PEARSON

Charles D. Miller • Vern E. Heeren • John Hornsby • Christopher Heeren

Mathematical Ideas

Third Custom Edition for Northern Virginia Community College

Taken from:
Mathematical Ideas, Thirteenth Edition
by Charles D. Miller, Vern E. Heeren, John Hornsby,
and Christopher Heeren, with Margaret L. Morrow
and Jill Van Newenhizen

Mathematical Ideas, Eighth Edition
by Charles D. Miller, Vern E. Heeren, and E. John Hornsby, Jr.

Mathematical Ideas, Eleventh Edition
by Charles D. Miller, Vern E. Heeren, and John Hornsby

Mathematical Ideas, Twelfth Edition
by Charles D. Miller, Vern E. Heeren, and John Hornsby,
with Margaret L. Morrow and Jill Van Newenhizen

Mathematical Ideas, Sixth Edition
by Charles D. Miller, Vern E. Heeren, and E. John Hornsby, Jr.

Cover Art: Courtesy of Pearson Learning Solutions.

Taken from:

Mathematical Ideas, Thirteenth Edition
by Charles D. Miller, Vern E. Heeren, John Hornsby, and Christopher Heeren, with Margaret L. Morrow
and Jill Van Newenhizen
Copyright © 2016, 2012, 2008 by Pearson Education, Inc.
New York, New York 10013

Mathematical Ideas, Eighth Edition
by Charles D. Miller, Vern E. Heeren, and E. John Hornsby, Jr.
Copyright © 1997 by Pearson Education, Inc.
Published by Addison-Wesley
Boston, Massachusetts 02116

Mathematical Ideas, Eleventh Edition
by Charles D. Miller, Vern E. Heeren, and John Hornsby
Copyright © 2008 by Pearson Education, Inc.
Published by Addison-Wesley

Mathematical Ideas, Twelfth Edition
by Charles D. Miller, Vern E. Heeren, and John Hornsby, with Margaret L. Morrow and Jill Van Newenhizen
Copyright © 2012, 2008, 2004 by Pearson Education, Inc.
Published by Addison-Wesley

Mathematical Ideas, Sixth Edition
by Charles D. Miller, Vern E. Heeren, and E. John Hornsby, Jr.
Copyright © 1990 by Pearson Education, Inc.
Published by Addison-Wesley

This special edition published in cooperation with Pearson Learning Solutions.

Pearson Learning Solutions, 501 Boylston Street, Suite 900, Boston, MA 02116
A Pearson Education Company
www.pearsoned.com

Printed in the United States of America

2 3 4 5 6 7 8 9 10 V056 18 17 16 15

000200010271978452

EEB

ISBN 10: 1-323-14594-X
ISBN 13: 978-1-323-14594-4

CONTENTS

Unless otherwise noted, content is taken from *Mathematical Ideas*, Thirteenth Edition, by Charles D. Miller, Vern E. Heeren, John Hornsby, and Christopher Heeren, with Margaret L. Morrow and Jill Van Newenhizen.

Content preceded by an asterisk is taken from *Mathematical Ideas*, Eleventh Edition, by Charles D. Miller, Vern E. Heeren, and John Hornsby.

Content preceded by two asterisks is taken from *Mathematical Ideas*, Twelfth Edition, by Charles D. Miller, Vern E. Heeren, and John Hornsby, with Margaret L. Morrow and Jill Van Newenhizen.

Introduction to Logic   89

Numeration Systems   145

5 Number Theory 215

6 The Real Numbers and Their Representations 257

7 The Basic Concepts of Algebra   329

10 Counting Methods 573

Personal Financial Management 747

Graph Theory 815

The Art of Problem Solving

1

Professor Terry Krieger, of Rochester (Minnesota) Community College, shares his thoughts about why he decided to become a mathematics teacher. He is an expert at the Rubik's Cube. Here, he explains how he mastered this classic problem.

*From a very young age I always enjoyed solving problems, especially problems involving numbers and patterns. There is something inherently beautiful in the process of discovering mathematical truth. Mathematics may be the only discipline in which different people, using wildly varied but logically sound methods, will arrive at the **same** correct result—not just once, but every time! It is this aspect of mathematics that led me to my career as an educator. As a mathematics instructor, I get to be part of, and sometimes guide, the discovery process.*

I received a Rubik's Cube as a gift my junior year of high school. I was fascinated by it. I devoted the better part of three months to solving it for the first time, sometimes working 3 or 4 hours per day on it.

There was a lot of trial and error involved. I devised a process that allowed me to move only a small number of pieces at a time while keeping other pieces in their places. Most of my moves affect only three or four of the 26 unique pieces of the puzzle. What sets my solution apart from those found in many books is that I hold the cube in a consistent position and work from the top to the bottom. Most book solutions work upward from the bottom.

My first breakthrough came when I realized that getting a single color on one face of the cube was not helpful if the colors along the edges of that face were placed improperly. In other words, it does no good to make the top of the cube all white if one of the edges along the white top shows green, yellow, and blue. It needs to be all green, for example.

I worked on the solution so much that I started seeing cube moves in my sleep. In fact, I figured out the moves for one of my most frustrating sticking points while sleeping. I just woke up knowing how to do it.

The eight corners of the cube represented a particularly difficult challenge for me. Finding a consistent method for placing the corners appropriately took many, many hours. To this day, the amount of time that it takes for me to solve a scrambled cube depends largely on the amount of time that it takes for me to place the corners.

When I first honed my technique, I was able to consistently solve the cube in 2 to 3 minutes. My average time is now about 65 seconds. My fastest time is 42 seconds.

Since figuring out how to solve the cube, I have experimented with other possible color patterns that can be formed. The most complicated one I have created leaves the cube with three different color stripes on all six faces. I have never met another person who can accomplish this arrangement.

1.1   SOLVING PROBLEMS BY INDUCTIVE REASONING

OBJECTIVES

1 Be able to distinguish between inductive and deductive reasoning.

2 Understand that in some cases, inductive reasoning may not lead to valid conclusions.

Characteristics of Inductive and Deductive Reasoning

The development of mathematics can be traced to the Egyptian and Babylonian cultures (3000 B.C.–A.D. 260) as a necessity for counting and problem solving. To solve a problem, a cookbook-like recipe was given, and it was followed repeatedly to solve similar problems. By observing that a specific method worked for a certain type of problem, the Babylonians and the Egyptians concluded that the same method would work for any similar type of problem. Such a conclusion is called a *conjecture*. A **conjecture** is an educated guess based on repeated observations of a particular process or pattern.

The method of reasoning just described is called *inductive reasoning*.

INDUCTIVE REASONING

Inductive reasoning is characterized by drawing a general conclusion (making a conjecture) from repeated observations of specific examples. The conjecture may or may not be true.

In testing a conjecture obtained by inductive reasoning, it takes only one example that does not work to prove the conjecture false. Such an example is called a **counterexample.**

Inductive reasoning provides a powerful method of drawing conclusions, but there is no assurance that the observed conjecture will always be true. For this reason, mathematicians are reluctant to accept a conjecture as an absolute truth until it is formally proved using methods of *deductive reasoning*. Deductive reasoning characterized the development and approach of Greek mathematics, as seen in the works of Euclid, Pythagoras, Archimedes, and others. During the classical Greek period (600 B.C.–A.D. 450), general concepts were applied to specific problems, resulting in a structured, logical development of mathematics.

DEDUCTIVE REASONING

Deductive reasoning is characterized by applying general principles to specific examples.

We now look at examples of these two types of reasoning. In this chapter, we often refer to the **natural,** or **counting, numbers.**

$$1, 2, 3, \ldots \quad \text{Natural (counting) numbers}$$

$$\uparrow$$

Ellipsis points

The three dots (*ellipsis points*) indicate that the numbers continue indefinitely in the pattern that has been established. The most probable rule for continuing this pattern is "Add 1 to the previous number," and this is indeed the rule that we follow.

Now consider the following list of natural numbers:

$$2, 9, 16, 23, 30.$$

What is the next number of this list? What is the pattern? After studying the numbers, we might see that $2 + 7 = 9$, and $9 + 7 = 16$. Do we add 16 and 7 to get 23? Do we add 23 and 7 to get 30? Yes. It seems that any number in the given list can be found by adding 7 to the preceding number, so the next number in the list would be $30 + 7 = 37$.

We set out to find the "next number" by reasoning from observation of the numbers in the list. We may have jumped from these observations to the general statement that any number in the list is 7 more than the preceding number. This is an example of inductive reasoning.

By using inductive reasoning, we concluded that 37 was the next number. Suppose the person making up the list has another answer in mind. The list of numbers

$$2, 9, 16, 23, 30$$

actually gives the dates of Mondays in June if June 1 falls on a Sunday. The next Monday after June 30 is July 7. With this pattern, the list continues as

$$2, 9, 16, 23, 30, 7, 14, 21, 28, \ldots.$$

See the calendar in **Figure 1.** The correct answer would then be 7. The process used to obtain the rule "add 7" in the preceding list reveals a main flaw of inductive reasoning. *We can never be sure that what is true in a specific case will be true in general. Inductive reasoning does not guarantee a true result, but it does provide a means of making a conjecture.*

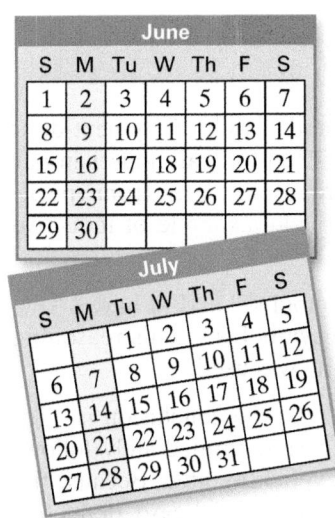

Figure 1

We now review some basic notation. Throughout this book, we use *exponents* to represent repeated multiplication.

$$\text{Base} \rightarrow 4^3 = 4 \cdot 4 \cdot 4 = 64 \qquad \text{4 is used as a factor 3 times.}$$

Exponent

EXPONENTIAL EXPRESSION

If a is a number and n is a counting number $(1, 2, 3, \ldots)$, then the exponential expression a^n is defined as follows.

$$a^n = \underbrace{a \cdot a \cdot a \cdot \ldots \cdot a}_{n \text{ factors of } a}$$

The number a is the **base** and n is the **exponent.**

With deductive reasoning, we use general statements and apply them to specific situations. For example, a basic rule for converting feet to inches is to multiply the number of feet by 12 in order to obtain the equivalent number of inches. This can be expressed as a formula.

$$\text{Number of inches} = 12 \times \text{number of feet}$$

This general rule can be applied to any specific case. For example, the number of inches in 3 feet is $12 \times 3 = 36$ inches.

Reasoning through a problem usually requires certain *premises*. A **premise** can be an assumption, law, rule, widely held idea, or observation. Then reason inductively or deductively from the premises to obtain a **conclusion.** The premises and conclusion make up a **logical argument.**

EXAMPLE 1 Identifying Premises and Conclusions

Identify each premise and the conclusion in each of the following arguments. Then tell whether each argument is an example of inductive or deductive reasoning.

(a) Our house is made of brick. Both of my next-door neighbors have brick houses. Therefore, all houses in our neighborhood are made of brick.

(b) All keyboards have the symbol @. I have a keyboard. My keyboard has the symbol @.

(c) Today is Tuesday. Tomorrow will be Wednesday.

Solution

(a) The premises are "Our house is made of brick" and "Both of my next-door neighbors have brick houses." The conclusion is "Therefore, all houses in our neighborhood are made of brick." Because the reasoning goes from specific examples to a general statement, the argument is an example of inductive reasoning (although it may very well be faulty).

(b) Here the premises are "All keyboards have the symbol @" and "I have a keyboard." The conclusion is "My keyboard has the symbol @." This reasoning goes from general to specific, so deductive reasoning was used.

(c) There is only one premise here, "Today is Tuesday." The conclusion is "Tomorrow will be Wednesday." The fact that Wednesday immediately follows Tuesday is being used, even though this fact is not explicitly stated. Because the conclusion comes from general facts that apply to this special case, deductive reasoning was used. ∎

While inductive reasoning may, at times, lead to false conclusions, in many cases it does provide correct results if we look for the most *probable* answer.

The Fibonacci Sequence

1, 1, 2, 3, 5, 8, 13, 21, ...

In the 2003 movie *A Wrinkle in Time*, young Charles Wallace, played by David Dorfman, is challenged to identify a particular sequence of numbers. He correctly identifies it as the **Fibonacci sequence.**

EXAMPLE 2 Predicting the Next Number in a Sequence

Use inductive reasoning to determine the *probable* next number in each list below.

(a) 5, 9, 13, 17, 21, 25, 29   **(b)** 1, 1, 2, 3, 5, 8, 13, 21   **(c)** 2, 4, 8, 16, 32

Solution

(a) Each number in the list is obtained by adding 4 to the previous number. The probable next number is $29 + 4 = 33$. (This is an example of an *arithmetic sequence.*)

(b) Beginning with the third number in the list, 2, each number is obtained by adding the two previous numbers in the list. That is,

$$1 + 1 = 2, \quad 1 + 2 = 3, \quad 2 + 3 = 5,$$

and so on. The probable next number in the list is $13 + 21 = 34$. (These are the first few terms of the *Fibonacci sequence.*)

(c) It appears here that to obtain each number after the first, we must double the previous number. Therefore, the probable next number is $32 \times 2 = 64$. (This is an example of a *geometric sequence.*) ∎

EXAMPLE 3 Predicting the Product of Two Numbers

Consider the list of equations. Predict the next multiplication fact in the list.

$$37 \times \ \ 3 = 111$$
$$37 \times \ \ 6 = 222$$
$$37 \times \ \ 9 = 333$$
$$37 \times 12 = 444$$

Solution

The left side of each equation has two factors, the first 37 and the second a multiple of 3, beginning with 3. Each product (answer) consists of three digits, all the same, beginning with 111 for 37×3. Thus, the next multiplication fact would be

$$37 \times 15 = 555, \quad \text{which is indeed true.} \quad ∎$$

Pitfalls of Inductive Reasoning

There are pitfalls associated with inductive reasoning. A classic example involves the maximum number of regions formed when chords are constructed in a circle. When two points on a circle are joined with a line segment, a *chord* is formed.

Locate a single point on a circle. Because no chords are formed, a single interior region is formed. See **Figure 2(a)** on the next page. Locate two points and draw a chord. Two interior regions are formed, as shown in **Figure 2(b).** Continue this pattern. Locate three points, and draw all possible chords. Four interior regions are formed, as shown in **Figure 2(c).** Four points yield 8 regions and five points yield 16 regions. See **Figures 2(d) and 2(e).**

The results of the preceding observations are summarized in **Table 1.** The pattern formed in the column headed "Number of Regions" is the same one we saw in **Example 2(c),** where we predicted that the next number would be 64. It seems here that for each additional point on the circle, the number of regions doubles.

Table 1

Number of Points	Number of Regions
1	1
2	2
3	4
4	8
5	16

(a)

(b)

(c)

(d)

(e)

Figure 2

Figure 3

A reasonable inductive conjecture would be that for six points, 32 regions would be formed. But as **Figure 3** indicates, there are *only 31 regions.* The pattern of doubling ends when the sixth point is considered. Adding a seventh point would yield 57 regions. The numbers obtained here are

$$1, 2, 4, 8, 16, 31, 57.$$

For *n* points on the circle, the number of regions is given by the formula

$$\frac{n^4 - 6n^3 + 23n^2 - 18n + 24}{24}. \quad *$$

1.1   EXERCISES

In Exercises 1–16, determine whether the reasoning is an example of deductive or inductive reasoning.

1. The next number in the pattern 2, 4, 6, 8, 10 is 12.

2. My dog barked and woke me up at 1:02 a.m., 2:03 a.m., and 3:04 a.m. So he will bark again and wake me up at 4:05 a.m.

3. To find the perimeter *P* of a square with side of length *s*, I can use the formula *P* = 4*s*. So the perimeter of a square with side of length 7 inches is 4 × 7 = 28 inches.

4. A company charges a 10% re-stocking fee for returning an item. So when I return a radio that cost $150, I will only get $135 back.

5. If the mechanic says that it will take seven days to repair your SUV, then it will actually take ten days. The mechanic says, "I figure it'll take exactly one week to fix it, ma'am." Then you can expect it to be ready ten days from now.

6. If you take your medicine, you'll feel a lot better. You take your medicine. Therefore, you'll feel a lot better.

7. It has rained every day for the past six days, and it is raining today as well. So it will also rain tomorrow.

8. Carrie's first five children were boys. If she has another baby, it will be a boy.

9. The 2000 movie *Cast Away* stars Tom Hanks as the only human survivor of a plane crash, stranded on a tropical island. He approximates his distance from where the plane lost radio contact to be 400 miles (a radius), and uses the formula for the area of a circle,

$$\text{Area} = \pi \, (\text{radius})^2$$

to determine that a search party would have to cover an area of over 500,000 square miles to look for him and his "pal" Wilson.

---

*For more information on this and other similar patterns, see "Counting Pizza Pieces and Other Combinatorial Problems," by Eugene Maier, in the January 1988 issue of *Mathematics Teacher,* pp. 22–26.

10. If the same number is subtracted from both sides of a true equation, the new equation is also true. I know that $9 + 18 = 27$. Therefore, $(9 + 18) - 13 = 27 - 13$.

11. If you build it, they will come. You build it. Therefore, they will come.

12. All men are mortal. Socrates is a man. Therefore, Socrates is mortal.

13. It is a fact that every student who ever attended Delgado University was accepted into graduate school. Because I am attending Delgado, I can expect to be accepted to graduate school, too.

14. For the past 126 years, a rare plant has bloomed in Columbia each summer, alternating between yellow and green flowers. Last summer, it bloomed with green flowers, so this summer it will bloom with yellow flowers.

15. In the sequence 5, 10, 15, 20, 25, . . . , the most probable next number is 30.

16. (This anecdote is adapted from a story by Howard Eves in *In Mathematical Circles*.) A scientist had a group of 100 fleas, and one by one he would tell each flea "Jump," and the flea would jump. Then with the same fleas, he yanked off their hind legs and repeated "Jump," but the fleas would not jump. He concluded that when a flea has its hind legs yanked off, it cannot hear.

17. Discuss the differences between inductive and deductive reasoning. Give an example of each.

18. Give an example of faulty inductive reasoning.

Determine the most probable next term in each of the following lists of numbers.

19. 6, 9, 12, 15, 18

20. 13, 18, 23, 28, 33

21. 3, 12, 48, 192, 768

22. 32, 16, 8, 4, 2

23. 3, 6, 9, 15, 24, 39

24. $\frac{1}{3}, \frac{3}{5}, \frac{5}{7}, \frac{7}{9}, \frac{9}{11}$

25. $\frac{1}{2}, \frac{3}{4}, \frac{5}{6}, \frac{7}{8}, \frac{9}{10}$

26. 1, 4, 9, 16, 25

27. 1, 8, 27, 64, 125

28. 2, 6, 12, 20, 30, 42

29. 4, 7, 12, 19, 28, 39

30. 27, 21, 16, 12, 9

31. 5, 3, 5, 5, 3, 5, 5, 5, 3, 5, 5, 5, 5, 3, 5, 5, 5, 5

32. 8, 2, 8, 2, 2, 8, 2, 2, 2, 8, 2, 2, 2, 2, 8, 2, 2, 2, 2

33. Construct a list of numbers similar to those in **Exercise 19** such that the most probable next number in the list is 60.

34. Construct a list of numbers similar to those in **Exercise 30** such that the most probable next number in the list is 8.

Use the list of equations and inductive reasoning to predict the next equation, and then verify your conjecture.

35.
$(9 \times 9) + 7 = 88$
$(98 \times 9) + 6 = 888$
$(987 \times 9) + 5 = 8888$
$(9876 \times 9) + 4 = 88{,}888$

36.
$(1 \times 9) + 2 = 11$
$(12 \times 9) + 3 = 111$
$(123 \times 9) + 4 = 1111$
$(1234 \times 9) + 5 = 11{,}111$

37.
$3367 \times \ 3 = 10{,}101$
$3367 \times \ 6 = 20{,}202$
$3367 \times \ 9 = 30{,}303$
$3367 \times 12 = 40{,}404$

38.
$15873 \times \ 7 = 111{,}111$
$15873 \times 14 = 222{,}222$
$15873 \times 21 = 333{,}333$
$15873 \times 28 = 444{,}444$

39.
$34 \times 34 = 1156$
$334 \times 334 = 111{,}556$
$3334 \times 3334 = 11{,}115{,}556$

40.
$11 \times 11 = 121$
$111 \times 111 = 12{,}321$
$1111 \times 1111 = 1{,}234{,}321$

41.
$$3 = \frac{3(2)}{2}$$
$$3 + 6 = \frac{6(3)}{2}$$
$$3 + 6 + 9 = \frac{9(4)}{2}$$
$$3 + 6 + 9 + 12 = \frac{12(5)}{2}$$

42.
$$2 = \ 4 - 2$$
$$2 + 4 = \ 8 - 2$$
$$2 + 4 + 8 = 16 - 2$$
$$2 + 4 + 8 + 16 = 32 - 2$$

43.
$$5(6) = 6(6 - 1)$$
$$5(6) + 5(36) = 6(36 - 1)$$
$$5(6) + 5(36) + 5(216) = 6(216 - 1)$$
$$5(6) + 5(36) + 5(216) + 5(1296) = 6(1296 - 1)$$

44.
$$3 = \frac{3(3-1)}{2}$$
$$3 + 9 = \frac{3(9-1)}{2}$$
$$3 + 9 + 27 = \frac{3(27-1)}{2}$$
$$3 + 9 + 27 + 81 = \frac{3(81-1)}{2}$$

45.
$$\frac{1}{2} = 1 - \frac{1}{2}$$
$$\frac{1}{2} + \frac{1}{4} = 1 - \frac{1}{4}$$
$$\frac{1}{2} + \frac{1}{4} + \frac{1}{8} = 1 - \frac{1}{8}$$
$$\frac{1}{2} + \frac{1}{4} + \frac{1}{8} + \frac{1}{16} = 1 - \frac{1}{16}$$

46.
$$\frac{1}{1 \cdot 2} = \frac{1}{2}$$
$$\frac{1}{1 \cdot 2} + \frac{1}{2 \cdot 3} = \frac{2}{3}$$
$$\frac{1}{1 \cdot 2} + \frac{1}{2 \cdot 3} + \frac{1}{3 \cdot 4} = \frac{3}{4}$$
$$\frac{1}{1 \cdot 2} + \frac{1}{2 \cdot 3} + \frac{1}{3 \cdot 4} + \frac{1}{4 \cdot 5} = \frac{4}{5}$$

Legend has it that the great mathematician Carl Friedrich Gauss (1777–1855) at a very young age was told by his teacher to find the sum of the first 100 *counting numbers. While his classmates toiled at the problem, Carl simply wrote down a single number and handed the correct answer in to his teacher. The young Carl explained that he observed that there were 50 pairs of numbers that each added up to* 101. *(See below.) So the sum of all the numbers must be* 50 × 101 = 5050.

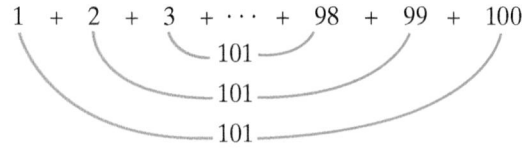

50 sums of 101 = 50 × 101 = 5050

Use the method of Gauss to find each sum.

47. $1 + 2 + 3 + \cdots + 200$ **48.** $1 + 2 + 3 + \cdots + 400$

49. $1 + 2 + 3 + \cdots + 800$ **50.** $1 + 2 + 3 + \cdots + 2000$

51. Modify the procedure of Gauss to find the sum $1 + 2 + 3 + \cdots + 175$.

52. Explain in your own words how the procedure of Gauss can be modified to find the sum $1 + 2 + 3 + \cdots + n$, where n is an odd natural number. (When an odd natural number is divided by 2, it leaves a remainder of 1.)

53. Modify the procedure of Gauss to find the sum $2 + 4 + 6 + \cdots + 100$.

54. Use the result of **Exercise 53** to find the sum $4 + 8 + 12 + \cdots + 200$.

55. What is the most probable next number in this list?

12, 1, 1, 1, 2, 1, 3

(*Hint:* Think about a clock with chimes.)

56. What is the next term in this list?

O, T, T, F, F, S, S, E, N, T

(*Hint:* Think about words and their relationship to numbers.)

57. Choose any three-digit number with all different digits, and follow these steps.

(a) Reverse the digits, and subtract the smaller from the larger. Record your result.

(b) Choose another three-digit number and repeat this process. Do this as many times as it takes for you to see a pattern in the different results you obtain. (*Hint:* What is the middle digit? What is the sum of the first and third digits?)

(c) Write an explanation of this pattern.

58. Choose any number, and follow these steps.

(a) Multiply by 2.   **(b)** Add 6.

(c) Divide by 2.   **(d)** Subtract the number you started with.

(e) Record your result.

Repeat the process, except in Step (b), add 8. Record your final result. Repeat the process once more, except in Step (b), add 10. Record your final result.

(f) Observe what you have done. Then use inductive reasoning to explain how to predict the final result.

59. Complete the following.

$142,857 \times 1 = $ _____ $142,857 \times 2 = $ _____

$142,857 \times 3 = $ _____ $142,857 \times 4 = $ _____

$142,857 \times 5 = $ _____ $142,857 \times 6 = $ _____

What pattern exists in the successive answers? Now multiply 142,857 by 7 to obtain an interesting result.

60. Refer to **Figures 2(b)–(e)** and **Figure 3**. Instead of counting interior regions of the circle, count the chords formed. Use inductive reasoning to predict the number of chords that would be formed if seven points were used.

1.2   AN APPLICATION OF INDUCTIVE REASONING: NUMBER PATTERNS

OBJECTIVES

1 Be able to recognize arithmetic and geometric sequences.

2 Be able to apply the method of successive differences to predict the next term in a sequence.

3 Be able to recognize number patterns.

4 Be able to use sum formulas.

5 Be able to recognize triangular, square, and pentagonal numbers.

Number Sequences

An ordered list of numbers such as

$$3, 9, 15, 21, 27, \ldots$$

is called a *sequence*. A **number sequence** is a list of numbers having a first number, a second number, a third number, and so on, called the **terms** of the sequence.

The sequence that begins

$$5, 9, 13, 17, 21, \ldots$$

is an *arithmetic sequence,* or *arithmetic progression.* In an **arithmetic sequence,** each term after the first is obtained by adding the same number, called the **common difference,** to the preceding term. To find the common difference, choose any term after the first and subtract from it the preceding term. If we choose $9 - 5$ (the second term minus the first term), for example, we see that the common difference is 4. To find the term following 21, we add 4 to get $21 + 4 = 25$.

The sequence that begins

$$2, 4, 8, 16, 32, \ldots$$

is a *geometric sequence,* or *geometric progression.* In a **geometric sequence,** each term after the first is obtained by multiplying the preceding term by the same number, called the **common ratio.** To find the common ratio, choose any term after the first and divide it by the preceding term. If we choose $\frac{4}{2}$ (the second term divided by the first term), for example, we see that the common ratio is 2. To find the term following 32, we multiply by 2 to get $32 \cdot 2 = 64$.

EXAMPLE 1   Identifying Arithmetic and Geometric Sequences

For each sequence, determine if it is an *arithmetic sequence,* a *geometric sequence,* or *neither.* If it is either arithmetic or geometric, give the next term in the sequence.

(a) $5, 10, 15, 20, 25, \ldots$ **(b)** $3, 12, 48, 192, 768, \ldots$ **(c)** $1, 4, 9, 16, 25, \ldots$

Solution

(a) If we choose *any* term after the first term, and subtract the preceding term, we find that the common difference is 5.

$$10 - 5 = 5 \qquad 15 - 10 = 5 \qquad 20 - 15 = 5 \qquad 25 - 20 = 5$$

Therefore, this is an arithmetic sequence. The next term in the sequence is

$$25 + 5 = 30.$$

(b) If any term after the first is multiplied by 4, the following term is obtained.

$$\frac{12}{3} = 4 \qquad \frac{48}{12} = 4 \qquad \frac{192}{48} = 4 \qquad \frac{768}{192} = 4$$

Therefore, this is a geometric sequence. The next term in the sequence is

$$768 \cdot 4 = 3072.$$

(c) Although there is a pattern here (the terms are the squares of the first five counting numbers), there is neither a common difference nor a common ratio. This is neither an arithmetic nor a geometric sequence.   ■

Successive Differences

Some sequences may present more difficulty than our earlier examples when making a conjecture about the next term. Often the **method of successive differences** may be applied in such cases. Consider the sequence

$$2, 6, 22, 56, 114, \dots.$$

Because the next term is not obvious, subtract the first term from the second term, the second from the third, the third from the fourth, and so on.

Now repeat the process with the sequence 4, 16, 34, 58 and continue repeating until the difference is a constant value, as shown in line (4).

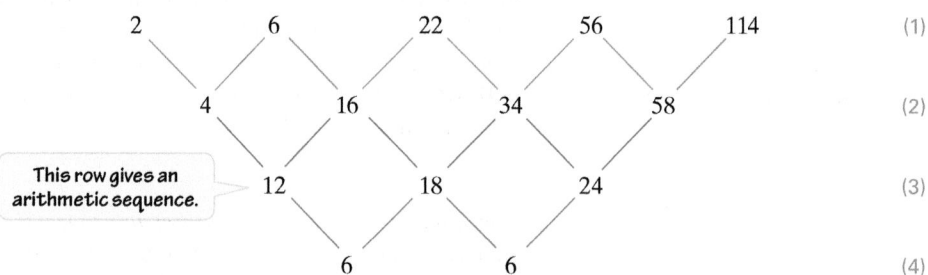

Once a line of constant values is obtained, simply work "backward" by adding until the desired term of the given sequence is obtained. Thus, for this pattern to continue, another 6 should appear in line (4), meaning that the next term in line (3) would have to be $24 + 6 = 30$. The next term in line (2) would be $58 + 30 = 88$. Finally, the next term in the given sequence would be $114 + 88 = \mathbf{202}$.

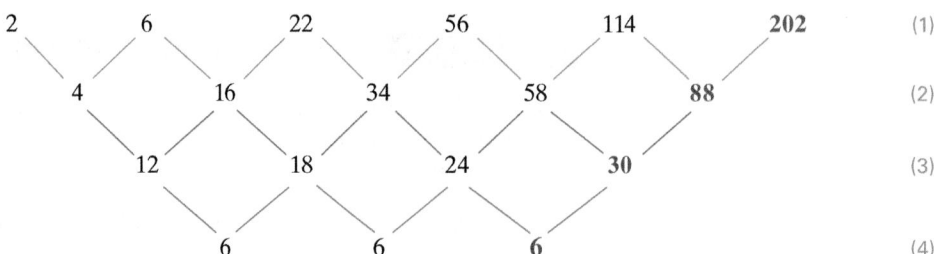

EXAMPLE 2 Using Successive Differences

Use successive differences to determine the next number in each sequence.

(a) $14, 22, 32, 44, \dots$ **(b)** $5, 15, 37, 77, 141, \dots$

Solution

(a) Subtract a term from the one that follows it, and continue until a pattern is observed.

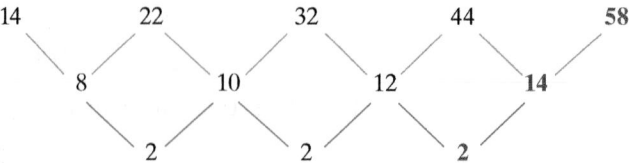

Once the row of 2s was obtained and extended, we were able to obtain

$$12 + 2 = 14, \quad \text{and} \quad 44 + 14 = 58 \quad \text{as shown above.}$$

The next number in the sequence is **58**.

(b) Proceed as before to obtain the following diagram.

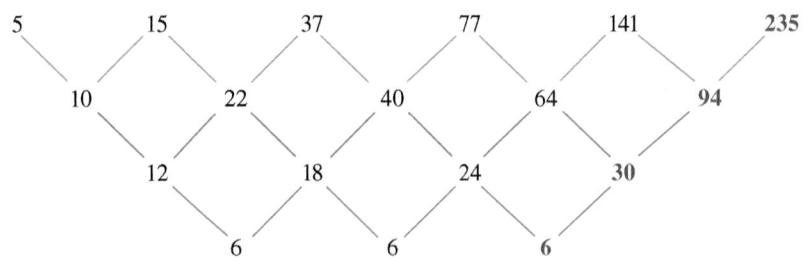

The numbers in the "diagonal" at the far right were obtained by adding: $24 + 6 = 30, 64 + 30 = 94$, and $141 + 94 = 235$. The next number in the sequence is **235**. ■

The method of successive differences does not always work. For example, try it on the Fibonacci sequence in **Example 2(b)** of **Section 1.1** and see what happens.

Number Patterns and Sum Formulas

Observe the following number pattern.

$$1 = 1^2$$
$$1 + 3 = 2^2$$
$$1 + 3 + 5 = 3^2$$
$$1 + 3 + 5 + 7 = 4^2$$
$$1 + 3 + 5 + 7 + 9 = 5^2$$

In each case, the left side of the equation is the indicated sum of consecutive odd counting numbers beginning with 1, and the right side is the square of the number of terms on the left side. Inductive reasoning would suggest that the next line in this pattern is as follows.

$$1 + 3 + 5 + 7 + 9 + 11 = 6^2$$

Evaluating each side shows that each side simplifies to 36.

We cannot conclude that this pattern will continue indefinitely, because observation of a finite number of examples does *not* guarantee that the pattern will continue. However, mathematicians have proved that this pattern does indeed continue indefinitely, using a method of proof called **mathematical induction.** (See any standard college algebra text.)

Any even counting number may be written in the form $2k$, where k is a counting number. It follows that the kth odd counting number is written $2k - 1$. For example, the **third** odd counting number, 5, can be written

$$2(3) - 1.$$

Using these ideas, we can write the result obtained above as follows.

SUM OF THE FIRST n ODD COUNTING NUMBERS

If n is any counting number, then the following is true.

$$1 + 3 + 5 + \cdots + (2n - 1) = n^2$$

EXAMPLE 3 Predicting the Next Equation in a List

In each of the following, several equations are given illustrating a suspected number pattern. Determine what the next equation would be, and verify that it is indeed a true statement.

(a)
$$1^2 = 1^3$$
$$(1 + 2)^2 = 1^3 + 2^3$$
$$(1 + 2 + 3)^2 = 1^3 + 2^3 + 3^3$$
$$(1 + 2 + 3 + 4)^2 = 1^3 + 2^3 + 3^3 + 4^3$$

(b)
$$1 = 1^3$$
$$3 + 5 = 2^3$$
$$7 + 9 + 11 = 3^3$$
$$13 + 15 + 17 + 19 = 4^3$$

(c)
$$1 = \frac{1 \cdot 2}{2}$$
$$1 + 2 = \frac{2 \cdot 3}{2}$$
$$1 + 2 + 3 = \frac{3 \cdot 4}{2}$$
$$1 + 2 + 3 + 4 = \frac{4 \cdot 5}{2}$$

(d)
$$12{,}345{,}679 \times 9 = 111{,}111{,}111$$
$$12{,}345{,}679 \times 18 = 222{,}222{,}222$$
$$12{,}345{,}679 \times 27 = 333{,}333{,}333$$
$$12{,}345{,}679 \times 36 = 444{,}444{,}444$$
$$12{,}345{,}679 \times 45 = 555{,}555{,}555$$

Notice that there is no 8 here.

Solution

(a) The left side of each equation is the square of the sum of the first n counting numbers, and the right side is the sum of their cubes. The next equation in the pattern would be

$$(1 + 2 + 3 + 4 + 5)^2 = 1^3 + 2^3 + 3^3 + 4^3 + 5^3.$$

Each side simplifies to 225, so the pattern is true for this equation.

(b) The left sides of the equations contain the sum of odd counting numbers, starting with the first (1) in the first equation, the second and third (3 and 5) in the second equation, the fourth, fifth, and sixth (7, 9, and 11) in the third equation, and so on. Each right side contains the cube (third power) of the number of terms on the left side. Following this pattern, the next equation would be

$$21 + 23 + 25 + 27 + 29 = 5^3,$$

which can be verified by computation.

(c) The left side of each equation gives the indicated sum of the first n counting numbers, and the right side is always of the form

$$\frac{n(n + 1)}{2}.$$

For the pattern to continue, the next equation would be

$$1 + 2 + 3 + 4 + 5 = \frac{5 \cdot 6}{2}.$$

Because each side simplifies to 15, the pattern is true for this equation.

(d) In each case, the first factor on the left is 12,345,679 and the second factor is a multiple of 9 (that is, 9, 18, 27, 36, 45). The right side consists of a nine-digit number, all digits of which are the same (that is, 1, 2, 3, 4, 5). For the pattern to continue, the next equation would be as follows.

$$12{,}345{,}679 \times 54 = 666{,}666{,}666$$

Verify that this is a true statement.

The patterns established in **Examples 3(a) and 3(c)** can be written as follows.

SPECIAL SUM FORMULAS

For any counting number n, the following are true.

$$(1 + 2 + 3 + \cdots + n)^2 = 1^3 + 2^3 + 3^3 + \cdots + n^3$$

$$1 + 2 + 3 + \cdots + n = \frac{n(n + 1)}{2}$$

We can provide a general deductive argument showing how the second equation is obtained.

Let S represent the sum $1 + 2 + 3 + \cdots + n$. This sum can also be written as $S = n + (n - 1) + (n - 2) + \cdots + 1$. Write these two equations as follows.

$$S = 1 \qquad + 2 \qquad + 3 \qquad + \cdots + n$$

$$\underline{S = n \qquad + (n - 1) + (n - 2) + \cdots + 1}$$

$$2S = (n + 1) + (n + 1) + (n + 1) + \cdots + (n + 1) \qquad \text{Add the corresponding sides.}$$

$$2S = n(n + 1) \qquad \text{There are } n \text{ terms of } n + 1.$$

$$S = \frac{n(n + 1)}{2} \qquad \text{Divide both sides by 2.}$$

Figurate Numbers

Pythagoras and his Pythagorean brotherhood studied numbers of geometric arrangements of points, such as **triangular numbers, square numbers,** and **pentagonal numbers. Figure 4** illustrates the first few of each of these types of numbers.

The **figurate numbers** possess numerous interesting patterns. For example, every square number greater than 1 is the sum of two consecutive triangular numbers. ($9 = 3 + 6, 25 = 10 + 15$, and so on.)

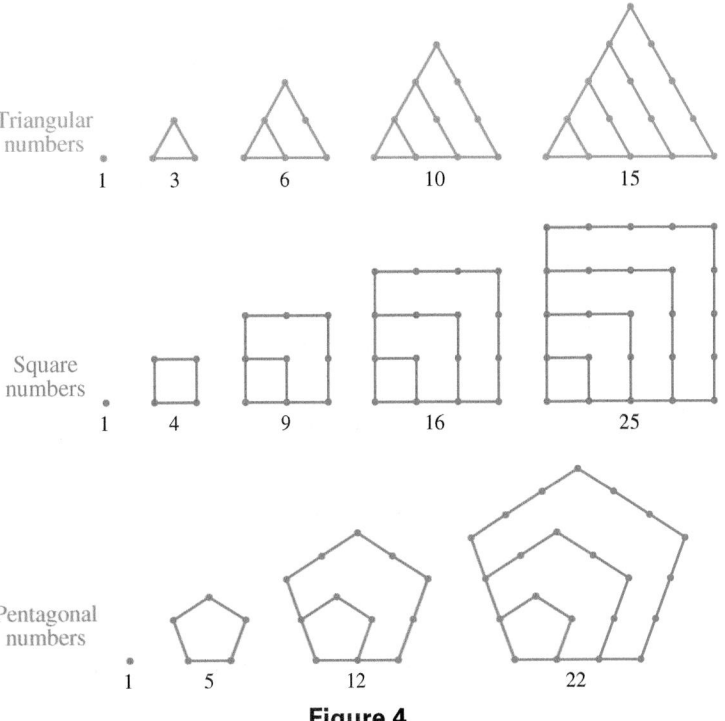

Triangular numbers
1   3   6   10   15

Square numbers
1   4   9   16   25

Pentagonal numbers
1   5   12   22

Figure 4

Every pentagonal number can be represented as the sum of a square number and a triangular number. (For example, $5 = 4 + 1$ and $12 = 9 + 3$.) Many other such relationships exist.

In the expression T_n, n is called a **subscript.** T_n is read **"T sub *n*,"** and it represents the triangular number in the *n*th position in the sequence. For example,

$$T_1 = 1, \quad T_2 = 3, \quad T_3 = 6, \quad \text{and} \quad T_4 = 10.$$

S_n and P_n represent the *n*th square and pentagonal numbers, respectively.

FORMULAS FOR TRIANGULAR, SQUARE, AND PENTAGONAL NUMBERS

For any natural number *n*, the following are true.

The *n*th triangular number is given by $\quad \mathbf{T_n} = \dfrac{n(n+1)}{2}.$

The *n*th square number is given by $\quad \mathbf{S_n} = \mathbf{n^2}.$

The *n*th pentagonal number is given by $\mathbf{P_n} = \dfrac{n(3n-1)}{2}.$

EXAMPLE 4 Using the Formulas for Figurate Numbers

Use the formulas to find each of the following.

(a) seventh triangular number   **(b)** twelfth square number

(c) sixth pentagonal number

Solution

(a) $T_7 = \dfrac{n(n+1)}{2} = \dfrac{7(7+1)}{2} = \dfrac{7(8)}{2} = \dfrac{56}{2} = 28$ Formula for a triangular number, with $n = 7$

(b) $S_{12} = n^2 = 12^2 = 144$ Formula for a square number, with $n = 12$

$12^2 = 12 \cdot 12$

Inside the brackets, multiply first and then subtract.

(c) $P_6 = \dfrac{n(3n-1)}{2} = \dfrac{6[3(6)-1]}{2} = \dfrac{6(18-1)}{2} = \dfrac{6(17)}{2} = 51$ ∎

EXAMPLE 5 Illustrating a Figurate Number Relationship

Show that the sixth pentagonal number is equal to the sum of 6 and 3 times the fifth triangular number.

Solution

From **Example 4(c)**, $P_6 = 51$. The fifth triangular number is 15. Thus,

$$51 = 6 + 3(15) = 6 + 45 = 51.$$ ∎

The general relationship examined in **Example 5** can be written as follows.

$$P_n = n + 3 \cdot T_{n-1} \quad (n \geq 2)$$

▌EXAMPLE 6 Predicting the Value of a Pentagonal Number

The first five pentagonal numbers are 1, 5, 12, 22, 35. Use the method of successive differences to predict the sixth pentagonal number.

Solution

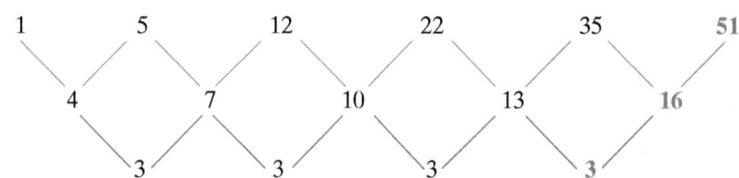

After the second line of successive differences, we work backward to find that the sixth pentagonal number is 51, which was also found in **Example 4(c).** ▪

FOR FURTHER THOUGHT

Kaprekar Constants

Take any four-digit number whose digits are all different. Arrange the digits in decreasing order, and then arrange them in increasing order. Now subtract. Repeat the process, called the *Kaprekar routine,* until the same result appears.

For example, suppose that we choose a number whose digits are 1, 5, 7, and 9, such as 1579.

9751	8721	7443	9963	6642	7641
−1579	−1278	−3447	−3699	−2466	−1467
8172	7443	3996	6264	4176	6174

Note that we have obtained the number 6174, and the process will lead to 6174 again. The number 6174 is called a **Kaprekar constant**. This number 6174 will always be generated eventually if this process is applied to such a four-digit number.

For Group or Individual Investigation

1. Apply the process of Kaprekar to a four-digit number of your choice, in which the digits are all different. How many steps did it take for you to arrive at 6174?

2. See **Exercises 77 and 78** in the exercise set that follows.

▍1.2 ▍ EXERCISES

For each sequence, determine if it is an arithmetic *sequence, a* geometric *sequence, or* neither. *If it is either arithmetic or geometric, give the next term in the sequence.*

1. 6, 16, 26, 36, 46, . . .

2. 8, 16, 24, 32, 40, . . .

3. 5, 15, 45, 135, 405, . . .

4. 2, 12, 72, 432, 2592, . . .

5. 1, 8, 27, 81, 243, . . .

6. 2, 8, 18, 32, 50, . . .

7. 256, 128, 64, 32, 16, . . .

8. 4096, 1024, 256, 64, 16, . . .

9. 1, 3, 4, 7, 11, . . .

10. 0, 1, 1, 2, 3, . . .

11. 12, 14, 16, 18, 20, . . .

12. 10, 50, 90, 130, 170, . . .

Use the method of successive differences to determine the next number in each sequence.

13. 1, 4, 11, 22, 37, 56, . . .

14. 3, 14, 31, 54, 83, 118, . . .

15. 6, 20, 50, 102, 182, 296, . . .

16. 1, 11, 35, 79, 149, 251, . . .

17. 0, 12, 72, 240, 600, 1260, 2352, . . .

18. 2, 57, 220, 575, 1230, 2317, . . .

19. 5, 34, 243, 1022, 3121, 7770, 16799, . . .

20. 3, 19, 165, 771, 2503, 6483, 14409, . . .

21. Refer to **Figures 2 and 3** in **Section 1.1.** The method of successive differences can be applied to the sequence of interior regions,

$$1, 2, 4, 8, 16, 31,$$

to find the number of regions determined by seven points on the circle. What is the next term in this sequence? How many regions would be determined by eight points? Verify this using the formula given at the end of that section.

22. The 1952 film *Hans Christian Andersen* stars Danny Kaye as the Danish writer of fairy tales. In a scene outside a schoolhouse window, Kaye sings a song to an inchworm. *Inchworm* was written for the film by the composer Frank Loesser and has been recorded by many artists, including Paul McCartney and Kenny Loggins. It was once featured on an episode of *The Muppets* and sung by Charles Aznavour.

As Kaye sings the song, the children in the school room are heard chanting addition facts: $2 + 2 = 4$, $4 + 4 = 8$, $8 + 8 = 16$, and so on.

(a) Use patterns to state the next addition fact (as heard in the movie).

(b) If the children were to extend their facts to the next four in the pattern, what would those facts be?

In Exercises 23–32, several equations are given illustrating a suspected number pattern. Determine what the next equation would be, and verify that it is indeed a true statement.

23. $(1 \times 9) - 1 = 8$
$(21 \times 9) - 1 = 188$
$(321 \times 9) - 1 = 2888$

24. $(1 \times 8) + 1 = 9$
$(12 \times 8) + 2 = 98$
$(123 \times 8) + 3 = 987$

25. $999,999 \times 2 = 1,999,998$
$999,999 \times 3 = 2,999,997$

26. $101 \times 101 = 10,201$
$10,101 \times 10,101 = 102,030,201$

27. $3^2 - 1^2 = 2^3$
$6^2 - 3^2 = 3^3$
$10^2 - 6^2 = 4^3$
$15^2 - 10^2 = 5^3$

28. $1 = 1^2$
$1 + 2 + 1 = 2^2$
$1 + 2 + 3 + 2 + 1 = 3^2$
$1 + 2 + 3 + 4 + 3 + 2 + 1 = 4^2$

29. $2^2 - 1^2 = 2 + 1$
$3^2 - 2^2 = 3 + 2$
$4^2 - 3^2 = 4 + 3$

30. $1^2 + 1 = 2^2 - 2$
$2^2 + 2 = 3^2 - 3$
$3^2 + 3 = 4^2 - 4$

31. $1 = 1 \times 1$
$1 + 5 = 2 \times 3$
$1 + 5 + 9 = 3 \times 5$

32. $1 + 2 = 3$
$4 + 5 + 6 = 7 + 8$
$9 + 10 + 11 + 12 = 13 + 14 + 15$

Use the formula $S = \frac{n(n+1)}{2}$ to find each sum.

33. $1 + 2 + 3 + \cdots + 300$

34. $1 + 2 + 3 + \cdots + 500$

35. $1 + 2 + 3 + \cdots + 675$

36. $1 + 2 + 3 + \cdots + 825$

Use the formula $S = n^2$ to find each sum. (Hint: To find n, add 1 to the last term and divide by 2.)

37. $1 + 3 + 5 + \cdots + 101$

38. $1 + 3 + 5 + \cdots + 49$

39. $1 + 3 + 5 + \cdots + 999$

40. $1 + 3 + 5 + \cdots + 301$

41. Use the formula for finding the sum

$$1 + 2 + 3 + \cdots + n$$

to discover a formula for finding the sum

$$2 + 4 + 6 + \cdots + 2n.$$

42. State in your own words the following formula discussed in this section.

$$(1 + 2 + 3 + \cdots + n)^2 = 1^3 + 2^3 + 3^3 + \cdots + n^3$$

43. Explain how the following diagram geometrically illustrates the formula $1 + 3 + 5 + 7 + 9 = 5^2$.

44. Explain how the following diagram geometrically illustrates the formula $1 + 2 + 3 + 4 = \frac{4 \times 5}{2}$.

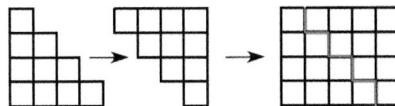

45. Use patterns to complete the table below.

Figurate Number	1st	2nd	3rd	4th	5th	6th	7th	8th
Triangular	1	3	6	10	15	21		
Square	1	4	9	16	25			
Pentagonal	1	5	12	22				
Hexagonal	1	6	15					
Heptagonal	1	7						
Octagonal	1							

46. The first five triangular, square, and pentagonal numbers can be obtained using sums of terms of sequences as shown below.

Triangular	Square	Pentagonal
$1 = 1$	$1 = 1$	$1 = 1$
$3 = 1 + 2$	$4 = 1 + 3$	$5 = 1 + 4$
$6 = 1 + 2 + 3$	$9 = 1 + 3 + 5$	$12 = 1 + 4 + 7$
$10 = 1 + 2 + 3 + 4$	$16 = 1 + 3 + 5 + 7$	$22 = 1 + 4 + 7 + 10$
$15 = 1 + 2 + 3 + 4 + 5$	$25 = 1 + 3 + 5 + 7 + 9$	$35 = 1 + 4 + 7 + 10 + 13$

Notice the successive differences of the added terms on the right sides of the equations. The next type of figurate number is the **hexagonal** number. (A hexagon has six sides.) Use the patterns above to predict the first five hexagonal numbers.

47. Eight times any triangular number, plus 1, is a square number. Show that this is true for the first four triangular numbers.

48. Divide the first triangular number by 3 and record the remainder. Divide the second triangular number by 3 and record the remainder. Repeat this procedure several more times. Do you notice a pattern?

49. Repeat **Exercise 48,** but instead use square numbers and divide by 4. What pattern is determined?

50. Exercises 48 and 49 are specific cases of the following: When the numbers in the sequence of n-agonal numbers are divided by n, the sequence of remainders obtained is a repeating sequence. Verify this for $n = 5$ and $n = 6$.

51. Every square number can be written as the sum of two triangular numbers. For example, $16 = 6 + 10$. This can be represented geometrically by dividing a square array of dots with a line as shown.

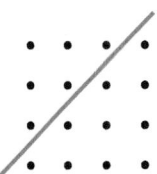

The triangular arrangement above the line represents 6, the one below the line represents 10, and the whole arrangement represents 16. Show how the square numbers 25 and 36 may likewise be geometrically represented as the sum of two triangular numbers.

52. A fraction is in *lowest terms* if the greatest common factor of its numerator and its denominator is 1. For example, $\frac{3}{8}$ is in lowest terms, but $\frac{4}{12}$ is not.

(a) For $n = 2$ to $n = 8$, form the fractions

$$\frac{n\text{th square number}}{(n + 1)\text{st square number}}.$$

(b) Repeat part (a) with triangular numbers.

(c) Use inductive reasoning to make a conjecture based on your results from parts (a) and (b), observing whether the fractions are in lowest terms.

*In addition to the formulas for T_n, S_n, and P_n, the following formulas are true for **hexagonal** numbers (H), **heptagonal** numbers (Hp), and **octagonal** numbers (O):*

$$H_n = \frac{n(4n - 2)}{2}, \quad Hp_n = \frac{n(5n - 3)}{2}, \quad O_n = \frac{n(6n - 4)}{2}.$$

Use these formulas to find each of the following.

53. the sixteenth square number

54. the eleventh triangular number

55. the ninth pentagonal number

56. the seventh hexagonal number

57. the tenth heptagonal number

58. the twelfth octagonal number

59. Observe the formulas given for H_n, Hp_n, and O_n, and use patterns and inductive reasoning to predict the formula for N_n, the *n*th **nonagonal** number. (A nonagon has nine sides.) Then use the fact that the sixth nonagonal number is 111 to further confirm your conjecture.

60. Use the result of **Exercise 59** to find the tenth nonagonal number.

Use inductive reasoning to answer each question.

61. If you add two consecutive triangular numbers, what kind of figurate number do you get?

62. If you add the squares of two consecutive triangular numbers, what kind of figurate number do you get?

63. Square a triangular number. Square the next triangular number. Subtract the smaller result from the larger. What kind of number do you get?

64. Choose a value of n greater than or equal to 2. Find T_{n-1}, multiply it by 3, and add n. What kind of figurate number do you get?

In an arithmetic sequence, the nth term a_n is given by the formula

$$a_n = a_1 + (n - 1)d,$$

where a_1 is the first term and d is the common difference. Similarly, in a geometric sequence, the nth term is given by

$$a_n = a_1 \cdot r^{n-1}.$$

Here r is the common ratio. In Exercises 65–76, use these formulas to determine the indicated term in the given sequence.

65. The eleventh term of $2, 6, 10, 14, \ldots$

66. The sixteenth term of $5, 15, 25, 35, \ldots$

67. The 21st term of $19, 39, 59, 79, \ldots$

68. The 36th term of $8, 38, 68, 98, \ldots$

69. The 101st term of $\frac{1}{2}, 1, \frac{3}{2}, 2, \ldots$

70. The 151st term of $0.75, 1.50, 2.25, 3.00, \ldots$

71. The eleventh term of $2, 4, 8, 16, \ldots$

72. The ninth term of $1, 4, 16, 64, \ldots$

73. The 12th term of $1, \frac{1}{2}, \frac{1}{4}, \frac{1}{8}, \ldots$

74. The 10th term of $1, \frac{1}{3}, \frac{1}{9}, \frac{1}{27}, \ldots$

75. The 8th term of $40, 10, \frac{5}{2}, \frac{5}{8}, \ldots$

76. The 9th term of $10, 2, \frac{2}{5}, \frac{2}{25}, \ldots$

77. In the *For Further Thought* investigation of this section, we saw that the number 6174 is a Kaprekar constant. Use the procedure described there, starting with a three-digit number of your choice whose digits are all different. You should arrive at a particular three-digit number that has the same property described for 6174. What is this three-digit number?

78. Applying the Kaprekar routine to a five-digit number does not reach a single repeating result but instead reaches one of the following ten numbers and then cycles repeatedly through a subset of these ten numbers.

53955, 59994, 61974, 62964, 63954,
71973, 74943, 75933, 82962, 83952

(a) Start with the number 45986 and determine which one of the ten numbers above is reached first.

(b) Start with a five-digit number of your own, and determine which one of the ten numbers is eventually reached first.

*The mathematical array of numbers known as **Pascal's triangle** consists of rows of numbers, each of which contains one more entry than the previous row. The first six rows are shown here.*

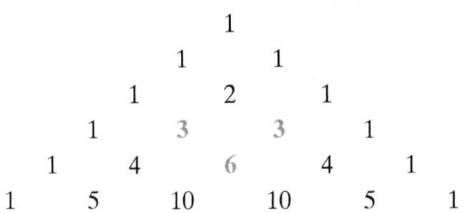

Refer to this array to answer Exercises 79–82.

79. Each row begins and ends with a 1. Discover a method whereby the other entries in a row can be determined from the entries in the row immediately above it. (*Hint:* See the entries in color above.) Find the next three rows of the triangle, and prepare a copy of the first nine rows for later reference.

80. Find the sum of the entries in each of the first eight rows. What is the pattern that emerges? Predict the sum of the entries in the ninth row, and confirm your prediction.

81. The first six rows of the triangle are arranged "flush left" here.

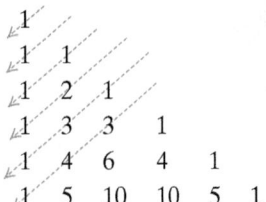

Add along the blue diagonal lines. Write these sums in order from left to right. What sequence is this?

82. Find the values of the first four powers of the number 11, starting with 11^0, which by definition is equal to 1. Predict what the next power of 11 will equal by observing the rows of Pascal's triangle. Confirm your prediction by actual computation.

1.3   STRATEGIES FOR PROBLEM SOLVING

OBJECTIVES

1 Know George Polya's four-step method of problem solving.

2 Be able to apply various strategies for solving problems.

A General Problem-Solving Method

In the first two sections of this chapter we stressed the importance of pattern recognition and the use of inductive reasoning in solving problems. Probably the most famous study of problem-solving techniques was developed by George Polya (1888–1985), among whose many publications was the modern classic *How to Solve It*. In this book, Polya proposed a four-step method for problem solving.

POLYA'S FOUR-STEP METHOD FOR PROBLEM SOLVING

Step 1   **Understand the problem.** You cannot solve a problem if you do not understand what you are asked to find. The problem must be read and analyzed carefully. You may need to read it several times. After you have done so, ask yourself, *"What must I find?"*

Step 2   **Devise a plan.** There are many ways to attack a problem. Decide what plan is appropriate for the particular problem you are solving.

Step 3   **Carry out the plan.** Once you know how to approach the problem, carry out your plan. You may run into "dead ends" and unforeseen roadblocks, but be persistent.

Step 4   **Look back and check.** Check your answer to see that it is reasonable. *Does it satisfy the conditions of the problem? Have you answered all the questions the problem asks? Can you solve the problem a different way and come up with the same answer?*

In Step 2 of Polya's problem-solving method, we are told to devise a plan. Here are some strategies that may prove useful.

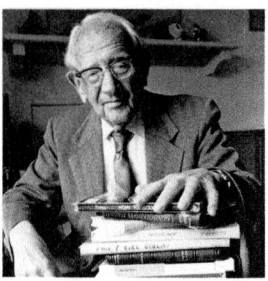

George Polya, author of the classic *How to Solve It*, died at the age of 97 on September 7, 1985. A native of Budapest, Hungary, he was once asked why there were so many good mathematicians to come out of Hungary at the turn of the century. He theorized that it was because mathematics is the cheapest science. It does not require any expensive equipment, only pencil and paper.

Polya authored or coauthored more than 250 papers in many languages, wrote a number of books, and was a brilliant lecturer and teacher. Yet, interestingly enough, he never learned to drive a car.

Problem-Solving Strategies

- Make a table or a chart.
- Look for a pattern.
- Solve a similar, simpler problem.
- Draw a sketch.
- Use inductive reasoning.
- Write an equation and solve it.

- If a formula applies, use it.
- Work backward.
- Guess and check.
- Use trial and error.
- Use common sense.
- Look for a "catch" if an answer seems too obvious or impossible.

Using a Table or Chart

EXAMPLE 1 Solving Fibonacci's Rabbit Problem

A man put a pair of rabbits in a cage. During the first month the rabbits produced no offspring but each month thereafter produced one new pair of rabbits. If each new pair thus produced reproduces in the same manner, how many pairs of rabbits will there be at the end of 1 year? (This problem is a famous one in the history of mathematics and first appeared in *Liber Abaci*, a book written by the Italian mathematician Leonardo Pisano (also known as Fibonacci) in the year 1202.)

Solution

Step 1   **Understand the problem.** We can reword the problem as follows:

> *How many pairs of rabbits will the man have at the end of one year if he starts with one pair, and they reproduce this way: During the first month of life, each pair produces no new rabbits, but each month thereafter each pair produces one new pair?*

Step 2   **Devise a plan.** Because there is a definite pattern to how the rabbits will reproduce, we can construct **Table 2.**

Table 2

Month	Number of Pairs at Start	Number of New Pairs Produced	Number of Pairs at End of Month
1st			
2nd			
3rd			
4th			
5th			
6th			
7th			
8th			
9th			
10th			
11th			
12th			

The answer will go here.

Fibonacci (1170–1250) discovered the sequence named after him in a problem on rabbits. Fibonacci ("son of Bonaccio") is one of several names for Leonardo of Pisa. His father managed a warehouse in present-day Bougie (or Bejaia), in Algeria. Thus it was that Leonardo Pisano studied with a Moorish teacher and learned the "Indian" numbers that the Moors and other Moslems brought with them in their westward drive.

Fibonacci wrote books on algebra, geometry, and trigonometry.

Step 3 **Carry out the plan.** At the start of the first month, there is only one pair of rabbits. No new pairs are produced during the first month, so there is $1 + 0 = 1$ pair present at the end of the first month. This pattern continues. In **Table 3,** we add the number in the first column of numbers to the number in the second column to get the number in the third.

Table 3

Month	Number of Pairs at Start	+	Number of New Pairs Produced	=	Number of Pairs at End of Month	
1st	1		0		1	$1 + 0 = 1$
2nd	1		1		2	$1 + 1 = 2$
3rd	2		1		3	$2 + 1 = 3$
4th	3		2		5	·
5th	5		3		8	·
6th	8		5		13	·
7th	13		8		21	·
8th	21		13		34	·
9th	34		21		55	·
10th	55		34		89	·
11th	89		55		144	·
12th	144		89		**233**	$144 + 89 = 233$

> The answer is the final entry.

There will be **233** pairs of rabbits at the end of one year.

Step 4 **Look back and check.** Go back and make sure that we have interpreted the problem correctly. Double-check the arithmetic. We have answered the question posed by the problem, so the problem is solved. ∎

On January 23, 2005, the CBS television network presented the first episode of *NUMB3RS*, a show focusing on how mathematics is used in solving crimes. David Krumholtz plays Charlie Eppes, a brilliant mathematician who assists his FBI agent brother (Rob Morrow).

In the first-season episode "Sabotage" (2/25/2005), one of the agents admits that she was not a good math student, and Charlie uses the **Fibonacci sequence** and its relationship to nature to enlighten her.

The sequence shown in color in **Table 3** is the Fibonacci sequence, mentioned in **Example 2(b)** of **Section 1.1.**

Working Backward

EXAMPLE 2 **Determining a Wager at the Track**

Ronnie goes to the racetrack with his buddies on a weekly basis. One week he tripled his money, but then lost $12. He took his money back the next week, doubled it, but then lost $40. The following week he tried again, taking his money back with him. He quadrupled it, and then played well enough to take that much home, a total of $224. How much did he start with the first week?

Solution

This problem asks us to find Ronnie's starting amount. Since we know his final amount, the method of working backward can be applied.

Because his final amount was $224 and this represents four times the amount he started with on the third week, we *divide* $224 by 4 to find that he started the third week with $56. Before he lost $40 the second week, he had this $56 plus the $40 he lost, giving him $96.

Augustus De Morgan was an English mathematician and philosopher, who served as professor at the University of London. He wrote numerous books, one of which was *A Budget of Paradoxes*. His work in set theory and logic led to laws that bear his name and are covered in other chapters.

The $96 represented double what he started with, so he started with $96 *divided by* 2, or $48, the second week. Repeating this process once more for the first week, before his $12 loss he had

$$\$48 + \$12 = \$60,$$

which represents triple what he started with. Therefore, he started with

$$\$60 \div 3 = \$20. \quad \text{Answer}$$

To check, observe the following equations that depict winnings and losses.

First week: $(3 \times \$20) - \$12 = \$60 - \$12 = \$48$
Second week: $(2 \times \$48) - \$40 = \$96 - \$40 = \$56$
Third week: $(4 \times \$56) = \$224$ His final amount   ∎

Using Trial and Error

Recall that $5^2 = 5 \cdot 5 = 25$. That is, 5 squared is 25. Thus, 25 is called a **perfect square,** a term that we use in **Example 3.**

1, 4, 9, 16, 25, 36, and so on   Perfect squares

EXAMPLE 3 Finding Augustus De Morgan's Birth Year

The mathematician Augustus De Morgan lived in the nineteenth century. He made the following statement: "I was x years old in the year x^2." In what year was he born?

Solution

We must find the year of De Morgan's birth. The problem tells us that he lived in the nineteenth century, which is another way of saying that he lived during the 1800s. One year of his life was a perfect square, so we must find a number between 1800 and 1900 that is a perfect square. Use trial and error.

$$42^2 = 42 \cdot 42 = 1764$$
$$43^2 = 43 \cdot 43 = 1849 \quad \boxed{\text{1849 is between 1800 and 1900.}}$$
$$44^2 = 44 \cdot 44 = 1936$$

The only natural number whose square is between 1800 and 1900 is 43, because $43^2 = 1849$. Therefore, De Morgan was 43 years old in 1849. The final step in solving the problem is to subtract 43 from 1849 to find the year of his birth.

$$1849 - 43 = 1806 \quad \boxed{\text{He was born in 1806.}}$$

To check this answer, look up De Morgan's birth date in a book dealing with mathematics history, such as *An Introduction to the History of Mathematics,* Sixth Edition, by Howard W. Eves.   ∎

Guessing and Checking

As mentioned above, $5^2 = 25$. The inverse procedure for squaring a number is called taking the **square root.** We indicate the positive square root using a **radical symbol** $\sqrt{\ }$. Thus, $\sqrt{25} = 5$. Also,

$$\sqrt{4} = 2, \quad \sqrt{9} = 3, \quad \sqrt{16} = 4, \quad \text{and so on.} \quad \text{Square roots}$$

The next problem deals with a square root and dates back to Hindu mathematics, circa 850.

EXAMPLE 4 Finding the Number of Camels

One-fourth of a herd of camels was seen in the forest. Twice the square root of that herd had gone to the mountain slopes, and 3 times 5 camels remained on the river-bank. What is the numerical measure of that herd of camels?

Solution

The numerical measure of a herd of camels must be a counting number. Because the problem mentions "one-fourth of a herd" and "the square root of that herd," the number of camels must be both a multiple of 4 and a perfect square, so that only whole numbers are used. The least counting number that satisfies both conditions is 4.

We write an equation where x represents the numerical measure of the herd, and then substitute 4 for x to see if it is a solution.

One-fourth of the herd		Twice the square root of that herd		3 times 5 camels		The numerical measure of the herd.
$\frac{1}{4}x$	$+$	$2\sqrt{x}$	$+$	$3 \cdot 5$	$=$	x

$$\frac{1}{4}(4) + 2\sqrt{4} + 3 \cdot 5 \stackrel{?}{=} 4 \quad \text{Let } x = 4.$$

$$1 + 4 + 15 \stackrel{?}{=} 4 \quad \sqrt{4} = 2$$

$$20 \neq 4$$

Because 4 is not the solution, try 16, the next perfect square that is a multiple of 4.

$$\frac{1}{4}(16) + 2\sqrt{16} + 3 \cdot 5 \stackrel{?}{=} 16 \quad \text{Let } x = 16.$$

$$4 + 8 + 15 \stackrel{?}{=} 16 \quad \sqrt{16} = 4$$

$$27 \neq 16$$

Because 16 is not a solution, try 36.

$$\frac{1}{4}(36) + 2\sqrt{36} + 3 \cdot 5 \stackrel{?}{=} 36 \quad \text{Let } x = 36.$$

$$9 + 12 + 15 \stackrel{?}{=} 36 \quad \sqrt{36} = 6$$

$$36 = 36$$

Thus, 36 is the numerical measure of the herd.

Check: "One-fourth of 36, plus twice the square root of 36, plus 3 times 5" gives 9 plus 12 plus 15, which equals 36. ∎

Considering a Similar, Simpler Problem

EXAMPLE 5 Finding the Units Digit of a Power

The digit farthest to the right in a counting number is called the *ones* or *units* digit, because it tells how many ones are contained in the number when grouping by tens is considered. What is the ones (or units) digit in 2^{4000}?

Solution

Recall that 2^{4000} means that 2 is used as a factor 4000 times.

$$2^{4000} = \underbrace{2 \times 2 \times 2 \times \cdots \times 2}_{4000 \text{ factors}}$$

Mathematics to Die For In the 1995 movie *Die Hard: With a Vengeance,* detective John McClane (Bruce Willis) is tormented by the villain Simon Gruber (Jeremy Irons), who has planted a bomb in a park. Gruber presents McClane and his partner Zeus Carver (Samuel L. Jackson) with a riddle for disarming it, but there is a time limit. The riddle requires that they get exactly 4 gallons of water using 3-gallon and 5-gallon jugs having no markers. They are able to solve it and defuse the bomb. Can you do it? (See the next page for the answer.)

To answer the question, we examine some smaller powers of 2 and then look for a pattern. We start with the exponent 1 and look at the first twelve powers of 2.

$$2^1 = 2 \qquad 2^5 = 32 \qquad 2^9 = 512$$
$$2^2 = 4 \qquad 2^6 = 64 \qquad 2^{10} = 1024$$
$$2^3 = 8 \qquad 2^7 = 128 \qquad 2^{11} = 2048$$
$$2^4 = 16 \qquad 2^8 = 256 \qquad 2^{12} = 4096$$

Notice that in any one of the four rows above, the ones digit is the same all the way across the row. The final row, which contains the exponents 4, 8, and 12, has the ones digit 6. Each of these exponents is divisible by 4, and because 4000 is divisible by 4, we can use inductive reasoning to predict that the units digit in 2^{4000} is **6**.

(*Note:* The units digit for any other power can be found if we divide the exponent by 4 and consider the remainder. Then compare the result to the list of powers above. For example, to find the units digit of 2^{543}, divide 543 by 4 to get a quotient of 135 and a remainder of **3**. The units digit is the same as that of 2^3, which is **8**.) ∎

Drawing a Sketch

EXAMPLE 6 Connecting the Dots

An array of nine dots is arranged in a 3×3 square, as shown in **Figure 5**. Is it possible to join the dots with exactly four straight line segments if you are not allowed to pick up your pencil from the paper and may not trace over a segment that has already been drawn? If so, show how.

Solution

Figure 6 shows three attempts. In each case, something is wrong. In the first sketch, one dot is not joined. In the second, the figure cannot be drawn without picking up your pencil from the paper or tracing over a line that has already been drawn. In the third figure, all dots have been joined, but you have used five line segments as well as retraced over the figure.

Figure 6

The conditions of the problem can be satisfied, as shown in **Figure 7.** We "went outside of the box," which was not prohibited by the conditions of the problem. This is an example of creative thinking—we used a strategy that often is not considered at first. ∎

Figure 5

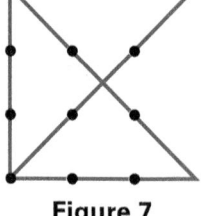

Figure 7

Using Common Sense

Problem-Solving Strategies

Some problems involve a "catch." They seem too easy or perhaps impossible at first because we tend to overlook an obvious situation. Look carefully at the use of language in such problems. And, of course, never forget to use common sense.

EXAMPLE 7 Determining Coin Denominations

Two currently minted United States coins together have a total value of $1.05. One is not a dollar. What are the two coins?

Solution

Our initial reaction might be, "The only way to have two such coins with a total of $1.05 is to have a nickel and a dollar, but the problem says that one of them is not a dollar." This statement is indeed true. What we must realize here is that the one that is not a dollar is the nickel, and the *other* coin is a dollar! So the two coins are a dollar and a nickel. ∎

1.3 EXERCISES

One of the most popular features in the journal Mathematics Teacher, *published by the National Council of Teachers of Mathematics, is the monthly calendar. It provides an interesting, unusual, or challenging problem for each day of the month. Some of these exercises, and others later in this text, are chosen from these calendars (the day, month, and year of publication of each problem are indicated). The authors want to thank the many contributors for permission to use these problems.*

Use the various problem-solving strategies to solve each problem. In many cases there is more than one possible approach, so be creative.

1. *Broken Elevator* A man enters a building on the first floor and runs up to the third floor in 20 seconds. At this rate, how many seconds would it take for the man to run from the first floor up to the sixth floor? (October 3, 2010)

2. *Saving Her Dollars* Every day Sally saved a penny, a dime, and a quarter. What is the least number of days required for her to save an amount equal to an integral (counting) number of dollars? (January 11, 2012)

3. *Do You Have a Match?* Move 4 of the matches in the figure to create exactly 3 equilateral triangles. (An *equilateral triangle* has all three sides the same length.) (February 20, 2011)

4. *Sudoku* Sudoku is an $n \times n$ puzzle that requires the solver to fill in all the squares using the integers 1 through n. Each row, column, and subrectangle contains exactly one of each number. Complete the $n \times n$ puzzle. (June 25, 2012)

			4
2			
	1		
		1	

5. *Break This Code* Each letter of the alphabet is assigned an integer, starting with A = 0, B = 1, and so on. The numbers repeat after every seven letters, so that G = 6, H = 0, and I = 1, continuing on to Z. What two-letter word is represented by the digits 16? (October 3, 2011)

6. *A Real Problem* We are given the following sequence:

PROBLEMSOLVINGPROBLEMSOLVINGPROB...

If the pattern continues, what letter will be in the 2012th position? (November 1, 2012)

7. *How Old Is Mommy?* A mother has two children whose ages differ by 5 years. The sum of the squares of their ages is 97. The square of the mother's age can be found by writing the squares of the children's ages one after the other as a four-digit number. How old is the mother? (March 9, 2012)

8. *An Alarming Situation* You have three alarms in your room. Your cell phone alarm is set to ring every 30 minutes, your computer alarm is set to ring every 20 minutes, and your clock alarm is set to ring every 45 minutes. If all three alarms go off simultaneously at 12:34 p.m., when is the next time that they will go off simultaneously? (November 2, 2012)

9. *Laundry Day* Every Monday evening, a mathematics teacher stops by the dry cleaners, drops off the shirts that he wore for the week, and picks up his previous week's load. If he wears a clean shirt every day, including Saturday and Sunday, what is the minimum number of shirts that he can own? (April 1, 2012)

10. *Pick an Envelope* Three envelopes contain a total of six bills. One envelope contains two $10 bills, one contains two $20 bills, and the third contains one $10 and one $20 bill. A label on each envelope indicates the sum of money in one of the other envelopes. It is possible to select one envelope, see one bill in that envelope, and then state the contents of all of the envelopes. Which envelope should you choose? (May 1, 2012)

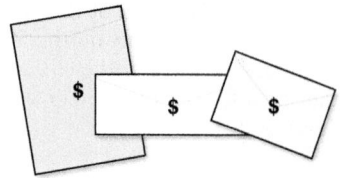

11. *Class Members* A classroom contains an equal number of boys and girls. If 8 girls leave, twice as many boys as girls remain. What was the original number of students present? (May 24, 2008)

12. *Give Me a Digit* Given a two-digit number, make a three-digit number by putting a 6 as the rightmost digit. Then add 6 to the resulting three-digit number and remove the rightmost digit to obtain another two-digit number. If the result is 76, what is the original two-digit number? (October 18, 2009)

13. *Missing Digit* Look for a pattern and find the missing digit x.

$$
\begin{array}{cccc}
3 & 2 & 4 & 8 \\
7 & 2 & 1 & 3 \\
8 & 4 & x & 5 \\
4 & 3 & 6 & 9 \\
\end{array}
$$

(February 14, 2009)

14. *Abundancy* An integer $n > 1$ is **abundant** if the sum of its proper divisors (positive integer divisors smaller than n) is greater than n. Find the smallest abundant integer. (November 27, 2009)

15. *Cross-Country Competition* The schools in an athletic conference compete in a cross-country meet to which each school sends three participants. Erin, Katelyn, and Iliana are the three representatives from one school. Erin finished the race in the middle position; Katelyn finished after Erin, in the 19th position; and Iliana finished 28th. How many schools took part in the race? (May 27, 2008)

16. *Gone Fishing* Four friends go fishing one day and bring home a total of 11 fish. If each person caught at least 1 fish, then which of the following *must* be true?

   A. One person caught exactly 2 fish.

   B. One person caught exactly 3 fish.

   C. One person caught fewer than 3 fish.

   D. One person caught more than 3 fish.

   E. Two people each caught more than 1 fish.

   (May 24, 2008)

17. *Cutting a Square in Half* In how many ways can a single straight line cut a square in half? (October 2, 2008)

18. *You Lie!* Max, Sam, and Brett were playing basketball. One of them broke a window, and the other two saw him break it. Max said, "I am innocent." Sam said, "Max and I are both innocent." Brett said, "Max and Sam are both innocent." If only one of them is telling the truth, who broke the window? (September 21, 2008)

19. *Bookworm Snack* A 26-volume encyclopedia (one for each letter) is placed on a bookshelf in alphabetical order from left to right. Each volume is 2 inches thick, including the front and back covers. Each cover is $\frac{1}{4}$ inch thick. A bookworm eats straight through the encyclopedia, beginning inside the front cover of volume A and ending after eating through the back cover of volume Z. How many inches of book did the bookworm eat? (November 12, 2008)

20. *Pick a Card, Any Card* Three face cards from an ordinary deck of playing cards lie facedown in a horizontal row and are arranged such that immediately to the right of a king is a queen or two queens, immediately to the left of a queen is a queen or two queens, immediately to the left of a heart is a spade or two spades, and immediately to the right of a spade is a spade or two spades. Name the three cards in order. (April 23, 2008)

21. *Catwoman's Cats* If you ask Batman's nemesis, Catwoman, how many cats she has, she answers with a riddle: "Five-sixths of my cats plus seven." How many cats does Catwoman have? (April 20, 2003)

22. *Pencil Collection* Bob gave four-fifths of his pencils to Barbara, then he gave two-thirds of the remaining pencils to Bonnie. If he ended up with ten pencils for himself, with how many did he start? (October 12, 2003)

23. *Adding Gasoline* The gasoline gauge on a van initially read $\frac{1}{8}$ full. When 15 gallons were added to the tank, the gauge read $\frac{3}{4}$ full. How many more gallons are needed to fill the tank? (November 25, 2004)

24. *Gasoline Tank Capacity* When 6 gallons of gasoline are put into a car's tank, the indicator goes from $\frac{1}{4}$ of a tank to $\frac{5}{8}$. What is the total capacity of the gasoline tank? (February 21, 2004)

25. *Number Pattern* What is the relationship between the rows of numbers?

18,	38,	24,	46,	42
8,	24,	8,	24,	8

(May 26, 2005)

26. *Locking Boxes* You and I each have one lock and a corresponding key. I want to mail you a box with a ring in it, but any box that is not locked will be emptied before it reaches its recipient. How can I safely send you the ring? (Note that you and I each have keys to our own lock but not to the other lock.) (May 4, 2004)

27. *Number in a Sequence* In the sequence 16, 80, 48, 64, A, B, C, D, each term beyond the second term is the arithmetic mean (average) of the two previous terms. What is the value of D? (April 26, 2004)

28. *Unknown Number* Cindy was asked by her teacher to subtract 3 from a certain number and then divide the result by 9. Instead, she subtracted 9 and then divided the result by 3, giving an answer of 43. What would her answer have been if she had worked the problem correctly? (September 3, 2004)

29. *Unfolding and Folding a Box* An unfolded box is shown below.

	2		
1	**3**	**5**	**6**
	4		

Which figure shows the box folded up? (November 7, 2001)

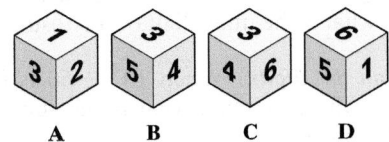

A   B   C   D

30. *Vertical Symmetry in States' Names* (If a vertical line is drawn through the center of a figure, and the left and right sides are reflections of each other across this line, the figure is said to have vertical symmetry.) When spelled with all capital letters, each letter in HAWAII has vertical symmetry. Find the name of a state whose letters all have vertical and horizontal symmetry. (September 11, 2001)

31. *Labeling Boxes* You are working in a store that has been very careless with the stock. Three boxes of socks are each incorrectly labeled. The labels say *red socks, green socks,* and *red and green socks.* How can you relabel the boxes correctly by taking only one sock out of one box, without looking inside the boxes? (October 22, 2001)

32. *Mr. Green's Age* At his birthday party, Mr. Green would not directly tell how old he was. He said, "If you add the year of my birth to this year, subtract the year of my tenth birthday and the year of my fiftieth birthday, and then add my present age, the result is eighty." How old was Mr. Green? (December 14, 1997)

33. *Sum of Hidden Dots on Dice* Three dice with faces numbered 1 through 6 are stacked as shown. Seven of the eighteen faces are visible, leaving eleven faces hidden on the back, on the bottom, and between dice. The total number of dots not visible in this view is _____.

A. 21
B. 22
C. 31
D. 41
E. 53

(September 17, 2001)

34. *Age of the Bus Driver* Today is your first day driving a city bus. When you leave downtown, you have twenty-three passengers. At the first stop, three people exit and five people get on the bus. At the second stop, eleven people exit and eight people get on the bus. At the third stop, five people exit and ten people get on. How old is the bus driver? (April 1, 2002)

35. *Matching Triangles and Squares* How can you connect each square with the triangle that has the same number? Lines cannot cross, enter a square or triangle, or go outside the diagram. (October 15, 1999)

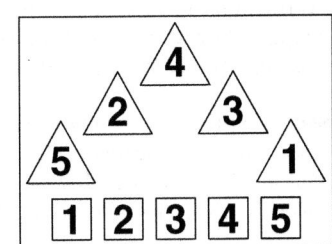

36. *Forming Perfect Square Sums* How must one place the integers from 1 to 15 in each of the spaces below in such a way that no number is repeated and the sum of the numbers in any two consecutive spaces is a perfect square? (November 11, 2001)

37. *Difference Triangle* Balls numbered 1 through 6 are arranged in a **difference triangle.** Note that in any row, the difference between the larger and the smaller of two successive balls is the number of the ball that appears below them. Arrange balls numbered 1 through 10 in a difference triangle. (May 6, 1998)

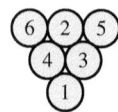

38. *Clock Face* By drawing two straight lines, divide the face of a clock into three regions such that the numbers in the regions have the same total. (October 28, 1998)

39. *Alphametric* If a, b, and c are digits for which

$$
\begin{array}{r}
7\ a\ 2 \\
-4\ 8\ b \\
\hline
c\ 7\ 3,
\end{array}
$$

then $a + b + c =$ ____ .

A. 14 **B.** 15 **C.** 16 **D.** 17 **E.** 18

(September 22, 1999)

40. *Perfect Square* Only one of these numbers is a perfect square. Which one is it? (October 8, 1997)

329476   389372   964328
326047   724203

41. *Sleeping on the Way to Grandma's House* While traveling to his grandmother's for Christmas, George fell asleep halfway through the journey. When he awoke, he still had to travel half the distance that he had traveled while sleeping. For what part of the entire journey had he been asleep? (December 25, 1998)

42. *Buckets of Water* You have brought two unmarked buckets to a stream. The buckets hold 7 gallons and 3 gallons of water, respectively. How can you obtain exactly 5 gallons of water to take home? (October 19, 1997)

43. *Counting Puzzle (Rectangles)* How many rectangles are in the figure? (March 27, 1997)

44. *Digit Puzzle* Place each of the digits 1, 2, 3, 4, 5, 6, 7, and 8 in separate boxes so that boxes that share common corners do not contain successive digits. (November 29, 1997)

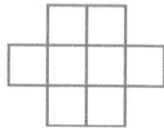

45. *Palindromic Number* (*Note*: A **palindromic number** is a number whose digits read the same left to right as right to left. For example, 383, 12321, and 9876789 are palindromic.) The odometer of the family car read 15951 when the driver noticed that the number was palindromic. "Curious," said the driver to herself. "It will be a long time before that happens again." But 2 hours later, the odometer showed a new palindromic number. (*Author's note:* Assume it was the next possible one.) How fast was the car driving in those 2 hours? (December 26, 1998)

46. *How Much Is That Doggie in the Window?* A man wishes to sell a puppy for $11. A customer who wants to buy it has only foreign currency. The exchange rate for the foreign currency is as follows: 11 round coins = $15, 11 square coins = $16, 11 triangular coins = $17. How many of each coin should the customer pay? (April 20, 2008)

47. *Final Digits of a Power of 7* What are the final two digits of 7^{1997}? (November 29, 1997)

48. *Units Digit of a Power of 3* If you raise 3 to the 324th power, what is the units digit of the result?

49. *Summing the Digits* When $10^{50} - 50$ is expressed as a single whole number, what is the sum of its digits? (April 7, 2008)

50. Frog Climbing up a Well A frog is at the bottom of a 20-foot well. Each day it crawls up 4 feet, but each night it slips back 3 feet. After how many days will the frog reach the top of the well?

51. Units Digit of a Power of 7 What is the units digit in 7^{491}?

52. Money Spent at a Bazaar Christine bought a book for $10 and then spent half her remaining money on a train ticket. She then bought lunch for $4 and spent half her remaining money at a bazaar. She left the bazaar with $8. How much money did she start with?

53. Going Postal Joanie wants to mail a package that requires $1.53 in postage. If she has only 5-cent and 8-cent stamps, what is the smallest number of stamps she could use that would total exactly $1.53? (August 20, 2008)

54. Counting Puzzle (Squares) How many squares are in the figure?

55. Matching Socks A drawer contains 20 black socks and 20 white socks. If the light is off and you reach into the drawer to get your socks, what is the minimum number of socks you must pull out in order to be sure that you have a matching pair?

56. Counting Puzzle (Triangles) How many triangles are in the figure?

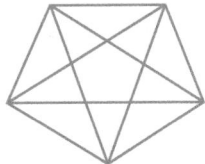

57. Perfect Number A **perfect number** is a counting number that is equal to the sum of all its counting number divisors except itself. For example, 28 is a perfect number because its divisors other than itself are 1, 2, 4, 7, and 14, and $1 + 2 + 4 + 7 + 14 = 28$. What is the least perfect number?

58. Naming Children Becky's mother has three daughters. She named her first daughter Penny and her second daughter Nichole. What did she name her third daughter?

59. Growth of a Lily Pad A lily pad grows so that each day it doubles its size. On the twentieth day of its life, it completely covers a pond. On what day was the pond half covered?

60. Interesting Property of a Sentence Comment on an interesting property of this sentence: "A man, a plan, a canal, Panama." (*Hint:* See **Exercise 45.**)

61. High School Graduation Year of Author One of the authors of this book graduated from high school in the year that satisfies these conditions: (1) The sum of the digits is 23; (2) The hundreds digit is 3 more than the tens digit; (3) No digit is an 8. In what year did he graduate?

62. Where in the World Is Matt Lauer? Matt Lauer is one of the hosts of the *Today* show on the NBC television network. From time to time he travels the world and is in a new location each day of the week, which is unknown even to his co-hosts back in the studio in New York. On one day, he decided to give them a riddle as a hint to where he would be on the following day. Here's the riddle:

> This country is an ANAGRAM of a SYNONYM of a HOMOPHONE of an EVEN PRIME NUMBER.

In what country was Matt going to be the following day? (If you are unfamiliar with some of the terms in capital letters, look up their definitions.)

63. Adam and Eve's Assets Eve said to Adam, "If you give me one dollar, then we will have the same amount of money." Adam then replied, "Eve, if you give me one dollar, I will have double the amount of money you are left with." How much does each have?

64. Missing Digits Puzzle In the addition problem below, some digits are missing, as indicated by the blanks. If the problem is done correctly, what is the sum of the missing digits?

$$
\begin{array}{r}
\_\ 3\ 5 \\
8\ \_\ 6 \\
+\ 1\ 4\ \_ \\
\hline
\_\ 4\ 0\ 8
\end{array}
$$

65. Missing Digits Puzzle Fill in the blanks so that the multiplication problem below uses all digits 0, 1, 2, 3, ..., 9 exactly once and is worked correctly.

$$
\begin{array}{r}
\_\ 0\ 2 \\
\times\quad 3\ \_ \\
\hline
\_\ 5,\ \_\ \_\ \_
\end{array}
$$

66. *Magic Square* A **magic square** is a square array of numbers that has the property that the sum of the numbers in any row, column, or diagonal is the same. Fill in the square below so that it becomes a magic square, and all digits 1, 2, 3, . . . , 9 are used exactly once.

6		8
	5	
		4

67. *Magic Square* Refer to **Exercise 66.** Complete the magic square below so that all counting numbers 1, 2, 3, . . . , 16 are used exactly once, and the sum in each row, column, or diagonal is 34.

6			9
	15		14
11		10	
16		13	

68. *Decimal Digit* What is the 100th digit in the decimal representation for $\frac{1}{7}$?

69. *Pitches in a Baseball Game* What is the minimum number of pitches that a baseball player who pitches a complete game can make in a regulation 9-inning baseball game?

70. *Weighing Coins* You have eight coins. Seven are genuine and one is a fake, which weighs a little less than the other seven. You have a balance scale, which you may use only three times. Tell how to locate the bad coin in three weighings. (Then show how to detect the bad coin in only *two* weighings.)

71. *Geometry Puzzle* When the diagram shown is folded to form a cube, what letter is opposite the face marked Z?

72. *Geometry Puzzle* Draw the following figure without picking up your pencil from the paper and without tracing over a line you have already drawn.

73. *Geometry Puzzle* Repeat **Exercise 72** for this figure.

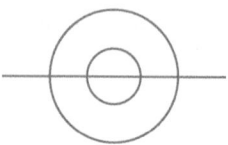

74. *Books on a Shelf* Volumes 1 and 2 of *The Complete Works of Wally Smart* are standing in numerical order from left to right on your bookshelf. Volume 1 has 450 pages and Volume 2 has 475 pages. Excluding the covers, how many pages are between page 1 of Volume 1 and page 475 of Volume 2?

75. *Paying for a Mint* Brian has an unlimited number of cents (pennies), nickels, and dimes. In how many different ways can he pay 15¢ for a chocolate mint? (For example, one way is 1 dime and 5 pennies.)

76. *Teenager's Age* A teenager's age increased by 2 gives a perfect square. Her age decreased by 10 gives the square root of that perfect square. She is 5 years older than her brother. How old is her brother?

77. *Area and Perimeter* Triangle *ABC* has sides 10, 24, and 26 cm long. A rectangle that has an area equal to that of the triangle is 3 cm wide. Find the perimeter of the rectangle. (November 13, 2008)

78. *Making Change* In how many different ways can you make change for a half dollar using currently minted U.S. coins, if cents (pennies) are not allowed?

79. *Ages* James, Dan, Jessica, and Cathy form a pair of married couples. Their ages are 36, 31, 30, and 29. Jessica is married to the oldest person in the group. James is older than Jessica but younger than Cathy. Who is married to whom, and what are their ages?

80. *Final Digit* What is the last digit of $49{,}327^{17783}$? (April 11, 2009)

81. *Geometry Puzzle* What is the maximum number of small squares in which we may place crosses (×) and not have any row, column, or diagonal completely filled with crosses? Illustrate your answer.

82. *Making Change* Webster has some pennies, dimes, and quarters in his pocket. When Josefa asks him for change for a dollar, Webster discovers that he cannot make the change exactly. What is the largest possible total value of the coins in his pocket? (October 5, 2009)

WHEN Will I Ever USE This ?

Suppose that you are an employee of a group home, and you have been assigned to provide the necessary items for a Thanksgiving meal for ten of the residents of the home, who will be preparing the meal for themselves. You decide that the dinner will be a traditional one: turkey, stuffing, cranberry sauce, yams, green bean casserole, rolls, and iced tea. You must go to the supermarket for these items and have decided to use cash to pay for them. Of course, you do not want to approach the checkout counter and not have enough for the purchase. You also know that a sales tax of 8.75% will be added to the total. You take your allotment of $80 in cash with you.

In a situation like this, it is not difficult to get a fairly accurate idea of what the total will be by mentally rounding each item (up or down) to the nearest dollar and keeping a running total along the way as you place items in the shopping cart. Here is an example of this procedure.

Item	Actual Cost	Estimate
18-lb turkey	$26.82	$30
12-pack of dinner rolls	2.29	2
15-oz container of margarine	2.79	3
40-oz can of yams	3.34	3
28-oz can of cranberry sauce	3.97	4
26-oz can of cream of mushroom soup	2.99	3
14-oz bag of herb stuffing	3.59	4
1-lb bag of pecans	8.79	9
50-oz can of green beans	2.59	3
28-oz can of onion flakes	2.19	2
22-bag pack of tea bags	4.29	4

Before reaching the checkout counter, look at the items in the basket (move from the top to the bottom in the third column) and add them, rounding off whenever doing so helps to simplify the computation. Here is one of many ways this can be done. (Remember, this is not an *exact* computation, so thought processes will vary.)

"30 plus 2 gives 32; I notice that the next three items total 10, so 32 plus 10 equals 42, which I will round down to 40; plus 3 gives 43; plus 4 gives 47, which I will round up to 50; I will round 9 to 10 and add 50 to 10 to give 60; the final three items total 9, which I will round down to 8 (because I rounded up just before) and add to 60 to get 68; 68 is about 70."

Before tax is added, the items total about $70. The sales tax is 8.75%, so round this to 10%. Taking 10% of a number is simple: Just move the decimal point one unit to the left. In this case, the tax will be about $7. So add 7 to 70 to get an approximate total of $77. It looks like $80 will cover the total cost.

Now, as the cashier rings up the purchase, the screen shows that the actual total cost is $63.65, the sales tax is $5.57, and the grand total is $69.22. The estimate is a bit high in this example (because most of the roundoffs were "upward"), but this is what "being in the ballpark" means: The estimate is close enough for our purpose.

Happy Thanksgiving.

1.4 NUMERACY IN TODAY'S WORLD

OBJECTIVES

1 Be able to use a calculator for routine mathematical operations.

2 Be able to use estimation techniques.

3 Be able to interpret information by reading circle, bar, and line graphs.

4 Be able to use writing skills to convey information about mathematics.

The familiar term *literacy* applies to language in the same way that the term **numeracy** applies to mathematics. It is virtually impossible to function in the world today without understanding fundamental number concepts. The basic ideas of calculating, estimating, interpreting data from graphs, and conveying mathematics via language and writing are among the skills required to be "numerate."

Calculation

The search for easier ways to calculate and compute has culminated in the development of hand-held calculators and computers. For the general population, a calculator that performs the operations of arithmetic and a few other functions is sufficient. These are known as **four-function calculators.** Students who take higher mathematics courses (engineers, for example) usually need the added power of **scientific calculators. Graphing calculators,** which actually plot graphs on small screens, are also available. *Always refer to your owner's manual if you need assistance in performing an operation with your calculator. If you need further help, ask your instructor or another student who is using the same model.*

Today's smartphones routinely include a calculator application (app). For example, Apple's iPhone has an app that serves as a four-function calculator when the phone is held vertically, but it becomes a scientific calculator when held horizontally. Furthermore, graphing calculator apps are available at little or no cost. Although it is not necessary to have a graphing calculator to study the material presented in this text, we occasionally include graphing calculator screens to support results obtained or to provide supplemental information.*

The screens that follow illustrate some common entries and operations.

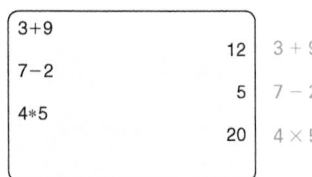

Screen A	
3+9	12
7−2	5
4*5	20

$3 + 9 = 12$
$7 - 2 = 5$
$4 \times 5 = 20$

A

Screen B	
24/20	1.2
Ans▶Frac	$\frac{6}{5}$
5−(8−7)	4

$\frac{24}{20} = 1.2$
$1.2 = \frac{6}{5}$
$5 - (8 - 7) = 4$

B

Screen C	
7^2	49
5^3	125
$\sqrt{81}$	9

$7^2 = 49$
$5^3 = 125$
$\sqrt{81} = 9$

C

Shown here is an example of a **calculator app** from a smartphone. Since the introduction of hand-held calculators in the early 1970s, the methods of everyday arithmetic have been drastically altered. One of the first consumer models available was the Texas Instruments SR-10, which sold for nearly $150 in 1973. It could perform the four operations of arithmetic and take square roots, but it could do very little more.

Screen A illustrates how two numbers can be added, subtracted, or multiplied. Screen B shows how two numbers can be divided, how the decimal quotient (stored in the memory cell Ans) can be converted into a fraction, and how parentheses can be used in a computation. Screen C shows how a number can be squared, how it can be cubed, and how its square root can be taken.

Screen D	
$\sqrt[3]{27}$	3
$\sqrt[4]{16}$	2
5^{-1}	.2

$\sqrt[3]{27} = 3$
$\sqrt[4]{16} = 2$
$5^{-1}\left(\text{or } \frac{1}{5}\right) = .2$

D

Screen E	
π	3.141592654
5!	120
6265804*8980591	5.627062301ᴇ13

$\pi \approx 3.141592654$
5! (or $1 \times 2 \times 3 \times 4 \times 5$) = 120
6,265,804 $\times$ 8,980,591 $\approx 5.627062301 \times 10^{13}$
$\approx$ indicates "is approximately equal to"

E

---

*Because it is one of the most popular graphing calculators, we include screens similar to those generated by the TI-83 Plus and TI-84 Plus from Texas Instruments.

The popular **TI-84 Plus** graphing calculator is shown here.

Screen D shows how other roots (cube root and fourth root) can be found, and how the reciprocal of a number can be found using -1 as an exponent. Screen E shows how π can be accessed with its own special key, how a *factorial* (as indicated by !) can be found, and how a result might be displayed in *scientific notation*. (The "E13" following 5.627062301 means that this number is multiplied by 10^{13}. This answer is still only an approximation, because the product $6,265,804 \times 8,980,591$ contains more digits than the calculator can display.)

In **Section 1.3** we presented a list of problem-solving strategies. As Terry Krieger points out in the chapter opener, "mathematics may be the only discipline in which different people, using wildly varied but logically sound methods, will arrive at the same correct result" with respect to solving problems. Sometimes more than one strategy can be used in a particular situation. In **Example 1,** we present a type of problem that has been around for thousands of years in various forms, and is solved by observing a pattern within a table. One ancient form of this problem deals with doubling a kernel of corn for each square on a checkerbord. (See http://mathforum.org/sanders/geometry/GP11Fable.html.) It illustrates an example of exponential growth, covered in more detail in a later chapter.

▊EXAMPLE 1 Calculating a Sum That Involves a Pattern

Following her success in *I Love Lucy*, Lucille Ball starred in *The Lucy Show*, which aired for six seasons on CBS in the 1960s. She worked for Mr. Mooney (Gale Gordon), who was very careful with his money.

In the September 26, 1966, show "Lucy, the Bean Queen," Lucy learned a lesson about saving money. Mr. Mooney had refused to lend her $1500 to buy furniture, because he claimed she did not know the value of money. He explained to her that if she were to save so that she would have one penny on Day 1, two pennies on Day 2, four pennies on Day 3, and so on, she would have more than enough money to buy her furniture after only nineteen days. Use a calculator to verify this fact.

Solution

A calculator will help in constructing **Table 4.**

Table 4

Day Number	Accumulated Savings on That Day	Day Number	Accumulated Savings on That Day
1	$0.01	11	$10.24
2	0.02	12	20.48
3	0.04	13	40.96
4	0.08	14	81.92
5	0.16	15	163.84
6	0.32	16	327.68
7	0.64	17	655.36
8	1.28	18	1310.72
9	2.56	19	2621.44
10	5.12		

So, indeed, Lucy will have accumulated $2621.44 on day 19, which is enough to buy the furniture.) ▮

Estimation

Although calculators can make life easier when it comes to computations, many times we need only estimate an answer to a problem, and in these cases, using a calculator may not be necessary or appropriate.

EXAMPLE 2   Estimating an Appropriate Number of Birdhouses

A birdhouse for swallows can accommodate up to 8 nests. How many birdhouses would be necessary to accommodate 58 nests?

Solution

If we divide 58 by 8 either by hand or with a calculator, we get 7.25. Can this possibly be the desired number? Of course not, because we cannot consider fractions of birdhouses. Do we need 7 or 8 birdhouses?

To provide nesting space for the nests left over after the 7 birdhouses (as indicated by the decimal fraction), we should plan to use 8 birdhouses. In this problem, we must round our answer *up* to the next counting number.   ■

EXAMPLE 3   Approximating Average Number of Yards per Carry

In 2013, Fred Jackson of the Buffalo Bills carried the football a total of 206 times for 890 yards (*Source:* www.nfl.com). Approximate his average number of yards per carry that year.

Solution

Because we are told only to find Jackson's approximate average, we can say that he carried about 200 times for about 900 yards, and his average was therefore about $\frac{900}{200} = 4.5$ yards per carry. (A calculator shows that his average to the nearest tenth was 4.3 yards per carry. Verify this.)   ■

In the introduction to his book *Innumeracy: Mathematical Illiteracy and Its Consequences,* Temple University professor **John Allen Paulos** writes

Innumeracy, *an inability to deal comfortably with the fundamental notions of number and chance, plagues far too many otherwise knowledgeable citizens.*
. . .

(W)e were watching the news and the TV weathercaster announced that there was a 50 percent chance of rain for Saturday and a 50 percent chance for Sunday, and concluded that there was therefore a 100 percent chance of rain that weekend. . . . (U)nlike other failings which are hidden, mathematical illiteracy is often flaunted. "I can't even balance my checkbook." "I'm a people person, not a numbers person." Or "I always hated math."

Interpretation of Graphs

In a **circle graph,** or **pie chart,** a circle is used to indicate the total of all the data categories represented. The circle is divided into sectors, or wedges (like pieces of a pie), whose sizes show the relative magnitudes of the categories. The sum of all the fractional parts must be 1 (for one whole circle).

EXAMPLE 4   Interpreting Information in a Circle Graph

In a recent month there were about 2100 million (2.1 billion) Internet users worldwide. The circle graph in **Figure 8** shows the approximate shares of these users living in various regions of the world.

(a) Which region had the largest share of Internet users? What was that share?

(b) Estimate the number of Internet users in North America.

(c) How many actual Internet users were there in North America?

Worldwide Internet Users by Region

North America 13%

Asia 44%

Other 20.5%

Europe 22.5%

Source: www.internetworldstats.com

Figure 8

Solution

(a) In the circle graph, the sector for Asia is the largest, so Asia had the largest share of Internet users, 44%.

(b) A share of 13% can be rounded down to 10%. Then find 10% of 2100 million by finding $\frac{1}{10}$ of 2100, or 210. There were *about* 210 million users in North America. (This estimate is low, because we rounded *down*.)

(c) To find the actual number of users, find 13% of 2100 million. We do this by multiplying 0.13 × 2100 million.

$$\underbrace{0.13}_{13\%} \quad \times \quad \underbrace{2100 \text{ million}}_{\substack{\text{of} \\ \text{total}}} \quad = \quad \underbrace{273 \text{ million}}_{\substack{\text{Actual number} \\ \text{of users in} \\ \text{North America}}}$$

■

A **bar graph** is used to show comparisons. It consists of a series of bars (or simulations of bars) arranged either vertically or horizontally. In a bar graph, values from two categories are paired with each other (for example, years with dollar amounts).

EXAMPLE 5 Interpreting Information in a Bar Graph

The bar graph in **Figure 9** shows annual per-capita spending on health care in the United States for the years 2004 through 2009.

Per-Capita Spending on Health Care

Source: U.S. Centers for Medicare and Medicaid Services.

Figure 9

(a) In what years was per-capita health care spending greater than $7000?

(b) Estimate per-capita health care spending in 2004 and 2008.

(c) Describe the change in per-capita spending as the years progressed.

Solution

(a) Locate 7000 on the vertical axis and follow the line across to the right. Three years—2007, 2008, and 2009—have bars that extend above the line for 7000, so per-capita health care spending was greater than $7000 in those years.

(b) Locate the top of the bar for 2004 and move horizontally across to the vertical scale to see that it is about 6000. Per-capita health care spending for 2004 was about $6000.

Similarly, follow the top of the bar for 2008 across to the vertical scale to see that it lies a little more than halfway between 7000 and 7500, so per-capita health care spending in 2008 was about $7300.

(c) As the years progressed, per-capita spending on health care increased steadily, from about $6000 in 2004 to about $7500 in 2009. ∎

A **line graph** is used to show changes or trends in data over time. To form a line graph, we connect a series of points representing data with line segments.

EXAMPLE 6 Interpreting Information in a Line Graph

The line graph in **Figure 10** shows average prices of a gallon of regular unleaded gasoline in the United States for the years 2004 through 2011.

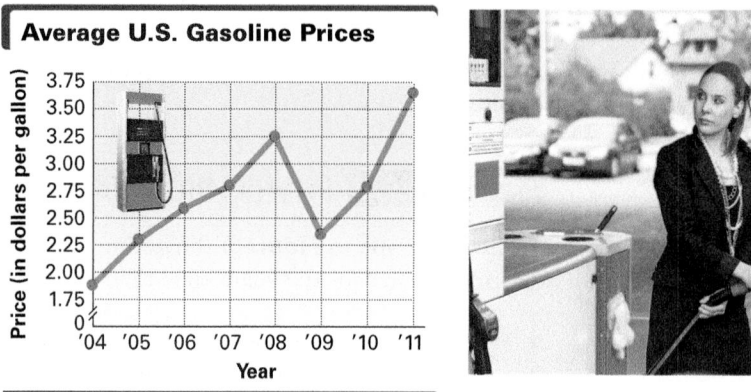

Source: U.S. Department of Energy.

Figure 10

(a) Between which years did the average price of a gallon of gasoline decrease?

(b) What was the general trend in the average price of a gallon of gasoline from 2004 through 2008?

(c) Estimate the average price of a gallon of gasoline in 2004 and in 2008. About how much did the price increase between 2004 and 2008?

Solution

(a) The line between 2008 and 2009 falls, so the average price of a gallon of gasoline decreased from 2008 to 2009.

(b) The line graph rises from 2004 to 2008, so the average price of a gallon of gasoline increased over those years.

(c) Move up from 2004 on the horizontal scale to the point plotted for 2004. This point is about halfway between the lines on the vertical scale for $1.75 and $2.00. Halfway between $1.75 and $2.00 would be about $1.88. Therefore, a gallon of gasoline cost about $1.88 in 2004.

Similarly, locate the point plotted for 2008. Moving across to the vertical scale, the graph indicates that the price for a gallon of gasoline in 2008 was about $3.25.

Between 2004 and 2008, the average price of a gallon of gasoline increased by about

$$\$3.25 - \$1.88 = \$1.37.$$ ∎

Mathematical writing takes many forms. One of the most famous author/ mathematicians was **Charles Dodgson** (1832–1898), who used the pen name **Lewis Carroll.**

Dodgson was a mathematics lecturer at Oxford University in England. Queen Victoria told Dodgson how much she enjoyed *Alice's Adventures in Wonderland* and how much she wanted to read his next book; he is said to have sent her *Symbolic Logic,* his most famous mathematical work.

The *Alice* books made Carroll famous. Late in life, however, Dodgson shunned attention and denied that he and Carroll were the same person, even though he gave away hundreds of signed copies to children and children's hospitals.

Communicating Mathematics through Language Skills

Research has indicated that the ability to express mathematical observations in writing can serve as a positive force in one's continued development as a mathematics student. The implementation of writing in the mathematics class can use several approaches.

One way of using writing in mathematics is to keep a **journal** in which you spend a few minutes explaining what happened in class that day. The journal entries may be general or specific, depending on the topic covered, the degree to which you understand the topic, your interest level at the time, and so on. Journal entries are usually written in informal language.

Although journal entries are for the most part informal writings in which the student's thoughts are allowed to roam freely, entries in **learning logs** are typically more formal. An instructor may pose a specific question for a student to answer in a learning log. In this text, we intersperse in each exercise set exercises that require written answers that are appropriate for answering in a learning log.

EXAMPLE 7 Writing an Answer to a Conceptual Exercise

Exercise 17 of **Section 1.1** reads as follows.

> *Discuss the differences between inductive and deductive reasoning. Give an example of each.*

Write a short paragraph to answer this exercise.

Solution

Here is one possible response.

> *Deductive reasoning occurs when you go from general ideas to specific ones. For example, I know that I can multiply both sides of $\frac{1}{2}x = 6$ by 2 to get $x = 12$, because I can multiply both sides of any equation by whatever I want (except 0). Inductive reasoning goes the other way. If I have a general conclusion from specific observations, that's inductive reasoning. Example – in the numbers 4, 8, 12, 16, and so on, I can conclude that the next number is 20, since I always add 4 to get the next number.*

The motto "Publish or perish" has long been around, implying that a scholar in pursuit of an academic position must publish in a journal in his or her field. There are numerous such journals in mathematics research and/or mathematics education. The National Council of Teachers of Mathematics publishes *Teaching Children Mathematics, Mathematics Teaching in the Middle School, Mathematics Teacher, Journal for Research in Mathematics Education, Mathematics Teacher Educator,* and *Student Explorations in Mathematics.* Refer to the Web site www.nctm.org to access these journals, or refer to print copies in your local library.

Writing a report on a journal article can help you understand what mathematicians do and what ideas mathematics teachers use to convey concepts to their students. Many professors in mathematics survey courses require short term papers of their students. In doing such research, students can become aware of the plethora of books and articles on mathematics and mathematicians, many written specifically for the layperson.

A list of important mathematicians, philosophers, and scientists follows.

Abel, N.	Cardano, G.	Gauss, C.	Noether, E.
Agnesi, M. G.	Copernicus, N.	Hilbert, D.	Pascal, B.
Agnesi, M. T.	De Morgan, A.	Kepler, J.	Plato
Al-Khowârizmi	Descartes, R.	Kronecker, L.	Polya, G.
Apollonius	Euler, L.	Lagrange, J.	Pythagoras
Archimedes	Fermat, P.	Leibniz, G.	Ramanujan, S.
Aristotle	Fibonacci	L'Hôspital, G.	Riemann, G.
Babbage, C.	(Leonardo	Lobachevsky, N.	Russell, B.
Bernoulli, Jakob	of Pisa)	Mandelbrot, B.	Somerville, M.
Bernoulli,	Galileo (Galileo	Napier, J.	Tartaglia, N.
Johann	Galilei)	Nash, J.	Whitehead, A.
Cantor, G.	Galois, E.	Newton, I.	Wiles, A.

The following topics in the history and development of mathematics can also be used for term papers.

Babylonian mathematics	Pascal's triangle
Egyptian mathematics	The origins of probability theory
The origin of zero	Women in mathematics
Plimpton 322	Mathematical paradoxes
The Rhind papyrus	Unsolved problems in mathematics
Origins of the Pythagorean theorem	The four-color theorem
The regular (Platonic) solids	The proof of Fermat's Last Theorem
The Pythagorean brotherhood	The search for large primes
The Golden Ratio (Golden Section)	Fractal geometry
The three famous construction problems of the Greeks	The co-inventors of calculus
The history of the approximations of π	The role of the computer in the study of mathematics
Euclid and his *Elements*	Mathematics and music
Early Chinese mathematics	Police mathematics
Early Hindu mathematics	The origins of complex numbers
Origin of the word *algebra*	Goldbach's conjecture
Magic squares	The use of the Internet in mathematics education
Figurate numbers	The development of graphing calculators
The Fibonacci sequence	Mathematics education reform movement
The Cardano/Tartaglia controversy	Multicultural mathematics
Historical methods of computation (logarithms, the abacus, Napier's rods, the slide rule, etc.)	The Riemann Hypothesis

1.4 EXERCISES

Perform the indicated operations, and give as many digits in your answer as shown on your calculator display. (The number of displayed digits may vary depending on the model used.)

1. $39.7 + (8.2 - 4.1)$

2. $2.8 \times (3.2 - 1.1)$

3. $\sqrt{5.56440921}$

4. $\sqrt{37.38711025}$

5. $\sqrt[3]{418.508992}$

6. $\sqrt[3]{700.227072}$

7. 2.67^2

8. 3.49^3

9. 5.76^5

10. 1.48^6

11. $\dfrac{14.32 - 8.1}{2 \times 3.11}$

12. $\dfrac{12.3 + 18.276}{3 \times 1.04}$

13. $\sqrt[5]{1.35}$

14. $\sqrt[6]{3.21}$

15. $\dfrac{\pi}{\sqrt{2}}$

16. $\dfrac{2\pi}{\sqrt{3}}$

17. $\sqrt[4]{\dfrac{2143}{22}}$

18. $\dfrac{12,345,679 \times 72}{\sqrt[3]{27}}$

19. $\dfrac{\sqrt{2}}{\sqrt[3]{6}}$

20. $\dfrac{\sqrt[3]{12}}{\sqrt{3}}$

21. Choose any number consisting of five digits. Multiply it by 9 on your calculator. Now add the digits in the answer. If the sum is more than 9, add the digits of this sum, and repeat until the sum is less than 10. Your answer will always be 9. Repeat the exercise with a number consisting of six digits. Does the same result hold?

22. Use your calculator to *square* the following two-digit numbers ending in 5: 15, 25, 35, 45, 55, 65, 75, 85. Write down your results, and examine the pattern that develops. Then use inductive reasoning to predict the value of 95^2. Write an explanation of how you can mentally square a two-digit number ending in 5.

Perform each calculation and observe the answers. Then fill in the blank with the appropriate response.

23. $\left(\dfrac{-3}{-8}\right)$; $\left(\dfrac{-5}{-4}\right)$; $\left(\dfrac{-2.7}{-4.3}\right)$

Dividing a negative number by another negative number gives a _____ product.
 (negative/positive)

24. $\left(5 * -4\right)$; $\left(-3 * 8\right)$; $\left(2.7 * -4.3\right)$

Multiplying a negative number by a positive number gives a _____ product.
 (negative/positive)

25. $\left(5.6^0\right)$; $\left(\pi^0\right)$; $\left(2^0\right)$; $\left(120^0\right)$

Raising a nonzero number to the power 0 gives a result of _____.

26. $\left(1^2\right)$; $\left(1^3\right)$; $\left(1^{-3}\right)$; $\left(1^0\right)$

Raising 1 to any power gives a result of _____.

27. $\left(\dfrac{1}{7}\right)$; $\left(\dfrac{1}{-9}\right)$; $\left(\dfrac{1}{3}\right)$; $\left(\dfrac{1}{-8}\right)$

The sign of the reciprocal of a number is _____ the sign of the number.
 (the same as/different from)

28. $\left(5 \div 0\right)$; $\left(9 \div 0\right)$; $\left(0 \div 0\right)$

Dividing a number by 0 gives a(n) _____ on a calculator.

29. $\left(0 \div 8\right)$; $\left(0 \div -2\right)$; $\left(0 \div \pi\right)$

Zero divided by a nonzero number gives a quotient of _____.

30. $\left(\sqrt{-3}\right)$; $\left(\sqrt{-4}\right)$; $\left(\sqrt{-10}\right)$

Taking the square root of a negative number gives a(n) _____ on a calculator.

31. $\left(-3 * -4 * -5\right)$; $\left(-3 * -4 * -5 * -6 * -7\right)$;

$\left(-3 * -4 * -5 * -6 * -7 * -8 * -9\right)$

Multiplying an *odd* number of negative numbers gives a _____ product.
 (positive/negative)

32. $\left(-3 * -4\right)$; $\left(-3 * -4 * -5 * -6\right)$;

$\left(-3 * -4 * -5 * -6 * -7 * -8\right)$

Multiplying an *even* number of negative numbers gives a _____ product.
 (positive/negative)

33. Find the decimal representation of $\frac{1}{6}$ on your calculator. Following the decimal point will be a 1 and a string of 6s. The final digit will be a 7 if your calculator *rounds off* or a 6 if it *truncates*. Which kind of calculator do you have?

34. Choose any three-digit number and enter the digits into a calculator. Then enter them again to get a six-digit number. Divide this six-digit number by 7. Divide the result by 13. Divide the result by 11. What is interesting about your answer? Explain why this happens.

35. Choose any digit except 0. Multiply it by 429. Now multiply the result by 259. What is interesting about your answer? Explain why this happens.

36. Refer to **Example 1.** If Lucy continues to double her savings amount each day, on what day will she become a millionaire?

Give an appropriate counting number answer to each question in Exercises 37–40. (Find the least counting number that will work.)

37. **Pages to Store Trading Cards** A plastic page designed to hold trading cards will hold up to 9 cards. How many pages will be needed to store 563 cards?

38. **Drawers for DVDs** A sliding drawer designed to hold DVD cases has 20 compartments. If Chris wants to house his collection of 408 Disney DVDs, how many such drawers will he need?

39. **Containers for African Violets** A gardener wants to fertilize 800 African violets. Each container of fertilizer will supply up to 60 plants. How many containers will she need to do the job?

40. **Fifth-Grade Teachers Needed** False River Academy has 155 fifth-grade students. The principal has decided that each fifth-grade teacher should have a maximum of 24 students. How many fifth-grade teachers does he need?

In Exercises 41–46, use estimation to determine the choice closest to the correct answer.

41. **Price per Acre of Land** To build a "millennium clock" on Mount Washington in Nevada that would tick once each year, chime once each century, and last at least 10,000 years, the nonprofit Long Now Foundation purchased 80 acres of land for $140,000. Which one of the following is the closest estimate to the price per acre?

    A. $1000   **B.** $2000   **C.** $4000   **D.** $11,200

42. **Time of a Round Trip** The distance from Seattle, Washington, to Springfield, Missouri, is 2009 miles. About how many hours would a round trip from Seattle to Springfield and back take a bus that averages 50 miles per hour for the entire trip?

    A. 60   **B.** 70   **C.** 80   **D.** 90

43. **People per Square Mile** Baton Rouge, LA has a population of 230,058 and covers 76.9 square miles. About how many people per square mile live in Baton Rouge?

    A. 3000   **B.** 300   **C.** 30   **D.** 30,000

44. **Revolutions of Mercury** The planet Mercury takes 88.0 Earth days to revolve around the sun once. Pluto takes 90,824.2 days to do the same. When Pluto has revolved around the sun once, about how many times will Mercury have revolved around the sun?

    A. 100,000   **B.** 10,000   **C.** 1000   **D.** 100

45. **Reception Average** In 2013, A. J. Green of the Cincinnati Bengals caught 98 passes for 1426 yards. His approximate number of yards gained per catch was _____.

    A. $\frac{1}{14}$ **B.** 0.07   **C.** 139,748   **D.** 14

46. **Area of the Sistine Chapel** The Sistine Chapel in Vatican City measures 40.5 meters by 13.5 meters.

Which is the closest approximation to its area?

    A. 110 meters   **B.** 55 meters
    C. 110 square meters   **D.** 600 square meters

Foreign-Born Americans Approximately 37.5 million people living in the United States in a recent year were born in other countries. The circle graph gives the share from each region of birth for these people. Use the graph to answer each question in Exercises 47–50.

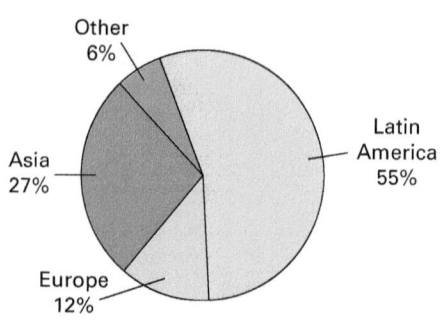

U.S. Foreign-Born Population by Region of Birth

Other 6%
Latin America 55%
Asia 27%
Europe 12%

Source: U.S. Census Bureau.

47. What share was from other regions?

48. What share was from Latin America or Asia?

49. How many people (in millions) were born in Europe?

50. How many more people (in millions) were born in Latin America than in Asia?

Milk Production   *The bar graph shows total U.S. milk production (in billions of pounds) for the years 2004 through 2010. Use the bar graph to work Exercises 51–54.*

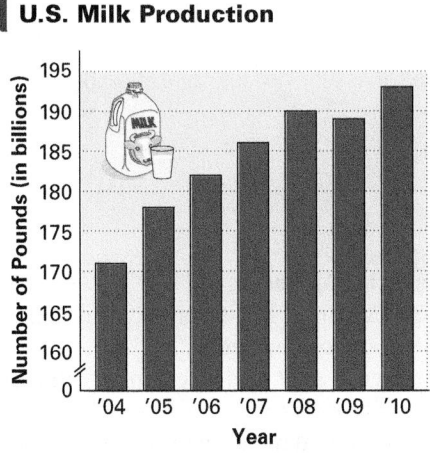

U.S. Milk Production

Source: U.S. Department of Agriculture.

51. In what years was U.S. milk production greater than 185 billion pounds?

52. In what years was U.S. milk production about the same?

53. Estimate U.S. milk production in 2004 and 2010.

54. Describe the change from 2004 to 2010.

U.S. Car Imports   *The line graph shows the number of new and used passenger cars (in millions) imported into the United States over the years 2005 through 2010. Use the line graph to work Exercises 55–58.*

Passenger Cars Imported into the U.S.

Source: U.S. Census Bureau.

55. Over which two consecutive years did the number of imported cars increase the most? About how much was this increase?

56. Estimate the number of cars imported during 2007, 2008, and 2009.

57. Describe the trend in car imports from 2006 to 2009.

58. During which year(s) were fewer than 6 millions cars imported into the United States?

Use effective writing skills to address the following.

59. ***Mathematics Web Sites***   The following Web sites provide a fascinating list of mathematics-related topics. Investigate, choose a topic that interests you, and report on it according to the guidelines provided by your instructor.

www.mathworld.wolfram.com

world.std.com/~reinhold/mathmovies.html

www.maths.surrey.ac.uk/hosted-sites/R.Knott/

http://dir.yahoo.com/Science/Mathematics/

www.cut-the-knot.org

www.ics.uci.edu/~eppstein/recmath.html

www.coolmathguy.com

ptri1.tripod.com

mathforum.org

rosettacode.org

plus.maths.org

60. ***The Simpsons***   The longest-running animated television series is *The Simpsons*, having begun in 1989. The Web site www.simpsonsmath.com explores the occurrence of mathematics in the episodes on a season-by-season basis. Watch several episodes and elaborate on the mathematics found in them.

61. ***Donald in Mathmagic Land***   One of the most popular mathematical films of all time is *Donald in Mathmagic Land*, a 1959 Disney short that is available on DVD. Spend an entertaining half-hour watching this film, and write a report on it according to the guidelines provided by your instructor.

62. ***Mathematics in Hollywood***   A theme of mathematics-related scenes in movies and television is found throughout this text. Prepare a report on one or more such scenes, and determine whether the mathematics involved is correct or incorrect. If correct, show why. If incorrect, find the correct answer.

CHAPTER 1 SUMMARY

KEY TERMS

1.1

conjecture
inductive reasoning
counterexample
deductive reasoning
natural (counting) numbers
base
exponent
premise
conclusion
logical argument

1.2

number sequence
terms of a sequence
arithmetic sequence
common difference
geometric sequence
common ratio
method of successive
    differences
mathematical
    induction

triangular, square, and
    pentagonal numbers
figurate number
subscript
Kaprekar constant

1.3

perfect square
square root
radical symbol

1.4

numeracy
four-function calculator
scientific calculator
graphing calculator
circle graph (pie chart)
bar graph
line graph
journal
learning log

TEST YOUR WORD POWER

See how well you have learned the vocabulary in this chapter.

1. A **conjecture** is
   A. a statement that has been proved to be true.
   B. an educated guess based on repeated observations.
   C. an example that shows that a general statement is false.
   D. an example of deductive reasoning.

2. An example of a **natural number** is
   A. 0. B. $\frac{1}{2}$. C. -1. D. 1.

3. An **arithmetic sequence** is
   A. a sequence that has a common difference between any two successive terms.
   B. a sequence that has a common sum of any two successive terms.
   C. a sequence that has a common ratio between any two successive terms.
   D. a sequence that can begin 1, 1, 2, 3, 5. . . .

4. A **geometric sequence** is
   A. a sequence that has a common difference between any two successive terms.
   B. a sequence that has a common sum of any two successive terms.
   C. a sequence that has a common ratio between any two successive terms.
   D. A sequence that can begin 1, 1, 2, 3, 5, ...

5. The symbol T_n, which uses the **subscript** n, is read
   A. "T to the nth power." B. "T times n."
   C. "T of n." D. "T sub n."

ANSWERS
1. B 2. D 3. A 4. C 5. D

QUICK REVIEW

Concepts	Examples
1.1 Solving Problems by Inductive Reasoning	
Inductive Reasoning Inductive reasoning is characterized by drawing a general conclusion (making a conjecture) from repeated observations of specific examples. The conjecture may or may not be true.	Consider the following: *When I square the first twenty numbers ending in 5, the result always ends in 25. Therefore, I make the conjecture that this happens in the twenty-first case.*
A general conclusion from inductive reasoning can be shown to be false by providing a single counterexample.	This is an example of inductive reasoning because a general conclusion follows from repeated observations.

Concepts	*Examples*
Deductive Reasoning Deductive reasoning is characterized by applying general principles to specific examples.	Consider the following: *The formula for finding the perimeter P of a rectangle with length L and width W is P = 2L + 2W. Therefore, the perimeter P is* $$2(5) + 2(3) = 16.$$ 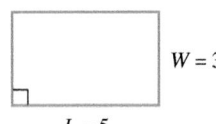 $W = 3$ $L = 5$ This is an example of deductive reasoning because a specific conclusion follows from a mathematical formula that is true in general.

1.2 An Application of Inductive Reasoning: Number Patterns

Sequences A number sequence is a list of numbers having a first number, a second number, a third number, and so on, which are called the terms of the sequence.	
Arithmetic Sequence In an arithmetic sequence, each term after the first is obtained by adding the same number, called the common difference.	The arithmetic sequence that begins $$2, 4, 6, 8$$ has common difference $4 - 2 = 2$, and the next term in the sequence is $8 + 2 = 10$.
Geometric Sequence In a geometric sequence, each term after the first is obtained by multiplying by the same number, called the common ratio.	The geometric sequence that begins $$4, 20, 100, 500$$ has common ratio $\frac{20}{4} = 5$, and the next term in the sequence is $500 \times 5 = 2500$.
Method of Successive Differences The next term in a sequence can sometimes be found by computing successive differences between terms until a pattern can be established.	The sequence that begins $$7, 15, 25, 37$$ has the following successive differences.

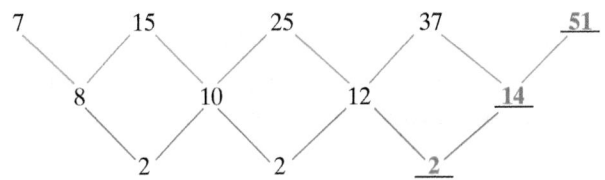

The next term in the sequence is $37 + 14 = 51$.

| **Figurate Numbers**
Figurate numbers, such as triangular, square, and pentagonal numbers, can be represented by geometric arrangements of points. | Triangular numbers ·   1   3   6   10   15

Square numbers ·   1   4   9   16   25

Pentagonal numbers ·   1   5   12   22 |

Concepts	*Examples*

1.3 **Strategies for Problem Solving**

Polya's Four-Step Method for Problem Solving

Step 1 Understand the problem.

Step 2 Devise a plan.

Step 3 Carry out the plan.

Step 4 Look back and check.

Problem-Solving Strategies

- Make a table or a chart.
- Look for a pattern.
- Solve a similar, simpler problem.
- Draw a sketch.
- Use inductive reasoning.
- Write an equation and solve it.
- If a formula applies, use it.
- Work backward.
- Guess and check.
- Use trial and error.
- Use common sense.
- Look for a "catch" if an answer seems too obvious or impossible.

What is the ones, or units, digit in 7^{350}?

Solution

We can observe a pattern in the table of simpler powers of 7. (Use a calculator.)

$7^1 = 7$	$7^5 = 16,807$	$7^9 = 40,353,607$
$7^2 = 49$	$7^6 = 117,649$	...
$7^3 = 343$	$7^7 = 823,543$	...
$7^4 = 2401$	$7^8 = 5,764,801$	...

The ones digit appears in a pattern of four digits over and over: 7, 9, 3, 1, 7, 9, 3, 1, ... If the exponent is divided by 4, the remainder helps predict the ones digit. If we divide the exponent 350 by 4, the quotient is 87 and the remainder is 2, just as it is in the second row above for 7^2 and 7^6, where the units digit is 9. So the units digit in 7^{350} is 9.

How many ways are there to make change equivalent to one dollar using only nickels, dimes, and quarters? You do not need at least one coin of each denomination. (December 26, 2013)

Solution (Verify each of the following by trial and error.)

If we start with 4 quarters, there is 1 way to make change for a dollar.

If we start with 3 quarters, there are 3 ways.

If we start with 2 quarters, there are 6 ways.

If we start with 1 quarter, there are 8 ways.

If we start with 0 quarters, there are 11 ways.

Thus, there are $1 + 3 + 6 + 8 + 11 = 29$ ways in all.

1.4 **Numeracy in Today's World**

There are a variety of types of calculators available; four-function, scientific, and graphing calculators are some of them.

In practical applications, it is often convenient to simply approximate to get an idea of an answer to a problem.

Circle graphs (pie charts), bar graphs, and line graphs are used in today's media to illustrate data in a compact way.

Percents of Students Who Return for Second Year (2-Year Public Institutions)

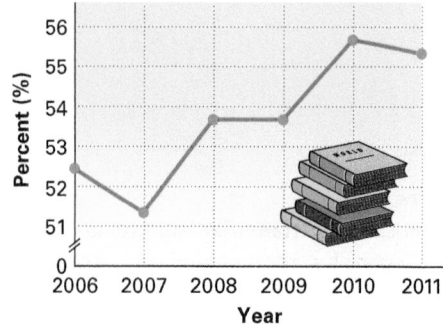

Source: ACT.

Over which two consecutive years did the percent stay the same? Estimate this percent.

Solution

The graph is horizontal between 2008 and 2009, at about 53.7%.

In Exercises 1 and 2, decide whether the reasoning involved is an example of inductive or deductive reasoning.

1. Michelle is a sales representative for a publishing company. For the past 16 years, she has exceeded her annual sales goal, primarily by selling mathematics textbooks. Therefore, she will also exceed her annual sales goal this year.

2. For all natural numbers n, n^2 is also a natural number. 176 is a natural number. Therefore, 176^2 is a natural number.

3. ***Counting Puzzle (Rectangles)*** How many rectangles of any size are in the figure shown? (September 10, 2001)

4. Use the list of equations and inductive reasoning to predict the next equation, and then verify your conjecture.

   $65,359,477,124,183 \times 17 = 1,111,111,111,111,111$
   $65,359,477,124,183 \times 34 = 2,222,222,222,222,222$
   $65,359,477,124,183 \times 51 = 3,333,333,333,333,333$

5. Use the method of successive differences to find the next term in the sequence

   $$3, 11, 31, 69, 131, 223, \ldots .$$

6. Find the sum $1 + 2 + 3 + \cdots + 250$.

7. Consider the following equations, where the left side of each is an octagonal number.

   $$1 = 1$$
   $$8 = 1 + 7$$
   $$21 = 1 + 7 + 13$$
   $$40 = 1 + 7 + 13 + 19$$

   Use the pattern established on the right sides to predict the next octagonal number. What is the next equation in the list?

8. Use the result of **Exercise 7** and the method of successive differences to find the first eight octagonal numbers. Then divide each by 4 and record the remainder. What is the pattern obtained?

9. Describe the pattern used to obtain the terms of the Fibonacci sequence below. What is the next term?

   $$1, 1, 2, 3, 5, 8, 13, 21, \ldots .$$

Use problem-solving strategies to solve each problem, taken from the date indicated in the monthly calendar of Mathematics Teacher.

10. ***Building a Fraction*** Each of the four digits 2, 4, 6, and 9 is placed in one of the boxes to form a fraction. The numerator and the denominator are both two-digit whole numbers. What is the smallest value of all the common fractions that can be formed? Express your answer as a common fraction. (November 17, 2004)

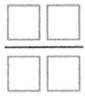

11. ***Units Digit of a Power of 9*** What is the units digit (ones digit) in the decimal representation of 9^{1997}? (January 27, 1997)

12. ***Counting Puzzle (Triangles)*** How many triangles are in this figure? (January 6, 2000)

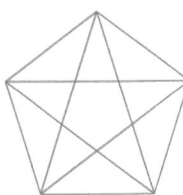

13. ***Make Them Equal*** Consider the following:

    $$1\ 2\ 3\ 4\ 5\ 6\ 7\ 8\ 9\ 0 = 100.$$

    Leaving all the numerals in the order given, insert addition and subtraction signs into the expression to make the equation true. (March 23, 2008)

14. ***Shrinkage*** Dr. Small is 36 inches tall, and Ms. Tall is 96 inches tall. If Dr. Small shrinks 2 inches per year and Ms. Tall grows $\frac{2}{3}$ of an inch per year, how tall will Ms. Tall be when Dr. Small disappears altogether? (November 2, 2007)

15. ***Units Digit of a Sum*** Find the units digit (ones digit) of the decimal numeral representing the number

    $$11^{11} + 14^{14} + 16^{16}. \text{ (February 14, 1994)}$$

16. Based on your knowledge of elementary arithmetic, describe the pattern that can be observed when the following operations are performed.

    $$9 \times 1, \quad 9 \times 2, \quad 9 \times 3, \ldots, \quad 9 \times 9$$

    (*Hint:* Add the digits in the answers. What do you notice?)

Use your calculator to evaluate each of the following. Give as many decimal places as the calculator displays.

17. $\sqrt{98.16}$

18. 3.25^3

19. *Basketball Scoring Results* During the 2012–13 NCAA women's basketball season, Brittney Griner of Baylor made 148 of her 208 free throw attempts. This means that for every 20 attempts, she made approximately _____ of them.

A. 10 **B.** 14 **C.** 8 **D.** 11

20. *Unemployment Rate* The line graph shows the overall unemployment rate in the U.S. civilian labor force for the years 2003 through 2010.

    (a) Between which pairs of consecutive years did the unemployment rate decrease?

    (b) What was the general trend in the unemployment rate between 2007 and 2010?

    (c) Estimate the overall unemployment rate in 2008 and 2009. About how much did the unemployment rate increase between 2008 and 2009?

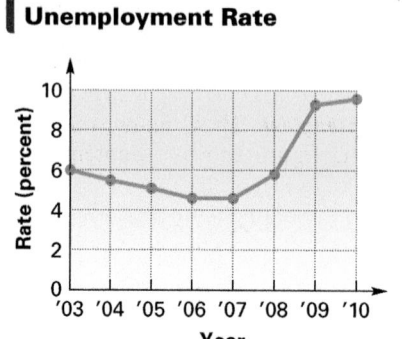

Unemployment Rate

Source: Bureau of Labor Statistics.

The Basic Concepts of Set Theory

2

For many reasons, the job outlook in the United States is good—and improving—for all types of nursing careers, as well as other health-related categories. Students may be considering groups of different training programs; lists of certificate or degree objectives; an array of employment opportunities; the pros and cons of different opportunities relative to upward mobility, stress level, and flexibility; and many others. The properties of these arrays, groups, and collections can be better understood by treating them all as *sets* (the mathematical term) and applying the methods presented in this chapter. (See, for example, the opening discussion of **Section 2.4** on page 71.)

Refer to the table on the next page. To the nearest tenth of a percent, what percentage increase is predicted for number of jobs over the decade 2012–2022 for RNs? For LPNs? (See page 50 for the answer.)

	2012 Median Salary	Number of Jobs in 2012	Predicted Increase in Number of Jobs, 2012–2022
Registered Nurses, RNs	$65,470	2,711,500	526,800
Licensed Practical (or Vocational) Nurses, LPNs (or LVNs)	$41,540	738,400	182,900

Source of data: www.bls.gov

2.1 SYMBOLS AND TERMINOLOGY

OBJECTIVES

1 Use three methods to designate sets.

2 Understand important categories of numbers, and determine cardinal numbers of sets.

3 Distinguish between finite and infinite sets.

4 Determine whether two sets are equal.

The basic ideas of set theory were developed by the German mathematician **Georg Cantor** (1845–1918) in about 1875. Cantor created a new field of theory and at the same time continued the long debate over infinity that began in ancient times. He developed counting by one-to-one correspondence to determine how many objects are contained in a set. Infinite sets differ from finite sets by not obeying the familiar law that the whole is greater than any of its parts.

Designating Sets

A **set** is a collection of objects. The objects belonging to the set are called the **elements,** or **members,** of the set. Sets are designated using the following three methods: (1) *word description,* (2) the *listing method,* and (3) *set-builder notation.*

The set of even counting numbers less than 10	Word description
$\{2, 4, 6, 8\}$	Listing method
$\{x \mid x$ is an even counting number less than $10\}$	Set-builder notation

The set-builder notation above is read "the set of all x such that x is an even counting number less than 10." Set-builder notation uses the algebraic idea of a *variable.* (Any symbol would do, but just as in other algebraic applications, the letter x is a common choice.)

Variable representing an element in general
↓
$$\{x \mid x \text{ is an even counting number less than } 10\}$$
↑
Criteria by which an element qualifies for membership in the set

Sets are commonly given names (usually capital letters), such as E for the set of all letters of the English alphabet.

$$E = \{a, b, c, d, e, f, g, h, i, j, k, l, m, n, o, p, q, r, s, t, u, v, w, x, y, z\}$$

The listing notation can often be shortened by establishing the pattern of elements included and using ellipsis points to indicate a continuation of the pattern.

$$E = \{a, b, c, d, \ldots, x, y, z\}, \quad \text{or} \quad E = \{a, b, c, d, e, \ldots, z\}$$

The set containing no elements is called the **empty set,** or **null set.** The symbol $\varnothing$ is used to denote the empty set, so $\varnothing$ and $\{\ \}$ have the same meaning. We do *not* denote the empty set with the symbol $\{\varnothing\}$ because this notation represents a set with one element (that element being the empty set).

EXAMPLE 1 **Listing Elements of Sets**

Give a complete listing of all the elements of each set.

(a) the set of counting numbers between eight and thirteen

(b) $\{5, 6, 7, \ldots, 13\}$

(c) $\{x \mid x$ is a counting number between 4 and 5$\}$

Solution

(a) This set can be denoted $\{9, 10, 11, 12\}$. (Notice that the word *between* excludes the endpoint values.)

(b) This set begins with the element 5, then 6, then 7, and so on, with each element obtained by adding 1 to the previous element in the list. This pattern stops at 13, so a complete listing is

$$\{5, 6, 7, 8, 9, 10, 11, 12, 13\}.$$

(c) There are no counting numbers between 4 and 5, so this is the empty set: $\{\ \}$, or $\varnothing$. ∎

For a set to be useful, it must be *well defined*. For example, the preceding set E of the letters of the English alphabet is well defined. Given the letter q, we know that q is an element of E. Given the Greek letter θ (theta), we know that it is not an element of set E.

However, given the set C of all good singers, and a particular singer, Adilah, it may not be possible to say whether

Adilah is an element of C or   Adilah is *not* an element of C.

The problem is the word "good"; how good is good? Because we cannot necessarily decide whether a given singer belongs to set C, set C is not well defined.

The fact that the letter q is an element of set E is denoted by using the symbol $\in$.

$\text{q} \in E$ This is read "q is an element of set E."

The letter θ is not an element of E. To show this, $\in$ with a slash mark is used.

$\theta \notin E$ This is read "θ is not an element of set E."

Many other mathematical symbols also have their meanings negated by use of a **slash mark.** The most common example, $\neq$, means "does not equal" or "is not equal to."

EXAMPLE 2 **Applying the Symbol $\in$**

Decide whether each statement is *true* or *false*.

(a) $4 \in \{1, 2, 5, 8, 13\}$ **(b)** $0 \in \{0, 1, 2, 3\}$ **(c)** $\dfrac{1}{5} \notin \left\{\dfrac{1}{3}, \dfrac{1}{4}, \dfrac{1}{6}\right\}$

Solution

(a) Because 4 is *not* an element of the set $\{1, 2, 5, 8, 13\}$, the statement is *false*.

(b) Because 0 is indeed an element of the set $\{0, 1, 2, 3\}$, the statement is *true*.

(c) This statement says that $\dfrac{1}{5}$ is not an element of the set $\left\{\dfrac{1}{3}, \dfrac{1}{4}, \dfrac{1}{6}\right\}$, which is *true*. ∎

Sets of Numbers and Cardinality

Important categories of numbers are summarized below.

Most concepts in this chapter will be illustrated using the **sets of numbers** shown here, not only to solidify understanding of these sets of numbers but also because all these sets are precisely, or "well," defined and therefore provide clear illustrations.

SETS OF NUMBERS

Natural numbers (or counting numbers) $\{1, 2, 3, 4, \dots\}$

Whole numbers $\{0, 1, 2, 3, 4, \dots\}$

Integers $\{\dots, -3, -2, -1, 0, 1, 2, 3, \dots\}$

Rational numbers $\left\{\frac{p}{q} \,\middle|\, p \text{ and } q \text{ are integers, and } q \neq 0\right\}$

(*Examples:* $\frac{3}{5}, -\frac{7}{9}, 5, 0$. Any rational number may be written as a terminating decimal number, such as 0.25, or a repeating decimal number, such as $0.666\dots$.)

Real numbers $\{x \,|\, x \text{ is a number that can be expressed as a decimal}\}$

Irrational numbers $\{x \,|\, x \text{ is a real number and } x \text{ cannot be expressed as a quotient of integers}\}$

(*Examples:* $\sqrt{2}$, $\sqrt[3]{4}$, π. Decimal representations of irrational numbers are neither terminating nor repeating.)

The number of elements in a set is called the **cardinal number,** or **cardinality,** of the set. The symbol

$$n(A), \quad \text{which is read "}\textbf{\textit{n} of \textit{A},}\text{"}$$

represents the cardinal number of set A. If elements are repeated in a set listing, they should not be counted more than once when determining the cardinal number of the set.

EXAMPLE 3 Finding Cardinal Numbers

Find the cardinal number of each set.

(a) $K = \{3, 9, 27, 81\}$ **(b)** $M = \{0\}$ **(c)** $B = \{1, 1, 2, 3, 2\}$

(d) $R = \{7, 8, \dots, 15, 16\}$ **(e)** $\varnothing$

Solution

(a) Set K contains four elements, so the cardinal number of set K is 4, and $n(K) = 4$.

(b) Set M contains only one element, 0, so $n(M) = 1$.

(c) Do not count repeated elements more than once. Set B has only three *distinct* elements, so $n(B) = 3$.

(d) Although only four elements are listed, the ellipsis points indicate that there are other elements in the set. Counting them all, we find that there are ten elements, so $n(R) = 10$.

(e) The empty set, $\varnothing$, contains no elements, so $n(\varnothing) = 0$.   ■

Finite and Infinite Sets

If the cardinal number of a set is a particular whole number (0 or a counting number), as in all parts of **Example 3,** we call that set a **finite set.** Given enough time, we could finish counting all the elements of any finite set and arrive at its cardinal number.

Some sets, however, are so large that we could never finish the counting process. The counting numbers themselves are such a set. Whenever a set is so large that its cardinal number is not found among the whole numbers, we call that set an **infinite set.**

Answers to the Chapter Opener questions

RNs: 19.4%

LPNs: 24.8%

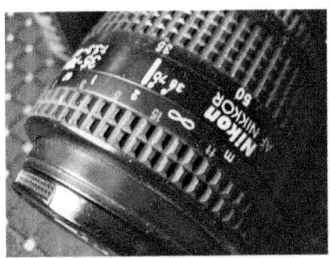

A close-up of a camera lens shows the **infinity symbol,** ∞, defined in this case as any distance greater than 1000 times the focal length of a lens.

The sign was invented by the mathematician John Wallis in 1655. Wallis used $1/\infty$ to represent an infinitely small quantity.

EXAMPLE 4 Designating an Infinite Set

Designate all odd counting numbers by the three common methods of set notation.

Solution

The set of all odd counting numbers   Word description

$\{1, 3, 5, 7, 9, \dots\}$ Listing method

$\{x \mid x \text{ is an odd counting number}\}$ Set-builder notation   ■

Equality of Sets

SET EQUALITY

Set A is **equal** to set B provided the following two conditions are met:

1. Every element of A is an element of B, and

2. Every element of B is an element of A.

Two sets are equal if they contain exactly the same elements, regardless of order.

$\{a, b, c, d\} = \{a, c, d, b\}$ Both sets contain exactly the same elements.

Repetition of elements in a set listing does not add new elements.

$\{1, 0, 1, 5, 3, 3\} = \{0, 1, 3, 5\}$ Both sets contain exactly the same elements.

EXAMPLE 5 Determining Whether Two Sets Are Equal

Are $\{-4, 3, 2, 5\}$ and $\{-4, 0, 3, 2, 5\}$ equal sets?

Solution

Every element of the first set is an element of the second. However, 0 is an element of the second and not of the first. The sets do not contain exactly the same elements.

$\{-4, 3, 2, 5\} \neq \{-4, 0, 3, 2, 5\}$ The sets are not equal.   ■

Two sets are **equivalent** if they have the *same number* of elements. (See **Exercises 87–90**.) Georg Cantor extended the idea of equivalence to infinite sets, used one-to-one correspondence to establish equivalence, and showed that, surprisingly, the natural numbers, the whole numbers, the integers, and the rational numbers are all equivalent. The elements of any one of these sets will match up, one-to-one, with those of any other, with no elements left over in either set. All these sets have cardinal number $\aleph_0$ (which is read **aleph null**).

However, the irrational numbers and the real numbers, though equivalent to one another, are of a higher infinite order than the sets mentioned above. Their cardinal number is denoted **c** (representing the **continuum** of points on a line).

EXAMPLE 6 Determining Whether Two Sets Are Equal

Decide whether each statement is *true* or *false*.

(a) $\{3\} = \{x \mid x \text{ is a counting number between 1 and 5}\}$

(b) $\{x \mid x \text{ is a negative whole number}\} = \{y \mid y \text{ is a number that is both rational and irrational}\}$

(c) $\{(0, 0), (1, 1), (2, 4)\} = \{(x, y) \mid x \text{ is a natural number less than 3, and } y = x^2\}$

Solution

(a) The set on the right contains *all* counting numbers between 1 and 5, namely 2, 3, and 4, while the set on the left contains *only* the number 3. Because the sets do not contain exactly the same elements, they are not equal. The statement is *false*.

(b) No whole numbers are negative, so the set on the left is ∅. By definition, if a number is rational, it cannot be irrational, so the set on the right is also ∅. Because each set is the empty set, the sets are equal. The statement is *true*.

(c) The first listed ordered pair in the set on the left has x-value 0, which is not a natural number. Therefore, the ordered pair $(0, 0)$ is not an element of the set on the right, even though the relationship $y = x^2$ is true for $(0, 0)$. Thus the sets are not equal. The statement is *false*.   ■

2.1   EXERCISES

Match each set in Group I with the appropriate description in Group II.

I

1. $\{1, 3, 5, 7, 9\}$

2. $\{x \mid x$ is an even integer greater than 4 and less than 6$\}$

3. $\{\ldots, -4, -3, -2, -1\}$

4. $\{\ldots, -5, -3, -1, 1, 3, 5, \ldots\}$

5. $\{2, 4, 8, 16, 32\}$

6. $\{\ldots, -4, -2, 0, 2, 4, \ldots\}$

7. $\{2, 4, 6, 8, 10\}$

8. $\{2, 4, 6, 8\}$

II

A. the set of all even integers

B. the set of the five least positive integer powers of 2

C. the set of even positive integers less than 10

D. the set of all odd integers

E. the set of all negative integers

F. the set of odd positive integers less than 10

G. $\varnothing$

H. the set of the five least positive integer multiples of 2

List all the elements of each set. Use set notation and the listing method to describe the set.

9. the set of all counting numbers less than or equal to 6

10. the set of all whole numbers greater than 8 and less than 18

11. the set of all whole numbers not greater than 4

12. the set of all natural numbers between 4 and 14

13. $\{6, 7, 8, \ldots, 14\}$

14. $\{3, 6, 9, 12, \ldots, 30\}$

15. $\{2, 4, 8, \ldots, 256\}$

16. $\{90, 87, 84, \ldots, 69\}$

17. $\{x \mid x$ is an even whole number less than 11$\}$

18. $\{x \mid x$ is an odd integer between -8 and 7$\}$

Denote each set by the listing method. There may be more than one correct answer.

19. the set of all multiples of 20 that are greater than 200

20. $\{x \mid x$ is a negative multiple of 6$\}$

21. the set of U.S. Great Lakes

22. the set of U.S. presidents who served after Richard Nixon and before Barack Obama

23. $\{x \mid x$ is the reciprocal of a natural number$\}$

24. $\{x \mid x$ is a positive integer power of 4$\}$

25. $\{(x, y) \mid x$ and y are whole numbers and $x^2 + y^2 = 25\}$

26. $\{(x, y) \mid x$ and y are integers, and $x^2 = 9y^2 + 16\}$

Denote each set by set-builder notation, using x as the variable. There may be more than one correct answer.

27. the set of all rational numbers

28. the set of all even natural numbers

29. $\{1, 3, 5, \ldots, 75\}$

30. $\{35, 40, 45, \ldots, 95\}$

Give a word description for each set. There may be more than one correct answer.

31. $\{-9, -8, -7, \ldots, 7, 8, 9\}$

32. $\left\{\dfrac{1}{2}, \dfrac{2}{3}, \dfrac{3}{4}, \ldots\right\}$

33. $\{$Alabama, Alaska, Arizona, $\ldots$, Wisconsin, Wyoming$\}$

34. $\{$Alaska, California, Hawaii, Oregon, Washington$\}$

Identify each set as finite or infinite.

35. $\{2, 4, 6, \ldots, 932\}$

36. $\{6, 12, 18\}$

37. $\left\{1, \dfrac{1}{2}, \dfrac{1}{3}, \dfrac{1}{4}, \ldots\right\}$

38. $\{3, 6, 9, \ldots\}$

39. $\{x \mid x$ is a natural number greater than 50$\}$

40. $\{x \mid x$ is a natural number less than 50$\}$

41. $\{x \mid x$ is a rational number$\}$

42. $\{x \mid x$ is a rational number between 0 and 1$\}$

Find n(A) for each set.

43. $A = \{0, 1, 2, 3, 4, 5, 6, 7\}$

44. $A = \{-3, -1, 1, 3, 5, 7, 9\}$

45. $A = \{2, 4, 6, \ldots, 1000\}$

46. $A = \{0, 1, 2, 3, \ldots, 2000\}$

47. $A = \{a, b, c, \ldots, z\}$

48. $A = \{x \mid x$ is a vowel in the English alphabet$\}$

49. $A = $ the set of integers between -20 and 20

50. $A = $ the set of sanctioned U.S. senate seats

51. $A = \left\{ \dfrac{1}{3}, \dfrac{2}{4}, \dfrac{3}{5}, \dfrac{4}{6}, \ldots, \dfrac{27}{29}, \dfrac{28}{30} \right\}$

52. $A = \left\{ \dfrac{1}{2}, -\dfrac{1}{2}, \dfrac{1}{3}, -\dfrac{1}{3}, \ldots, \dfrac{1}{10}, -\dfrac{1}{10} \right\}$

53. Although x is a consonant, why can we write

$$\text{``}x \text{ is a vowel in the English alphabet''}$$

   in **Exercise 48?**

54. Explain how **Exercise 51** can be answered without actually listing and then counting all the elements.

Identify each set as well defined *or* not well defined.

55. $\{x \mid x$ is a real number$\}$

56. $\{x \mid x$ is a good athlete$\}$

57. $\{x \mid x$ is a difficult course$\}$

58. $\{x \mid x$ is a counting number less than 2$\}$

Fill each blank with either $\in$ or $\notin$ to make each statement true.

59. 3 ___ $\{2, 4, 5, 7\}$ **60.** -4 ___ $\{4, 7, 8, 12\}$

61. 8 ___ $\{3, 8, 12, 18\}$ **62.** 0 ___ $\{-2, 0, 5, 9\}$

63. 8 ___ $\{10 - 2, 10\}$ **64.** $\{6\}$ ___ $\{5 + 1, 6 + 1\}$

65. Is the statement $\{0\} = \varnothing$ true, or is it false?

66. The statement

$$3 \in \{9 - 6, 8 - 6, 7 - 6\}$$

is true even though the *symbol* 3 does not appear in the set. Explain.

Write true *or* false *for each statement.*

67. $3 \in \{2, 5, 6, 8\}$ **68.** $m \in \{l, m, n, o, p\}$

69. $c \in \{c, d, a, b\}$ **70.** $2 \in \{-2, 5, 8, 9\}$

71. $\{k, c, r, a\} = \{k, c, a, r\}$ **72.** $\{e, h, a, n\} = \{a, h, e, n\}$

73. $\{5, 8, 9\} = \{5, 8, 9, 0\}$ **74.** $\{3, 7\} = \{3, 7, 0\}$

75. $\{4\} \in \{\{3\}, \{4\}, \{5\}\}$ **76.** $4 \in \{\{3\}, \{4\}, \{5\}\}$

77. $\{x \mid x$ is a natural number less than 3$\} = \{1, 2\}$

78. $\{x \mid x$ is a natural number greater than 10$\}$
   $= \{11, 12, 13, \ldots\}$

Write true *or* false *for each statement in Exercises 79–84.*

   Let $A = \{2, 4, 6, 8, 10, 12\}$, $B = \{2, 4, 8, 10\}$,
              and $C = \{4, 10, 12\}$.

79. $4 \in A$ **80.** $10 \in B$

81. $4 \notin C$ **82.** $10 \notin A$

83. Every element of C is also an element of A.

84. Every element of C is also an element of B.

85. The human mind likes to create collections. Why do you suppose this is so? In your explanation, use one or more particular "collections," mathematical or otherwise.

86. Explain the difference between a well-defined set and a set that is not well defined. Give examples, and use terms introduced in this section.

*Two sets are **equal** if they contain identical elements. Two sets are **equivalent** if they contain the same number of elements (but not necessarily the same elements). For each condition, give an example or explain why it is impossible.*

87. two sets that are neither equal nor equivalent

88. two sets that are equal but not equivalent

89. two sets that are equivalent but not equal

90. two sets that are both equal and equivalent

91. *Hiring Nurses*   A medical organization plans to hire three nurses from the pool of applicants shown.

Name	Certification
Bernice	RN
Heather	RN
Marcy	LVN
Natalie	LVN
Susan	RN

Show all possible sets of hires that would include

(a) two RNs and one LVN.

(b) one RN and two LVNs.

(c) no LVNs.

92. *Burning Calories*   Candice Cotton likes cotton candy, each serving of which contains 220 calories. To burn off unwanted calories, Candice participates in her favorite activities, shown in the next column, in increments of 1 hour and never repeats a given activity on a given day.

Activity	Symbol	Calories Burned per Hour
Volleyball	v	160
Golf	g	260
Canoeing	c	340
Swimming	s	410
Running	r	680

(a) On Monday, Candice has time for no more than two hours of activities. List all possible sets of activities that would burn off at least the number of calories obtained from three cotton candies.

(b) Assume that Candice can afford up to three hours of time for activities on Wednesday. List all sets of activities that would burn off at least the number of calories in five cotton candies.

(c) Candice can spend up to four hours in activities on Saturday. List all sets of activities that would burn off at least the number of calories in seven cotton candies.

2.2   VENN DIAGRAMS AND SUBSETS

OBJECTIVES

1 Use Venn diagrams to depict set relationships.

2 Determine the complement of a set within a universal set.

3 Determine whether one set is a subset of another.

4 Understand the distinction between a subset and a proper subset.

5 Determine the number of subsets of a given set.

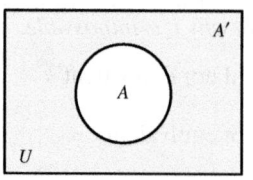

The entire region bounded by the rectangle represents the universal set *U*, and the portion bounded by the circle represents set *A*.

Figure 1

Venn Diagrams

In most discussions, there is either a stated or an implied **universe of discourse.** The universe of discourse includes all things under discussion at a given time. For example, if the topic of interest is what courses to offer at a vocational school, the universe of discourse might be all students at the school, or the board of trustees of the school, or the members of a local overseer board, or the members of a state regulatory agency, or perhaps all these groups of people.

In set theory, the universe of discourse is called the **universal set,** typically designated by the letter *U.* The universal set might change from one discussion to another.

Also in set theory, we commonly use **Venn diagrams,** developed by the logician John Venn (1834–1923). In these diagrams, the universal set is represented by a rectangle, and other sets of interest within the universal set are depicted by circular regions (sometimes ovals or other shapes). See **Figure 1.**

Complement of a Set

The colored region inside *U* and outside the circle in **Figure 1** is labeled *A′* (read "*A* prime"). This set, called the *complement* of *A*, contains all elements that are contained in *U* but are not contained in *A*.

> **THE COMPLEMENT OF A SET**
>
> For any set *A* within a universal set *U*, the **complement** of *A*, written *A′*, is the set of elements of *U* that are not elements of *A*. That is,
>
> $$A' = \{x \mid x \in U \text{ and } x \notin A\}.$$

▌EXAMPLE 1   Finding Complements

Find each set.

Let $U = \{a, b, c, d, e, f, g, h\}$, $M = \{a, b, e, f\}$,   and $N = \{b, d, e, g, h\}$.

(a) M' **(b)** N'

Solution

(a) Set M' contains all the elements of set U that are *not* in set M. Because set M contains a, b, e, and f, these elements will be disqualified from belonging to set M'.

$$M' = \{c, d, g, h\}$$

(b) Set N' contains all the elements of U that are not in set N, so $N' = \{a, c, f\}$. ▪

Consider the complement of the universal set, U'. The set U' is found by selecting all the elements of U that do not belong to U. There are no such elements, so there can be no elements in set U'. This means that for any universal set U,

$$U' = \varnothing.$$

Now consider the complement of the empty set, $\varnothing'$. The set $\varnothing'$ includes all elements of U that do *not* belong to $\varnothing$. All elements of U qualify, because none of them belongs to $\varnothing$. Therefore, for any universal set U,

$$\varnothing' = U.$$

Subsets of a Set

Suppose that we are given the universal set $U = \{1, 2, 3, 4, 5\}$, while $A = \{1, 2, 3\}$. Every element of set A is also an element of set U. Because of this, set A is called a *subset* of set U, written

$$A \subseteq U.$$

("A is not a subset of set U" would be written $A \nsubseteq U$.)

A Venn diagram showing that set M is a subset of set N is shown in **Figure 2**.

Figure 2

SUBSET OF A SET
Set A is a **subset** of set B if every element of A is also an element of B. This is written $A \subseteq B$.

▌EXAMPLE 2   Determining If One Set Is a Subset of Another

Write $\subseteq$ or $\nsubseteq$ in each blank to make a true statement.

(a) $\{3, 4, 5, 6\}$ _____ $\{3, 4, 5, 6, 8\}$ **(b)** $\{1, 2, 6\}$ _____ $\{2, 4, 6, 8\}$

(c) $\{5, 6, 7, 8\}$ _____ $\{6, 5, 8, 7\}$

Solution

(a) Because every element of $\{3, 4, 5, 6\}$ is also an element of $\{3, 4, 5, 6, 8\}$, the first set is a subset of the second, so $\subseteq$ goes in the blank.

$$\{\mathbf{3, 4, 5, 6}\} \subseteq \{3, 4, 5, 6, 8\}$$

(b) $\{\mathbf{1}, 2, 6\} \nsubseteq \{2, 4, 6, 8\}$ 1 does not belong to $\{2, 4, 6, 8\}$.

(c) $\{5, 6, 7, 8\} \subseteq \{6, 5, 8, 7\}$ ▪

As **Example 2(c)** suggests, every set is a subset of itself.

$$B \subseteq B, \quad \text{for any set } B.$$

> **SET EQUALITY (ALTERNATIVE DEFINITION)**
>
> Suppose A and B are sets. Then $A = B$ if $A \subseteq B$ and $B \subseteq A$ are both true.

Proper Subsets

Suppose that we are given the following sets.

$$B = \{5, 6, 7, 8\} \quad \text{and} \quad A = \{6, 7\}$$

A is a subset of B, but A is not all of B. There is at least one element in B that is not in A. (Actually, in this case there are two such elements, 5 and 8.) In this situation, A is called a *proper subset* of B, written $A \subset B$.

Notice the similarity of the subset symbols, $\subset$ and $\subseteq$, to the inequality symbols from algebra, $<$ and $\leq$.

> **PROPER SUBSET OF A SET**
>
> Set A is a **proper subset** of set B if $A \subseteq B$ and $A \neq B$. This is written $\boldsymbol{A \subset B}$.

EXAMPLE 3 Determining Subsets and Proper Subsets

Decide whether $\subset$, $\subseteq$, or both could be placed in each blank to make a true statement.

(a) $\{5, 6, 7\}$ _____ $\{5, 6, 7, 8\}$ **(b)** $\{a, b, c\}$ _____ $\{a, b, c\}$

Solution

(a) Every element of $\{5, 6, 7\}$ is contained in $\{5, 6, 7, 8\}$, so $\subseteq$ could be placed in the blank. Also, the element 8 belongs to $\{5, 6, 7, 8\}$ but not to $\{5, 6, 7\}$, making $\{5, 6, 7\}$ a proper subset of $\{5, 6, 7, 8\}$. Thus $\subset$ could also be placed in the blank.

(b) The set $\{a, b, c\}$ is a subset of $\{a, b, c\}$. Because the two sets are equal, $\{a, b, c\}$ is not a proper subset of $\{a, b, c\}$. Only $\subseteq$ may be placed in the blank. ∎

Set A is a subset of set B if every element of set A is also an element of set B. Alternatively, we say that set A is a subset of set B if there are no elements of A that are not also elements of B. Thus, the empty set is a subset of any set.

$$\varnothing \subseteq B, \quad \text{for any set } B.$$

This is true because it is not possible to find any element of $\varnothing$ that is not also in B. (There are no elements in $\varnothing$.) The empty set $\varnothing$ is a proper subset of every set except itself.

$$\varnothing \subset B \quad \text{if } B \text{ is any set other than } \varnothing.$$

Every set (except $\varnothing$) has at least two subsets, $\varnothing$ and the set itself.

One-to-one correspondence was employed by Georg Cantor to establish many controversial facts about infinite sets. For example, the correspondence

$$\{1, 2, 3, 4, \dots, n, \dots\}$$
$$\updownarrow \updownarrow \updownarrow \updownarrow \quad \updownarrow$$
$$\{2, 4, 6, 8, \dots, 2n, \dots\},$$

which can be continued indefinitely without leaving any elements in either set unpaired, shows that the counting numbers and the even counting numbers are equivalent (have the same number of elements), even though logic may seem to say that the first set has twice as many elements as the second.

EXAMPLE 4 Listing All Subsets of a Set

Find all possible subsets of each set.

(a) $\{7, 8\}$ **(b)** $\{a, b, c\}$

Solution

(a) By trial and error, the set $\{7, 8\}$ has four subsets: $\varnothing$, $\{7\}$, $\{8\}$, $\{7, 8\}$.

(b) Here, trial and error leads to eight subsets for $\{a, b, c\}$:

$$\varnothing, \{a\}, \{b\}, \{c\}, \{a, b\}, \{a, c\}, \{b, c\}, \{a, b, c\}. \quad ∎$$

Counting Subsets

In **Example 4,** the subsets of $\{7, 8\}$ and the subsets of $\{a, b, c\}$ were found by trial and error. An alternative method involves drawing a **tree diagram,** a systematic way of listing all the subsets of a given set. See **Figure 3.**

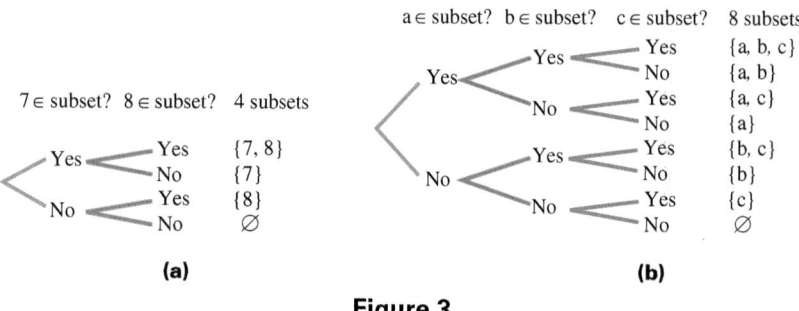

Figure 3

In **Example 4,** we determined the number of subsets of a given set by making a list of all such subsets and then counting them. The tree diagram method also produced a list of all possible subsets. To obtain a formula for finding the number of subsets, we use inductive reasoning. That is, we observe particular cases to try to discover a general pattern.

Begin with the set containing the least number of elements possible—the empty set. This set, $\varnothing$, has only one subset, $\varnothing$ itself. Next, a set with one element has only two subsets, itself and $\varnothing$. These facts, together with those obtained in **Example 4** for sets with two and three elements, are summarized here.

Number of elements	0	1	2	3
Number of subsets	1	2	4	8

This chart suggests that as the number of elements of the set increases by one, the number of subsets doubles. If so, then the number of subsets in each case might be a power of 2. Since every number in the second row of the chart is indeed a power of 2, add this information to the chart.

Number of elements	0	1	2	3
Number of subsets	$1 = 2^0$	$2 = 2^1$	$4 = 2^2$	$8 = 2^3$

This chart shows that the number of elements in each case is the same as the exponent on the base 2. Inductive reasoning gives the following generalization.

NUMBER OF SUBSETS

The number of subsets of a set with n elements is $\mathbf{2^n}$.

Because the value 2^n includes the set itself, we must subtract 1 from this value to obtain the number of proper subsets of a set containing n elements.

NUMBER OF PROPER SUBSETS

The number of proper subsets of a set with n elements is $\mathbf{2^n - 1}$.

Powers of 2

$2^0 = 1$
$2^1 = 2$
$2^2 = 2 \cdot 2 = 4$
$2^3 = 2 \cdot 2 \cdot 2 = 8$
$2^4 = 2 \cdot 2 \cdot 2 \cdot 2 = 16$
$2^5 = 32$
$2^6 = 64$
$2^7 = 128$
$2^8 = 256$
$2^9 = 512$
$2^{10} = 1024$
$2^{11} = 2048$
$2^{12} = 4096$
$2^{15} = 32,768$
$2^{20} = 1,048,576$
$2^{25} = 33,554,432$
$2^{30} = 1,073,741,824$

As shown in **Chapter 1,** although inductive reasoning is a good way of *discovering* principles or arriving at a *conjecture*, it does not provide a proof that the conjecture is true in general. The two formulas above are true, by observation, for $n = 0, 1, 2,$ and 3. (For a general proof, see **Exercise 63** at the end of this section.)

EXAMPLE 5 Finding Numbers of Subsets and Proper Subsets

Find the number of subsets and the number of proper subsets of each set.

(a) $\{3, 4, 5, 6, 7\}$ **(b)** $\{1, 2, 3, 4, 5, 9, 12, 14\}$

Solution

(a) This set has 5 elements and $2^5 = 2 \cdot 2 \cdot 2 \cdot 2 \cdot 2 = 32$ subsets. Of these,

$$2^5 - 1 = 32 - 1 = 31 \text{ are proper subsets.}$$

(b) This set has 8 elements. There are $2^8 = 256$ subsets and 255 proper subsets. ■

2.2 EXERCISES

Match each set or sets in Column I with the appropriate description in Column II.

I	II
1. $\{p\}, \{q\}, \{p, q\}, \varnothing$	**A.** the proper subsets of $\{p, q\}$
2. $\{p\}, \{q\}, \varnothing$	**B.** the complement of $\{c, d\}$, if $U = \{a, b, c, d\}$
3. $\{a, b\}$	**C.** the complement of U
4. $\varnothing$	**D.** the subsets of $\{p, q\}$

Insert $\subseteq$ or $\nsubseteq$ in each blank to obtain a true statement.

5. $\{-2, 0, 2\}$ ____ $\{-2, -1, 1, 2\}$

6. $\{M, W, F\}$ ____ $\{S, M, T, W, Th\}$

7. $\{2, 5\}$ ____ $\{0, 1, 5, 3, 7, 2\}$

8. $\{a, n, d\}$ ____ $\{r, a, n, d, y\}$

9. $\varnothing$ ____ $\{a, b, c, d, e\}$

10. $\varnothing$ ____ $\varnothing$

11. $\{-5, 2, 9\}$ ____ $\{x \mid x \text{ is an odd integer}\}$

12. $\left\{1, 2, \dfrac{9}{3}\right\}$ ____ the set of rational numbers

Decide whether $\subset$, $\subseteq$, both, or neither can be placed in each blank to make the statement true.

13. $\{P, Q, R\}$ ____ $\{P, Q, R, S\}$

14. $\{\text{red, blue, yellow}\}$ ____ $\{\text{yellow, blue, red}\}$

15. $\{9, 1, 7, 3, 5\}$ ____ $\{1, 3, 5, 7, 9\}$

16. $\{S, M, T, W, Th\}$ ____ $\{W, E, E, K\}$

17. $\varnothing$ ____ $\{0\}$

18. $\varnothing$ ____ $\varnothing$

19. $\{0, 1, 2, 3\}$ ____ $\{1, 2, 3, 4\}$

20. $\left\{\dfrac{5}{6}, \dfrac{9}{8}\right\}$ ____ $\left\{\dfrac{6}{5}, \dfrac{8}{9}\right\}$

For Exercises 21–36, tell whether each statement is true *or* false. *U is the universal set.*

Let $U = \{a, b, c, d, e, f, g\}$, $A = \{a, e\}$,
$B = \{a, b, e, f, g\}$, $C = \{b, f, g\}$,   *and* $D = \{d, e\}$.

21. $A \subset U$ **22.** $C \nsubseteq U$

23. $D \subseteq B$ **24.** $D \nsubseteq A$

25. $A \subset B$ **26.** $B \subseteq C$

27. $\varnothing \nsubseteq A$ **28.** $\varnothing \subseteq D$

29. $D \nsubseteq B$ **30.** $A \nsubseteq B$

31. There are exactly 6 subsets of C.

32. There are exactly 31 subsets of B.

33. There are exactly 3 proper subsets of A.

34. There are exactly 4 subsets of D.

35. The Venn diagram below correctly represents the relationship among sets *A*, *D*, and *U*.

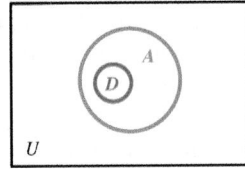

36. The Venn diagram below correctly represents the relationship among sets *B*, *C*, and *U*.

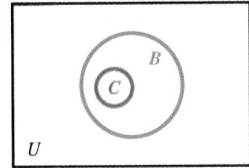

For Exercises 37–40, find **(a)** *the number of subsets and* **(b)** *the number of proper subsets of each set.*

37. {a, b, c, d, e, f }

38. the set of days of the week

39. {x | x is an odd integer between −4 and 6}

40. {x | x is an even whole number less than 4}

For Exercises 41–44, let U = {1, 2, 3, 4, 5, 6, 7, 8, 9, 10} and find the complement of each set.

41. *U*

42. ∅

43. {1, 2, 3, 4, 6, 8}

44. {2, 5, 9, 10}

Vacationing in California *Terry is planning a trip with her two sons to California. In weighing her options concerning whether to fly or drive from their home in Iowa, she has listed the following considerations.*

Fly to California	Drive to California
Higher cost	Lower cost
Educational	Educational
More time to see the sights in California	Less time to see the sights in California
Cannot visit friends along the way	Can visit friends along the way

Refer to the table for Exercises 45–50.

45. Find the smallest universal set *U* that contains all listed considerations of both options.

Let F represent the set of considerations of the flying option and let D represent the set of considerations of the driving option. Use the universal set from ***Exercise 45.***

46. Give the set *F′*.   **47.** Give the set *D′*.

Find the set of elements common to both sets in Exercises 48–50.

48. *F* and *D*   **49.** *F′* and *D′*

50. *F* and *D′*

Meeting in the Conference Room *Amie, Bruce, Corey, Dwayne, and Eric, members of an architectural firm, plan to meet in the company conference room to discuss the project coordinator's plans for their next project. Denoting these five people by* A, B, C, D, *and* E, *list all the possible sets of this group in which the given number of them can gather.*

51. five people   **52.** four people

53. three people   **54.** two people

55. one person   **56.** no people

57. Find the total number of ways that members of this group can gather. (*Hint:* Find the total number of sets in your answers to **Exercises 51–56**.)

58. How does your answer in **Exercise 57** compare with the number of subsets of a set of five elements? Interpret the answer to **Exercise 57** in terms of subsets.

59. ***Selecting a Club Delegation*** The twenty-five members of the mathematics club must send a delegation to a meeting for student groups at their school. The delegation can include as many members of the club as desired, but at least one member must attend. How many different delegations are possible? (*Mathematics Teacher* calendar problem)

60. In **Exercise 59,** suppose ten of the club members say they do not want to be part of the delegation. Now how many delegations are possible?

61. ***Selecting Bills*** Suppose you have the bills shown here.

(a) How many sums of money can you make using nonempty subsets of these bills?

(b) Repeat part (a) without the condition "nonempty."

62. *Selecting Coins* The photo shows a group of obsolete U.S. coins, consisting of one each of the penny, nickel, dime, quarter, and half dollar. Repeat **Exercise 61,** replacing "bill(s)" with "coin(s)."

63. In discovering the expression (2^n) for finding the number of subsets of a set with n elements, we observed that for the first few values of n, increasing the number of elements by one doubles the number of subsets.

Here, you can prove the formula in general by showing that the same is true for any value of n. Assume set A has n elements and s subsets. Now add one additional element, say e, to the set A. (We now have a new set, say B, with $n + 1$ elements.) Divide the subsets of B into those that do not contain e and those that do.

(a) How many subsets of B do not contain e? (*Hint:* Each of these is a subset of the original set A.)

(b) How many subsets of B do contain e? (*Hint:* Each of these would be a subset of the original set A, with the additional element e included.)

(c) What is the total number of subsets of B?

(d) What do you conclude?

64. Explain why $\varnothing$ is both a subset and an element of $\{\varnothing\}$.

2.3 SET OPERATIONS

OBJECTIVES

1 Determine intersections of sets.

2 Determine unions of sets.

3 Determine the difference of two sets.

4 Understand ordered pairs and their uses.

5 Determine Cartesian products of sets.

6 Analyze sets and set operations with Venn diagrams.

7 Apply De Morgan's laws for sets.

Figure 4

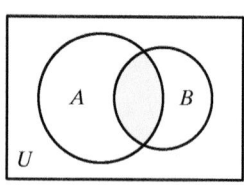

$A \cap B$
Figure 5

Intersection of Sets

Two candidates, Aimee and Darien, are running for a seat on the city council. A voter deciding for whom she should vote recalled the campaign promises, each given a code letter, made by the candidates.

Honest Aimee	**Determined Darien**
Spend less money, *m*	Spend less money, *m*
Emphasize traffic law enforcement, *t*	Crack down on crooked politicians, *p*
Increase service to suburban areas, *s*	Increase service to the city, *c*

The only promise common to both candidates is promise m, to spend less money. Suppose we take each candidate's promises to be a set. The promises of Aimee give the set $\{m, t, s\}$, while the promises of Darien give $\{m, p, c\}$. The common element m belongs to the *intersection* of the two sets, as shown in color in the Venn diagram in **Figure 4.**

$$\{m, t, s\} \cap \{m, p, c\} = \{m\} \quad \cap \text{ represents set intersection.}$$

The intersection of two sets is itself a set.

> **INTERSECTION OF SETS**
>
> The **intersection** of sets A and B, written $A \cap B$, is the set of elements common to both A and B.
>
> $$A \cap B = \{x \mid x \in A \text{ and } x \in B\}$$

Form the intersection of sets A and B by taking all the elements included in both sets, as shown in color in **Figure 5.**

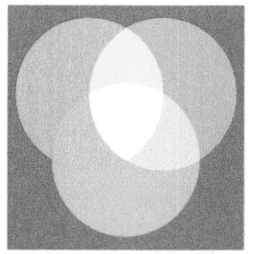

White light can be viewed as the intersection of the three primary colors.

EXAMPLE 1 Finding Intersections

Find each intersection.

(a) $\{3, 4, 5, 6, 7\} \cap \{4, 6, 8, 10\}$ **(b)** $\{9, 14, 25, 30\} \cap \{10, 17, 19, 38, 52\}$

(c) $\{5, 9, 11\} \cap \varnothing$

Solution

(a) The elements common to both sets are 4 and 6.

$$\{3, 4, 5, 6, 7\} \cap \{4, 6, 8, 10\} = \{4, 6\}$$

(b) These two sets have no elements in common.

$$\{9, 14, 25, 30\} \cap \{10, 17, 19, 38, 52\} = \varnothing$$

(c) There are no elements in $\varnothing$, so there can be no elements belonging to both $\{5, 9, 11\}$ and $\varnothing$.

$$\{5, 9, 11\} \cap \varnothing = \varnothing$$ ∎

Examples 1(b) and 1(c) show two sets that have no elements in common. Sets with no elements in common are called **disjoint sets**. (See **Figure 6**.) A set of dogs and a set of cats would be disjoint sets.

Sets A and B are disjoint if $A \cap B = \varnothing$.

Disjoint sets

Figure 6

Union of Sets

Referring again to the lists of campaign promises, suppose a pollster wants to summarize the types of promises made by the candidates. The pollster would need to study *all* the promises made by *either* candidate, or the set

$$\{m, t, s, p, c\}.$$

This set is the *union* of the sets of promises, as shown in color in the Venn diagram in **Figure 7**.

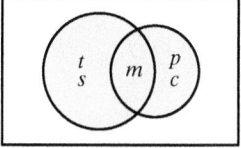

Figure 7

> Be careful not to confuse this symbol with the universal set U.

$$\{m, t, s\} \cup \{m, p, c\} = \{m, t, s, p, c\}$$ ∪ denotes set union.

Again, the union of two sets is a set.

UNION OF SETS

The **union** of sets A and B, written $A \cup B$, is the set of all elements belonging to either A or B.

$$A \cup B = \{x \mid x \in A \text{ or } x \in B\}$$

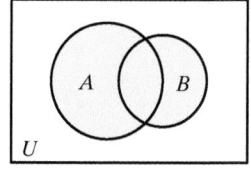

$A \cup B$

Figure 8

Form the union of sets A and B by first taking every element of set A and then also including every element of set B that is not already listed. See Figure 8.

EXAMPLE 2 Finding Unions

Find each union.

(a) $\{2, 4, 6\} \cup \{4, 6, 8, 10, 12\}$ **(b)** $\{a, b, d, f, g, h\} \cup \{c, f, g, h, k\}$

(c) $\{3, 4, 5\} \cup \varnothing$

Solution

(a) Start by listing all the elements from the first set, 2, 4, and 6. Then list all the elements from the second set that are not in the first set, 8, 10, and 12. The union is made up of *all* these elements.

$$\{2, 4, 6\} \cup \{4, 6, 8, 10, 12\} = \{2, 4, 6, 8, 10, 12\}$$

(b) $\{a, b, d, f, g, h\} \cup \{c, f, g, h, k\} = \{a, b, c, d, f, g, h, k\}$

(c) Because there are no elements in $\varnothing$, the union of $\{3, 4, 5\}$ and $\varnothing$ contains only the elements 3, 4, and 5.

$$\{3, 4, 5\} \cup \varnothing = \{3, 4, 5\}$$ ∎

Recall from the previous section that A' represents the *complement* of set A. ***Set A' is formed by taking every element of the universal set U that is not in set A.***

EXAMPLE 3 Finding Intersections and Unions of Complements

Find each set. Let

$$U = \{1, 2, 3, 4, 5, 6, 9\}, \quad A = \{1, 2, 3, 4\}, \quad B = \{2, 4, 6\}, \quad \text{and} \quad C = \{1, 3, 6, 9\}.$$

(a) $A' \cap B$ **(b)** $B' \cup C'$ **(c)** $A \cap (B \cup C')$ **(d)** $(B \cup C)'$

Solution

(a) First identify the elements of set A', the elements of U that are not in set A.

$$A' = \{5, 6, 9\}$$

Now, find $A' \cap B$, the set of elements belonging both to A' and to B.

$$A' \cap B = \{5, 6, 9\} \cap \{2, 4, 6\} = \{6\}$$

(b) $B' \cup C' = \{1, 3, 5, 9\} \cup \{2, 4, 5\} = \{1, 2, 3, 4, 5, 9\}$

(c) First find the set inside the parentheses.

$$B \cup C' = \{2, 4, 6\} \cup \{2, 4, 5\} = \{2, 4, 5, 6\}$$

Now, find the intersection of this set with A.

$$\begin{aligned} A \cap (B \cup C') &= A \cap \{2, 4, 5, 6\} \\ &= \{1, 2, 3, 4\} \cap \{2, 4, 5, 6\} \\ &= \{2, 4\} \end{aligned}$$

(d) $B \cup C = \{2, 4, 6\} \cup \{1, 3, 6, 9\} = \{1, 2, 3, 4, 6, 9\}$,   so

$$(B \cup C)' = \{5\}.$$ ∎

Comparing **Examples 3(b) and 3(d),** we see that, interestingly, $(B \cup C)'$ is not the same as $B' \cup C'$. This fact will be investigated further later in this section.

Comparing Properties

The arithmetic operations of addition and multiplication, when applied to numbers, have some familiar properties. If a, b, and c are *real numbers,* then the **commutative property of addition** says that the order of the numbers being added makes no difference:

$$a + b = b + a.$$

(Is there a **commutative property of multiplication?**) The **associative property of addition** says that when three numbers are added, the grouping used makes no difference:

$$(a + b) + c = a + (b + c).$$

(Is there an **associative property of multiplication?**) The number 0 is called the **identity element for addition** since adding it to any number does not change that number:

$$a + 0 = a.$$

(What is the **identity element for multiplication?**) Finally, the **distributive property of multiplication over addition** says that

$$a(b + c) = ab + ac.$$

(Is there a distributive property of addition over multiplication?)

For Group or Individual Investigation

Now consider the operations of union and intersection, applied to sets. By recalling definitions, trying examples, or using Venn diagrams, answer the following questions.

1. Is set union commutative?   Set intersection?
2. Is set union associative?   Set intersection?
3. Is there an identity element for set union? If so, what is it? How about set intersection?
4. Is set intersection distributive over set union? Is set union distributive over set intersection?

EXAMPLE 4 **Describing Sets in Words**

Describe each set in words.

(a) $A \cap (B \cup C')$ **(b)** $(A' \cup C') \cap B'$

Solution

(a) This set might be described as "the set of all elements that are in A, and also are in B or not in C."

(b) One possibility is "the set of all elements that are not in A or not in C, and also are not in B." ■

Difference of Sets

Suppose that $A = \{1, 2, 3, \ldots, 10\}$ and $B = \{2, 4, 6, 8, 10\}$. If the elements of B are excluded (or taken away) from A, the set $C = \{1, 3, 5, 7, 9\}$ is obtained. C is called the *difference* of sets A and B.

DIFFERENCE OF SETS

The **difference** of sets A and B, written $A - B$, is the set of all elements belonging to set A and not to set B.

$$A - B = \{x \mid x \in A \text{ and } x \notin B\}$$

Assume a universal set U containing both A and B. Then because $x \notin B$ has the same meaning as $x \in B'$, the set difference $A - B$ can also be described as

$$\{x \mid x \in A \text{ and } x \in B'\}, \quad \text{or} \quad A \cap B'.$$

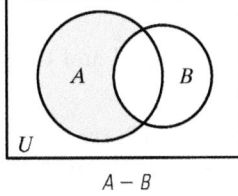

$A - B$

Figure 9

Figure 9 illustrates the idea of set difference. The region in color represents $A - B$.

EXAMPLE 5 Finding Set Differences

Find each set.

$$\text{Let } U = \{1, 2, 3, 4, 5, 6, 7\}, \quad A = \{1, 2, 3, 4, 5, 6\},$$
$$B = \{2, 3, 6\}, \quad \text{and} \quad C = \{3, 5, 7\}.$$

(a) $A - B$ **(b)** $B - A$ **(c)** $(A - B) \cup C'$

Solution

(a) Begin with set A and exclude any elements found also in set B.

$$A - B = \{1, 2, 3, 4, 5, 6\} - \{2, 3, 6\} = \{1, 4, 5\}$$

(b) To be in $B - A$, an element must be in set B and not in set A. But all elements of B are also in A. Thus, $B - A = \varnothing$.

(c) From part (a), $A - B = \{1, 4, 5\}$. Also, $C' = \{1, 2, 4, 6\}$.

$$(A - B) \cup C' = \{1, 2, 4, 5, 6\}$$ ■

The results in **Examples 5(a) and 5(b)** illustrate that, in general,

$$A - B \neq B - A.$$

Ordered Pairs

When writing a set that contains several elements, the order in which the elements appear is not relevant. For example,

$$\{1, 5\} = \{5, 1\}.$$

However, there are many instances in mathematics where, when two objects are paired, the order in which the objects are written is important. This leads to the idea of *ordered pair*. When writing ordered pairs, use parentheses rather than braces, which are reserved for writing sets.

ORDERED PAIRS

In the **ordered pair** (a, b), a is called the **first component** and b is called the **second component**. In general, $(a, b) \neq (b, a)$.

Two ordered pairs (a, b) and (c, d) are **equal** provided that their first components are equal and their second components are equal.

$$(a, b) = (c, d) \quad \textit{if and only if} \quad a = c \quad \textit{and} \quad b = d.$$

EXAMPLE 6 Determining Equality of Sets and of Ordered Pairs

Decide whether each statement is *true* or *false*.

(a) $(3, 4) = (5 - 2, 1 + 3)$ **(b)** $\{3, 4\} \neq \{4, 3\}$ **(c)** $(7, 4) = (4, 7)$

Solution

(a) Because $3 = 5 - 2$ and $4 = 1 + 3$, the first components are equal and the second components are equal. The statement is *true*.

(b) Because these are sets and not ordered pairs, the order in which the elements are listed is not important. Because these sets are equal, the statement is *false*.

(c) The ordered pairs $(7, 4)$ and $(4, 7)$ are not equal because their corresponding components are not equal. The statement is *false*. ■

Cartesian Product of Sets

A set may contain ordered pairs as elements. If A and B are sets, then each element of A can be paired with each element of B, and the results can be written as ordered pairs. The set of all such ordered pairs is called the *Cartesian product* of A and B, which is written $A \times B$ and read **"A cross B."** The name comes from that of the French mathematician René Descartes, profiled in **Chapter 8.**

CARTESIAN PRODUCT OF SETS

The **Cartesian product** of sets A and B is defined as follows.

$$A \times B = \{(a, b) \mid a \in A \text{ and } b \in B\}$$

EXAMPLE 7 Finding Cartesian Products

Let $A = \{1, 5, 9\}$ and $B = \{6, 7\}$. Find each set.

(a) $A \times B$ **(b)** $B \times A$

Solution

(a) Pair each element of A with each element of B. Write the results as ordered pairs, with the element of A written first and the element of B written second. Write as a set.

$$A \times B = \{(1, 6), (1, 7), (5, 6), (5, 7), (9, 6), (9, 7)\}$$

(b) Because B is listed first, this set will consist of ordered pairs that have their components interchanged when compared to those in part (a).

$$B \times A = \{(6, 1), (7, 1), (6, 5), (7, 5), (6, 9), (7, 9)\} \qquad \blacksquare$$

The order in which the ordered pairs themselves are listed is not important. For example, another way to write $B \times A$ in **Example 7(b)** would be

$$\{(6, 1), (6, 5), (6, 9), (7, 1), (7, 5), (7, 9)\}.$$

From **Example 7** it can be seen that, in general,

$$A \times B \neq B \times A,$$

because they do not contain exactly the same ordered pairs. However, each set contains the same *number* of elements, six. Furthermore, $n(A) = 3$, $n(B) = 2$, and $n(A \times B) = n(B \times A) = 6$. Because $3 \cdot 2 = 6$, one might conclude that the cardinal number of the Cartesian product of two sets is equal to the product of the cardinal numbers of the sets. In general, this conclusion is correct.

CARDINAL NUMBER OF A CARTESIAN PRODUCT

If $n(A) = a$ and $n(B) = b$, then the following is true.

$$n(A \times B) = n(B \times A) = n(A) \cdot n(B) = n(B) \cdot n(A) = ab = ba$$

EXAMPLE 8 Finding Cardinal Numbers of Cartesian Products

Find $n(A \times B)$ and $n(B \times A)$ from the given information.

(a) $A = \{a, b, c, d, e, f, g\}$ and $B = \{2, 4, 6\}$ **(b)** $n(A) = 24$ and $n(B) = 5$

Solution

(a) Because $n(A) = 7$ and $n(B) = 3$, $n(A \times B)$ and $n(B \times A)$ both equal $7 \cdot 3$, or 21.

(b) $n(A \times B) = n(B \times A) = 24 \cdot 5 = 5 \cdot 24 = 120$ ■

An **operation** is a rule or procedure by which one or more objects are used to obtain another object. The most common operations on sets are summarized in the following box.

SET OPERATIONS

Let A and B be any sets within a universal set U.

The **complement** of A, written A', is

$$A' = \{x \mid x \in U \text{ and } x \notin A\}.$$

The **intersection** of A and B is

$$A \cap B = \{x \mid x \in A \text{ and } x \in B\}.$$

The **union** of A and B is

$$A \cup B = \{x \mid x \in A \text{ or } x \in B\}.$$

The **difference** of A and B is

$$A - B = \{x \mid x \in A \text{ and } x \notin B\}.$$

The **Cartesian product** of A and B is

$$A \times B = \{(x, y) \mid x \in A \text{ and } y \in B\}.$$

More on Venn Diagrams

It is often helpful to use numbers in Venn diagrams, as in **Figures 10, 11, and 12,** depending on whether the discussion involves one, two, or three (distinct) sets, respectively. In each case, the numbers are neither elements nor cardinal numbers, but simply arbitrary labels for the various regions within the diagram.

In **Figure 11,** region 3 includes the elements belonging to both A and B, while region 4 includes those elements (if any) belonging to B but not to A. How would you describe region 7 in **Figure 12?**

Figure 10

Figure 11

Figure 12

Figure 13

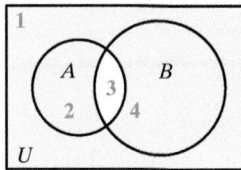

Figure 14

EXAMPLE 9 Shading Venn Diagrams to Represent Sets

Draw a Venn diagram similar to **Figure 11,** and shade the region or regions representing each set.

(a) $A' \cap B$ **(b)** $A' \cup B'$

Solution

(a) See **Figure 11.** Set A' contains all the elements outside of set A—in other words, the elements in regions 1 and 4. Set B contains the elements in regions 3 and 4. The intersection of sets A' and B is made up of the elements in the region common to (1 and 4) and (3 and 4), which is region 4. Thus, $A' \cap B$ is represented by region 4, shown in color in **Figure 13.** This region can also be described as $B - A$.

(b) Again, set A' is represented by regions 1 and 4, and B' is made up of regions 1 and 2. The union of A' and B', the set $A' \cup B'$, is made up of the elements belonging to the union of (1 and 4) with (1 and 2)—that is, regions 1, 2, and 4, shown in color in **Figure 14.** ◼

EXAMPLE 10 Locating Elements in a Venn Diagram

Place the elements of the sets in their proper locations in a Venn diagram.

Let $U = \{q, r, s, t, u, v, w, x, y, z\}$, $A = \{r, s, t, u, v\}$, and $B = \{t, v, x\}$.

Solution

Because $A \cap B = \{t, v\}$, elements t and v are placed in region 3 in **Figure 15.** The remaining elements of A, that is, r, s, and u, go in region 2. The figure shows the proper placement of all other elements. ◼

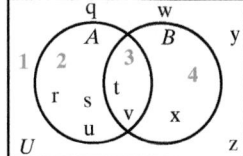

Figure 15

EXAMPLE 11 Shading a Set in a Venn Diagram

Shade the set $(A' \cap B') \cap C$ in a Venn diagram similar to the one in **Figure 12.**

Solution

Work first inside the parentheses. Set A' is made up of the regions outside set A, or regions 1, 6, 7, and 8. Set B' is made up of regions 1, 2, 5, and 6. The intersection of these sets is given by the overlap of regions 1, 6, 7, 8 and 1, 2, 5, 6, or regions 1 and 6.

For the final Venn diagram, find the intersection of regions 1 and 6 with set C. Set C is made up of regions 4, 5, 6, and 7. The overlap of regions 1, 6 and 4, 5, 6, 7 is region 6, the region shown in color in **Figure 16.** ◼

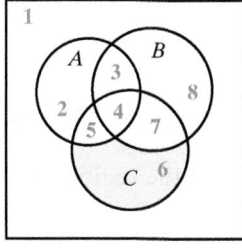

$(A' \cap B') \cap C$

Figure 16

EXAMPLE 12 Verifying a Statement Using a Venn Diagram

Suppose $A, B \subseteq U$. Is the statement $(A \cap B)' = A' \cup B'$ true for every choice of sets A and B?

Solution

Use the regions labeled in **Figure 11.** Set $A \cap B$ is made up of region 3, so $(A \cap B)'$ is made up of regions 1, 2, and 4. These regions are shown in color in **Figure 17(a)** on the next page.

To identify set $A' \cup B'$, proceed as in **Example 9(b).** The result, shown in **Figure 14,** is repeated in **Figure 17(b)** on the next page.

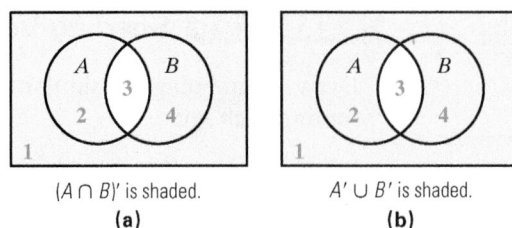

$(A \cap B)'$ is shaded.
(a)

$A' \cup B'$ is shaded.
(b)

Figure 17

The fact that the same regions are in color in both Venn diagrams suggests that

$$(A \cap B)' = A' \cup B'.$$

De Morgan's Laws

The result of **Example 12** can be stated in words.

> *The complement of the intersection of two sets is equal to the union of the complements of the two sets.*

Interchanging the words "intersection" and "union" produces another true statement.

> *The complement of the union of two sets is equal to the intersection of the complements of the two sets.*

Both of these "laws" were established by the British logician Augustus De Morgan (1806–1871), profiled on **page 22.** They are stated in set symbols as follows.

DE MORGAN'S LAWS FOR SETS

For any sets A and B, where $A, B \subseteq U$,

$$(A \cap B)' = A' \cup B' \quad \text{and} \quad (A \cup B)' = A' \cap B'.$$

The Venn diagrams in **Figure 17** strongly suggest the truth of the first of De Morgan's laws. They provide a *conjecture*. Actual proofs of De Morgan's laws would require methods used in more advanced courses in set theory.

EXAMPLE 13 **Describing Venn Diagram Regions Using Symbols**

For the Venn diagrams, write several symbolic descriptions of the region in color, using $A, B, C, \cap, \cup, -,$ and $'$ as necessary.

(a)

(b)

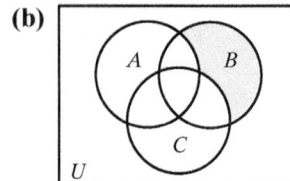

Solution

(a) The region in color can be described as belonging to all three sets, A and B and C. Therefore, the region corresponds to

$$(A \cap B) \cap C, \quad \text{or} \quad A \cap (B \cap C), \quad \text{or} \quad A \cap B \cap C.$$

(b) The region in color is in set B and is not in A and is not in C. Because it is not in A, it is in A', and similarly it is in C'. The region can be described as

$$B \cap A' \cap C', \quad \text{or} \quad B - (A \cup C), \quad \text{or} \quad B \cap (A \cup C)'.$$

2.3 EXERCISES

Match each term in Group I with the appropriate description from A–F in Group II. Assume that A and B are sets.

I

1. the intersection of A and B

2. the union of A and B

3. the difference of A and B

4. the complement of A

5. the Cartesian product of A and B

6. the difference of B and A

II

A. the set of elements in A that are not in B

B. the set of elements common to both A and B

C. the set of elements in the universal set that are not in A

D. the set of elements in B that are not in A

E. the set of ordered pairs such that each first element is from A and each second element is from B, with every element of A paired with every element of B

F. the set of elements that are in A or in B or in both A and B

Perform the indicated operations, and designate each answer using the listing method.

$$Let \quad U = \{a, b, c, d, e, f, g\}, \quad X = \{a, c, e, g\},$$
$$Y = \{a, b, c\}, \quad and \quad Z = \{b, c, d, e, f\}.$$

7. $X \cap Y$

8. $X \cup Y$

9. $Y \cup Z$

10. $Y \cap Z$

11. X'

12. Y'

13. $X' \cap Y'$

14. $X' \cap Z$

15. $X \cup (Y \cap Z)$

16. $Y \cap (X \cup Z)$

17. $X - Y$

18. $Y - X$

19. $(Z \cup X')' \cap Y$

20. $(Y \cap X')' \cup Z'$

21. $X \cap (X - Y)$

22. $Y \cup (Y - X)$

23. $X' - Y$

24. $Y' - (X \cap Z)$

Describe each set in words.

25. $A \cup (B' \cap C')$

26. $(A \cap B') \cup (B \cap A')$

27. $(C - B) \cup A$

28. $(A' \cap B') \cup C'$

Adverse Effects of Tobacco and Alcohol *The table lists some common adverse effects of prolonged tobacco and alcohol use.*

Tobacco	Alcohol
Emphysema, e	Liver damage, l
Heart damage, h	Brain damage, b
Cancer, c	Heart damage, h

In Exercises 29–32, let T be the set of listed effects of tobacco and A be the set of listed effects of alcohol. Find each set.

29. the smallest possible universal set U that includes all the effects listed

30. $T \cap A$

31. $T \cup A$

32. $T \cap A'$

An accountant is sorting tax returns in her files that require attention in the next week.

Describe in words each set in Exercises 33–36.

Let U = the set of all tax returns in the file,

A = the set of all tax returns with itemized deductions,

B = the set of all tax returns showing business income,

C = the set of all tax returns filed in 2014,

D = the set of all tax returns selected for audit.

33. $C - A$

34. $D \cup A'$

35. $(A \cup B) - D$

36. $(C \cap A) \cap B'$

For Exercises 37–40, assume that A and B represent any two sets. Identify each statement as either always true *or* not always true.

37. $(A \cap B) \subseteq A$

38. $A \subseteq (A \cap B)$

39. $n(A \cup B) = n(A) + n(B)$

40. $n(A \cup B) = n(A) + n(B) - n(A \cap B)$

For Exercises 41–44, use your results in parts (a) and (b) to answer part (c).

Let $U = \{1, 2, 3, 4, 5\}$, $X = \{1, 3, 5\}$, $Y = \{1, 2, 3\}$,
and $Z = \{3, 4, 5\}$.

41. (a) Find $X \cup Y$.   **(b)** Find $Y \cup X$.

   (c) State a conjecture.

42. (a) Find $X \cap Y$.   **(b)** Find $Y \cap X$.

   (c) State a conjecture.

43. (a) Find $X \cup (Y \cup Z)$.   **(b)** Find $(X \cup Y) \cup Z$.

   (c) State a conjecture.

44. (a) Find $X \cap (Y \cap Z)$.   **(b)** Find $(X \cap Y) \cap Z$.

   (c) State a conjecture.

Decide whether each statement is true *or* false.

45. $(3, 2) = (5 - 2, 1 + 1)$

46. $(2, 13) = (13, 2)$

47. $\{6, 3\} = \{3, 6\}$

48. $\{(5, 9), (4, 8), (4, 2)\} = \{(4, 8), (5, 9), (2, 4)\}$

Find $A \times B$ and $B \times A$, for A and B defined as follows.

49. $A = \{d, o, g\}$, $B = \{p, i, g\}$

50. $A = \{3, 6, 9, 12\}$, $B = \{6, 8\}$

Use the given information to find $n(A \times B)$ and $n(B \times A)$.

51. $n(A) = 35$ and $n(B) = 6$

52. $n(A) = 13$ and $n(B) = 5$

Find the cardinal number specified.

53. If $n(A \times B) = 72$ and $n(A) = 12$, find $n(B)$.

54. If $n(A \times B) = 300$ and $n(B) = 30$, find $n(A)$.

Place the elements of these sets in the proper locations in the given Venn diagram.

55. Let $U = \{a, b, c, d, e, f, g\}$,
   $A = \{b, d, f, g\}$,
   $B = \{a, b, d, e, g\}$.

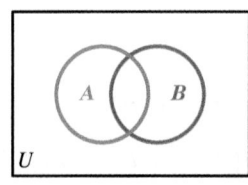

56. Let $U = \{5, 6, 7, 8, 9, 10, 11, 12, 13\}$,
   $M = \{5, 8, 10, 11\}$,
   $N = \{5, 6, 7, 9, 10\}$.

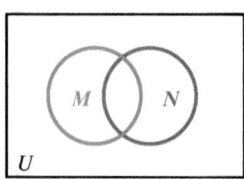

Use a Venn diagram similar to the one shown below to shade each set.

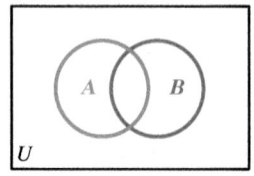

57. $A' \cup B$ 　　　　　　　**58.** $A' \cap B'$

59. $B \cap A'$ 　　　　　　　**60.** $A \cup B$

61. $B' \cap B$ 　　　　　　　**62.** $A' \cup A$

63. $B' \cup (A' \cap B')$ 　　　**64.** $(A - B) \cup (B - A)$

In Exercises 65 and 66, place the elements of the sets in the proper locations in a Venn diagram similar to the one shown below.

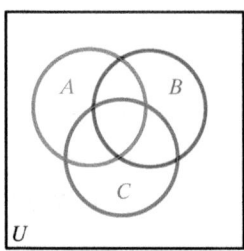

65. Let $U = \{m, n, o, p, q, r, s, t, u, v, w\}$,
   $A = \{m, n, p, q, r, t\}$,
   $B = \{m, o, p, q, s, u\}$,
   $C = \{m, o, p, r, s, t, u, v\}$.

66. Let $U = \{1, 2, 3, 4, 5, 6, 7, 8, 9\}$,
   $A = \{1, 3, 5, 7\}$,
   $B = \{1, 3, 4, 6, 8\}$,
   $C = \{1, 4, 5, 6, 7, 9\}$.

Use a Venn diagram to shade each set.

67. $(A \cap B) \cap C$ 　　　　　**68.** $(A' \cap B) \cap C$

69. $(A' \cap B') \cap C$ 　　　　**70.** $(A \cap C') \cap B$

71. $(A \cap B') \cap C'$ 　　　　**72.** $(A \cap B)' \cup C$

Write a description of each shaded area. Use the symbols A, B, C, ∩, ∪, −, and '. Different answers are possible.

73.

74.

75.

76.

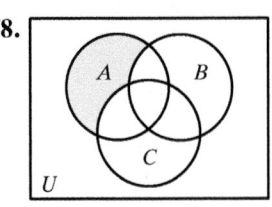

77.

78.

Suppose A and B are sets. Describe the conditions under which each statement would be true.

79. $A = A - B$

80. $A = B - A$

81. $A = A - \varnothing$

82. $A \cap \varnothing = \varnothing$

83. $A \cup B = A$

84. $A \cap B = B$

For Exercises 85–88, draw two Venn diagrams to decide whether the statement is always true *or* not always true.

85. $(A \cap B) \subseteq A$

86. $(A \cup B) \subseteq A$

87. If $A \subseteq B$, then $A \cup B = A$.

88. If $A \subseteq B$, then $A \cap B = A$.

89. Explain why, if A and B are sets, it is not necessarily true that $n(A - B) = n(A) - n(B)$. Give a counterexample.

90. The five set operations listed on **page 66** are applied to subsets of U (that is, to A and/or B). Is the result always a subset of U also? Explain why or why not.

2.4   SURVEYS AND CARDINAL NUMBERS

OBJECTIVES

1 Analyze survey results.

2 Apply the cardinal number formula.

3 Interpret information from tables.

Surveys

As suggested in the chapter opener, the techniques of set theory can be applied to many different groups of people (or objects). The problems addressed sometimes require analyzing known information about certain subsets to obtain cardinal numbers of other subsets. In this section, we apply three problem-solving strategies to such problems:

Venn diagrams,   cardinal number formulas,   and   tables.

The "known information" is quite often (although not always) obtained by conducting a survey.

Suppose a group of attendees at an educational seminar, all of whom desire to become registered nurses (RNs), are asked their preferences among the three traditional ways to become an RN, and the following information is produced.

23 would consider pursuing the Bachelor of Science in Nursing (BSN).

16 would consider pursuing the Associate Degree in Nursing (ADN).

7 would consider a Diploma program (Diploma).

10 would consider both the BSN and the ADN.

5 would consider both the BSN and the Diploma.

3 would consider both the ADN and the Diploma.

2 would consider all three options.

4 are looking for an option other than these three.

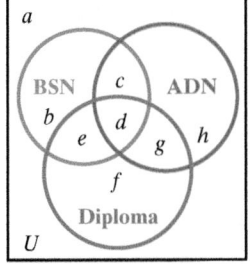

Figure 18

To determine the total number of attendees surveyed, we cannot just add the eight numbers above because there is some overlap. For example, in **Figure 18,** the 23 who like the BSN option should not be positioned in region b but, rather, should be distributed among regions b, c, d, and e in a way that is consistent with all of the data. (Region b actually contains those who like the BSN but neither of the other two options.)

Because, at the start, we do not know how to distribute the 23 who like the BSN, we look first for some more manageable data. The smallest total listed, the 2 who like all three options, can be placed in region *d* (the intersection of the three sets). The 4 who like none of the three must go into region *a*. Then, the 10 who like the BSN and the ADN must go into regions *c* and *d*. Because region *d* already contains 2 attendees, we must place

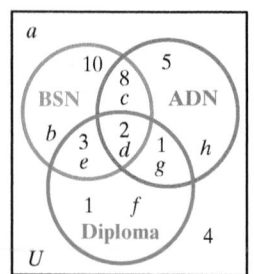

Figure 19

$$10 - 2 = 8 \quad \text{in region } c.$$

Because 5 like BSN and Diploma (regions *d* and *e*), we place

$$5 - 2 = 3 \quad \text{in region } e.$$

Now that regions *c*, *d*, and *e* contain 8, 2, and 3, respectively, we must place

$$23 - 8 - 2 - 3 = 10 \quad \text{in region } b.$$

By similar reasoning, all regions are assigned their correct numbers. See **Figure 19.**

EXAMPLE 1 **Analyzing a Survey**

Using the survey data on personal preferences for nursing preparation, as summarized in **Figure 19,** answer each question.

(a) How many persons like the BSN option only?

(b) How many persons like exactly two of these three options?

(c) How many persons were surveyed?

Solution

(a) A person who likes BSN only does not like ADN and does not like Diploma. These persons are inside the regions for BSN and outside the regions for ADN and Diploma. Region *b* is the appropriate region in **Figure 19,** and we see that ten persons like BSN only.

(b) The persons in regions *c*, *e*, and *g* like exactly two of the three options. The total number of such persons is

$$8 + 3 + 1 = 12.$$

(c) Each person surveyed has been placed in exactly one region of **Figure 19,** so the total number surveyed is the sum of the numbers in all eight regions:

$$4 + 10 + 8 + 2 + 3 + 1 + 1 + 5 = 34. \qquad \blacksquare$$

Cardinal Number Formula

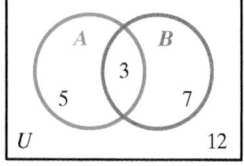

Figure 20

If the numbers shown in **Figure 20** are the cardinal numbers of the individual regions, then

$$n(A) = 5 + 3 = 8, \quad n(B) = 3 + 7 = 10, \quad n(A \cap B) = 3,$$

and

$$n(A \cup B) = 5 + 3 + 7 = 15.$$

Notice that $n(A \cup B) = n(A) + n(B) - n(A \cap B)$ because $15 = 8 + 10 - 3$. This relationship is true for any two sets *A* and *B*.

CARDINAL NUMBER FORMULA

For any two sets *A* and *B*, the following is true.

$$n(A \cup B) = n(A) + n(B) - n(A \cap B)$$

The cardinal number formula can be rearranged to find any one of its four terms when the others are known.

▒EXAMPLE 2 Applying the Cardinal Number Formula

Find $n(A)$ if $n(A \cup B) = 22$, $n(A \cap B) = 8$, and $n(B) = 12$.

Solution

We solve the cardinal number formula for $n(A)$.

$$n(A) = n(A \cup B) - n(B) + n(A \cap B)$$
$$= 22 - 12 + 8$$
$$= 18$$

Sometimes, even when information is presented as in **Example 2,** it is more convenient to fit that information into a Venn diagram as in **Example 1.**

WHEN ᐳ Will I ᐳ Ever USE ᐳ This ᐳ ?

Suppose you run a small construction company, building a few "spec" homes at a time. This week's work will require the following jobs:

　Hanging drywall (D),　Installing roofing (R),　Doing electrical work (E).

You will assign 9 workers, with job skills as described here.

6 of the 9 can do D	5 can do both D and E
4 can do R	4 can do both R and E
7 can do E	4 can do all three

1. Construct a Venn diagram to decide how many of your workers have

    (a) exactly two of the three skills

    (b) none of the three skills

    (c) no more than one of the three skills.

2. Which skill is common to the greatest number of workers, and how many possess that skill?

EXAMPLE 3 Analyzing Data in a Report

Scott, who leads a group of software engineers who investigate illegal activities on social networking sites, reported the following information.

T = the set of group members following patterns on Twitter

F = the set of group members following patterns on Facebook

L = the set of group members following patterns on LinkedIn

$$n(T) = 13 \quad n(T \cap F) = 9 \quad n(T \cap F \cap L) = 5$$
$$n(F) = 16 \quad n(F \cap L) = 10 \quad n(T' \cap F' \cap L') = 3$$
$$n(L) = 13 \quad n(T \cap L) = 6$$

How many engineers are in Scott's group?

Solution

The data supplied by Scott are reflected in **Figure 21.** The sum of the numbers in the diagram gives the total number of engineers in the group.

$$3 + 3 + 1 + 2 + 5 + 5 + 4 + 2 = 25 \qquad ■$$

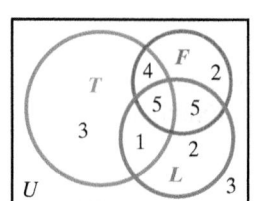

Figure 21

Tables

Sometimes information appears in a table rather than a Venn diagram, but the basic ideas of union and intersection still apply.

EXAMPLE 4 Analyzing Data in a Table

Melanie, the officer in charge of the cafeteria on a military base, wanted to know if the beverage that enlisted men and women preferred with lunch depended on their ages. On a given day, Melanie categorized her lunch patrons according to age and preferred beverage, recording the results in a table.

		Beverage			
		Cola (*C*)	Iced Tea (*I*)	Sweet Tea (*S*)	Totals
Age	18–25 (*Y*)	45	10	35	90
	26–33 (*M*)	20	25	30	75
	Over 33 (*O*)	5	30	20	55
	Totals	70	65	85	220

Using the letters in the table, find the number of people in each set.

(a) $Y \cap C$ **(b)** $O' \cup I$

Solution

(a) The set Y includes all personnel represented across the top row of the table (90 in all), while C includes the 70 down the left column. The intersection of these two sets is just the upper left entry, 45 people.

(b) The set O' excludes the bottom row, so it includes the first and second rows. The set I includes the middle column only. The union of the two sets represents

$$45 + 10 + 35 + 20 + 25 + 30 + 30 = 195 \text{ people.} \qquad ■$$

Use the numerals representing cardinalities in the Venn diagrams to give the cardinality of each set specified.

1.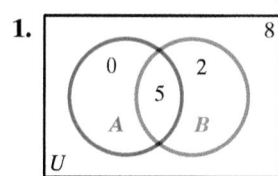

(a) $A \cap B$ (b) $A \cup B$
(c) $A \cap B'$ (d) $A' \cap B$
(e) $A' \cap B'$

2.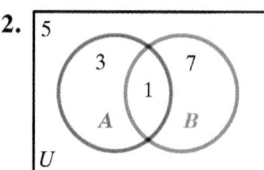

(a) $A \cap B$ (b) $A \cup B$
(c) $A \cap B'$ (d) $A' \cap B$
(e) $A' \cap B'$

3.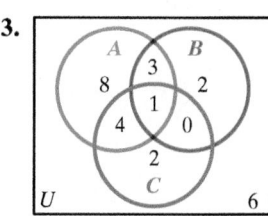

(a) $A \cap B \cap C$ (b) $A \cap B \cap C'$
(c) $A \cap B' \cap C$ (d) $A' \cap B \cap C$
(e) $A' \cap B' \cap C$ (f) $A \cap B' \cap C'$
(g) $A' \cap B \cap C'$ (h) $A' \cap B' \cap C'$

4.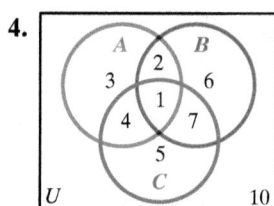

(a) $A \cap B \cap C$ (b) $A \cap B \cap C'$
(c) $A \cap B' \cap C$ (d) $A' \cap B \cap C$
(e) $A' \cap B' \cap C$ (f) $A \cap B' \cap C'$
(g) $A' \cap B \cap C'$ (h) $A' \cap B' \cap C'$

In Exercises 5–10, make use of an appropriate formula.

5. Find the value of $n(A \cup B)$ if $n(A) = 12, n(B) = 14$, and $n(A \cap B) = 5$.

6. Find the value of $n(A \cup B)$ if $n(A) = 16, n(B) = 28$, and $n(A \cap B) = 5$.

7. Find the value of $n(A \cap B)$ if $n(A) = 20, n(B) = 12$, and $n(A \cup B) = 25$.

8. Find the value of $n(A \cap B)$ if $n(A) = 20, n(B) = 24$, and $n(A \cup B) = 30$.

9. Find the value of $n(A)$ if $n(B) = 35, n(A \cap B) = 15$, and $n(A \cup B) = 55$.

10. Find the value of $n(B)$ if $n(A) = 20, n(A \cap B) = 6$, and $n(A \cup B) = 30$.

Draw a Venn diagram and use the given information to fill in the number of elements in each region.

11. $n(A) = 19, \ n(B) = 13, \ n(A \cup B) = 25, \ n(A') = 11$

12. $n(U) = 43, \ n(A) = 25, \ n(A \cap B) = 5, \ n(B') = 30$

13. $n(A') = 25, \ n(B) = 28, \ n(A' \cup B') = 40,$
$n(A \cap B) = 10$

14. $n(A \cup B) = 15, \ n(A \cap B) = 8, \ n(A) = 13,$
$n(A' \cup B') = 11$

15. $n(A) = 57, \ n(A \cap B) = 35, \ n(A \cup B) = 81,$
$n(A \cap B \cap C) = 15, \ n(A \cap C) = 21, n(B \cap C) = 25,$
$n(C) = 49, \ n(B') = 52$

16. $n(A) = 24, \ n(B) = 24, \ n(C) = 26, \ n(A \cap B) = 10,$
$n(B \cap C) = 8, \ n(A \cap C) = 15, \ n(A \cap B \cap C) = 6,$
$n(U) = 50$

17. $n(A) = 15, \ n(A \cap B \cap C) = 5, \ n(A \cap C) = 13,$
$n(A \cap B') = 9, n(B \cap C) = 8, n(A' \cap B' \cap C') = 21,$
$n(B \cap C') = 3, \ n(B \cup C) = 32$

18. $n(A \cap B) = 21, \ n(A \cap B \cap C) = 6, \ n(A \cap C) = 26,$
$n(B \cap C) = 7, \ n(A \cap C') = 20, \ n(B \cap C') = 25,$
$n(C) = 40, \ n(A' \cap B' \cap C') = 2$

Use Venn diagrams to work each problem.

19. *Writing and Producing Music* Joe Long worked on 9 music projects last year.

Joe Long, Bob Gaudio, Tommy DeVito, and Frankie Valli
The Four Seasons

He wrote and produced 3 projects.
He wrote a total of 5 projects.
He produced a total of 7 projects.

(a) How many projects did he write but not produce?
(b) How many projects did he produce but not write?

20. Compact Disc Collection   Gitti is a fan of the music of Paul Simon and Art Garfunkel. In her collection of 25 compact discs, she has the following:

>   5 on which both Simon and Garfunkel sing
>
>   7 on which Simon sings
>
>   8 on which Garfunkel sings
>
>   15 on which neither Simon nor Garfunkel sings.

(a) How many of her compact discs feature only Paul Simon?

(b) How many of her compact discs feature only Art Garfunkel?

(c) How many feature at least one of these two artists?

(d) How many feature at most one of these two artists?

21. Student Response to Classical Composers   The 65 students in a classical music lecture class were polled, with the following results:

>   37 like Wolfgang Amadeus Mozart
>
>   36 like Ludwig van Beethoven
>
>   31 like Franz Joseph Haydn
>
>   14 like Mozart and Beethoven
>
>   21 like Mozart and Haydn
>
>   14 like Beethoven and Haydn
>
>   8 like all three composers.

How many of these students like:

(a) exactly two of these composers?

(b) exactly one of these composers?

(c) none of these composers?

(d) Mozart, but neither Beethoven nor Haydn?

(e) Haydn and exactly one of the other two?

(f) no more than two of these composers?

22. Financial Aid for Students   At a southern university, half of the 48 mathematics majors were receiving federal financial aid.

>   5 had Pell Grants
>
>   14 participated in the College Work Study Program
>
>   4 had TOPS scholarships
>
>   2 had TOPS scholarships and participated in Work Study.
>
>   Those with Pell Grants had no other federal aid.

How many of the 48 math majors had:

(a) no federal aid?

(b) more than one of these three forms of aid?

(c) federal aid other than these three forms?

(d) a TOPS scholarship or Work Study?

(e) exactly one of these three forms of aid?

(f) no more than one of these three forms of aid?

23. Animated Movies   A middle school counselor, attempting to correlate school performance with leisure interests, found the following information for a group of students:

>   34 had seen *Despicable Me*
>
>   29 had seen *Epic*
>
>   26 had seen *Turbo*
>
>   16 had seen *Despicable Me* and *Epic*
>
>   12 had seen *Despicable Me* and *Turbo*
>
>   10 had seen *Epic* and *Turbo*
>
>   4 had seen all three of these films
>
>   5 had seen none of the three films.

(a) How many students had seen *Turbo* only?

(b) How many had seen exactly two of the films?

(c) How many students were surveyed?

24. Non-Mainline Religious Beliefs   140 U.S. adults were surveyed.

Let A = the set of respondents who believe in astrology,

　　R = the set of respondents who believe in reincarnation,

　　Y = the set of respondents who believe in the spirituality of yoga.

The survey revealed the following information:

$$n(A) = 35 \qquad n(R \cap Y) = 8$$
$$n(R) = 36 \qquad n(A \cap Y) = 10$$
$$n(Y) = 32 \qquad n(A \cap R \cap Y) = 6$$
$$n(A \cap R) = 19$$

How many of the respondents believe in:

(a) astrology but not reincarnation?

(b) at least one of these three things?

(c) reincarnation but neither of the others?

(d) exactly two of these three things?

(e) none of the three?

25. *Survey on Attitudes toward Religion* Researchers interviewed a number of people and recorded the following data. Of all the respondents:

240 think Hollywood is unfriendly toward religion

160 think the media are unfriendly toward religion

181 think scientists are unfriendly toward religion

145 think both Hollywood and the media are unfriendly toward religion

122 think both scientists and the media are unfriendly toward religion

80 think exactly two of these groups are unfriendly toward religion

110 think all three groups are unfriendly toward religion

219 think none of these three groups is unfriendly toward religion.

How many respondents:

(a) were surveyed?

(b) think exactly one of these three groups is unfriendly toward religion?

26. *Student Goals* Sofia, who sells college textbooks, interviewed first-year students on a community college campus to find out the main goals of today's students.

Let W = the set of those who want to be wealthy,

F = the set of those who want to raise a family,

E = the set of those who want to become experts in their fields.

Sofia's findings are summarized here.

$$n(W) = 160 \qquad n(E \cap F) = 90$$
$$n(F) = 140 \qquad n(W \cap F \cap E) = 80$$
$$n(E) = 130 \qquad n(E') = 95$$
$$n(W \cap F) = 95 \qquad n[(W \cup F \cup E)'] = 10$$

Find the total number of students interviewed.

27. *Hospital Patient Symptoms* A survey was conducted among 75 patients admitted to a hospital cardiac unit during a two-week period.

Let B = the set of patients with high blood pressure,

C = the set of patients with high cholesterol levels,

S = the set of patients who smoke cigarettes.

The survey produced the following data.

$$n(B) = 47 \qquad n(B \cap S) = 33$$
$$n(C) = 46 \qquad n(B \cap C) = 31$$
$$n(S) = 52 \qquad n(B \cap C \cap S) = 21$$
$$n[(B \cap C) \cup (B \cap S) \cup (C \cap S)] = 51$$

Find the number of these patients who:

(a) had either high blood pressure or high cholesterol levels, but not both

(b) had fewer than two of the indications listed

(c) were smokers but had neither high blood pressure nor high cholesterol levels

(d) did not have exactly two of the indications listed.

28. *Song Themes* It was once said that country-western songs emphasize three basic themes: love, prison, and trucks. A survey of the local country-western radio station produced the following data.

12 songs about a truck driver who is in love while in prison

13 about a prisoner in love

28 about a person in love

18 about a truck driver in love

3 about a truck driver in prison who is not in love

2 about people in prison who are not in love and do not drive trucks

8 about people who are out of prison, are not in love, and do not drive trucks

16 about truck drivers who are not in prison

(a) How many songs were surveyed?

Find the number of songs about:

(b) truck drivers

(c) prisoners

(d) truck drivers in prison

(e) people not in prison

(f) people not in love.

29. Use the figure to find the numbers of the regions belonging to each set.

(a) $A \cap B \cap C \cap D$

(b) $A \cup B \cup C \cup D$

(c) $(A \cap B) \cup (C \cap D)$

(d) $(A' \cap B') \cap (C \cup D)$

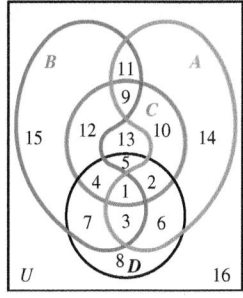

30. *Sports Viewing* A survey of 130 TV viewers was taken.

> 52 watch football
>
> 56 watch basketball
>
> 62 watch tennis
>
> 60 watch golf
>
> 21 watch football and basketball
>
> 19 watch football and tennis
>
> 22 watch basketball and tennis
>
> 27 watch football and golf
>
> 30 watch basketball and golf
>
> 21 watch tennis and golf
>
> 3 watch football, basketball, and tennis
>
> 15 watch football, basketball, and golf
>
> 10 watch football, tennis, and golf
>
> 10 watch basketball, tennis, and golf
>
> 3 watch all four of these sports
>
> 5 don't watch any of these four sports

Use a Venn diagram to answer these questions.

(a) How many of these viewers watch football, basketball, and tennis, but not golf?

(b) How many watch exactly one of these four sports?

(c) How many watch exactly two of these four sports?

Solve each problem.

31. *Basketball Positions* Sakda runs a basketball program in California. On the first day of the season, 60 young women showed up and were categorized by age level and by preferred basketball position, as shown in the following table.

| | Position | | | |
	Guard (G)	Forward (F)	Center (N)	Totals
Junior High (J)	9	6	4	19
Age **Senior High (S)**	12	5	9	26
College (C)	5	8	2	15
Totals	26	19	15	60

Using the set labels (letters) in the table, find the number of players in each of the following sets.

(a) $J \cap G$ **(b)** $S \cap N$

(c) $N \cup (S \cap F)$ **(d)** $S' \cap (G \cup N)$

(e) $(S \cap N') \cup (C \cap G')$ **(f)** $N' \cap (S' \cap C')$

32. *Army Housing* A study of U.S. Army housing trends categorized personnel as commissioned officers (*C*), warrant officers (*W*), or enlisted (*E*), and categorized their living facilities as on-base (*B*), rented off-base (*R*), or owned off-base (*O*). One survey yielded the following data.

| | | Facilities | | | |
		B	R	O	Totals
	C	12	29	54	95
Personnel	**W**	4	5	6	15
	E	374	71	285	730
	Totals	390	105	345	840

Find the number of personnel in each of the following sets.

(a) $W \cap O$

(b) $C \cup B$

(c) $R' \cup W'$

(d) $(C \cup W) \cap (B \cup R)$

(e) $(C \cap B) \cup (E \cap O)$

(f) $B \cap (W \cup R)'$

33. Could the information of **Example 4** have been presented in a Venn diagram similar to those in **Examples 1 and 3?** If so, construct such a diagram. Otherwise, explain the essential difference of **Example 4.**

34. Explain how a cardinal number formula can be derived for the case where *three* sets occur. Specifically, give a formula relating $n(A \cup B \cup C)$ to

$$n(A), \ n(B), \ n(C), \ n(A \cap B), \ n(A \cap C),$$
$$n(B \cap C), \ \text{and} \ n(A \cap B \cap C).$$

Illustrate with a Venn diagram.

CHAPTER 2 SUMMARY

KEY TERMS

2.1

set
elements
members
empty (null) set
natural (counting) numbers
whole numbers

integers
rational numbers
real numbers
irrational numbers
cardinal number
  (cardinality)
finite set
infinite set

2.2

universal set
Venn diagram
complement (of a set)
subset (of a set)
proper subset (of a set)
tree diagram

2.3

intersection (of sets)
disjoint sets
union (of sets)
difference (of sets)
ordered pairs
Cartesian product (of sets)
operation (on sets)

NEW SYMBOLS

$\varnothing$	empty set (or null set)
$\in$	is an element of
$\notin$	is not an element of
$n(A)$	cardinal number of set A
$\aleph_0$	aleph null
U	universal set
A'	complement of set A
$\subseteq$	is a subset of

$\not\subset$	is not a subset of
$\subset$	is a proper subset of
$\cap$	intersection (of sets)
$\cup$	union (of sets)
$-$	difference (of sets)
(a, b)	ordered pair
$\times$	Cartesian product

TEST YOUR WORD POWER

See how well you have learned the vocabulary in this chapter.

1. In an **ordered pair,**
   A. the components are always numbers of the same type.
   B. the first component must be less than the second.
   C. the components can be any kinds of objects.
   D. the first component is a subset of the second component.

2. The **complement** of a set
   A. contains only some, but not all, of that set's elements.
   B. contains the same number of elements as the given set.
   C. always contains fewer elements than the given set.
   D. cannot be determined until a universal set is given.

3. Any **subset** of set A
   A. must have fewer elements than A.
   B. has fewer elements than A only if it is a proper subset.
   C. is an element of A.
   D. contains all the elements of A, plus at least one additional element.

4. Examples of **operations on sets** are
   A. union, intersection, and subset.
   B. Cartesian product, difference, and proper subset.
   C. complement, supplement, and intersection.
   D. complement, union, and Cartesian product.

5. The **set difference $A - B$** must have cardinality
   A. $n(A) - n(B)$.
   B. less than or equal to $n(A)$.
   C. greater than or equal to $n(B)$.
   D. less than $n(A)$.

6. The **cardinal number formula** says that
   A. $n(A \cup B) = n(A) + n(B) - n(A \cap B)$.
   B. $n(A \cup B) = n(A) + n(B) + n(A \cap B)$.
   C. $n(A \cup B) = n(A) + n(B)$.
   D. $n(A \cup B) = n(A) \cdot n(B)$.

ANSWERS

1. C **2.** D **3.** B **4.** D **5.** B **6.** A

QUICK REVIEW

Concepts	*Examples*

2.1 Symbols and Terminology

Designating Sets
Sets are designated using the following methods:

   (1) word descriptions,

   (2) the listing method,

   (3) set-builder notation.

The set of odd counting numbers less than 7

$\{1, 3, 5\}$

$\{x \mid x \text{ is an odd counting number and } x < 7\}$

All are equal.

The **cardinal number** of a set is the number of elements it contains.

If $A = \{10, 20, 30, ..., 80\}$, then $n(A) = 8$.

Equal sets have exactly the same elements.

$\{a, e, i, o, u\} = \{i, o, u, a, e\}, \quad \{q, r, s, t\} \neq \{q, p, s, t\}$

2.2 Venn Diagrams and Subsets

Sets are normally discussed within the context of a designated **universal set, U**.

Let $U = \{x \mid x \text{ is a whole number}\}$

and

$\qquad A = \{x \mid x \text{ is an even whole number}\}.$

The **complement** of a set A contains all elements in U that are not in A.

Then $A' = \{x \mid x \text{ is an odd whole number}\}.$

Set B is a **subset** of set A if every element of B is also an element of A.

Let $U = \{2, 3, 5, 7\}, \quad A = \{3, 5, 7\}, \quad$ and $\quad B = \{5\}.$
Then $A' = \{2\}$ and $B \subseteq A.$

Set B is a **proper subset** of A if $B \subseteq A$ and $B \neq A$.

For the sets A and B given above, $B \subset A.$

If a set has cardinal number n, it has 2^n subsets and $2^n - 1$ proper subsets.

If $D = \{x, y, z\}$, then $n(D) = 3.$
D has $2^3 = 8$ subsets and $2^3 - 1 = 8 - 1 = 7$ proper subsets.

2.3 Set Operations

Intersection of sets

$$A \cap B = \{x \mid x \in A \text{ and } x \in B\}$$

$\{1, 2, 7\} \cap \{5, 7, 9, 11\} = \{7\}$

Union of sets

$$A \cup B = \{x \mid x \in A \text{ or } x \in B\}$$

$\{20, 40, 60\} \cup \{40, 60, 80\} = \{20, 40, 60, 80\}$

Difference of sets

$$A - B = \{x \mid x \in A \text{ and } x \notin B\}$$

$\{5, 6, 7, 8\} - \{1, 3, 5, 7\} = \{6, 8\}$

Cartesian product of sets

$$A \times B = \{(a, b) \mid a \in A \text{ and } b \in B\}$$

$\{1, 2\} \times \{30, 40, 50\}$
$\quad = \{(1, 30), (1, 40), (1, 50), (2, 30), (2, 40), (2, 50)\}$

Cardinal number of a Cartesian product

If $n(A) = a$ and $n(B) = b$, then

$$n(A \times B) = n(A) \cdot n(B) = ab.$$

If $A = \{2, 4, 6, 8\}$ and $B = \{3, 7\}$, then

$$n(A \times B) = n(A) \cdot n(B) = 4 \cdot 2 = 8.$$

Verify by listing the elements of $A \times B$.

$\{(2, 3), (2, 7), (4, 3), (4, 7), (6, 3), (6, 7), (8, 3), (8, 7)\}$

It, indeed, has 8 elements.

Concepts	*Examples*
Numbering the regions in a Venn diagram facilitates identification of various sets and relationships among them.	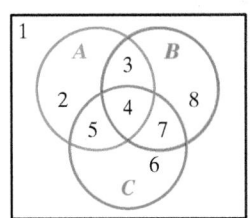

A consists of regions 2, 3, 4, and 5.

$A \cap B$ consists of regions 3 and 4.

$B \cup C$ consists of regions 3, 4, 5, 6, 7, and 8.

$(A \cup B) \cap C'$ consists of regions 2, 3, and 8.

$A \cap B \cap C$ consists of region 4.

$(A \cup B \cup C)'$ consists of region 1.

$A - C$ consists of regions 2 and 3.

De Morgan's Laws

For any sets A and B, where $A, B \subseteq U$, the following are true.

$$(A \cap B)' = A' \cup B'$$

Let $U = \{1, 2, 3, 4, \ldots, 9\}$, $A = \{2, 4, 6, 8\}$, and $B = \{4, 5, 6, 7\}$.

Then $A \cap B = \{4, 6\}$,

so $(A \cap B)' = \{1, 2, 3, 5, 7, 8, 9\}$. ⟵

Also $A' = \{1, 3, 5, 7, 9\}$ and $B' = \{1, 2, 3, 8, 9\}$, ⊦ Same

so $A' \cup B' = \{1, 2, 3, 5, 7, 8, 9\}$. ⟵

Using the same sets A and B as above,

$$A \cup B = \{2, 4, 5, 6, 7, 8\},$$

$$(A \cup B)' = A' \cap B'$$

so $(A \cup B)' = \{1, 3, 9\}$. ⟵

Also, $A' = \{1, 3, 5, 7, 9\}$ and $B' = \{1, 2, 3, 8, 9\}$, ⊦ Same

so $A' \cap B' = \{1, 3, 9\}$. ⟵

2.4 Surveys and Cardinal Numbers

Cardinal Number Formula

For any two sets A and B, the following is true.

$$n(A \cup B) = n(A) + n(B) - n(A \cap B)$$

Suppose $n(A) = 5, n(B) = 12$, and $n(A \cup B) = 10$. Then, to find $n(A \cap B)$, first solve the formula for that term.

$$n(A \cap B) = n(A) + n(B) - n(A \cup B)$$

$$= 5 + 12 - 10 = 7$$

Enter known facts in a Venn diagram to find desired facts.

Given $n(A) = 12, n(B) = 27, n(A \cup B) = 32$, and $n(U) = 50$, find $n(A - B)$ and $n[(A \cap B)']$.

$$n(A \cap B) = n(A) + n(B) - n(A \cup B)$$

$$= 12 + 27 - 32$$

$$= 7$$

Then the cardinalities of all regions can be entered in the diagram, starting with 7 in the center.

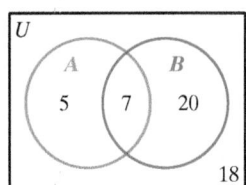

Now observe that $n(A - B) = 5$ and $n[(A \cap B)'] = 18 + 5 + 20 = 43$.

CHAPTER 2 TEST

In Exercises 1–14, let

$U = \{a, b, c, d, e, f, g, h\}$, $A = \{a, b, c, d\}$,
$B = \{b, e, a, d\}$, *and* $C = \{e, a\}$.

Find each set.

1. $A \cup C$ **2.** $B \cap A$

3. B' **4.** $A - (B \cap C')$

Identify each statement as true *or* false.

5. $e \in A$ **6.** $C \subseteq B$

7. $B \subset (A \cup C)$ **8.** $c \notin C$

9. $n[(A \cup B) - C] = 4$ **10.** $\varnothing \not\subset C$

11. $A \cap B'$ is equivalent to $B \cap A'$

12. $(A \cup B)' = A' \cap B'$

Find each of the following.

13. $n(B \times A)$

14. the number of proper subsets of B

Give a word description for each set.

15. $\{-3, -1, 1, 3, 5, 7, 9\}$

16. $\{\text{Sun, Mon, Tue}, \dots, \text{Sat}\}$

Express each set in set-builder notation.

17. $\{-1, -2, -3, -4, \dots\}$

18. $\{24, 32, 40, 48, \dots, 88\}$

Place $\subset$, $\subseteq$, both, *or* neither *in each blank to make a true statement.*

19. $\varnothing$ _____ $\{x \mid x \text{ is a counting number between 20 and 21}\}$

20. $\{3, 5, 7\}$ _____ $\{4, 5, 6, 7, 8, 9, 10\}$

Shade each set in an appropriate Venn diagram.

21. $X \cup Y'$ **22.** $X' \cap Y'$

23. $(X \cup Y) - Z$

24. $[(X \cap Y) \cup (X \cap Z)] - (Y \cap Z)$

25. State De Morgan's laws for sets in words rather than symbols.

Facts about Inventions The table lists ten inventions, together with other pertinent data.

Invention	Date	Inventor	Nation
Adding machine	1642	Pascal	France
Baking powder	1843	Bird	England
Electric razor	1917	Schick	U.S.
Fiber optics	1955	Kapany	England
Geiger counter	1913	Geiger	Germany
Pendulum clock	1657	Huygens	Holland
Radar	1940	Watson-Watt	Scotland
Telegraph	1837	Morse	U.S.
Thermometer	1593	Galileo	Italy
Zipper	1891	Judson	U.S.

Let $U = $ the set of all ten inventions,
$A = $ the set of items invented in the United States,
and $T = $ the set of items invented in the twentieth century.

List the elements of each set.

26. $A \cap T$ **27.** $(A \cup T)'$ **28.** $T' - A'$

29. The numerals in the Venn diagram indicate the number of elements in each particular subset. Determine the number of elements in each set.

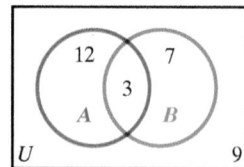

(a) $A \cup B$ **(b)** $A \cap B'$

(c) $(A \cap B)'$

30. *Financial Aid to College Students* Three sources of financial aid are government grants, private scholarships, and the colleges themselves. Susan, a financial aid director of a private college, surveyed the records of 100 sophomores and found the following:

    49 receive government grants

    55 receive private scholarships

    43 receive aid from the college

    23 receive government grants and private scholarships

    18 receive government grants and aid from the college

    28 receive private scholarships and aid from the college

    8 receive help from all three sources.

How many of the students in the survey:

(a) have government grants only?

(b) have scholarships but not government grants?

(c) receive financial aid from only one of these sources?

(d) receive aid from exactly two of these sources?

(e) receive no financial aid from any of these sources?

(f) receive no aid from the college or the government?

EXTENSION   INFINITE SETS AND THEIR CARDINALITIES

OBJECTIVES

1 One-to-One Correspondence and Equivalent Sets

2 The Cardinal Number $\aleph_0$

3 Infinite Sets

4 Sets That Are Not Countable

The word **paradox** in Greek originally meant "wrong opinion" as opposed to orthodox, which meant "right opinion." Over the years, the word came to mean self-contradiction.

Before the twentieth century it was considered a paradox that any set could be placed into one-to-one correspondence with a proper subset of itself. This paradox, called **Galileo's paradox** after the sixteenth-century mathematician and scientist **Galileo** (see the picture), is now explained by saying that the ability to make such a correspondence is how we distinguish infinite sets from finite sets. What is true for finite sets is not necessarily true for infinite sets.

One-to-One Correspondence and Equivalent Sets

Georg Cantor met with much resistance in the late 1800s when he first developed modern set theory because of his ideas on infinite sets. The results discussed here, however, are commonly accepted today.

1. The cardinal number of a set is the number of elements it contains.

2. Two sets are *equivalent* if their cardinal numbers are equal.

3. A set is *infinite* if its cardinal number is "too large" to be found among the whole numbers.

We can easily establish the equivalence of two finite sets by counting their elements and comparing their cardinal numbers. But the elements of an infinite set cannot be counted in the same sense. Cantor addressed this difficulty using the idea of a **one-to-one correspondence** between sets. The sets $A = \{1, 2, 3\}$ and $B = \{3, 6, 9\}$, for example, can be placed in such correspondence as follows (among other ways):

$$\{1, \quad 2, \quad 3\}$$
$$\updownarrow \quad \updownarrow \quad \updownarrow \; .$$
$$\{3, \quad 6, \quad 9\}$$

This correspondence is "one-to-one" because each element of each set is paired with exactly one element of the other set. The equivalence of A and B is denoted $A \sim B$.

On the other hand, the sets $C = \{1, 8, 12\}$ and $C = \{6, 11\}$ are *not* equivalent. Any correspondence between them, such as

$$\{1, \quad 8, \quad 12\}$$
$$\updownarrow \qquad \text{↕↗}$$
$$\{6, \qquad 11\}$$

is not one-to-one. (Two different elements from C must be paired with a single element of D.)

Cantor extended this idea that one-to-one correspondence establishes equivalence to his study of infinite sets.

The Cardinal Number $\aleph_0$

The most basic infinite set is the set of counting numbers, $\{1, 2, 3, 4, 5, \ldots\}$.. The counting numbers are said to have the infinite cardinal number $\aleph_0$ (the first Hebrew letter, aleph, with a zero subscript, read "aleph-null"). Think of $\aleph_0$. as being the "smallest" infinite cardinal number. To the question "How many counting numbers are there?", we answer "There are $\aleph_0$ of them."

Now, any set that can be placed in a one-to-one correspondence with the counting numbers will have the same cardinal number, or $\aleph_0$. There are many such sets.

EXAMPLE 1 Showing that {0, 1, 2, 3, . . .} Has Cardinal Number $\aleph_0$

Verify that the set of whole numbers $\{0, 1, 2, 3, . . .\}$ has cardinal number $\aleph_0$.

Solution

We know that $\aleph_0$ is the cardinal number of the set of counting numbers (by definition). To show that another set, such as the whole numbers, also has $\aleph_0$ as its cardinal number, we must show that set to be equivalent to the set of counting numbers. Equivalence is established by a one-to-one correspondence between the two sets.

$$\{1, \quad 2, \quad 3, \quad 4, \quad 5, \quad 6, . . ., \quad n, \quad . . .\} \quad \text{Counting numbers}$$
$$\updownarrow \quad \updownarrow \quad \updownarrow \quad \updownarrow \quad \updownarrow \quad \updownarrow \qquad \updownarrow \qquad \updownarrow$$
$$\{0, \quad 1, \quad 2, \quad 3, \quad 4, \quad 5, . . ., \quad n-1, \quad . . .\} \quad \text{Whole numbers}$$

The pairing of the counting number n with the whole number $n - 1$ continues indefinitely, with neither set containing any element not used up in the pairing process. Even though the set of whole numbers has an additional element (the number 0) compared to the set of counting numbers, the correspondence proves that both sets have the same cardinal number, $\aleph_0$. ■

The result in **Example 1** shows that intuition is a poor guide for dealing with infinite sets. Because the sets of counting numbers and whole numbers can be placed in a one-to-one correspondence, the two sets have the same cardinal number.

Infinite Sets The set $\{5, 6, 7\}$ is a proper subset of the set $\{5, 6, 7, 8\}$, and there is no way to place these two sets in a one-to-one correspondence. However, the set of counting numbers is a proper subset of the set of whole numbers, and **Example 1** showed that these two sets *can* be placed in a one-to-one correspondence. This important property is used in the formal definition of an infinite set.

> **INFINITE SET**
>
> A set is **infinite** if it can be placed in a one-to-one correspondence with a proper subset of itself.

EXAMPLE 2 Showing that {. . . , −3, −2, −1, 0, 1, 2, 3, . . .} Has Cardinal Number $\aleph_0$

Verify that the set of integers $\{. . . , -3, -2, -1, 0, 1, 2, 3, . . .\}$ has cardinal number $\aleph_0$.

Solution

A one-to-one correspondence can be set up between the set of integers and the set of counting numbers.

$$\{1, \; 2, \quad 3, \; 4, \; 5, \; 6, \; 7, \; . . ., \; 2n, \; 2n+1, \; . . .\}$$
$$\updownarrow \; \updownarrow \; \updownarrow \; \updownarrow \; \updownarrow \; \updownarrow \; \updownarrow \qquad \updownarrow \qquad \updownarrow$$
$$\{0, \; 1, \; -1, \; 2, \; -2, \; 3, \; -3, \; . . ., \; n, \quad -n, \quad . . .\}$$

Because of this one-to-one correspondence, the cardinal number of the set of integers is the same as the cardinal number of the set of counting numbers, $\aleph_0$. ■

Aleph and other letters of the **Hebrew alphabet** are shown on a Kabbalistic diagram representing one of the ten emanations of God during Creation. Kabbalah, the ultramystical tradition within Judaism, arose in the fifth century and peaked in the sixteenth century in both Palestine and Poland.

Kabbalists believed that the Bible held mysteries that could be discovered in permutations, combinations, and anagrams of its very letters. Each letter in the aleph-bet has a numerical value (aleph = 1), and thus a numeration system exists. The letter Y stands for 10, so 15 should be YH (10 + 5). However, YH is a form of the Holy Name, so instead TW (9 + 6) is the symbol.

The one-to-one correspondence of **Example 2** proves that the set of integers is infinite—it was placed in one-to-one correspondence with a proper subset of itself.

As shown by **Example 2,** there are just as many integers as there are counting numbers. This result is not at all intuitive, and the next result is even less so. There is an infinite number of fractions between any two counting numbers. For example, there is an infinite set of fractions $\left\{ \frac{1}{2}, \frac{3}{4}, \frac{7}{8}, \frac{15}{16}, \frac{31}{32}, \ldots \right\}$ between the count ing numbers 0 and 1. This should imply that there are "more" fractions than counting numbers. However, there are just as many fractions as counting numbers.

EXAMPLE 3   **Showing that the Set of Rational Numbers Has Cardinal Number $\aleph_0$**

Verify that the cardinal number of the set of rational numbers is $\aleph_0$.

Solution

First show that a one-to-one correspondence may be set up between the set of non-negative rational numbers and the counting numbers. This is done by the following ingenious scheme, devised by Georg Cantor.

Look at **Figure 22** in this page. The nonnegative rational numbers whose denominators are 1 are written in the first row. Those whose denominators are 2 are written in the second row, and so on. Every nonnegative rational number appears in this list sooner or later. For example, $\frac{327}{189}$ is in row 189 and column 327.

To set up a one-to-one correspondence between the set of nonnegative rationals and the set of counting numbers, follow the path drawn in **Figure 22.** Let $\frac{0}{1}$ correspond to 1, let $\frac{1}{1}$ correspond to 2, $\frac{2}{1}$ to 3, $\frac{1}{2}$ to 4 $\left(\text{skip } \frac{2}{2}, \text{ since } \frac{2}{2} = \frac{1}{1}\right)$, $\frac{1}{3}$ to 5, $\frac{1}{4}$ to 6, and so on. The numbers under the colored disks are omitted because they can be reduced to lower terms, and were thus included earlier in the listing.

This procedure sets up a one-to-one correspondence between the set of non-negative rationals and the counting numbers, showing that both of these sets have the same cardinal number, $\aleph_0$. Now by using the method of **Example 2** (i.e., letting each negative number follow its corresponding positive number), we can extend this correspondence to include negative rational numbers as well. Thus, the set of all rational numbers has cardinal number $\aleph_0$.

Figure 22   ■

The Barber Paradox is a version of a paradox of set theory that Bertrand Russell proposed in the early twentieth century.

1. The men in a village are of two types: men who do not shave themselves and men who do.
2. The village barber shaves all men who do not shave themselves and he shaves only those men.

But who shaves the barber?
The barber cannot shave himself. If he did, he would fall into the category of men who shave themselves. However, (2) above states that the barber does not shave such men.

So the barber does not shave himself. But then he falls into the category of men who do not shave themselves. According to (2), the barber shaves all of these men; hence, the barber shaves himself, too.

We find that the barber cannot shave himself, yet the barber does shave himself—a paradox.

Zeno's paradox of the Tortoise and Achilles was given in its original form by Zeno of Elea.

In the original story, the Tortoise is able to convince Achilles (the Greek hero of Homer's *The Illiad*) that in a race, given a small head start, the Tortoise is always able to defeat Achilles. (See the **Chapter Opener** and **Exercises 51 and 52** in this **Extension**.) The resolution of this paradox is discussed on the Web site www.mathacademy.com.

A set is called **countable** if it is finite or if it has cardinal number $\aleph_0$. All the infinite sets of numbers discussed so far—the counting numbers, the whole numbers, the integers, and the rational numbers—are countable.

Sets That Are Not Countable

EXAMPLE 4 **Showing that the Set of Real Numbers Does Not Have Cardinal Number $\aleph_0$**

Verify that the set of all real numbers does not have cardinal number $\aleph_0$.

Solution

There are two possibilities:
1. The set of real numbers has cardinal number $\aleph_0$.
2. The set of real numbers does not have cardinal number $\aleph_0$.

If we assume that the first statement is true, then a one-to-one correspondence can be set up between the set of real numbers and the set of counting numbers.

In a later chapter, we show that every real number can be written as a decimal number (or simply "decimal"). Thus, in the one-to-one correspondence we are assuming, some decimal corresponds to the counting number 1, some decimal corresponds to 2, and so on. Suppose the correspondence begins as follows:

$$1 \leftrightarrow 0.68458429006\ldots$$
$$2 \leftrightarrow 0.13479201038\ldots$$
$$3 \leftrightarrow 0.37291568341\ldots$$
$$4 \leftrightarrow 0.935223671611\ldots$$

and so on.

Assuming the existence of a one-to-one correspondence between the counting numbers and the real numbers means that every decimal is in the list above. Let's construct a new decimal K as follows. The first decimal in the above list has 6 as its first digit. Let K start as $K = 0.4\ldots$. We picked 4 because $4 \neq 6$. (We could have used any other digit except 6.) Because the second digit of the second decimal in the list is 3, we let $K = 0.45\ldots$ (because $5 \neq 3$). The third digit of the third decimal is 2, so let $K = 0.457\ldots$ (because $7 \neq 2$). The fourth digit of the fourth decimal is 2, so let $K = 0.4573\ldots$ (because $3 \neq 2$). Continue defining K in this way.

Is K in the list that we assumed to contain all decimals? The first decimal in the list differs from K in at least the first position (K starts with 4, and the first decimal in the list starts with 6). The second decimal in the list differs from K in at least the second position, and the nth decimal in the list differs from K in at least the nth position. Every decimal in the list differs from K in at least one position, so that K cannot possibly be in the list. In summary:

We assume every decimal is in the list above.
The decimal K is not in the list.

Because these statements cannot both be true, the original assumption has led to a contradiction. This forces the acceptance of the only possible alternative to the original assumption: It is not possible to set up a one-to-one correspondence between the set of reals and the set of counting numbers. The cardinal number of the set of reals is not equal to $\aleph_0$. ∎

The set of counting numbers is a proper subset of the set of real numbers. Because of this, it would seem reasonable to say that the cardinal number of the set of reals, commonly written c, is greater than $\aleph_0$. (The letter c here represents *continuum*.) Other, even larger, infinite cardinal numbers can be constructed. For example, the set of all subsets of the set of real numbers has a cardinal number larger than c. Continuing this process of finding cardinal numbers of sets of subsets, more and more, larger and larger infinite cardinal numbers are produced.

The six most important infinite sets of numbers were listed in **Section 2.1.** All of them have been dealt with in this **Extension,** except the irrational numbers. The irrationals have decimal representations, so they are all included among the real numbers. Because the irrationals are a subset of the reals, you might guess that the irrationals have cardinal number $\aleph_0$, just like the rationals. However, because the union of the rationals and the irrationals is all the reals, that would imply that the cardinality of the union of two disjoint countable sets is c. But **Example 2** showed that this is not the case. A better guess is that the cardinal number of the irrationals is c (the same as that of the reals). This is, in fact, true.

CARDINAL NUMBERS OF INFINITE NUMBER SETS

Infinite Set	Cardinal Number
Natural or counting numbers	$\aleph_0$
Whole numbers	$\aleph_0$
Integers	$\aleph_0$
Rational numbers	$\aleph_0$
Irrational numbers	c
Real numbers	c

EXTENSION EXERCISES

Match each set in Column I with the set in Column II that has the same cardinality. Give the cardinal number.

I

1. $\{6\}$

2. $\{-16, 14, 3\}$

3. $\{x \mid x \text{ is a natural number}\}$

4. $\{x \mid x \text{ is a real number}\}$

5. $\{x \mid x \text{ is an integer between } 5 \text{ and } 6\}$

6. $\{x \mid x \text{ is an integer that satisfies } x^2 = 100\}$

II

A. $\{x \mid x \text{ is a rational number}\}$

B. $\{26\}$

C. $\{x \mid x \text{ is an irrational number}\}$

D. $\{x, y, z\}$

E. $\{x \mid x \text{ is a real number that satisfies } x^2 = 25\}$

F. $\{x \mid x \text{ is an integer that is both even and odd}\}$

Place each pair of sets into a one-to-one correspondence, if possible.

7. $\{I, II, III\}$ and $x, y, z\}$

8. $\{a, b, c, d\}$ and $\{2, 4, 6\}$

9. $\{a, d, d, i, t, i, o, n\}$ and $\{a, n, s, w, e, r\}$

10. $\{\text{Obama, Clinton, Bush}\}$ and $\{\text{Michelle, Hillary, Laura}\}$

Give the cardinal number of each set.

11. $\{a, b, c, d, \dots, k\}$

12. $\{9, 12, 15, \dots, 36\}$

13. $\emptyset$

14. $\{0\}$

15. $\{300, 400, 500, \dots\}$

16. $\{-35, -28, -21, \dots, 56\}$

17. $\left\{ -\dfrac{1}{4}, -\dfrac{1}{8}, -\dfrac{1}{12}, \dots \right\}$

18. $\{x \mid x \text{ is an even integer}\}$

19. $\{x \mid x \text{ is an odd counting number}\}$

20. $\{b, a, 1, 1, a, d\}$

21. $\{\text{Jan, Feb, Mar, \dots, Dec}\}$

22. $\{\text{Alabama, Alaska, Arizona, \dots, Wisconsin, Wyoming}\}$

23. Lew Lefton has revised the old song "100 Bottles of Beer on the Wall" to illustrate a property of infinite cardinal numbers.

Fill in the blank in the first verse of Lefton's composition:

$\aleph_0$ bottles of beer on the wall, $\aleph_0$ bottles of beer, take one down and pass it around, ___ $\aleph_0$ bottles of beer on the wall. (*Source:* http://people.math.gatech.edu/~llefton)

$\aleph_0 - 1 = 0$

24. Two one-to-one correspondences are considered "different" if some elements are paired differently in one than in the other.

{a, b, c}   {a, b, c}
↕ ↕ ↕   and   ↕ ↕ ↕   are different,
{a, b, c}   {c, b, a}

{a, b, c}   {b, c, a}
while   ↕ ↕ ↕   and   ↕ ↕ ↕   are not.
{c, a, b}   {a, b, c}

(a) How many *different* correspondences can be set up between the two sets {Jamie Foxx, Mike Myers, Madonna} and {Austin Powers, Ray Charles, Eva Peron}?

(b) Which one of these correspondences pairs each person with the appropriate famous movie role?

Determine whether each pair of sets is equal, equivalent, both, *or* neither.

25. {u, v, w}, {v, u, w}   **26.** {48, 6}, {4, 86}

27. {X, Y, Z}, {x, y, z}

28. {top}, {pot}

29. $\{x \mid x$ is a positive real number$\}$,

   $\{x \mid x$ is a negative real number$\}$

30. $\{x \mid x$ is a positive rational number$\}$,

   $\{x \mid x$ is a negative real number$\}$

Show that each set has cardinal number $\aleph_0$ *by setting up a one-to-one correspondence between the given set and the set of counting numbers.*

31. the set of positive even integers

32. $\{-10, -20, -30, -40, \ldots\}$

33. $\{1{,}000{,}000, 2{,}000{,}000, 3{,}000{,}000, \ldots\}$

34. the set of odd integers

35. $\{2, 4, 8, 16, 32, \ldots\}$
   (*Hint:* $4 = 2^2$, $8 = 2^3$, $16 = 2^4$, and so on)

36. $\{-17, -22, -27, -32, \ldots\}$

In Exercises 37–40, identify the given statement as always true *or* not always true. *If not* always true, *give a counterexample.*

37. If A and B are infinite sets, then A is equivalent to B.

38. If set A is an infinite set and set B can be put in a one-to-one correspondence with a proper subset of A, then B must be infinite.

39. If A is an infinite set and A is not equivalent to the set of counting numbers, then $n(A) = c$

40. If A and B are both countably infinite sets, then $n(A \cup B) = \aleph_0$.

Exercises 41 and 42 are geometric applications of the concept of infinity.

41. The set of real numbers can be represented by an infinite line, extending indefinitely in both directions. Each point on the line corresponds to a unique real number, and each real number corresponds to a unique point on the line.

(a) Use the figure below, where the line segment between 0 and 1 has been bent into a semicircle and positioned above the line, to prove that

   $\{x \mid x$ is a real number between 0 and 1$\}$ *is equivalent to* $\{x \mid x$ is a real number$\}$.

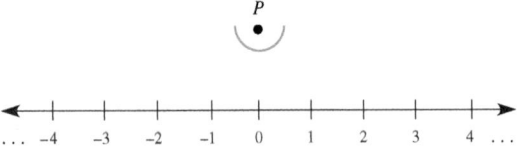

(b) What fact does part (a) establish about the set of real numbers?

42. Show that the two vertical line segments shown here both have the same number of points.

Show that each set can be placed in a one-to-one correspondence with a proper subset of itself to prove that the set is infinite.

43. $\{3, 6, 9, 12, \ldots\}$ **44.** $\{4, 7, 10, 13, 16, \ldots\}$

45. $\left\{\dfrac{3}{3}, \dfrac{3}{8}, \dfrac{3}{12}, \dfrac{3}{16}, \ldots\right\}$ **46.** $\left\{1, \dfrac{4}{3}, \dfrac{5}{3}, 2, \ldots\right\}$

47. $\left\{\dfrac{1}{9}, \dfrac{1}{18}, \dfrac{1}{27}, \dfrac{1}{36}, \ldots\right\}$ **48.** $\{-3, -5, -9, -17, \ldots\}$

49. Describe the distinction between *equal* and *equivalent* sets.

50. Explain how the correspondence suggested in **Example 4** shows that the set of real numbers between 0 and 1 is not countable.

The Paradoxes of Zeno The **Chapter Opener** discussed the scene in the movie I.Q. that deals with Zeno's paradox. Zeno was born about 496 B.C. in southern Italy. Two forms of his paradox are given below. What is your explanation for the following two examples of Zeno's paradoxes?

51. Achilles, if he starts out behind a tortoise, can never overtake the tortoise even if he runs faster.

Suppose Tortoise has a head start of one meter and goes one-tenth as fast as Achilles. When Achilles reaches the point where Tortoise started, Tortoise is then one-tenth meter ahead. When Achilles reaches *that* point, Tortoise is one-hundredth meter ahead. And so on. Achilles gets closer but can never catch up.

52. Motion itself cannot occur.

You cannot travel one meter until after you have first gone a half meter. But you cannot go a half meter until after you have first gone a quarter meter. And so on. Even the tiniest motion cannot occur because a tinier motion would have to occur first.

Introduction to Logic

3

To capture the imagination of their readers, authors of fantasy literature (such as J. R. R. Tolkien, J. K. Rowling, and Lewis Carroll) have long used magical imagery, including riddles. Such a riddle confronts a hero named Humphrey, who finds himself trapped in a magical maze with only two exits.

> *One door to freedom opens wide,*
> *The other naught but dungeon hides.*
> *Twin watchers, one by truth is bound,*
> *The other never truth will sound.*
>
> *The watcher here shall speak when he*
> *Spies a man who would be free.*
> *Name him Lying Troll or Truthful,*
> *Rightly named he shall be useful.*
>
> *If he moves, then be not late,*
> *Choose a door and seal thy fate.*

As Humphrey approaches the troll, it speaks:

"If truly Truthful Troll I be,
then go thou east, and be thou free."

Logic, the topic of this chapter, is useful to authors in the creation of such puzzles—and also to readers in solving them.

3.1 STATEMENTS AND QUANTIFIERS

OBJECTIVES

1 Distinguish between statements and non-statements.

2 Compose negations of statements.

3 Translate between words and symbols.

4 Interpret statements with quantifiers and form their negations.

5 Find truth values of statements involving quantifiers and number sets.

Statements

This section introduces the study of **symbolic logic,** which uses letters to represent statements, and symbols for words such as *and, or, not.* Logic is used to determine the **truth value** (that is, the truth or falsity) of statements with multiple parts. The truth value of such statements depends on their components.

Many kinds of sentences occur in ordinary language, including factual statements, opinions, commands, and questions. Symbolic logic discusses only statements that involve facts. A **statement** is a declarative sentence that is either true or false, but not both simultaneously.

> Electronic mail provides a means of communication. } Statements
> $12 + 6 = 13$ Each is either true or false.

> Access the file.   } Not statements
> Did the Seahawks win the Super Bowl?   Each cannot be
> Dustin Pedroia is a better baseball player than Miguel Cabrera.   identified as being
> This sentence is false.   either true or false.

Of the sentences that are not statements, the first is a command, and the second is a question. The third is an opinion. "This sentence is false" is a paradox: If we assume it is true, then it is false, and if we assume it is false, then it is true.

A **compound statement** may be formed by combining two or more statements. The statements making up a compound statement are called **component statements.** Various **logical connectives,** or simply **connectives,** such as *and, or, not,* and *if . . . then,* can be used in forming compound statements. (Although a statement such as "Today is not Tuesday" does not consist of two component statements, for convenience it is considered compound, because its truth value is determined by noting the truth value of a different statement, "Today is Tuesday.")

EXAMPLE 1 Deciding Whether a Statement Is Compound

Decide whether each statement is compound. If so, identify the connective.

(a) Lord Byron wrote sonnets, and the poem exhibits iambic pentameter.

(b) You can pay me now, or you can pay me later.

(c) If it's on the Internet, then it must be true.

(d) My pistol was made by Smith and Wesson.

Solution

(a) This statement is compound, because it is made up of the component statements "Lord Byron wrote sonnets" and "the poem exhibits iambic pentameter." The connective is *and.*

(b) The connective here is *or.* The statement is compound.

(c) The connective here is *if . . . then,* discussed in more detail in **Section 3.3.** The statement is compound.

(d) Although the word "and" is used in this statement, it is not used as a *logical* connective. It is part of the name of the manufacturer. The statement is not compound. ∎

Negations

The sentence "Anthony Mansella has a red truck" is a statement. The **negation** of this statement is "Anthony Mansella does not have a red truck." ***The negation of a true statement is false, and the negation of a false statement is true.***

Gottfried Leibniz (1646–1716) was a wide-ranging philosopher and a universalist who tried to patch up Catholic–Protestant conflicts. He promoted cultural exchange between Europe and the East. Chinese ideograms led him to search for a universal symbolism. He was an early inventor of **symbolic logic.**

EXAMPLE 2 Forming Negations

Form the negation of each statement.

(a) That city has a mayor.   **(b)** The moon is not a planet.

Solution

(a) To negate this statement, we introduce *not* into the sentence: "That city does not have a mayor."

(b) The negation is "The moon is a planet." ∎

One way to detect incorrect negations is to check truth values. *A negation must have the opposite truth value from the original statement.*

The next example uses some of the inequality symbols in **Table 1.** In the case of an inequality involving a variable, the negation must have the opposite truth value for *any* replacement of the variable.

```
TEST  LOGIC
1:=
2:≠
3:>
4:≥
5:<
6:≤
```

The TEST menu of the TI-83/84 Plus calculator allows the user to test the truth value of statements involving =, ≠, >, ≥, <, and ≤. If a statement is true, it returns a 1. If a statement is false, it returns a 0.

Table 1

Symbolism	Meaning	Examples	
$a < b$	a is less than b	$4 < 9$	$\frac{1}{2} < \frac{3}{4}$
$a > b$	a is greater than b	$6 > 2$	$-5 > -11$
$a \leq b$	a is less than or equal to b	$8 \leq 10$	$3 \leq 3$
$a \geq b$	a is greater than or equal to b	$-2 \geq -3$	$-5 \geq -5$

4 < 9 is true, as indicated by the 1.
4 > 9 is false, as indicated by the 0.

EXAMPLE 3 Negating Inequalities

Give a negation of each inequality. Do *not* use a slash symbol.

(a) $x < 9$ **(b)** $7x + 11y \geq 77$

Solution

(a) The negation of "x is less than 9" is "x is *not* less than 9." Because we cannot use "not," which would require writing $x \not< 9$, phrase the negation as "x is greater than or equal to 9," or

$$x \geq 9.$$

(b) The negation, with no slash, is

$$7x + 11y < 77.$$ ∎

Symbols

The study of logic uses symbols. Statements are represented with letters, such as *p*, *q*, or *r*. Several symbols for connectives are shown in **Table 2**.

Table 2

Connective	Symbol	Type of Statement
and	∧	Conjunction
or	∨	Disjunction
not	~	Negation

The symbol ~ represents the connective *not*. If *p* represents the statement "Barack Obama was president in 2014," then ~*p* represents "Barack Obama was *not* president in 2014."

EXAMPLE 4 Translating from Symbols to Words

Let *p* represent the statement "Nursing informatics is a growing field," and let *q* represent "Critical care will always be in demand." Translate each statement from symbols to words.

(a) $p \vee q$ **(b)** $\sim p \wedge q$ **(c)** $\sim (p \vee q)$ **(d)** $\sim (p \wedge q)$

Solution

(a) From the table, ∨ symbolizes *or*. Thus, $p \vee q$ represents

Nursing informatics is a growing field, or critical care will always be in demand.

(b) Nursing informatics is not a growing field and critical care will always be in demand.

(c) It is not the case that nursing informatics is a growing field or critical care will always be in demand. (This is usually translated as **"Neither *p* nor *q*."**)

(d) It is not the case that nursing informatics is a growing field and critical care will always be in demand. ∎

Quantifiers

Quantifiers are used to indicate *how many* cases of a particular situation exist. The words ***all, each, every,*** and ***no(ne)*** are **universal quantifiers,** while words and phrases such as ***some, there exists,*** and ***(for) at least one*** are **existential quantifiers.**

Be careful when forming the negation of a statement involving quantifiers. A statement and its negation must have opposite truth values in all possible cases. Consider this statement.

All girls in the group are named Mary.

Many people would write the negation of this statement as "No girls in the group are named Mary" or "All girls in the group are not named Mary." But neither of these is correct. To see why, look at the three groups below.

Group I: Mary Jane Payne, Mary Meyer, Mary O'Hara

Group II: Mary Johnson, Lisa Pollak, Margaret Watson

Group III: Donna Garbarino, Paula Story, Rhonda Alessi, Kim Falgout

These groups contain all possibilities that need to be considered. In Group I, *all* girls are named Mary. In Group II, *some* girls are named Mary (and some are not). In Group III, *no* girls are named Mary.

Aristotle, the first to systematize the logic we use in everyday life, appears above in a detail from the painting *The School of Athens,* by Raphael. He is shown debating a point with his teacher **Plato.**

Consider **Table 3**. Keep in mind that "some" means "at least one (and possibly all)."

Table 3 Truth Value as Applied to:

	Group I	Group II	Group III
(1) All girls in the group are named Mary. (Given)	T	F	F
(2) No girls in the group are named Mary. (Possible negation)	F	F	T
(3) All girls in the group are not named Mary. (Possible negation)	F	F	T
(4) Some girls in the group are not named Mary. (Possible negation)	F	T	T

Negation (applies to rows (1) and (4))

The negation of the given statement (1) must have opposite truth values in *all* cases. It can be seen that statements (2) and (3) do not satisfy this condition (for Group II), but statement (4) does. It may be concluded that the correct negation for "All girls in the group are named Mary" is "Some girls in the group are not named Mary." Other ways of stating the negation include the following.

Not all girls in the group are named Mary.

It is not the case that all girls in the group are named Mary.

At least one girl in the group is not named Mary.

Table 4 shows how to find the negation of a statement involving quantifiers.

Table 4 Negations of Quantified Statements

Statement	Negation
All do.	Some do not. (Equivalently: Not all do.)
Some do.	None do. (Equivalently: All do not.)

The negation of the negation of a statement is simply the statement itself. For instance, the negations of the statements in the Negation column are simply the corresponding original statements in the Statement column.

EXAMPLE 5 Forming Negations of Quantified Statements

Form the negation of each statement.

(a) Some cats have fleas.   **(b)** Some cats do not have fleas.

(c) No cats have fleas.

Solution

(a) Because *some* means "at least one," the statement "Some cats have fleas" is really the same as "At least one cat has fleas." The negation of this is

"No cat has fleas."

(b) The statement "Some cats do not have fleas" claims that at least one cat, somewhere, does not have fleas. The negation of this is

"All cats have fleas."

(c) The negation is "Some cats have fleas."   Avoid the incorrect answer "All cats have fleas."

Quantifiers and Number Sets

Earlier we introduced sets of numbers.

SETS OF NUMBERS

Natural numbers (or counting numbers) $\{1, 2, 3, 4, \dots\}$

Whole numbers $\{0, 1, 2, 3, 4, \dots\}$

Integers $\{\dots, -3, -2, -1, 0, 1, 2, 3, \dots\}$

Rational numbers $\left\{\frac{p}{q} \,\middle|\, p \text{ and } q \text{ are integers, and } q \neq 0\right\}$

Real numbers $\{x \mid x \text{ is a number that can be written as a decimal}\}$

Irrational numbers $\{x \mid x \text{ is a real number and } x \text{ cannot be written as a quotient of integers}\}$

EXAMPLE 6 **Deciding Whether Quantified Statements Are True or False**

Decide whether each statement involving a quantifier is *true* or *false*.

(a) There exists a whole number that is not a natural number.

(b) Every integer is a natural number.

(c) Every natural number is a rational number.

(d) There exists an irrational number that is not real.

Solution

(a) Because there is such a whole number (it is 0), this statement is true.

(b) This statement is false, because we can find at least one integer that is not a natural number. For example, -1 is an integer but is not a natural number.

(c) Because every natural number can be written as a fraction with denominator 1, this statement is true.

(d) In order to be an irrational number, a number must first be real. Because we cannot give an irrational number that is not real, this statement is false. (Had we been able to find at least one, the statement would have been true.)   ■

3.1   EXERCISES

Decide whether each is a statement or is not a statement.

1. February 2, 2009, was a Monday.

2. The ZIP code for Oscar, Louisiana, is 70762.

3. Listen, my children, and you shall hear of the midnight ride of Paul Revere.

4. Did you yield to oncoming traffic?

5. $5 + 9 \neq 14$ and $4 - 1 = 12$

6. $5 + 9 \neq 12$ or $4 - 2 = 5$

7. Some numbers are positive.

8. Grover Cleveland was president of the United States in 1885 and 1897.

9. Accidents are the main cause of deaths of children under the age of 7.

10. It is projected that in the United States between 2010 and 2020, there will be over 500,000 job openings per year for elementary school teachers, with median annual salaries of about $51,000.

11. Where are you going tomorrow?

12. Behave yourself and sit down.

13. Kevin "Catfish" McCarthy once took a prolonged continuous shower for 340 hours, 40 minutes.

14. One gallon of milk weighs more than 3 pounds.

Decide whether each statement is compound.

15. I read the *Detroit Free Press,* and I read the *Sacramento Bee.*

16. My brother got married in Copenhagen.

17. Tomorrow is Saturday.

18. Jing is younger than 18 years of age, and so is her friend Shu-fen.

19. Jay's wife loves Ben and Jerry's ice cream.

20. The sign on the back of the car read "Canada or bust!"

21. If Lorri sells her quota, then Michelle will be happy.

22. If Bobby is a politician, then Mitch is a crook.

Write a negation for each statement.

23. Her aunt's name is Hermione.

24. No rain fell in southern California today.

25. Some books are longer than this book.

26. All students present will get another chance.

27. No computer repairman can play blackjack.

28. Some people have all the luck.

29. Everybody loves somebody sometime.

30. Everyone needs a friend.

31. The trash needs to be collected.

32. Every architect who wants a job can find one.

Give a negation of each inequality. Do not use a slash symbol.

33. $x > 12$

34. $x < -6$

35. $x \geq 5$

36. $x \leq 19$

37. Try to negate the sentence "The exact number of words in this sentence is ten" and see what happens. Explain the problem that arises.

38. Explain why the negation of "$x > 5$" is not "$x < 5$."

Let p represent the statement "She has green eyes" *and let q represent the statement* "He is 60 years old." *Translate each symbolic compound statement into words.*

39. $\sim p$

40. $\sim q$

41. $p \wedge q$

42. $p \vee q$

43. $\sim p \vee q$

44. $p \wedge \sim q$

45. $\sim p \vee \sim q$

46. $\sim p \wedge \sim q$

47. $\sim(\sim p \wedge q)$

48. $\sim(p \vee \sim q)$

Let p represent the statement "Tyler collects DVDs" *and let q represent the statement* "Josh is an art major." *Convert each compound statement into symbols.*

49. Tyler collects DVDs and Josh is not an art major.

50. Tyler does not collect DVDs or Josh is not an art major.

51. Tyler does not collect DVDs or Josh is an art major.

52. Josh is an art major and Tyler does not collect DVDs.

53. Neither Tyler collects DVDs nor Josh is an art major.

54. Either Josh is an art major or Tyler collects DVDs, and it is not the case that both Josh is an art major and Tyler collects DVDs.

55. Incorrect use of quantifiers often is heard in everyday language. Suppose you hear that a local electronics chain is having a 40% off sale, and the radio advertisement states "All items are not available in all stores." Do you think that, literally translated, the ad really means what it says? What do you think is really meant? Explain your answer.

56. Repeat **Exercise 55** for the following: "All people don't have the time to devote to maintaining their vehicles properly."

Refer to the groups of art labeled A, B, and C, and identify by letter the group or groups that satisfy the given statements involving quantifiers in Exercises 57–64.

A

B

C

57. All pictures have frames.

58. No picture has a frame.

59. At least one picture does not have a frame.

60. Not every picture has a frame.

61. At least one picture has a frame.

62. No picture does not have a frame.

63. All pictures do not have frames.

64. Not every picture does not have a frame.

Decide whether each statement in Exercises 65–74 involving a quantifier is true *or* false.

65. Every whole number is an integer.

66. Every integer is a whole number.

67. There exists a natural number that is not an integer.

68. There exists an integer that is not a natural number.

69. All rational numbers are real numbers.

70. All irrational numbers are real numbers.

71. Some rational numbers are not integers.

72. Some whole numbers are not rational numbers.

73. Each whole number is a positive number.

74. Each rational number is a positive number.

75. Explain the difference between the statements "All students did not pass the test" and "Not all students passed the test."

76. The statement "For some real number x, $x^2 \geq 0$" is true. However, your friend does not understand why, because he claims that $x^2 \geq 0$ is true for *all* real numbers x (and not *some*). How would you explain his misconception to him?

77. Write the following statement using "every": There is no one here who has not made mistakes before.

78. Only one of these statements is true. Which one is it?

A. For some real number x, $x \not< 0$.

B. For all real numbers x, $x^3 > 0$.

C. For all real numbers x less than 0, x^2 is also less than 0.

D. For some real number x, $x^2 < 0$.

Symbolic logic also uses symbols for quantifiers. The symbol for the existential quantifier is

$$\exists \quad (a \text{ rotated } E),$$

and the symbol for the universal quantifier is

$$\forall \quad (an \text{ inverted } A).$$

The statement "For some x, p is true" can be symbolized

$$(\exists x)(p).$$

The statement "For all x, p is true" can be symbolized

$$(\forall x)(p).$$

The negation of $(\exists x)(p)$ is

$$(\forall x)(\sim p),$$

and the negation of $(\forall x)(p)$ is

$$(\exists x)(\sim p).$$

79. Refer to **Example 5.** If we let c represent "cat" and f represent "The cat has fleas," then the statement "Some cats have fleas" can be represented by $(\exists c)(f)$. Use symbols to express the negation of this statement.

80. Use symbols to express the statements for parts (b) and (c) of **Example 5** and their negations. Verify that the symbolic expressions translate to the negations found in the text.

3.2   TRUTH TABLES AND EQUIVALENT STATEMENTS

OBJECTIVES

1 Find the truth value of a conjunction.

2 Find the truth value of a disjunction.

3 Find the truth values for compound mathematical statements.

4 Construct truth tables for compound statements.

5 Understand and determine equivalence of statements.

6 Use De Morgan's laws to find negations of compound statements.

Conjunctions

Truth values of component statements are used to find truth values of compound statements. To begin, we must decide on truth values of the **conjunction p and q,** symbolized $p \land q.$ Here, the connective *and* implies the idea of "both." The following statement is true, because each component statement is true.

Monday immediately follows Sunday, and March immediately follows February.
True

On the other hand, the following statement is false, even though part of the statement (Monday immediately follows Sunday) is true.

Monday immediately follows Sunday, and March immediately follows January.
False

For the conjunction $p \land q$ to be true, both p and q must be true. This result is summarized by a table, called a **truth table,** which shows truth values of $p \land q$ for all four possible combinations of truth values for the component statements p and q.

TRUTH TABLE FOR THE CONJUNCTION p and q

	p and q	
p	q	$p \land q$
T	T	T
T	F	F
F	T	F
F	F	F

The calculator returns a 0 for

5 > 3 *and* 6 < 0,

indicating that the statement is false.

EXAMPLE 1   Finding the Truth Value of a Conjunction

Let p represent "$5 > 3$" and let q represent "$6 < 0$." Find the truth value of $p \land q$.

Solution

Here p is true and q is false. The second row of the conjunction truth table shows that $p \land q$ is false in this case.   ■

In some cases, the logical connective *but* is used in compound statements.

He wants to go to the mountains but she wants to go to the beach.

Here, *but* is used in place of *and* to give a different emphasis to the statement. We consider this statement as we would consider the conjunction using the word *and*. The truth table for the conjunction, given above, would apply.

Disjunctions

In ordinary language, the word *or* can be ambiguous. The expression "this or that" can mean either "this or that or both," or "this or that but not both." For example, consider the following statement.

I will paint the wall or I will paint the ceiling.

This statement probably means: "I will paint the wall or I will paint the ceiling or I will paint both."

On the other hand, consider the following statement.

I will wear my glasses or my contact lenses.

It probably means "I will wear my glasses, or I will wear my contacts, but I will not wear both."

The symbol ∨ represents the first *or* described. That is,

$p \lor q$ means   "p or q or both."   Disjunction

With this meaning of *or*, $p \lor q$ is called the **inclusive disjunction,** or just the **disjunction** of p and q. In everyday language, the disjunction implies the idea of "either." For example, consider the following disjunction.

I have a quarter or I have a dime.

It is true whenever I have either a quarter, a dime, or both. The only way this disjunction could be false would be if I had neither coin. *The disjunction $p \lor q$ is false only if both component statements are false.*

TRUTH TABLE FOR THE DISJUNCTION p or q

		p or q
p	q	$p \lor q$
T	T	T
T	F	T
F	T	T
F	F	F

The calculator returns a 1 for

$5 > 3 \text{ or } 6 < 0,$

indicating that the statement is true.

EXAMPLE 2 Finding the Truth Value of a Disjunction

Let p represent "$5 > 3$" and let q represent "$6 < 0$." Find the truth value of $p \lor q$.

Solution

Here, as in **Example 1,** p is true and q is false. The second row of the disjunction truth table shows that $p \lor q$ is true. ■

The symbol $\geq$ is read **"is greater than or equal to,"** while $\leq$ is read **"is less than or equal to."** If a and b are real numbers, then $a \leq b$ is true if $a < b$ or $a = b$. See **Table 5.**

Table 5

Statement	Reason It Is True
$8 \geq 8$	$8 = 8$
$3 \geq 1$	$3 > 1$
$-5 \leq -3$	$-5 < -3$
$-4 \leq -4$	$-4 = -4$

Negations

The **negation** of a statement p, symbolized **$\sim p$,** must have the opposite truth value from the statement p itself. This leads to the truth table for the negation.

TRUTH TABLE FOR THE NEGATION   not p

	not p
p	$\sim p$
T	F
F	T

EXAMPLE 3 Finding the Truth Value of a Compound Statement

Suppose p is false, q is true, and r is false. What is the truth value of the compound statement $\sim p \wedge (q \vee \sim r)$?

Solution

Here parentheses are used to group q and $\sim r$ together. Work first inside the parentheses. Because r is false, $\sim r$ will be true. Because $\sim r$ is true and q is true, the truth value of $q \vee \sim r$ is T, as shown in the first row of the *or* truth table.

Because p is false, $\sim p$ is true, and the truth value of $\sim p \wedge (q \vee \sim r)$ is found in the top row of the *and* truth table. The statement

$$\sim p \wedge (q \vee \sim r) \quad \text{is true.}$$

We can use a shortcut symbolic method that involves replacing the statements with their truth values, letting T represent a true statement and F represent a false statement.

$$\sim p \wedge (q \vee \sim r)$$
$$\sim F \wedge (T \vee \sim F) \quad \text{← Work within parentheses first.}$$
$$T \wedge (T \vee T) \quad \sim\text{F gives T.}$$
$$T \wedge T \quad \text{T} \vee \text{T gives T.}$$

The compound statement is true. $\rightarrow$ T $\quad$ T $\wedge$ T gives T. ∎

Mathematical Statements

We can use truth tables to determine the truth values of compound mathematical statements.

EXAMPLE 4 Deciding Whether Compound Mathematical Statements Are True or False

Let p represent the statement $3 > 2$, q represent $5 < 4$, and r represent $3 < 8$. Decide whether each statement is *true* or *false*.

(a) $\sim p \wedge \sim q$ **(b)** $\sim (p \wedge q)$ **(c)** $(\sim p \wedge r) \vee (\sim q \wedge \sim p)$

Solution

(a) Because p is true, $\sim p$ is false. By the *and* truth table, if one part of an "and" statement is false, the entire statement is false.

$$\sim p \wedge \sim q \quad \text{is false.}$$

(b) For $\sim (p \wedge q)$, first work within the parentheses. Because p is true and q is false, $p \wedge q$ is false by the *and* truth table. Next, apply the negation. The negation of a false statement is true.

$$\sim (p \wedge q) \quad \text{is true.}$$

(c) Here p is true, q is false, and r is true. This makes $\sim p$ false and $\sim q$ true. By the *and* truth table, $\sim p \wedge r$ is false, and $\sim q \wedge \sim p$ is also false. By the *or* truth table,

$$(\sim p \wedge r) \vee (\sim q \wedge \sim p) \quad \text{is false.}$$
$$\qquad \downarrow \qquad\qquad \downarrow$$
$$\qquad \text{F} \quad \vee \quad \text{F}$$

(Alternatively, see **Example 8(b)**.) ∎

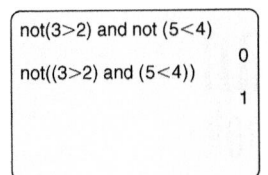

Example 4(a) explains why

$$\sim (3 > 2) \wedge \sim (5 < 4)$$

is false. The calculator returns a 0. For a true statement such as

$$\sim [(3 > 2) \wedge (5 < 4)]$$

from **Example 4(b)**, it returns a 1.

When a quantifier is used with a conjunction or a disjunction, we must be careful in determining the truth value, as shown in the following example.

George Boole (1815–1864) grew up in poverty. His father, a London tradesman, gave him his first mathematics lessons and taught him to make optical instruments. Boole was largely self-educated. At 16 he worked in an elementary school and by age 20 had opened his own school. He studied mathematics in his spare time. He died of lung disease at age 49.

Boole's ideas have been used in the design of computers, telephone systems, and search engines.

EXAMPLE 5 Deciding Whether Quantified Mathematical Statements Are True or False

Decide whether each statement is *true* or *false*.

(a) For some real number x, $x < 5$ and $x > 2$.

(b) For every real number x, $x > 0$ or $x < 1$.

(c) For all real numbers x, $x^2 > 0$.

Solution

(a) Because "some" is an *existential* quantifier, we need only find one real number x that makes both component statements true, and $x = 3$ is such a number. The statement is true by the *and* truth table.

(b) No matter which real number might be tried as a replacement for x, at least one of the two statements

$$x > 0, \quad x < 1$$

will be true. Because an "or" statement is true if one or both component statements are true, the entire statement as given is true.

(c) Because "for all" is a *universal* quantifier, we need only find one case in which the inequality is false to make the entire statement false. Can we find a real number whose square is not positive (that is, not greater than 0)? Yes, we can— 0 is such a number. In fact 0 is the *only* real number whose square is not positive. This statement is false. ∎

FOR FURTHER THOUGHT

Whose Picture Am I Looking At?

Raymond Smullyan is one of today's foremost writers of logic puzzles. This professor of mathematics and philosophy is now retired from Indiana University and has written several books on recreational logic, including *What Is the Name of This Book?*, *The Lady or the Tiger?*, and *The Gödelian Puzzle Book*. The first of these includes the following puzzle, which has been around for many years.

For Group or Individual Investigation

A man was looking at a portrait. Someone asked him, "Whose picture are you looking at?" He replied: "Brothers and sisters, I have none, but this man's father is my father's son." ("This man's father" means, of course, the father of the man in the picture.)

Whose picture was the man looking at? (The answer is on **page 102**.)

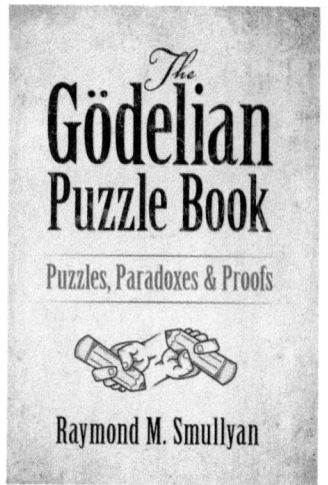

Truth Tables

In the preceding examples, the truth value for a given statement was found by going back to the basic truth tables. It is generally easier to first create a complete truth table for the given statement itself. Then final truth values can be read directly from this table.

In this book we use the standard format shown in the margin for listing the possible truth values in compound statements involving two component statements.

p	q	Compound Statement
T	T	
T	F	
F	T	
F	F	

▋EXAMPLE 6 Constructing a Truth Table

Consider the statement $(\sim p \wedge q) \vee \sim q$.

(a) Construct a truth table.

(b) Suppose both p and q are true. Find the truth value of the compound statement.

Solution

(a) As shown below, begin by listing all possible combinations of truth values for p and q. Then list the truth values of $\sim p$, which are the opposite of those of p.

Use the "$\sim p$" and "q" columns, along with the *and* truth table, to find the truth values of $\sim p \wedge q$. List them in a separate column.

Next include a column for $\sim q$.

p	q	$\sim p$	$\sim p \wedge q$	$\sim q$
T	T	F	F	F
T	F	F	F	T
F	T	T	T	F
F	F	T	F	T

Finally, make a column for the entire compound statement. To find the truth values, use *or* to combine $\sim p \wedge q$ with $\sim q$ and refer to the *or* truth table.

p	q	$\sim p$	$\sim p \wedge q$	$\sim q$	$(\sim p \wedge q) \vee \sim q$
T	T	F	F	F	F
T	F	F	F	T	T
F	T	T	T	F	T
F	F	T	F	T	T

(b) Look in the first row of the final truth table above, where both p and q have truth value T. Read across the row to find that the compound statement is false. ▋

▋EXAMPLE 7 Constructing a Truth Table

Construct the truth table for $p \wedge (\sim p \vee \sim q)$.

Solution

p	q	$\sim p$	$\sim q$	$\sim p \vee \sim q$	$p \wedge (\sim p \vee \sim q)$
T	T	F	F	F	F
T	F	F	T	T	T
F	T	T	F	T	F
F	F	T	T	T	F

▋

If a compound statement involves three component statements p, q, and r, we will use the following standard format in setting up the truth table.

p	q	r	**Compound Statement**
T	T	T	
T	T	F	
T	F	T	
T	F	F	
F	T	T	
F	T	F	
F	F	T	
F	F	F	

Emilie, Marquise du Châtelet
(1706–1749) participated in the scientific activity of the generation after Newton and Leibniz. Educated in science, music, and literature, she was studying mathematics at the time (1733) she began a long intellectual relationship with the philosopher **François Voltaire** (1694–1778). She and Voltaire competed independently in 1738 for a prize offered by the French Academy on the subject of fire. Although du Châtelet did not win, her dissertation was published by the academy in 1744.

EXAMPLE 8 Constructing a Truth Table

Consider the statement $(\sim p \wedge r) \vee (\sim q \wedge \sim p)$.

(a) Construct a truth table.

(b) Suppose p is true, q is false, and r is true. Find the truth value of this statement.

Solution

(a) There are three component statements: p, q, and r. The truth table thus requires eight rows to list all possible combinations of truth values of p, q, and r. The final truth table can be found in much the same way as the ones earlier.

p	q	r	$\sim p$	$\sim p \wedge r$	$\sim q$	$\sim q \wedge \sim p$	$(\sim p \wedge r) \vee (\sim q \wedge \sim p)$
T	T	T	F	F	F	F	F
T	T	F	F	F	F	F	F
T	F	T	F	F	T	F	F
T	F	F	F	F	T	F	F
F	T	T	T	T	F	F	T
F	T	F	T	F	F	F	F
F	F	T	T	T	T	T	T
F	F	F	T	F	T	T	T

(b) By the third row of the truth table in part (a), the compound statement is false. (This is an alternative method for working part (c) of **Example 4**.) ∎

Problem-Solving Strategy

One strategy for problem solving is to notice a pattern and then use inductive reasoning. This strategy is applied in the next example.

EXAMPLE 9 Using Inductive Reasoning

Suppose that n is a counting number, and a logical statement is composed of n component statements. How many rows will appear in the truth table for the compound statement?

Solution

We examine some of the earlier truth tables in this section. The truth table for the negation has one statement and two rows. The truth tables for the conjunction and the disjunction have two component statements, and each has four rows. The truth table in **Example 8(a)** has three component statements and eight rows.

Summarizing these in **Table 6** (seen in the margin) reveals a pattern encountered earlier. Inductive reasoning leads us to the conjecture that if a logical statement is composed of n component statements, it will have 2^n rows. This can be proved using more advanced concepts. ∎

Table 6

Number of Statements	Number of Rows
1	$2 = 2^1$
2	$4 = 2^2$
3	$8 = 2^3$

The result of **Example 9** is reminiscent of the formula for the number of subsets of a set having n elements.

NUMBER OF ROWS IN A TRUTH TABLE

A logical statement having n component statements will have 2^n rows in its truth table.

Alternative Method for Constructing Truth Tables

After making a reasonable number of truth tables, some people prefer the shortcut method shown in **Example 10,** which repeats **Examples 6 and 8.**

EXAMPLE 10 Constructing Truth Tables

Construct the truth table for each compound statement.

(a) $(\sim p \wedge q) \vee \sim q$ **(b)** $(\sim p \wedge r) \vee (\sim q \wedge \sim p)$

Solution

(a) Start by inserting truth values for $\sim p$ and for q. Then use the *and* truth table to obtain the truth values for $\sim p \wedge q$.

p	q	$(\sim p$	$\wedge$	$q)$	$\vee$	$\sim q$
T	T	F		T		
T	F	F		F		
F	T	T		T		
F	F	T		F		

p	q	$(\sim p$	$\wedge$	$q)$	$\vee$	$\sim q$
T	T	F	F	T		
T	F	F	F	F		
F	T	T	T	T		
F	F	T	F	F		

Now disregard the two preliminary columns of truth values for $\sim p$ and for q, and insert truth values for $\sim q$. Finally, use the *or* truth table.

p	q	$(\sim p \wedge q)$	$\vee$	$\sim q$
T	T	F		F
T	F	F		T
F	T	T		F
F	F	F		T

p	q	$(\sim p \wedge q)$	$\vee$	$\sim q$
T	T	F	F	F
T	F	F	T	T
F	T	T	T	F
F	F	F	T	T

These steps can be summarized as follows.

p	q	$(\sim p$	$\wedge$	$q)$	$\vee$	$\sim q$
T	T	F	F	T	F	F
T	F	F	F	F	T	T
F	T	T	T	T	T	F
F	F	T	F	F	T	T
		①	②	①	④	③

> The circled numbers indicate the order in which the various columns of the truth table were found.

(b) Work as follows.

p	q	r	$(\sim p$	$\wedge$	$r)$	$\vee$	$(\sim q$	$\wedge$	$\sim p)$
T	T	T	F	F	T	F	F	F	F
T	T	F	F	F	F	F	F	F	F
T	F	T	F	F	T	F	T	F	F
T	F	F	F	F	F	F	T	F	F
F	T	T	T	T	T	T	F	F	T
F	T	F	T	F	F	F	F	F	T
F	F	T	T	T	T	T	T	T	T
F	F	F	T	F	F	T	T	T	T
			①	②	①	⑤	③	④	③

> The circled numbers indicate the order.

■

Equivalent Statements and De Morgan's Laws

Two statements are **equivalent** if they have the same truth value in *every* possible situation. The columns of the two truth tables that were the last to be completed will be the same for equivalent statements.

Ada Lovelace (1815–1852) was born Augusta Ada Byron. Her talents as a mathematician and logician led to her work with **Charles Babbage** (1791–1871) on his Analytical Engine, the first programmable mechanical computer. Lovelace's notes on this machine include what is regarded by many as the first computer program and reveal her visionary belief that computing machines would have applications beyond numerical calculations.

▦ EXAMPLE 11 Deciding Whether Two Statements Are Equivalent

Are the following two statements equivalent?

$$\sim p \wedge \sim q \quad \text{and} \quad \sim(p \vee q)$$

Solution

Construct a truth table for each statement.

p	q	$\sim p \wedge \sim q$		p	q	$\sim(p \vee q)$
T	T	F		T	T	F
T	F	F		T	F	F
F	T	F		F	T	F
F	F	T		F	F	T

Because the truth values are the same in all cases, as shown in the columns in color, the statements $\sim p \wedge \sim q$ and $\sim(p \vee q)$ are equivalent.

$$\sim p \wedge \sim q \equiv \sim(p \vee q) \qquad \text{The symbol} \equiv \text{denotes equivalence.} \qquad ■$$

In the same way, the statements $\sim p \vee \sim q$ and $\sim(p \wedge q)$ are equivalent. We call these equivalences *De Morgan's laws*.

DE MORGAN'S LAWS FOR LOGICAL STATEMENTS

Compare **De Morgan's Laws** for logical statements with the set theoretical version on **page 68**.

For any statements p and q, the following equivalences are valid.

$$\sim(p \vee q) \equiv \sim p \wedge \sim q \quad \text{and} \quad \sim(p \wedge q) \equiv \sim p \vee \sim q$$

▦ EXAMPLE 12 Applying De Morgan's Laws

Find a negation of each statement by applying De Morgan's laws.

(a) I got an A or I got a B.   **(b)** She won't try and he will succeed.

(c) $\sim p \vee (q \wedge \sim p)$

Solution

(a) If p represents "I got an A" and q represents "I got a B," then the compound statement is symbolized $p \vee q$. The negation of $p \vee q$ is $\sim(p \vee q)$. By one of De Morgan's laws, this is equivalent to $\sim p \wedge \sim q$, or, in words,

> **I didn't get an A and I didn't get a B.**

This negation is reasonable—the original statement says that I got either an A or a B. The negation says that I didn't get *either* grade.

(b) From De Morgan's laws, $\sim(p \wedge q) \equiv \sim p \vee \sim q$, so the negation becomes

> **She will try or he won't succeed.**

(c) Negate both component statements and change $\vee$ to $\wedge$.

$$\sim[\sim p \vee (q \wedge \sim p)] \equiv p \wedge \sim(q \wedge \sim p)$$
$$\equiv p \wedge (\sim q \vee \sim(\sim p)) \qquad \text{Apply De Morgan's law again.}$$
$$\equiv p \wedge (\sim q \vee p)$$

A truth table will show that the statements

$$\sim p \vee (q \wedge \sim p) \quad \text{and} \quad p \wedge (\sim q \vee p) \quad \text{are negations of each other.} \qquad ■$$

FOR FURTHER THOUGHT

The Logic Behind Computers

Computer designers use *logic gates* at the foundation of digital circuits. Logic gates treat the binary digits 0 and 1 as logical values, and give a single output of 1 or 0 based on the input value(s), which also have a value of 1 or 0. Since 1 and 0 are the only digits in the binary number system, that system is the perfect bridge between logic and numerical computation (as Leibniz realized).

There are three basic logic gates: the AND gate, the OR gate, and the NOT gate, whose symbols and truth tables follow.

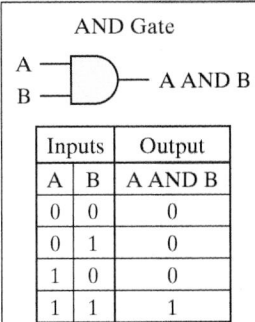

Inputs		Output
A	B	A AND B
0	0	0
0	1	0
1	0	0
1	1	1

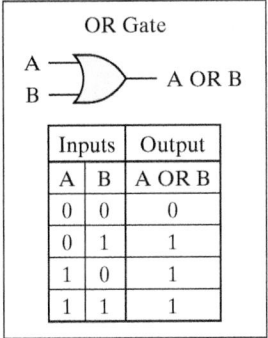

Inputs		Output
A	B	A OR B
0	0	0
0	1	1
1	0	1
1	1	1

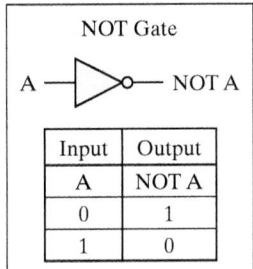

Input	Output
A	NOT A
0	1
1	0

Other logic gates include NAND, NOR (the negations of AND and OR, respectively), XOR (exclusive OR—see **Exercise 77** in this section), and XNOR (the negation of XOR). Their symbols are shown below.

Early logic gates were constructed with electrical relays and vacuum tubes, but the development of semiconductors and the transistor have made possible the placement of millions of logic gates in integrated circuits, microchips that perform billions of logical calculations per second. More recently, logic gates have even been fashioned from biological organisms and DNA.

There are some excellent Android Apps (such as Logic Simulator, free in the Android Play Store) for simulating logic circuits. The simulator shown allows the user to add logic gates, switches (connected to inputs), and light bulbs (connected to outputs). Red highlighting indicates where current is flowing. These four screenshots show the truth values for the XOR logic gate.

For Group or Individual Investigation

1. Create the truth table for A XOR B using the accompanying screenshots. (Remember that the red nodes are "hot," which is indicated by a 1 or a T in the truth table.)

2. Charles Peirce (1839–1914) showed that all of the logic gates we have mentioned could be constructed using only NAND gates. Construct a truth table for the logic circuit below to show that it is equivalent to the XOR gate. *Hint:* The output of the circuit shown is

   [A NAND (A NAND B)] NAND [(A NAND B) NAND B],

   which is equivalent to

   $\sim(\sim(A \wedge \sim(A \wedge B)) \wedge \sim(\sim(A \wedge B) \wedge B))$.

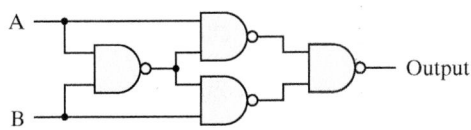

3. Download and install an app to simulate logic gates, and use it to verify your truth table from **Exercise 2**. One image of the simulated circuit is shown below.

4. Use the simulator to build circuits to verify De Morgan's laws for logic.

3.2 EXERCISES

Use the concepts introduced in this section to answer Exercises 1–8.

1. If q is false, what must be the truth value of the statement $(p \wedge {\sim}q) \wedge q$?

2. If q is true, what must be the truth value of the statement $q \vee (q \wedge {\sim}p)$?

3. If the statement $p \wedge q$ is true, and p is true, then q must be _____.

4. If the statement $p \vee q$ is false, and p is false, then q must be _____.

5. If $p \vee (q \wedge {\sim}q)$ is true, what must be the truth value of p?

6. If $p \wedge {\sim}(q \vee r)$ is true, what must be the truth value of the component statements?

7. If ${\sim}(p \vee q)$ is true, what must be the truth values of the component statements?

8. If ${\sim}(p \wedge q)$ is false, what must be the truth values of the component statements?

Let p represent a false statement and let q represent a true statement. Find the truth value of the given compound statement.

9. ${\sim}p$

10. ${\sim}q$

11. $p \vee q$

12. $p \wedge q$

13. $p \vee {\sim}q$

14. ${\sim}p \wedge q$

15. ${\sim}p \vee {\sim}q$

16. $p \wedge {\sim}q$

17. ${\sim}(p \wedge {\sim}q)$

18. ${\sim}({\sim}p \vee {\sim}q)$

19. ${\sim}[{\sim}p \wedge ({\sim}q \vee p)]$

20. ${\sim}[({\sim}p \wedge {\sim}q) \vee {\sim}q]$

21. Is the statement $6 \geq 2$ a conjunction or a disjunction? Why?

22. Why is the statement $8 \geq 3$ true? Why is $5 \geq 5$ true?

Let p represent a true statement, and let q and r represent false statements. Find the truth value of the given compound statement.

23. $(p \wedge r) \vee {\sim}q$

24. $(q \vee {\sim}r) \wedge p$

25. $p \wedge (q \vee r)$

26. $({\sim}p \wedge q) \vee {\sim}r$

27. ${\sim}(p \wedge q) \wedge (r \vee {\sim}q)$

28. $({\sim}r \wedge {\sim}q) \vee ({\sim}r \wedge q)$

29. ${\sim}[({\sim}p \wedge q) \vee r]$

30. ${\sim}[r \vee ({\sim}q \wedge {\sim}p)]$

31. ${\sim}[{\sim}q \vee (r \wedge {\sim}p)]$

32. ${\sim}(p \vee q) \wedge {\sim}(p \wedge q)$

Let p represent the statement $16 < 8$, let q represent the statement $5 \not> 4$, and let r represent the statement $17 \leq 17$. Find the truth value of the given compound statement.

33. $p \wedge r$

34. $p \vee {\sim}q$

35. ${\sim}q \vee {\sim}r$

36. ${\sim}p \wedge {\sim}r$

37. $(p \wedge q) \vee r$

38. ${\sim}p \vee ({\sim}r \vee {\sim}q)$

39. $({\sim}r \wedge q) \vee {\sim}p$

40. ${\sim}(p \vee {\sim}q) \vee {\sim}r$

Give the number of rows in the truth table for each compound statement.

41. $p \vee {\sim}r$

42. $p \wedge (r \wedge {\sim}s)$

43. $({\sim}p \wedge q) \vee ({\sim}r \vee {\sim}s) \wedge r$

44. $[(p \vee q) \wedge (r \wedge s)] \wedge (t \vee {\sim}p)$

45. $[({\sim}p \wedge {\sim}q) \wedge ({\sim}r \wedge s \wedge {\sim}t)] \wedge ({\sim}u \vee {\sim}v)$

46. $[({\sim}p \wedge {\sim}q) \vee ({\sim}r \vee {\sim}s)]$
$\quad \vee [({\sim}m \wedge {\sim}n) \wedge (u \wedge {\sim}v)]$

47. If the truth table for a certain compound statement has 64 rows, how many distinct component statements does it have?

48. Is it possible for the truth table of a compound statement to have exactly 54 rows? Why or why not?

Construct a truth table for each compound statement.

49. ${\sim}p \wedge q$

50. ${\sim}p \vee {\sim}q$

51. ${\sim}(p \wedge q)$

52. $p \vee {\sim}q$

53. $(q \vee {\sim}p) \vee {\sim}q$

54. $(p \wedge {\sim}q) \wedge p$

55. $(p \vee {\sim}q) \wedge (p \wedge q)$

56. $({\sim}p \wedge {\sim}q) \vee ({\sim}p \vee q)$

57. $({\sim}p \wedge q) \wedge r$

58. $r \vee (p \wedge {\sim}q)$

59. $({\sim}p \wedge {\sim}q) \vee ({\sim}r \vee {\sim}p)$

60. $({\sim}r \vee {\sim}p) \wedge ({\sim}p \vee {\sim}q)$

61. ${\sim}({\sim}p \wedge {\sim}q) \vee ({\sim}r \vee {\sim}s)$

62. $({\sim}r \vee s) \wedge ({\sim}p \wedge q)$

Use one of De Morgan's laws to write the negation of each statement.

63. You can pay me now or you can pay me later.

64. I am not going or she is going.

65. It is summer and there is no snow.

66. $\frac{1}{2}$ is a positive number and -9 is less than zero.

67. I said yes but she said no.

68. Dan tried to sell the software, but he was unable to do so.

69. $6 - 1 = 5$ and $9 + 13 \neq 7$

70. $8 < 10$ or $5 \neq 2$

71. Prancer or Vixen will lead Santa's reindeer sleigh next Christmas.

72. The lawyer and the client appeared in court.

Identify each statement as true *or* false.

73. For every real number x, $x < 14$ or $x > 6$.

74. For every real number x, $x > 9$ or $x < 9$.

75. There exists an integer n such that $n > 0$ and $n < 0$.

76. For some integer n, $n \geq 3$ and $n \leq 3$.

77. Complete the truth table for *exclusive disjunction*. The symbol $\underline{\vee}$ represents "one or the other is true, but not both."

p	q	$p \underline{\vee} q$
T	T	
T	F	
F	T	
F	F	

Exclusive disjunction

78. Attorneys sometimes use the phrase "and/or." This phrase corresponds to which usage of the word *or:* inclusive or exclusive disjunction?

Decide whether each compound statement is true *or* false. *Remember that* $\underline{\vee}$ *is the exclusive disjunction of* **Exercise 77.**

79. $3 + 1 = 4 \underline{\vee} 2 + 5 = 7$

80. $3 + 1 = 4 \underline{\vee} 2 + 5 = 10$

81. $3 + 1 = 6 \underline{\vee} 2 + 5 = 7$

82. $3 + 1 = 12 \underline{\vee} 2 + 5 = 10$

83. In his book *The Lady or the Tiger and Other Logic Puzzles,* Raymond Smullyan proposes the following problem. It is taken from the classic Frank Stockton short story, in which a prisoner must make a choice between two doors: behind one is a beautiful lady, and behind the other is a hungry tiger.

What if each door has a sign, and the man knows that only one sign is true?

The sign on Door 1 reads:

IN THIS ROOM THERE IS A LADY AND IN THE OTHER ROOM THERE IS A TIGER.

The sign on Door 2 reads:

IN ONE OF THESE ROOMS THERE IS A LADY AND IN ONE OF THESE ROOMS THERE IS A TIGER.

With this information, the man is able to choose the correct door. Can you?

84. (a) Build truth tables for

$$p \vee (q \wedge r) \quad \text{and} \quad (p \vee q) \wedge (p \vee r).$$

Decide whether it can be said that "OR distributes over AND." Explain.

(b) Build truth tables for

$$p \wedge (q \vee r) \quad \text{and} \quad (p \wedge q) \vee (p \wedge r).$$

Decide whether it can be said that "AND distributes over OR." Explain.

(c) Describe how the logical equivalences developed in parts (a) and (b) are related to the set-theoretical equations

$$X \cup (Y \cap Z) = (X \cup Y) \cap (X \cup Z)$$

and

$$X \cap (Y \cup Z) = (X \cap Y) \cup (X \cap Z).$$

85. De Morgan's law

$$\sim(p \vee q) \equiv \sim p \wedge \sim q$$

can be stated verbally, "The negation of a disjunction is equivalent to the conjunction of the negations." Give a similar verbal statement of

$$\sim(p \wedge q) \equiv \sim p \vee \sim q.$$

3.3 THE CONDITIONAL AND CIRCUITS

OBJECTIVES

1 Understand the structure of the conditional statement.

2 Determine the truth values of conditional statements.

3 Express a conditional statement as a disjunction.

4 Express the negation of a conditional statement.

5 Use circuits to model conditional statements.

In his April 21, 1989, five-star review of **Field of Dreams,** the *Chicago Sun-Times* movie critic Roger Ebert gave an explanation of why the movie has become an American classic.

There is a speech in this movie about baseball that is so simple and true that it is heartbreaking. And the whole attitude toward the players reflects that attitude. Why do they come back from the great beyond and play in this cornfield? Not to make any kind of vast, earthshattering statement, but simply to hit a few and field a few, and remind us of a good and innocent time.

The photo above was taken in 2007 in Dyersville, Iowa, at the actual scene of the filming. The carving "Ray Loves Annie" in the bleacher seats can be seen in a quick shot during the movie. It has weathered over time.

What famous **conditional statement** inspired Ray to build a baseball field in his cornfield?

Conditionals

"If truly Truthful Troll I be,
then go thou east, and be thou free."

This of course is the statement uttered by the troll on the second page of this chapter. A more modern paraphrase would be, "*If* I am the troll who always tells the truth, *then* the door to the east is the one that leads to freedom."

The troll's utterance is an example of a conditional statement. A **conditional** statement is a compound statement that uses the connective *if . . . then.*

If I read for too long, *then* I get tired.

If looks could kill, *then* I would be dead.

If he doesn't get back soon, *then* you should go look for him.

Conditional statements

In each of these conditional statements, the component coming after the word *if* gives a condition (but not necessarily the only condition) under which the statement coming after *then* will be true. For example, "If it is over 90°, then I'll go to the mountains" tells one possible condition under which I will go to the mountains—if the temperature is over 90°.

The conditional is written with an arrow and symbolized as follows.

$$p \rightarrow q \qquad \text{If } p, \text{ then } q.$$

We read $p \rightarrow q$ as "***p* implies *q***" or "**If *p*, then *q*.**" In the conditional $p \rightarrow q$, the statement *p* is the **antecedent,** while *q* is the **consequent.**

The conditional connective may not always be explicitly stated. That is, it may be "hidden" in an everyday expression. For example, consider the following statement.

Quitters never win.

It can be written in *if . . . then* form as

If you're a quitter, *then* you will never win.

As another example, consider this statement.

It is difficult to study when you are distracted.

It can be written

If you are distracted, *then* it is difficult to study.

In the quotation "If you aim at nothing, you will hit it every time," the word "then" is not stated but understood from the context of the statement. "You aim at nothing" is the antecedent, and "you will hit it every time" is the consequent.

The conditional truth table is more difficult to define than the tables in the previous section. To see how to define the conditional truth table, imagine you have bought a used car (with financing from the car dealer), and the used-car salesman says,

If you fail to make your payment on time, *then* your car will be taken.

Let *p* represent "You fail to make your payment on time," and let *q* represent "Your car will be taken." There are four combinations of truth values for the two component statements.

The importance of **symbols** was emphasized by the American philosopher-logician **Charles Sanders Peirce** (1839–1914), who asserted the nature of humans as symbol-using or sign-using organisms. Symbolic notation is half of mathematics, Bertrand Russell once said.

As we consider these four possibilities, it is helpful to ask,

"Did the salesman lie?"

If so, then the conditional statement is considered false. Otherwise, the conditional statement is considered true.

Possibility	Failed to Pay on Time?	Car Taken?	
1	Yes	Yes	p is T, q is T.
2	Yes	No	p is T, q is F.
3	No	Yes	p is F, q is T.
4	No	No	p is F, q is F.

The four possibilities are as follows.

1. In the first case, assume you failed to make your payment on time, and your car *was* taken (p is T, q is T). The salesman told the truth, so place T in the first row of the truth table. (We do not claim that your car was taken *because* you failed to pay on time. It may be gone for a completely different reason.)

2. In the second case, assume that you failed to make your payment on time, and your car was *not* taken (p is T, q is F). The salesman lied (gave a false statement), so place an F in the second row of the truth table.

You Lie! (or Do You?) Granted, the T for Case 3 is less obvious than the F for Case 2. However, the laws of symbolic logic permit only one of two truth values. Since no lie can be established in Case 3, we give the salesman the benefit of the doubt. Likewise, *any* conditional statement is declared to be true whenever its antecedent is false.

3. In the third case, assume that you paid on time, but your car was taken anyway (p is F, q is T). The salesman did *not* lie. He only said what would happen if you were late on payments, not what would happen if you paid on time. (The crime here is stealing, not lying.) Since we cannot say that the salesman lied, place a T in the third row of the truth table.

4. Finally, assume that you made timely payment, and your car was not taken (p is F, q is F). This certainly does not contradict the salesman's statement, so place a T in the last row of the truth table.

The completed truth table for the conditional is defined as follows.

TRUTH TABLE FOR THE CONDITIONAL   If p, then q

	If p, then q	
p	q	$p \rightarrow q$
T	T	T
T	F	F
F	T	T
F	F	T

The use of the conditional connective in no way implies a cause-and-effect relationship. Any two statements may have an arrow placed between them to create a compound statement. Consider this example.

If I pass mathematics, then the sun will rise the next day.

It is true, because the consequent is true. (See the special characteristics following **Example 1** on the next page.) There is, however, no cause-and-effect connection between my passing mathematics and the rising of the sun. The sun will rise no matter what grade I get.

```
PROGRAM:PARITY
: Prompt N
: If N/2 = int (N/2)
:Then
: Disp "EVEN"
:
:
```

```
PROGRAM:PARITY

:
: Else
: Disp "ODD"
: End
:
```

```
prgmPARITY
N = ?7
ODD
                    Done
```

```
prgmPARITY
N = ?6
EVEN
                    Done
```

Conditional statements are useful in writing programs. The short program in the first two screens determines whether an integer is even. Notice the lines that begin with *If* and *Then*.

EXAMPLE 1 Finding the Truth Value of a Conditional

Given that p, q, and r are all false, find the truth value of the following statement.

$$(p \rightarrow \sim q) \rightarrow (\sim r \rightarrow q)$$

Solution

Using the shortcut method explained in **Example 3** of the previous section, we can replace p, q, and r with F (since each is false) and proceed as before, using the negation and conditional truth tables as necessary.

$$
\begin{array}{ccc}
(p \rightarrow \sim q) & \rightarrow & (\sim r \rightarrow q) \\
(F \rightarrow \sim F) & \rightarrow & (\sim F \rightarrow F) \\
(F \rightarrow T) & \rightarrow & (T \rightarrow F) \quad \text{Use the negation truth table.} \\
T & \rightarrow & F \quad \text{Use the conditional truth table.} \\
& F &
\end{array}
$$

The statement $(p \rightarrow \sim q) \rightarrow (\sim r \rightarrow q)$ is false when p, q, and r are all false. ∎

SPECIAL CHARACTERISTICS OF CONDITIONAL STATEMENTS

1. $p \rightarrow q$ is false only when the antecedent is *true* and the consequent is *false*.

2. If the antecedent is *false*, then $p \rightarrow q$ is automatically *true*.

3. If the consequent is *true*, then $p \rightarrow q$ is automatically *true*.

EXAMPLE 2 Determining Whether Conditionals Are True or False

Write *true* or *false* for each statement. Here T represents a true statement, and F represents a false statement.

(a) $T \rightarrow (7 = 3)$ **(b)** $(8 < 2) \rightarrow F$ **(c)** $(4 \neq 3 + 1) \rightarrow T$

Solution

(a) Because the antecedent is true, while the consequent, $7 = 3$, is false, the given statement is false by the first point mentioned above.

(b) The antecedent is false, so the given statement is true by the second observation.

(c) The consequent is true, making the statement true by the third characteristic of conditional statements. ∎

EXAMPLE 3 Constructing Truth Tables

Construct a truth table for each statement.

(a) $(\sim p \rightarrow \sim q) \rightarrow (\sim p \wedge q)$ **(b)** $(p \rightarrow q) \rightarrow (\sim p \vee q)$

Solution

(a) Insert the truth values of $\sim p$ and $\sim q$. Find the truth values of $\sim p \rightarrow \sim q$.

p	q	$\sim p$	$\sim q$	$\sim p \rightarrow \sim q$
T	T	F	F	T
T	F	F	T	T
F	T	T	F	F
F	F	T	T	T

Next use $\sim p$ and q to find the truth values of $\sim p \wedge q$.

p	q	$\sim p$	$\sim q$	$\sim p \rightarrow \sim q$	$\sim p \wedge q$
T	T	F	F	T	F
T	F	F	T	T	F
F	T	T	F	F	T
F	F	T	T	T	F

Now find the truth values of $(\sim p \rightarrow \sim q) \rightarrow (\sim p \wedge q)$.

p	q	$\sim p$	$\sim q$	$\sim p \rightarrow \sim q$	$\sim p \wedge q$	$(\sim p \rightarrow \sim q) \rightarrow (\sim p \wedge q)$
T	T	F	F	T	F	F
T	F	F	T	T	F	F
F	T	T	F	F	T	T
F	F	T	T	T	F	F

(b) For $(p \rightarrow q) \rightarrow (\sim p \vee q)$, go through steps similar to the ones above.

p	q	$p \rightarrow q$	$\sim p$	$\sim p \vee q$	$(p \rightarrow q) \rightarrow (\sim p \vee q)$
T	T	T	F	T	T
T	F	F	F	F	T
F	T	T	T	T	T
F	F	T	T	T	T

As the truth table in **Example 3(b)** shows, the statement

$$(p \rightarrow q) \rightarrow (\sim p \vee q)$$

is always true, no matter what the truth values of the components. Such a statement is called a **tautology.** Several other examples of tautologies (as can be checked by forming truth tables) are

$$p \vee \sim p, \quad p \rightarrow p, \quad \text{and} \quad (\sim p \vee \sim q) \rightarrow \sim (p \wedge q). \quad \text{Tautologies}$$

The truth tables in **Example 3** also could have been found by the alternative method shown in **Section 3.2.**

Writing a Conditional as a Disjunction

p	q	$p \rightarrow q$
T	T	T
T	F	F
F	T	T
F	F	T

Recall that the truth table for the conditional (repeated in the margin) shows that $p \rightarrow q$ is false only when p is true and q is false. But we also know that the disjunction is false for only one combination of component truth values, and it is easy to see that $\sim p \vee q$ will be false only when p is true and q is false, as the following truth table indicates.

p	q	$\sim p$	$\vee$	q
T	T	F	T	T
T	F	F	F	F
F	T	T	T	T
F	F	T	T	F

Thus we see that the disjunction $\sim p \vee q$ is equivalent to the conditional $p \rightarrow q$.

WRITING A CONDITIONAL AS A DISJUNCTION

$p \rightarrow q$ is equivalent to $\sim p \vee q$.

We now know that

$$p \rightarrow q \equiv \sim p \vee q,$$

so the negation of the conditional is

$$\sim(p \rightarrow q) \equiv \sim(\sim p \vee q).$$

Applying De Morgan's law to the right side of the above equivalence gives the negation as a conjunction.

NEGATION OF $p \rightarrow q$

The negation of $p \rightarrow q$ is $p \wedge \sim q.$

EXAMPLE 4 Determining Negations

Determine the negation of each statement.

(a) If I'm hungry, I will eat.   **(b)** All dogs have fleas.

Solution

> Do not try to negate a conditional with another conditional.

(a) If p represents "I'm hungry" and q represents "I will eat," then the given statement can be symbolized by $p \rightarrow q$. The negation of $p \rightarrow q$, as shown earlier, is $p \wedge \sim q$, so the negation of the statement is

$$\text{I'm hungry and I will not eat.}$$

(b) First, we must restate the given statement in *if . . . then* form.

$$\text{If it is a dog, then it has fleas.}$$

Based on our earlier discussion, the negation is

$$\text{It is a dog and it does not have fleas.} \qquad \blacksquare$$

As seen in **Example 4,** the negation of a conditional statement is written as a conjunction.

EXAMPLE 5 Determining Statements Equivalent to Conditionals

Write each conditional as an equivalent statement without using *if . . . then.*

(a) If the Indians win the pennant, then Johnny will go to the World Series.

(b) If it's Borden's, it's got to be good.

Solution

(a) Because the conditional $p \rightarrow q$ is equivalent to $\sim p \vee q$, let p represent "The Indians win the pennant" and q represent "Johnny will go to the World Series." Restate the conditional as

$$\text{The Indians do not win the pennant or Johnny will go to the World Series.}$$

(b) If p represents "it's Borden's" and if q represents "it's got to be good," the conditional may be restated as

$$\text{It's not Borden's or it's got to be good.} \qquad \blacksquare$$

Figure 1

Figure 2

Figure 3

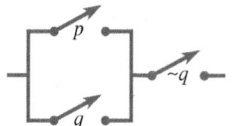

Figure 4

Switch Position	Current	Truth Value
Closed	flows	T
Open	stops	F

Circuits

One of the first nonmathematical applications of symbolic logic was seen in the master's thesis of Claude Shannon in 1937. Shannon showed how logic could be used to design electrical circuits. His work was immediately used by computer designers. Then in the developmental stage, computers could be simplified and built for less money using the ideas of Shannon.

To see how Shannon's ideas work, look at the electrical switch shown in **Figure 1**. We assume that current will flow through this switch when it is closed and not when it is open.

Figure 2 shows two switches connected in *series*. In such a circuit, current will flow only when both switches are closed. Note how closely a series circuit corresponds to the conjunction $p \land q$. We know that $p \land q$ is true only when both p and q are true.

A circuit corresponding to the disjunction $p \lor q$ can be found by drawing a *parallel* circuit, as in **Figure 3**. Here, current flows if either p *or* q is closed or if both p *and* q are closed.

The circuit in **Figure 4** corresponds to the statement $(p \lor q) \land \sim q$, which is a compound statement involving both a conjunction and a disjunction.

Simplifying an electrical circuit depends on the idea of equivalent statements from **Section 3.2**. Recall that two statements are equivalent if they have the same truth table final column. The symbol $\equiv$ is used to indicate that the two statements are equivalent. Some equivalent statements are shown in the following box.

EQUIVALENT STATEMENTS USED TO SIMPLIFY CIRCUITS

$$p \lor (q \land r) \equiv (p \lor q) \land (p \lor r) \qquad p \lor p \equiv p$$

$$p \land (q \lor r) \equiv (p \land q) \lor (p \land r) \qquad p \land p \equiv p$$

$$p \rightarrow q \equiv \sim q \rightarrow \sim p \qquad \sim(p \land q) \equiv \sim p \lor \sim q$$

$$p \rightarrow q \equiv \sim p \lor q \qquad \sim(p \lor q) \equiv \sim p \land \sim q$$

If T represents any true statement and F represents any false statement, then

$$p \lor T \equiv T \qquad p \lor \sim p \equiv T$$

$$p \land F \equiv F \qquad p \land \sim p \equiv F.$$

Circuits can be used as models of compound statements, with a closed switch corresponding to T (current flowing) and an open switch corresponding to F (current not flowing).

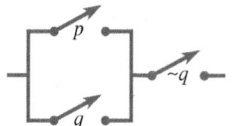

Figure 5

EXAMPLE 6   Simplifying a Circuit

Simplify the circuit of **Figure 5**.

Solution

At the top of **Figure 5**, p and q are connected in series, and at the bottom, p and r are connected in series. These are interpreted as the compound statements $p \land q$ and $p \land r$, respectively. These two conjunctions are connected in parallel, as indicated by the figure treated as a whole.

Write the disjunction of the two conjunctions.

$$(p \land q) \lor (p \land r)$$

Figure 6

(Think of the two switches labeled "*p*" as being controlled by the same lever.) By one of the pairs of equivalent statements in the preceding box,

$$(p \land q) \lor (p \land r) \equiv p \land (q \lor r),$$

which has the circuit of **Figure 6.** This circuit is logically equivalent to the one in **Figure 5,** and yet it contains only three switches instead of four—which might well lead to a large savings in manufacturing costs. ∎

Figure 7

EXAMPLE 7 Drawing a Circuit for a Conditional Statement

Draw a circuit for $p \to (q \land \sim r)$.

Solution

From the list of equivalent statements in the box, $p \to q$ is equivalent to $\sim p \lor q$. This equivalence gives $p \to (q \land \sim r) \equiv \sim p \lor (q \land \sim r)$, which has the circuit diagram in **Figure 7.** ∎

WHEN Will I Ever USE This ?

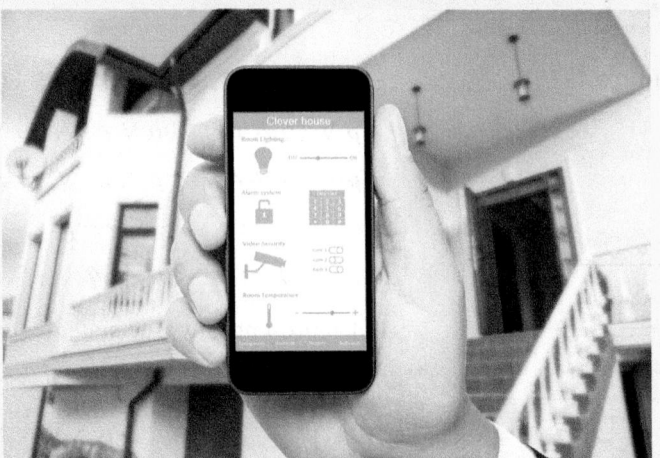

Suppose you are a home-monitoring and control system designer. A home-owner wants the capability of turning his air-conditioning system on or off at home via his smartphone (in case he forgets before leaving for vacation). You will need to install a control module for the AC unit that receives signals from your customer's smartphone.

Draw a circuit that will allow the AC unit to turn on when both a master switch and the control module are activated, and when either (or both) of two thermostats is (or are) triggered. Then write a logical statement for the circuit.

Since the master switch (*m*) and the control module (*c*) both need to be activated, they must be connected in series, followed by two thermostats T_1 and T_2 in parallel (because only one needs to be triggered). The circuit is shown below, and the corresponding logical statement is $m \land c \land (T_1 \lor T_2)$.

3.3 EXERCISES

Rewrite each statement using the if . . . then *connective. Rearrange the wording or add words as necessary.*

1. You can do it if you just believe.

2. It must be bad for you if it's sweet.

3. Every even integer divisible by 5 is divisible by 10.

4. No perfect square integers have units digit 2, 3, 7, or 8.

5. No grizzly bears live in California.

6. No guinea pigs get lonely.

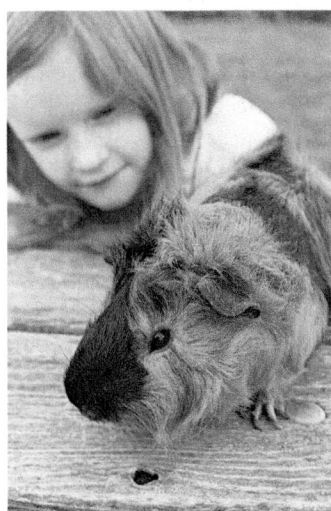

7. Surfers can't stay away from the beach.

8. Running Bear loves Little White Dove.

Decide whether each statement is true *or* false.

9. If the antecedent of a conditional statement is false, the conditional statement is true.

10. If the consequent of a conditional statement is true, the conditional statement is true.

11. If q is true, then $(p \wedge (q \rightarrow r)) \rightarrow q$ is true.

12. If p is true, then $\sim p \rightarrow (q \vee r)$ is true.

13. The negation of "If pigs fly, I'll believe it" is "If pigs don't fly, I won't believe it."

14. The statements "If it flies, then it's a bird" and "It does not fly or it's a bird" are logically equivalent.

15. Given that $\sim p$ is true and q is false, the conditional $p \rightarrow q$ is true.

16. Given that $\sim p$ is false and q is false, the conditional $p \rightarrow q$ is true.

17. Explain why the statement "If $3 > 5$, then $4 < 6$" is true.

18. In a few sentences, explain how to determine the truth value of a conditional statement.

Tell whether each conditional is true (T) *or* false (F).

19. $T \rightarrow (7 < 3)$

20. $F \rightarrow (4 \neq 8)$

21. $F \rightarrow (5 \neq 5)$

22. $(8 \geq 8) \rightarrow F$

23. $(5^2 \neq 25) \rightarrow (8 - 8 = 16)$

24. $(5 = 12 - 7) \rightarrow (9 > 0)$

Let s represent "She sings for a living," *let p represent* "he fixes cars," *and let m represent* "they collect classics." *Express each compound statement in words.*

25. $\sim m \rightarrow p$

26. $p \rightarrow \sim m$

27. $s \rightarrow (m \wedge p)$

28. $(s \wedge p) \rightarrow m$

29. $\sim p \rightarrow (\sim m \vee s)$

30. $(\sim s \vee \sim m) \rightarrow \sim p$

Let b represent "I take my ball," *let s represent* "it is sunny," *and let p represent* "the park is open." *Write each compound statement in symbols.*

31. If I take my ball, then the park is open.

32. If I do not take my ball, then it is not sunny.

33. The park is open, and if it is sunny then I do not take my ball.

34. I take my ball, or if the park is open then it is sunny.

35. It is sunny if the park is open.

36. I'll take my ball if it is not sunny.

Find the truth value of each statement. Assume that p and r are false, and q is true.

37. $\sim r \to q$

38. $q \to p$

39. $p \to q$

40. $\sim r \to p$

41. $\sim p \to (q \land r)$

42. $(\sim r \lor p) \to p$

43. $\sim q \to (p \land r)$

44. $(\sim p \land \sim q) \to (p \land \sim r)$

45. $(p \to \sim q) \to (\sim p \land \sim r)$

46. $[(p \to \sim q) \land (p \to r)] \to r$

47. Explain why we know that

$$[r \lor (p \lor s)] \to [(p \lor q) \lor \sim p]$$

is true, even if we are not given the truth values of p, q, r, and s.

48. Construct a true statement involving a conditional, a conjunction, a disjunction, and a negation (not necessarily in that order) that consists of component statements p, q, and r, with all of these component statements false.

Construct a truth table for each statement. Identify any tautologies.

49. $\sim q \to p$

50. $(\sim q \to \sim p) \to \sim q$

51. $(\sim p \to q) \to p$

52. $(p \land q) \to (p \lor q)$

53. $(p \lor q) \to (q \lor p)$

54. $(\sim p \to \sim q) \to (p \land q)$

55. $[(r \lor p) \land \sim q] \to p$

56. $[(r \land p) \land (p \land q)] \to p$

57. $(\sim r \to s) \lor (p \to \sim q)$

58. $(\sim p \land \sim q) \to (s \to r)$

59. What is the minimum number of Fs that must appear in the final column of a truth table for us to be assured that the statement is not a tautology?

60. If all truth values in the final column of a truth table are F, how can we easily transform the statement into a tautology?

Write the negation of each statement. Remember that the negation of $p \to q$ is $p \land \sim q$.

61. If that is an authentic Coach bag, I'll be surprised.

62. If Muley Jones hits that note, he will shatter glass.

63. If the bullfighter doesn't get going, he's going to get gored.

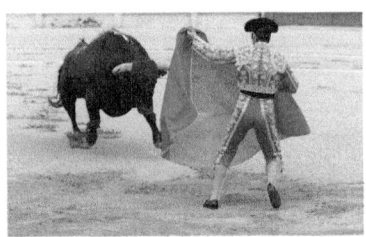

64. If you don't say "I do," then you'll regret it for the rest of your life.

65. "If you want to be happy for the rest of your life, never make a pretty woman your wife." *Jimmy Soul*

66. "If I had a hammer, I'd hammer in the morning." *Lee Hayes and Pete Seeger*

Write each statement as an equivalent statement that does not use the if . . . then connective. Remember that

$$p \to q \quad \text{is equivalent to} \quad \sim p \lor q.$$

67. If you give your plants tender, loving care, they flourish.

68. If you scratch my back, I'll scratch yours.

69. If she doesn't, he will.

70. If I say "black," she says "white."

71. All residents of Pensacola are residents of Florida.

72. All women were once girls.

Use truth tables to decide which of the pairs of statements are equivalent.

73. $p \to q$; $\sim p \lor q$

74. $\sim (p \to q)$; $p \land \sim q$

75. $p \to q$; $\sim q \to \sim p$

76. $p \to q$; $q \to p$

77. $p \to \sim q$; $\sim p \lor \sim q$

78. $\sim p \land q$; $\sim p \to q$

79. $q \rightarrow \sim p; \quad p \rightarrow \sim q$

80. $\sim (p \vee q) \rightarrow r; \quad (p \vee q) \vee r$

Write a logical statement representing each of the following circuits. Simplify each circuit when possible.

81.

82.

83.

84.

85.

86.

Draw circuits representing the following statements as they are given. Simplify if possible.

87. $p \wedge (q \vee \sim p)$

88. $(\sim p \wedge \sim q) \wedge \sim r$

89. $(p \vee q) \wedge (\sim p \wedge \sim q)$

90. $(\sim q \wedge \sim p) \vee (\sim p \vee q)$

91. $[(p \vee q) \wedge r] \wedge \sim p$

92. $[(\sim p \wedge \sim r) \vee \sim q] \wedge (\sim p \wedge r)$

93. $\sim q \rightarrow (\sim p \rightarrow q)$

94. $\sim p \rightarrow (\sim p \vee \sim q)$

95. Refer to **Figures 5 and 6** in **Example 6.** Suppose the cost of the use of one switch for an hour is $0.06. By using the circuit in **Figure 6** rather than the circuit in **Figure 5,** what is the savings for a year of 365 days, assuming that the circuit is in continuous use?

96. Explain why the circuit shown will always have exactly one open switch. What does this circuit simplify to?

97. Refer to the "For Further Thought" at the end of **Section 3.2.** Verify that the logic circuit shown below is equivalent to the conditional statement $A \rightarrow B$.

3.4   THE CONDITIONAL AND RELATED STATEMENTS

OBJECTIVES

1 Determine the converse, inverse, and contrapositive of a conditional statement.

2 Translate conditional statements into alternative forms.

3 Understand the structure of the biconditional.

4 Summarize the truth tables of compound statements.

Converse, Inverse, and Contrapositive

Many mathematical properties and theorems are stated in *if . . . then* form. Any conditional statement $p \rightarrow q$ is made up of an antecedent p and a consequent q. If they are interchanged, negated, or both, a new conditional statement is formed. Suppose that we begin with a conditional statement.

If you stay, then I go.   Conditional statement

By interchanging the antecedent ("you stay") and the consequent ("I go"), we obtain a new conditional statement.

If I go, then you stay.   Converse

This new conditional is called the **converse** of the given conditional statement.

By negating both the antecedent and the consequent, we obtain the **inverse** of the given conditional statement.

If you do not stay, then I do not go.   Inverse

Alfred North Whitehead (1861–1947) and Bertrand Russell worked together on *Principia Mathematica*. During that time, Whitehead was teaching mathematics at Cambridge University and had written *Universal Algebra*. In 1910 he went to the University of London, exploring not only the philosophical basis of science but also the "aims of education" (as he called one of his books). It was as a philosopher that he was invited to Harvard University in 1924. Whitehead died at the age of 86 in Cambridge, Massachusetts.

If the antecedent and the consequent are both interchanged *and* negated, the **contrapositive** of the given conditional statement is formed.

If I do not go, then you do not stay.   Contrapositive

These three related statements for the conditional $p \rightarrow q$ are summarized below.

RELATED CONDITIONAL STATEMENTS		
Conditional Statement	$p \rightarrow q$	(If p, then q.)
Converse	$q \rightarrow p$	(If q, then p.)
Inverse	$\sim p \rightarrow \sim q$	(If not p, then not q.)
Contrapositive	$\sim q \rightarrow \sim p$	(If not q, then not p.)

Notice that the inverse is the contrapositive of the converse.

EXAMPLE 1 **Determining Related Conditional Statements**

Determine each of the following, given the conditional statement

If I am running, then I am moving.

(a) the converse   **(b)** the inverse   **(c)** the contrapositive

Solution

(a) Let p represent "I am running" and q represent "I am moving." Then the given statement may be written $p \rightarrow q$. The converse, $q \rightarrow p$, is

If I am moving, then I am running.

The converse is not necessarily true, even though the given statement is true.

(b) The inverse of $p \rightarrow q$ is $\sim p \rightarrow \sim q$. Thus the inverse is

If I am not running, then I am not moving.

Again, this is not necessarily true.

(c) The contrapositive, $\sim q \rightarrow \sim p$, is

If I am not moving, then I am not running.

The contrapositive, like the given conditional statement, is true.   ∎

Example 1 shows that the converse and inverse of a true statement need not be true. They *can* be true, but they need not be. The relationships between the related conditionals are shown in the truth table that follows.

		Conditional	Converse	Inverse	Contrapositive
p	q	$p \rightarrow q$	$q \rightarrow p$	$\sim p \rightarrow \sim q$	$\sim q \rightarrow \sim p$
T	T	T	T	T	T
T	F	F	T	T	F
F	T	T	F	F	T
F	F	T	T	T	T

Equivalent (Conditional — Contrapositive)
Equivalent (Converse — Inverse)

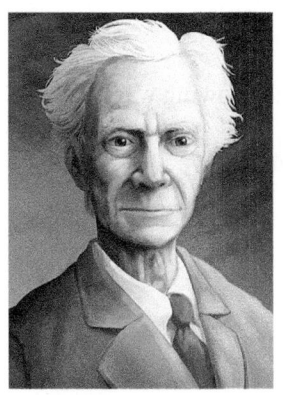

Bertrand Russell (1872–1970) was a student of Whitehead's before they wrote the *Principia*. Like his teacher, Russell turned toward philosophy. His works include a critique of Leibniz, analyses of mind and of matter, and a history of Western thought.

Russell became a public figure because of his involvement in social issues. Deeply aware of human loneliness, he was "passionately desirous of finding ways of diminishing this tragic isolation." During World War I he was an antiwar crusader, and he was imprisoned briefly. Again in the 1960s he championed peace. He wrote many books on social issues, winning the Nobel Prize for Literature in 1950.

As this truth table shows,

1. *A conditional statement and its contrapositive always have the same truth value,* making it possible to replace any statement with its contrapositive without affecting the logical meaning.

2. *The converse and inverse always have the same truth value.*

> **EQUIVALENCES**
>
> A conditional statement and its contrapositive are equivalent. Also, the converse and the inverse are equivalent.

EXAMPLE 2 **Determining Related Conditional Statements**

For the conditional statement $\sim p \to q$, write each of the following.

(a) the converse   **(b)** the inverse   **(c)** the contrapositive

Solution

(a) The converse of $\sim p \to q$ is $q \to \sim p$.

(b) The inverse is $\sim (\sim p) \to \sim q$, which simplifies to $p \to \sim q$.

(c) The contrapositive is $\sim q \to \sim (\sim p)$, which simplifies to $\sim q \to p$. ∎

Alternative Forms of "If *p*, then *q*"

The conditional statement "If p, then q" can be stated in several other ways in English. Consider this statement.

> If you take Tylenol, then you will find relief from your symptoms.

It can also be written as follows.

> Taking Tylenol is *sufficient* for relieving your symptoms.

According to this statement, taking Tylenol is enough to relieve your symptoms. Taking other medications or using other treatment techniques *might* also result in symptom relief, but at least we *know* that taking Tylenol will. Thus $p \to q$ can be written "p is sufficient for q." Knowing that p has occurred is sufficient to guarantee that q will also occur.

On the other hand, consider this statement, which has a different structure.

> Fresh ingredients are necessary for making a good pizza.   (*)

This statement claims that fresh ingredients are one condition for making a good pizza. But there may be other conditions (such as a working oven, for example). The statement labeled (*) could be written as

> If you want good pizza, then you need fresh ingredients.

As this example suggests, $p \to q$ is the same as "q is necessary for p." In other words, if q doesn't happen, then neither will p. Notice how this idea is closely related to the idea of equivalence between a conditional statement and its contrapositive.

Kurt Gödel (1906–1978) is widely regarded as the most influential mathematical logician of the twentieth century. He proved by his Incompleteness Theorem that the search for a set of axioms from which all mathematical truths could be proved was futile. In particular, "the vast structure of the *Principia Mathematica* of Whitehead and Russell was inadequate for deciding all mathematical questions."

After the death of his friend **Albert Einstein** (1879–1955), Gödel developed paranoia, and his life ended tragically when, convinced he was being poisoned, he refused to eat, essentially starving himself to death.

COMMON TRANSLATIONS OF $p \rightarrow q$

The conditional $p \rightarrow q$ can be translated in any of the following ways, none of which depends on the truth or falsity of $p \rightarrow q$.

If p, then q.	**p is sufficient for q.**
If p, q.	**q is necessary for p.**
p implies q.	**All p are q.**
p only if q.	**q if p.**

Example: If you live in Alamogordo, then you live in New Mexico. Statement

You live in New Mexico if you live in Alamogordo.
You live in Alamogordo only if you live in New Mexico.
Living in New Mexico is necessary for living in Alamogordo.
Living in Alamogordo is sufficient for living in New Mexico.
All residents of Alamogordo are residents of New Mexico.
Being a resident of Alamogordo implies residency in New Mexico.

Common translations

EXAMPLE 3 Rewording Conditional Statements

Rewrite each statement in the form "If p, then q."

(a) You'll get sick if you eat that.

(b) Go to the doctor only if your temperature exceeds 101°F.

(c) Everyone at the game had a great time.

Solution

(a) If you eat that, then you'll get sick.

(b) If you go to the doctor, then your temperature exceeds 101°F.

(c) If you were at the game, then you had a great time. ∎

EXAMPLE 4 Translating from Words to Symbols

Let p represent "A triangle is equilateral," and let q represent "A triangle has three sides of equal length." Write each of the following in symbols.

(a) A triangle is equilateral if it has three sides of equal length.

(b) A triangle is equilateral only if it has three sides of equal length.

Solution

(a) $q \rightarrow p$ **(b)** $p \rightarrow q$ ∎

Biconditionals

The compound statement **p if and only if q** (often abbreviated **p iff q**) is called a **biconditional**. It is symbolized $p \leftrightarrow q$ and is interpreted as the conjunction of the two conditionals $p \rightarrow q$ and $q \rightarrow p$.

Using symbols, the conjunction of the conditionals $p \rightarrow q$ and $q \rightarrow p$ is written $(q \rightarrow p) \wedge (p \rightarrow q)$ so that, by definition,

$$p \leftrightarrow q \equiv (q \rightarrow p) \wedge (p \rightarrow q). \quad \text{Biconditional}$$

The truth table for the biconditional $p \leftrightarrow q$ can be determined using this definition.

Principia Mathematica, the title chosen by Whitehead and Russell, was a deliberate reference to *Philosophiae naturalis principia mathematica,* or "mathematical principles of the philosophy of nature," Isaac Newton's epochal work of 1687. Newton's *Principia* pictured a kind of "clockwork universe" that ran via his Law of Gravitation. Newton independently invented the calculus, unaware that Leibniz had published his own formulation of it earlier.

TRUTH TABLE FOR THE BICONDITIONAL   *p* if and only if *q*

p if and only if *q*

p	q	$p \leftrightarrow q$
T	T	T
T	F	F
F	T	F
F	F	T

A biconditional is true when both component statements have the same truth value. It is false when they have different truth values.

EXAMPLE 5 **Determining Whether Biconditionals Are True or False**

Determine whether each biconditional statement is *true* or *false*.

(a) $6 + 8 = 14$ if and only if $11 + 5 = 16$

(b) $6 = 5$ if and only if $12 \neq 12$

(c) Mars is a moon if and only if Jupiter is a planet.

Solution

(a) Both $6 + 8 = 14$ and $11 + 5 = 16$ are true. By the truth table for the biconditional, this biconditional is true.

(b) Both component statements are false, so by the last line of the truth table for the biconditional, this biconditional statement is true.

(c) Because the first component Mars is a moon is false, and the second is true, this biconditional statement is false.   ∎

Summary of Truth Tables

Truth tables have been derived for several important types of compound statements.

SUMMARY OF BASIC TRUTH TABLES

1. $\sim p$, the **negation** of p, has truth value opposite that of p.

2. $p \wedge q$, the **conjunction,** is true only when both p and q are true.

3. $p \vee q$, the **disjunction,** is false only when both p and q are false.

4. $p \rightarrow q$, the **conditional,** is false only when p is true and q is false.

5. $p \leftrightarrow q$, the **biconditional,** is true only when both p and q have the same truth value.

3.4 EXERCISES

*For each given conditional statement (or statement that can be written as a conditional), write (**a**) the converse, (**b**) the inverse, and (**c**) the contrapositive in* if . . . then *form. In some of the exercises, it may be helpful to first restate the given statement in* if . . . then *form.*

1. If beauty were a minute, then you would be an hour.

2. If you lead, then I will follow.

3. If it ain't broke, don't fix it.

4. If I had a nickel for each time that happened, I would be rich.

5. Walking in front of a moving car is dangerous to your health.

6. Milk contains calcium.

7. Birds of a feather flock together.

8. A rolling stone gathers no moss.

9. If you build it, he will come.

10. Where there's smoke, there's fire.

11. $p \rightarrow \sim q$ **12.** $\sim p \rightarrow q$

13. $\sim p \rightarrow \sim q$ **14.** $\sim q \rightarrow \sim p$

15. $p \rightarrow (q \vee r)$ (*Hint:* Use one of De Morgan's laws as necessary.)

16. $(r \vee \sim q) \rightarrow p$ (*Hint:* Use one of De Morgan's laws as necessary.)

17. Discuss the equivalences that exist among a given conditional statement, its converse, its inverse, and its contrapositive.

18. State the contrapositive of "If the square of a natural number is odd, then the natural number is odd." The two statements must have the same truth value. Use several examples and inductive reasoning to decide whether both are true or both are false.

Write each statement in the form "if p, then q."

19. If the Kings go to the playoffs, pigs will fly.

20. If I score 90% or higher on my test, I'll go to a movie.

21. Legs of 3 and 4 imply a hypotenuse of 5.

22. "This is a leap year" implies that next year is not.

23. All whole numbers are rational numbers.

24. No irrational numbers are rational.

25. Doing logic puzzles is sufficient for driving me crazy.

26. Being in Kalamazoo is sufficient for being in Michigan.

27. Two coats of paint are necessary to cover the graffiti.

28. Being an environmentalist is necessary for being elected.

29. Employment will improve only if the economy recovers.

30. The economy will recover only if employment improves.

31. No whole numbers are not integers.

32. No integers are irrational numbers.

33. The Phillies will win the pennant when their pitching improves.

34. The grass will be greener when we're on the other side.

35. A rectangle is a parallelogram with perpendicular adjacent sides.

36. A square is a rectangle with two adjacent sides equal.

37. A triangle with two perpendicular sides is a right triangle.

38. A parallelogram is a four-sided figure with opposite sides parallel.

39. The square of a three-digit number whose units digit is 5 will end in 25.

40. An integer whose units digit is 0 or 5 is divisible by 5.

41. One of the following statements is not equivalent to all the others. Which one is it?

A. *r* only if *s*.   **B.** *r* implies *s*.

C. If *r*, then *s*.   **D.** *r* is necessary for *s*.

42. Many students have difficulty interpreting *necessary* and *sufficient*. Use the statement "Being in Vancouver is sufficient for being in North America" to explain why "*p* is sufficient for *q*" translates as "if *p*, then *q*."

43. Use the statement "To be an integer, it is necessary that a number be rational" to explain why "*p* is necessary for *q*" translates as "if *q*, then *p*."

44. Explain why the statement "A week has eight days if and only if October has forty days" is true.

Identify each statement as true *or* false.

45. $6 = 9 - 3$ if and only if $8 + 2 = 10$.

46. $3 + 1 \neq 7$ if and only if $8 \neq 8$.

47. $8 + 7 \neq 15$ if and only if $3 \times 5 \neq 8$.

48. $6 \times 2 = 18$ if and only if $9 + 7 \neq 16$.

49. George H. W. Bush was president if and only if George W. Bush was not president.

50. McDonald's sells Whoppers if and only if Apple manufactures Ipods.

Two statements that can both be true about the same object are **consistent.** *For example, "It is green" and "It weighs 60 pounds" are consistent statements. Statements that cannot both be true about the same object are called* **contrary.** *"It is a Nissan" and "It is a Mazda" are contrary. In Exercises 51–55, label each pair of statements as either* contrary *or* consistent.

51. Michael Jackson is alive. Michael Jackson is dead.

52. That book is nonfiction. That same book costs more than $150.

53. This number is a whole number. This same number is irrational.

54. This number is positive. This same number is a natural number.

55. This number is an integer. This same number is a rational number.

56. Refer to the "For Further Thought" on **page 105** at the end of **Section 3.2.** Verify that the logic circuit at the top of the next column (consisting of only NOR gates) is equivalent to the biconditional $A \leftrightarrow B$. Build a truth table for the statement $\sim(p \veebar q)$ (the negation of the Exclusive OR statement). What is the relationship between this and the biconditional?

Exercises 57 and 58 refer to the Chapter Opener on **page 89.** *Humphrey the hero deduced from the riddle that there are twin trolls who take shifts guarding the magical doors. One of them tells only truths, the other only lies. When the troll standing guard sees Humphrey, he says,*

> *"If truly Truthful Troll I be, then go thou east and be thou free."*

Humphrey needs to decide which troll he is addressing, call him by name, and tell him which door he would like opened.

> *There are two things Humphrey must get right: the name of the troll and the proper door. If he misidentifies the troll, no door will be opened. If he correctly names the troll and picks the wrong door, he will be confined to the dungeon behind it.*

57. Because the troll either always lies or always tells the truth, Humphrey knows that

(1) if the troll is Truthful Troll, then the conditional statement he uttered is true, and

(2) if the conditional statement he uttered is true, then he is Truthful Troll.

Let p represent "the troll is Truthful Troll" and let q represent "the door to the east leads to freedom." Express the statements in (1) and (2) in symbolic form.

58. The conjunction of the answers from **Exercise 57** is a biconditional that must be true.

(a) Build a truth table for this biconditional.

(b) Use the fact that it *must* be true to solve Humphrey's riddle.

3.5 ANALYZING ARGUMENTS WITH EULER DIAGRAMS

OBJECTIVES

1 Define logical arguments.

2 Use Euler diagrams to analyze arguments with universal quantifiers.

3 Use Euler diagrams to analyze arguments with existential quantifiers.

Logical Arguments

With inductive reasoning we observe patterns to solve problems. Now we study how deductive reasoning may be used to determine whether logical arguments are valid or invalid.

A logical argument is made up of **premises** (assumptions, laws, rules, widely held ideas, or observations) and a **conclusion.** Recall that *deductive* reasoning involves drawing specific conclusions from given general premises. When reasoning from the premises of an argument to obtain a conclusion, we want the argument to be valid.

Leonhard Euler (1707–1783) won the Academy prize and edged out du Châtelet and Voltaire. That was a minor achievement, as was the invention of "Euler circles" (which antedated Venn diagrams). Euler was the most prolific mathematician of his generation despite blindness that forced him to dictate from memory.

VALID AND INVALID ARGUMENTS

An argument is **valid** if the fact that all the premises are true forces the conclusion to be true. An argument that is not valid is **invalid.** It is called a **fallacy.**

"Valid" and "true" do not have the same meaning—an argument can be valid even though the conclusion is false (see Example 4), *or invalid even though the conclusion is true* (see Example 6).

Arguments with Universal Quantifiers

Several techniques can be used to check whether an argument is valid. One such technique is based on **Euler diagrams.**

Leonhard Euler (pronounced "Oiler") was one of the greatest mathematicians who ever lived. He is immortalized in mathematics history with the important irrational number e, named in his honor. This number appears throughout mathematics and is discussed in **Chapters 6 and 8.**

▦EXAMPLE 1 Using an Euler Diagram to Determine Validity

Is the following argument valid?

> No accidents happen on purpose.
> Spilling the beans was an accident.
> _____
> The beans were not spilled on purpose.

Solution

To begin, draw regions to represent the first premise. Because no accidents happen on purpose, the region for "accidents" goes outside the region for "things that happen on purpose," as shown in **Figure 8.**

The second premise, "Spilling the beans was an accident," suggests that "spilling the beans" belongs in the region representing "accidents." Let x represent "spilling the beans." **Figure 9** shows that "spilling the beans" is not in the region for "things that happen on purpose." If both premises are true, the conclusion that the beans were not spilled on purpose is also true. The argument is valid. ∎

Figure 8

Things that happen on purpose

Accidents

Figure 9

Things that happen on purpose

Accidents
x

▦EXAMPLE 2 Using an Euler Diagram to Determine Validity

Is the following argument valid?

> All rainy days are cloudy.
> Today is not cloudy.
> _____
> Today is not rainy.

Solution

In **Figure 10,** the region for "rainy days" is drawn entirely inside the region for "cloudy days." Since "Today is *not* cloudy," place an x for "today" *outside* the region for "cloudy days." See **Figure 11.** Placing the x outside the region for "cloudy days" forces it also to be outside the region for "rainy days." Thus, if the two premises are true, then it is also true that today is not rainy. The argument is valid.

Figure 10

Cloudy days

Rainy days

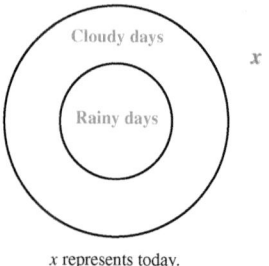

Cloudy days

Rainy days

x

x represents today.
Figure 11 ∎

EXAMPLE 3   Using an Euler Diagram to Determine Validity

Is the following argument valid?

All magnolia trees have green leaves.

That plant has green leaves.

That plant is a magnolia tree.

Solution

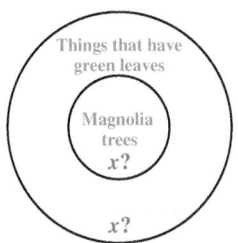

Figure 12

The region for "magnolia trees" goes entirely inside the region for "things that have green leaves." See **Figure 12.** The *x* that represents "that plant" must go inside the region for "things that have green leaves," but it can go either inside or outside the region for "magnolia trees." Even if the premises are true, we are not forced to accept the conclusion as true. This argument is invalid. It is a fallacy.   ■

EXAMPLE 4   Using an Euler Diagram to Determine Validity

Is the following argument valid?

All expensive things are desirable.

All desirable things make you feel good.

All things that make you feel good make you live longer.

All expensive things make you live longer.

Solution

A diagram for the argument is given in **Figure 13.** If each premise is true, then the conclusion must be true because the region for "expensive things" lies completely within the region for "things that make you live longer." Thus, the argument is valid. (This argument is an example of the fact that a *valid* argument need *not* have a true conclusion.)

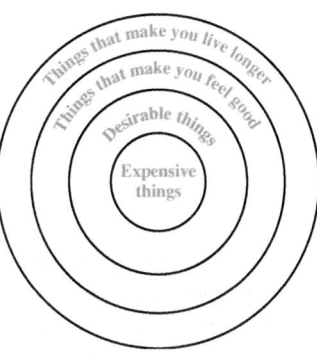

Figure 13   ■

Arguments with Existential Quantifiers

EXAMPLE 5   Using an Euler Diagram to Determine Validity

Is the following argument valid?

Many students drive Hondas.

I am a student.

I drive a Honda.

Solution

Figure 14

Figure 15

The first premise is sketched in **Figure 14,** where many (but not necessarily *all*) students drive Hondas. There are two possibilities for *I,* as shown in **Figure 15.** One possibility is that *I* drive a Honda. The other is that *I* don't. Since the truth of the premises does not force the conclusion to be true, the argument is invalid.   ■

▓ EXAMPLE 6 Using an Euler Diagram to Determine Validity

Is the following argument valid?

> All fish swim.
> All whales swim.
> _____
> A whale is not a fish.

Solution

The premises lead to two possibilities. **Figure 16** shows the set of fish and the set of whales as intersecting, while **Figure 17** does not. Both diagrams are valid interpretations of the given premises, but only one supports the conclusion.

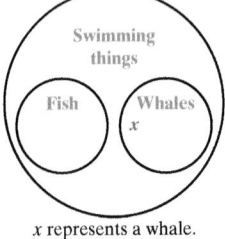

x represents a whale.   *x* represents a whale.

Figure 16   **Figure 17**

Because the truth of the premises does not force the conclusion to be true, the argument is invalid. Even though we know the conclusion to be true, this knowledge is not deduced from the premises. ■

FOR FURTHER THOUGHT

Common Fallacies

Discussions in everyday conversation, politics, and advertising provide a nearly endless stream of examples of **fallacies**—arguments exhibiting illogical reasoning. There are many general forms of fallacies, and we now present descriptions and examples of some of the more common ones. (Much of this list is adapted from the document Reader Mission Critical, located on the San Jose State University Web site, www.sjsu.edu)

1. **Circular Reasoning** (also called *Begging the Question*) The person making the argument assumes to be true what he is trying to prove.

   Husband: What makes you say that this dress makes you look fat?

   Wife: Because it does.

   Here the wife makes her case by stating what she wants to prove.

2. **False Dilemma** (also called the *Either-Or Fallacy,* or the *Black and White Fallacy*) Presenting two options with the assumption that they are contradictions (that is, the truth of one implies the falsity of the other) when in fact they are not, is the basis of a common fallacy.

Politician: America: Love it or leave it.

This argument implies only two choices. It is possible that someone may love America and yet leave, while someone else may not love America and yet stay.

3. **Loaded Question and Complex Claims** This fallacy involves one person asking a question or making a statement that is constructed in such a way as to obtain an answer in which the responder agrees to something with which he does not actually agree.

   Teenager Beth to her father: I hope you enjoyed embarrassing me in front of my friends.

   If Beth gets the expected response "No, I didn't enjoy it," the answer allows Beth to interpret that while her father didn't enjoy it, he did indeed embarrass her.

4. **Post Hoc Reasoning** An argument that is based on the false belief that if event A preceded event B, then A must have caused B is called *post hoc reasoning.*

   Johnny: I wore my Hawaiian shirt while watching all three playoff games, and my team won all three games. So I am going to wear that shirt every time I watch them.

The fact that Johnny put the same shirt on before each game has nothing to do with the outcomes of the games.

5. **Red Herring** (also called *Smoke Screen,* or *Wild Goose Chase*) This fallacy involves introducing an irrelevant topic to divert attention away from the original topic, allowing the person making the argument to seemingly prevail.

(The following script is from a political advertisement during the 2008 presidential campaign, intended to establish that John McCain lacked understanding of the economy.)

Maybe you're struggling just to pay the mortgage on your home. But recently, John McCain said, "The fundamentals of our economy are strong." Hmm. Then again, that same day, when asked how many houses he owns, McCain lost track. He couldn't remember. Well, it's seven. Seven houses. And here's one house America can't afford to let John McCain move into (showing a picture of the White House).

The advertisement shifted the focus to the number of houses McCain owned, which had nothing to do with the state of the economy, or the ability of "average" citizens to make their mortgage payments.

6. **Shifting the Burden of Proof** A person making a claim usually is required to support that claim. In this fallacy, if the claim is difficult to support, that person turns the burden of proof of that claim over to someone else.

Employee: You accuse me of embezzling money? That's ridiculous.

Employer: Well, until you can prove otherwise, you will just have to accept it as true.

If money has been disappearing, it is up to the employer to prove that this employee is guilty. The burden of proof is on the employer, but he is insinuating that the employee must prove that he is not the one taking the money.

7. **Straw Man** This fallacy involves creating a false image (like a scarecrow, or straw man) of someone else's position in an argument.

Dan Quayle: I have as much experience in the Congress as Jack Kennedy did when he sought the presidency.

Lloyd Bentsen: Senator, I served with Jack Kennedy. I knew Jack Kennedy. Jack Kennedy was a friend of mine. And Senator, you're no Jack Kennedy.

Dan Quayle: That was really uncalled for, Senator.

Lloyd Bentsen: You're the one that was making the comparison, Senator.

While this was the defining moment of the 1988 vice-presidential debate, Bentsen expertly used the straw man fallacy. Quayle did not compare himself or his accomplishments to those of Kennedy, but merely stated that he had spent as much time in Congress as Kennedy had when the latter ran for president.

For Group or Individual Investigation

Use the Internet to investigate the following additional logical fallacies.

Appeal to Authority	Appeal to Common	Common Practice
Two Wrongs	Belief	Wishful
Appeal to Fear	Indirect Consequences	Thinking
Appeal to Prejudice	Appeal to Loyalty	Appeal to Pity
Guilt by Association	Appeal to Spite	Appeal to Vanity
	Slippery Slope	Hasty Generalization

3.5   EXERCISES

Decide whether each argument is valid or invalid.

1. All amusement parks have thrill rides.
   Universal Orlando is an amusement park.

   Universal Orlando has thrill rides.

2. All disc jockeys play music.
   Calvin is a disc jockey.

   Calvin plays music.

3. All celebrities have problems.
That man has problems.

That man is a celebrity.

4. All Southerners speak with an accent.
Nick speaks with an accent.

Nick is a Southerner.

5. All dogs love to bury bones.
Puddles does not love to bury bones.

Puddles is not a dog.

6. All vice presidents use cell phones.
Bob does not use a cell phone.

Bob is not a vice president.

7. All residents of Colorado know how to breathe thin air.
Julie knows how to breathe thin air.

Julie lives in Colorado.

8. All drivers must have a photo I.D.
Kay has a photo I.D.

Kay is a driver.

9. Some dinosaurs were plant eaters.
Danny was a plant eater.

Danny was a dinosaur.

10. Some philosophers are absent minded.
Nicole is a philosopher.

Nicole is absent minded.

11. Many nurses belong to unions.
Heather is a nurse.

Heather belongs to a union.

12. Some trucks have sound systems.
Some trucks have gun racks.

Some trucks with sound systems have gun racks.

13. Refer to **Example 3.** If the second premise and the conclusion were interchanged, would the argument then be valid?

14. Refer to **Example 4.** Give a different conclusion from the one given there so that the argument is still valid.

Construct a valid argument based on the Euler diagram shown.

15.

x represents Erin.

16.

x represents vaccinations.

As mentioned in the text, an argument can have a true conclusion yet be invalid. In these exercises, each argument has a true conclusion. Identify each argument as valid *or* invalid.

17. All birds fly.
All planes fly.

A bird is not a plane.

18. All actors have cars.
All cars use gas.

All actors have gas.

19. All chickens have beaks.
All hens are chickens.

All hens have beaks.

20. All chickens have beaks.
All birds have beaks.

All chickens are birds.

21. Amarillo is northeast of El Paso.
Amarillo is northeast of Deming.

El Paso is northeast of Deming.

22. Beaverton is north of Salem.
Salem is north of Lebanon.

Beaverton is north of Lebanon.

23. No whole numbers are negative.
-3 is negative.

-3 is not a whole number.

24. A scalene triangle has a longest side.
A scalene triangle has a largest angle.

The largest angle in a scalene triangle is opposite the longest side.

In Exercises 25–30, the premises marked A, B, *and* C *are followed by several possible conclusions. Take each conclusion in turn, and check whether the resulting argument is* valid *or* invalid.

A. *All people who drive contribute to air pollution.*

B. *All people who contribute to air pollution make life a little worse.*

C. *Some people who live in a suburb make life a little worse.*

25. Some people who live in a suburb contribute to air pollution.

26. Some people who live in a suburb drive.

27. Suburban residents never drive.

28. Some people who contribute to air pollution live in a suburb.

29. Some people who make life a little worse live in a suburb.

30. All people who drive make life a little worse.

| 3.6 | **ANALYZING ARGUMENTS WITH TRUTH TABLES** |

OBJECTIVES

1 Use truth tables to determine validity of arguments.

2 Recognize valid and invalid argument forms.

3 Be familiar with the arguments of Lewis Carroll.

Using Truth Tables to Determine Validity

In **Section 3.5** we used Euler diagrams to test the validity of arguments. While Euler diagrams often work well for simple arguments, difficulties can develop with more complex ones, because Euler diagrams must show every possible case. In complex arguments, it is hard to be sure that all cases have been considered.

In deciding whether to use Euler diagrams to test the validity of an argument, look for quantifiers such as "all," "some," or "no." These words often indicate arguments best tested by Euler diagrams. If these words are absent, it may be better to use truth tables to test the validity of an argument.

EXAMPLE 1 Using a Truth Table to Determine Validity

Determine whether the argument is *valid* or *invalid*.

> If there is a problem, then I must fix it.
> There is a problem.
> ———————————————
> I must fix it.

Solution

To test the validity of this argument, we begin by assigning the letters p and q to represent these statements.

p represents "There is a problem."

q represents "I must fix it."

Now we write the two premises and the conclusion in symbols.

Premise 1: $p \rightarrow q$
Premise 2: p
—————————
Conclusion: q

To decide if this argument is valid, we must determine whether the conjunction of both premises implies the conclusion for all possible combinations of truth values for p and q. Therefore, write the conjunction of the premises as the antecedent of a conditional statement, and write the conclusion as the consequent.

$$[(p \rightarrow q) \quad \wedge \quad p] \quad \rightarrow \quad q$$

premise   and   premise   implies   conclusion

Finally, construct the truth table for this conditional statement, as shown below.

p	q	$p \rightarrow q$	$(p \rightarrow q) \wedge p$	$[(p \rightarrow q) \wedge p] \rightarrow q$
T	T	T	T	T
T	F	F	F	T
F	T	T	F	T
F	F	T	F	T

Because the final column, shown in color, indicates that the conditional statement that represents the argument is true for all possible truth values of p and q, the statement is a tautology. Thus, the argument is valid. ∎

In the 2007 Spanish film **La Habitacion de Fermat (Fermat's Room)**, four mathematicians are invited to dinner, only to discover that the room in which they are meeting is designed to eventually crush them as walls creep in closer and closer. The only way for them to delay the inevitable is to answer enigmas, questions, puzzles, problems, and riddles that they are receiving on a cell phone.

One of the enigmas deals with a hermetically sealed room that contains a single light bulb. There are three switches outside the room, all of them are off, and only one of these switches controls the bulb. You are allowed to flip any or all of the switches as many times as you wish before you enter the room, but once you enter, you cannot return to the switches outside. How can you determine which one controls the bulb? (The answer is on **page 130.**)

Answer to the Light Bulb question on page 129.

Label the switches 1, 2, and 3. Turn switch 1 on and leave it on for several minutes. Then turn switch 1 off, turn switch 2 on, and then immediately enter the room. If the bulb is on, then you know that switch 2 controls it. If the bulb is off, touch it to see if it is still warm. If it is, then switch 1 controls it. If the bulb is not warm, then switch 3 controls it.

The pattern of the argument in **Example 1**

$$p \rightarrow q$$
$$\underline{p}$$
$$q$$

is called **modus ponens,** or the *law of detachment.*

To test the validity of an argument using a truth table, follow the steps in the box.

TESTING THE VALIDITY OF AN ARGUMENT WITH A TRUTH TABLE

Step 1 Assign a letter to represent each component statement in the argument.

Step 2 Express each premise and the conclusion symbolically.

Step 3 Form the symbolic statement of the entire argument by writing the *conjunction* of *all* the premises as the antecedent of a conditional statement, and the conclusion of the argument as the consequent.

Step 4 Complete the truth table for the conditional statement formed in Step 3. If it is a tautology, then the argument is valid; otherwise, it is invalid.

EXAMPLE 2 Using a Truth Table to Determine Validity

Determine whether the argument is *valid* or *invalid*.

If my check arrives in time, I'll register for fall semester.
I've registered for fall semester.
_____
My check arrived in time.

Solution

Let p represent "My check arrives (arrived) in time." Let q represent "I'll register (I've registered) for fall semester." The argument can be written as follows.

$$p \rightarrow q$$
$$\underline{q}$$
$$p$$

To test for validity, construct a truth table for the statement $[(p \rightarrow q) \land q] \rightarrow p$.

p	q	$p \rightarrow q$	$(p \rightarrow q) \land q$	$[(p \rightarrow q) \land q] \rightarrow p$
T	T	T	T	T
T	F	F	F	T
F	T	T	T	F
F	F	T	F	T

The final column of the truth table contains an F. The argument is invalid. ∎

If a conditional and its converse were logically equivalent, then an argument of the type found in **Example 2** would be valid. Because a conditional and its converse are *not* equivalent, the argument is an example of what is sometimes called the **fallacy of the converse.**

EXAMPLE 3 Using a Truth Table to Determine Validity

Determine whether the argument is *valid* or *invalid*.

If I can avoid sweets, I can avoid the dentist.
I can't avoid the dentist.
_____
I can't avoid sweets.

Solution

If p represents "I can avoid sweets" and q represents "I can avoid the dentist," the argument is written as follows.

$$p \to q$$
$$\dfrac{\sim q}{\sim p}$$

The symbolic statement of the entire argument is as follows.

$$[(p \to q) \land \sim q] \to \sim p$$

The truth table for this argument indicates a tautology, and the argument is valid.

p	q	$p \to q$	$\sim q$	$(p \to q) \land \sim q$	$\sim p$	$[(p \to q) \land \sim q] \to \sim p$
T	T	T	F	F	F	T
T	F	F	T	F	F	T
F	T	T	F	F	T	T
F	F	T	T	T	T	T

The pattern of reasoning of this example is called **modus tollens,** or the *law of contraposition,* or *indirect reasoning.* ∎

With reasoning similar to that used to name the fallacy of the converse, the fallacy

$$p \to q$$
$$\dfrac{\sim p}{\sim q}$$

Concluding $\sim q$ from $\sim p$ wrongly assumes $\sim p \to \sim q$, the *inverse* of the given premise $p \to q$.

is called the **fallacy of the inverse.** An example of such a fallacy is "If it rains, I get wet. It doesn't rain. Therefore, I don't get wet."

EXAMPLE 4 Using a Truth Table to Determine Validity

Determine whether the argument is *valid* or *invalid.*

> I'll buy a car or I'll take a vacation.
> I won't buy a car.
> ─────────────────────────────
> I'll take a vacation.

Solution

If p represents "I'll buy a car" and q represents "I'll take a vacation," the argument is symbolized as follows.

$$p \lor q$$
$$\dfrac{\sim p}{q}$$

We must set up a truth table for the statement $[(p \lor q) \land \sim p] \to q$.

p	q	$p \lor q$	$\sim p$	$(p \lor q) \land \sim p$	$[(p \lor q) \land \sim p] \to q$
T	T	T	F	F	T
T	F	T	F	F	T
F	T	T	T	T	T
F	F	F	T	F	T

The statement is a tautology and the argument is valid. Any argument of this form is valid by the law of **disjunctive syllogism.** ∎

EXAMPLE 5 Using a Truth Table to Determine Validity

Determine whether the argument is *valid* or *invalid*.

> If it squeaks, then I use WD-40.
> If I use WD-40, then I must go to the hardware store.
> _____
> If it squeaks, then I must go to the hardware store.

Solution

Let p represent "It squeaks," let q represent "I use WD-40," and let r represent "I must go to the hardware store." The argument takes on the following form.

$$p \rightarrow q$$
$$q \rightarrow r$$
$$\overline{p \rightarrow r}$$

Make a truth table for this statement, which requires eight rows.

$$[(p \rightarrow q) \wedge (q \rightarrow r)] \rightarrow (p \rightarrow r)$$

p	q	r	$p \rightarrow q$	$q \rightarrow r$	$p \rightarrow r$	$(p \rightarrow q) \wedge (q \rightarrow r)$	$[(p \rightarrow q) \wedge (q \rightarrow r)] \rightarrow (p \rightarrow r)$
T	T	T	T	T	T	T	T
T	T	F	T	F	F	F	T
T	F	T	F	T	T	F	T
T	F	F	F	T	F	F	T
F	T	T	T	T	T	T	T
F	T	F	T	F	T	F	T
F	F	T	T	T	T	T	T
F	F	F	T	T	T	T	T

This argument is valid because the final statement is a tautology. This pattern of argument is called **reasoning by transitivity,** or the *law of hypothetical syllogism.* ∎

Valid and Invalid Argument Forms

A summary of the valid forms of argument presented so far follows.

In a scene near the beginning of the 1974 film *Monty Python and the Holy Grail,* an amazing application of **poor logic** leads to the apparent demise of a supposed witch. Some peasants have forced a young woman to wear a nose made of wood. The convoluted argument they make is this: Witches and wood are both burned, and because witches are made of wood, and wood floats, and ducks also float, if she weighs the same as a duck, then she is made of wood and, therefore, is a witch!

VALID ARGUMENT FORMS

Modus Ponens	Modus Tollens	Disjunctive Syllogism	Reasoning by Transitivity
$p \rightarrow q$	$p \rightarrow q$	$p \vee q$	$p \rightarrow q$
$\dfrac{p}{q}$	$\dfrac{\sim q}{\sim p}$	$\dfrac{\sim p}{q}$	$\dfrac{q \rightarrow r}{p \rightarrow r}$

The following is a summary of invalid forms (or fallacies).

INVALID ARGUMENT FORMS (FALLACIES)

Fallacy of the Converse	Fallacy of the Inverse
$p \rightarrow q$	$p \rightarrow q$
$\dfrac{q}{p}$	$\dfrac{\sim p}{\sim q}$

Setting the Table Correctly If an argument has the form

$$p_1$$
$$p_2$$
$$\vdots$$
$$\frac{p_n,}{c}$$

then **Step 3** in the testing process calls for the statement

$$(p_1 \wedge p_2 \wedge \ldots \wedge p_n) \to c.$$

EXAMPLE 6 Using a Truth Table to Determine Validity

Determine whether the argument is *valid* or *invalid*.

> If Eddie goes to town, then Mabel stays at home.
> If Mabel does not stay at home, then Rita will cook.
> Rita will not cook. Therefore, Eddie does not go to town.

Solution

In an argument written in this manner, the premises are given first, and the conclusion is the statement that follows the word "Therefore." Let *p* represent "Eddie goes to town," let *q* represent "Mabel stays at home," and let *r* represent "Rita will cook." Then the argument is symbolized as follows.

$$p \to q$$
$$\sim q \to r$$
$$\frac{\sim r}{\sim p}$$

When an argument contains more than two premises, it is necessary to determine the truth values of the conjunction of *all* of them.

> ***If at least one premise in a conjunction of several premises is false, then the entire conjunction is false.***

To test validity, set up a truth table for this statement.

$$[(p \to q) \wedge (\sim q \to r) \wedge \sim r] \to \sim p$$

p	*q*	*r*	*p → q*	~*q*	~*q → r*	~*r*	(*p → q*) ∧ (~*q → r*) ∧ ~*r*	~*p*	[(*p → q*) ∧ (~*q → r*) ∧ ~*r*] → ~*p*
T	T	T	T	F	T	F	F	F	T
T	T	F	T	F	T	T	T	F	F
T	F	T	F	T	T	F	F	F	T
T	F	F	F	T	F	T	F	F	T
F	T	T	T	F	T	F	F	T	T
F	T	F	T	F	T	T	T	T	T
F	F	T	T	T	T	F	F	T	T
F	F	F	T	T	F	T	F	T	T

Because the final column does not contain all Ts, the statement is not a tautology. The argument is invalid. ∎

Arguments of Lewis Carroll

Consider the following verse, which has been around for many years.

> *For want of a nail, the shoe was lost.*
> *For want of a shoe, the horse was lost.*
> *For want of a horse, the rider was lost.*
> *For want of a rider, the battle was lost.*
> *For want of a battle, the war was lost.*
> *Therefore, for want of a nail, the war was lost.*

Each line of the verse may be written as an *if . . . then* statement. For example, the first line may be restated as "If a nail is lost, then the shoe is lost." The conclusion, "For want of a nail, the war was lost," follows from the premises, because repeated use of the law of transitivity applies. Arguments such as the one used by Lewis Carroll in the next example often take a similar form.

Alice's Adventures in Wonderland is the most famous work of **Charles Dodgson** (1832–1898), better known as **Lewis Carroll,** who was a mathematician and logician. He popularized recreational mathematics with this story and its sequel, *Through the Looking-Glass.* More than a century later, Raymond Smullyan continues this genre in his book *Alice in Puzzle-land* and many others.

EXAMPLE 7 Supplying a Conclusion to Ensure Validity

Supply a conclusion that yields a valid argument for the following premises.

> Babies are illogical.
>
> Nobody is despised who can manage a crocodile.
>
> Illogical persons are despised.

Solution

First, write each premise in the form *if . . . then. . . .*

> If you are a baby, then you are illogical.
>
> If you can manage a crocodile, then you are not despised.
>
> If you are illogical, then you are despised.

Let p represent "you are a baby," let q represent "you are logical," let r represent "you can manage a crocodile," and let s represent "you are despised." The statements can be written symbolically.

$$p \rightarrow \sim q$$
$$r \rightarrow \sim s$$
$$\sim q \rightarrow s$$

Begin with any letter that appears only once. Here p appears only once. Using the contrapositive of $r \rightarrow \sim s$, which is $s \rightarrow \sim r$, rearrange the statements as follows.

$$p \rightarrow \sim q$$
$$\sim q \rightarrow s$$
$$s \rightarrow \sim r$$

From the three statements, repeated use of reasoning by transitivity gives the conclusion

$$p \rightarrow \sim r,\ \text{which leads to a valid argument.}$$

In words, the conclusion is "If you are a baby, then you cannot manage a crocodile," or, as Lewis Carroll would have written it, "Babies cannot manage crocodiles." ∎

WHEN Will I Ever USE This ?

Suppose you are a pediatric nurse administering flu vaccination for a 6-year-old patient. The flowchart on the next page is a dosing algorithm provided by the CDC for children 6 months to 8 years of age.

Influenza Dosing Algorithm

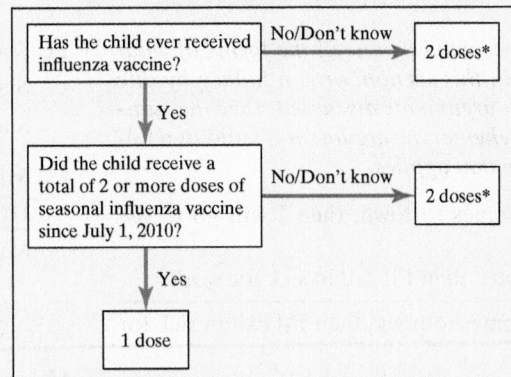

* Doses should be administered at least 4 weeks apart.
Source: cdc.gov

The patient was vaccinated for the first time last year, so you place the patient on a 2-dose regimen. Use a truth table to determine the validity of your action.

We let

p be "The child has received flu vaccine in the past,"

q be "The child has received 2 or more doses of flu vaccine since July 1, 2010,"

and r be "The child needs 2 doses this season."

Then the algorithm and your treatment decision can be expressed symbolically by the following argument.

$$(p \wedge q) \leftrightarrow \sim r$$
$$\underline{\sim q}$$
$$r$$

Make a truth table for the argument. Since there are three component statements, we require eight rows.

p	q	r	$[((p$	$\wedge$	$q)$	$\leftrightarrow$	$\sim r)$	$\wedge$	$\sim q]$	$\rightarrow$	r
T	T	T								T	T
T	T	F	T	T	T	T	T	F	F	T	F
T	F	T								T	T
T	F	F	T	F	F	F	T	F	T	T	F
F	T	T								T	T
F	T	F	F	F	T	F	T	F	F	T	F
F	F	T								T	T
F	F	F	F	F	F	F	T	F	T	T	F
			①	②	①	④	③	⑥	⑤	⑧	⑦

The truth table shows that your argument is a tautology, so your action was valid according to the CDC.

Note that in the odd rows of the table, we used the fact that the consequent r was true to conclude that the conditional was true, thus avoiding the effort required to "build" those rows piece by piece. In the even rows, we used the shortcut method introduced in **Example 10** of **Section 3.2**.

3.6 EXERCISES

Each argument either is valid by one of the forms of valid arguments discussed in this section, or is a fallacy by one of the forms of invalid arguments discussed. (See the summary boxes.) Decide whether the argument is valid *or a fallacy, and give the form that applies.*

1. If Rascal Flatts comes to town, then I will go to the concert.

If I go to the concert, then I'll call in sick for work.

If Rascal Flatts comes to town, then I'll call in sick for work.

2. If you use binoculars, then you get a glimpse of the bald eagle.

If you get a glimpse of the bald eagle, then you'll be amazed.

If you use binoculars, then you'll be amazed.

3. If Marina works hard enough, she will get a promotion.

Marina works hard enough.

She will get a promotion.

4. If Isaiah's ankle heals on time, he'll play this season.

His ankle heals on time.

He'll play this season.

5. If he doesn't have to get up at 3:00 A.M., he's ecstatic.

He's ecstatic.

He doesn't have to get up at 3:00 A.M.

6. "A mathematician is a device for turning coffee into theorems." (quote from Paul Erdos)

You turn coffee into theorems.

You are a mathematician.

7. If Clayton pitches, the Dodgers win.

The Dodgers do not win.

Clayton does not pitch.

8. If Josh plays, the opponent gets shut out.

The opponent does not get shut out.

Josh does not play.

9. "If you're going through hell, keep going." (quote from Winston Churchill)

You're not going through hell.

Don't keep going.

10. "If you can't get rid of the skeleton in your closet, you'd best teach it to dance." (quote from George Bernard Shaw)

You can get rid of the skeleton in your closet.

You'd best not teach it to dance.

11. She uses e-commerce or she pays by credit card.

She does not pay by credit card.

She uses e-commerce.

12. Mia kicks or Drew passes.

Drew does not pass.

Mia kicks.

Use a truth table to determine whether the argument is valid *or* invalid.

13. $p \lor q$
p
$\sim q$

14. $p \land \sim q$
p
$\sim q$

15. $\sim p \rightarrow \sim q$
q
p

16. $p \lor \sim q$
p
$\sim q$

17. $p \rightarrow q$
$q \rightarrow p$
$p \land q$

18. $\sim p \rightarrow q$
p
$\sim q$

19. $p \rightarrow \sim q$
q
$\sim p$

20. $p \rightarrow \sim q$
$\sim p$
$\sim q$

21. $(p \rightarrow q) \land (q \rightarrow p)$
p
$p \lor q$

22. $(p \land q) \lor (p \lor q)$
q
p

23. $(\sim p \lor q) \land (\sim p \rightarrow q)$
p
$\sim q$

24. $(r \land p) \rightarrow (r \lor q)$
$q \land p$
$r \lor p$

25. $(\sim p \land r) \rightarrow (p \lor q)$
$\sim r \rightarrow p$
$q \rightarrow r$

26. $(p \rightarrow \sim q) \lor (q \rightarrow \sim r)$
$p \lor \sim r$
$r \rightarrow p$

27. Earlier we showed how to analyze arguments using Euler diagrams. Refer to **Example 5** in this section, restate each premise and the conclusion using a quantifier, and then draw an Euler diagram to illustrate the relationship.

28. Explain in a few sentences how to determine the statement for which a truth table will be constructed so that the arguments that follow in **Exercises 29–38** can be analyzed for validity.

Determine whether each argument is valid *or* invalid.

29. Joey loves to watch movies. If Terry likes to jog, then Joey does not love to watch movies. If Terry does not like to jog, then Carrie drives a school bus. Therefore, Carrie drives a school bus.

30. If Hurricane Gustave hit that grove of trees, then the trees are devastated. People plant trees when disasters strike and the trees are not devastated. Therefore, if people plant trees when disasters strike, then Hurricane Gustave did not hit that grove of trees.

31. If Yoda is my favorite *Star Wars* character, then I hate Darth Vader. I hate Luke Skywalker or Darth Vader. I don't hate Luke Skywalker. Therefore, Yoda is not my favorite character.

32. Carrie Underwood sings or Joe Jonas is not a teen idol. If Joe Jonas is not a teen idol, then Jennifer Hudson does not win a Grammy. Jennifer Hudson wins a Grammy. Therefore, Carrie Underwood does not sing.

33. The Cowboys will make the playoffs if and only if Troy comes back to play. Jerry doesn't coach the Cowboys or Troy comes back to play. Jerry does coach the Cowboys. Therefore, the Cowboys will not be in the playoffs.

34. If I've got you under my skin, then you are deep in the heart of me. If you are deep in the heart of me, then you are not really a part of me. You are deep in the heart of me or you are really a part of me. Therefore, if I've got you under my skin, then you are really a part of me.

35. If Dr. Hardy is a department chairman, then he lives in Atlanta. He lives in Atlanta and his first name is Larry. Therefore, if his first name is not Larry, then he is not a department chairman.

36. If I were your woman and you were my man, then I'd never stop loving you. I've stopped loving you. Therefore, I am not your woman or you are not my man.

37. All men are created equal. All people who are created equal are women. Therefore, all men are women.

38. All men are mortal. Socrates is a man. Therefore, Socrates is mortal.

39. A recent DirecTV commercial had the following script: "When the cable company keeps you on hold, you feel trapped. When you feel trapped, you need to feel free. When you need to feel free, you try hang-gliding. When you try hang-gliding, you crash into things. When you crash into things, the grid goes down. When the grid goes down, crime goes up, and when crime goes up, your dad gets punched over a can of soup . . . "

(a) Use reasoning by transitivity and all the component statements to draw a valid conclusion.

(b) If we added the line, "Your dad does not get punched over a can of soup," what valid conclusion could be drawn?

40. Molly made the following observation: "If I want to determine whether an argument leading to the statement

$$[(p \to q) \land \sim q] \to \sim p$$

is valid, I only need to consider the lines of the truth table that lead to T for the column that is headed $(p \to q) \land \sim q$." Molly was very perceptive. Can you explain why her observation was correct?

In the arguments used by Lewis Carroll, it is helpful to restate a premise in if . . . then *form in order to more easily identify a valid conclusion. The following premises come from Lewis Carroll. Write each premise in* if . . . then *form.*

41. All my poultry are ducks.

42. None of your sons can do logic.

43. Guinea pigs are hopelessly ignorant of music.

44. No teetotalers are pawnbrokers.

45. No teachable kitten has green eyes.

46. Opium-eaters have no self-command.

47. I have not filed any of them that I can read.

48. All of them written on blue paper are filed.

Exercises 49–54 involve premises from Lewis Carroll. Write each premise in symbols, and then, in the final part, give a conclusion that yields a valid argument.

49. Let *p* be "it is a duck," *q* be "it is my poultry," *r* be "one is an officer," and *s* be "one is willing to waltz."

(a) No ducks are willing to waltz.

(b) No officers ever decline to waltz.

(c) All my poultry are ducks.

(d) Give a conclusion that yields a valid argument.

50. Let *p* be "one is able to do logic," *q* be "one is fit to serve on a jury," *r* be "one is sane," and *s* be "he is your son."

   (a) Everyone who is sane can do logic.

   (b) No lunatics are fit to serve on a jury.

   (c) None of your sons can do logic.

   (d) Give a conclusion that yields a valid argument.

51. Let *p* be "one is honest," *q* be "one is a pawnbroker," *r* be "one is a promise-breaker," *s* be "one is trustworthy," *t* be "one is very communicative," and *u* be "one is a wine-drinker."

   (a) Promise-breakers are untrustworthy.

   (b) Wine-drinkers are very communicative.

   (c) A person who keeps a promise is honest.

   (d) No teetotalers are pawnbrokers. (*Hint:* Assume "teetotaler" is the opposite of "wine-drinker.")

   (e) One can always trust a very communicative person.

   (f) Give a conclusion that yields a valid argument.

52. Let *p* be "it is a guinea pig," *q* be "it is hopelessly ignorant of music," *r* be "it keeps silent while the *Moonlight Sonata* is being played," and *s* be "it appreciates Beethoven."

   (a) Nobody who really appreciates Beethoven fails to keep silent while the *Moonlight Sonata* is being played.

   (b) Guinea pigs are hopelessly ignorant of music.

   (c) No one who is hopelessly ignorant of music ever keeps silent while the *Moonlight Sonata* is being played.

   (d) Give a conclusion that yields a valid argument.

53. Let *p* be "it begins with 'Dear Sir'," *q* be "it is crossed," *r* be "it is dated," *s* be "it is filed," *t* be "it is in black ink,"

u be "it is in the third person," *v* be "I can read it," *w* be "it is on blue paper," *x* be "it is on one sheet," and *y* be "it is written by Brown."

   (a) All the dated letters are written on blue paper.

   (b) None of them are in black ink, except those that are written in the third person.

   (c) I have not filed any of them that I can read.

   (d) None of them that are written on one sheet are undated.

   (e) All of them that are not crossed are in black ink.

   (f) All of them written by Brown begin with "Dear Sir."

   (g) All of them written on blue paper are filed.

   (h) None of them written on more than one sheet are crossed.

   (i) None of them that begin with "Dear Sir" are written in the third person.

   (j) Give a conclusion that yields a valid argument.

54. Let *p* be "he is going to a party," *q* be "he brushes his hair," *r* be "he has self-command," *s* be "he looks fascinating," *t* be "he is an opium-eater," *u* be "he is tidy," and *v* be "he wears white kid gloves."

   (a) No one who is going to a party ever fails to brush his hair.

   (b) No one looks fascinating if he is untidy.

   (c) Opium-eaters have no self-command.

   (d) Everyone who has brushed his hair looks fascinating.

   (e) No one wears white kid gloves unless he is going to a party. (*Hint:* "*a* unless *b*" ≡ ~*b* → *a*.)

   (f) A man is always untidy if he has no self-command.

   (g) Give a conclusion that yields a valid argument.

CHAPTER 3   # SUMMARY

KEY TERMS

3.1	**3.2**	**3.4**	fallacy
symbolic logic	conjunction	converse	Euler diagram
truth value	truth table	inverse	
statement	disjunction	contrapositive	**3.6**
compound statement	equivalent statements	biconditional	modus ponens
component statements	**3.3**	**3.5**	modus tollens
connectives	conditional statement	argument	disjunctive syllogism
negation	antecedent	premises	fallacy of the converse
quantifiers	consequent	conclusion	fallacy of the inverse
	tautology	valid	reasoning by transitivity

NEW SYMBOLS

∨   disjunction
∧   conjunction
~   negation

→   implication
↔   biconditional
≡   equivalence

TEST YOUR WORD POWER

See how well you have learned the vocabulary in this chapter.

1. A **statement** is
   A. a sentence that asks a question, the answer to which may be true or false.
   B. a directive giving specific instructions.
   C. a sentence declaring something that is either true or false, but not both at the same time.
   D. a paradoxical sentence with no truth value.

2. A **disjunction** (inclusive) is
   A. a compound statement that is true only if both of its component statements are true.
   B. a compound statement that is true if one or both of its component statements is/are true.
   C. a compound statement that is false if either of its component statements is false.
   D. a compound statement that is true if exactly one of its component statements is true.

3. A **conditional** statement is
   A. a statement that may be true or false, depending on some condition.
   B. an idea that can be stated only under certain conditions.
   C. a statement using the connective *if . . . then*.
   D. a statement the antecedent of which is implied by the consequent.

4. The **inverse** of a conditional statement is
   A. the result when the antecedent and consequent are negated.
   B. the result when the antecedent and consequent are interchanged.
   C. the result when the antecedent and consequent are interchanged and negated.
   D. logically equivalent to the conditional.

5. A **fallacy** is
   A. an argument with a false conclusion.
   B. an argument whose conclusion is not supported by the premises.
   C. a valid argument.
   D. an argument containing at least one false premise.

6. **Fallacy of the converse** is
   A. the reason the converse of a conditional is not equivalent to the conditional.
   B. an invalid argument form that assumes the converse of a premise.
   C. an invalid argument form that denies the converse of a premise.
   D. an invalid argument form that assumes the inverse of a premise.

ANSWERS
1. C 2. B 3. C 4. A 5. B 6. B

QUICK REVIEW

Concepts	*Examples*
3.1 Statements and Quantifiers	Consider the following statement.
A **statement** is a declarative sentence that is either true or false (not both simultaneously).	"If it rains this month, then we'll have a green spring."
A **compound statement** is made up of two or more **component statements** joined by **connectives** (*not, and, or, if . . . then*).	It is a compound statement made up of the following two component statements joined by the connective *if . . . then*. "It rains this month" and "We'll have a green spring,"

Quantifiers indicate how many members in a group being considered exhibit a particular property or characteristic. Universal quantifiers indicate *all* members, and existential quantifiers indicate *at least one* member.	The statement
	
	      "All five of those birds can fly"
	
	 contains a universal quantifier. Its negation is
	
	      "At least one of those five birds cannot fly,"

The **negation** of a statement has the opposite truth value of that statement in all cases.	which contains an existential quantifier.

Concepts	*Examples*

3.2 Truth Tables and Equivalent Statements

Given two component statements p and q, their **conjunction** is symbolized $p \wedge q$ and is true only when both component statements are true.

p	q	$p \wedge q$	$p \vee q$
T	T	T	T
T	F	F	T
F	T	F	T
F	F	F	F

Their **disjunction**, symbolized $p \vee q$, is false only when both component statements are false.

If p represents "$7 < 10$" and q represents "$4 < 3$," then the second row of the truth table above shows that $p \wedge q$ is false and $p \vee q$ is true.

The truth value of a compound statement is found by substituting T or F for each component statement, and then working from inside parentheses out, determining truth values for larger parts of the overall statement, until the entire statement has been evaluated.

When this process is carried out for all possible combinations of truth values for the component statements, a **truth table** results.

The truth table for the statement $\sim p \vee (q \wedge p)$ is shown below, with circled numbers indicating the order in which columns were determined.

p	q	$\sim p$	$\vee$	$(q$	$\wedge$	$p)$
T	T	F	T	T	T	T
T	F	F	F	F	F	T
F	T	T	T	T	F	F
F	F	T	T	F	F	F
		①	③	①	②	①

Equivalent statements have the same truth value for all combinations of truth values for the component statements. To determine whether two statements are equivalent, construct truth tables for both and see if the final truth values agree in all rows.

The statements $\sim(p \wedge q)$ and $\sim p \vee \sim q$ are equivalent, as shown in the table.

p	q	$\sim$	$(p$	$\wedge$	$q)$	$\sim p$	$\vee$	$\sim q$
T	T	F	T	T	T	F	F	F
T	F	T	T	F	F	F	T	T
F	T	T	F	F	T	T	T	F
F	F	T	F	F	F	T	T	T

De Morgan's laws can be used to quickly find negations of disjunctions and conjunctions.

$$\sim(p \vee q) \equiv \sim p \wedge \sim q$$
$$\sim(p \wedge q) \equiv \sim p \vee \sim q$$

To find the negation of the statement "I love chess and I had breakfast," let p represent "I love chess" and let q represent "I had breakfast." Then the above statement becomes $p \wedge q$. Its negation $\sim(p \wedge q) \equiv \sim p \vee \sim q$ translates to

"I don't love chess or I didn't have breakfast."

3.3 The Conditional and Circuits

A **conditional statement** uses the *if . . . then* connective and is symbolized $p \rightarrow q$, where p is the **antecedent** and q is the **consequent.**

If p represents "You are mighty" and q represents "I am flighty," then the conditional statement $p \rightarrow q$ is expressed as

"*If* you are mighty, *then* I am flighty."

The conditional is false if the antecedent is true and if the consequent is false. Otherwise, the conditional is true. This is because q is only *required* to be true on the *condition* that p is true, but q may "voluntarily" be true even if p is false. That is, p is sufficient for q, but not necessary.

The statement $(6 < 1) \rightarrow (3 = 7)$ is true because the antecedent is false.

The statement "If you are reading this book, then it is the year 1937" is false, because the antecedent is true and the consequent is false.

Concepts   **Examples**

The conditional $p \rightarrow q$ is equivalent to the disjunction $\sim p \vee q$, and its negation is $p \wedge \sim q$, as shown by a comparison of their truth tables.

p	q	$p \rightarrow q$	$\sim p \vee q$	$p \wedge \sim q$
T	T	T T T	F T T	T F F
T	F	T F F	F F F	T T T
F	T	F T T	T T T	F F F
F	F	F T F	T T F	F F T

The statement "All mice love cheese" can be stated, "*If* it's a mouse, *then* it loves cheese." This is equivalent to saying, "It's not a mouse or it loves cheese." The negation of this statement is "It's a mouse and it does not love cheese."

Electrical circuits are analogous to logical statements, with *parallel* circuits corresponding to disjunctions, and *series* circuits corresponding to conjunctions. Each switch (modeled by an arrow) represents a component statement. When a switch is closed, it allows current to pass through. The circuit represents a true statement when current flows from one end of the circuit to the other.

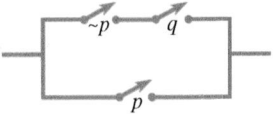

This corresponds to the logical statement $p \vee (\sim p \wedge q)$. Current will flow from one end to the other if p is true *or* if p is false and q is true. This statement is equivalent to

$$(p \vee \sim p) \wedge (p \vee q), \quad \text{which simplifies to} \quad p \vee q.$$

3.4 The Conditional and Related Statements

Given a conditional statement $p \rightarrow q$, its **converse, inverse,** and **contrapositive** are defined as follows.

Consider the statement "If it's a pie, it tastes good."

$$\text{Converse: } q \rightarrow p$$
$$\text{Inverse: } \sim p \rightarrow \sim q$$
$$\text{Contrapositive: } \sim q \rightarrow \sim p$$

Converse: "If it tastes good, it's a pie."

Inverse: "If it's not a pie, it doesn't taste good."

Contrapositive: "If it doesn't taste good, it's not a pie."

The conditional $p \rightarrow q$ can be translated in many ways:

If p, then q.	p is sufficient for q.
If p, q.	q is necessary for p.
p implies q.	All p are q.
p only if q.	q if p.

Statement	If . . . then form
You'll be sorry if I go.	If I go, then you'll be sorry.
Today is Tuesday only if yesterday was Monday.	If today is Tuesday, then yesterday was Monday.
All nurses wear comfortable shoes.	If you are a nurse, then you wear comfortable shoes.

For the **biconditional** statement "p if and only if q,"

$$p \leftrightarrow q \equiv (p \rightarrow q) \wedge (q \rightarrow p).$$

It is true only when p and q have the same truth value.

The statement "$5 < 9$ if and only if $3 > 7$" is false because the component statements have opposite truth values. The first is true, while the second is false.

Summary of Basic Truth Tables

1. $\sim p$, the **negation** of p, has truth value opposite that of p.
2. $p \wedge q$, the **conjunction,** is true only when both p and q are true.
3. $p \vee q$, the **disjunction,** is false only when both p and q are false.
4. $p \rightarrow q$, the **conditional,** is false only when p is true and q is false.
5. $p \leftrightarrow q$, the **biconditional,** is true only when both p and q have the same truth value.

p	$\sim p$
T	F
F	T

p	q	$p \wedge q$	$p \vee q$	$p \rightarrow q$	$p \leftrightarrow q$
T	T	T T T	T T T	T T T	T T T
T	F	T F F	T T F	T F F	T F F
F	T	F F T	F T T	F T T	F F T
F	F	F F F	F F F	F T F	F T F

Concepts	*Examples*

3.5 **Analyzing Arguments with Euler Diagrams**

A logical **argument** consists of premises and a conclusion. An argument is considered **valid** if the truth of the premises forces the conclusion to be true. Otherwise, it is **invalid.**

Euler diagrams can be used to determine whether an argument is valid or invalid.

To draw a Euler diagram, follow these steps:

1. Use the first premise to draw regions. (Arguments with multiple premises may involve multiple regions.)

2. Place an *x* in the diagram to represent the subject of the argument.

Consider this argument. Notice the universal quantifier "all."

All dogs are animals.
Dotty is a dog.
_____
Dotty is an animal.

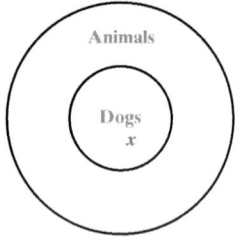

x represents Dotty.

We see from the Euler diagram that the truth of the premises forces the conclusion, that Dotty is an animal, to be true. Thus the argument is valid.

Consider the following argument. Notice the existential quantifier "some."

Some animals are warmblooded.
Albie is an animal.
_____
Albie is warmblooded.

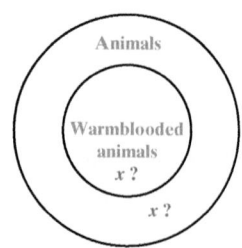

x represents Albie.

We see from the Euler diagram that the location of *x* is uncertain, so the truth of the premises does not force the conclusion to be true. Thus, the argument is invalid.

3.6 **Analyzing Arguments with Truth Tables**

An argument with premises $p_1, p_2, \ldots, p_n$ and conclusion c can be tested for validity by constructing a truth table for the statement

$$(p_1 \wedge p_2 \wedge \ldots \wedge p_n) \rightarrow c.$$

If all rows yield T for this statement (that is, if it is a tautology), then the argument is valid. Otherwise, the argument is invalid.

Valid Argument Forms

Modus Ponens	Modus Tollens	Disjunctive Syllogism	Reasoning by Transitivity
$p \rightarrow q$	$p \rightarrow q$	$p \vee q$	$p \rightarrow q$
p	$\sim q$	$\sim p$	$q \rightarrow r$
q	$\sim p$	q	$p \rightarrow r$

Consider this argument. "If I eat ice cream, I regret it later. I didn't regret it later. Therefore, I didn't eat ice cream."

Let p represent "I eat ice cream" and q represent "I regret it later." Then the argument can be expressed as the compound statement

$$[(p \rightarrow q) \wedge \sim q] \rightarrow \sim p.$$

Test its validity using a truth table, which shows that the statement is a tautology. The argument is valid (by **modus tollens**).

p	q	$[(p$	$\rightarrow$	$q)$	$\wedge$	$\sim q]$	$\rightarrow$	$\sim p$
T	T				F	F	T	F
T	F	T	F	F	F	T	T	F
F	T						T	T
F	F						T	T

Concepts	Examples

Invalid Argument Forms

Fallacy of the Converse	Fallacy of the Inverse
$p \rightarrow q$	$p \rightarrow q$
q	$\sim p$
p	$\sim q$

Consider this argument.

> If I drink coffee, I get jittery.
> I didn't drink coffee.
> _____
> I don't get jittery.

Let p represent "I drink coffee" and q represent "I get jittery."

Test the argument, using a truth table for the statement

$$[(p \rightarrow q) \wedge \sim p] \rightarrow \sim q.$$

p	q	$[(p$	$\rightarrow$	$q)$	$\wedge$	$\sim p]$	$\rightarrow$	$\sim q$
T	T		T		F	F	T	F
T	F						T	T
F	T		T		T	T	F	F
F	F						T	T

This argument is invalid by **fallacy of the inverse.**

CHAPTER 3   TEST

Write a negation for each statement.

1. $6 - 3 = 3$

2. All men are created equal.

3. Some members of the class went on the field trip.

4. If I fall in love, it will be forever.

5. She applied and did not get a student loan.

Let p represent "You will love me" and let q represent "I will love you." Write each statement in symbols.

6. If you won't love me, then I will love you.

7. I will love you if you will love me.

8. I won't love you if and only if you won't love me.

Using the same statements as for Exercises 6–8, write each of the following in words.

9. $\sim p \wedge q$ **10.** $\sim (p \vee \sim q)$

In each of the following, assume that p is true and that q and r are false. Find the truth value of each statement.

11. $\sim q \wedge \sim r$ **12.** $r \vee (p \wedge \sim q)$

13. $r \rightarrow (s \vee r)$ (The truth value of the statement s is unknown.)

14. $p \leftrightarrow (p \rightarrow q)$

15. Explain in your own words why, if p is a statement, the biconditional $p \leftrightarrow \sim p$ must be false.

16. State the necessary conditions for each of the following.

  (a) a conditional statement to be false

  (b) a conjunction to be true

  (c) a disjunction to be false

  (d) a biconditional to be true

Construct a truth table for each of the following.

17. $p \wedge (\sim p \vee q)$

18. $\sim (p \wedge q) \rightarrow (\sim p \vee \sim q)$

Decide whether each statement is true *or* false.

19. Some negative integers are whole numbers.

20. All irrational numbers are real numbers.

Write each conditional statement in if . . . then *form.*

21. All integers are rational numbers.

22. Being a rhombus is sufficient for a polygon to be a quadrilateral.

23. Being divisible by 2 is necessary for a number to be divisible by 4.

24. She digs dinosaur bones only if she is a paleontologist.

For each statement in Exercises 25 and 26, write (**a**) *the converse,* (**b**) *the inverse, and* (**c**) *the contrapositive.*

25. If a picture paints a thousand words, the graph will help me understand it.

26. $\sim p \rightarrow (q \wedge r)$ (Use one of De Morgan's laws as necessary.)

27. Use an Euler diagram to determine whether the argument is *valid* or *invalid*.

All members of that athletic club save money.

Don is a member of that athletic club.

Don saves money.

28. Match each argument in parts (a)–(d) in the next column with the law that justifies its validity, or the fallacy of which it is an example, in choices A–F.

A. Modus ponens

B. Modus tollens

C. Reasoning by transitivity

D. Disjunctive syllogism

E. Fallacy of the converse

F. Fallacy of the inverse

(a) If he eats liver, then he'll eat anything.

He eats liver.

He'll eat anything.

(b) If you use your seat belt, you will be safer.

You don't use your seat belt.

You won't be safer.

(c) If I hear *Mr. Bojangles,* I think of her.

If I think of her, I smile.

If I hear *Mr. Bojangles,* I smile.

(d) She sings or she dances.

She does not sing.

She dances.

Use a truth table to determine whether each argument is valid *or* invalid.

29. If I write a check, it will bounce. If the bank guarantees it, then it does not bounce. The bank guarantees it. Therefore, I don't write a check.

30. $\sim p \rightarrow \sim q$

$q \rightarrow p$

$p \vee q$

Numeration Systems

4

Network administrators oversee the operation and maintenance of computer networks for businesses and organizations. In order to ensure that computers can communicate with other hosts on the network and the Internet, each computer must be assigned an IP address. Often, for reasons of security or efficiency, an administrator may divide the network into subnetworks. Tasks like these require an understanding of some of the numeration systems covered in this chapter.

Symbols designed to represent objects or ideas are among the oldest inventions of humans. These Indian symbols in Arizona are several hundred years old.

Tally sticks like this one were used by the English in about 1400 A.D. to keep track of financial transactions. Each notch stands for one pound sterling.

Mathematical and Numeration Systems

Earlier we introduced and studied the concept of a *set*, a collection of elements. A set, in itself, may have no particular structure. But when we introduce *ways of combining the elements* (called *operations*) and *ways of comparing the elements* (called *relations*), we obtain a **mathematical system**.

MATHEMATICAL SYSTEM

A **mathematical system** is made up of three components:

1. a set of elements;
2. one or more operations for combining the elements;
3. one or more relations for comparing the elements.

A familiar example of a mathematical system is the set of whole numbers {0, 1, 2, 3, . . . }, along with the operation of addition and the relation of equality.

Historically, the earliest mathematical system to be developed involved the set of counting numbers or at least a limited subset of the first few counting numbers. The various ways of symbolizing and working with the counting numbers are called **numeration systems.** The symbols of a numeration system are called **numerals.**

Numeration systems have developed over many millennia of human history. Ancient documents provide insight into methods used by the early Sumerian peoples, the Egyptians, the Babylonians, the Greeks, the Romans, the Chinese, the Hindus, and the Mayan people.

A practical method of keeping accounts by matching may have developed as humans established permanent settlements and began to grow crops and raise livestock. People might have kept track of the number of sheep in a flock by matching pebbles with the sheep, for example. The pebbles could then be kept as a record of the number of sheep.

A more efficient method is to keep a **tally stick.** With a tally stick, one notch or **tally** is made on a stick for each sheep. Tally sticks and tally marks have been found that appear to be many thousands of years old. Tally marks are still used today: for example, nine items are tallied by writing ⵜⵜⵜⵜ ⵗⵗⵗⵗ.

4.1 HISTORICAL NUMERATION SYSTEMS

Basics of Numeration

The various ways of symbolizing and working with the counting numbers are called **numeration systems.** The symbols representing the numbers are called **numerals.**

Numeration systems have developed over many millennia of human history. Ancient documents provide insight into methods used by the early Sumerian peoples, the Egyptians, the Babylonians, the Greeks, the Romans, the Chinese, the Hindus, and the Mayan people, as well as others.

Keeping accounts by matching may have developed as humans established permanent settlements and began to grow crops and raise livestock. People might have kept track of the number of sheep in a flock by matching pebbles with the sheep, for example. The pebbles could then be kept as a record of the number of sheep.

A more efficient method is to keep a **tally stick.** With a tally stick, one notch or **tally** is made on a stick for each sheep. Tally marks provide a crude and inefficient numeration system. For example, the numeral for the number thirteen might be

$$|\,|\,|\,|\,|\,|\,|\,|\,|\,|\,|\,|\,|\,, \leftarrow 13\text{ tally marks}$$

which requires the recording of 13 symbols, and later interpretation requires careful counting of symbols.

Even today, tally marks are used, especially when keeping track of things that occur one or a few at a time, over space or time. To facilitate the counting of the tally, we often use a sort of "grouping" technique as we go.

 $\leftarrow$ Numeral (tally) for 13

A long evolution of numeration systems throughout recorded history would take us from tally marks to our own modern system, the **Hindu-Arabic system,** which utilizes the set of symbols

$$\{1, 2, 3, 4, 5, 6, 7, 8, 9, 0\}.$$

Ancient Egyptian Numeration

An essential feature common to all more advanced numeration systems is **grouping,** which allows for less repetition of symbols, making numerals easier to interpret. Most historical systems, including our own, have used groups of ten, reflecting the common practice of learning to count by using the fingers. The size of the groupings (again, usually ten) is called the **base** of the number system.

The ancient Egyptian system is an example of a **simple grouping system.** It utilized ten as its base, and its various symbols are shown in **Table 1** on the next page. The symbol for 1 ($|$) is repeated, in a tally scheme, for 2, 3, and so on up to 9. A new symbol is introduced for 10 ($\cap$), and that symbol is repeated for 20, 30, and so on, up to 90. This pattern enabled the Egyptians to express numbers up to 9,999,999 with just the seven symbols shown in the table.

The numbers denoted by the seven Egyptian symbols are all *powers* of the base ten.

$$10^0 = 1, \quad 10^1 = 10, \quad 10^2 = 100, \quad 10^3 = 1000, \quad 10^4 = 10,000,$$

$$10^5 = 100,000, \quad 10^6 = 1,000,000$$

These expressions, called *exponential expressions,* were first defined in **Section 1.1.** In the expression 10^4, for example, 10 is the *base* and 4 is the *exponent.* Recall that the exponent indicates the number of repeated factors of the base to be multiplied.

Tally sticks like this one were used by the English in about 1400 A.D. to keep track of financial transactions. Each notch stands for one pound sterling.

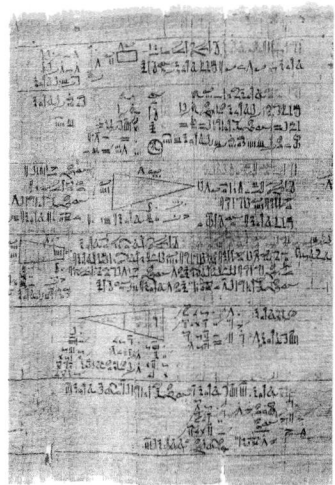

Much of our knowledge of **Egyptian mathematics** comes from the **Rhind papyrus,** from about 3800 years ago. A small portion of this papyrus, showing methods for finding the area of a triangle, is reproduced here.

Table 1 Early Egyptian Symbols

Number	Symbol	Description
1	I	Stroke
10	∩	Heel bone
100	୨	Scroll
1000	⌠	Lotus flower
10,000	∕	Pointing finger
100,000	⌢	Burbot fish
1,000,000	𝕏	Astonished person

EXAMPLE 1 Interpreting an Egyptian Numeral

Write the number below in Hindu-Arabic form.

⌢⌢⌠⌠⌠⌠୨୨୨∩∩∩∩∩III
∩∩∩∩IIII

Solution

Refer to **Table 1** for the values of the Egyptian symbols. Each ⌢ represents 100,000. Therefore, two ⌢s represent 2 · 100,000, or 200,000. Proceed as shown.

two	⌢	2 · 100,000 =	200,000
four	⌠	4 · 1000 =	4000
three	୨	3 · 100 =	300
nine	∩	9 · 10 =	90
seven	I	7 · 1 =	7

204,397 ← Answer

EXAMPLE 2 Creating an Egyptian Numeral

Write 376,248 in Egyptian form.

Solution

$$3 \quad 7 \quad 6, \quad 2 \quad 4 \quad 8$$
$$\downarrow \quad \downarrow \quad \downarrow \quad \downarrow \quad \downarrow \quad \downarrow$$

⌢⌢∕∕∕ ⌠⌠⌠ ୨୨∩∩IIII   Refer to Table 1 as needed.
⌢ ∕∕∕∕⌠⌠⌠ ∩∩IIII

The position or order of the symbols makes no difference in a simple grouping system. Each of the numerals ୨୨∩∩∩IIIII, IIIII∩∩୨୨, and II∩∩୨୨∩II would be interpreted as 234. In **Examples 1 and 2,** like symbols are grouped together, and groups of greater-valued symbols are positioned to the left.

A simple grouping system is well suited to addition and subtraction.

An Egyptian tomb painting shows scribes tallying the count of a grain harvest. **Egyptian mathematics** was oriented more to practicality than was Greek or Babylonian mathematics, although the Egyptians did have a formula for finding the volume of a certain portion of a pyramid.

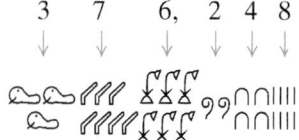

⌠⌠ ୨୨ ∩∩∩ II
+ ⌠ ୨୨୨ ∩ IIIIII

We use a + sign for convenience and draw a line under the numbers being added, although the Egyptians did not do this.

Sum: ⌠⌠⌠ ୨୨୨ ∩∩ IIII
୨୨ ∩∩ IIII

Two Is plus six Is is equal to eight Is, and so on.

Archaeological investigation has provided much of what we know about the numeration systems of ancient peoples.

Regrouping, or "carrying," is needed when more than nine of the same symbol result.

$$\ell \ \ \underset{\text{ΔΔ}}{\text{ΔΔ}} \ \ 99 \ \ \begin{matrix}\cap\cap\cap\cap\\\cap\cap\cap\end{matrix} \ \ ||$$

$$+ \ \ell\ell \ \ \ \ \ 999 \ \ \begin{matrix}\cap\cap\cap\\\cap\cap\end{matrix} \ \ \begin{matrix}||\\|||\end{matrix}$$

Regrouped answer:

Sum: $\ \ \ell\ell\ell\ell\underset{\text{ΔΔ}}{\text{ΔΔ}}\begin{matrix}999\cap\cap\cap\cap\cap\cap||||\\99\ \cap\cap\cap\cap\cap\cap\ |||\end{matrix}$ $\ell\ell\ell\ell\underset{\text{ΔΔ}}{\text{ΔΔ}}\begin{matrix}999\cap\cap\ |||\\999\ \ ||||\end{matrix}$

$\longrightarrow$ ten $\cap$ = one 9 $\longrightarrow$

Subtraction is done in much the same way, as shown in the next example.

EXAMPLE 3 Subtracting Egyptian Numerals

Work each subtraction problem.

(a) $\begin{matrix}999 \ \cap\cap \ ||||\\ 99 \ \ \cap\cap \ |||\end{matrix}$ **(b)** $99\cap\cap\cap\cap \ ||$
$\underline{- \ 9 \ \ \cap\cap \ \ ||||}$

$\underline{- \ 999 \ \cap \ \ ||||}$

Solution

(a)

$\begin{matrix}999 \ \cap\cap \ ||||\\ 99 \ \ \cap\cap \ |||\end{matrix}$

$\underline{- \ 999 \ \cap \ \ ||||}$ As with addition, work from right to left and subtract.

Difference: $99 \ \cap\cap\cap \ |||$

(b) To subtract four ls from two ls, "borrow" one heel bone, which is equivalent to ten ls. Finish the problem after writing ten additional ls on the right.

Regrouped: $99 \cap\cap\cap\begin{matrix}||||||\\||||||\end{matrix}$ one $\cap$ = ten ls

$\underline{- \ 9 \ \ \cap\cap \ \ ||||}$

Difference: $9 \ \ \cap \ \ ||||||||$

A procedure such as those described above is called an **algorithm:** a rule or method for working a problem. The Egyptians used an interesting algorithm for multiplication that requires only an ability to add and to double numbers, as shown in **Example 4.** For convenience, this example uses our symbols rather than theirs.

EXAMPLE 4 Using the Egyptian Multiplication Algorithm

A rectangular room in an archaeological excavation measures 19 cubits by 70 cubits. (A cubit, based on the length of the forearm, from the elbow to the tip of the middle finger, was approximately 18 inches.) Find the area of the room.

Solution

Multiply the width and length to find the area of a rectangle. Build two columns of numbers as shown at the top of the next page. Start the first column with 1, the second with 70. Each column is built downward by doubling the number above. Keep going until the first column contains numbers that can be added to equal 19. Then add the corresponding numbers from the second column.

	→	1	70 ←
	→	2	140 ←
$1 + 2 + 16 = 19$		4	280	$70 + 140 + 1120 = 1330$
		8	560
	→	16	1120 ←

Thus $19 \cdot 70 = 1330$, and the area of the given room is 1330 square cubits. ∎

Ancient Roman Numeration

Roman numerals are still used today, mainly for decorative purposes, on clock faces, for heading numbers in outlines, chapter numbers in books, copyright dates of movies, and so on. The base is again 10, with distinct symbols for 1, 10, 100, and 1000. The Romans, however, deviated from pure simple grouping in several ways. For the symbols and some examples, see **Tables 2 and 3**, respectively.

Table 2 Roman Symbols

Number	Symbol
1	I
5	V
10	X
50	L
100	C
500	D
1000	M

Table 3

Selected Roman Numerals

Number	Numeral
6	VI
12	XII
19	XIX
30	XXX
49	XLIX
85	LXXXV
25,040	$\overline{\text{XXV}}\text{XL}$
35,000	$\overline{\text{XXXV}}$
5,105,004	$\overline{\overline{\text{V}}}\overline{\text{CV}}\text{IV}$
7,000,000	$\overline{\overline{\text{VII}}}$

SPECIAL FEATURES OF THE ROMAN SYSTEM

1. In addition to symbols for 1, 10, 100, and 1000, "extra" symbols denote 5, 50, and 500. This allows less symbol repetition within a numeral. It is like a secondary base-five grouping functioning within the base-ten simple grouping.

2. A *subtractive feature* was introduced, whereby a smaller-valued symbol, placed immediately to the left of one of larger value, meant to subtract. Thus IV = 4, while VI = 6. Only certain combinations were used in this way:
   (a) I preceded only V or X.
   (b) X preceded only L or C.
   (c) C preceded only D or M.

3. A *multiplicative feature,* rather than more symbols, allowed for larger numbers:
   (a) A bar over a numeral meant to multiply by 1000.
   (b) A double bar meant to multiply by 1000^2 — that is, by 1,000,000.

Adding and subtracting with Roman numerals is very similar to the Egyptian method, except that the subtractive feature of the Roman system sometimes makes the processes more involved. With Roman numerals we cannot add IV and VII to get the sum VVIII by simply combining like symbols. (Even XIII would be incorrect.) The safest method is to rewrite IV as IIII, then add IIII and VII, getting VIIIIII. We convert this to VVI, and then to XI by regrouping. Subtraction, which is similar, is shown in the following example.

EXAMPLE 5 Subtracting Roman Numerals

Janus, a Roman official, has 26 servants. If, on a given Saturday, he has excused 14 of them to attend a Lucky Lyres concert at the Forum, how many are still at home to serve the banquet?

Solution

To find the answer, we subtract XIV from XXVI. Set up the problem in terms of simple grouping numerals (that is, XIV is rewritten as XIIII).

Problem:	XXVI	Problem restated without	XXVI
	− XIV	subtractive notation:	− XIIII
Regrouped:		XXIIIIII	
		− XIIII	
		XII ← Answer	

Since four **I**s cannot be subtracted from one **I,** we have "borrowed" in the top numeral, writing XXVI as XXIIIIII. The subtraction can then be carried out. Janus has 12 servants home for the banquet. ∎

Computation, in early forms, was often aided by mechanical devices just as it is today. The Roman merchants, in particular, did their figuring on a counting board, or **counter,** on which lines or grooves represented 1s, 10s, 100s, etc., and on which the spaces between the lines represented 5s, 50s, 500s, and so on. Discs or beads (called *calculi,* the word for "pebbles") were positioned on the board to denote numbers, and *calculations* were carried out by moving the discs around and simplifying.

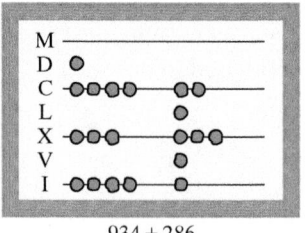

934

Figure 1

EXAMPLE 6 Adding on a Roman Counting Board

A Roman merchant wants to calculate the sum 934 + 286. Use counting boards to carry out the following steps.

(a) Represent the first number, 934.

(b) Represent the second number, 286, beside the first.

(c) Represent the sum, in simplified form.

Solution

(a) See **Figure 1.**   **(b)** See **Figure 2.**

934 + 286

Figure 2

(c) See **Figure 3.** The simplified answer is MCCXX, or 1220. In the process of simplification, five discs on the bottom line were replaced by a single disc in the V space. This made two Vs that were replaced by an additional disc on the X line. Five of those on the X line were then replaced by one in the L space, and this process continued until the disc on the M line finally appeared. ∎

Classical Chinese Numeration

The preceding examples show that simple grouping, although an improvement over tallying, still requires considerable repetition of symbols. To denote 90, for example, the ancient Egyptian system must utilize nine ∩s: ∩∩∩∩∩ ∩∩∩∩ . If an additional symbol (a "multiplier") was introduced to represent nine, say "9," then 90 could be denoted 9 ∩ . All possible numbers of repetitions of powers of the base could be handled by introducing a separate multiplier symbol for each counting number less than the base.

1220

Figure 3

Table 4

Chinese Symbols

Number	Symbol
1	∼
2	⸌
3	⸨
4	⊖
5	五
6	六
7	㇠
8	入
9	㇅
10	十
100	百
1000	千
0	零

Just such a system was developed long ago in China. We show the predominant Chinese version, which used the symbols shown in **Table 4**. We call this type of system a **multiplicative grouping system.** In general, a numeral in such a system would contain pairs of symbols, each pair containing a multiplier (with some counting-number value less than the base) and then a power of the base. The Chinese numerals are read from top to bottom rather than from left to right.

If the Chinese system were *pure* multiplicative grouping, the number 2018 would be denoted as shown in **Figure 4**. But three special features of the system show that they had started to move beyond multiplicative grouping toward something more efficient.

⸌	2
千	1000
	+
零	0
	·
百	100
	+
∼	1
	·
十	10
	+
入	8
∼	1

2018 in pure multiplicative grouping

Figure 4

SPECIAL FEATURES OF THE CHINESE SYSTEM

1. A single symbol, rather than a pair, denotes the number of 1s. The multiplier $(1, 2, 3, 4, \ldots,$ or 9) is written, but the power of the base (10^0) is omitted. See **Figure 5** (and also **Examples 7(a), (b), and (c)**).

2. In the 10s pair, if the multiplier is 1 it is omitted. See **Figure 6** (and **Example 8(a)**).

3. When a particular power of the base is totally missing, the omission is denoted with the zero symbol. See **Figure 7** (and **Examples 7(b) and 8(b)**). If two or more consecutive powers are missing, just one zero symbol denotes the total omission. (See **Example 7(c)**.) The omission of 1s and 10s and any other powers occurring at the extreme bottom of a numeral need not be denoted at all. (See **Example 7(d)**.)

Note that, for clarification in the following examples, we have emphasized the grouping into pairs by spacing and by colored braces. These features were *not* part of the actual numerals in practice.

⸌	2		⸌	2
千	1000		千	1000
	+			+
零	0		零	0
百	100		百	100
	+			+
∼	1		十	10
	·			+
十	10		入	8
	+			
入	8			

2018 with feature 1   2018 with features 1 and 2

Figure 5   **Figure 6**

⸌	2
千	1000
	+
零	0
	+
十	10
	+
入	8

2018 with features 1, 2, and 3

Figure 7

EXAMPLE 7   Interpreting Chinese Numerals

Interpret each Chinese numeral.

(a) ⸨ 十 二 百 六 十 ⊖

(b) ㇠ 百 零 ⸨

(c) 五 千 零 ㇅

(d) ⊖ 千 ⸌ 百

Solution

(a)
$$\left.\begin{array}{c} ⸨ \\ 千 \end{array}\right\} 3 \cdot 1000 = 3000$$

$$\left.\begin{array}{c} ∼ \\ 百 \end{array}\right\} 1 \cdot 100 = 100$$

$$\left.\begin{array}{c} 六 \\ 十 \end{array}\right\} 6 \cdot 10 = 60$$

$$⊖ \qquad 4(\cdot 1) = 4$$

Total: $\overline{3164}$

(b)
$$\left.\begin{array}{c} ㇠ \\ 百 \end{array}\right\} 7 \cdot 100 = 700$$

$$零 \qquad 0(\cdot 10) = 00$$

$$⸨ \qquad 3(\cdot 1) = 3$$

Total: $\overline{703}$

This illustration is of a **quipu**. In *Ethnomathematics: A Multicultural View of Mathematical Ideas*, Marcia Ascher writes:

A quipu is an assemblage of colored knotted cotton cords. Cotton cordage and cloth were of unparalleled importance in Inca culture. The colors of the cords, the way the cords are connected, the relative placement of the cords, the spaces between the cords, the types of knots on the individual cords, and the relative placement of the knots are all part of the logical-numerical recording.

(c)

$$5 \cdot 1000 = 5000$$
$$0(\cdot 100) = 000$$
$$0(\cdot 10) = 00$$
$$9(\cdot 1) = 9$$
Total: 5009

(d)

$$4 \cdot 1000 = 4000$$
$$2 \cdot 100 = 200$$
Total: 4200

EXAMPLE 8 Creating Chinese Numerals

Write a Chinese numeral for each number.

(a) 614   **(b)** 5090

Solution

(a) The number 614 is made up of six 100s, one 10, and four 1s, as depicted at the right.

$6 \cdot 100$:
$(1 \cdot)10$:
$4(\cdot 1)$:

(b) The number 5090 consists of five 1000s, no 100s, and nine 10s (no 1s).

$5 \cdot 1000$:
$0(\cdot 100)$:
$9 \cdot 10$:

4.1 EXERCISES

Convert each Egyptian numeral to Hindu-Arabic form.

1. ⟨ egyptian numeral ⟩

2. ⟨ egyptian numeral ⟩

3. ⟨ egyptian numeral ⟩

4. ⟨ egyptian numeral ⟩

Convert each Hindu-Arabic numeral to Egyptian form.

5. 23,135   **6.** 427

7. 8,657,000   **8.** 306,090

Chapter 1 of the book of Numbers in the Bible describes a census of the draft-eligible men of Israel after Moses led them out of Egypt into the Desert of Sinai, about 1450 B.C. Write an Egyptian numeral for the number of available men from each tribe listed.

9. 59,300 from the tribe of Simeon

10. 46,500 from the tribe of Reuben

11. 74,600 from the tribe of Judah

12. 45,650 from the tribe of Gad

13. 62,700 from the tribe of Dan

14. 32,200 from the tribe of Manasseh

Convert each Roman numeral to Hindu-Arabic form.

15. CLXXIII   **16.** MDXCVII

17. $\overline{\text{XIV}}$ **18.** $\overline{\overline{\text{V}}}\,\overline{\text{CXXI}}\text{CD}$

Convert each Hindu-Arabic numeral to Roman form.

19. 2861   **20.** 749

21. 25,619   **22.** 6,402,524

Convert each Chinese numeral to Hindu-Arabic form.

23. ⟨ chinese numeral ⟩   **24.** ⟨ chinese numeral ⟩   **25.** ⟨ chinese numeral ⟩   **26.** ⟨ chinese numeral ⟩

Convert each Hindu-Arabic numeral to Chinese form.

27. 965   **28.** 63

29. 7012   **30.** 2416

Though Chinese art forms began before written history, their highest development was achieved during four particular dynasties. Write traditional Chinese numerals for the beginning and ending dates of each dynasty listed.

31. Ming (1368 to 1644)

32. Sung (960 to 1279)

33. T'ang (618 to 907)

34. Han (202 B.C. to A.D. 220)

Work each addition or subtraction problem, using regrouping as necessary. Convert each answer to Hindu-Arabic form.

35.

$$9 \;\; \overset{\cap\cap}{\cap\cap} \;\; || $$
$$+ \;\; \overset{\cap\cap\cap}{\cap\cap\cap} |||| $$

36.

$$99 \cap\cap \overset{||||}{|||} $$
$$+ \; 9 \overset{\cap\cap\cap}{\cap\cap} \overset{||}{|||} $$

37.

$$\mathcal{I}\mathcal{I}\mathcal{I} \mathcal{\xi}\mathcal{\xi} \qquad \cap \;\; |||$$
$$+ \; \mathcal{I}\mathcal{I} \; \mathcal{\xi} \; \overset{99}{999} \overset{\cap\cap\cap\cap||||}{\cap\cap\cap\cap\cap||||}$$

38.

$$\mathcal{\xi}\mathcal{\xi}\mathcal{\xi} \overset{99}{999} \overset{\cap\cap}{\cap\cap} \; ||$$
$$+ \mathcal{\xi}\mathcal{\xi} \overset{999}{999} \cap\cap \overset{|||}{|||}$$

39.

$$99\cap\cap\cap||||$$
$$- \; 9 \; \cap\cap \;\; |$$

40.

$$\overset{\cap\cap\cap|||}{\cap\cap \;\; |||}$$
$$- \cap\cap\cap ||||$$

41.

$$\mathcal{I} \; \mathcal{\xi} \quad 99 ||||$$
$$- \; \mathcal{\xi}\mathcal{\xi}\mathcal{\xi} \overset{999}{999} \overset{|||}{|||}$$

42.

$$\mathcal{\xi} \overset{999}{99} \cap\cap\cap \overset{|||}{|||}$$
$$- \; 99 \overset{\cap\cap\cap}{\cap\cap\cap\cap} |||$$

43. MCDXII
  + DCIX

44. $\overline{\text{XXIII}}$CXIX
  + $\overline{\text{XIV}}$CDXII

45. MCCCXXII
  − CDXIX

46. $\overline{\text{XII}}$CCCVI
  − MMCXXXII

Use the Egyptian algorithm to find each product.

47. 32 · 47   **48.** 29 · 75

49. 64 · 127   **50.** 52 · 131

In Exercises 51 and 52, convert all numbers to Egyptian numerals. Multiply using the Egyptian algorithm, and add using the Egyptian symbols. Give the final answer using a Hindu-Arabic numeral.

51. *Value of a Biblical Treasure* The book of Ezra in the Bible describes the return of the exiles to Jerusalem. To rebuild the temple, the King of Persia gave them the following items: thirty golden basins, a thousand silver basins, four hundred ten silver bowls, and thirty golden bowls. Find the total value of this treasure if each gold basin is worth 3000 shekels, each silver basin is worth 500 shekels, each silver bowl is worth 50 shekels, and each golden bowl is worth 400 shekels.

52. *Total Bill for King Solomon* King Solomon told the King of Tyre (now Lebanon) that he needed the best cedar for his temple, and that he would "pay you for your men whatever sum you fix." Find the total bill to Solomon if the King of Tyre used the following numbers of men: 5500 tree cutters at 2 shekels per week each, for a total of 7 weeks; 4600 sawers of wood at 3 shekels per week each, for a total of 32 weeks; and 900 sailors at 1 shekel per week each, for a total of 16 weeks.

Explain why each step would be an improvement in the development of numeration systems.

53. progressing from carrying groups of pebbles to making tally marks on a stick

54. progressing from tallying to simple grouping

55. utilizing a subtractive technique within simple grouping, as the Romans did

56. progressing from simple grouping to multiplicative grouping

The ancient Egyptian system described in this section was simple grouping, used a base of ten, and contained seven distinct symbols. The largest number expressible in that system is 9,999,999. Identify the largest number expressible in each of the following simple grouping systems. (In Exercises 61–64, d can be any counting number.)

57. base ten, five distinct symbols

58. base ten, ten distinct symbols

59. base five, five distinct symbols

60. base five, ten distinct symbols

61. base ten, d distinct symbols

62. base five, d distinct symbols

63. base seven, d distinct symbols

64. base b, d distinct symbols (where b is any counting number 2 or greater)

65. The Chinese system presented in the text has symbols for 1 through 9 and also for 10, 100, and 1000. What is the greatest number expressible in that system?

66. The Chinese system did eventually adopt two additional symbols, for 10,000 and 100,000. What greatest number could then be expressed?

4.2   MORE HISTORICAL NUMERATION SYSTEMS

OBJECTIVES

1 Understand the basic features of positional numeration systems.

2 Understand Hindu-Arabic numeration.

3 Understand Babylonian numeration.

4 Understand Mayan numeration.

5 Understand Greek numeration.

Basics of Positional Numeration

A simple grouping system relies on repetition of symbols to denote the number of each power of the base. A multiplicative grouping system uses multipliers in place of repetition, which is more efficient. The ultimate in efficiency is attained with a **positional system** in which only multipliers are used. The various powers of the base require no separate symbols, because the power associated with each multiplier can be understood from the position that the multiplier occupies in the numeral.

If the Chinese system had evolved into a positional system, then the numeral for 7482 could have been written

$$
\begin{array}{c}
\text{七} \\
\text{田} \\
\text{入} \\
\text{二}
\end{array}
\quad \text{rather than} \quad
\begin{array}{c}
\text{七} \\
\text{十} \\
\text{田} \\
\text{百} \\
\text{入} \\
\text{十} \\
\text{二}
\end{array}.
$$

In the positional version on the left, the lowest symbol is understood to represent two 1s (10^0), the next one up denotes eight 10s (10^1), then four 100s (10^2), then seven 1000s (10^3). Each symbol in a numeral now has both a *face value,* associated with that particular symbol (the multiplier value), and a *place value* (a power of the base), associated with the place, or position, occupied by the symbol.

POSITIONAL NUMERATION

In a positional numeral, each symbol (called a **digit**) conveys two things:

1. **face value**—the inherent value of the symbol

2. **place value**—the power of the base that is associated with the position that the digit occupies in the numeral.

Hindu-Arabic Numeration

The place values in a Hindu-Arabic numeral, from right to left, are 1, 10, 100, 1000, and so on. The three 4s in the number 46,424 all have the same face value but different place values. The first 4, on the left, denotes four 10,000s, the next one denotes four 100s, and the one on the right denotes four 1s. Place values (in base ten) are named as shown here.

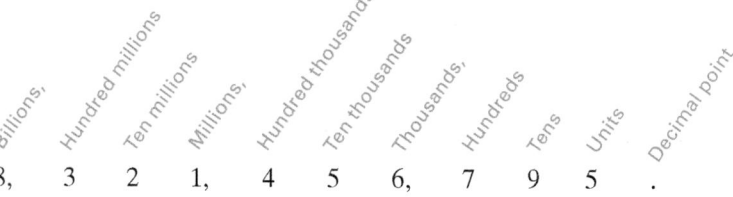

This numeral is read as eight billion, three hundred twenty-one million, four hundred fifty-six thousand, seven hundred ninety-five.

To work successfully, a positional system must have a symbol for zero to serve as a **placeholder** in case one or more powers of the base are not needed. Because of this requirement, some early numeration systems took a long time to evolve into a positional form, or never did. Although the traditional Chinese system does utilize a zero symbol, it never did incorporate all the features of a positional system, but remained essentially a multiplicative grouping system.

The one numeration system that did achieve the maximum efficiency of positional form is our own system, the **Hindu-Arabic** system. Its symbols have been traced to the Hindus of 200 B.C. They were picked up by the Arabs and eventually transmitted to Spain, where a late tenth-century version appeared like this:

$$I\ Z\ 7\ \chi\ y\ 6\ 7\ 8\ \vartheta.$$

The earliest stages of the system evolved under the influence of navigational, trade, engineering, and military requirements. And in early modern times, the advance of astronomy and other sciences led to a structure well suited to fast and accurate computation.

The purely positional form that the system finally assumed was introduced to the West by Leonardo Fibonacci of Pisa (1170–1250) early in the thirteenth century, but widespread acceptance of standardized symbols and form was not achieved until the invention of printing during the fifteenth century. Since that time, no better system of numeration has been devised, and the positional base-ten Hindu-Arabic system is commonly used around the world today.

The Hindu-Arabic system and notation will be investigated further in **Sections 4.3 and 4.4**. The systems we consider next, the Babylonian and the Mayan, achieved the main ideas of positional numeration without fully developing them.

Babylonian Numeration

The Babylonians used a base of 60 in their system. Because of this, in theory they would then need distinct symbols for numbers from 1 through 59 (just as we have symbols for 1 through 9). However, the Babylonian method of writing on clay with wedge-shaped sticks gave rise to only *two* symbols, as shown in **Table 5**. The number 47 would be written

⟨⟨⟨⟨▼▼▼▼▼▼▼   or   ⟨⟨▼▼▼▼ .   The number 47
⟨⟨ ▼▼▼

Since the Babylonian system had base sixty, the "digit" on the right in a multidigit number represented the number of 1s, with the second "digit" from the right giving the number of 60s. The third digit would give the number of 3600s $(60 \cdot 60 = 3600)$, and so on.

Table 5

Babylonian Symbols

Number	Symbol
1	▼
10	⟨

SPECIAL FEATURES OF THE BABYLONIAN SYSTEM

1. Rather than using distinct symbols for each number less than the base (sixty), the Babylonians expressed face values in base-ten simple grouping, using only the two symbols

⟨ for 10   and   ▼ for 1.

The system is, therefore, base-ten simple grouping *within* base-sixty positional.

2. The earliest Babylonian system lacked a placeholder symbol (zero), so missing powers of the base were difficult to express. Blank spaces within a numeral would be subject to misinterpretation.

EXAMPLE 1 Converting Babylonian Numerals to Hindu-Arabic

Convert each Babylonian numeral to Hindu-Arabic form.

(a) ⟨⟨⟨⟨⟨⟨▼▼▼ **(b)** ⟨⟨⟨▼▼▼▼ ⟨⟨ ▼▼▼▼ ⟨⟨▼▼ **(c)** ⟨⟨▼▼▼▼▼⟨▼⟨⟨⟨▼▼▼▼▼▼

Solution

(a) Here we have five 10s and three 1s.

$$5 \cdot 10 = 50$$
$$3 \cdot 1 = \underline{3}$$
$$53 \leftarrow \text{Answer}$$

(b) This "two-digit" Babylonian number represents twenty-two 1s and fifty-eight 60s.

$$22 \cdot 1 = 22$$
$$58 \cdot 60 = \underline{3480}$$
$$3502 \leftarrow \text{Answer}$$

(c) Here we have a three-digit number.

$$36 \cdot 1 = 36$$
$$11 \cdot 60 = 660$$
$$25 \cdot 3600 = \underline{90{,}000}$$
$$90{,}696 \leftarrow \text{Answer}$$

EXAMPLE 2 Converting Hindu-Arabic Numerals to Babylonian

Convert each Hindu-Arabic numeral to Babylonian form.

(a) 733 **(b)** 75,904 **(c)** 43,233

Solution

(a) To write 733 in Babylonian, we will need some 60s and some 1s. Divide 60 into 733. The quotient is 12, with a remainder of 13. Thus we need twelve 60s and thirteen 1s.

⟨▼▼⟨▼▼▼ ← 733

(b) For 75,904, we need some 3600s, as well as some 60s and some 1s. Divide 75,904 by 3600. The answer is 21, with a remainder of 304. Divide 304 by 60. The quotient is 5, with a remainder of 4.

⟨⟨▼ ▼▼▼▼▼ ▼▼▼▼ ← 75,904

(c) Divide 43,233 by 3600. The answer is 12, with a remainder of 33. We need no 60s here. In a system such as ours we would use a 0 to show that no 60s are needed. Since the early Babylonians had no such symbol, they merely left a space.

⟨▼▼ ⟨⟨⟨▼▼▼ ← 43,233

Example 2(c) illustrates the problem presented by the lack of a symbol for zero. In our system we know that 202 is not the same as 2002 or 20,002. The lack of a zero symbol was a major difficulty with the very early Babylonian system. A symbol for zero was introduced about 300 B.C.

Mayan Numeration

The Mayan Indians of Central America and Mexico also used what is basically a positional system. Like the Babylonians, the Mayans did not use base ten—they used base twenty, with a twist. In a true base-twenty system, the digits would represent 1s, 20s, $20 \cdot 20 = 400$s, $20 \cdot 400 = 8000$s, and so on. The Mayans used 1s, 20s, $18 \cdot 20 = 360$s, $20 \cdot 360 = 7200$s, and so on. It is possible that they multiplied 20 by 18 (instead of 20) because $18 \cdot 20$ is close to the number of days in a year, convenient for astronomy. The symbols of the Mayan system are shown in **Table 6**.

Table 6

Mayan Symbols

Number	Symbol
0	◉
1	.
5	—

The Mayans were one of the first civilizations to invent a placeholder. They had a zero symbol many hundreds of years before it reached western Europe. Mayan numerals are written from top to bottom, just as in the classical Chinese system.

> **SPECIAL FEATURES OF THE MAYAN SYSTEM**
>
> 1. Rather than using distinct symbols for each number less than the base (twenty), the Mayans expressed face values in base-five simple grouping, using only the two symbols — for 5 and · for 1. The system is, therefore, base-five simple grouping *within* base-twenty positional.
>
> 2. Place values in base-twenty would normally be
>
> $$1, \quad 20, \quad 20^2 = 400, \quad 20^3 = 8000, \quad 20^4 = 160,000, \quad \text{and so on.}$$
>
>   However, the Mayans multiplied by 18 rather than 20 in just one case, so the place values are
>
> $$1, \quad 20, \quad 20 \cdot 18 = 360, \quad 360 \cdot 20 = 7200, \quad 7200 \cdot 20 = 144,000, \quad \text{and so on.}$$

EXAMPLE 3   Converting Mayan Numerals to Hindu-Arabic

Convert each Mayan numeral to Hindu-Arabic form.

(a)   **(b)**

Solution

(a) The top group of symbols represents two 360s, the middle group represents nine 20s, and the bottom group represents eleven 1s.

$$
\begin{aligned}
2 \cdot 360 &= 720 \\
9 \cdot 20 &= 180 \\
11 \cdot 1 &= \underline{11} \\
&\ 911 \leftarrow \text{Answer}
\end{aligned}
$$

(b)

$$
\begin{aligned}
6 \cdot 360 &= 2160 \\
0 \cdot 20 &= 0 \\
13 \cdot 1 &= \underline{13} \\
&\ 2173 \leftarrow \text{Answer}
\end{aligned}
$$

EXAMPLE 4   Converting Hindu-Arabic Numerals to Mayan

Convert each Hindu-Arabic numeral to Mayan form.

(a) 277   **(b)** 1238

Solution

(a) The number 277 requires thirteen 20s (divide 277 by 20) and seventeen 1s.

← 277

(b) Divide 1238 by 360. The quotient is 3, with remainder 158. Divide 158 by 20. The quotient is 7, with remainder 18. Thus we need three 360s, seven 20s, and eighteen 1s.

← 1238

Table 7
Greek Symbols

Number	Symbol
1	α
2	β
3	γ
4	δ
5	ϵ
6	ς
7	ζ
8	η
9	θ
10	ι
20	κ
30	λ
40	μ
50	ν
60	ξ
70	o
80	π
90	$\varqoppa$
100	ρ
200	σ
300	τ
400	υ
500	ϕ
600	χ
700	ψ
800	ω
900	λ

Greek Numeration

The classical Greeks of Ionia assigned values to the 24 letters of their ordinary alphabet, together with three obsolete Phoenician letters (the digamma ς for 6, the koppa $\varqoppa$ for 90, and the sampi λ for 900). See **Table 7**. This scheme, usually called a **ciphered system,** makes all counting numbers less than 1000 easily represented. It avoids repetitions of symbols but requires vast multiplication tables for 27 distinct symbols. Computation would be very burdensome. The base is 10, but the system is quite different from simple grouping, multiplicative grouping, or positional.

■ EXAMPLE 5 Converting Greek Numerals to Hindu-Arabic

Convert each Greek numeral to Hindu-Arabic form.

(a) $\lambda\alpha$ **(b)** $\tau\xi\epsilon$ **(c)** $\lambda\varqoppa\theta$ **(d)** $\chi\delta$

Solution

(a) 31 **(b)** 365 **(c)** 999 **(d)** 604 ■

For numbers larger than 999, the Greeks introduced two additional techniques.

SPECIAL FEATURES OF THE GREEK SYSTEM

1. Multiples of 1000 (up to 9000) are indicated with a small stroke next to a units symbol. For example, 9000 would be denoted ${}_\prime\theta$.

2. Multiples of 10,000 are indicated by the letter M (from the word *myriad,* meaning ten thousand) with the multiple (a units symbol) shown above the M. The number 50,000 would be denoted $\overset{\epsilon}{M}$.

■ EXAMPLE 6 Converting Hindu-Arabic Numerals to Greek

Convert each Hindu-Arabic numeral to Greek form.

(a) 3000 **(b)** 40,000 **(c)** 7694 **(d)** 88,888

Solution

(a) ${}_\prime\gamma$ **(b)** $\overset{\delta}{M}$ **(c)** ${}_\prime\zeta\chi\varqoppa\delta$ **(d)** $\overset{\eta}{M}\eta\omega\pi\eta$ ■

4.2 EXERCISES

Identify each numeral in Exercises 1–20 as Babylonian, Mayan, or Greek. Give the equivalent in the Hindu-Arabic system.

1. ⠶

2. ⟨⟨▼▼

3. ⟨⟨⟨▼▼

4. ▦

5. $\sigma\lambda\delta$

6. $\omega o\beta$

7. ⠗

8. ▦

9. ⟨⟨▼⟨⟨▼▼

10. ⟨▼▼▼▼⟨⟨▼▼

11. ⟨⟨▼▼ ⟨⟨▼ ⟨⟨▼

12. ⟨⟨⟨▼▼▼ ⟨⟨ ▼▼ ⟨⟨⟨▼

13. 🔹

14. 🔹

15. 🔹

16. 🔹

17. ⟨⟨▼▼⟨⟨▼⟨▼▼▼▼

18. ⟨⟨ ▼▼ ⟨⟨ ▼▼▼▼▼ ⟨⟨ ⟨⟨▼▼ ⟨ ⟨⟨▼▼▼

19. $\overset{\alpha}{M}{}_\prime\epsilon\rho\mu\theta$

20. $\overset{\eta}{M}\omega\eta$

Write each number as a Babylonian numeral.

21. 21 **22.** 32 **23.** 293

24. 412 **25.** 1514 **26.** 3280

27. 5190 **28.** 43,205 **29.**

30. ⋅ ◯ ⋅ **31.** $\chi\kappa\epsilon$ **32.** $\overset{\beta}{M}$

Write each number as a Mayan numeral.

33. 12 **34.** 32 **35.** 151

36. 208 **37.** 4694 **38.** 4328

39. ⟨ᵞᵞᵞᵞ⟨⟨⟨ᵞᵞᵞᵞ⟨ᵞ ᵞᵞᵞ ⟨⟨⟨ᵞᵞᵞᵞ⟨ᵞ

40. ⟨ᵞᵞᵞᵞ ᵞᵞᵞ⟨ᵞᵞᵞᵞ ᵞᵞᵞ ᵞᵞᵞ⟨ᵞᵞᵞᵞ

41. $\tau\nu\theta$ **42.** $\tau\pi\alpha$

Write each number as a Greek numeral.

43. 39 **44.** 51 **45.** 92

46. 106 **47.** 412 **48.** 381

49. 2769 **50.** 9814 **51.** 54,726

52. 80,102 **53.** ⟨ᵞ⟨⟨ᵞ **54.** ᵞ⟨ᵞ⟨ᵞᵞ

55. ⋅⋅ ⋅⋅⋅ ⋅⋅⋅ **56.** ⋅⋅⋅ ◯ ⋅⋅ ⋅⋅⋅

4.3 ARITHMETIC IN THE HINDU-ARABIC SYSTEM

OBJECTIVES

1 Express Hindu-Arabic numerals in expanded form.

2 Explore historical calculation devices.

Expanded Form

The historical development of numeration culminated in positional systems. The most successful of these is the Hindu-Arabic system, which has base ten and, therefore, has place values that are powers of 10. Exponential expressions, or powers, are the basis of expanded form in a positional system.

EXAMPLE 1 Evaluating Powers

Find each power.

(a) 10^3 **(b)** 7^2 **(c)** 2^8

Solution

(a) $10^3 = 10 \cdot 10 \cdot 10 = 1000$
(10^3 is read "10 cubed," or "10 to the third power.")

(b) $7^2 = 7 \cdot 7 = 49$
(7^2 is read "7 squared," or "7 to the second power.")

(c) $2^8 = 2 \cdot 2 \cdot 2 \cdot 2 \cdot 2 \cdot 2 \cdot 2 \cdot 2 = 256$
(2^8 is read "2 to the eighth power.") ∎

To simplify work with exponents, it is agreed that

$$a^0 = 1, \quad \text{for any nonzero number } a.$$

Thus, $7^0 = 1, 52^0 = 1$, and so on. At the same time,

$$a^1 = a, \quad \text{for any number } a.$$

For example, $8^1 = 8$, and $25^1 = 25$. The exponent 1 is usually omitted.

By using exponents, numbers can be written in **expanded form** in which the value of the digit in each position is made clear. For example,

$$924 = 900 + 20 + 4$$
$$= (9 \cdot 100) + (2 \cdot 10) + (4 \cdot 1)$$
$$= (9 \cdot 10^2) + (2 \cdot 10^1) + (4 \cdot 10^0). \quad \text{100} = 10^2, 10 = 10^1, \text{ and } 1 = 10^0$$

This Iranian stamp should remind us that counting on fingers (and toes) is an age-old practice. In fact, our word **digit**, referring to the numerals 0–9, comes from a Latin word for "finger" (or "toe"). Aristotle first noted the relationships between fingers and base ten in Greek numeration. Anthropologists go along with the notion. Some cultures, however, have used two, three, or four as number bases, for example, counting on the joints of the fingers or the spaces between them.

There is much evidence that early humans (in various cultures) used their fingers to represent numbers. As calculations became more complicated, **finger reckoning,** as illustrated above, became popular. The Romans became adept at this sort of calculating, carrying it to 10,000 or perhaps higher.

EXAMPLE 2 Writing Numbers in Expanded Form

Write each number in expanded form.

(a) 1906 **(b)** 46,424

Solution

(a) $1906 = (1 \cdot 10^3) + (9 \cdot 10^2) + (0 \cdot 10^1) + (6 \cdot 10^0)$

Because $0 \cdot 10^1 = 0$, this term could be omitted, but the form is clearer with it included.

(b) $46{,}424 = (4 \cdot 10^4) + (6 \cdot 10^3) + (4 \cdot 10^2) + (2 \cdot 10^1) + (4 \cdot 10^0)$ ∎

EXAMPLE 3 Simplifying Expanded Numbers

Simplify each expansion.

(a) $(3 \cdot 10^5) + (2 \cdot 10^4) + (6 \cdot 10^3) + (8 \cdot 10^2) + (7 \cdot 10^1) + (9 \cdot 10^0)$

(b) $(2 \cdot 10^1) + (8 \cdot 10^0)$

Solution

(a) $(3 \cdot 10^5) + (2 \cdot 10^4) + (6 \cdot 10^3) + (8 \cdot 10^2) + (7 \cdot 10^1) + (9 \cdot 10^0) = 326{,}879$

(b) $(2 \cdot 10^1) + (8 \cdot 10^0) = 28$ ∎

Expanded notation and the **distributive property** can be used to see why standard algorithms for addition and subtraction really work.

DISTRIBUTIVE PROPERTY

For all real numbers a, b, and c,

$$(b \cdot a) + (c \cdot a) = (b + c) \cdot a.$$

Example: $\quad (3 \cdot 10^4) + (2 \cdot 10^4) = (3 + 2) \cdot 10^4$

$$= 5 \cdot 10^4$$

Finger Counting The first digits many people used for counting were their fingers. In Africa the Zulu used the method shown here to count to ten. They started on the left hand with palm up and fist closed. The Zulu finger positions for 1–5 are shown above on the left. The Zulu finger positions for 6–10 are shown on the right.

EXAMPLE 4 Adding Expanded Forms

Use expanded notation to add 23 and 64.

Solution

$$
\begin{aligned}
23 &= (2 \cdot 10^1) + (3 \cdot 10^0) \\
+\,64 &= (6 \cdot 10^1) + (4 \cdot 10^0) \\
\hline
& (8 \cdot 10^1) + (7 \cdot 10^0) = 87 \quad \text{Sum}
\end{aligned}
$$
∎

EXAMPLE 5 Subtracting Expanded Forms

Use expanded notation to subtract 254 from 695.

Solution

$$
\begin{aligned}
695 &= (6 \cdot 10^2) + (9 \cdot 10^1) + (5 \cdot 10^0) \\
-\,254 &= (2 \cdot 10^2) + (5 \cdot 10^1) + (4 \cdot 10^0) \\
\hline
& (4 \cdot 10^2) + (4 \cdot 10^1) + (1 \cdot 10^0) = 441 \quad \text{Difference}
\end{aligned}
$$
∎

The **Carmen de Algorismo** (opening verses shown here) by Alexander de Villa Dei, thirteenth century, popularized the new art of "algorismus":

> ... from these twice five figures 0 9 8 7 6 5 4 3 2 1 of the Indians we benefit ...

The *Carmen* related that Algor, an Indian king, invented the art. But actually, "algorism" (or "algorithm") comes in a roundabout way from the name Muhammad ibn Musa al-Khorârizmi, an Arabian mathematician of the ninth century, whose arithmetic book was translated into Latin. Furthermore, this Muhammad's book on equations, *Hisab al-jabr w'almuqâbalah*, yielded the term "algebra" in a similar way.

EXAMPLE 6 Carrying in Expanded Form

Use expanded notation to add 75 and 48.

Solution

$$75 = (7 \cdot 10^1) + (5 \cdot 10^0)$$
$$\underline{+\,48 = (4 \cdot 10^1) + (8 \cdot 10^0)}$$
$$(11 \cdot 10^1) + (13 \cdot 10^0)$$

The units position (10^0) has room for only one digit, so we modify $13 \cdot 10^0$.

$$13 \cdot 10^0 = (10 \cdot 10^0) + (3 \cdot 10^0) \qquad \text{Distributive property}$$
$$= (1 \cdot 10^1) + (3 \cdot 10^0) \qquad 10 \cdot 10^0 = 1 \cdot 10^1$$

The 1 from 13 moved to the left (carried) from the units position to the tens position.

$$\overbrace{\qquad\qquad}^{13 \cdot 10^0}$$
$$(11 \cdot 10^1) + (1 \cdot 10^1) + (3 \cdot 10^0)$$
$$= (12 \cdot 10^1) + (3 \cdot 10^0) \qquad \text{Distributive property}$$
$$= (10 \cdot 10^1) + (2 \cdot 10^1) + (3 \cdot 10^0) \qquad \text{Modify } 12 \cdot 10^1.$$
$$= (1 \cdot 10^2) + (2 \cdot 10^1) + (3 \cdot 10^0) \qquad 10 \cdot 10^1 = 1 \cdot 10^2$$
$$= 123 \qquad \text{Sum} \qquad ■$$

EXAMPLE 7 Borrowing in Expanded Form

Use expanded notation to subtract 186 from 364.

Solution

$$364 = (3 \cdot 10^2) + (6 \cdot 10^1) + (4 \cdot 10^0)$$
$$\underline{-186 = (1 \cdot 10^2) + (8 \cdot 10^1) + (6 \cdot 10^0)}$$

We cannot subtract 6 from 4. The units position borrows from the tens position.

$$(3 \cdot 10^2) + (6 \cdot 10^1) + (4 \cdot 10^0)$$
$$= (3 \cdot 10^2) + (5 \cdot 10^1) + (1 \cdot 10^1) + (4 \cdot 10^0) \qquad \text{Distributive property}$$
$$= (3 \cdot 10^2) + (5 \cdot 10^1) + (10 \cdot 10^0) + (4 \cdot 10^0) \qquad 1 \cdot 10^1 = 10 \cdot 10^0$$
$$= (3 \cdot 10^2) + (5 \cdot 10^1) + (14 \cdot 10^0) \qquad \text{Distributive property}$$

We cannot take 8 from 5 in the tens position, so we borrow from the hundreds.

$$(3 \cdot 10^2) + (5 \cdot 10^1) + (14 \cdot 10^0)$$
$$= (2 \cdot 10^2) + (1 \cdot 10^2) + (5 \cdot 10^1) + (14 \cdot 10^0) \qquad \text{Distributive property}$$
$$= (2 \cdot 10^2) + (10 \cdot 10^1) + (5 \cdot 10^1) + (14 \cdot 10^0) \qquad 1 \cdot 10^2 = 10 \cdot 10^1$$
$$= (2 \cdot 10^2) + (15 \cdot 10^1) + (14 \cdot 10^0) \qquad \text{Distributive property}$$

Now we can complete the subtraction.

$$(2 \cdot 10^2) + (15 \cdot 10^1) + (14 \cdot 10^0)$$
$$\underline{-(1 \cdot 10^2) + (8 \cdot 10^1) + (6 \cdot 10^0)}$$
$$(1 \cdot 10^2) + (7 \cdot 10^1) + (8 \cdot 10^0) = 178 \qquad \text{Difference} \qquad ■$$

Smartphones perform mathematical calculations and many other functions as well.

Examples 4–7 used expanded notation and the distributive property to clarify our usual addition and subtraction methods. In practice, our actual work for these four problems would appear as follows.

$$
\begin{array}{cccc}
23 & 695 & 75 & \overset{1}{}\overset{2\ 15}{\cancel{3}\cancel{6}^1 4} \\
+\ 64 & -\ 254 & +\ 48 & -\ 1\ 8\ 6 \\
\hline
87 & 441 & 123 & 1\ 7\ 8 \\
\end{array}
$$

The procedures seen in this section also work for positional systems with bases other than ten.

Historical Calculation Devices

Because our numeration system is based on powers of ten, it is often called the **decimal system,** from the Latin word *decem,* meaning ten.* Over the years, many methods have been devised for speeding calculations in the decimal system.

One of the oldest calculation methods is the **abacus,** a device made with a series of rods with sliding beads and a dividing bar. Reading from right to left, the rods have values of 1, 10, 100, 1000, and so on. The bead above the bar has five times the value of those below. Beads moved *toward* the bar are in the "active" position, and those toward the frame are ignored. In our illustrations of *abaci* (plural form of *abacus*), such as in **Figure 8**, the activated beads are shown in black.

$$10^4 \quad 10^3 \quad 10^2 \quad 10^1 \quad 10^0$$

Figure 8

EXAMPLE 8 Reading an Abacus

What number is shown on the abacus in **Figure 8**?

Solution

Find the number as follows.

Beads above the bar have five times the value.

$$(3 \cdot 10{,}000) + (1 \cdot 1000) + [(1 \cdot 500) + (2 \cdot 100)] + 0 \cdot 10 + [(1 \cdot 5) + (1 \cdot 1)]$$
$$= 30{,}000 + 1000 + (500 + 200) + 0 + (5 + 1)$$
$$= 31{,}706 \qquad \blacksquare$$

The **speed and accuracy of the abacus** are well known, according to www .ucmasusa.com. In a contest held between a Japanese **soroban** (the Japanese version of the abacus) expert and a highly skilled desk-calculator operator, the abacus won on addition, subtraction, division, and combinations of these operations. The electronic calculator won only on multiplication.

As paper became more readily available, people gradually switched from devices like the abacus (though these still are commonly used in some areas) to paper-and-pencil methods of calculation. One early scheme, used in India and Persia, was the **lattice method,** which arranged products of single digits into a diagonalized lattice.

December was the tenth month in an old form of the calendar. It is interesting to note that *decem* became *dix* in the French language; a ten-dollar bill, called a "dixie," was in use in New Orleans before the Civil War. "Dixie Land" was a nickname for that city before Dixie came to refer to all the Southern states, as in Daniel D. Emmett's song, written in 1859.

John Napier's most significant mathematical contribution, developed over a period of at least 20 years, was the concept of **logarithms,** which, among other things, allow multiplication and division to be accomplished with addition and subtraction. It was a great computational advantage given the state of mathematics at the time (1614).

Napier, a supporter of John Knox and James I, published a widely read anti-Catholic work that analyzed the biblical book of Revelation. He concluded that the Pope was the Antichrist and that the Creator would end the world between 1688 and 1700. Napier is one of many who, over the years, have miscalculated the end of the world.

EXAMPLE 9   Using the Lattice Method for Products

Find the product $38 \cdot 794$ by the lattice method.

Solution

Step 1   Write the problem, with one number at the side and one across the top.

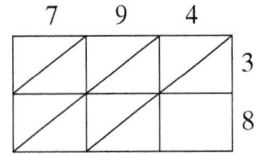

Step 2   Within the lattice, write the products of all pairs of digits from the top and side.

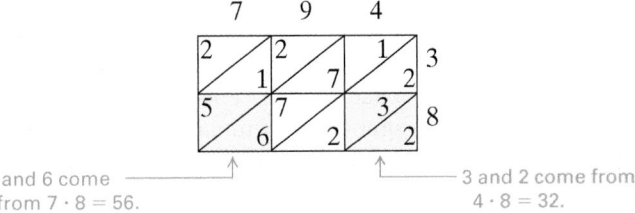

5 and 6 come from $7 \cdot 8 = 56.$ 3 and 2 come from $4 \cdot 8 = 32.$

Step 3   Starting at the right of the lattice, add diagonally, carrying as necessary.

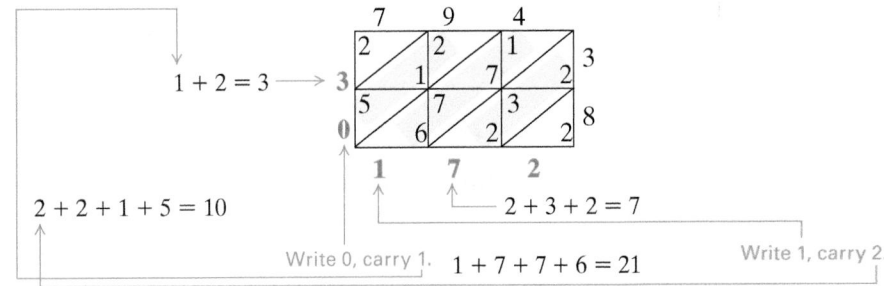

$1 + 2 = 3$

$2 + 2 + 1 + 5 = 10$

Write 0, carry 1. $1 + 7 + 7 + 6 = 21$

$2 + 3 + 2 = 7$

Write 1, carry 2.

Step 4   Read the answer around the left side and bottom: $38 \cdot 794 = \mathbf{30{,}172.}$ ■

The Scottish mathematician John Napier (1550–1617) introduced a significant calculating tool called **Napier's rods,** or **Napier's bones.** Napier's invention, based on the lattice method of multiplication, is widely acknowledged as a very early forerunner of modern computers. It consisted of a set of strips, several for each digit 0 through 9, on which multiples of each digit appeared in a sort of lattice column. See **Figure 9.**

An additional strip, the *index,* is laid beside any of the others to indicate the multiplier at each level. **Figure 10** shows that $7 \times 2806 = \mathbf{19{,}642.}$

Napier's rods were an early step toward modern computers.

Figure 9

Figure 10

Free on the Android Market is an **app for Napier's rods** (or "Napier's abacus"). The app prompts the user for a number and then generates a picture showing the rods for those digits next to the index.

For a way to include a little magic with your calculations, check out http://digicc.com/fido.

Figure 11

```
    4 1 9 8
   1 2 5 9 4  3
     8 3 9 6  2
   2 9 3 8 6  7
   3 0 3 5 1 5 4
```

EXAMPLE 10 Multiplying with Napier's Rods

Use Napier's rods to find the product of 723 and 4198.

Solution

We line up the rods for 4, 1, 9, and 8 next to the index, as in **Figure 11**. The product $3 \cdot 4198$ is found as described in **Example 9** and written at the bottom of the figure. Then $2 \cdot 4198$ is found similarly and written below, shifted one place to the left. (Why?) Finally, the product $7 \cdot 4198$ is written shifted two places to the left.

The final answer is found by addition.

$$723 \cdot 4198 = 3{,}035{,}154$$ ∎

Another paper-and-pencil method of multiplication is the **Russian peasant method,** which is similar to the Egyptian method of doubling explained in **Section 4.1.** To multiply 37 and 42 by the Russian peasant method, make two columns headed by 37 and 42. Form the first column by dividing 37 by 2 again and again, ignoring any remainders. Stop when 1 is obtained. Form the second column by doubling each number down the column.

Divide by 2, ignoring remainders.	37	42	Double each number.
	18	84	
	9	168	
	4	336	
	2	672	
	1	1344	

Now add up only the second-column numbers that correspond to odd numbers in the first column. Omit those corresponding to even numbers in the first column.

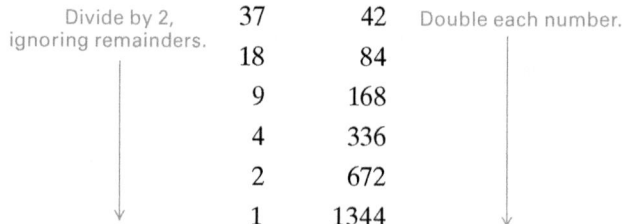

$$37 \cdot 42 = 42 + 168 + 1344 = 1554 \leftarrow \text{Answer}$$

Most people use standard algorithms for adding and subtracting, carrying or borrowing when appropriate, as illustrated following **Example 7.** An interesting alternative is the **nines complement method** for subtracting. To use this method, we first agree that the nines complement of a digit n is $9 - n$. For example, the nines complement of 0 is 9, of 1 is 8, of 2 is 7, and so on, down to the nines complement of 9, which is 0.

To carry out the nines complement method, complete the following steps:

Step 1 Align the digits as in the standard subtraction algorithm.

Step 2 Add leading zeros, if necessary, in the subtrahend so that both numbers have the same number of digits.

Step 3 Replace each digit in the subtrahend with its nines complement, and then add.

Step 4 Finally, delete the leading digit (1), and add 1 to the remaining part of the sum.

EXAMPLE 11 Using the Nines Complement Method

Use the nines complement method to subtract 2803 − 647.

Solution

Step 1	Step 2	Step 3	Step 4
2803	2803	2803	2155
− 647	− 0647	+ 9352	+ 1
		12,155	2156 Difference ∎

FOR FURTHER THOUGHT

Calculating on the Abacus

The abacus has been (and still is) used to perform rapid calculations. Add 526 and 362 as shown.

Start with 526 on the abacus.

To add 362, start by "activating" an additional 2 on the 1s rod.

Next, activate an additional 6 on the 10s rod.

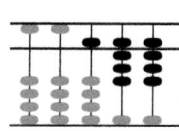

Finally, activate an additional 3 on the 100s rod.

The sum, read from the abacus, is 888.
For problems where carrying or borrowing is required, it takes a little more thought and skill.

For Group or Individual Investigation

1. Use an abacus to add: 13,728 + 61,455. Explain each step of your procedure.

2. Use an abacus to subtract: 6512 − 4816. Explain each step of your procedure.

4.3 EXERCISES

Write each number in expanded form.

1. 73   **2.** 265   **3.** 8335   **4.** 12,398

5. three thousand, six hundred twenty-four

6. fifty-two thousand, one hundred eighteen

7. fourteen million, two hundred six thousand, forty

8. two hundred twelve million, eleven thousand, nine hundred sixteen

Simplify each expansion.

9. $(7 \cdot 10^1) + (5 \cdot 10^0)$

10. $(8 \cdot 10^2) + (2 \cdot 10^1) + (0 \cdot 10^0)$

11. $(4 \cdot 10^3) + (3 \cdot 10^2) + (8 \cdot 10^1) + (0 \cdot 10^0)$

12. $(5 \cdot 10^5) + (0 \cdot 10^4) + (3 \cdot 10^3) + (5 \cdot 10^2) + (6 \cdot 10^1) + (8 \cdot 10^0)$

13. $(7 \cdot 10^7) + (4 \cdot 10^5) + (1 \cdot 10^3) + (9 \cdot 10^0)$

14. $(3 \cdot 10^8) + (8 \cdot 10^6) + (2 \cdot 10^4) + (3 \cdot 10^0)$

In each of the following, add in expanded notation.

15. 37 + 42   **16.** 732 + 417

In each of the following, subtract in expanded notation.

17. 85 − 32   **18.** 835 − 534

Perform each addition using expanded notation.

19. 64 + 45   **20.** 663 + 272

21. 434 + 299   **22.** 6755 + 4827

Perform each subtraction using expanded notation.

23. 54 − 48   **24.** 383 − 78

25. 855 − 649   **26.** 816 − 335

Perform each subtraction using the nines complement method.

27. 283 − 41   **28.** 536 − 425

29. 50,000 − 199   **30.** 40,002 − 4846

Identify the number represented on each abacus.

31.

32.

33.

34.

Sketch an abacus to show each number.

35. 38

36. 183

37. 2547

38. 70,163

Use the lattice method to find each product.

39. 65 · 29

40. 32 · 741

41. 525 · 73

42. 912 · 483

*Refer to **Example 10** where Napier's rods were used. Then complete Exercises 43 and 44.*

43. Find the product of 723 and 4198 by completing the lattice process shown here.

44. Explain how Napier's rods could have been used in **Example 10** to set up one complete lattice product rather than adding three individual (shifted) lattice products. Illustrate with a sketch.

*Use Napier's rods (**Figure 9**) to find each product.*

45. 8 · 62

46. 32 · 73

47. 26 · 8354

48. 526 · 4863

Use the Russian peasant method to find each product.

49. 5 · 92

50. 41 · 53

51. 62 · 529

52. 145 · 63

The Hindu-Arabic system is positional and uses ten as the base. Describe any advantages or disadvantages that may have resulted in each case.

53. Suppose the base had been larger, say twelve or twenty.

54. Suppose the base had been smaller, maybe five or eight.

4.4 CONVERSION BETWEEN NUMBER BASES

OBJECTIVES

1 Convert numerals from one base to another.

2 Use different bases in the context of computer mathematics.

General Base Conversions

In this section we consider bases other than ten, but we use the familiar Hindu-Arabic symbols. We indicate bases other than ten with a spelled-out subscript, as in the numeral 43_{five}. **Whenever a number appears without a subscript, it is assumed that the intended base is ten.** Be careful how you read (or verbalize) numerals here. The numeral 43_{five} is read "four three base five." (Do *not* read it as "forty-three," as that terminology implies base ten and names a totally different number.)

Table 8 gives powers of some numbers used as alternative bases.

Table 8 Selected Powers of Some Alternative Number Bases

	Fourth Power	Third Power	Second Power	First Power	Zero Power
Base two	16	8	4	2	1
Base five	625	125	25	5	1
Base seven	2401	343	49	7	1
Base eight	4096	512	64	8	1
Base sixteen	65,536	4096	256	16	1

For example, the base-two row of **Table 8** indicates that

$$2^4 = 16, \quad 2^3 = 8, \quad 2^2 = 4, \quad 2^1 = 2, \quad \text{and} \quad 2^0 = 1.$$

Table 9

Base-Five Numerals

Base Ten	Base Five	Base Ten	Base Five
0	0	16	31
1	1	17	32
2	2	18	33
3	3	19	34
4	4	20	40
5	10	21	41
6	11	22	42
7	12	23	43
8	13	24	44
9	14	25	100
10	20	26	101
11	21	27	102
12	22	28	103
13	23	29	104
14	24	30	110
15	30	31	111

We begin with the base-five system, which requires just five distinct symbols: 0, 1, 2, 3, and 4. **Table 9** compares base-five and decimal (base-ten) numerals for the whole numbers 0 through 31. Notice that because only the symbols 0, 1, 2, 3, and 4 are used in base five, we must use two digits in base five when we get to 5_{ten}.

5_{ten} is expressed as one 5 and no 1s—that is, as 10_{five}.

6_{ten} becomes 11_{five} (one 5 and one 1).

While base five uses fewer distinct symbols than base ten (an apparent advantage because there are fewer symbols to learn), it often requires more digits than base ten to denote the same number (a disadvantage because more symbols must be written).

You will find that in any base, if you denote the base "b," then the base itself will be 10_b, just as occurred in base five. For example,

$7_{\text{ten}} = 10_{\text{seven}}, \quad 16_{\text{ten}} = 10_{\text{sixteen}},$ and so on.

EXAMPLE 1 **Converting from Base Five to Base Ten**

Convert 1342_{five} to decimal form.

Solution

Referring to the powers of five in **Table 8**, we see that this number has one 125, three 25s, four 5s, and two 1s.

$$1342_{\text{five}} = (1 \cdot 125) + (3 \cdot 25) + (4 \cdot 5) + (2 \cdot 1)$$
$$= 125 + 75 + 20 + 2$$
$$= 222 \qquad \blacksquare$$

A shortcut for converting from base five to decimal form, which is *particularly useful when you use a calculator,* can be derived as follows.

$$1342_{\text{five}} = (1 \cdot 5^3) + (3 \cdot 5^2) + (4 \cdot 5) + 2$$
$$= ((1 \cdot 5^2) + (3 \cdot 5) + 4) \cdot 5 + 2 \quad \text{Factor 5 out of the three quantities in parentheses.}$$
$$= (((1 \cdot 5) + 3) \cdot 5 + 4) \cdot 5 + 2 \quad \text{Factor 5 out of the two "inner" quantities.}$$

The inner parentheses around $1 \cdot 5$ are not needed because the product is done automatically before the 3 is added. Therefore, we can write

$$1342_{\text{five}} = ((1 \cdot 5 + 3) \cdot 5 + 4) \cdot 5 + 2 = 222.$$

This series of products and sums is easily done as an uninterrupted sequence of operations on a calculator, with no intermediate results written down. The same method works for converting to base ten from any other base.

CALCULATOR SHORTCUT FOR BASE CONVERSION

To convert from another base to decimal form, follow these steps.

Step 1 Start with the first digit on the left and multiply by the base.

Step 2 Then add the next digit, multiply again by the base, and so on.

Step 3 Add the last digit on the right. ***Do not multiply it by the base.***

With some calculators, only the digits, the multiplications, and the additions need to be entered in order. With others, you may need to press the ⊟ key following each addition of a digit. If you handle grouped expressions on your calculator by actually entering parentheses, then enter the expression just as illustrated above and in the following example. (The number of left parentheses to start with will be two fewer than the number of digits in the original numeral.)

EXAMPLE 2 **Using the Calculator Shortcut**

Use the calculator shortcut to convert 244314_{five} to decimal form.

Solution

$$244314_{\text{five}} = ((((2 \cdot 5 + 4) \cdot 5 + 4) \cdot 5 + 3) \cdot 5 + 1) \cdot 5 + 4$$

$$= 9334 \qquad \boxed{\text{Note the four left parentheses for a 6-digit numeral.}}$$

EXAMPLE 3 **Converting from Base Ten to Base Five**

Convert 497 from decimal form to base five.

Solution

The base-five place values, starting from the right, are

$$1, \quad 5, \quad 25, \quad 125, \quad 625, \quad \text{and so on.}$$

Because 497 is between 125 and 625, it will require no 625s, but some 125s, as well as possibly some 25s, 5s, and 1s.

- Dividing 497 by 125 yields a quotient of 3, which is the proper number of 125s.

- The remainder, 122, is divided by 25 (the next place value) to find the proper number of 25s. The quotient is 4, with remainder 22, so we need four 25s.

- Dividing 22 by 5 yields 4, with remainder 2, so we need four 5s.

- Dividing 2 by 1 yields 2 (with remainder 0), so we need two 1s.

Thus 497 consists of three 125s, four 25s, four 5s, and two 1s, so $497 = 3442_{\text{five}}$.
More concisely, this process can be written as follows.

$$497 \div 125 = 3 \qquad \text{Remainder } 122$$
$$122 \div 25 = 4 \qquad \text{Remainder } 22$$
$$22 \div 5 = 4 \qquad \text{Remainder } 2$$
$$2 \div 1 = 2 \qquad \text{Remainder } 0$$
$$497 = 3442_{\text{five}}$$

Check:
$$3442_{\text{five}} = (3 \cdot 125) + (4 \cdot 25) + (4 \cdot 5) + (2 \cdot 1)$$
$$= 375 + 100 + 20 + 2$$
$$= 497 \checkmark$$

The symbol here is the ancient Chinese **"yin-yang,"** in which the black and the white enfold each other, each containing a part of the other. A kind of duality is conveyed between destructive (yin) and beneficial (yang) aspects.

Leibniz (1646–1716) studied Chinese ideograms in search of a universal symbolic language and promoted East–West cultural contact.

Niels Bohr (1885–1962), famous Danish Nobel laureate in physics (atomic theory), adopted the yin-yang symbol in his coat of arms to depict his principle of *complementarity,* which he believed was fundamental to reality at the deepest levels. Bohr also pushed for East–West cooperation.

In its 1992 edition, *The World Book Dictionary* first judged "yin-yang" to have been used enough to become a permanent part of our ever-changing language, assigning to it the definition "made up of opposites."

The calculator shortcut for converting from another base to decimal form involved repeated *multiplications* by the other base. (See **Example 2.**) A shortcut for converting from decimal form to another base makes use of repeated *divisions* by the other base. Just divide the original decimal numeral, and the resulting quotients in turn, by the desired base until the quotient 0 appears.

Woven fabric is a binary system of threads going lengthwise (warp threads—tan in the diagram above) and threads going crosswise (weft or woof). At any point in a fabric, either warp or weft is on top, and the variation creates the pattern.

Nineteenth-century looms for weaving operated using punched cards "programmed" for a pattern. The looms were set up with hooked needles, the hooks holding the warp. Where there were holes in cards, the needles moved, the warp lifted, and the weft passed under. Where no holes were, the warp did not lift, and the weft was on top. The system parallels the on–off system in calculators and computers. In fact, these looms were models in the development of modern calculating machinery.

Joseph Marie Jacquard (1752–1834) is credited with improving the mechanical loom so that mass production of fabric was feasible.

▌EXAMPLE 4▐ Using a Shortcut to Convert from Base Ten

Repeat **Example 3** using the shortcut just described.

Solution

Remainder

$$
\begin{array}{r|l}
5 & 497 \\
5 & 99 \leftarrow 2 \\
5 & 19 \leftarrow 4 \\
5 & 3 \leftarrow 4 \\
& 0 \leftarrow 3
\end{array}
$$

Read the answer from the remainder column, reading from the bottom up.

$$497 = 3442_{\text{five}}$$

To see why this shortcut works, notice the following:

- The first division shows that four hundred ninety-seven 1s are equivalent to ninety-nine 5s and two 1s. (The two 1s are set aside and account for the last digit of the answer.)
- The second division shows that ninety-nine 5s are equivalent to nineteen 25s and four 5s. (The four 5s account for the next digit of the answer.)
- The third division shows that nineteen 25s are equivalent to three 125s and four 25s. (The four 25s account for the next digit of the answer.)
- The fourth (and final) division shows that the three 125s are equivalent to no 625s and three 125s. The remainders, as they are obtained *from top to bottom*, give the number of 1s, then 5s, then 25s, then 125s.

The methods for converting between bases ten and five, including the shortcuts, can be adapted for conversions between base ten and any other base.

▌EXAMPLE 5▐ Converting from Base Seven to Base Ten

Convert 6343_{seven} to decimal form, by expanding in powers, and by using the calculator shortcut.

Solution

$$
\begin{aligned}
6343_{\text{seven}} &= (6 \cdot 7^3) + (3 \cdot 7^2) + (4 \cdot 7^1) + (3 \cdot 7^0) \\
&= (6 \cdot 343) + (3 \cdot 49) + (4 \cdot 7) + (3 \cdot 1) \\
&= 2236
\end{aligned}
$$

Calculator shortcut: $\quad 6343_{\text{seven}} = ((6 \cdot 7 + 3) \cdot 7 + 4) \cdot 7 + 3 = 2236.$

▌EXAMPLE 6▐ Converting from Base Ten to Base Seven

Convert 7508 to base seven.

Solution

Divide 7508 by 7, then divide the resulting quotient by 7, until a quotient of 0 results.

Remainder

$$
\begin{array}{r|l}
7 & 7508 \\
7 & 1072 \leftarrow 4 \\
7 & 153 \leftarrow 1 \\
7 & 21 \leftarrow 6 \\
7 & 3 \leftarrow 0 \\
& 0 \leftarrow 3
\end{array}
$$

From the remainders, reading bottom to top, $\quad 7508 = 30614_{\text{seven}}.$

To handle conversions between arbitrary bases (where neither is ten), go from the given base to base ten and then to the desired base.

EXAMPLE 7 Converting between Two Bases Other Than Ten

Convert 3164_{seven} to base five.

Solution

Convert to decimal form.

$$
\begin{aligned}
3164_{\text{seven}} &= (3 \cdot 7^3) + (1 \cdot 7^2) + (6 \cdot 7^1) + (4 \cdot 7^0) \\
&= (3 \cdot 343) + (1 \cdot 49) + (6 \cdot 7) + (4 \cdot 1) \\
&= 1029 + 49 + 42 + 4 \\
&= 1124
\end{aligned}
$$

Convert this decimal result to base five.

Remainder

$$
\begin{array}{r}
5\,\lfloor 1124 \\
5\,\lfloor 224 \quad \longleftarrow \quad 4 \\
5\,\lfloor 44 \quad \longleftarrow \quad 4 \\
5\,\lfloor 8 \quad \longleftarrow \quad 4 \\
5\,\lfloor 1 \quad \longleftarrow \quad 3 \\
0 \quad \longleftarrow \quad 1
\end{array}
$$

From the remainders, $3164_{\text{seven}} = 13444_{\text{five}}$. ∎

Table 10

Base-Two Numerals

Base Ten	Base Two	Base Ten	Base Two
0	0	16	10000
1	1	17	10001
2	10	18	10010
3	11	19	10011
4	100	20	10100
5	101	21	10101
6	110	22	10110
7	111	23	10111
8	1000	24	11000
9	1001	25	11001
10	1010	26	11010
11	1011	27	11011
12	1100	28	11100
13	1101	29	11101
14	1110	30	11110
15	1111	31	11111

Computer Mathematics

There are three alternative base systems that are most useful in computer applications—**binary** (base two), **octal** (base eight), and **hexadecimal** (base sixteen).

Computers and handheld calculators use the binary system for their internal calculations because that system consists of only two symbols, 0 and 1. All numbers can then be represented by electronic "switches," where "on" indicates 1 and "off" indicates 0. The octal and hexadecimal systems have been used extensively by programmers who work with internal computer codes and for communication between the CPU (central processing unit) and a printer or other output device.

The binary system is extreme in that it has only two available symbols (0 and 1). Thus, representing numbers in binary form requires more digits than in any other base. **Table 10** shows the whole numbers up to 31 expressed in binary form.

EXAMPLE 8 Converting from Binary to Decimal

Convert 110101_{two} to decimal form.

Solution

$$
\begin{aligned}
110101_{\text{two}} &= (1 \cdot 2^5) + (1 \cdot 2^4) + (0 \cdot 2^3) + (1 \cdot 2^2) + (0 \cdot 2^1) + (1 \cdot 2^0) \\
&= (1 \cdot 32) + (1 \cdot 16) + (0 \cdot 8) + (1 \cdot 4) + (0 \cdot 2) + (1 \cdot 1) \\
&= 32 + 16 + 0 + 4 + 0 + 1 \\
&= 53
\end{aligned}
$$

Calculator shortcut: $110101_{\text{two}} = ((((1 \cdot 2 + 1) \cdot 2 + 0) \cdot 2 + 1) \cdot 2 + 0) \cdot 2 + 1$

$$= 53$$

Note the four left parentheses for a 6-digit numeral. ∎

EXAMPLE 9 Converting from Decimal to Octal

Convert 9583 to octal form.

Solution

Divide repeatedly by 8, writing the remainders at the side.

Remainder

$$
\begin{array}{r r}
8\,\rlap{\underline{}}|\,9583 & \\
8\,\rlap{\underline{}}|\,1197 & \leftarrow\ 7 \\
8\,\rlap{\underline{}}|\,149 & \leftarrow\ 5 \\
8\,\rlap{\underline{}}|\,18 & \leftarrow\ 5 \\
8\,\rlap{\underline{}}|\,2 & \leftarrow\ 2 \\
0 & \leftarrow\ 2
\end{array}
$$

From the remainders, $9583 = 22557_{\text{eight}}$.

The hexadecimal system, having base sixteen (and 16 being greater than 10), presents a new problem. Because distinct symbols are needed for all whole numbers from 0 up to one less than the base, base sixteen requires more symbols than are normally used in our decimal system. Computer programmers commonly use the letters **A, B, C, D, E, and F** as hexadecimal digits for **the numbers ten through fifteen, respectively.**

EXAMPLE 10 Converting from Hexadecimal to Decimal

Convert $\text{FA5}_{\text{sixteen}}$ to decimal form.

Solution

$$
\begin{aligned}
\mathbf{FA5}_{\text{sixteen}} &= (\mathbf{15} \cdot 16^2) + (\mathbf{10} \cdot 16^1) + (5 \cdot 16^0) \\
&= 3840 + 160 + 5 \\
&= 4005
\end{aligned}
$$

F and A represent 15 and 10, respectively.

EXAMPLE 11 Converting from Decimal to Hexadecimal

Convert 748 from decimal form to hexadecimal form.

Solution

Use repeated division by 16.

Hexadecimal
Remainder   notation

$$
\begin{array}{r r r}
16\,\rlap{\underline{}}|\,748 & & \\
16\,\rlap{\underline{}}|\,46 & \leftarrow\ 12 & \leftarrow\ \text{C} \\
16\,\rlap{\underline{}}|\,2 & \leftarrow\ 14 & \leftarrow\ \text{E} \\
0 & \leftarrow\ 2 & \leftarrow\ 2
\end{array}
$$

From the remainders at the right, $748 = 2\text{EC}_{\text{sixteen}}$.

The decimal whole numbers 0 through 17 are shown in **Table 11** on the next page, along with their equivalents in the common computer-oriented bases (two, eight, and sixteen). Conversions among binary, octal, and hexadecimal can generally be accomplished by the shortcuts illustrated in the remaining examples.

The binary system is the natural one for internal computer workings because of its compatibility with the two-state electronic switches. It is very cumbersome, however, for human use, because so many digits occur even in the numerals for relatively small numbers. The octal and hexadecimal systems are the choices of computer programmers mainly because of their close relationship with the binary system. ***Both eight and sixteen are powers of two.***

Table 11 Some Decimal Equivalents in the Common Computer-Oriented Bases

Decimal (Base Ten)	Hexadecimal (Base Sixteen)	Octal (Base Eight)	Binary (Base Two)
0	0	0	0
1	1	1	1
2	2	2	10
3	3	3	11
4	4	4	100
5	5	5	101
6	6	6	110
7	7	7	111
8	8	10	1000
9	9	11	1001
10	A	12	1010
11	B	13	1011
12	C	14	1100
13	D	15	1101
14	E	16	1110
15	F	17	1111
16	10	20	10000
17	11	21	10001

Table 12

Octal	Binary
0	000
1	001
2	010
3	011
4	100
5	101
6	110
7	111

When conversions involve one base that is a power of the other, there is a quick conversion shortcut available. For example, because $8 = 2^3$, every octal digit (0 through 7) can be expressed as a 3-digit binary numeral. See **Table 12**.

EXAMPLE 12 Converting from Octal to Binary

Convert 473_{eight} to binary form.

Solution

Replace each octal digit with its 3-digit binary equivalent. (Leading zeros can be omitted only when they occur in the leftmost group.) Combine the equivalents into a single binary numeral.

$$
\begin{array}{ccc}
4 & 7 & 3_{\text{eight}} \\
\downarrow & \downarrow & \downarrow \\
100 & 111 & 011_{\text{two}}
\end{array}
$$

$$473_{\text{eight}} = 100111011_{\text{two}} \quad \blacksquare$$

EXAMPLE 13 Converting from Binary to Octal

Convert 10011110_{two} to octal form.

Solution

Start at the right and break the digits into groups of three. Then convert the groups to their octal equivalents.

$$
\begin{array}{ccc}
10 & 011 & 110_{\text{two}} \\
\downarrow & \downarrow & \downarrow \\
2 & 3 & 6_{\text{eight}}
\end{array}
$$

Finally, $10011110_{\text{two}} = 236_{\text{eight}}$. $\quad \blacksquare$

The following message was seen on the front of a T-shirt. "There are only 10 types of people in the world: Those who understand **binary** and those who don't." Do YOU understand this message?

Because $16 = 2^4$, every hexadecimal digit can be equated to a 4-digit binary numeral (see **Table 13** below), and conversions between binary and hexadecimal forms can be done in a manner similar to that used in **Examples 12 and 13.**

EXAMPLE 14   Converting from Hexadecimal to Binary

Convert $8B4F_{sixteen}$ to binary form.

Solution

Each hexadecimal digit yields a 4-digit binary equivalent.

$$
\begin{array}{cccc}
8 & B & 4 & F_{sixteen} \\
\downarrow & \downarrow & \downarrow & \downarrow \\
1000 & 1011 & 0100 & 1111_{two}
\end{array}
$$

Combining these groups of digits, $8B4F_{sixteen} = 1000101101001111_{two}.$ ∎

Several games and tricks are based on the binary system. For example, **Table 14** can be used to find the age of a person 31 years old or younger. The person need only tell you the columns that contain his or her age. For example, suppose Kathy says that her age appears in columns B, C, and D. To find her age, add the numbers from the top row of these columns:

$$\text{Kathy is } 2 + 4 + 8 = 14 \text{ years old.}$$

Do you see how this trick works? (See **Exercises 65–68.**)

Table 13

Hexadecimal	Binary
0	0000
1	0001
2	0010
3	0011
4	0100
5	0101
6	0110
7	0111
8	1000
9	1001
A	1010
B	1011
C	1100
D	1101
E	1110
F	1111

Table 14

A	B	C	D	E
1	2	4	8	16
3	3	5	9	17
5	6	6	10	18
7	7	7	11	19
9	10	12	12	20
11	11	13	13	21
13	14	14	14	22
15	15	15	15	23
17	18	20	24	24
19	19	21	25	25
21	22	22	26	26
23	23	23	27	27
25	26	28	28	28
27	27	29	29	29
29	30	30	30	30
31	31	31	31	31

In the world of computers, each binary digit is called a **bit,** and eight bits are called a **byte.** Computers receive, process, and transmit sequences of 1s and 0s (binary code). When one computer sends information to another computer, it *encapsulates* the information with binary strings that indicate, among other things, file type (such as text, photo, or video) and the *address* of the target computer. This Internet Protocol (IP) address is expressed in **dotted decimal notation,** which features four decimal numerals, each ranging from 0 to 255, separated by decimal points.

EXAMPLE 15 Converting an IP Address

Convert the IP address 192.168.1.108 to binary form.

Solution

Each decimal numeral ranging from 0 to 255 can be expressed in eight bits.

$$192 = 128 + 64 = 2^7 + 2^6 \qquad\qquad = 11000000_{two}$$
$$168 = 128 + 32 + 8 = 2^7 + 2^5 + 2^3 \qquad = 10101000_{two}$$
$$1 = 2^0 \qquad\qquad = 00000001_{two}$$
$$108 = 64 + 32 + 8 + 4 = 2^6 + 2^5 + 2^3 + 2^2 = 01101100_{two}$$

Thus the binary representation for this IP address is as follows.

$$11000000.10101000.00000001.01101100$$

WHEN Will I Ever USE This ?

Suppose you are a network administrator for a company that has a network address of 192.168.3.0. The *subnet mask* for your network is 255.255.255.0, which means that the first twenty-four bits of any IP address in your network are used to designate the network address. The last eight bits are available to be assigned to individual computers within your network.

$$\underbrace{11000000.10101000.00000011.}_{\text{Network field}}\underbrace{00000000}_{\text{Host field}}$$

You have been directed by the owner of the company to set up subnetworks within the network—one for management and one for employees. This will enable you to keep certain information (such as personnel files and financial data) on company servers from being viewed by employees who have no business seeing them. The management subnet will only need up to 20 computers (hosts) connected, but the employee subnet will need as many as 50.

1. What new subnet mask should be used to set up your subnetworks?

2. What IP addresses will be available for assignment to computers on each subnetwork?

Because the largest subnet will need to host as many as 50 computers, you will need at least six bits allocated to hosts. (Five bits would not be enough because that would allow for only $2^5 = 32$ host addresses.)

Since the current network address allows eight bits for hosts within the network, you decide to borrow the two highest-order bits to use for subnets, leaving the last six for hosts.

11000000.10101000.00000011. 00 000000

Network field   Subnet Host
field   field

A subnet mask has all 1s in the network and subnet fields, and all 0s in the host field. Thus the new subnet mask is

11111111.11111111.11111111. 11 000000,

Network field   Subnet Host
field   field

which is expressed in dotted decimal notation as follows.

255.255.255.192
11000000

Note that this configuration will allow for four subnets, each having 62 addresses available for hosts, as shown in **Table 15**. (The host addresses come in blocks of 64, but the first is reserved for the subnetwork address, and the last, with all 1s in the host field, is reserved as a "broadcast" address for use when messages need to be sent to all hosts on the subnetwork.)

Table 15

Subnet	Subnetwork Address	Range of Host Addresses	Broadcast Address
00	192.168.3.0	192.168.3.1–192.168.3.62	192.168.3.63
01	192.168.3.64	192.168.3.65–192.168.3.126	192.168.3.127
10	192.168.3.128	192.168.3.129–192.168.3.190	192.168.3.191
11	192.168.3.192	192.168.3.193–192.168.3.254	192.168.3.255

You decide to assign the 01 subnet (with address 192.168.3.64) to management, and the 10 subnet (with address 192.168.3.128) to employees. The topology of your company's newly configured network is shown in **Figure 12**.

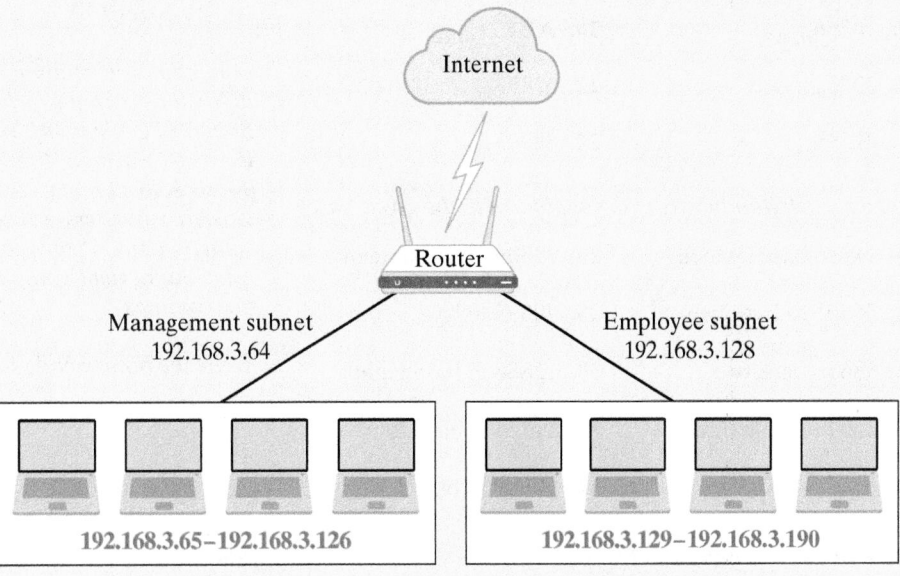

Figure 12

The router can now be programmed to filter traffic between the management and employee subnetworks.

List the first twenty counting numbers in each base.

1. seven (Only digits 0 through 6 are used in base seven.)

2. eight (Only digits 0 through 7 are used.)

3. nine (Only digits 0 through 8 are used.)

4. sixteen (The digits 0, 1, 2, . . . , 9, A, B, C, D, E, F are used in base sixteen.)

Write (in the same base) the counting numbers just before and just after the given number. (Do not convert to base ten.)

5. 14_{five}

6. 555_{six}

7. $B6F_{sixteen}$

8. 10111_{two}

Determine the number of distinct symbols needed in each of the following positional systems.

9. base three

10. base seven

11. base eleven

12. base sixteen

Determine, in each base, the least and greatest four-digit numbers and their decimal equivalents.

13. three

14. sixteen

Convert each number to decimal form by expanding in powers and by using the calculator shortcut.

15. $3BC_{sixteen}$

16. 34432_{five}

17. 2366_{seven}

18. 101101110_{two}

19. 70266_{eight}

20. $ABCD_{sixteen}$

21. 2023_{four}

22. 6185_{nine}

23. 41533_{six}

24. 88703_{nine}

Convert each number from decimal form to the given base.

25. 147 to base sixteen

26. 2730 to base sixteen

27. 36401 to base five

28. 70893 to base seven

29. 586 to base two

30. 12888 to base eight

31. 8407 to base three

32. 11028 to base four

33. 9346 to base six

34. 99999 to base nine

Make each conversion as indicated.

35. 43_{five} to base seven

36. 27_{eight} to base five

37. 6748_{nine} to base four

38. $C02_{sixteen}$ to base seven

Convert each number from octal form to binary form.

39. 367_{eight}

40. 2406_{eight}

Convert each number from binary form to octal form.

41. 100110111_{two}

42. 11010111101_{two}

Make each conversion as indicated.

43. $DC_{sixteen}$ to binary

44. $F111_{sixteen}$ to binary

45. 101101_{two} to hexadecimal

46. 101111011101000_{two} to hexadecimal

Identify the greatest number from each list.

47. 42_{seven}, 37_{eight}, $1D_{sixteen}$

48. 1101110_{two}, 414_{five}, $6F_{sixteen}$

There is a theory that twelve would be a better base than ten for general use. This is mainly because twelve has more divisors (1, 2, 3, 4, 6, 12) than ten (1, 2, 5, 10), which makes fractions easier in base twelve. The base-twelve system is called the **duodecimal system.** *In the decimal system we speak of a one, a ten, and a hundred (and so on); in the duodecimal system we say a* one, *a* dozen *(twelve), and a* gross *(twelve squared, or one hundred forty-four).*

49. Adam's clients ordered 9 gross, 10 dozen, and 11 copies of *The King* during 2014. How many copies was that in base ten?

50. Which amount is greater: 3 gross, 6 dozen or 2 gross, 19 dozen?

One common method of converting symbols into binary digits for computer processing is called **ASCII** *(American Standard Code of Information Interchange). The uppercase letters A through Z are assigned the numbers 65 through 90, so A has binary code 1000001 and Z has code 1011010. Lowercase letters a through z have codes 97 through 122 (that is, 1100001 through 1111010). ASCII codes, as well as other numerical computer output, normally appear without commas.*

Write the binary code for each letter.

51. C

52. X

53. k

54. q

Break each code into groups of seven digits and write as letters.

55. 1001000100010110011001010000

56. 1000011100100010101011000011001011

Translate each word into an ASCII string of binary digits. (Be sure to distinguish uppercase and lowercase letters.)

57. New

58. Orleans

*Exercises 59–62 refer to the **When Will I Ever Use This?** feature on **page 168**.*

59. Explain why an IP address like 192.168.3.30 is a 32-bit address, and convert it to binary.

60. What subnet mask would you use to split a network with address 192.168.7.0 into 8 subnetworks, each having room for 30 hosts?

If the IP address and subnet mask for a computer are known, then the network address can be found by performing a bitwise logical AND on the IP address and subnet mask. That is, convert the dotted decimal address and mask into binary form, AND them together bit-by-bit, and convert the result back to dotted decimal form.

61. Suppose your computer's IP address is 192.172.3.67 and the subnet mask is 255.255.255.192. What is the network address for the network your computer is on?

62. If a computer's IP address is 192.168.3.135, and the subnet mask is 255.255.255.224, what is the network address?

63. Explain why the octal and hexadecimal systems are convenient for people who code for computers.

64. There are thirty-seven counting numbers whose base eight numerals contain two digits but whose base three numerals contain four digits. Find the least and greatest of these numbers.

*Refer to **Table 14** for Exercises 65–68.*

65. After observing the binary forms of the numbers 1–31, identify a common property of all **Table 14** numbers in each of the following columns.

(a) Column A

(b) Column B

(c) Column C

(d) Column D

(e) Column E

66. Explain how the "trick" of **Table 14** works.

67. How many columns would be needed for **Table 14** to include all ages up to 63?

68. How many columns would be needed for **Table 14** to include all ages up to 127?

In our decimal system, we distinguish odd and even numbers by looking at their ones (or units) digits. If the ones digit is even (0, 2, 4, 6, or 8), the number is even. If the ones digit is odd (1, 3, 5, 7, or 9), the number is odd. For Exercises 69–76, determine whether this same criterion works for numbers expressed in the given bases.

69. two   **70.** three   **71.** four

72. five   **73.** six   **74.** seven

75. eight   **76.** nine

77. Consider all even bases. If the above criterion works for all, explain why. If not, find a criterion that does work for all even bases.

78. Consider all odd bases. If the above criterion works for all, explain why. If not, find a criterion that does work for all odd bases.

Determine whether the given base-five numeral represents one that is divisible by five.

79. 3204_{five} **80.** 200_{five}

81. 2310_{five} **82.** 342_{five}

83. If you want to multiply a decimal numeral by 10, what do you do?

84. If you want to multiply a binary numeral by 2, what do you do?

85. Explain why your answers to **Exercises 83 and 84** are correct.

86. If a binary numeral ends in 0, then it is even. How would you divide such a number in half?

*Recall that conversions between binary and octal are simplified because eight is a power of 2: $8 = 2^3$. (See **Examples 12 and 13**.) The same is true of conversions between binary and hexadecimal, because $16 = 2^4$. (See **Example 14**.) Direct conversion between octal and hexadecimal does not work the same way, because 16 is not a power of 8. Explain how to carry out each conversion without using base ten, and give an example.*

87. hexadecimal to octal   **88.** octal to hexadecimal

Devise a method (similar to the one for conversions between binary, octal, and hexadecimal) for converting between base three and base nine, and use it to carry out each conversion.

89. 6504_{nine} to base three

90. 81170_{nine} to base three

91. 212201221_{three} to base nine

92. 200121021_{three} to base nine

The colors seen on a computer screen consist of combinations of the primary colors red (R), green (G), and blue (B). The intensity of each of the three ranges from 0 to 255. This allows

$$255^3 = 16,581,375 \text{ distinct colors}$$

(at least theoretically), where a particular color's designation may require up to 9 digits.

For example, the (R, G, B) designation for black is (0, 0, 0), white is (255, 255, 255), and gray is (128, 128, 128).

But the colors are coded in **HTML** *(HyperText Markup Language) in hexadecimal, so each primary color intensity then requires no more than two digits.* $(255 = \text{FF}_{sixteen}.)$ *White is coded FFFFFF, and black is 000000.*

Give similar HTML codes for the following colors.

93. gray

94. yellow (255, 255, 0)

95. hot pink (255, 105, 180)

96. the color (171, 205, 239)

CHAPTER 4 SUMMARY

KEY TERMS

4.1

numeral
numeration system
tally stick
tally
Hindu-Arabic system
grouping
base
simple grouping system
algorithm

multiplicative grouping system

4.2

positional system
digit
face value
place value
placeholder
ciphered system

4.3

expanded form
distributive property
decimal system
abacus
lattice method
Napier's rods
Russian peasant method
nines complement method

4.4

binary
octal
hexadecimal
bit
byte
dotted decimal notation

TEST YOUR WORD POWER

See how well you have learned the vocabulary in this chapter.

1. A **simple grouping system** is
 A. a numeration system that uses group position to determine values of numerals.
 B. a numeration system in which the order of the symbols in a numeral makes no difference.
 C. a numeration system that uses grouping symbols (such as parentheses) to simplify numerals.
 D. a system that constructs numerals by grouping different numbers together.

2. A **positional system** is
 A. a numeration system that features a different symbol for each power of the base.
 B. a numeration system that works differently depending on the context in which it is used.
 C. a numeration system that is extremely efficient because only multipliers are used.
 D. a system that uses position to determine the face values of the digits.

3. Napier's rods (or bones) is the name of
 A. a calculating device based on the lattice method for multiplication.

 B. a device containing sliding beads and a dividing bar used to speed calculations.
 C. a device based on the Russian peasant method for multiplication.
 D. an adding machine designed around the nines complement method of subtraction.

4. The **hexadecimal** numeration system is
 A. a numeration system needing twelve distinct symbols.
 B. a base-sixteen numeration system using symbols 0–9, A, B, C, D, E, and F.
 C. a base-six numeration system with multipliers corresponding to the vertices of a hexagon.
 D. a system having fewer symbols than the octal numeration system.

ANSWERS
1. B **2.** C **3.** A **4.** B

QUICK REVIEW

Concepts	*Examples*

4.1 Historical Numeration Systems

Numeration systems use symbols called **numerals** to represent numbers. Ancient Egyptian numeration is an example of a **simple grouping system.** It is a base-ten system that uses a different symbol to represent each power of 10 (from 10^0 to 10^6).

Early Egyptian Symbols

Number	Symbol
1	I
10	∩
100	⌐
1000	↑
10,000	∂
100,000	⌐
1,000,000	⌐

Add 123,223 + 3104 using ancient Egyptian numeration.

The sum can be translated to our Hindu-Arabic system as

126,327.

The ancient Roman numeration system is also base ten, but it has symbols for 5, 50, and 500 as well. It uses a subtractive feature (involving writing a smaller-valued symbol immediately to the left of a larger-valued symbol) to reduce repetition of symbols, and a multiplicative feature in which a bar over a symbol means to multiply it by 1000, and a double-bar indicates multiplication by 1,000,000.

Express the difference 20,236 − 10,125 in Roman numerals.

$$\overline{XX}CCXXXVI$$
$$- \quad \overline{X}CXXV$$
$$\overline{X}CXI$$

Translating the result to Hindu-Arabic numeration gives

10,111.

Classical Chinese numeration is a base-ten **multiplicative grouping system,** with some modifications. Pairs of symbols are written, each including a multiplier (with value less than the base) and a symbol representing a power of the base. The modifications involve exceptions, which include omitting the symbol for 10^0 when displaying the number of 1s, omitting the multiplier for the 10s if the multiplier is 1, and using a single zero symbol in place of one, two, or more consecutive "missing" powers of 10.

Express the numeral 2014 in the classical Chinese numeration system.

4.2 More Historical Numeration Systems

Positional systems rely on the position of each symbol to determine its place value (that is, for which power of the base it is a multiplier).

In our Hindu-Arabic (base-ten) numeration system, the numeral

3024

means "three thousand twenty-four." The digit 3 is in the *thousands* place, the placeholder 0 is in the *hundreds* place, the digit 2 is in the *tens* place, and 4 is in the *ones* place.

Concepts	*Examples*

The Babylonian numeration system features only two symbols.

Babylonian Symbols

Number	Symbol
1	▼
10	◄

These symbols are grouped to express the numbers 1–59. The groups are then positioned to represent powers of 60, the base of the system.

The Mayan numeration system uses three symbols.

Mayan Symbols

Number	Symbol
0	👁
1	•
5	—

Most notable is the presence of a symbol for zero. The **place values** in the Mayan system are 1, 20, 360, 7200, 144,000, and so on. Each place value is 20 times the previous place value, with the exception that $360 = 18 \cdot 20$. Thus it is essentially a base-twenty positional system using simple groupings of symbols to form multipliers with face values ranging from 0 to 19.

Greek numeration is a **ciphered system,** using 27 distinct symbols. These symbols can be used to express numbers less than 1000 easily. Multiples of 1000 and 10,000 require the use of special features.

The Babylonian numeral

$$\underbrace{\text{◄◄▼▼▼}}_{23 \cdot 3600} \quad \underbrace{\text{◄▼▼}}_{12 \cdot 60} \quad \underbrace{\text{▼▼▼▼}}_{4 \cdot 1}$$

represents

$23 \cdot 3600 + 12 \cdot 60 + 4 \cdot 1 = 83{,}524.$ Hindu-Arabic form

To convert the numeral 83,524 to a Babylonian numeral, divide 83,524 by 3600 (since 3600 is the largest power of 60 that divides into 83,524) to get a quotient of 23 and a remainder of 724. Divide 724 by 60 to get a quotient of 12 with a remainder of 4. Then express these multiples of powers of 60 using the symbols as shown above.

The Mayan numeral

$$\begin{array}{l} \cdots \longleftarrow 8 \cdot 360 \\ 👁 \longleftarrow 0 \cdot 20 \\ \overset{\cdots}{=} \longleftarrow 12 \cdot 1 \end{array}$$

represents

$8 \cdot 360 + 0 \cdot 20 + 12 \cdot 1 = 2892.$ Hindu-Arabic form

To convert the Hindu-Arabic numeral 948 to a Mayan numeral, divide by 360, and divide the remainder by 20 to see that

$$948 = 2 \cdot 360 + 11 \cdot 20 + 8.$$

In Mayan, this is written as follows.

$$\begin{array}{c} \cdot\cdot \\ = \\ \cdots \end{array}$$

Since α represents 1, ϕ represents 500, μ represents 40, and β represents 2, the Greek numeral $\overset{\alpha}{\text{M}}\phi\mu\beta$ represents

$$10{,}000 + 500 + 40 + 2 = 10{,}542.$$

The Hindu-Arabic numeral 837 is expressed in Greek numeration as follows.

$$\omega\lambda\zeta$$

4.3 Arithmetic in the Hindu-Arabic System

Since the Hindu-Arabic system is a positional base-ten numeration system, the digits in a numeral are multipliers for powers of 10. Writing a numeral in **expanded form** makes this clear.

Adding numerals using expanded form makes clear the need to "carry" when the sum includes more than nine of any power of 10. Similarly, expanded notation makes clear the need to "borrow" when subtracting a larger number of a power of 10 from a smaller number.

Write the numeral 4132 in expanded form.

$$4 \cdot 10^3 + 1 \cdot 10^2 + 3 \cdot 10^1 + 2 \cdot 10^0$$

Add 67 and 56 using expanded notation.

$$\begin{array}{r} 67 = (6 \cdot 10^1) \ + (7 \cdot 10^0) \\ + \ 56 = (5 \cdot 10^1) \ + (6 \cdot 10^0) \\ \hline (11 \cdot 10^1) + (13 \cdot 10^0) \end{array}$$

We must rewrite both products in this sum.

Concepts	Examples

$11 \cdot 10^1 = (10 + 1) \cdot 10^1 = 1 \cdot 10^2 + 1 \cdot 10^1$, and

$13 \cdot 10^0 = (10 + 3) \cdot 10^0 = 1 \cdot 10^1 + 3 \cdot 10^0$,

so the sum $11 \cdot 10^1 + 13 \cdot 10$ becomes

$$(1 \cdot 10^2 + 1 \cdot 10^1) + (1 \cdot 10^1 + 3 \cdot 10^0)$$
$$= 1 \cdot 10^2 + (1 \cdot 10^1 + 1 \cdot 10^1) + 3 \cdot 10^0$$
$$= 1 \cdot 10^2 + 2 \cdot 10^1 + 3 \cdot 10^0 = 123.$$
$$= 123.$$

Over time, several calculation devices have been invented to make calculation with Hindu-Arabic numerals more efficient. Two examples are the **abacus** and **Napier's rods.** The abacus consists of a series of rods (corresponding to powers of 10), beads (for the multipliers), and a dividing bar which separates 5s (above the rod in the figure at right) from 1s (below the rod in the figure at right). Napier's rods contain strips of numbers that facilitate use of the **lattice method** for multiplication.

The abacus shows the number 11,707.

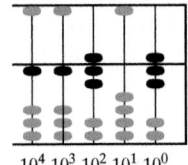

$10^4 \; 10^3 \; 10^2 \; 10^1 \; 10^0$

Napier's rods show the multiplication of $6 \cdot 2305$.

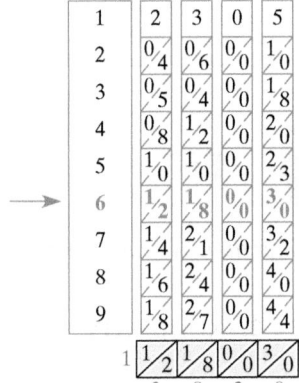

The product is 13,830.

The **nines complement method** of subtraction involves replacing the digits in the subtrahend with their nines complements, adding the resulting number to the minuend, and then deleting the leading 1 and adding 1 to the result.

Calculate the difference $625 - 48$ using the nines complement method.

```
 625      625     576
-048      951       1
         1576     577  ← Answer
```

4.4 Conversion between Number Bases

Any base-n positional numeration system needs n distinct symbols for expressing numbers.

The hexadecimal (base-sixteen) system uses 0–9 and A, B, C, D, E, and F as digits.

Converting from Another Base to Decimal Form

Step 1   Start with the first digit on the left and multiply by the base.

Step 2   Then add the next digit, multiply again by the base, and so on.

Step 3   Add the last digit on the right. ***Do not multiply it by the base.***

Convert the base-five numeral 1214_{five} to decimal form.

$$1214_{\text{five}} = ((1 \cdot 5 + 2) \cdot 5 + 1) \cdot 5 + 4 = 184$$

Concepts	Examples

We can convert from decimal to any other base n by dividing the decimal numeral by the other base repeatedly, recording the remainders, and dividing quotients until the quotient 0 appears. Then write the remainders in reverse order.

Computers operate on the basis of the binary system, using 1s and 0s corresponding to switch states of "on" and "off", respectively. Because 8 and 16 are powers of 2, the octal and hexadecimal systems are also helpful in condensing data into shorter strings of symbols.

Because $8 = 2^3$, each digit in the octal system can be expressed as three digits ("bits") in the binary system.

Decimal-to-binary conversion is helpful when working with IP addresses and networking configurations.

Octal	Binary
0	000
1	001
2	010
3	011
4	100
5	101
6	110
7	111

Convert 395 to base four as shown.

$$
\begin{array}{r}
4\,\lfloor 395 \\
4\,\lfloor 98 \leftarrow 3 \\
4\,\lfloor 24 \leftarrow 2 \\
4\,\lfloor 6 \leftarrow 0 \\
4\,\lfloor 1 \leftarrow 2 \\
4\,\lfloor 0 \leftarrow 1
\end{array}
$$

Remainder

Thus $395 = 12023_{\text{four}}$.

Convert the octal numeral 375_{eight} to binary. Replace each digit with its three-bit representation.

$$375_{\text{eight}} = \underbrace{011}_{3}\underbrace{111}_{7}\underbrace{101}_{5}{}_{\text{two}}$$

Express the IP address 192.168.5.35 in binary form.

11000000.10101000.00000101.00100011

CHAPTER 4   TEST

In each case, identify the numeration system, and give the Hindu-Arabic equivalent.

1. ⌐ 99 99 999 ∩∩∩ ‖ ‖

2. $\overline{\text{XCDLXXIV}}$

3. 𒐱 百 λ + 五

4. ⟨⟨▼▼ ⟨⟨▼ ⟨▼▼⟨⟨

5. ◎

6. $\overset{\epsilon}{\text{M}}, \gamma\phi\kappa\delta$

Perform each operation using the alternative algorithm specified.

7. $23 \cdot 45$ (Russian peasant or Egyptian method)

8. $246 \cdot 97$ (Lattice method)

9. $21,425 - 8198$ (Nines complement method)

Convert each number to base ten.

10. 243_{five}

11. 100101_{two}

12. $\text{BEEF}_{\text{sixteen}}$

Convert as indicated.

13. 49 to binary

14. 2930 to base five

15. 10101110_{two} to octal

16. 7215_{eight} to hexadecimal

17. 5041_{six} to decimal

18. $\text{BAD}_{\text{sixteen}}$ to binary

Briefly explain each of the following.

19. the advantage of multiplicative grouping over simple grouping

20. the advantage of positional over multiplicative grouping

21. the advantage, in a positional numeration system, of a smaller base over a larger base

22. the advantage, in a positional numeration system, of a larger base over a smaller base

23. Explain a quick method to convert a base-nine numeral to base three.

24. Illustrate your method from **Exercise 23** by converting 765_{nine} to base three.

4.5   CLOCK ARITHMETIC AND MODULAR SYSTEMS

Figure 9

Plus 2 hours

$5 + 2 = 7$

Figure 10

Plus 9 hours

$8 + 9 = 5$

Figure 11

Plus 3 hours

$11 + 3 = 2$

Figure 12

Finite Systems and Clock Arithmetic

At the beginning of this chapter we described a "mathematical system" as

1. a set of elements along with

2. one or more operations for combining those elements, and

3. one or more relations for comparing those elements.

The numeration systems studied in the first three sections mainly involved the set of whole numbers. The operations were mostly addition and multiplication, and the relation was that of equality. Because the set of whole numbers is infinite, that system is an **infinite mathematical system.** In this section, we consider some **finite mathematical systems,** based on finite sets.

The **12-hour clock system** is based on an ordinary clock face, except that 12 is replaced by 0 so that the finite set of the system is {0, 1, 2, 3, 4, 5, 6, 7, 8, 9, 10, 11}. (We will need just one hand on our clock.) See Figure 9.

As an operation for this clock system, addition is defined as follows: add by moving the hour hand in a *clockwise* direction. For example, to add 5 and 2 on a clock, first move the hand to 5, as in Figure 10. Then, to add 2, move the hand 2 more hours in a clockwise direction. The hand stops at 7, so

$$5 + 2 = 7.$$

This result agrees with traditional addition. However, the sum of two numbers from the 12-hour clock system is not always what might be expected, as the following example shows.

EXAMPLE 1   Finding Clock Sums by Hand Rotations

Find each sum in 12-hour clock arithmetic.

(a) $8 + 9$ **(b)** $11 + 3$

Solution

(a) Move the hand to 8, as in Figure 11. Then advance the hand clockwise through 9 more hours. It stops at 5, so $8 + 9 = 5$.

(b) To find $11 + 3$, proceed as shown in Figure 12. Check that $11 + 3 = 2$.

Because there are infinitely many whole numbers, it is not possible to write a complete table of addition facts for that set. Such a table, to show the sum of every possible pair of whole numbers, would have infinite numbers of rows and columns, making it impossible to construct.

On the other hand, the 12-hour clock system uses only the whole numbers 0, 1, 2, 3, 4, 5, 6, 7, 8, 9, 10, and 11. In effect, the clock face serves to "reduce" the infinite set of whole numbers to the finite set {0, 1, 2, 3, 4, 5, 6, 7, 8, 9, 10, 11}. No matter how large a whole number results from additions (clockwise motions around the clock), the result is always equivalent, in this system, to one of the numbers 0 through 11. A table of all possible sums for this system requires only 12 rows and 12 columns. The 12-hour clock **addition table** is shown in Table 16 on the following page. The significance of the colored diagonal line will be discussed later.

ASCENSION

Plagued by serious maritime mishaps linked to navigational difficulties, several European governments offered prizes for an effective method of determining longitude. The largest prize was 20,000 pounds (equivalent to several million dollars in today's currency) offered by the British Parliament in the Longitude Act of 1714. While famed scientists, academics, and politicians pursued an answer in the stars, **John Harrison,** a clock maker, set about to build a clock that could maintain accuracy at sea. This turned out to be the key, and Harrison's **Chronometer** eventually earned him the prize.

For a fascinating account of this drama and of Harrison's struggle to collect his prize money from the government, see the book *The Illustrated Longitude* by Dava Sobel and William J. H. Andrewes.

▚▚▚ EXAMPLE 2 Finding Clock Sums by Addition Table

Use the 12-hour clock addition table to find each sum.

(a) $7 + 11$ **(b)** $11 + 1$

Solution

(a) Rather than following rotations around the clock face, we simply refer to the table. Find 7 on the left of the addition table and 11 across the top. The intersection of the row headed 7 and the column headed 11 gives the number 6. Thus, $7 + 11 = 6$.

(b) Also from the table, $11 + 1 = 0$. ■

Mathematical systems are characterized by the properties they possess, specifically, the properties of their operations and relations. Five properties that many of the most commonly applied systems have are the *closure, commutative, associative, identity,* and *inverse properties.* We can check whether the 12-hour clock system has these properties.

Table 16 12-Hour Clock Addition

+	0	1	2	3	4	5	6	7	8	9	10	11
0	0	1	2	3	4	5	6	7	8	9	10	11
1	1	2	3	4	5	6	7	8	9	10	11	0
2	2	3	4	5	6	7	8	9	10	11	0	1
3	3	4	5	6	7	8	9	10	11	0	1	2
4	4	5	6	7	8	9	10	11	0	1	2	3
5	5	6	7	8	9	10	11	0	1	2	3	4
6	6	7	8	9	10	11	0	1	2	3	4	5
7	7	8	9	10	11	0	1	2	3	4	5	6
8	8	9	10	11	0	1	2	3	4	5	6	7
9	9	10	11	0	1	2	3	4	5	6	7	8
10	10	11	0	1	2	3	4	5	6	7	8	9
11	11	0	1	2	3	4	5	6	7	8	9	10

Table 16 shows that the sum of two numbers on a clock face is always a number on the clock face. That is, if a and b are any clock numbers in the set of the system, then $a + b$ is also in the set of the system. Therefore, the system has the **closure property.** (The set of the system is *closed* under clock addition.)

Notice also that in this system $9 + 6$ and $6 + 9$ both yield 3. And the answers, the two 3s, are located in positions that are mirror images of one another with respect to the diagonal line shown. Observe another case—the results for $5 + 8$ and $8 + 5$ are also located symmetrically with respect to the diagonal line, and both results are 1. The entries throughout the entire table occur in equal, diagonally symmetric, pairs. This means that for any clock numbers a and b, $a + b = b + a$. The system, therefore, has the **commutative property**.

The next question is: When any three elements are combined in a given order, say $a + b + c$, does it matter whether the first and second or the second and third are associated initially? In other words, is it true that, for any elements a, b, and c in the 12-hour clock system, $(a + b) + c = a + (b + c)$?

EXAMPLE 3 Checking the Associative Property for Clock Addition

Is 12-hour clock addition associative?

Solution

It would take lots of work to prove that the required relationship *always* holds. But a few examples should either disprove it (by revealing a *counterexample*—a case where it fails to hold), or should make it at least plausible. Using the clock numbers 4, 5, and 9, we see that

$$(4 + 5) + 9 = 9 + 9 \qquad 4 + (5 + 9) = 4 + 2$$
$$= 6 \qquad\qquad\qquad = 6.$$

Thus, $(4 + 5) + 9 = 4 + (5 + 9)$. Try another example:

$$(7 + 6) + 3 = 1 + 3 \qquad 7 + (6 + 3) = 7 + 9$$
$$= 4 \qquad\qquad\qquad = 4.$$

So $(7 + 6) + 3 = 7 + (6 + 3)$. Any other examples checked also will work. The 12-hour clock system therefore has the **associative property.** ∎

Our next question is whether the clock face contains some element (number) that, when combined with any element (in either order), produces that same element. Such an element (call it e) would satisfy $a + e = a$ and $e + a = a$ for any element a of the system. Notice in Table 16 that $4 + 0 = 0 + 4 = 4$, $6 + 0 = 0 + 6 = 6$, and so on. The number 0 is the required *identity element*. The system has the **identity property.**

Generally, if a finite system has an identity element e, it can be located easily in the operation table. Check the body of Table 16 for a column that is identical to the column at the left side of the table. Because the column under 0 meets this requirement, $a + 0 = a$ holds for all elements a in the system. Thus, 0 is *possibly* the identity. Now locate 0 at the left of the table. Because the corresponding row is identical to the row at the top of the table, $0 + a = a$ also holds for all elements a, which is the other requirement of an identity element. Hence, 0 is *indeed* the identity.

Our 12-hour clock system can be expanded to include operations besides addition. For example, subtraction can be performed on a 12-hour clock. Subtraction may be interpreted on the clock face by a movement in the *counterclockwise* direction. For example, to perform the subtraction $2 - 5$, begin at 2 and move 5 hours counterclockwise, ending at 9, as shown in Figure 13. Therefore, in this system,

$$2 - 5 = 9.$$

In our usual system, subtraction may be checked by addition, and this is also the case in clock arithmetic. To check that $2 - 5 = 9$, simply add $9 + 5$, either by using rotation on the clock face or consulting the addition table. In either case, the result is 2, verifying the accuracy of this subtraction.

The *additive inverse*, $-a$, of an element a in clock arithmetic is the element that satisfies this statement: $a + (-a) = 0$ and $(-a) + a = 0$. Such an element, if it exists, can be determined either on the clock face or by using the addition table, as shown in the next example.

Minus 5 hours

$2 - 5 = 9$

Figure 13

A **chess clock** or double clock is used to time chess, backgammon, and Scrabble games. Push one button, and that clock stops—the other begins simultaneously. When a player's allotted time for the game has expired, that player will lose if he or she has not made the required number of moves.

Mathematics and chess both involve structured relationships and demand logical thinking. Emanuel Lasker achieved mastery in both fields. He was best known as a World Chess Champion for 27 years, until 1921. Lasker also was famous in mathematical circles for his work concerning the theory of primary ideals, algebraic analogies of prime numbers. An important result, the Lasker-Noether theorem, bears his name along with that of Emmy Noether. Noether extended Lasker's work. Her father been Lasker's Ph.D. advisor.

EXAMPLE 4 Finding Additive Inverses in Clock Arithmetic

Determine the additive inverse, if it exists, for each number in 12-hour clock arithmetic.

(a) 8   **(b)** 2

Solution

(a) Use the clock face to solve the equation

$$8 + x = 0.$$
$$x = 4 \qquad \text{It is 4 hours from 8 to 0.}$$

The additive inverse of 8 is 4.

(b) Refer to the addition table to solve the equation.

$$2 + x = 0.$$
$$x = 10 \qquad \text{The row headed 2 has 0 in the column headed 10.}$$

The additive inverse of 2 is 10.   ■

The methods used in Example 4 may be used to verify that *every* element of the system has an additive inverse (also in the system). So the system has the **inverse property.**

A simpler way to verify the inverse property, if you have the table, is to make sure the identity element appears exactly once in each row, and that the pair of elements that produces it also produces it in the opposite order. (This last condition is automatically true if the commutative property holds for the system.) For example, note in Table 16 that row 3 contains one 0, under the 9, so $3 + 9 = 0$, and that row 9 contains 0, under the 3, so $9 + 3 = 0$ also. Therefore, 3 and 9 are inverses.

Table 17 lists all the elements and their additive inverses. Notice that one element, 6, is its own inverse for addition.

Table 17 Inverses for 12-Hour Clock Addition

Clock value a	0	1	2	3	4	5	6	7	8	9	10	11
Additive inverse $-a$	0	11	10	9	8	7	6	5	4	3	2	1

Using the additive inverse symbol, we can say that in clock arithmetic,

$$-5 = 7, \qquad -11 = 1, \qquad -10 = 2, \qquad \text{and so on.}$$

We have now seen that the 12-hour clock system, with addition, has all five properties that we set out to check: closure, commutative, associative, identity, and inverse. Having discussed additive inverses, we can define subtraction formally. Notice that the definition is the same as for ordinary subtraction of whole numbers.

SUBTRACTION ON A CLOCK

If a and b are elements in clock arithmetic, then the **difference, $a - b$,** is defined as

$$a - b = a + (-b)$$

EXAMPLE 5 Finding Clock Differences

Find each difference.

(a) $8 - 5$ **(b)** $6 - 11$

Solution

(a) $8 - 5 = 8 + (-5)$ Use the definition of subtraction.

$\qquad = 8 + 7$ The additive inverse of 5 is 7, from the table of inverses.

$\qquad = 3$

This result agrees with traditional arithmetic. Check by adding 5 and 3; the sum is 8.

(b) $6 - 11 = 6 + (-11)$

$\qquad = 6 + 1$ The additive inverse of 11 is 1.

$\qquad = 7$ ∎

Clock numbers can also be multiplied. For example,

$$5 \cdot 4 = 4 + 4 + 4 + 4 + 4 = 8. \qquad \text{Add five 4s.}$$

EXAMPLE 6 Finding Clock Products

Find each product, using clock arithmetic.

(a) $6 \cdot 9$ **(b)** $3 \cdot 4$ **(c)** $6 \cdot 0$ **(d)** $0 \cdot 8$

Solution

(a) $6 \cdot 9 = 9 + 9 + 9 + 9 + 9 + 9 = 6$ **(b)** $3 \cdot 4 = 4 + 4 + 4 = 0$

(c) $6 \cdot 0 = 0 + 0 + 0 + 0 + 0 + 0 = 0$ **(d)** $0 \cdot 8 = 0$ ∎

Some properties of the system of 12-hour clock numbers with the operation of multiplication will be investigated in Exercises 6–8.

Modular Systems

We now expand the ideas of clock arithmetic to **modular systems** in general. Recall that 12-hour clock arithmetic was set up so that answers were always whole numbers less than 12. For example, $8 + 6 = 2$. The traditional sum, $8 + 6 = 14$, reflects the fact that moving the clock hand forward 8 hours from 0, and then forward another 6 hours, amounts to moving it forward 14 hours total. But because the final position of the clock is at 2, we see that 14 and 2 are, in a sense, equivalent. More formally, we say that 14 and 2 are **congruent modulo** 12 (or **congruent mod** 12), which is written

$$14 \equiv 2 \ (\text{mod } 12) \qquad \text{The sign} \equiv \text{indicates congruence.}$$

By observing clock hand movements, you can also see that, for example,

$$26 \equiv 2 \ (\text{mod } 12), \qquad 38 \equiv 2 \ (\text{mod } 12), \qquad \text{and so on.}$$

In each case, the congruence is true because the difference of the two congruent numbers is a multiple of 12:

$$14 - 2 = 12 = 1 \cdot 12, \quad 26 - 2 = 24 = 2 \cdot 12, \quad 38 - 2 = 36 = 3 \cdot 12.$$

This suggests the following definition

CONGRUENCE MODULO *m*

The integers *a* and *b* are **congruent modulo *m*** (where *m* is a natural number greater than 1 called the **modulus**) if and only if the difference $a - b$ is divisible by *m*. Symbolically, this congruence is written

$$a \equiv b \ (\text{mod } m).$$

Because being divisible by *m* is the same as being a multiple of *m,* we can say that

$a \equiv b \ (\text{mod } m)$ if and only if $a - b = km$ for some integer *k*.

EXAMPLE 7 **Checking the Truth of Modular Equations**

Decide whether each statement is *true* or *false*.

(a) $16 \equiv 2 \ (\text{mod } 2)$ **(b)** $49 \equiv 32 \ (\text{mod } 5)$ **(c)** $30 \equiv 345 \ (\text{mod } 7)$

Solution

(a) The difference $16 - 10 = 6$ is divisible by 2, so $16 \equiv 10 \ (\text{mod } 2)$ is true.

(b) The statement $49 \equiv 32 \ (\text{mod } 5)$ is false, because $49 - 32 = 17$, which is not divisible by 5.

(c) The statement $30 \equiv 345 \ (\text{mod } 7)$ is true, because $30 - 345 = 315$ is divisible by 7. (It doesn't matter if we find $30 - 345$ or $345 - 30$.) ∎

There is another method of determining if two numbers, *a* and *b*, are congruent modulo *m*.

CRITERION FOR CONGRUENCE

$a \equiv b \ (\text{mod } m)$ if and only if the same remainder is obtained when *a* and *b* are divided by *m*.

For example, we know that $27 \equiv 9 \ (\text{mod } 6)$ because $27 - 9 = 18$, which is divisible by 6. Now, if 27 is divided by 6, the quotient is 4 and the remainder is 3. Also, if 9 is divided by 6, the quotient is 1 and the remainder is 3. According to the criterion above, $27 \equiv 9 \ (\text{mod } 6)$ since both remainders are the same.

Addition, subtraction, and multiplication can be performed in any modular system just as with clock numbers. Because final answers should be whole numbers less than the modulus, we can first find an answer using ordinary arithmetic. Then, as long as the answer is nonnegative, simply divide it by the modulus and keep the remainder. This produces the smallest nonnegative integer that is congruent (modulo *m*) to the ordinary answer.

EXAMPLE 8 **Performing Modular Arithmetic**

Find each sum, difference, or product.

(a) $(9 + 14 \ (\text{mod } 3)$ **(b)** $27 - 5 \ (\text{mod } 6)$ **(c)** $(50 + 34) \ (\text{mod } 7)$
(d) $(8 \cdot 9) \ (\text{mod } 10)$ **(e)** $12 \cdot 10 \ (\text{mod } 5)$

Solution

(a) First add 9 and 14 to get 23. Then divide 23 by 3. The remainder is 2, so we obtain $23 \equiv 2 \pmod 3$ and
$$(9 + 14) \equiv 2 \pmod 3.$$

(b) $27 - 5 = 22$. Divide 22 by 6, obtaining 4 as a remainder:
$$(27 - 5) \equiv 4 \pmod 6.$$

(c) $50 + 34 = 84$. When 84 is divided by 7, a remainder of 0 is found:
$$(50 + 34) \equiv 0 \pmod 7.$$

(d) Since $8 \cdot 9 = 72$, and 72 leaves a remainder of 2 when divided by 10,
$$(8 \cdot 9) \equiv 2 \pmod{10}.$$

(e) $(12 \cdot 10) \pmod 5 = 120 \equiv 0 \pmod 5$ ∎

Problem-Solving Hint

Modular systems can often be applied to questions involving cyclical changes. For example, our method of dividing time into weeks causes the days to repeatedly cycle through the same pattern of seven. Suppose today is Sunday and we want to know what day of the week it will be 45 days from now. Because we don't care how many weeks will pass between now and then, we can discard the largest whole number of weeks in 45 days and keep the remainder. (We are finding the smallest nonnegative integer that is congruent to 45 modulo 7.) Dividing 45 by 7 leaves remainder 3, so the desired day of the week is 3 days past Sunday, or *Wednesday*.

EXAMPLE 9 Using Modular Methods to Find the Day of the Week

If today is Thursday, November 12, and *next* year is a leap year, what day of the week will it be one year from today?

Solution

A modulo 7 system applies here, but we need to know the number of days between today and one year from today. Today's date, November 12, is unimportant except that it shows we are later in the year than the end of February and therefore the next year (starting today) will contain 366 days. (This would not be so if today were, say, January 12.) Now dividing 366 by 7 produces 52 with remainder 2. Two days past Thursday is our answer. That is, one year from today will be a Saturday. ∎

Problem-Solving Hint

A modular system (mod m) allows only a fixed set of remainder values, 0, 1, 2, ..., $m - 1$. One practical approach to solving modular equations, at least when m is reasonably small, is to simply try all these integers. For each solution found in this way, others can be found by adding multiples of the modulus to it.

EXAMPLE 10 Solving Modular Equations

Solve each modular equation for whole number solutions.

(a) $(3 + x) \equiv 5 \pmod 7$ **(b)** $5x \equiv 4 \pmod 9$

(c) $6x \equiv 3 \pmod 8$ **(d)** $8x \equiv 8 \pmod 8$

Solution

(a) Because dividing 5 by 7 yields remainder 5, the criterion for congruence is that the given equation is true only if dividing $3 + x$ by 7 also yields remainder 5. Try replacing x, in turn, by 0, 1, 2, 3, 4, 5, and 6.

$x = 0$: $(3 + 0) \equiv 5 \pmod 7$ is false.   The remainder is 3.

$x = 1$: $(3 + 1) \equiv 5 \pmod 7$ is false.   The remainder is 4.

$x = 2$: $(3 + 2) \equiv 5 \pmod 7$ is true.   The remainder is 5.

Try $x = 3$, $x = 4$, $x = 5$, and $x = 6$ to see that none work. Of the integers from 0 through 6, only 2 is a solution of the equation $(3 + x) \equiv 5 \pmod 7$.

Because 2 is a solution, find other solutions to this mod 7 equation by repeatedly adding 7:

$$2 + 7 = 9, \quad 9 + 7 = 16, \quad 16 + 7 = 23, \quad \text{and so on.}$$

The set of all nonnegative solutions of $(3 + x) \equiv 5 \pmod 7$ is

$$\{2, 9, 16, 23, 30, 37, \dots\}.$$

(b) Dividing 4 by 9 yields remainder 4. Because the modulus is 9, check the remainders when $5x$ is divided by 9 for $x = 0, 1, 2, 3, 4, 5, 6, 7,$ and 8.

$x = 0$: $5 \cdot 0 \equiv 5 \pmod 9$ is false.   The remainder is 0.

$x = 1$: $5 \cdot 1 \equiv 4 \pmod 9$ is false.   The remainder is 5.

Continue trying numbers. Only $x = 8$ works:

$$5 \cdot 8 = 40 \equiv 4 \pmod 9. \quad \text{The remainder is 4.}$$

The set of all nonnegative solutions to the equation $5x \equiv 4 \pmod 9$ is

$$\{8, 8 + 9, 8 + 9 + 9, 8 + 9 + 9 + 9, \dots\} \quad \text{or} \quad \{8, 17, 26, 35, 44, 53, \dots\}.$$

(c) To solve $6x \equiv 3 \pmod 8$, try the numbers 0, 1, 2, 3, 4, 5, 6, and 7. None work. Therefore, the equation $6x \equiv 3 \pmod 8$ has no solutions. Write the set of all solutions as the empty set, $\varnothing$

This result is reasonable because $6x$ will always be even, no matter which whole number is used for x. Because $6x$ is even and 3 is odd, the difference $6x - 3$ will be odd and therefore not divisible by 8.

(d) To solve $8x \equiv 8 \pmod 8$, trying the integers 0, 1, 2, 3, 4, 5, 6, and 7. *Any* replacement will work. The solution set is $\{0, 1, 2, 3, \dots\}$. ∎

Some problems can be solved by writing down two or more modular equations and finding their common solutions. The next example illustrates the process.

EXAMPLE 11 Finding the Number of Discs in a CD Collection

Julio wants to arrange his CD collection in equal size stacks, but after trying stacks of 4, stacks of 5, and stacks of 6, he finds that there is always 1 disc left over. Assuming Julio owns more than one CD, what is the least possible number of discs in his collection?

Solution

The given information leads to three modular equations,

$$x \equiv 1 \pmod 4, \quad x \equiv 1 \pmod 5, \quad \text{and} \quad x \equiv 1 \pmod 6.$$

For the first equation, try $x = 0$, $x = 1$, $x = 2$, and $x = 3$. The value 1 works, as it does for the other two equations as well. So the solution sets are, respectively,

$$\{1, 5, 9, 13, 17, 21, 25, 29, 33, 37, 41, 45, 49, 53, 57, 61, 65, 69. \ldots\},$$
$$\{1, 6, 11, 16, 21, 26, 31, 36, 41, 46, 51, 56, 61, 66, 71, 76, \ldots\},$$

and
$$\{1, 7, 13, 19, 25, 31, 37, 43, 49, 55, 61, \ldots\}.$$

The least common solution greater than 1 is 61, so the least possible number of discs in the collection is 61. ∎

EXAMPLE 12 Applying Congruences to a Construction Problem

A dry-wall contractor is ordering materials to finish a 17-foot-by-45-foot room. The wallboard panels come in 4-foot widths. Show that, after uncut panels are applied, all four walls will require additional partial strips of the same width.

Solution

The width of any partial strip needed will be the remainder when the wall length is divided by 4 (the panel width). In terms of congruence, we must show that $17 \equiv 45$ (mod 4). By the criterion for congruence, we see that this is true because both 17 and 45 give the same remainder (namely 1) when divided by 4. A 1-foot partial strip will be required for each wall. (In this case four 1-foot strips can be cut from a single panel, so there will be no waste.) ∎

FOR FURTHER THOUGHT

A Card Trick

Many card "tricks" that have been around for years are really not illusions at all but are based on mathematical properties that allow anyone to do them with no special conjuring abilities. One of them is based on mod 14 arithmetic.

In this trick, suits play no role. Each card has a numerical value: 1 for ace, 2 for two, . . . , 11 for jack, 12 for queen, and 13 for king. The deck is shuffled and given to a spectator, who is instructed to place the deck of cards face up on a table and is told to follow the procedure described: The top card is removed from the deck and laid on the table with its face up. (We shall call it the "starter" card.) The starter card will be at the bottom of a pile. In order to form a pile, note the value of the starter card, and then add cards on top of it while counting up to 13. For example, if the starter card is a six, pile up seven cards on top of it. If it is a jack, add two cards to it, and so on.

When the first pile is completed, it is picked up and placed face down. The next card from the deck becomes the starter card for the next pile, and the process is repeated. This continues until all cards are used or until there are not enough cards to complete the last pile. Any cards that are left over are put aside, face down, for later use. We will refer to these as "leftovers."

The performer then requests that a spectator choose three piles at random. The remaining piles are added to the leftovers. The spectator is then instructed to turn over any two top cards from the piles. The performer is then able to determine the value of the third top card.

The secret to the trick is that the performer adds the values of the two top cards that were turned over, and then adds 10 to this sum. The performer then counts off this number of cards from the leftovers. The number of cards remaining in the leftovers is the value of the remaining top card!

For Group or Individual Investigation

1. Obtain a deck of playing cards and perform the "trick" as described above. (As with many activities, you'll find that doing it is simpler than describing it.) Does it work?

2. Explain why this procedure works. (If you want to see how someone else explained it, using modulo 14 arithmetic, see "An Old Card Trick Revisited," by Barry C. Felps, in the December 1976 issue of the journal The *Mathematics Teacher.*)

4.5 EXERCISES

Find each difference on the 12-hour clock.

1. 8 - 3   **2.** 4 - 9   **3.** 2 - 8   **4.** 0 - 3

5. Complete the 12-hour clock multiplication table below. You can use repeated addition and the addition table (for example, $3 \cdot 7 = 7 + 7 + 7 + 2 + 7 + 9$) or use mod 12 multiplication techniques, as in Example 8, parts (d) and (e).

·	0	1	2	3	4	5	6	7	8	9	10	11
0	0	0	0	0	0	0	0	0	0	0	0	0
1	0	1	2	3	4	5	6	7	8	9	10	11
2	0	2	4	6	8	10		2	4		8	
3	0	3	6	9	0	3	6			3	6	
4	0	4	8			8		4			4	8
5	0	5	10	3	8		6	11	4			
6	0	6	0		0	6	0	6		6		6
7	0	7	2	9				1			10	
8	0	8	4	0				8	4		8	4
9	0	9			0		6		0			
10	0	10	8			2						2
11	0	11										1

By referring to your table in Exercise 5, determine which properties hold for the system of 12-hour clock numbers with the operation of multiplication.

6. closure   **7.** commutative

8. identity (If so, what is the identity element?)

A 5-hour clock system utilizes the set $\{0, 1, 2, 3, 4\}$, and relates to the clock face shown here.

5-hour clock

9. Complete this 5-hour clock addition table.

+	0	1	2	3	4
0	0	1	2	3	4
1	1	2	3	4	
2	2	3	4		1
3	3	4			
4	4			3	

Which properties are satisfied by the system of 5-hour clock numbers with the operation of addition?

10. closure

11. commutative

12. identity (If so, what is the identity element?)

13. inverse (If so, name the inverse of each element.)

14. Complete this 5-hour clock multiplication table.

·	0	1	2	3	4
0	0	0	0	0	0
1	0	1	2	3	4
2	0	2	4		
3	0	3			
4	0	4			

Determine which properties hold for the system of 5-hour clock numbers with the operation of multiplication.

15. closure   **16.**   commutative

17. identity (If so, what is the identity element?)

In clock arithmetic, as in ordinary arithmetic, $a - b = d$ is true if and only if $b + d = a$. Similarly, $a \div b = q$ if and only if $b \cdot q = a$.
    Use the idea above and your 5-hour clock multiplication table of Exercise 14 to find each quotient on a 5-hour clock.

18. $1 \div 3$ **19.** $3 \div 1$

20. $2 \div 3$ **21.** $3 \div 2$

22. Is division commutative on a 5-hour clock? Explain.

23. Is there an answer for $4 \div 0$ on a 5-hour clock? Find it or explain why not.

The military uses a 24-hour clock to avoid the problems of "A.M." and "P.M." For example, 1100 hours is 11 A.M., while 2100 hours is 9 P.M. (12 noon + 9 hours). In these designations, the last two digits represent minutes, and the digits before that represent hours. Find each sum in the 24-hour clock system.

24. $1400 + 500$ **25.** $1300 + 1800$

26. $0750 + 1630$ **27.** $1545 + 0815$

28. Explain how the following three statements can *all* be true. (*Hint:* Think of clocks.)

$$1145 + 1135 = 2280$$
$$1145 + 1135 = 1120$$
$$1145 + 1135 = 2320$$

Answer true *or* false *for each statement.*

29. $5 \equiv 19 \pmod 3$ **30.** $35 \equiv 8 \pmod 9$

31. $5445 \equiv 0 \pmod 3$ **32.** $7021 \equiv 4202 \pmod 6$

Work each modular arithmetic problem.

33. $(12 + 7)(\bmod 4)$ **34.** $(62 + 95)(\bmod 9)$

35. $(35 - 22)(\bmod 5)$ **36.** $(82 - 45)(\bmod 3)$

37. $(5 \cdot 8)(\bmod 3)$ **38.** $(32 \cdot 21)(\bmod 8)$

39. $[4 \cdot (13 + 6)](\bmod 11)$

40. $[(10 + 7) \cdot (5 + 3)](\bmod 10)$

41. The text described how to do arithmetic mod m when the ordinary answer comes out nonnegative. Explain what to do when the ordinary answer is negative.

Work each modular arithmetic problem.

42. $(3 - 27)(\bmod 5)$ **43.** $(16 - 60)(\bmod 7)$

44. $[(-8) \cdot 11](\bmod 3)$ **45.** $[2 \cdot (-23)](\bmod 5)$

In Exercises 46 and 47:
(a) *Complete the given addition table.*
(b) *Decide whether the closure, commutative, identity, and inverse properties are satisfied.*
(c) *If the inverse property is satisfied, give the inverse of each number.*

46. mod 4

+	0	1	2	3
0	0	1	2	3
1				
2				
3				

47. mod 7

+	0	1	2	3	4	5	6
0	0	1	2	3	4	5	6
1	1	2	3	4	5	6	
2							
3							
4							
5							
6							

In Exercises 48–51:
(a) *Complete the given multiplication table.*
(b) *Decide whether the closure, commutative, identity, and inverse properties are satisfied.*
(c) *Give the inverse of each nonzero number that has an inverse.*

48. mod 2

·	0	1
0	0	0
1	0	

49. mod 3

·	0	1	2
0	0	0	0
1	0	1	2
2	0	2	

50. mod 4

·	0	1	2	3
0	0	0	0	0
1	0	1	2	3
2	0	2		
3	0	3		

51. mod 9

·	0	1	2	3	4	5	6	7	8
0	0	0	0	0	0	0	0	0	0
1	0	1	2	3	4	5	6	7	8
2	0	2	4	6	8		5		
3	0	3	6	0		6		3	6
4	0	4	8		7		6		5
5	0	5	1		2		3	8	
6	0	6	3	0	6	3	0	6	3
7	0	7	5			8			2
8	0	8	7		4	3			1

52. Explain why a modular system containing the number 0 cannot satisfy the inverse property for multiplication.

Find all nonnegative solutions for each equation.

53. $x \equiv 3 \;(\bmod 7)$

54. $(2 + x) \equiv 7 \;(\bmod 3)$

55. $6x \equiv 2 \;(\bmod 2)$

56. $(5x - 3) \equiv 7 \;(\bmod 4)$

Solve each problem.

57. *Odometer Readings* For many years automobile odometers showed five whole number digits and a digit for tenths of a mile. For those odometers showing just five whole number digits, totals are recorded according to what modulus?

58. *Distance Traveled by a Car* If a car's five-digit whole number odometer shows a reading of 29,306, *in theory* how many miles might the car have traveled?

59. *Determining Day of the Week* Refer to Example 9 in the text. (Recall that *next* year is a leap year.) Assuming today was Thursday, January 12, answer the following questions.
(a) How many days would the next year (starting today) contain?
(b) What day of the week would occur one year from today?

60. *Silver Spoon Collection* Roxanna Parker has a collection of silver spoons from all over the world. She finds that she can arrange her spoons in sets of 7 with 6 left over, sets of 8 with 1 left over, or sets of 15 with 3 left over. If Roxanna has fewer than 200 spoons, how many are there?

61. ***Piles of Ticket Stubs*** Lawrence Rosenthal finds that whether he sorts his White Sox ticket stubs into piles of 10, piles of 15, or piles of 20, there are always 2 left over. What is the least number of stubs he could have (assuming he has more than 2)?

62. ***Determining a Range of Dates*** Assume again, as in Example 9, that *next* year is a leap year. If the next year (starting today) does *not* contain 366 days, what is the range of possible dates for today?

63. ***Flight Attendant Schedules*** Robin Strang and Kristyn Wasag, flight attendants for two different airlines, are close friends and like to get together as often as possible. Robin flies a 21-day schedule (including days off), which then repeats, while Kristyn has a repeating 30-day schedule. Both of their routines include layovers in Chicago, New Orleans, and San Francisco. The table below shows which days of each of their individual schedules they are in these cities. (Assume the first day of a cycle is day number 1.)

	Days in Chicago	**Days in New Orleans**	**Days in San Francisco**
Robin	1, 2, 8	5, 12	6, 18, 19
Kristyn	23, 29, 30	5, 6, 17	8, 10, 15, 20, 25

If today is July 1 and both are starting their schedules today (day 1), list the days during July and August that they will be able to see each other in each of the three cities.

The following formula can be used to find the day of the week on which a given year begins.* Here y represents the year (which must be after 1582, when our current calendar began). First calculate

$$a = y + [(y-1)/4] - [(y-1)/100]$$
$$+ [(y-1)/400],$$

where [x] represents the greatest integer less than or equal to x. (For example, [9.2] = 9, and [π] = 3.) After finding a, find the smallest nonnegative integer b such that

$$a \equiv b \pmod 7.$$

Then b gives the day of January 1, with b = 0 representing Sunday, b = 1 Monday, and so on.

Find the day of the week on which January 1 would occur in each year.

64. 1812   **65.** 1865

66. 2006   **67.** 2020

Some people believe that Friday the thirteenth is unlucky. The table* below shows the months that will have a Friday the thirteenth if the first day of the year is known. A year is a leap year if it is divisible by 4. The only exception to this rule is that a century year (1900, for example) is a leap year only when it is divisible by 400.

First Day of Year	**Non-leap Year**	**Leap Year**
Sunday	Jan., Oct.	Jan., April, July
Monday	April, July	Sept., Dec.
Tuesday	Sept., Dec.	June
Wednesday	June	March, Nov.
Thursday	Feb., March, Nov.	Feb., Aug.
Friday	August	May
Saturday	May	Oct.

Use the table to determine the months that have a Friday the thirteenth for each year.

68. 2007   **69.** 2008

70. 2009   **71.** 2200

72. Modular arithmetic can be used to create **residue designs.** For example, the designs (11, 3) and (65, 3) are shown here.

 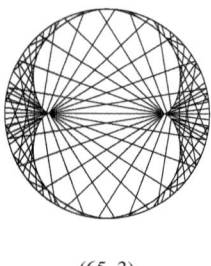

(11, 3)   (65, 3)

To see how such designs are created, construct a new design, (11, 5), by proceeding as follows.

(a) Draw a circle and divide the circumference into 10 equal parts. Label the division points as 1, 2, 3, . . . , 10.

(b) Since $1 \cdot 5 \equiv 5 \pmod{11}$, connect 1 and 5. (We use 5 as a multiplier because we are making an (11, 5) design.)

(c) $2 \cdot 5 \equiv 10 \pmod{11}$
Therefore, connect 2 and ____ .

(d) $3 \cdot 5 \equiv$ ____ $\pmod{11}$
Connect 3 and ____.

(e) $4 \cdot 5 \equiv$ ____ $\pmod{11}$
Connect 4 and ____.

(f) $5 \cdot 5 \equiv$ ____ (mod 11)
   Connect 5 and ____.

(g) $6 \cdot 5 \equiv$ ____ (mod 11)
   Connect 6 and ____.

(h) $7 \cdot 5 \equiv$ ____ (mod 11)
   Connect 7 and ____.

(i) $8 \cdot 5 \equiv$ ____ (mod 11)
   Connect 8 and ____.

(j) $9 \cdot 5 \equiv$ ____ (mod 11)
   Connect 9 and ____.

(k) $10 \cdot 5 \equiv$ ____ (mod 11)
   Connect 10 and ____.

(l) You might want to shade some of the regions you have found to make an interesting pattern. For more information, see "Residue Designs," by Phil Locke in *The Mathematics Teacher*, March 1972, pages 260–263.

Identification numbers are used in various ways for many kinds of different products.* Books, for example, are assigned International Standard Book Numbers (ISBNs). Each ISBN is a ten-digit number. It includes a check digit, which is determined on the basis of modular arithmetic. The ISBN for one version of this book is

$$0\text{-}321\text{-}36146\text{-}6$$

The first digit, 0, identifies the book as being published in an English-speaking country. The next digits, 321, identify the publisher, while 36146 identifies this particular book.

---

*For an interesting general discussion, see "The Mathematics of Identification Numbers," by Joseph A. Gallian in *The College Mathematics Journal*, May 1991, p. 194.

The final digit, 6, is a check digit. To find this check digit, start at the left and multiply the digits of the ISBN by 10, 9, 8, 7, 6, 5, 4, 3, and 2, respectively. Then add these products. For this book we get

$$(10 \cdot 0) + (9 \cdot 3) + (8 \cdot 2) + (7 \cdot 1) + (6 \cdot 3)$$
$$+ (5 \cdot 6) + (4 \cdot 1) + (3 \cdot 4) + (2 \cdot 6) = 126.$$

The check digit is the smallest number that must be added to this result to get a multiple of 11. Because $126 + 6 = 132$, a multiple of 11, the check digit is 6. (It is possible to have a check "digit" of 10; the letter X is used instead of 10.)

When an order for this book is received, the ISBN is entered into a computer, and the check digit evaluated. If this result does not match the check digit on the order, the order will not be processed. Does each ISBN have the correct check digit?

73. 0-275-98341-2

74. 0-374-29288-7

Find the appropriate check digit for each ISBN. (Note: The positions of hyphens (or spaces) may vary (or there may be none), but this does not affect the determination of the check digit.)

75. Man of the Century, by Jonathan Kwitny, 0-8050-2688- _____

76. *Winning*, by Jack Welch, 0-06-075394- _____

77. *1776*, by David McCullough, 0-7432-2671- _____

78. *The Da Vinci Code*, by Dan Brown, 0-385-50420- _____

4.6 PROPERTIES OF MATHEMATICAL SYSTEMS

OBJECTIVES
1. An Abstract System
2. Closure Property
3. Commutative Property
4. Associative Property
5. Identity Property
6. Inverse Property
7. Distributive Property

An Abstract System

Clock arithmetic and modular systems, discussed in the previous section, were built upon ordinary numbers and involved familiar operations such as addition, subtraction, multiplication, and division. We begin this section by presenting a more abstract system, where the elements and the operations have no implied mathematical significance. This way, we can concentrate on investigating the properties of the system without preconceived notions of what they may be.

To begin, we introduce a finite mathematical system made up of the set of elements $\{a, b, c, d\}$ and an operation we will write with the symbol ☆. We define the system in Table 18, an **operation table** that shows how operation ☆ combines any two elements from the set $\{a, b, c, d\}$. To use the table to find, say, c ☆ d, first locate c on the left, and d across the top. This row and column intersect at b, so that

$$c ☆ d = b.$$

Table 18

☆	*a*	*b*	*c*	*d*
a	*a*	*b*	*c*	*d*
b	*b*	*d*	*a*	*c*
c	*c*	*a*	*d*	*b*
d	*d*	*c*	*b*	*a*

As with clock arithmetic, the important properties we shall look for in this system are the following: *closure, commutative, associative, identity,* and *inverse.*

Closure Property

For this system to be closed under the operation ☆, the answer to any possible combination of elements from the system must be in the set $\{a, b, c, d\}$. A glance at Table 18 shows that the answers in the body of the table are all elements of this set. This means that the system is closed. If an element other than a, b, c, or d had appeared in the body of the table, or if any position in the body of the table had contained no entry, the system would not have been closed.

Table 19

☆	*a*	*b*	*c*	*d*
a	*a*	*b*	*c*	*d*
b	*b*	*d*	*a*	*c*
c	*c*	*a*	*d*	*b*
d	*d*	*c*	*b*	*a*

Commutative Property

In order for the system to have the commutative property, it must be true that $\Gamma \mathbin{\text{☆}} \Delta = \Delta \mathbin{\text{☆}} \Gamma$, where Γ and Δ stand for any elements from the set $\{a, b, c, d\}$. For example,

$$c \mathbin{\text{☆}} d = b \quad \text{and} \quad d \mathbin{\text{☆}} c = b, \quad \text{so} \quad c \mathbin{\text{☆}} d = d \mathbin{\text{☆}} c.$$

To see that the same is true for *all* choices of Γ and Δ, observe that Table 19 is symmetric with respect to the diagonal line shown. This "diagonal line test" establishes that ☆ is a commutative operation for this system.

Associative Property

The system is associative if $(\Gamma \mathbin{\text{☆}} \Delta) \mathbin{\text{☆}} Y = \Gamma \mathbin{\text{☆}} (\Delta \mathbin{\text{☆}} Y)$, where Γ, Δ, and Y represent any elements from the set $\{a, b, c, d\}$. There is no quick way to check a table for the associative property, as there is for the commutative property. All we can do is try some examples. Using the table that defines operation ☆,

$$(a \mathbin{\text{☆}} d) \mathbin{\text{☆}} b = d \mathbin{\text{☆}} b = c, \quad \text{and} \quad a \mathbin{\text{☆}} (d \mathbin{\text{☆}} b) = a \mathbin{\text{☆}} c = c,$$

so that

$$(a \mathbin{\text{☆}} d) \mathbin{\text{☆}} b = a \mathbin{\text{☆}} (d \mathbin{\text{☆}} b).$$

In the same way,

$$b \mathbin{\text{☆}} (c \mathbin{\text{☆}} d) = (b \mathbin{\text{☆}} c) \mathbin{\text{☆}} d.$$

In both these examples, changing the location of parentheses did not change the answers. Because the two examples worked, we suspect that the system is associative. We cannot be sure of this, however, unless every possible choice of three letters from the set is checked. (Although we have not completely verified it here, this system does, in fact, satisfy the associative property.)

Identity Property

For the identity property to hold, there must be an element Δ from the set of the system such that $\Delta \mathbin{\text{☆}} X = X$ and $X \mathbin{\text{☆}} \Delta = X$, where X represents any element from the set $\{a, b, c, d\}$. We can see that a is such an element as follows. In Table 19, the column below a (at the top) is identical to the column at the left, and the row across from a (at the left) is identical to the row at the top. Therefore, a is in fact the identity element of the system. (It is shown in more advanced courses that if a system has an identity element, it has *only* one.)

Inverse Property

We found earlier that a is the identity element for the system using operation ☆. If there is an inverse in this system for, say, the element b, and if Δ represents the inverse of b, then

$$b \mathbin{\text{☆}} \Delta = a \quad \text{and} \quad \Delta \mathbin{\text{☆}} b = a \text{ (because } a \text{ is the identity element).}$$

Bernard Bolzano (1781–1848) was an early exponent of rigor and precision in mathematics. Many early results in such areas as calculus were produced by the masters in the field; these masters knew what they were doing and produced accurate results. However, their sloppy arguments caused trouble in the hands of the less gifted. The work of Bolzano and others helped put mathematics on a strong footing.

Inspecting the table for operation ☆ shows that Δ can be replaced with c:

$$b ☆ c = a \quad \text{and} \quad c ☆ b = a.$$

So we see that c is the inverse of b.

We can inspect the table to see if every element of our system has an inverse in the system. We see (in Table 19) that the identity element a appears once in each row, and that, in each case, the pair of elements that produces a also produces it in the opposite order. Therefore, we conclude that the system satisfies the inverse property.

In summary, the mathematical system made up of the set $\{a, b, c, d\}$ and operation ☆ satisfies the closure, commutative, associative, identity, and inverse properties.

POTENTIAL PROPERTIES OF A SINGLE-OPERATION SYSTEM

Here a, b, and c represent elements from the set of any system, and ∘ represents the operation of the system.

Closure   The system is closed if for all elements a and b,

$$a \circ b$$

is in the set of the system.

Commutative   The system has the commutative property if

$$a \circ b = b \circ a$$

for all elements a and b of the system.

Associative   The system has the associative property if

$$(a \circ b) \circ c = a \circ (b \circ c)$$

for every choice of three elements a, b, and c of the system.

Identity   The system has the identity property if there exists an identity element e (where e is in the set of the system) such that

$$a \circ e = a \quad \text{and} \quad e \circ a = a$$

for every element a of the system.

Inverse   The system has the inverse property if, for every element a of the system, there is an element x in the system such that

$$a \circ x = e \quad \text{and} \quad x \circ a = e,$$

where e is the identity element of the system.

▉▉▉ EXAMPLE 1   Identifying the Properties of a System

Table 20 on the next page defines a system consisting of the set $\{0, 1, 2, 3, 4, 5\}$ under an operation designated ⊗. Which properties above are satisfied by this system?

Solution

All the numbers in the body of the table come from the set $\{0, 1, 2, 3, 4, 5\}$, so the system is closed. If we draw a line from upper left to lower right, we could fold the table along this line and have the corresponding elements match; the system has the commutative property.

Table 20

$\otimes$	0	1	2	3	4	5
0	0	0	0	0	0	0
1	0	1	2	3	4	5
2	0	2	4	0	2	4
3	0	3	0	3	0	3
4	0	4	2	0	4	2
5	0	5	4	3	2	1

To check for the associative property, try some examples:

$$2 \otimes (3 \otimes 5) = 2 \otimes 3 = 0 \quad \text{and} \quad (2 \otimes 3) \otimes 5 = 0 \otimes 5 = 0,$$

so that
$$2 \otimes (3 \otimes 5) = (2 \otimes 3) \otimes 5.$$

Also,
$$5 \otimes (4 \otimes 2) = (5 \otimes 4) \otimes 2.$$

Any other examples that we might try would also work. The system has the associative property.

Because the column at the left of the operation table is repeated under 1 in the body of the table, 1 is a candidate for the identity element in the system. To be sure that 1 is the identity element here, check that the row corresponding to 1 at the left is identical with the row at the top of the table. Since it is, 1 is indeed the identity element.

To find inverse elements, look for the identity element, 1, in the rows of the table. The identity element appears in the second row, $1 \otimes 1 = 1$; and in the bottom row, $5 \otimes 5 = 1$; so 1 and 5 both are their own inverses. There is no identity element in the rows opposite the numbers 0, 2, 3, and 4, so none of these elements has an inverse.

In summary, the system made up of the set $\{0, 1, 2, 3, 4, 5\}$ under this operation $\otimes$ satisfies the closure, associative, commutative, and identity properties, but not the inverse property. ∎

Table 21

$\boxtimes$	1	2	3	4	5	6
1	1	2	3	4	5	6
2	2	4	6	1	3	5
3	3	6	2	5	1	4
4	4	1	5	2	6	3
5	5	3	1	6	4	2
6	6	5	4	3	2	1

EXAMPLE 2 Identifying the Properties of a System

Table 21 defines a system consisting of the set of numbers $\{1, 2, 3, 4, 5, 6\}$ under an operation designated $\boxtimes$. Which properties are satisfied by this system?

Solution

Notice here that 0 is not an element of this system. This is perfectly legitimate. Because we are defining the system, we can include (or exclude) whatever we wish. Check that the system satisfies the closure, commutative, associative, and identity properties, with identity element 1. Let us now check for inverses. The element 1 is its own inverse, because $1 \boxtimes 1 = 1$. In row 2, the identity element 1 appears under the number 4, so $2 \boxtimes 4 = 1$ (and $4 \boxtimes 2 = 1$), with 2 and 4 inverses of each other. Also, 3 and 5 are inverses of each other, and 6 is its own inverse. Because each number in the set of the system has an inverse, the system satisfies the inverse property. ∎

Distributive Property

When a mathematical system has two operations, rather than just one, we can look for the **distributive property.**

DISTRIBUTIVE PROPERTY

Let $\star$ and $\circ$ be two operations defined for elements in the same set. Then $\star$ is distributive over $\circ$ if

$$a \star (b \circ c) = (a \star b) \circ (a \star c)$$

for every choice of elements a, b, and c from the set.

It is a well-known fact that multiplication is distributive over (or with respect to) addition on the set of real numbers. For example,

$$5 \cdot (8 + 3) = 5 \cdot 11 = 55 \quad \text{and} \quad 5 \cdot 8 + 5 \cdot 3 = 40 + 15 = 55,$$

so
$$5 \cdot (8 + 3) = 5 \cdot 8 + 5 \cdot 3.$$

▦ EXAMPLE 3 Testing for the Distributive Property

Is addition distributive over multiplication on the set of whole numbers?

Solution

To find out, replace ☆ with addition ($+$) and ∘ with multiplication ($\cdot$) in the statement of the distributive property at the bottom of the previous page:

$$a + (b \cdot c) = (a + b) \cdot (a + c). \quad \text{Is this true in general?}$$

We need to find out whether this statement is true for *every* choice of three whole numbers that we might make. Try an example. If $a = 3$, $b = 4$ and $c = 5$,

$$a + (b \cdot c) = 3 + (4 \cdot 5) = 3 + 20 = 23,$$

while
$$(a + b) \cdot (a + c) = (3 + 4) \cdot (3 + 5) = 7 \cdot 8 = 56.$$

Since $23 \neq 56$, we have $3 + (4 \cdot 5) \neq (3 + 4) \cdot (3 + 5)$. This false result is a *counterexample* (an example showing that a general statement is false). This counterexample shows that addition is *not* distributive over multiplication on the whole numbers. ■

The final example illustrates how the distributive property may hold for an abstract finite system.

Table 22

☆	*a*	*b*	*c*	*d*	*e*
a	*a*	*a*	*a*	*a*	*a*
b	*a*	*b*	*c*	*d*	*e*
c	*a*	*c*	*e*	*b*	*d*
d	*a*	*d*	*b*	*e*	*c*
e	*a*	*e*	*d*	*c*	*b*

Table 23

∘	*a*	*b*	*c*	*d*	*e*
a	*a*	*b*	*c*	*d*	*e*
b	*b*	*c*	*d*	*e*	*a*
c	*c*	*d*	*e*	*a*	*b*
d	*d*	*e*	*a*	*b*	*c*
e	*e*	*a*	*b*	*c*	*d*

▦ EXAMPLE 4 Testing for the Distributive Property

Suppose that the set $\{a, b, c, d, e\}$ has two operations ☆ and ∘ defined by Tables 22 and 23. The distributive property of ☆ with respect to ∘ holds in this system. Verify for the following case: $e \; ☆ \; (d \circ b) = (e \; ☆ \; d) \circ (e \; ☆ \; b)$.

Solution

First evaluate the left side of the equation by using the tables.

$$e \; ☆ \; (d \circ b) = e \; ☆ \; e \quad \text{Use the ∘ table.}$$
$$= b \quad \text{Use the ☆ table.}$$

Now, evaluate the right side of the equation.

$$(e \; ☆ \; d) \circ (e \; ☆ \; b) = c \circ e \quad \text{Use the ☆ table twice.}$$
$$= b \quad \text{Use the ∘ table.}$$

Each time the final result is b; the distributive property is verified for this case. ■

4.6   EXERCISES

For each system in Exercises 1–10, decide which of the properties of single-operation systems are satisfied. If the identity property is satisfied, give the identity element. If the inverse property is satisfied, give the inverse of each element. If the identity property is satisfied but the inverse property is not, name the elements that have no inverses.

1. {1, 2}; operation ⊗

⊗	1	2
1	1	2
2	2	1

2. {1, 2, 3, 4}; operation ⊗

⊗	1	2	3	4
1	1	2	3	4
2	2	4	1	3
3	3	1	4	2
4	4	3	2	1

3. {1, 2, 3, 4, 5, 6, 7}; operation ⊠

⊠	1	2	3	4	5	6	7
1	1	2	3	4	5	6	7
2	2	4	6	0	2	4	6
3	3	6	1	4	7	2	5
4	4	0	4	0	4	0	4
5	5	2	7	4	1	6	3
6	6	4	2	0	6	4	2
7	7	6	5	4	3	2	1

4. {1, 2, 3, 4, 5}; operation ⊠

⊠	1	2	3	4	5
1	1	2	3	4	5
2	2	4	0	2	4
3	3	0	3	0	3
4	4	2	0	4	2
5	5	4	3	2	1

5. {1, 3, 5, 7, 9}; operation ☆

☆	1	3	5	7	9
1	1	3	5	7	9
3	3	9	5	1	7
5	5	5	5	5	5
7	7	1	5	9	3
9	9	7	5	3	1

6. {1, 3, 5, 7}; operation ☆

☆	1	3	5	7
1	1	3	5	7
3	3	1	7	5
5	5	7	1	3
7	7	5	3	1

7. {A, B, F}; operation *

*	A	B	F
A	B	F	A
B	F	A	B
F	A	B	F

8. {m, n, p}; operation J

J	m	n	p
m	n	p	n
n	p	m	n
p	n	n	m

9. {r, s, t, u}; operation Z

Z	r	s	t	u
r	u	t	r	s
s	t	u	s	r
t	r	s	t	u
u	s	r	u	t

10. {A, J, T, U}; operation #

#	A	J	T	U
A	A	J	T	U
J	J	T	U	A
T	T	U	A	J
U	U	A	J	T

The tables in the finite mathematical systems that we developed in this section can be obtained in a variety of ways. For example, let us begin with a square, as shown in the figure. Let the symbols a, b, c, and d be defined as shown in the figure.

Let *a* represent zero rotation— leave the original square as is.

Let *b* represent rotation of 90° clockwise from original position.

Let *c* represent rotation of 180° clockwise from original position.

Let *d* represent rotation of 270° clockwise from original position.

Define an operation □ for these letters as follows. To evaluate b □ c, for example, first perform b by rotating the square 90°. (See the figure.) Then perform operation c by rotating the square an additional 180°. The net result is the same as if we had performed d only. Thus,

$$b \square c = d.$$

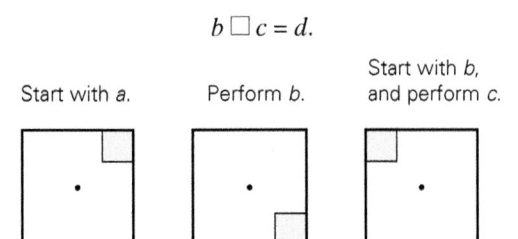

Start with *a*. Perform *b*. Start with *b*, and perform *c*.

Use this method to find each of the following.

11. $b \square d$ **12.** $b \square b$

13. $d \square b$ **14.** $a \square b$

Solve each problem.

15. Complete the table at the right for the system of square rotations described above.

□	a	b	c	d
a	a	b	c	d
b	b	c		a
c	c		a	
d	d	a		

16. Which of the properties from this section are satisfied by this system?

17. Define a universal set *U* as the set of counting numbers. Form a new set that contains all possible subsets of *U*. This new set of subsets together with the operation of set intersection forms a mathematical system. Which of the properties listed in this section are satisfied by this system?

18. Replace the word "intersection" with the word "union" in Exercise 17; then answer the same question.

19. Complete the table at the right so that the result is *not* the same as operation □ of Exercise 15, but so that the five properties listed in this section still hold.

	a	b	c	d
a				
b				
c				
d				

Try examples to help you decide whether each operation, when applied to the integers, satisfies the distributive property.

20. subtraction with respect to multiplication

21. addition with respect to subtraction

22. subtraction with respect to addition

Recall that Example 3 provided a counterexample for the general statement

$$a + (b \cdot c) = (a + b) \cdot (a + c).$$

Thus, addition is not *distributive with respect to multiplication. Now work Exercises 23–26.*

23. Decide if the statement above is true for each of the following sets of values.

   (a) $a = 2, b = -5, c = 4$

   (b) $a = -7, \ b = 5, c = 3$

   (c) $a = -8, b = 14, c = -5$

   (d) $a = 1, b = 6, c = -6$

24. Find another set of *a, b,* and *c* values that make the statement true.

25. Under what general conditions will the statement above be true?

26. Explain why, regardless of the results in Exercises 23–25, addition is still *not* distributive with respect to multiplication.

27. Give the conditions under which each equation would be true.
   (a) $a + (b - c) = (a + b) - (a + c)$
   (b) $a - (b + c) = (a - b) + (a - c)$

28. (a) Find values of *a, b* and *c* such that

$$a - (b \cdot c) = (a - b) \cdot (a - c).$$

   (b) Does this mean that subtraction is distributive with respect to multiplication? Explain.

Verify for the mathematical system of Example 4, defined by Tables 22 and 23, that the distributive property holds for each case.

29. $c \star (d \circ e) = (c \star d) \circ (c \star e)$

30. $a \star (a \circ b) = (a \star a) \circ (a \star b)$

31. $d \star (e \circ c) = (d \star e) \circ (d \star c)$

32. $b \star (b \circ b) = (b \star b) \circ (b \star b)$

Exercises 33 and 34 are for students who have studied sets.

33. Use Venn diagrams to show that the distributive property for union with respect to intersection holds for sets *A, B,* and *C.* That is,

$$A \cup (B \cap C) = (A \cup B) \cap (A \cup C).$$

34. Use Venn diagrams to show that *another* distributive property holds for sets *A, B,* and *C.* It is the distributive property of intersection with respect to union.

$$A \cup (B \cup C) = (A \cap B) \cup (A \cap C).$$

Exercises 35 and 36 are for students who have studied logic.

35. Use truth tables to show that the following distributive property holds:

$$p \vee (q \wedge r) \equiv (p \vee q) \wedge (p \vee r)$$

36. Use truth tables to show that *another* distributive property holds:

$$p \wedge (q \vee r) \equiv (p \wedge q) \vee (p \wedge r)$$

4.7 GROUPS

OBJECTIVES
1 Groups
2 Symmetry Groups
3 Permutation

Groups

We have considered some mathematical systems, most of which have satisfied some or all of the closure, associative, commutative, identity, inverse, and distributive properties. Systems are commonly classified according to which properties they satisfy. One important category, when a single operation is considered, is the mathematical *group*, which we define here.

GROUP

A mathematical system is called a **group** if, under its operation, it satisfies the closure, associative, identity, and inverse properties.

Some sets of numbers, under certain operations, form groups. Others do not.

EXAMPLE 1 Checking the Group Properties

Does the set {−1, 1} under the operation of multiplication form a group?

Solution

Check the necessary four properties.

Closure The given system leads to the multiplication table below. All entries in the body of the table are either −1 or 1; the system is closed.

·	−1	1
−1	1	−1
1	−1	1

Niels Henrik Abel (1802–1829) of Norway was identified in childhood as a mathematical genius but never received in his lifetime the professional recognition his work deserved.

At 16, influenced by a perceptive teacher, he read the works of Newton, Euler, and Lagrange. One of Abel's achievements was the demonstration that a general formula for solving fifth-degree equations does not exist. The quadratic formula (for equations of degree 2) is well known, and formulas do exist for solving third- and fourth-degree equations. Abel's accomplishment ended a search that had lasted for years.

In the study of abstract algebra, groups that have the commutative property are referred to as **abelian groups** in honor of Abel. He died of tuberculosis at age 27.

Associative Try some examples:

$$-1 \cdot (-1 \cdot 1) = -1 \cdot (-1) = 1$$

and

$$[-1 \cdot (-1)] \cdot 1 = 1 \cdot 1 = 1,$$

so

$$-1 \cdot (-1 \cdot 1) = [-1 \cdot (-1)] \cdot 1.$$

Also

$$1 \cdot [(-1) \cdot 1] = 1 \cdot (-1) = -1$$

and

$$[1 \cdot (-1)] \cdot 1 = -1 \cdot 1 = -1,$$

so

$$1 \cdot [(-1) \cdot 1] = [1 \cdot (-1)] \cdot 1.$$

Any other examples likewise will work. This system satisfies the associative property.

Identity The operation table for the system shows that the identity element is 1. (The column under 1 is identical to the column at the left, and the row to the right of 1 is identical to the row at the top.)

Inverse Check in the table that -1 is its own inverse, because $-1 \cdot (-1) = 1$ (the identity element); also, 1 is its own inverse.

All four of the properties are satisfied, so the system is a group. ∎

EXAMPLE 2 Checking the Group Properties

Does the set $\{-1, 1\}$ under the operation of addition form a group?

Solution

The addition table below shows that closure is not satisfied, so there is no need to check further. The system is not a group.

+	−1	1
−1	−2	0
1	0	2

∎

EXAMPLE 3 Checking the Group Properties

Does the set of integers $\{\ldots, -3, -2, -1, 0, 1, 2, 3, \ldots\}$ under the operation of addition form a group?

Solution

Check the required properties.

Closure The sum of any two integers is an integer; the system is closed.

Associative Try some examples:

$$2 + (5 + 8) = 2 + 13 = 15$$

and

$$(2 + 5) + 8 = 7 + 8 = 15,$$

so

$$2 + (5 + 8) = (2 + 5) + 8.$$

Also

$$-4 + (7 + 14) = -4 + 21 = 17$$

and

$$(-4 + 7) + 14 = 3 + 14 = 17,$$

so

$$-4 + (7 + 14) = (-4 + 7) + 14.$$

Apparently, addition of integers is associative.

Amalie ("Emmy") Noether
(1882–1935) was an outstanding mathematician in the field of **abstract algebra.** She studied and worked in Germany at a time when it was very difficult for a woman to do so. At the University of Erlangen in 1900, Noether was one of only two women. Although she could attend classes, professors could and did deny her the right to take the exams for their courses. Not until 1904 was Noether allowed to officially register. She completed her doctorate four years later.

In 1916 Emmy Noether went to Göttingen to work with David Hilbert on the general theory of relativity. But even with Hilbert's backing and prestige, it was three years before the faculty voted to make Noether a *Privatdozent,* the lowest rank in the faculty. In 1922 Noether was made an unofficial professor (or assistant). She received no pay for this post, although she was given a small stipend to lecture in algebra.

Noether's area of interest was abstract algebra, particularly structures called rings and ideals. (Groups are structures, too, with different properties.) One special type of ring bears her name; she was the first to study its properties.

Identity   We know that $a + 0 = a$ and $0 + a = a$ for any integer a. The identity element for addition of integers is 0.

Inverse   Given any integer a, its additive inverse, $-a$, is also an integer. For example, 5 and -5 are inverses. The system satisfies the inverse property.

Since all four properties are satisfied, this (infinite) system *is* a group. ∎

Symmetry Groups

Groups can be built upon sets of objects other than numbers. An example is the group of **symmetries of a square,** which we now develop. First, cut out a small square, and label it as shown in Figure 14.

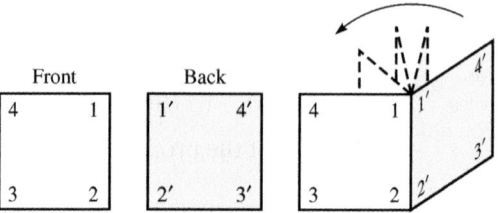

Figure 14

Make sure that 1 is in front of 1′, 2 is in front of 2′, 3 is in front of 3′, and 4 is in front of 4′. Let the letter M represent a clockwise rotation of 90° *about the center of the square* (marked with a dot in Figure 15). Let N represent a rotation of 180°, and so on. A list of the symmetries of a square is given in Figure 15.

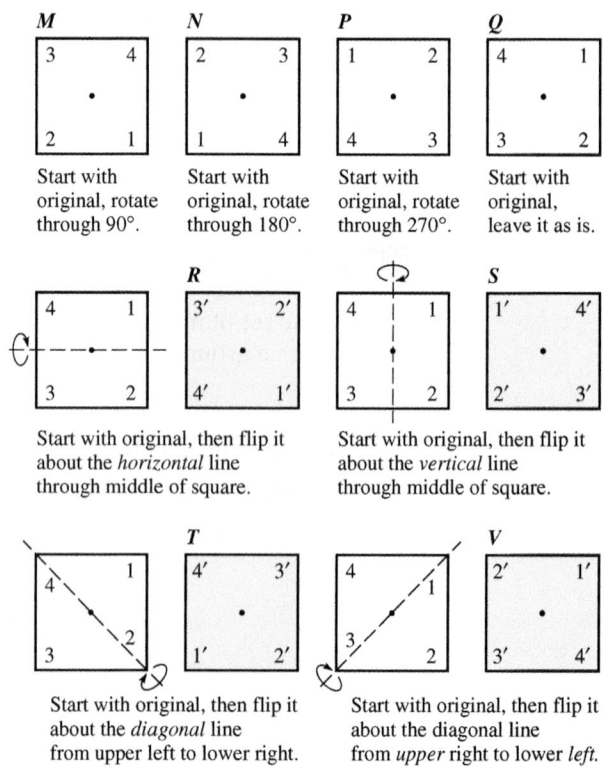

Symmetries of a square

Figure 15

Évariste Galois (1811–1832), as a young Frenchman, agreed to fight a duel. He had been engaged in profound mathematical research for some time. Now, anticipating the possibility of his death, he summarized the essentials of his discoveries in a letter to a friend. The next day Galois was killed. He was not yet 21 years old when he died.

It was not until 1846 that Galois's theories were published. Mathematicians began to appreciate the importance of Galois's work, which centered on solving equations by using groups. Galois found a way to derive a group that corresponds to each equation. So-called **Galois groups** form an important part of modern abstract algebra.

Combine symmetries as follows: Let *NP* represent *N* followed by *P*. Performing *N* and then *P* is the same as performing just *M*, so that *NP* = *M*. See Figure 16.

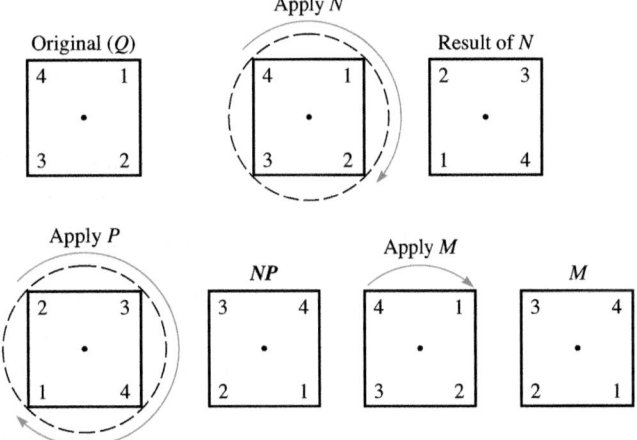

Think of N as advancing each corner two quarter turns clockwise. Thus 4 goes from upper left to lower right. To this result apply P, which advances each corner three quarter turns. Thus 2 goes from upper left to lower left. The result, NP, is the same as advancing each (original) corner one quarter turn, which M does. Thus NP = M.

Figure 16

A 2005 book by Mario Livio, titled *The Equation That Couldn't Be Solved: How Mathematical Genius Discovered the Language of Symmetry,* explores the story of Galois and Abel.

EXAMPLE 4 Combining Symmetries of a Square

Find *RT* using the symmetries of Figure 15.

Solution

First, perform *R* by flipping the square about a horizontal line through the middle. Then, perform *T* by flipping the result of *R* about a diagonal from upper left to lower right. The result of *RT* is the same as performing only *M*, so that *RT* = *M*. ■

The method in Example 4 can be used to complete Table 24 for combining the symmetries of a square.

Table 24

□	*M*	*N*	*P*	*Q*	*R*	*S*	*T*	*V*
M	N	P	Q	M	V	T	R	S
N	P	Q	M	N	S	R	V	T
P	Q	M	N	P	T	V	S	R
Q	M	N	P	Q	R	S	T	V
R	T	S	V	R	Q	N	M	P
S	V	R	T	S	N	Q	P	M
T	S	V	R	T	P	M	Q	N
V	R	T	S	V	M	P	N	Q

▓▓ EXAMPLE 5 Verifying the Group Properties

Show that the system made up of the symmetries of a square is a group.

Solution

For the system to be a group, it must satisfy the closure, associative, identity, and inverse properties.

Closure	All the entries in the body of Table 24 come from the set {*M, N, P, Q, R, S, T, V*}. Thus, the system is closed.
Associative	Try examples:

$$P(MT) = P(R) = T.$$

Also, $\quad P(MT) = (Q)T = T,$

so that $\quad P(MT) = (PM)T.$

Other similar examples also work. (See Exercises 25–28.) Thus, the system has the associative property.

Identity	The column at the left in the table is repeated under *Q*. Check that *Q* is indeed the identity element.
Inverse	In the first row, *Q* appears under *P*. Check that *M* and *P* are inverses of each other. In fact, every element in the system has an inverse. (See Exercises 29–34.)

Because all four properties are satisfied, the system is a group. ▓

▓▓ EXAMPLE 6 Verifying that a System Has a Subgroup

Table 25

□	*M*	*N*	*P*	*Q*
M	*M*	*P*	*Q*	*M*
N	*P*	*Q*	*M*	*N*
P	*Q*	*M*	*N*	*P*
Q	*M*	*N*	*P*	*Q*

Form a mathematical system by using only the set {*M, N, P, Q*} from the group of symmetries of a square. Is this new system a group?

Solution

Table 25 for the elements {*M, N, P, Q*} is just one corner of the table for the entire system. Verify that the system represented by this table satisfies all four properties and thus is a group. This new group is a *subgroup* of the original group of the symmetries of a square. ▓

Permutation Groups

A very useful example of a group comes from studying the arrangements, or permutations, of a list of numbers. Start with the symbols 1-2-3, in that order.

There are several ways in which the order could be changed—for example, 2-3-1. This rearrangement is written

1-2-3

2-3-1.

Replace 1 with 2, replace 2 with 3, and replace 3 with 1. In the same way,

1-2-3

3-1-2

means replace 1 with 3, 2 with 1, and 3 with 2, while

1-2-3

3-2-1

Much research in group theory has been devoted to "simple" groups (which are not at all simple). These groups are fundamental—other groups are built up from them. One of the largest of these simple groups has

$2^{46} \cdot 3^{20} \cdot 5^9 \cdot 7^6 \cdot 11^2 \cdot 13^3 \cdot$
$17 \cdot 19 \cdot 23 \cdot 29 \cdot 31 \cdot 41 \cdot$
$47 \cdot 59 \cdot 71$

different elements. This huge number of elements is why the group is called the **"monster group."** If this "monster group" contains too many elements, how about the "baby monster" simple group, with only

$2^{41} \cdot 3^{13} \cdot 5^6 \cdot 7^2 \cdot 11 \cdot 13 \cdot$
$17 \cdot 19 \cdot 23 \cdot 31 \cdot 47$

different elements? (For more information, see "The Classification of the Finite Simple Groups," by Michael Aschbacher in *The Mathematical Intelligencer*, Issue 2, 1981.)

says to replace 1 with 3, leave the 2 unchanged, and replace 3 with 1. All possible rearrangements of the symbols 1–2–3 are listed below where, for convenience, a name has been given to each rearrangement.

A^*: 1-2-3 B^*: 1-2-3 C^*: 1-2-3 D^*: 1-2-3 E^*: 1-2-3 F^*: 1-2-3
      2-3-1   2-1-3   1-2-3   1-3-2   3-1-2   3-2-1

Two rearrangements can be combined as with the symmetries of a square; for example, the symbol B^*F^* means to first apply B^* to 1-2-3 and then apply F^* to the result. Rearrangement B^* changes 1-2-3 into 2-1-3. Then apply F^* to this result: 1 becomes 3, 2 is unchanged, and 3 becomes 1. In summary:

The net result of B^*F^* is to change 1-2-3 into 2-3-1, which is exactly what A^* does to 1-2-3. Therefore,

$$B^*F^* = A^*.$$

EXAMPLE 7 Combining Rearrangements

Find D^*E^*.

Solution

Use the procedure described above.

1-2-3
1-3-2   Rearrange according to D^*.
3   E^* replaces 1 with 3.
3 1 E^* replaces 2 with 1.
3-2-1 E^* replaces 3 with 2.

The result is that D^*E^* converts 1-2-3 into 3-2-1, as does F^*, so

$$D^*E^* = F^*.$$

As further examples, $A^*B^* = D^*$ and $F^*E^* = B^*$.

Once again, we see that we encountered a mathematical system: the set $\{A^*, B^*, C^*, D^*, E^*, F^*\}$ and the operation of the combination of two rearrangements. To see whether this system is a group, check the requirements.

Closure   Combine any two rearrangements and the result is another rearrangement, so the system is closed.

Elie-Joseph Cartan (1869–1951) did extensive work in **group theory.** His 1894 doctoral thesis completely categorized all finite groups known at the time. The classification of *all* finite groups took 150 years and culminated with the monster group (see page 209) constructed in 1980 by Robert Griess, Jr.

Throughout the last half of the twentieth century, physicists were able to apply the structure of some of these groups to improve their understanding of the basic particles of matter and their quantum interactions, thereby enabling them to formulate ever better theories of the fundamental forces of nature.

Associative   Try an example:

First $(B*D*)A* = E*A* = C*.$
Also $B*(D*A*) = B*B* = C*$
so that $(B*D*)A* = B*(D*A*).$

Because other examples will work out similarly, the system is associative.

Identity   The identity element is $C*$. If x is any rearrangement, then we have $xC* = C*x = x.$

Inverse   Does each rearrangement have an inverse rearrangement? Begin with the basic order 1-2-3 and then apply, say $B*$, resulting in 2-1-3. The inverse of $B*$ must convert this 2-1-3 back into 1-2-3, by changing 2 into 1 and 1 into 2. But $B*$ itself will do this. Hence, $B*B* = C*$ and $B*$ is its own inverse. By the same process, $E*$ and $A*$ are inverses of each other. Also, each of $C*$, $D*$, and $F*$ is its own inverse.

Because all four requirements are satisfied, the system is a group. Rearrangements are also referred to as *permutations,* so this group is sometimes called the **permutation group on three symbols**. The total number of different permutations of a given number of symbols can be determined by techniques described in the chapter on counting methods.

4.7   EXERCISES

What is wrong with the way in which each question is stated?

1. Do the integers form a group?

2. Does multiplication satisfy all of the group properties?

Decide whether each system is a group. If not a group, identify all properties that are not satisfied. (Recall that any system failing to satisfy the identity property automatically fails to satisfy the inverse property also.) For the finite systems, it may help to construct tables. For infinite systems, try some examples to help you decide.

3. $\{0\}$; multiplication

4. $\{0\}$; addition

5. $\{0, 1\}$; addition

6. $\{0\}$; subtraction

7. $\{-1, 1\}$; division

8. $\{0, 1\}$; multiplication

9. $\{-1, 0, 1\}$; multiplication

10. $\{-1, 0, 1\}$; addition

11. integers; subtraction

12. integers; multiplication

13. odd integers; multiplication

14. counting numbers; addition

15. rational numbers; addition

16. even integers; addition

17. prime numbers; addition

18. nonzero rational numbers; multiplication

19. Explain why a *finite* group based on the operation of ordinary addition of numbers cannot contain the element 1.

20. Explain why a group based on the operation of ordinary addition of numbers *must* contain the element 0.

Exercises 21–34 apply to the system of symmetries of a square presented in the text. Find each combination.

21. *RN*   **22.** *PR*

23. *TV*   **24.** *VP*

Verify each statement.

25. $N(TR) = (NT)R$

26. $V(PS) = (VP)S$

27. $T(VN) = (TV)N$

28. $S(MR) = (SM)R$

Find the inverse of each element.

29. *N*   **30.** *Q*   **31.** *R*

32. *S*   **33.** *T*   **34.** *V*

A group that also satisfies the commutative property is called a **commutative group** *(or an* **abelian group**, *after Niels Henrik Abel). Determine whether each group is commutative.*

35. the group of symmetries of a square

36. the subgroup of Example 6

37. the integers under addition

38. the permutation group on three symbols

Give illustrations to support your answers for Exercises 39–42.

39. Produce a mathematical system with two operations which is a group under one operation but not a group under the other operation.

40. Explain what property is gained when the system of counting numbers is extended to the system of whole numbers.

41. Explain what property is gained when the system of whole numbers is extended to the system of integers.

42. Explain what property is gained when the system of integers is extended to the system of rational numbers.

Consider the following set of "actions" (A, B, C, and D) on three symbols (a, b, and c):

A: a   b   c   B: a   b   c
   a   b   c   c   b   a

C: a   b   c   D: a   b   c
   a −b   c   c −b   a

The resulting system is somewhat similar to the permutation group on three symbols discussed in the text, except that not all possible rearrangements of a, b, and c are included, and two of the actions involve sign changes. The operation of the system is the combination of actions as follows, for example, BD represents B followed by D:

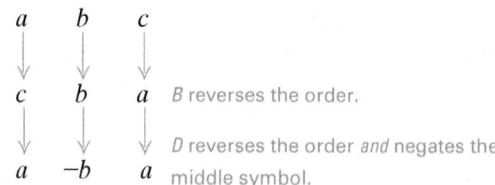

B reverses the order.

D reverses the order *and* negates the middle symbol.

The net result, from beginning to end, is simply to negate the middle symbol, which is exactly what C does. Therefore, BD = C.

43. Verify, for yourself, the entries shown in the following operation table and fill in the missing entries.

	A	*B*	*C*	*D*
A	*A*	*B*	*C*	*D*
B	*B*	*A*		*C*
C	*C*		*A*	
D	*D*			*A*

44. **(a)** Is there an identity element in this system?
   (b) If so, what is it?

45. **(a)** Is closure satisfied by this system?
   (b) Explain.

46. **(a)** Is this system commutative?
   (b) Explain.

47. **(a)** Is the distributive property satisfied in this system?
   (b) Explain.

48. **(a)** Assuming the associative property is satisfied, is the system a group?
   (b) Explain.

Collaborative Investigation

A Perpetual Calendar Algorithm

In this chapter we examined some alternative algorithms for arithmetic computations. Algorithms appear in various places in mathematics and computer science, and in each case give us a specified method of carrying out a procedure that produces a desired result. The algorithm that follows allows us to find the day of the week on which a particular date occurred or will occur.

In applying the algorithm, you will need to know whether a particular year is a leap year. In general, if a year is divisible (evenly) by 4, it is a leap year. However, there are exceptions. Century years, such as 1800 and 1900, are not leap years, despite the fact that they are divisible by 4. Furthermore, as an exception to the exception, a century year that is divisible by 400 (such as the year 2000) is a leap year.

In groups of three to five students, read the algorithm and then work the Topics for Discussion.

The Algorithm

This algorithm requires several *key numbers*. Key numbers for the month, day, and century are determined by the following tables.

Month	Key
January	1 (0 if a leap year)
February	4 (3 if a leap year)
March	4
April	0
May	2
June	5
July	0
August	3
September	6
October	1
November	4
December	6

Day	Key		Century	Key
Saturday	0		1700s	4
Sunday	1		1800s	2
Monday	2		1900s	0
Tuesday	3		2000s	6
Wednesday	4			
Thursday	5			
Friday	6			

The algorithm works as follows. (We use October 12, 1949, as an example.)

Step 1 Obtain the following five numbers.

	Example
1. The number formed by the last two digits of the year	49
2. The number in Step 1, divided by 4, with the remainder ignored	12
3. The month key (1 for October in our example)	1
4. The day of the month (12 for October 12)	12
5. The century key (0 for the 1900s)	0

Step 2 Add these five numbers. $\overline{74}$

Step 3 Divide the sum by 7, and retain the remainder. $\left(\frac{74}{7} = 10, \text{ with remainder } 4\right)$

Step 4 Find this remainder in the day key table. (The number 4 implies that October 12, 1949 was a Wednesday.)

Topics for Discussion

1. Have each person in the group determine the day of the week on which he or she was born.

2. Among the group members, discuss whether the following poem applies. (This is all in good fun, of course.)

   Monday's child is fair of face,
   Tuesday's child is full of grace.
   Wednesday's child is full of woe,
   Thursday's child has far to go.
   Friday's child is loving and giving,
   Saturday's child works hard for a living.
   But the child that is born on the Sabbath
   day is bonny and good, happy and gay.

3. Determine the day of the week on which the following important historical events occurred.
   (a) December 7, 1941 (the bombing of Pearl Harbor)
   (b) November 22, 1963 (the assassination of John F. Kennedy)
   (c) July 4, 1976 (the bicentennial of the United States)
   (d) January 1, 2000 (the "dreaded" Y2K day)
   (e) September 11, 2001 (the terrorist attacks on the United States)

CHAPTER 4   TEST

1. For the numeral ⟨numeral symbols⟩, identify the numeration system, and give the Hindu-Arabic equivalent.

2. Simplify:
$(7 \cdot 10^3) + (5 \cdot 10^2) + (6 \cdot 10^1) + (1 \cdot 10^0)$.

3. Write in expanded notation: 60,923.

4. $37 \cdot 54$ (Russian peasant or Egyptian method)

5. $236 \cdot 94$ (Lattice method)

6. $21{,}325 - 8498$ (Nines complement method)

Convert each number to base ten.

7. 324_{five} **8.** 110010_{two} **9.** $\text{DEAF}_{\text{sixteen}}$

Convert as indicated.

10. 49 to base two

11. 2930 to base five

12. 10101110_{two} to base eight

13. Find all positive solutions for the equation

$$3x - 1 \equiv 2 \ (\text{mod } 5).$$

14. Find each quantity on the 12-hour-clock.
(a) $8 + 9$ (b) $4 \cdot 10$
(c) -3 (d) $3 - 7$

15. Work each modular arithmetic problem.
(a) $(7 + 11) \ (\text{mod } 5)$ (b) $(8 \cdot 15) \ (\text{mod } 17)$

16. *Two-Dollar Bill Collection* Alec has a collection of two-dollar bills which he can arrange in groups of 5 with 3 left over, groups of 7 with 6 left over, or groups of 10 with 8 left over. What is the least number of bills he could have?

Briefly explain each of the following.

17. the advantage of multiplicative grouping over simple grouping

18. the advantage, in a positional numeration system, of a smaller base over a larger base

19. the advantage, in a positional numeration system, of a larger base over a smaller base

Answer the questions in Exercises 20–22.

20. For addition of whole numbers, what is the identity element?

21. For multiplication of rational numbers, what is the inverse of 3?

22. For any whole numbers a, b, and c, $(a + b) + c = (b + a) + c$. What property does this illustrate?

Consider the mathematical system with the set {1, 3, 5, 7} and with the operation of multiplication modulo 8.

23. Complete the operation table for the system.

∘	1	3	5	7
1	1	3	5	7
3	3	1		5
5	5		1	
7	7		3	

24. (a) Is there an identity element in this system?
(b) If so, what is it?

25. (a) Is closure satisfied by this system?
(b) Explain.

26. (a) Is this system commutative?
(b) Explain.

27. (a) Is the distributive property satisfied in this system?
(b) Explain.

28. (a) Assuming the associative property is satisfied, is the system a group?
(b) Explain.

Number Theory

5

The modern criminal justice system, like most other areas of government, the military, commerce, and personal life, is highly dependent on computer technology and the mathematical theory and algorithms underlying it. Our money, safety, and identity are protected by public key **cryptography,** which includes the processes of **encrypting** (coding) and **decrypting** (decoding) crucial information. Cryptography involves two kinds of problems:

1. Given two prime numbers, find their product.
2. Given the product, find its two prime factors.

You will learn about prime numbers in **Section 5.1.**

Cryptography systems utilize extremely large prime numbers, which are the subject of **Section 5.2.** The success of encryption depends on the fact that, given today's state of computer hardware and software, and given large enough primes, **Problem 1** above can be done, but **Problem 2** *cannot* be done, even with the most powerful computers available.

5.1 PRIME AND COMPOSITE NUMBERS

OBJECTIVES
1 Identify prime and composite numbers.
2 Apply divisibility tests for natural numbers.
3 Apply the fundamental theorem of arithmetic.

Do not confuse $b\,|\,a$ with b/a. The expression $b\,|\,a$ denotes the *statement* "b divides a." For example, $3\,|\,12$ is a true statement, while $5\,|\,14$ is a false statement. On the other hand, b/a denotes the *operation* "b divided by a." For example, $28/4$ yields the result 7.

The ideas of **even** and **odd natural numbers** are based on the concept of divisibility. A natural number is even if it is divisible by 2 and odd if it is not. Every even number can be written in the form $2k$ (for some natural number k), while every odd number can be written in the form $2k - 1$. Here is another way to say the same thing: 2 divides every even number but fails to divide every odd number. (If a is even, then $2\,|\,a$, whereas if a is odd, then $2\nmid a$.)

Primes, Composites, and Divisibility

The famous German mathematician Carl Friedrich Gauss once remarked, "Mathematics is the Queen of Science, and number theory is the Queen of Mathematics." **Number theory** is devoted to the study of the properties of the **natural numbers,** which are also called the **counting numbers** and the **positive integers.**

$$N = \{1, 2, 3, \dots\}$$

A key concept of number theory is the idea of *divisibility*. One counting number is *divisible* by another if dividing the first by the second leaves a remainder 0.

DIVISIBILITY

The natural number a is **divisible** by the natural number b if there exists a natural number k such that $a = bk$. If b divides a, then we write $b\,|\,a.$

Notice that if b divides a, then the quotient a/b or $\frac{a}{b}$ is a natural number. For example, 4 divides 20 because there exists a natural number k such that

$$20 = 4k.$$

The value of k here is 5, because

$$20 = 4 \cdot 5.$$

The natural number 20 is not divisible by 7, since there is no natural number k satisfying $20 = 7k$. Alternatively, "20 divided by 7 gives quotient 2 with remainder 6," and since there is a nonzero remainder, divisibility does not hold. We write $7\nmid 20$ to indicate that 7 does *not* divide 20.

If the natural number a is divisible by the natural number b, then b is a **factor** (or **divisor**) of a, and a is a **multiple** of b. For example, 5 is a factor of 30, and 30 is a multiple of 5. Also, 6 is a factor of 30, and 30 is a multiple of 6. The number 30 equals $6 \cdot 5$. This product $6 \cdot 5$ is called a **factorization** of 30. Other factorizations of 30 include

$$3 \cdot 10, \quad 2 \cdot 15, \quad 1 \cdot 30, \quad \text{and} \quad 2 \cdot 3 \cdot 5.$$

EXAMPLE 1 Checking Divisibility

Decide whether the first number is divisible by the second.

(a) 45; 9 **(b)** 60; 7 **(c)** 19; 19 **(d)** 26; 1

Solution

(a) Is there a natural number k that satisfies $45 = 9k$? The answer is yes, because $45 = 9 \cdot 5$, and 5 is a natural number. Therefore, 9 divides 45, written $9\,|\,45$.

(b) Because the quotient $60 \div 7$ is not a natural number, 60 is not divisible by 7, written $7\nmid 60$.

(c) The quotient $19 \div 19$ is the natural number 1, so 19 is divisible by 19. (***In fact, any natural number is divisible by itself.***)

(d) The quotient $26 \div 1$ is the natural number 26, so 26 is divisible by 1. (***In fact, any natural number is divisible by 1.***)

For any natural number a, it is true that $a\,|\,a$ and also that $1\,|\,a$.

EXAMPLE 2 Finding Factors

Find all the natural number factors of each number.

(a) 36   **(b)** 50   **(c)** 11

Solution

(a) To find the factors of 36, try to divide 36 by 1, 2, 3, 4, 5, 6, and so on. This gives the following natural number factors of 36: 1, 2, 3, 4, 6, 9, 12, 18, and 36.

(b) The factors of 50 are 1, 2, 5, 10, 25, and 50.

(c) The only natural number factors of 11 are 11 and 1.   ∎

How to Use Up Lots of Chalk In 1903, the mathematician F. N. Cole presented before a meeting of the American Mathematical Society his discovery of a factorization of the number

$$2^{67} - 1.$$

He walked up to the chalkboard, raised 2 to the 67th power, and then subtracted 1. Then he moved over to another part of the board and multiplied out

$$193{,}707{,}721 \times 761{,}838{,}257{,}287.$$

The two calculations agreed, and Cole received a standing ovation for a presentation that did not include a single word.

PRIME AND COMPOSITE NUMBERS

A natural number greater than 1 that has only itself and 1 as factors is called a **prime number.** A natural number greater than 1 that is not prime is called **composite.**

Mathematicians agree that the natural number 1 is neither prime nor composite.

ALTERNATIVE DEFINITION OF A PRIME NUMBER

A **prime number** is a natural number that has *exactly* two different natural number factors (which clarifies that 1 is not a prime).

There is a systematic method for identifying prime numbers in a list of numbers: $2, 3, \ldots, n$. The method, known as the **Sieve of Eratosthenes,** is named after the Greek geographer, poet, astronomer, and mathematician (about 276–192 B.C.).

To construct such a sieve, list all the natural numbers from 2 through some given natural number n, such as 100. The number 2 is prime, but all other multiples of 2 (4, 6, 8, 10, and so on) are composite. Circle the prime 2, and cross out all other multiples of 2. The next number not crossed out and not circled is 3, the next prime. Circle the 3, and cross out all other multiples of 3 (6, 9, 12, 15, and so on) that are not already crossed out. Circle the next prime, 5, and cross out all other multiples of 5 not already crossed out. Continue this process for all primes less than or equal to the square root of the last number in the list. For this list, we may stop with 7, because the next prime, 11, is greater than the square root of 100, which is 10. At this stage, simply circle all remaining numbers that are not crossed out.

Table 1 shows the Sieve of Eratosthenes for $2, 3, 4, \ldots, 100$.

Table 1 Sieve of Eratosthenes

The 25 primes between 1 and 100 are circled.

In the October 1, 1994 issue of *Science News*, Ivars Peterson gave a fascinating account of the discovery of a 75-year-old **factoring machine** ("Cranking Out Primes: Tracking Down a Long-lost Factoring Machine"). In 1989, Jeffrey Shallit of the University of Waterloo in Ontario came across an article in an obscure 1920 French journal, in which the author, Eugene Olivier Carissan, reported his invention of the factoring apparatus. Shallit and two colleagues embarked on a search for the machine. They contacted all telephone subscribers in France named Carissan and received a reply from Eugene Carissan's daughter. The machine was still in existence and in working condition, stored in a drawer at an astronomical observatory in Floirac, near Bordeaux.

Peterson explains in the article how the apparatus works. Using the machine, Carissan took just ten minutes to prove that 708,158,977 is a prime number, and he was able to factor a 13-digit number. While this cannot compare to what technology can accomplish today, it was a significant achievement for Carissan's day.

EXAMPLE 3 Identifying Prime and Composite Numbers

Decide whether each number is prime or composite.

(a) 89   **(b)** 83,572   **(c)** 629

Solution

(a) Because 89 is circled in **Table 1,** it is prime. If 89 had a smaller prime factor, 89 would have been crossed out as a multiple of that factor.

(b) The number 83,572 is even, so it is divisible by 2. It is composite.

> ***There is only one even prime, the number 2 itself.***

(c) For 629 to be composite, there must be a number other than 629 and 1 that divides into it with remainder 0. Start by trying 2, and then 3. Neither works. There is no need to try 4. (If 4 divides with remainder 0 into a number, then 2 will also.) Try 5. There is no need to try 6 or any succeeding even number. (Why?) Try 7. Try 11. (Why not try 9?) Try 13. Keep trying numbers until one works, or until a number is tried whose square exceeds the given number, 629. Try 17.

$$629 \div 17 = 37$$

The number 629 is composite, since

$$629 = 17 \cdot 37.$$ ∎

An aid in determining whether a natural number is divisible by another natural number is called a **divisibility test. Table 2** shows tests for divisibility by the natural numbers 2 through 12 (except for 7 and 11, which are covered in the exercises).

Table 2 Divisibility Tests for Natural Numbers

Divisible by	Test	Example
2	Number ends in 0, 2, 4, 6, or 8. (The last digit is even.)	9,489,994 ends in 4; it is divisible by 2.
3	Sum of the digits is divisible by 3.	897,432 is divisible by 3, since $8 + 9 + 7 + 4 + 3 + 2 = 33$ is divisible by 3.
4	Last two digits form a number divisible by 4.	7,693,432 is divisible by 4, since 32 is divisible by 4.
5	Number ends in 0 or 5.	890 and 7635 are divisible by 5.
6	Number is divisible by both 2 and 3.	27,342 is divisible by 6 since it is divisible by both 2 and 3.
8	Last three digits form a number divisible by 8.	1,437,816 is divisible by 8, since 816 is divisible by 8.
9	Sum of the digits is divisible by 9.	428,376,105 is divisible by 9 since the sum of the digits is 36, which is divisible by 9.
10	The last digit is 0.	897,463,940 is divisible by 10.
12	Number is divisible by both 4 and 3.	376,984,032 is divisible by 12.

The following program, written by Charles W. Gantner and provided courtesy of Texas Instruments, can be used on the TI-83 Plus calculator to list all primes less than or equal to a given natural number *N*.

```
PROGRAM: PRIMES
: Disp "INPUT N ≥ 2"
: Disp "TO GET"
: Disp "PRIMES ≤ N"
: Input N
: 2 → T
: Disp T
: 1 → A
: Lbl 1
: A + 2 → A
: 3 → B
: If A > N
: Stop
: Lbl 2
: If B ≤ √(A)
: Goto 3
: Disp A
: Pause
: Goto 1
: Lbl 3
: If A/B ≤ int (A/B)
: Goto 1
: B + 2 → B
: Goto 2
```

```
prgmPRIMES

INPUT N≥2
TO GET
PRIMES ≤ N
?6
```

```
TO GET
PRIMES ≤ N
?6
                    2
                    3
                    5
                 Done
```

The display indicates that the primes less than or equal to 6 are 2, 3, and 5.

EXAMPLE 4 Applying Divisibility Tests

In each case, decide whether the first number is divisible by the second.

(a) 2,984,094; 4   **(b)** 2,429,806,514; 9

Solution

(a) The last two digits form the number 94. Since 94 is not divisible by 4, the given number is not divisible by 4.

(b) The sum of the digits is

$$2 + 4 + 2 + 9 + 8 + 0 + 6 + 5 + 1 + 4 = 41,$$

which is not divisible by 9. The given number is, therefore, not divisible by 9. ∎

The Fundamental Theorem of Arithmetic

A *composite* number can be thought of as "composed" of smaller factors. For example, 42 is composite since $42 = 6 \cdot 7$. If the smaller factors are all primes, then we have a *prime factorization*. For example, $42 = 2 \cdot 3 \cdot 7$.

THE FUNDAMENTAL THEOREM OF ARITHMETIC

Every natural number can be expressed in one and only one way as a product of primes (if the order of the factors is disregarded). This unique product of primes is called the **prime factorization** of the natural number.

Because a prime natural number is not composed of smaller factors, its prime factorization is simply itself. For example, $17 = 17$.

EXAMPLE 5 Finding the Unique Prime Factorization of a Composite Number

Find the prime factorization of the number 1320.

Solution

We use a "factor tree." The factor tree can start with $1320 = 2 \cdot 660$, as shown below on the left. Then $660 = 2 \cdot 330$, and so on, until every branch of the tree ends with a prime. All the resulting prime factors are shown circled in the diagram.

Alternatively, the same factorization is obtained by repeated division by primes, as shown on the right. (In general, you would divide by the primes 2, 3, 5, 7, 11, and so on, each as many times as possible, until the answer is no longer composite.)

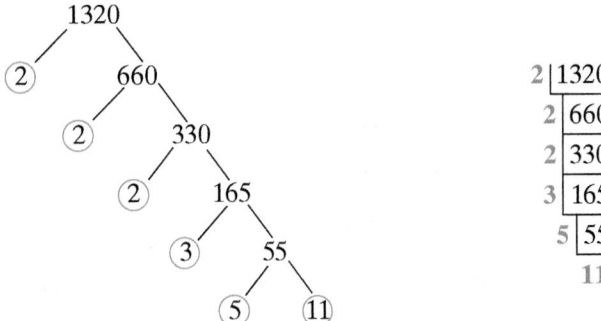

By either method, the prime factorization, in exponential form, is

$$1320 = 2^3 \cdot 3 \cdot 5 \cdot 11. \quad {\scriptstyle 2 \cdot 2 \cdot 2 = 2^3}$$ ∎

FOR FURTHER THOUGHT

Prime Factor Splicing

Prime factor splicing (PFS) has received increasing attention in recent years. A good basic explanation can be found in the article "Home Primes and Their Families," in *Mathematics Teacher*, vol. 107, no. 8, April 2014. Like many topics in number theory, PFS concerns easily stated problems but quickly leads to difficult and unanswered questions. Here is the process:

• Begin with a composite natural number, say 15.
• Obtain its prime factorization: $15 = 3 \cdot 5$
• Form a new natural number by arranging all the prime factors, in ascending order: 35
• Repeat the steps until a prime number is produced, called the **home prime.** For 15, we can summarize the entire process as shown here.

$$15 = 3 \cdot 5 \rightarrow 35 = 5 \cdot 7 \rightarrow 57 = 3 \cdot 19 \rightarrow 319 = 11 \cdot 29$$
$$\rightarrow 1129 \text{ (a prime)}$$

If we call the prime 1129 the "parent," then the composite 15 is its "child." If two or more children are found to have the same parent, call them "siblings." The Sieve of Eratosthenes (see **page 217**) provides plenty of composites to get started. We consider just a few arbitrarily chosen examples here. To do very much prime factor splicing, you would want to use some computer algebra system (CAS) for the factoring. In the case above, the child is 15, the parent is 1129, and the four arrows show that it took four iterations to get from child to parent.

For Group or Individual Investigation

Complete the table, and then answer the questions that follow it.

Child	Number of Iterations	Parent
4	_____	_____
6	_____	_____
9	_____	_____
10	_____	_____
12	_____	_____
22	_____	_____
25	_____	_____
33	_____	_____
46	_____	_____
55	_____	_____

Questions

• Is it possible for a child to have more than one parent?
• Can a parent have more than one child?
• It is possible for PFS to require at least _____ iterations.
• It is possible for a family to include at least _____ siblings.
• Show that if 49 and 77 both have parents, they must be the same.

Interesting Facts

• The child 80 requires 31 iterations and has a 48-digit prime parent.
• 49 and 77 have been "spliced" to at least 110 and 109 iterations, respectively, and no one knows whether a parent exists for them.

5.1 EXERCISES

Decide whether each statement is true *or* false.

1. If n is a natural number and $9 \mid n$, then $3 \mid n$.

2. If n is a natural number and $5 \mid n$, then $10 \mid n$.

3. Every natural number is divisible by 1.

4. There are no even prime numbers.

5. 1 is the least prime number.

6. Every natural number is both a factor and a multiple of itself.

7. If 16 divides a natural number, then 2, 4, and 8 must also divide that natural number.

8. The prime number 53 has exactly two natural number factors.

Find all natural number factors of each number.

9. 12

10. 20

11. 28

12. 172

Use divisibility tests to decide whether the given number is divisible by each number.

(a) 2 **(b)** 3 **(c)** 4 **(d)** 5 **(e)** 6 **(f)** 8

(g) 9 **(h)** 10 **(i)** 12

13. 321

14. 540

15. 36,360

16. 123,456,789

17. (a) In constructing the Sieve of Eratosthenes for 2 through 100, we said that any composite in that range had to be a multiple of some prime less than or equal to 7 (since the next prime, 11, is greater than the square root of 100). Explain.

(b) To extend the Sieve of Eratosthenes to 200, what is the largest prime whose multiples would have to be considered?

(c) Complete this statement: In seeking prime factors of a given number, we need only consider all primes up to and including the _____ of that number, since a prime factor greater than the _____ can occur only if there is at least one other prime factor less than the _____.

(d) Complete this statement: If no prime less than or equal to $\sqrt{n}$ divides n, then n is a _____ number.

18. (a) Continue the Sieve of Eratosthenes in **Table 1** from 101 to 200 and list the primes between 100 and 200. How many are there?

(b) From your list in part (a), verify that the numbers 197 and 199 are both prime.

19. In your list for **Exercise 18(a),** consider the six largest primes less than 200. Which pairs of these would have products that end in the digit 7?

20. By checking your pairs of primes from **Exercise 19,** give the prime factorization of 35,657.

21. List two primes that are consecutive natural numbers. Can there be any others?

22. Can there be three primes that are consecutive natural numbers? Explain.

23. For a natural number to be divisible by both 2 and 5, what must be true about its last digit?

24. Consider the divisibility tests for 2, 4, and 8 (all powers of 2). Use inductive reasoning to predict the divisibility test for 16. Then use the test to show that 456,882,320 is divisible by 16.

25. Redraw the factor tree of **Example 5,** assuming that you first observe that $1320 = 12 \cdot 110$, then that $12 = 3 \cdot 4$ and $110 = 10 \cdot 11$. Complete the process and give the resulting prime factorization.

26. Explain how your result in **Exercise 25** illustrates the fundamental theorem of arithmetic.

Find the prime factorization of each composite number.

27. 126

28. 825

29. 1183

30. 340

Here is a divisibility test for 7.

(a) *Double the last digit of the given number, and subtract this value from the given number with the last digit omitted.*

(b) *Repeat the process of part (a) as many times as necessary until it is clear whether the number obtained is divisible by 7.*

(c) *If the final number obtained is divisible by 7, then the given number also is divisible by 7. If the final number is not divisible by 7, then neither is the given number.*

Use this divisibility test to determine whether each number is divisible by 7.

31. 226,233

32. 548,184

33. 496,312

34. 368,597

Here is a divisibility test for 11.

(a) *Starting at the left of the given number, add together every other digit.*

(b) *Add together the remaining digits.*

(c) *Subtract the smaller of the two sums from the larger. (If they are the same, the difference is 0.)*

(d) *If the final number obtained is divisible by 11, then the given number also is divisible by 11. If the final number is not divisible by 11, then neither is the given number.*

Use this divisibility test to determine whether each number is divisible by 11.

35. 6,524,846

36. 108,410,313

37. 60,128,459,358

38. 29,630,419,088

39. Consider the divisibility test for the composite number 6, and make a conjecture for the divisibility test for the composite number 15.

40. Give two factorizations of the number 75 that are not prime factorizations.

Determine all possible digit replacements for x so that the first number is divisible by the second. For example, 37,58x is divisible by 2 if

$$x = 0, 2, 4, 6, \text{ or } 8.$$

41. 398,87x; 2

42. 2,45x,765; 3

43. 64,537,84x; 4

44. 2,143,89x; 5

45. 985,23x; 6

46. 23, x54,470; 10

*There is a method to determine the **number of divisors** of a composite number. To do this, write the composite number in its prime factored form, using exponents. Add 1 to each exponent and multiply these numbers. Their product gives the number of divisors of the composite number. For example,*

$$24 = 2^3 \cdot 3 = 2^3 \cdot 3^1.$$

Now add 1 to each exponent:

$$3 + 1 = 4, \ 1 + 1 = 2.$$

Multiply $4 \cdot 2$ to get 8. There are 8 divisors of 24. (Because 24 is rather small, this can be verified easily. The divisors are 1, 2, 3, 4, 6, 8, 12, and 24—a total of eight, as predicted.)

Find the number of divisors of each composite number.

47. 105

48. 156

49. $5^8 \cdot 29^2$

50. $2^4 \cdot 7^2 \cdot 13^3$

Leap years occur when the year number is divisible by 4. An exception to this occurs when the year number is divisible by 100 (that is, it ends in two zeros). In such a case, the number must be divisible by 400 in order for the year to be a leap year. Determine which years are leap years.

51. 1556

52. 1990

53. 2200

54. 2400

55. Why is the following *not* a valid divisibility test for the number 8? "A number is divisible by 8 if it is divisible by both 4 and 2." Support your answer with an appropriate example.

56. Choose any three consecutive natural numbers, multiply them together, and divide the product by 6. Repeat this several times, using different choices of three consecutive numbers. Make a conjecture concerning the result.

57. Explain why the product of three consecutive natural numbers must be divisible by 6. Include examples in your explanation.

58. Choose any 6-digit number consisting of three digits followed by the same three digits in the same order (for example, 467,467). Divide by 13. Divide by 11. Divide by 7. What do you notice? Why do you think this happens?

*One of the authors has three sons who were born, from eldest to youngest, on August 30, August 31, and October 14. For most (but not all) of each year, their ages are spaced two years from the eldest to the middle and three years from the middle to the youngest. In 2011, their ages were three consecutive prime numbers for a period of exactly 44 days. This same situation had also occurred in exactly two previous years. Use this information for **Exercises 59–62**. (Hint: Consult the Sieve of Eratosthenes on **page 217** for a listing of all primes less than 100.)*

59. Which were the "two previous years" referred to above?

60. What were the years of birth of the three sons?

61. In what year will the same situation next occur?

62. What will be the ages of the three sons at that time?

5.2 LARGE PRIME NUMBERS

OBJECTIVES

1 Understand the infinitude of primes.

2 Investigate several categories of prime numbers.

3 Learn how large primes are identified.

The Infinitude of Primes

One important basic result about prime numbers was proved by Euclid around 300 B.C., namely that there are infinitely many primes. This means that no matter how large a prime we identify, there are always others even larger. Euclid's proof remains today as one of the most elegant proofs in all of mathematics. (An *elegant* mathematical proof is one that demonstrates the desired result in a most direct, concise manner. Mathematicians strive for elegance in their proofs.) It is called a **proof by contradiction.**

A statement can be proved by contradiction as follows: Assume that the negation of the statement is true, and use that assumption to produce some sort of contradiction, or absurdity. Logically, the fact that the negation of the original statement leads to a contradiction means that the original statement must be true.

To better understand a particular part of the proof that there are infinitely many primes, first examine the following argument.

Suppose that $M = 2 \cdot 3 \cdot 5 \cdot 7 + 1 = 211$. Now M is the product of the first four prime numbers, plus 1. If we divide 211 by each of the primes 2, 3, 5, and 7, the remainder is always 1.

$$
\begin{array}{cccc}
105 & 70 & 42 & 30 \\
2\overline{)211} & 3\overline{)211} & 5\overline{)211} & 7\overline{)211} \\
\underline{210} & \underline{210} & \underline{210} & \underline{210} \\
1 & 1 & 1 & 1
\end{array}
$$

All remainders are 1.

Thus 211 is not divisible by any of the primes 2, 3, 5, and 7.

Now we can present Euclid's proof that there are infinitely many primes. If *there is no largest prime number,* then there must be infinitely many primes.

EXAMPLE 1   Proving the Infinitude of Primes

Prove by contradiction that there are infinitely many primes.

Solution

Suppose there is a largest prime number, called P. Form the number M such that

$$M = p_1 \cdot p_2 \cdot p_3 \cdots P + 1,$$

where $p_1, p_2, p_3, \ldots, P$ represent all the primes less than or equal to P. Now the number M must be either prime or composite.

1. Suppose that M is prime.
   M is obviously larger than P, so if M is prime, it is larger than the assumed largest prime P. We have reached a *contradiction*.

2. Suppose that M is composite.
   If M is composite, it must have a prime factor. But none of $p_1, p_2, p_3, \ldots, P$ is a factor of M, because division by each will leave a remainder of 1. (Recall the above argument.) So if M has a prime factor, it must be greater than P. But this is a *contradiction,* because P is the assumed largest prime.

In either case 1 or case 2, we reach a contradiction. The whole argument was based on the assumption that a largest prime exists, but this leads to contradictions, so there must be no largest prime, or, equivalently, ***there are infinitely many primes.*** ∎

We could never investigate all infinitely many primes directly. So, historically, people have observed properties of the smaller, familiar, ones and then tried to either "disprove" the property (usually by finding counterexamples) or prove it (usually by some deductive argument).

Here is one way to **partition** the natural numbers (divide them into disjoint subsets).

Set A: all natural numbers of the form $4k$

Set B: all natural numbers of the form $4k + 1$

Set C: all natural numbers of the form $4k + 2$

Set D: all natural numbers of the form $4k + 3$

In each case, k is some whole number, except that for set A, k cannot be 0. (Why?) Every natural number is now contained in exactly one of the sets A, B, C, or D. Any number of the form $4k + 4$ would be in subset A, because

$$4k + 4 = 4(k + 1).$$

Any number of the form $4k + 5$ would be in subset B, because

$$4k + 5 = 4(k + 1) + 1, \quad \text{and so on.}$$

Marin Mersenne (1588–1648), in his *Cogitata Physico-Mathematica* (1644), claimed that M_n was prime for $n = 2, 3, 5, 7, 13, 17, 19, 31, 67, 127,$ and 257, and composite for all other prime numbers n less than 257. Other mathematicians at the time knew that Mersenne could not have actually tested all these values, but no one else could prove or disprove them either. It was more then 300 years before all primes up to 257 were legitimately checked out, and Mersenne was finally revealed to have made five errors:

M_{61} is prime.

M_{67} is composite.

M_{89} is prime.

M_{107} is prime.

M_{257} is composite.

At one time, $2^{11,213} - 1$ was the largest known **Mersenne prime.** To honor its discovery, the Urbana, Illinois, post office used the cancellation picture above.

The subset A consists of all the multiples of 4. Each of these is divisible by 4; hence, each is not a prime. Now consider C. Because

$$4k + 2 = 2(2k + 1),$$

each member is divisible by 2; hence, each is not a prime (except for 2 itself).

Under this partitioning, all primes other than 2 must be in either B or D.

EXAMPLE 2 Partitioning the Natural Numbers

List the first eight members of each of the infinite sets A, B, C, and D.

Solution

$A = \{4, 8, 12, 16, 20, 24, 28, 32, \dots\}$; $B = \{1, 5, 9, 13, 17, 21, 25, 29, \dots\}$

$C = \{2, 6, 10, 14, 18, 22, 26, 30, \dots\}$; $D = \{3, 7, 11, 15, 19, 23, 27, 31, \dots\}$ ■

As mentioned earlier, sets A and C contain no primes except 2. All other primes must lie in sets B and D. (In fact, there are infinitely many primes in each.)

EXAMPLE 3 Identifying Primes of the Forms $4k + 1$ and $4k + 3$

Identify all primes *specifically listed* in the following infinite sets of **Example 2.**

(a) set B **(b)** set D

Solution

(a) $5, 13, 17, 29$ **(b)** $3, 7, 11, 19, 23, 31$ ■

Pierre de Fermat (profiled on **page 239**) proved that every prime number of the form $4k + 1$ can be expressed as the sum of two squares.

EXAMPLE 4 Expressing Primes as Sums of Squares

Express each prime in the solution of **Example 3(a)** as a sum of two squares.

Solution

$5 = 1^2 + 2^2$; $13 = 2^2 + 3^2$; $17 = 1^2 + 4^2$; $29 = 2^2 + 5^2$ ■

The Search for Large Primes

Identifying larger and larger prime numbers and factoring large composite numbers into their prime components is of great practical importance today, because it is the basis of modern **cryptography systems.** (See the chapter opener.)

No reasonable formula has ever been found that will consistently generate prime numbers, much less "generate all primes." The most useful attempt, named to honor the French monk Marin Mersenne (1588–1648), follows.

MERSENNE NUMBERS AND MERSENNE PRIMES

For $n = 1, 2, 3, \dots$, the **Mersenne numbers** are those generated by the formula

$$M_n = 2^n - 1.$$

(1) If n is composite, then M_n is also composite.

(2) If n is prime, then M_n may be either prime or composite.

The prime values of M_n are called the **Mersenne primes.** Large primes being verified currently are typically Mersenne primes.

Long before Mersenne's time, there was general agreement on statement (1) in the box. (**Exercises 23–25** show how to find a factor of $2^n - 1$ whenever n is composite.) However, some early writers did not agree with statement (2), believing instead (incorrectly) that a prime n would always produce a prime M_n.

EXAMPLE 5 Finding Mersenne Numbers

Find each Mersenne number M_n for $n = 2$, 3, and 5.

Solution

$$M_2 = 2^2 - 1 = 3 \quad {\scriptstyle 2^2 = 2 \cdot 2 = 4}$$
$$M_3 = 2^3 - 1 = 7 \quad {\scriptstyle 2^3 = 2 \cdot 2 \cdot 2 = 8}$$
$$M_5 = 2^5 - 1 = 31 \quad {\scriptstyle 2^5 = 2 \cdot 2 \cdot 2 \cdot 2 \cdot 2 = 32}$$

Note that all three values, 3, 7, and 31, are indeed primes. ∎

It turns out that $M_7 = 2^7 - 1 = 127$ is also a prime (see **Exercise 18(a)** of **Section 5.1**), but it was discovered in 1536 that

$$M_{11} = 2^{11} - 1 = 2047 \quad \text{is not prime (since it is } 23 \cdot 89).$$

So prime values of n do* not *always produce prime M_n. Which prime values of n *do* produce prime Mersenne numbers (the so-called **Mersenne primes**)? No way was ever found to identify, in general, which prime values of n result in Mersenne primes. It is a matter of checking out each prime n value individually—not an easy task given that the Mersenne numbers rapidly become very large.

The Mersenne prime search yielded results slowly. By about 1600, M_n had been verified as prime for all prime n up to 19 (except for 11, as mentioned above). The next one was M_{31}, verified by Euler sometime between 1752 and 1772.

In 1876, French mathematician Edouard Lucas used a clever test he had developed to show that M_{127} (a 39-digit number) is prime. In the 1930s Lucas's method was further simplified by D. H. Lehmer, and the testing of Mersenne numbers for primality has been done ever since with the Lucas-Lehmer test. In 1952 an early computer verified that M_{521}, M_{607}, M_{1279}, M_{2203}, and M_{2281} are primes.

Over the last half century, most new record-breaking primes have been identified by computer algorithms devised and implemented by mathematicians and programmers. In 1996, the **Great Internet Mersenne Prime Search (GIMPS)** was launched and now involves well over 900,000 CPUs worldwide. Of the 48 Mersenne primes presently known, the GIMPS program has discovered the fourteen largest ones. The latest one found (as of summer 2014),

$$M_{57,885,161} = 2^{57,885,161} - 1,$$

has 17,425,170 digits.

During the same general period that Mersenne was thinking about prime numbers, Pierre de Fermat (about 1601–1665) conjectured that the formula

$$2^{2^n} + 1$$

would always produce a prime, for any whole number value of n. **Table 3** on the next page shows how this formula generates the first four **Fermat numbers,** which are all primes. The fifth Fermat number (from $n = 4$) is likewise prime. Fermat had verified these first five by around 1630. But the sixth Fermat number (from $n = 5$) turns out to be 4,294,967,297, which is *not* prime. (See **Exercises 15 and 16.**)

Prime Does Pay Since August 23, 2008, GIMPS has offered participants (individuals or groups) these awards:

- $3000 GIMPS research award for a new Mersenne prime with fewer than 100,000,000 (decimal) digits
- $50,000 for the first prime discovered with at least 100,000,000 (decimal) digits

This second award is one-third of $150,000 offered by the Electronic Frontier Foundation (EFF). GIMPS plans to retain another $50,000 for expenses and the final $50,000 to fund past and/or future awards. EFF seeks, by its sponsorship, to "encourage the harmonious integration of Internet innovation into the whole of society."

As of late 2014, no more Fermat primes had been found. All F_n were known to be composite for $5 \leq n \leq 32$, but only F_0 to F_{11} had been completely factored.

Table 3 The Generation of Fermat Numbers

n	2^n	2^{2^n}	$2^{2^n} + 1$
0	1	2	3
1	2	4	5
2	4	16	17
3	8	256	257

Of historical interest are a couple of polynomial formulas that produce primes. (A *polynomial* in a given variable involves adding or subtracting integer multiples of whole number powers of the variable. Discussed in **Section 7.6,** polynomials are among the most basic mathematical functions.) In 1732, Leonhard Euler offered the formula

$$n^2 - n + 41, \quad \text{Euler's formula}$$

which generates primes for n up to 40 and fails at $n = 41$. In 1879, E. B. Escott produced more primes with the formula

$$n^2 - 79n + 1601, \quad \text{Escott's formula}$$

which first fails at $n = 80$.

EXAMPLE 6 Finding Numbers Using Euler's and Escott's Formulas

Find the first five numbers produced by each of the polynomial formulas of Euler and Escott.

Solution

Table 4 shows the required numbers.

Table 4 A Few Polynomial-Generated Prime Numbers

n	Euler formula $n^2 - n + 41$	Escott formula $n^2 - 79n + 1601$
1	41	1523
2	43	1447
3	47	1373
4	53	1301
5	61	1231

All values found here are primes. (Use **Table 1** to verify the Euler values.) ∎

Actually, it is not hard to prove that there can be no polynomial that will consistently generate primes. More complicated mathematical formulas exist for generating primes, but none produced so far can be practically applied in a reasonable amount of time, even using the fastest computers.

WHEN Will I Ever USE This ?

Imagine working for the U.S. Department of Justice as part of the effort to control cybercrime. Your work would surely involve Internet security. A recent ransomware scheme involved encrypting victims' computer files and then demanding payment for the decryption key to regain access.)

The chapter opener described the central role of multiplying large primes and factoring their products in public key cryptography. Another key mathematical component is **modular systems.** The partitioning of the natural numbers described on **page 223** is an example. In that case every natural number n was, in a sense, equated with one of just four numbers, 0, 1, 2, 3 — the remainders when n is divided by 4. In general, the divisor, any natural number greater than 1, is called the modulus (m), and the remainder, called the **residue,** is denoted n (mod m). For example,

$$849{,}657{,}221 \ (\text{mod } 215)$$

denotes the remainder when 849,657,221 is divided by 215. Using a calculator may produce

$$\frac{849{,}657{,}221}{215} = 3951894.051.$$

Subtract the integer part, 3951894. (We want the remainder only, represented by the fractional part.) Now the calculator may display

$$.0511628.$$

Multiply this result by the divisor, 215, to obtain 11. (Round if necessary — A slight error may result from the calculator's inherent limited number of significant digits.) The desired remainder, or residue, is 11. This establishes that

$$849{,}657{,}221 = 3{,}951{,}894 \cdot 215 + 11.$$

Now consider an even larger number. Try to find the remainder when 11^{14} is divided by 18. The number 11^{14} is so large that the calculator displays it in exponential notation:

$$11^{14} = 3.797498336\text{E}14$$

and

$$\frac{11^{14}}{18} = 2.109721298\text{E}13.$$

The calculator cannot display enough significant digits to reveal the integer portion of the result, so we cannot proceed as before. But we can apply a rule of exponents (see **Chapter 7**) and modular arithmetic as follows.

$$11^{14} \ (\text{mod } 18) = 11^{7+7} \ (\text{mod } 18) \qquad 14 = 7 + 7$$

$$= (11^7 \cdot 11^7) \ (\text{mod } 18) \qquad \text{Rule of exponents}$$

$$= [11^7 \ (\text{mod } 18)] \cdot [11^7 \ (\text{mod } 18)] \qquad \text{Modular arithmetic}$$

Now

$$11^7 = 19{,}487{,}171 \qquad \text{Use a calculator.}$$

$$\frac{19{,}487{,}171}{18} = 1082620.6\overline{1}$$

and

$$.6\overline{1} \cdot 18 = 11.$$

Therefore,

$$11^7 \ (\text{mod } 18) = 11$$

$$11^{14} \ (\text{mod } 18) = 11 \cdot 11 = 121$$

$$\frac{121}{18} = 6.7\overline{2}$$

$$.7\overline{2} \cdot 18 = 13.$$

The desired remainder, or residue, is 13.

These examples give a hint of the mathematics involved. But in practice the numbers would be much, much larger, and high-powered computers would be used.

5.2 EXERCISES

In Exercises 1–6 decide whether each statement is true *or* false.

1. A proof by contradiction assumes the negation of a statement and proceeds until a contradiction is encountered.

2. Marin Mersenne gave the first proof that there are infinitely many prime numbers.

3. If n is prime, then $2^n - 1$ must be prime also.

4. There are infinitely many Fermat numbers.

5. There can be no polynomial formula that consistently generates prime numbers.

6. As of late 2014, only five Fermat primes had ever been found.

7. Find the next three primes, of the form $4k + 1$, *not* listed specifically in **Example 3(a),** and express them as sums of squares.

8. Recall the first few perfect squares: 1, 4, 9, 16, 25. Try writing the numbers of the form $4k + 3$ listed in **Example 3(b)** as sums of two squares. Then complete this statement: The primes tested, of the form $4k + 3$, _____ be expressed as the sum of two squares. (Fermat claimed, but did not prove, that *no* prime of the form $4k + 3$ was the sum of two squares. Euler proved it 100 years later.)

9. Explain how the expressions $4k$, $4k + 1$, $4k + 2$, and $4k + 3$ serve to "partition" the natural numbers.

10. Explain why **Example 4** does not prove that every prime of the form $4k + 1$ can be expressed as a sum of two squares.

11. Evaluate Euler's polynomial formula for each of the following, and determine whether each value is prime or composite. If composite, give the prime factorization.

(a) $n = 41$

(b) $n = 42$

(c) $n = 43$

12. Consider your answers for **Exercise 11,** and choose the correct completion: For $n > 41$, Euler's formula produces a prime

A. never.   **B.** sometimes.   **C.** always.

13. Evaluate Escott's polynomial formula for each of the following, and determine whether each value is prime or composite. If composite, give the prime factorization.

(a) $n = 80$

(b) $n = 81$

(c) $n = 82$

14. Consider your answers for **Exercise 13,** and choose the correct completion: For $n > 80$, Escott's formula produces a prime

A. never.   **B.** sometimes.   **C.** always.

15. (a) Evaluate the Fermat number F_4: $2^{2^n} + 1$ for $n = 4$.

(b) In seeking possible prime factors of the Fermat number of part (a), what is the largest potential prime factor that one would have to try? (As stated in the text, F_4 is in fact prime.)

16. (a) Verify the value given in the text for the "sixth" Fermat number ($2^{2^5} + 1$).

(b) Divide this Fermat number by 641 and express it in factored form. (Euler discovered this factorization in 1732, proving that the sixth Fermat number is not prime.)

17. The 48th Mersenne prime was identified in the text. Write a short report on when, how, and by whom it was found.

18. The margin note on Marin Mersenne on **page 224** cites a 1644 claim that was not totally resolved for some 300 years. Find out when, and by whom, Mersenne's five errors were demonstrated. (*Hint:* One was mentioned in the margin note on **page 217.**)

19. Why do you suppose it normally takes up to a few years to discover each new Mersenne prime?

20. In Euclid's proof that there is no largest prime, we formed a number M by taking the product of primes and adding 1. Observe the pattern below.

$M = 2 + 1 = 3$	(3 is prime)
$M = 2 \cdot 3 + 1 = 7$	(7 is prime)
$M = 2 \cdot 3 \cdot 5 + 1 = 31$	(31 is prime)
$M = 2 \cdot 3 \cdot 5 \cdot 7 + 1 = 211$	(211 is prime)
$M = 2 \cdot 3 \cdot 5 \cdot 7 \cdot 11 + 1 = 2311$	(2311 is prime)

It may seem as though this pattern will always yield a prime number. Now evaluate

$$M = 2 \cdot 3 \cdot 5 \cdot 7 \cdot 11 \cdot 13 + 1.$$

21. Is the final value of M computed in **Exercise 20** prime or composite? If it is composite, give its prime factorization.

22. Explain in your own words the proof by Euclid that there is no largest prime.

The text stated that the Mersenne number M_n is composite whenever n is composite. Exercises 23–26 develop one way in which you can always find a factor of such a Mersenne number.

23. For the composite number $n = 6$, find

$$M_n = 2^n - 1.$$

24. Notice that $p = 3$ is a prime factor of $n = 6$. Find $2^p - 1$ for $p = 3$. Is $2^p - 1$ a factor of $2^n - 1$?

25. Complete this statement: If p is a prime factor of n, then _____ is a factor of the Mersenne number $2^n - 1$.

26. Find $M_n = 2^n - 1$ for $n = 10$.

27. Use the statement of **Exercise 25** to find two distinct factors of M_{10}.

28. Do you think this procedure will always produce *prime* factors of M_n for composite n? (*Hint:* Consider $n = 22$ and its prime factor $p = 11$, and recall the statement following **Example 5.**) Explain.

29. Explain why large prime numbers are important in modern cryptography systems.

30. Describe the difference between Mersenne *numbers* and Mersenne *primes*.

5.3   SELECTED TOPICS FROM NUMBER THEORY

The mathematician **Albert Wilansky,** when phoning his brother-in-law, Mr. Smith, noticed an interesting property concerning Smith's phone number (493–7775). The number 4,937,775 is composite, and its prime factorization is

$$3 \cdot 5 \cdot 5 \cdot 65{,}837.$$

When the digits of the phone number are added, the result, 42, is equal to the sum of the digits in the prime factors:

$$3 + 5 + 5 + 6 + 5 + 8 + 3 + 7 = 42.$$

Wilansky termed such a number a **Smith number.** In 1985 it was proved that there are infinitely many Smith numbers, but there still are many unanswered questions about them.

Perfect Numbers

In **Chapter 1,** we introduced figurate numbers, a topic investigated by the Pythagoreans, a group of Greek mathematicians and musicians who held their meetings in secret. In this section we examine some of the other special numbers that fascinated the Pythagoreans and are still studied by mathematicians today.

Divisors of a natural number were covered in **Section 5.1.** The **proper divisors** of a natural number include all divisors of the number except the number itself. For example, the proper divisors of 8 are 1, 2, and 4. (8 is *not* a proper divisor of 8.)

> **PERFECT NUMBERS**
>
> A natural number is said to be **perfect** if it is equal to the sum of its proper divisors.

Is 8 perfect? No, because $1 + 2 + 4 = 7$, and $7 \neq 8$. The least perfect number is 6, because the proper divisors of 6 are 1, 2, and 3, and

$$1 + 2 + 3 = 6. \quad \text{6 is perfect.}$$

EXAMPLE 1 Verifying a Perfect Number

Show that 28 is a perfect number.

Solution

The proper divisors of 28 are 1, 2, 4, 7, and 14. The sum of these is 28:

$$1 + 2 + 4 + 7 + 14 = 28.$$

By the definition, 28 is perfect. ∎

The numbers 6 and 28 are the two least perfect numbers. The next two are 496 and 8128. The pattern of these first four perfect numbers led early writers to conjecture that

1. The nth perfect number contains exactly n digits.
2. The even perfect numbers end in the digits 6 and 8, alternately.

} Conjectures NOT NECESSARILY TRUE

(**Exercises 39–41** will help you analyze these conjectures.)

There still are many unanswered questions about perfect numbers. Euclid showed that the following is true.

If $2^n - 1$ is prime, then $2^{n-1}(2^n - 1)$ is perfect, and conversely.

Because the prime values of $2^n - 1$ are the Mersenne primes (discussed in the previous section), this means that for every new Mersenne prime discovered, another perfect number is automatically revealed. (Hence, as of summer 2014, there were 48 known perfect numbers.) Also, it is known that the following is true.

All even perfect numbers must take the form $2^{n-1}(2^n - 1)$.

It is strongly suspected that no odd perfect numbers exist. (Any odd one would have at least eight different prime factors and would have at least 300 decimal digits.) Therefore, Euclid and the early Greeks most likely identified the form of all perfect numbers.

Deficient and Abundant Numbers

Earlier we saw that 8 is not perfect because it is not equal to the sum of its proper divisors ($8 \neq 7$). Next we define two alternative categories for natural numbers that are *not* perfect.

DEFICIENT AND ABUNDANT NUMBERS

A natural number is **deficient** if it is greater than the sum of its proper divisors. It is **abundant** if it is less than the sum of its proper divisors.

Based on this definition, a *deficient number* is one with proper divisors that add up to less than the number itself, while an *abundant number* is one with proper divisors that add up to more than the number itself. For example, because the proper divisors of 8 (1, 2, and 4) add up to 7, which is less than 8, the number 8 is deficient.

EXAMPLE 2   Identifying Deficient and Abundant Numbers

Decide whether each number is deficient or abundant.

(a) 12   **(b)** 10

Solution

(a) The proper divisors of 12 are 1, 2, 3, 4, and 6. The sum of these divisors is 16. Because $16 > 12$, the number 12 is abundant.

(b) The proper divisors of 10 are 1, 2, and 5. Since $1 + 2 + 5 = 8$, and $8 < 10$, the number 10 is deficient.   ∎

Amicable (Friendly) Numbers

Suppose that we add the proper divisors of 284.

$$1 + 2 + 4 + 71 + 142 = 220$$

Their sum is 220. Now, add the proper divisors of 220.

$$1 + 2 + 4 + 5 + 10 + 11 + 20 + 22 + 44 + 55 + 110 = 284$$

The sum of the proper divisors of 220 is 284, while the sum of the proper divisors of 284 is 220. Number pairs with this property are said to be *amicable,* or *friendly.*

AMICABLE OR FRIENDLY NUMBERS

The natural numbers a and b are **amicable, or friendly,** if the sum of the proper divisors of a is b, and the sum of the proper divisors of b is a.

The smallest pair of amicable numbers, 220 and 284, was known to the Pythagoreans, but it was not until 1636 that Fermat found the next pair, 17,296 and 18,416. Many more pairs were found over the next few decades, but it took a 16-year-old Italian boy named Nicolo Paganini to discover, in the year 1866, that the pair of amicable numbers 1184 and 1210 had been overlooked for centuries!

Today, powerful computers continually extend the lists of known amicable pairs. The last time we checked, nearly twelve million pairs were known. It still is unknown, however, whether there are infinitely many such pairs. No one has found an amicable pair without prime factors in common, but the possibility of such a pair has not been eliminated.

An extension of the idea of amicable numbers results in **sociable numbers.** In a chain of sociable numbers, the sum of the proper divisors of each number is the next number in the chain, and the sum of the proper divisors of the last number in the chain is the first number. Here is a 5-link chain of sociable numbers:

12,496

14,288

15,472

14,536

14,264.

The number 14,316 starts a 28-link chain of sociable numbers.

A Dull Number? The Indian mathematician **Srinivasa Ramanujan** (1887–1920) developed many ideas in number theory. His friend and collaborator on occasion was G. H. Hardy, also a number theorist and professor at Cambridge University in England.

A story has been told about Ramanujan that illustrates his genius. Hardy once mentioned to Ramanujan that he had just taken a taxicab with a rather dull number: 1729. Ramanujan countered by saying that this number isn't dull at all; it is the smallest natural number that can be expressed as the sum of two cubes in two different ways:

$$1^3 + 12^3 = 1729$$
and $\quad 9^3 + 10^3 = 1729.$

Show that 85 can be written as the sum of two *squares* in two ways.

Goldbach's Conjecture

The mathematician Christian Goldbach (1690–1764) stated the following conjecture (guess), which is one of the most famous unsolved problems in mathematics. Mathematicians have tried to prove the conjecture but have not succeeded. However, the conjecture has been verified (as of late 2014) for numbers up to 4×10^{18}.

> **GOLDBACH'S CONJECTURE (NOT PROVED)**
>
> Every even number greater than 2 can be written as the sum of two prime numbers.
>
> *Examples:* $8 = 5 + 3$
> $10 = 5 + 5 \text{ (or } 10 = 7 + 3)$

EXAMPLE 3 Expressing Numbers as Sums of Primes

Write each even number as the sum of two primes.

(a) 18   **(b)** 60

Solution

(a) $18 = 5 + 13$. Another way of writing it is $7 + 11$. Notice that $1 + 17$ is *not* valid because by definition 1 is not a prime number.

(b) $60 = 7 + 53$. Can you find other ways? Why is $3 + 57$ not valid? ∎

Twin Primes

Prime numbers that differ by 2 are called **twin primes.** Some twin prime pairs are

3 and 5,   5 and 7,   11 and 13,   and so on.

Like Goldbach's conjecture, the following conjecture about twin primes has never been proved. Interestingly, however, on May 13, 2013, substantial progress was made toward proofs of *both* the twin prime conjecture and Goldbach's conjecture. Two mathematicians, one in New Hampshire and one in Paris, proved conditions that get us significantly closer to proofs of the two famous conjectures.

Mathematics professor Gregory Larkin, played by Jeff Bridges, woos colleague Rose Morgan (Barbra Streisand) in the 1996 film *The Mirror Has Two Faces.* Larkin's research and book focus on the **twin prime conjecture,** which he correctly states in a dinner scene. He is amazed that his nonmathematician friend actually understands what he is talking about.

> **TWIN PRIME CONJECTURE (NOT PROVED)**
>
> There are infinitely many pairs of twin primes.

You may wish to verify that there are eight such pairs less than 100, using the Sieve of Eratosthenes in **Table 1.** As of summer 2014, the largest known twin primes were

$$3,756,801,695,685 \cdot 2^{666,669} \pm 1. \quad \text{Each contains 200,700 digits.}$$

Recall from **Section 5.2** that Euclid's proof of the infinitude of primes used numbers of the form

$$p_1 \cdot p_2 \cdot p_3 \cdots p_n + 1,$$

that is, the product of the first n primes, plus 1. It may seem that any such number must be prime, but that is not so. (See **Exercises 20 and 21** of **Section 5.2.**) However, this form often does produce primes (as does the same form with the plus replaced by a minus).

Sophie Germain (1776–1831) studied at the École Polytechnique in Paris in a day when female students were not admitted. A **Sophie Germain prime** is a prime p for which $2p + 1$ also is prime. Lately, large Sophie Germain primes have been discovered at the rate of one or more per year. As of late 2014, the largest one known was $18{,}543{,}637{,}900{,}515 \cdot 2^{666{,}667} - 1$, which has 200,701 digits.

(*Source:* www.primes.utm.edu)

The popular animated television series *The Simpsons* provides not only humor and social commentary but also lessons in mathematics. One episode depicted the equation

$$1782^{12} + 1841^{12} = 1922^{12},$$

which, according to **Fermat's Last Theorem,** cannot be true. Your calculator may indicate that the equation is true, but this is because it cannot accurately display powers of this size. Actually, 1782^{12} must be an *even* number because *an even number to any power is even.* Also, 1841^{12} must be *odd,* because *an odd number to any power is odd.* So the sum on the left must be *odd,* because

$$even + odd = odd.$$

Similarly, 1922^{12} must be *even.* So the equation states that an odd number equals an even number, which is impossible. (See www.simpsonsmath.com)

When *all* the primes up to p_n are included, the resulting numbers, if prime, are called **primorial primes.** They are denoted

$$p\# \pm 1.$$

For example, $5\# + 1 = 2 \cdot 3 \cdot 5 + 1 = 31$ is a primorial prime. (In late 2014, the largest known primorial prime was $1{,}098{,}133\# - 1$, a number with 476,311 digits.) The primorial primes are a popular place to look for twin primes.

EXAMPLE 4 Verifying Twin Primes

Verify that the primorial formula $p\# \pm 1$ produces twin prime pairs for both **(a)** $p = 3$ and **(b)** $p = 5$.

Solution

(a) $3\# \pm 1 = 2 \cdot 3 \pm 1 = 6 \pm 1 = 5$ and 7 Twin primes

> Multiply, then add and subtract.

(b) $5\# \pm 1 = 2 \cdot 3 \cdot 5 \pm 1 = 30 \pm 1 = 29$ and 31 Twin primes   ∎

Fermat's Last Theorem

In any right triangle with shorter sides (legs) a and b, and longest side (hypotenuse) c, the equation $a^2 + b^2 = c^2$ will hold true. This is the famous Pythagorean theorem. For example,

$$3^2 + 4^2 = 5^2 \quad \text{\small $a = 3, b = 4, c = 5$}$$
$$9 + 16 = 25 \quad \text{\small Apply the exponents.}$$
$$25 = 25. \quad \text{\small True}$$

It is known that there are infinitely many such triples (a, b, c) that satisfy the equation $a^2 + b^2 = c^2$. Is something similar true of the equation

$$a^n + b^n = c^n$$

for natural numbers $n \geq 3$? Pierre de Fermat, who is profiled in a margin note on **page 239,** thought that not only were there not infinitely many such triples, but that there were, in fact, none. He made the following claim in the 1600s.

> **FERMAT'S LAST THEOREM (PROVED IN THE 1990s)**
>
> For *any* natural number $n \geq 3$, there are *no* triples (a, b, c) that satisfy the equation
>
> $$a^n + b^n = c^n.$$

Fermat's assertion was the object of some 350 years of attempts by mathematicians to provide a suitable proof. While it was verified for many specific cases (Fermat himself proved it for $n = 3$), a proof of the general case could not be found until the Princeton mathematician Andrew Wiles announced a proof in the spring of 1993. Although some flaws were discovered in his argument, Wiles was able, by the fall of 1994, to repair the proof.

There were probably about 100 mathematicians around the world qualified to understand the Wiles proof. ***Today Fermat's Last Theorem finally is regarded by the mathematics community as officially proved.***

EXAMPLE 5 Applying a Theorem Proved by Fermat

One of the theorems legitimately proved by Fermat is as follows:

Every odd prime can be expressed as the difference
of two squares in one and only one way.

Express each odd prime as the difference of two squares.

(a) 3   **(b)** 7

Solution

(a) $3 = 4 - 1 = 2^2 - 1^2$ **(b)** $7 = 16 - 9 = 4^2 - 3^2$ ∎

FOR FURTHER THOUGHT

Curious and Interesting

One of the most remarkable books on number theory is *The Penguin Dictionary of Curious and Interesting Numbers* (1986) by David Wells. This book contains fascinating numbers and their properties, including the following.

- There are only three sets of three digits that form prime numbers in all possible arrangements: {1, 1, 3}, {1, 9, 9}, {3, 3, 7}.
- Find the sum of the cubes of the digits of 136:

$$1^3 + 3^3 + 6^3 = 244.$$

Repeat the process with the digits of 244:

$$2^3 + 4^3 + 4^3 = 136.$$

We're back to where we started.

- 635,318,657 is the least number that can be expressed as the sum of two fourth powers in two ways:

$$635{,}318{,}657 = 59^4 + 158^4 = 133^4 + 134^4.$$

- The number 24,678,050 has an interesting property:

$$24{,}678{,}050 = 2^8 + 4^8 + 6^8 + 7^8 + 8^8 + 0^8$$
$$+ 5^8 + 0^8.$$

- The number 54,748 has a similar interesting property:

$$54{,}748 = 5^5 + 4^5 + 7^5 + 4^5 + 8^5.$$

- The number 3435 has this property:

$$3435 = 3^3 + 4^4 + 3^3 + 5^5.$$

For anyone whose curiosity is piqued by such facts, the book mentioned above is for you!

For Group or Individual Investigation

Have each student in the class choose a three-digit number that is a multiple of 3. Add the cubes of the digits. Repeat the process until the same number is obtained over and over. Then, have the students compare their results. What is curious and interesting about this process?

5.3 EXERCISES

In Exercises 1–10 decide whether each statement is true *or* false.

1. Given a prime number, no matter how large, there is always another prime even larger.

2. The prime numbers 2 and 3 are twin primes.

3. The first and third perfect numbers both end in the digit 6, and the second and fourth perfect numbers both end in the digits 28.

4. For every Mersenne prime, there is a corresponding perfect number.

5. All prime numbers are deficient.

6. The equation $17 + 51 = 68$ verifies Goldbach's conjecture for the number 68.

7. Even perfect numbers are more plentiful than Mersenne primes.

8. The twin prime conjecture was proved in 2013.

9. The number $2^5(2^6 - 1)$ is perfect.

10. Every natural number greater than 1 must be one of the following: prime, abundant, or deficient.

11. The proper divisors of 496 are 1, 2, 4, 8, 16, 31, 62, 124, and 248. Use this information to verify that 496 is perfect.

12. The proper divisors of 8128 are 1, 2, 4, 8, 16, 32, 64, 127, 254, 508, 1016, 2032, and 4064. Use this information to verify that 8128 is perfect.

13. As mentioned in the text, when $2^n - 1$ is prime,

$$2^{n-1}(2^n - 1)$$

is perfect. By letting $n = 2, 3, 5$, and 7, we obtain the first four perfect numbers. Show that $2^n - 1$ is prime for $n = 13$, and then find the decimal digit representation for the fifth perfect number.

14. In the summer of 2014, the largest known prime number was $2^{57,885,161} - 1$. Use the formula in **Exercise 13** to write an expression for the perfect number generated by this prime number.

15. It has been proved that the reciprocals of *all* the positive divisors of a perfect number have a sum of 2. Verify this for the perfect number 28.

16. Consider the following equations.

$$6 = 1 + 2 + 3$$
$$28 = 1 + 2 + 3 + 4 + 5 + 6 + 7$$

Show that a similar equation is valid for the third perfect number, 496.

Determine whether each number is abundant *or* deficient.

17. 32   **18.** 60   **19.** 84   **20.** 75

21. There are four abundant numbers between 1 and 25. Find them. (*Hint:* They are all even, and no prime number is abundant.)

22. Explain why a prime number must be deficient.

23. There are no odd abundant numbers less than 945. If 945 has proper divisors 1, 3, 5, 7, 9, 15, 21, 27, 35, 45, 63, 105, 135, 189, and 315, determine whether it is abundant or deficient.

24. Explain in your own words the terms *perfect number, abundant number,* and *deficient number.*

25. The proper divisors of 1184 are 1, 2, 4, 8, 16, 32, 37, 74, 148, 296, and 592. The proper divisors of 1210 are 1, 2, 5, 10, 11, 22, 55, 110, 121, 242, and 605. Verify that 16-year-old Nicolo Paganini was correct about these two numbers in 1866. See the subsection "Amicable (Friendly) Numbers."

26. An Arabian mathematician of the ninth century stated the following: "If the three numbers

$$x = 3 \cdot 2^{n-1} - 1,$$
$$y = 3 \cdot 2^n - 1,$$
and $$z = 9 \cdot 2^{2n-1} - 1$$

are all prime and $n \geq 2$, then $2^n xy$ and $2^n z$ are amicable numbers."

(a) Use $n = 2$, and show that the result is the least pair of amicable numbers, namely 220 and 284.

(b) Use $n = 4$ to obtain another pair of amicable numbers.

Write each even number as the sum of two primes. (There may be more than one way to do this.)

27. 12   **28.** 24   **29.** 40   **30.** 54

31. Joseph Louis Lagrange (1736–1813) conjectured that every odd natural number greater than 5 can be written as a sum $a + 2b$, where a and b are both primes.

(a) Verify this for the odd natural number 11.

(b) Verify that the odd natural number 17 can be written in this form in four different ways.

32. Another unproved conjecture in number theory states that every natural number multiple of 6 can be written as the difference of two primes. Verify this for 12 and 24.

Find one pair of twin primes between the two numbers given.

33. 45, 65   **34.** 65, 85

Pierre de Fermat provided proofs of many theorems in number theory. Exercises 35–38 investigate some of these theorems.

35. If p is prime and the natural numbers a and p have no common factor except 1, then $a^{p-1} - 1$ is divisible by p.

(a) Verify this for $p = 5$ and $a = 3$.

(b) Verify this for $p = 7$ and $a = 2$.

36. Every odd prime can be expressed as the difference of two squares in one and only one way.

(a) Find this one way for the prime number 5.

(b) Find this one way for the prime number 11.

37. There is only one solution in natural numbers for $a^2 + 2 = b^3$, and it is $a = 5, b = 3$. Verify this solution.

38. There are only two solutions in integers for $a^2 + 4 = b^3$. One solution is $a = 2, b = 2$. Find the other solution.

The first four perfect numbers were identified in the text: 6, 28, 496, and 8128. The next two are 33,550,336 and 8,589,869,056. Use this information about perfect numbers to work Exercises 39–41.

39. Verify that each of these six perfect numbers ends in either 6 or 28. (In fact, this is true of all even perfect numbers.)

40. Is conjecture (1) in the text (that the nth perfect number contains exactly n digits) true or false? Explain.

41. Is conjecture (2) in the text (that the even perfect numbers end in the digits 6 and 8, alternately) true or false? Explain.

*According to the Web site www.shyamsundergupta.com/ amicable.htm, a natural number is **happy** if the process of repeatedly summing the squares of its decimal digits finally ends in 1. For example, the least natural number (greater than 1) that is happy is 7, as shown here.*

$$7^2 = 49, \quad 4^2 + 9^2 = 97, \quad 9^2 + 7^2 = 130,$$
$$1^2 + 3^2 + 0^2 = 10, \quad 1^2 + 0^2 = 1.$$

*An amicable pair is a **happy amicable pair** if and only if both members of the pair are happy numbers. (The first 5000 amicable pairs include only 111 that are happy amicable pairs.) For each amicable pair, determine whether neither, one, or both of the members are happy, and whether the pair is a happy amicable pair.*

42. 220 and 284

43. 1184 and 1210

44. 10,572,550 and 10,854,650

45. 35,361,326 and 40,117,714

46. If the early Greeks knew the form of all even perfect numbers, namely $2^{n-1}(2^n - 1)$, then why did they not discover all the ones that are known today?

47. Explain why the primorial formula $p\# \pm 1$ does not result in a pair of twin primes for the prime value $p = 2$.

48. **(a)** What two numbers does the primorial formula produce for $p = 7$?

   (b) Which, if either, of these numbers is prime?

49. Choose the correct completion: The primorial formula produces twin primes

   A. never.   **B.** sometimes.   **C.** always.

*See the margin note (on **page 233**) defining a Sophie Germain prime, and complete this table.*

	p	$2p+1$	Is p a Sophie Germain prime?
50.	2	_____	_____
51.	3	_____	_____
52.	5	_____	_____
53.	7	_____	_____

Factorial primes *are of the form* $n! \pm 1$ *for natural numbers n. (n! denotes "n factorial," the product of all natural numbers up to n, not just the primes as in the primorial primes. For example,* $4! = 1 \cdot 2 \cdot 3 \cdot 4 = 24$.*) As of late 2014, the largest verified factorial prime was* $150{,}209! + 1$, *which has 712,355 digits. Find the missing entries in the following table.*

n	$n!$	$n! - 1$	$n! + 1$	Is $n! - 1$ prime?	Is $n! + 1$ prime?
	2	2	1	3	no	yes
54.	3	_____	_____	_____	_____	_____
55.	4	_____	_____	_____	_____	_____
56.	5	_____	_____	_____	_____	_____

57. Explain why the factorial prime formula does not give twin primes for $n = 2$.

Based on the preceding table, complete each statement with one of the following:

A. *never,*   **B.** *sometimes, or*   **C.** *always.*

When applied to particular values of n, the factorial prime formula $n! \pm 1$ produces

58. no primes _____   **59.** exactly one prime _____

60. twin primes _____

*Because it does not equal the sum of its proper divisors, an abundant number is not perfect, but it is called **pseudoperfect** if it is equal to the sum of a subset of its proper divisors. For example, 12, an abundant number, has proper divisors 1, 2, 3, 4, and 6.* $12 \neq 1 + 2 + 3 + 4 + 6$, *but* $12 = 2 + 4 + 6$. *(Also,* $12 = 1 + 2 + 3 + 6$.*)*
Show that each number is pseudoperfect.

61. 18   (Show it with two different sums.)

62. 24   (Show it with five different sums.)

*Abundant numbers are so commonly pseudoperfect that when we find one that isn't, we call it **weird**. There are no weird numbers less than 70. Do the following exercises to investigate 70.*

63. Show that 70 is abundant.

64. Show that 70 is *not* pseudoperfect and must therefore be the smallest weird number. (Among the first 10,000 counting numbers, there are only seven weird ones: 70, 863, 4030, 5830, 7192, 7912, and 9272.)

The following number is known as Belphegor's prime.

One nonillion, sixty-six quadrillion, six hundred trillion, one

Belphegor, who is referred to in many literary works, is one of the seven princes of hell, known for tempting men toward particular evils. Exercises 65–68 refer to Belphegor's prime.

65. Write out the decimal form of the number. (It is a "palindrome"—that is, it reads the same backward and forward. And in keeping with its name, it actually is a prime.)

66. What are the "middle three" digits? (The biblical book of Revelation calls this "the number of the beast.")

67. How many zeroes are on each side of the middle three digits?

68. With what digit does Belphegor's prime begin and end?

5.4   GREATEST COMMON FACTOR AND LEAST COMMON MULTIPLE

Greatest Common Factor

The *greatest common factor* is defined as follows.

GREATEST COMMON FACTOR

The **greatest common factor (GCF)** of a group of natural numbers is the largest natural number that is a factor of all the numbers in the group.

Examples: 18 is the GCF of 36 and 54, because 18 is the largest natural number that divides both 36 and 54.

1 is the GCF of 7 and 16.

The greatest common factor is often called the *greatest common divisor*. Greatest common factors can be found by using prime factorizations. To determine the GCF of 36 and 54, first write the prime factorization of each number.

$$36 = 2^2 \cdot 3^2$$
$$54 = 2^1 \cdot 3^3$$

The GCF is the product of the primes common to the factorizations, with each prime raised to the power indicated by the *least* exponent that it has in any factorization. Here, the prime 2 has 1 as the least exponent (in $54 = 2^1 \cdot 3^3$), while the prime 3 has 2 as the least exponent (in $36 = 2^2 \cdot 3^2$).

$$\text{GCF} = 2^1 \cdot 3^2 = 2 \cdot 9 = 18$$

We summarize as follows.

FINDING THE GREATEST COMMON FACTOR (PRIME FACTORS METHOD)

Step 1   Write the prime factorization of each number.

Step 2   Choose all primes common to *all* factorizations, with each prime raised to the *least* exponent that it has in any factorization.

Step 3   Form the product of all the numbers in Step 2. This product is the greatest common factor.

EXAMPLE 1   **Finding the Greatest Common Factor by the Prime Factors Method**

Find the greatest common factor of 360 and 2700.

Solution

Write the prime factorization of each number.

$$360 = 2^3 \cdot 3^2 \cdot 5 \qquad 2700 = 2^2 \cdot 3^3 \cdot 5^2$$

Find the primes common to both factorizations, with each prime having as its exponent the *least* exponent from either product.

> Use the least exponents.

$$\text{GCF} = 2^2 \cdot 3^2 \cdot 5 = 180$$

The greatest common factor of 360 and 2700 is 180.

gcd(360,2700)
180

The calculator shows that the greatest common divisor (factor) of 360 and 2700 is 180. Compare with **Example 1.**

EXAMPLE 2 Finding the Greatest Common Factor by the Prime Factors Method

Find the greatest common factor of 720, 1000, and 1800.

Solution

Write the prime factorization for each number.

$$720 = 2^4 \cdot 3^2 \cdot 5$$
$$1000 = 2^3 \cdot 5^3$$
$$1800 = 2^3 \cdot 3^2 \cdot 5^2$$

Use the smallest exponent on each prime common to the factorizations.

$$\text{GCF} = 2^3 \cdot 5 = 40$$

(The prime 3 is not used in the greatest common factor because it does not appear in the prime factorization of 1000.)   ∎

EXAMPLE 3 Finding the Greatest Common Factor by the Prime Factors Method

Find the greatest common factor of 80 and 63.

Solution

$$80 = 2^4 \cdot 5$$
$$63 = 3^2 \cdot 7$$

There are no primes in common here, so the GCF is 1. The number 1 is the largest number that will divide into both 80 and 63.   ∎

Two numbers, such as 80 and 63, with a greatest common factor of 1 are called **relatively prime numbers**—that is, they are prime *relative* to one another. (They have no common factors other than 1.)

Another method of finding the greatest common factor involves dividing the numbers by common prime factors.

FINDING THE GREATEST COMMON FACTOR (DIVIDING BY PRIME FACTORS METHOD)

Step 1 Write the numbers in a row.

Step 2 Divide each of the numbers by a common prime factor. Try 2, then try 3, and so on.

Step 3 Divide the quotients by a common prime factor. Continue until no prime will divide into all the quotients.

Step 4 The product of the primes in Steps 2 and 3 is the greatest common factor.

EXAMPLE 4   Finding the Greatest Common Factor by Dividing by Prime Factors

Find the greatest common factor of 12, 18, and 60.

Solution

Write the numbers in a row and divide by 2.

$$
\begin{array}{r|rrr}
2 & 12 & 18 & 60 \\
\hline
 & 6 & 9 & 30
\end{array}
$$

The numbers 6, 9, and 30 are not all divisible by 2, but they are divisible by 3.

$$
\begin{array}{r|rrr}
2 & 12 & 18 & 60 \\
\hline
3 & 6 & 9 & 30 \\
\hline
 & 2 & 3 & 10
\end{array}
$$

No prime divides into 2, 3, and 10, so the greatest common factor of the numbers 12, 18, and 60 is given by the product of the primes on the left, 2 and 3.

$$
\begin{array}{r|rrr}
2 & 12 & 18 & 60 \\
\hline
3 & 6 & 9 & 30 \\
\hline
 & 2 & 3 & 10
\end{array}
$$

$$2 \cdot 3 = 6$$

The GCF of 12, 18, and 60 is 6. ∎

gcd(12,gcd(18,60))
6

The **greatest common divisor** is symbolized GCD or gcd. This screen uses the fact that

gcd(a, b, c) = gcd(a, gcd(b, c)).

Compare with **Example 4.**

Another method of finding the greatest common factor of two numbers (but not more than two) is called the **Euclidean algorithm.***

EXAMPLE 5   Finding the Greatest Common Factor Using the Euclidean Algorithm

Use the Euclidean algorithm to find the greatest common factor of 90 and 168.

Solution

Step 1 Begin by dividing the larger, 168, by the smaller, 90. Disregard the quotient, but note the remainder.

$$
\begin{array}{r}
1 \\
90\overline{)168} \\
\underline{90} \\
78
\end{array}
$$

Step 2 Divide the smaller of the two numbers by the remainder obtained in Step 1. Once again, note the remainder.

$$
\begin{array}{r}
1 \\
78\overline{)90} \\
\underline{78} \\
12
\end{array}
$$

Step 3 Continue dividing the successive remainders as many times as necessary to obtain a remainder of 0.

$$
\begin{array}{r}
6 \\
12\overline{)78} \\
\underline{72} \\
6
\end{array}
$$

6   Greatest common factor

Step 4 The *last positive remainder* in this process is the greatest common factor of 90 and 168. It can be seen that their GCF is 6.

$$
\begin{array}{r}
2 \\
6\overline{)12} \\
\underline{12} \\
0
\end{array}
$$

∎

Pierre de Fermat (about 1601–1665), a government official who did not interest himself in mathematics until he was past 30, devoted leisure time to its study. He was a worthy scholar, best known for his work in number theory. His other major contributions involved certain applications in geometry and his original work in probability.

Much of Fermat's best work survived only on loose sheets or jotted, without proof, in the margins of works that he read.

*For a proof that this process does indeed give the greatest common factor, see *Elementary Introduction to Number Theory, Second Edition*, by Calvin T. Long, pp. 34–35.

The Euclidean algorithm is particularly useful if the two numbers are difficult to factor into primes. We summarize the algorithm here.

FINDING THE GREATEST COMMON FACTOR (EUCLIDEAN ALGORITHM)

To find the greatest common factor of two unequal numbers, divide the larger by the smaller. Note the remainder, and divide the previous divisor by this remainder. Continue the process until a remainder of 0 is obtained. The greatest common factor is the last positive remainder obtained.

Least Common Multiple

Closely related to the idea of the greatest common factor is the concept of the *least common multiple.*

LEAST COMMON MULTIPLE

The **least common multiple (LCM)** of a group of natural numbers is the smallest natural number that is a multiple of all the numbers in the group.

Example: 30 is the LCM of 15 and 10 because 30 is the smallest number that appears in both sets of multiples.

Multiples of 15: $\{15, 30, 45, 60, 75, 90, 105, \ldots\}$

Multiples of 10: $\{10, 20, 30, 40, 50, 60, 70, \ldots\}$

```
lcm(15,10)
                    30
```

The least common multiple of 15 and 10 is 30.

The set of natural numbers that are multiples of *both* 15 and 10 form the set of *common multiples:*

$$\{30, 60, 90, 120, \ldots\}.$$

While there are infinitely many common multiples, the *least* common multiple is observed to be 30.

A method similar to the first one given for the greatest common factor may be used to find the least common multiple of a group of numbers.

FINDING THE LEAST COMMON MULTIPLE (PRIME FACTORS METHOD)

Step 1   Write the prime factorization of each number.

Step 2   Choose all primes belonging to *any* factorization, with each prime raised to the power indicated by the *greatest* exponent that it has in any factorization.

Step 3   Form the product of all the numbers in Step 2. This product is the least common multiple.

```
lcm(135,lcm(280,300))
                   37800
```

The least common multiple of 135, 280, and 300 is 37,800. Compare with **Example 6.**

▓▓ EXAMPLE 6 Finding the Least Common Multiple by the Prime Factors Method

Find the least common multiple of 135, 280, and 300.

Solution

Write the prime factorizations:

$$135 = 3^3 \cdot 5, \quad 280 = 2^3 \cdot 5 \cdot 7, \quad \text{and} \quad 300 = 2^2 \cdot 3 \cdot 5^2.$$

Form the product of all the primes that appear in *any* of the factorizations. Use the *greatest* exponent from any factorization.

> Use the greatest exponents.

$$\text{LCM} = 2^3 \cdot 3^3 \cdot 5^2 \cdot 7 = 37,800$$

The least natural number divisible by 135, 280, and 300 is 37,800.   ∎

The least common multiple of a group of numbers can also be found by dividing by prime factors. The process is slightly different from that for finding the GCF.

FINDING THE LEAST COMMON MULTIPLE (DIVIDING BY PRIME FACTORS METHOD)

Step 1   Write the numbers in a row.

Step 2   Divide each of the numbers by a common prime factor. Try 2, then try 3, and so on.

Step 3   Divide the quotients by a common prime factor. When no prime will divide all quotients, but a prime will divide some of them, divide where possible and bring any nondivisible quotients down. Continue until no prime will divide any two quotients.

Step 4   The product of all prime divisors from Steps 2 and 3 as well as all remaining quotients is the least common multiple.

EXAMPLE 7   Finding the Least Common Multiple by Dividing by Prime Factors

Find the least common multiple of 12, 18, and 60.

Solution

Proceed just as in **Example 4** to obtain the following.

$$
\begin{array}{r|rrr}
2 & 12 & 18 & 60 \\
3 & 6 & 9 & 30 \\
\hline
  & 2 & 3 & 10 \\
\end{array}
$$

Now, even though no prime will divide 2, 3, and 10, the prime 2 will divide 2 and 10. Divide the 2 and the 10 and bring down the 3.

$$
\begin{array}{r|rrr}
2 & 12 & 18 & 60 \\
3 & 6 & 9 & 30 \\
2 & 2 & 3 & 10 \\
\hline
  & 1 & 3 & 5 \\
\end{array}
$$

$2 \cdot 3 \cdot 2 \cdot 1 \cdot 3 \cdot 5 = 180$

The LCM of 12, 18, and 60 is 180.   ∎

The least common multiple of two numbers m and n can be obtained by dividing their product by their greatest common factor.

FINDING THE LEAST COMMON MULTIPLE (FORMULA)

The least common multiple of m and n can be computed as follows.

$$\text{LCM} = \frac{m \cdot n}{\text{GCF of } m \text{ and } n}$$

(This method works only for two numbers, not for more than two.)

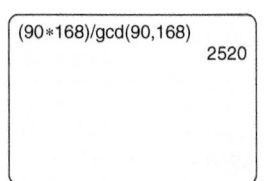

(90*168)/gcd(90,168)
                2520

This supports the result in **Example 8.**

EXAMPLE 8 Finding the Least Common Multiple by Formula

Use the formula to find the least common multiple of 90 and 168.

Solution

In **Example 5** we used the Euclidean algorithm to find that the greatest common factor of 90 and 168 is 6. Therefore, the formula gives us

$$\text{Least common multiple of 90 and 168} = \frac{90 \cdot 168}{6} = 2520.$$ ∎

Problem-Solving Strategy

Problems that deal with questions such as "How many objects will there be in each group if each group contains the same number of objects?" and "When will two events occur at the same time?" can sometimes be solved using the ideas of greatest common factor and least common multiple.

EXAMPLE 9 Finding Common Starting Times of Movie Cycles

The King Theatre and the Star Theatre run movies continuously, and each starts its first feature at 1:00 P.M. If the movie shown at the King lasts 80 minutes and the movie shown at the Star lasts 2 hours, when will the two movies again start at the same time?

Solution

First, convert 2 hours to 120 minutes. The question can be restated as follows: "What is the smallest number of minutes it will take for the two movies to start at the same time again?" This is equivalent to asking, "What is the least common multiple of 80 and 120?"

Using any of the methods described in this section, we find that the least common multiple of 80 and 120 is 240. Therefore, it will take 240 minutes, or $\frac{240}{60} = 4$ hours, for the movies to start at the same time again. By adding 4 hours to 1:00 P.M., we find that they will start together again at 5:00 P.M. ∎

EXAMPLE 10 Finding the Greatest Common Size of Stacks of Cards

Joshua has 450 football cards and 840 baseball cards. He wants to place them in stacks on a table so that each stack has the same number of cards, and no stack has different types of cards within it. What is the greatest number of cards that he can have in each stack?

Solution

Here, we are looking for the greatest number that will divide evenly into 450 and 840. This is, of course, the greatest common factor of 450 and 840. Using any of the methods described in this section, we find that

greatest common factor of 450 and 840 = 30.

Therefore, the greatest number of cards he can have in each stack is 30. He will have 15 stacks of 30 football cards and 28 stacks of 30 baseball cards. ∎

WHEN Will I Ever USE This ?

Addition and subtraction of fractions normally involve identifying the least common denominator, which is the LCM of all denominators. Suppose, for example, that a nurse needs the total displacement (volume) of the following quantities combined.

$$\frac{1}{5} \text{ teacup, } \frac{2}{3} \text{ cup, } 5 \text{ teaspoons, and } 3 \text{ tablespoons}$$

(In practice, the fractions would normally first be converted to decimal equivalents in metric units, but we illustrate the math here with the common fractions and non-metric units.)

The conversions necessary to obtain common units (in this case, ounces) are shown in the table.

1 teaspoon	=	$\frac{1}{6}$ ounce
1 tablespoon	=	$\frac{1}{2}$ ounce
1 teacup	=	6 ounces
1 cup	=	8 ounces

Thus

$$\frac{1}{5} \text{ teacup} = \frac{1}{5}(6 \text{ ounces}) = \frac{6}{5} \text{ ounces,}$$

$$\frac{2}{3} \text{ cup} = \frac{2}{3}(8 \text{ ounces}) = \frac{16}{3} \text{ ounces,}$$

$$5 \text{ teaspoons} = 5\left(\frac{1}{6} \text{ ounce}\right) = \frac{5}{6} \text{ ounces,}$$

$$3 \text{ tablespoons} = 3\left(\frac{1}{2} \text{ ounce}\right) = \frac{3}{2} \text{ ounces,}$$

and we need the sum $\frac{6}{5} + \frac{16}{3} + \frac{5}{6} + \frac{3}{2}$. One method of finding the least common denominator is dividing by prime factors.

$$
\begin{array}{c|cccc}
2 & 2 & 3 & 5 & 6 \\
\hline
3 & 1 & 3 & 5 & 3 \\
\hline
5 & 1 & 1 & 5 & 1 \\
\hline
& 1 & 1 & 1 & 1
\end{array}
\quad \text{LCM} = 2 \cdot 3 \cdot 5 \cdot 1 \cdot 1 \cdot 1 \cdot 1 = 30
$$

Using 30 as the least common denominator, we obtain

$$
\frac{6}{5} + \frac{16}{3} + \frac{5}{6} + \frac{3}{2} = \frac{6}{5} \cdot \frac{6}{6} + \frac{16}{3} \cdot \frac{10}{10} + \frac{5}{6} \cdot \frac{5}{5} + \frac{3}{2} \cdot \frac{15}{15}
$$

$$
= \frac{36}{30} + \frac{160}{30} + \frac{25}{30} + \frac{45}{30}
$$

$$
= \frac{36 + 160 + 25 + 45}{30}
$$

$$
= \frac{266}{30} = 8\frac{26}{30}.
$$

The combined total is $8\frac{26}{30}$ ounces, or, in decimal form, about 8.867 ounces.

5.4 EXERCISES

Decide whether each statement is true *or* false.

1. No two even natural numbers can be relatively prime.

2. Two different prime numbers must be relatively prime.

3. If p is a prime number, then the greatest common factor of p and p^2 is p^2.

4. If p is a prime number, then the least common multiple of p and p^2 is p^3.

5. There is no prime number p such that the greatest common factor of p and 2 is 2.

6. The set of all common multiples of two given natural numbers is infinite.

7. Any two natural numbers have at least one common factor.

8. The least common multiple of two different primes is their product.

9. No two composite numbers can be relatively prime.

10. The product of any two natural numbers is equal to the product of their least common multiple and their greatest common factor.

Use the prime factors method to find the greatest common factor of each group of numbers.

11. 84 and 140

12. 315 and 90

13. 275 and 132

14. 264 and 504

15. 68, 102, and 425

16. 765, 780, and 990

Use the method of dividing by prime factors to find the greatest common factor of each group of numbers.

17. 150 and 260

18. 237 and 395

19. 600 and 90

20. 330 and 255

21. 84, 90, and 210

22. 585, 1680, and 990

Use the Euclidean algorithm to find the greatest common factor of each group of numbers.

23. 18 and 60

24. 77 and 84

25. 36 and 90

26. 72 and 90

27. 945 and 450

28. 200 and 350

Use the prime factors method to find the least common multiple of each group of numbers.

29. 48 and 60

30. 21 and 35

31. 81 and 45

32. 84 and 98

33. 20, 30, and 50

34. 15, 21, and 45

Use the method of dividing by prime factors to find the least common multiple of each group of numbers.

35. 27 and 36

36. 21 and 56

37. 63 and 99

38. 16, 120, and 216

39. 48, 54, and 60

40. 154, 165, and 2310

*Use the formula given in the text on **page 241** and the results of **Exercises 23–28** to find the least common multiple of each group of numbers.*

41. 18 and 60

42. 77 and 84

43. 36 and 90

44. 72 and 90

45. 945 and 450

46. 200 and 350

47. Explain in your own words how to find the greatest common factor of a group of numbers.

48. Explain in your own words how to find the least common multiple of a group of numbers.

49. If p, q, and r are different primes, and a, b, and c are natural numbers such that $a < b < c$,

   (a) what is the greatest common factor of $p^a q^c r^b$ and $p^b q^a r^c$?

   (b) what is the least common multiple of $p^b q^a$, $q^b r^c$, and $p^a r^b$?

50. Find **(a)** the greatest common factor and **(b)** the least common multiple of $2^{25} \cdot 5^{17} \cdot 7^{21}$ and $2^{28} \cdot 5^{22} \cdot 7^{13}$. Leave your answers in prime factored form.

It is possible to extend the Euclidean algorithm in order to find the greatest common factor of more than two numbers. For example, if we wish to find the greatest common factor of 150, 210, and 240, we can first use the algorithm to find the greatest common factor of two of these (say, for example, 150 and 210). Then we find the greatest common factor of that result and the third number, 240. The final result is the greatest common factor of the original group of numbers.

Use the Euclidean algorithm as just described to find the greatest common factor of each group of numbers.

51. 90, 105, and 315

52. 48, 315, and 450

53. 144, 180, and 192

54. 180, 210, and 630

55. Suppose that the least common multiple of p and q is pq. What can we say about p and q?

56. Suppose that the least common multiple of p and q is q. What can we say about p and q?

57. Recall some of your early experiences in mathematics (for example, in the elementary grade classroom). What topic involving fractions required the use of the least common multiple? Give an example.

58. Recall some of your experiences in elementary algebra. What topics required the use of the greatest common factor? Give an example.

*Refer to **Examples 9 and 10** to solve each problem.*

59. *Inspecting Calculators*   Jameel and Fahima work on an assembly line, inspecting electronic calculators. Jameel inspects the electronics of every sixteenth calculator, while Fahima inspects the workmanship of every thirty-sixth calculator. If they both start working at the same time, which calculator will be the first that they both inspect?

60. *Night Off for Security Guards*   Tomas and Jenny work as security guards at a factory. Tomas has every sixth night off, and Jenny has every tenth night off. If both are off on July 1, what is the next night that they will both be off together?

61. *Stacking Coins*   Suyín has 240 pennies and 288 nickels. She wants to place them all in stacks so that each stack has the same number of coins, and each stack contains only one denomination of coin. What is the greatest number of coins that she can place in each stack?

62. *Bicycle Racing*   Aki and Felipe are in a bicycle race, following a circular track. If they start at the same place and travel in the same direction, and Aki completes a revolution every 40 seconds, which Felipe takes 45 seconds to complete each revolution, how long will it take them before they reach the starting point again simultaneously?

63. *Selling Books*   Azad sold some books at $24 each and used the money to buy some concert tickets at $50 each. He had no money left over after buying the tickets. What is the least amount of money he could have earned from selling the books? What is the least number of books he could have sold?

64. *Sawing Lumber*   Terri has some pieces of two-by-four lumber. Some are 60 inches long, and some are 72 inches long. All of them must be sawn into shorter pieces. If all sawn pieces must be the same length, what is the longest such piece so that no lumber is left over?

5.5 THE FIBONACCI SEQUENCE AND THE GOLDEN RATIO

OBJECTIVES

1 Work with the Fibonacci sequence.

2 Understand the golden ratio.

3 See relationships between the Fibonacci sequence and the golden ratio.

The Fibonacci Sequence

One of the most famous problems in elementary mathematics comes from the book *Liber Abaci,* written in 1202 by Leonardo of Pisa, a.k.a. Fibonacci. The problem is as follows:

> A man put a pair of rabbits in a cage. During the first month the rabbits produced no offspring, but each month thereafter produced one new pair of rabbits. If each new pair thus produced reproduces in the same manner, how many pairs of rabbits will there be at the end of one year?

The solution of this problem leads to a sequence of numbers known as the **Fibonacci sequence.** Here are the first fifteen terms of the Fibonacci sequence:

$$1, 1, 2, 3, 5, 8, 13, 21, 34, 55, 89, 144, 233, 377, 610.$$

The solution of **Fibonacci's rabbit problem** is examined in **Chapter 1, pages 20–21.**

After the first two terms (both 1) in the sequence, each term is obtained by adding the two previous terms. For example, the third term is obtained by adding $1 + 1$ to get 2, the fourth term is obtained by adding $1 + 2$ to get 3, and so on. This can be described by a mathematical formula known as a **recursion formula.**

If F_n represents the Fibonacci number in the nth position in the sequence, then

$$F_1 = 1$$
$$F_2 = 1$$
$$F_n = F_{n-2} + F_{n-1}, \quad \text{for } n \geq 3.$$

Using the recursion formula $F_n = F_{n-2} + F_{n-1}$, we obtain

$$F_3 = F_1 + F_2 = 1 + 1 = 2, \quad F_4 = F_2 + F_3 = 1 + 2 = 3, \quad \text{and so on.}$$

The **Fibonacci Association** is a research organization dedicated to investigation into the **Fibonacci sequence** and related topics. Check your library to see if it has the journal *Fibonacci Quarterly.* The first two journals of 1963 contain a basic introduction to the Fibonacci sequence.

The Fibonacci sequence exhibits many interesting patterns, and by inductive reasoning we can make many conjectures about these patterns. However, simply observing a finite number of examples does not provide a proof of a statement. Proofs of the properties of the Fibonacci sequence often involve mathematical induction (covered in college algebra texts). Here we simply observe some of the patterns and do not attempt to provide proofs.

EXAMPLE 1 Observing a Pattern of the Fibonacci Numbers

Find the sum of the squares of the first n Fibonacci numbers for $n = 1, 2, 3, 4, 5$, and examine the pattern. Generalize this relationship.

Solution

$$1^2 = 1 = 1 \cdot 1 = F_1 \cdot F_2$$

$$1^2 + 1^2 = 2 = 1 \cdot 2 = F_2 \cdot F_3$$

$$1^2 + 1^2 + 2^2 = 6 = 2 \cdot 3 = F_3 \cdot F_4$$

$$1^2 + 1^2 + 2^2 + 3^2 = 15 = 3 \cdot 5 = F_4 \cdot F_5$$

$$1^2 + 1^2 + 2^2 + 3^2 + 5^2 = 40 = 5 \cdot 8 = F_5 \cdot F_6$$

The sum of the squares of the first n Fibonacci numbers seems to always be the product of F_n and F_{n+1}. This has been proved to be true, in general, using mathematical induction. ∎

The following program for the TI-83 Plus utilizes the *Binet form* of the *n*th Fibonacci number (see **Exercises 33–36**) to determine its value.

```
PROGRAM: FIB
: ClrHome
: Disp "WHICH TERM"
: Disp "OF THE"
: Disp "SEQUENCE DO"
: Disp "YOU WANT?"
: Input N
: (1 + √(5))/2 → A
: (1 − √(5))/2 → B
: (A^N − B^N)/√(5) → F
: Disp F
```

```
WHICH TERM
OF THE
SEQUENCE DO
YOU WANT?
?20
                6765
                Done
```

This screen indicates that the twentieth Fibonacci number is 6765.

Fibonacci Fun To observe one of the many interesting properties of the Fibonacci sequence, do the following.

1. Choose any term after the first and square it.
2. Multiply the terms before and after the term chosen in Step 1.
3. Subtract the smaller value from the larger.
4. What is your result?

Try this procedure beginning with several different Fibonacci terms. **The result is always the same.**

EXAMPLE 2 Observing the Fibonacci Sequence in a Long Division Problem

Observe the steps of the long-division algorithm used to find the first few decimal places of the reciprocal of 89, the eleventh Fibonacci number. Locate occurrences of the terms of the Fibonacci sequence in the algorithm.

Solution

$$
\begin{array}{r}
.011235\ldots \\
89\overline{)1.000000\ldots} \\
\underline{89} \\
110 \\
\underline{89} \\
210 \\
\underline{178} \\
320 \\
\underline{267} \\
530 \\
\underline{445} \\
850\ldots
\end{array}
$$

Notice that after the 0 in the tenths place, the next five digits are the first five terms of the Fibonacci sequence. In addition, as indicated in color in the process, the digits 1, 1, 2, 3, 5, 8 appear in the division steps. Now, look at the digits next to the ones in color, beginning with the second "1"; they, too, are 1, 1, 2, 3, 5, ...

If the division process is continued past the final step shown above, the pattern seems to stop, because to ten decimal places, $\frac{1}{89} \approx 0.0112359551$. (The decimal representation actually begins to repeat later in the process, since $\frac{1}{89}$ is a rational number.) However, the sum below indicates how the Fibonacci numbers are actually "hidden" in this decimal.

$$
\begin{array}{l}
0.01 \\
0.001 \\
0.0002 \\
0.00003 \\
0.000005 \\
0.0000008 \\
0.00000013 \\
0.000000021 \\
0.0000000034 \\
0.00000000055 \\
\underline{0.000000000089} \\
\frac{1}{89} = 0.0112359550.\ldots
\end{array}
$$

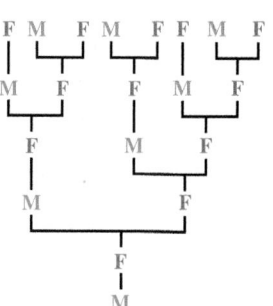

Figure 1

Fibonacci patterns have been found in numerous places in nature. For example, male honeybees (drones) hatch from eggs that have not been fertilized, so a male bee has only one parent, a female. On the other hand, female honeybees hatch from fertilized eggs, so a female has two parents, one male and one female. **Figure 1** shows several generations of ancestors for a male honeybee.

Notice that in the first generation, starting at the bottom, there is 1 bee, in the second there is 1 bee, in the third there are 2 bees, and so on. These are the terms of the Fibonacci sequence. Furthermore, beginning with the second generation, the numbers of female bees form the sequence, and beginning with the third generation, the numbers of male bees also form the sequence.

A fraction such as

$$1 + \cfrac{1}{1 + \cfrac{1}{1 + \cfrac{1}{1 + \cdots}}}$$

is called a **continued fraction**. This continued fraction can be evaluated as follows.

Let $x = 1 + \cfrac{1}{1 + \cfrac{1}{1 + \cdots}}$

Then $x = 1 + \dfrac{1}{x}$

$$x^2 = x + 1$$

$$x^2 - x - 1 = 0.$$

By the quadratic formula from algebra,

$$x = \frac{1 \pm \sqrt{1 - 4(1)(-1)}}{2(1)}$$

$$x = \frac{1 \pm \sqrt{5}}{2}.$$

Notice that the positive solution is the **golden ratio.**

Successive terms in the Fibonacci sequence also appear in some plants. For example, the photo on the left below shows the double spiraling of a daisy head, with 21 clockwise spirals and 34 counterclockwise spirals. These numbers are successive terms in the sequence.

Most pineapples (see the photo on the right below) exhibit the Fibonacci sequence in the following way: Count the spirals formed by the "scales" of the cone, first counting from lower left to upper right. Then count the spirals from lower right to upper left. You should find that in one direction you get 8 spirals, and in the other you get 13 spirals, once again successive terms of the Fibonacci sequence. Many pinecones exhibit 5 and 8 spirals, and the cone of the giant sequoia has 3 and 5 spirals.

The Golden Ratio

If we consider the quotients of successive Fibonacci numbers, a pattern emerges.

$\dfrac{1}{1} = 1$	$\dfrac{5}{3} = 1.666\ldots$	$\dfrac{21}{13} \approx 1.615384615$	$\dfrac{89}{55} = 1.618181818\ldots$
$\dfrac{2}{1} = 2$	$\dfrac{8}{5} = 1.6$	$\dfrac{34}{21} \approx 1.619047619$	
$\dfrac{3}{2} = 1.5$	$\dfrac{13}{8} = 1.625$	$\dfrac{55}{34} \approx 1.617647059$	

These quotients seem to be approaching some "limiting value" close to 1.618. In fact, as we go farther into the sequence, these quotients approach the number

$$\mathbf{\frac{1 + \sqrt{5}}{2}}, \quad \text{Golden ratio}$$

known as the **golden ratio** and often symbolized by $\boldsymbol{\phi}$, the Greek letter phi.

The golden ratio appears over and over in art, architecture, music, and nature. Its origins go back to the days of the ancient Greeks, who thought that a golden rectangle exhibited the most aesthetically pleasing proportions.

A **golden rectangle** is one that can be divided into a square and another (smaller) rectangle the same shape as the original rectangle. (See **Figure 2.**) If we let the smaller rectangle have length L and width W, as shown in the figure, then we see that the original rectangle has length $L + W$ and width L. Both rectangles (being "golden") have their lengths and widths in the golden ratio, ϕ, so we have

$$\frac{L}{W} = \frac{L + W}{L}$$

$$\frac{L}{W} = \frac{L}{L} + \frac{W}{L} \quad \text{Write the right side as the sum of two fractions.}$$

Figure 2

$$\phi = 1 + \frac{1}{\phi} \quad \text{Substitute } \frac{L}{W} = \phi, \frac{L}{L} = 1, \text{ and } \frac{W}{L} = \frac{1}{\phi}.$$

$$\phi^2 = \phi + 1 \quad \text{Multiply both sides by } \phi.$$

$$\phi^2 - \phi - 1 = 0. \quad \text{Write in standard quadratic form.}$$

Using the quadratic formula from algebra, the positive solution of this equation is found to be $\frac{1 + \sqrt{5}}{2} \approx 1.618033989$, the golden ratio.

The Parthenon (see the photo), built on the Acropolis in ancient Athens during the fifth century B.C., is an example of architecture exhibiting many distinct golden rectangles.

To see an interesting connection between the terms of the Fibonacci sequence, the golden ratio, and a phenomenon of nature, we can start with a rectangle measuring 89 by 55 units. (See **Figure 3.**) This is a very close approximation to a golden rectangle. Within this rectangle a square is then constructed, 55 units on a side. The remaining rectangle is also approximately a golden rectangle, measuring 55 units by 34 units. Each time this process is repeated, a square and an approximate golden rectangle are formed.

As indicated in **Figure 3,** vertices of the squares may be joined by a smooth curve known as a *spiral*. This spiral resembles the outline of a cross section of the shell of the chambered nautilus, as shown in the photo.

A Golden Rectangle in Art The rectangle outlining the figure in *St. Jerome* by Leonardo da Vinci is an example of a golden rectangle.

Figure 3

FOR FURTHER THOUGHT

Mathematical Animation

The 1959 animated film *Donald in Mathmagic Land* has endured for over 50 years as a classic. It provides a 25-minute trip with Donald Duck, led by the Spirit of Mathematics, through the world of mathematics. Several minutes of the film are devoted to the golden ratio (or, as it is termed there, the golden section).

© Disney Enterprises, Inc.

Disney provides animation to explain the golden ratio in a way that the printed word simply cannot do. The golden ratio is seen in architecture, nature, and the human body.

For Group or Individual Investigation

1. Verify the following Fibonacci pattern in the conifer family. Obtain a pineapple, and count spirals formed by the "scales" of the cone, first counting from lower left to upper right. Then count the spirals from lower right to upper left. What do you find?

2. Two popular sizes of index cards are 3″ by 5″ and 5″ by 8″. Why do you think that these are industry-standard sizes?

3. Divide your height by the height to your navel. Find a class average. What value does this come close to?

| 5.5 | **EXERCISES** |

Answer each question concerning the Fibonacci sequence or the golden ratio.

1. The fifteenth Fibonacci number is 610 and the seventeenth Fibonacci number is 1597. What is the value of the sixteenth Fibonacci number?

2. Recall that F_n represents the Fibonacci number in the nth position in the sequence. Find all values of n such that $F_n = n$.

3. Write the "parity" (o for odd, e for even) of each of the first twelve terms of the Fibonacci sequence.

4. From the pattern shown in the parity sequence, determine the parity of the one-hundredth term.

5. What is the exact value of the golden ratio?

6. What is the approximate value of the golden ratio to the nearest thousandth?

In each of Exercises 7–14, a pattern is established involving terms of the Fibonacci sequence. Use inductive reasoning to make a conjecture concerning the next equation in the pattern, and verify it. You may wish to refer to the first few terms of the sequence given in the text.

7. $1 = 2 - 1$
$1 + 1 = 3 - 1$
$1 + 1 + 2 = 5 - 1$
$1 + 1 + 2 + 3 = 8 - 1$

8. $1 = 2 - 1$
$1 + 3 = 5 - 1$
$1 + 3 + 8 = 13 - 1$
$1 + 3 + 8 + 21 = 34 - 1$

9. $1 = 1$
$1 + 2 = 3$
$1 + 2 + 5 = 8$
$1 + 2 + 5 + 13 = 21$

10. $1^2 + 1^2 = 2$
$1^2 + 2^2 = 5$
$2^2 + 3^2 = 13$
$3^2 + 5^2 = 34$

11. $2^2 - 1^2 = 3$
$3^2 - 1^2 = 8$
$5^2 - 2^2 = 21$
$8^2 - 3^2 = 55$

12. $2^3 + 1^3 - 1^3 = 8$
$3^3 + 2^3 - 1^3 = 34$
$5^3 + 3^3 - 2^3 = 144$
$8^3 + 5^3 - 3^3 = 610$

13. $1 = 1^2$
$1 - 2 = -1^2$
$1 - 2 + 5 = 2^2$
$1 - 2 + 5 - 13 = -3^2$

14. $1 - 1 = -1 + 1$
$1 - 1 + 2 = 1 + 1$
$1 - 1 + 2 - 3 = -2 + 1$
$1 - 1 + 2 - 3 + 5 = 3 + 1$

15. Every natural number can be expressed as a sum of Fibonacci numbers, where no number is used more than once. For example,

$$25 = 21 + 3 + 1.$$

Express each of the following in this way.

(a) 39   **(b)** 59   **(c)** 99

16. It has been shown that if m divides n, then F_m is a factor of F_n. Show that this is true for the following values of m and n.

(a) $m = 3, n = 6$ **(b)** $m = 4, n = 12$
(c) $m = 5, n = 15$

17. It has been shown that if the greatest common factor of m and n is r, then the greatest common factor of F_m and F_n is F_r. Show that this is true for the following values of m and n.

(a) $m = 10, n = 4$ **(b)** $m = 12, n = 6$
(c) $m = 14, n = 6$

18. For any prime number p except 2 or 5, either F_{p+1} or F_{p-1} is divisible by p. Show that this is true for the following values of p.

(a) $p = 3$ **(b)** $p = 7$ **(c)** $p = 11$

19. Earlier we saw that if a term of the Fibonacci sequence is squared and then the product of the terms on each side of the term is found, there will always be a difference of 1. Follow the steps below, choosing the sixth Fibonacci number, 8.

(a) Square 8. Multiply the terms of the sequence two positions away from 8 (i.e., 3 and 21). Subtract the smaller result from the larger, and record your answer.

(b) Square 8. Multiply the terms of the sequence three positions away from 8. Once again, subtract the smaller result from the larger, and record your answer.

(c) Repeat the process, moving four terms away from 8.

(d) Make a conjecture about what will happen when you repeat the process, moving five terms away. Verify your answer.

20. A Number Trick   Here is a number trick that you can perform. Ask someone to pick any two numbers at random and to write them down. Ask the person to determine a third number by adding the first and second, a fourth number by adding the second and third, and so on, until ten numbers are determined. Then ask the person to add these ten numbers. You will be able to give the sum before the person even completes the list, because the sum will always be 11 times the seventh number in the list. Verify that this is true, by using x and y as the first two numbers arbitrarily chosen. (*Hint:* Remember the distributive property from algebra.)

Another Fibonacci-type sequence that has been studied by mathematicians is the **Lucas sequence,** *named after a French mathematician of the nineteenth century. The first nine terms of the Lucas sequence are*

$$1, 3, 4, 7, 11, 18, 29, 47, 76.$$

21. What is the tenth term of the Lucas sequence?

22. Choose any term of the Lucas sequence and square it. Then multiply the terms on either side of the one you chose. Subtract the smaller result from the larger. Repeat this for a different term of the sequence. Do you get the same result? Make a conjecture about this pattern.

23. The first term of the Lucas sequence is 1. Add the first and third terms. Record your answer. Now add the first, third, and fifth terms and record your answer. Continue this pattern, each time adding another term that is in an *odd* position in the sequence. What do you notice about all of your sums?

24. The second term of the Lucas sequence is 3. Add the second and fourth terms. Record your answer. Now add the second, fourth, and sixth terms and record your answer. Continue this pattern, each time adding another term that is in an *even* position of the sequence. What do you notice about all of your sums?

25. Many interesting patterns exist among the terms of the Fibonacci sequence and the Lucas sequence. Make a conjecture about the next equation that would appear in each of the lists, and then verify it.

(a) $1 \cdot 1 = 1$
$1 \cdot 3 = 3$
$2 \cdot 4 = 8$
$3 \cdot 7 = 21$
$5 \cdot 11 = 55$

(b) $1 + 2 = 3$
$1 + 3 = 4$
$2 + 5 = 7$
$3 + 8 = 11$
$5 + 13 = 18$

(c) $1 + 1 = 2 \cdot 1$
$1 + 3 = 2 \cdot 2$
$2 + 4 = 2 \cdot 3$
$3 + 7 = 2 \cdot 5$
$5 + 11 = 2 \cdot 8$

(d) $1 + 4 = 5 \cdot 1$
$3 + 7 = 5 \cdot 2$
$4 + 11 = 5 \cdot 3$
$7 + 18 = 5 \cdot 5$
$11 + 29 = 5 \cdot 8$

26. In the text we illustrate that the quotients of successive terms of the Fibonacci sequence approach the golden ratio. Make a similar observation for the terms of the Lucas sequence; that is, find the decimal approximations for the quotients

$$\frac{3}{1}, \frac{4}{3}, \frac{7}{4}, \frac{11}{7}, \frac{18}{11}, \frac{29}{18},$$

and so on, using a calculator. Then make a conjecture about what seems to be happening.

Recall the **Pythagorean theorem** *from geometry: If a right triangle has legs of lengths a and b and hypotenuse of length c, then*

$$a^2 + b^2 = c^2.$$

Suppose that we choose any four successive terms of the Fibonacci sequence. Multiply the first and fourth. Double the product of the second and third. Add the squares of the second and third. The three results obtained form a **Pythagorean triple** *(three numbers that satisfy the equation $a^2 + b^2 = c^2$). Find the Pythagorean triple obtained this way, using the four given successive terms of the Fibonacci sequence.*

27. $1, 1, 2, 3$ **28.** $2, 3, 5, 8$ **29.** $5, 8, 13, 21$

30. Look at the values of the hypotenuse (c) in the answers to **Exercises 27–29.** What do you notice about each of them?

31. The following array of numbers is called **Pascal's triangle.**

$$
\begin{array}{ccccccccccccc}
 & & & & & & 1 & & & & & & \\
 & & & & & 1 & & 1 & & & & & \\
 & & & & 1 & & 2 & & 1 & & & & \\
 & & & 1 & & 3 & & 3 & & 1 & & & \\
 & & 1 & & 4 & & 6 & & 4 & & 1 & & \\
 & 1 & & 5 & & 10 & & 10 & & 5 & & 1 & \\
1 & & 6 & & 15 & & 20 & & 15 & & 6 & & 1
\end{array}
$$

This array is important in the study of counting techniques and probability (see later chapters) and appears in algebra in the binomial theorem. If the triangular array is written in a different form, as follows, and the sums along the diagonals as indicated by the dashed lines are found, there is an interesting occurrence. What do you find when the numbers are added?

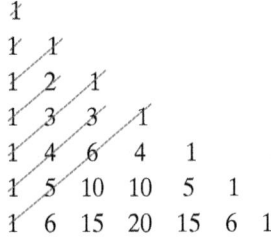

32. Write a paragraph explaining some of the occurrences of the Fibonacci sequence and the golden ratio in your everyday surroundings.

Exercises 33–36 require a scientific calculator.

33. The positive solution of $x^2 - x - 1 = 0$ is

$$\frac{1 + \sqrt{5}}{2},$$

as indicated in the text. The negative solution is

$$\frac{1 - \sqrt{5}}{2}.$$

Find the decimal approximations for both. What similarity do you notice between the two decimals?

34. In some cases, writers define the golden ratio to be the reciprocal of $\frac{1 + \sqrt{5}}{2}$. Find a decimal approximation for the reciprocal of $\frac{1 + \sqrt{5}}{2}$. What similarity do you notice between the decimals for $\frac{1 + \sqrt{5}}{2}$ and its reciprocal?

A remarkable relationship exists between the two solutions of the equation $x^2 - x - 1 = 0$, which are

$$\phi = \frac{1 + \sqrt{5}}{2} \quad and \quad \overline{\phi} = \frac{1 - \sqrt{5}}{2},$$

and the Fibonacci numbers. To find the nth Fibonacci number without using the recursion formula, use a calculator to evaluate

$$\frac{\phi^n - \overline{\phi}^n}{\sqrt{5}}.$$

Thus, to find the thirteenth Fibonacci number, evaluate

$$\frac{\left(\frac{1 + \sqrt{5}}{2}\right)^{13} - \left(\frac{1 - \sqrt{5}}{2}\right)^{13}}{\sqrt{5}}.$$

*This form is known as the **Binet form** of the nth Fibonacci number. Use the Binet form and a calculator to find the nth Fibonacci number for each of the following values of n.*

35. $n = 16$ **36.** $n = 24$

CHAPTER 5	**SUMMARY**

KEY TERMS

5.1

number theory
prime number
composite number
divisibility
divisibility tests
factor
divisor
multiple
factorization
prime factorization

Sieve of Eratosthenes
fundamental theorem
    of arithmetic
cryptography
modular systems

5.2

proof by contradiction
Mersenne number
Mersenne prime
partition

5.3

perfect number
deficient number
abundant number
amicable (friendly)
    numbers
Goldbach's conjecture
twin primes
primordial primes
Fermat's Last Theorem

5.4

greatest common factor (GCF)
relatively prime numbers
Euclidean algorithm
least common multiple (LCM)

5.5

Fibonacci sequence
Fibonacci numbers
golden ratio
golden rectangle

NEW SYMBOLS

$a \mid b$ a divides b ϕ the golden ratio

TEST YOUR WORD POWER

See how well you have learned the vocabulary in this chapter.

1. In mathematics, **number theory** in general deals with
  A. the properties of the rational numbers.
  B. operations on fractions.
  C. the properties of the natural numbers.
  D. only those numbers that are prime.

2. A **prime number** is
  A. divisible by 2, whereas a composite number is not.
  B. divisible by itself and 1 only.
  C. one of the finite set of numbers discovered by Marin Mersenne.
  D. any number expressible in the form $2^p - 1$, where p is a prime.

3. A **partition** of a set is
   A. a rule that separates half of its elements from the other half.
   B. a subset that contains some but not all of the elements of the set.
   C. a rule by which all elements of the set can be identified.
   D. a division of all elements of the set into disjoint subsets.

4. A natural number that is less than the sum of its **proper divisors** is
   A. an **abundant** number.
   B. a **perfect** number.
   C. a **deficient** number.
   D. a **Fermat number.**

5. An **amicable** pair consists of two numbers that are
   A. either both prime or both composite.
   B. either both odd or both even.
   C. each equal to the sum of the proper divisors of the other.
   D. one Fermat number and one Mersenne number.

6. **Goldbach's conjecture**
   A. was formulated over 300 years before it was proved.
   B. has to do with two *n*th powers summing to a third *n*th power.
   C. has to do with expressing natural numbers as products of primes.
   D. has to do with expressing natural numbers as sums of primes.

7. The so-called **twin primes**
   A. always occur in pairs that differ by 2.
   B. always occur in pairs that differ by 1.
   C. cannot exceed 10^{100}.
   D. have finally all been identified.

8. **Fermat's Last Theorem**
   A. was proved by Euler about 100 years after Fermat stated it.
   B. has never been proved, but most mathematicians believe it is true.
   C. was proved by Wiles in the 1990s.
   D. says that the equation $a^n + b^n = c^n$ cannot be true for $n = 2$.

ANSWERS
1. C 2. B 3. D 4. A
5. C 6. D 7. A 8. C

QUICK REVIEW

Concepts	Examples

5.1 Prime and Composite Numbers

The natural number a is divisible by the natural number b, or, equivalently, "b divides a" (denoted $b \mid a$), if there exists a natural number k such that $a = bk$.

$2 \mid 14$, since $14 = 2 \cdot 7$ ($k = 7$). 2 is a factor of 14, and 14 is a multiple of 2.

In the equation above, we say that b is a **factor** (or **divisor**) of a and that a is a multiple of b.

$2 \nmid 13$, since there is no suitable k. Here $13 = 2 \cdot 6.5$ (and $k = 6.5$ is *not* a natural number).

A **factorization** of a natural number expresses it as a product of some, or all, of its divisors.

$2 \cdot 12$, $3 \cdot 8$, $4 \cdot 6$, $2 \cdot 2 \cdot 6$, $2 \cdot 3 \cdot 4$, $2 \cdot 2 \cdot 2 \cdot 3$
Factorizations of 24

A **prime number** is greater than 1 and has only itself and 1 as factors.

17 is prime. Its only factors are 1 and 17.

A **composite number** is greater than 1 and is *not* prime—that is, it has at least one factor other than itself and 1.

10 is composite. In addition to 1 and 10, it has the factors 2 and 5.

Divisibility tests can help determine the factors of a given natural number.

54,086,226 is divisible by 3 since the sum of its digits

$$5 + 4 + 0 + 8 + 6 + 2 + 2 + 6 = 33$$

is divisible by 3.

258,784 is *not* divisible by 3 since the sum of its digits

$$2 + 5 + 8 + 7 + 8 + 4 = 34$$

is *not* divisible by 3.

Concepts	Examples
A factorization with prime factors only is a number's **prime factorization**.	The prime factorization of 24 is $$2 \cdot 2 \cdot 2 \cdot 3.$$
The **fundamental theorem of arithmetic** states that the prime factorization of a number is unique (if the order of the factors is disregarded).	24 has no other prime factorization except rearrangements of the factors shown above, such as $2 \cdot 3 \cdot 2 \cdot 2$ and $3 \cdot 2 \cdot 2 \cdot 2$.
A natural number's prime factorization can be determined by using a **factor tree** or by using **repeated division by primes**.	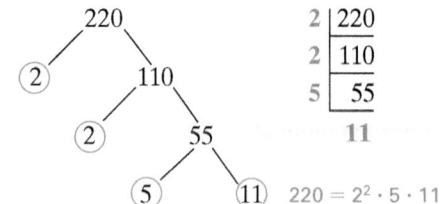 $220 = 2^2 \cdot 5 \cdot 11$

5.2 Large Prime Numbers

Modern **cryptography systems** are based on large prime numbers.	Cryptography systems, in practice, use primes so huge that the most powerful computers can multiply them but *cannot* factor their product.
Large primes are found today mainly among the **Mersenne numbers**.	The largest Mersenne prime discovered, as of summer 2014, is $2^{57,885,161} - 1$. It has 17,425,170 digits.

5.3 Selected Topics from Number Theory

The **proper divisors** of a natural number are all of its divisors except the number itself.	42 has proper divisors 1, 2, 3, 6, 7, 14, and 21.
A natural number is **perfect** if the sum of its proper divisors equals the number itself.	28 has proper divisors 1, 2, 4, 7, and 14. $$28 = 1 + 2 + 4 + 7 + 14$$
All even perfect numbers are of the form $2^{n-1}(2^n - 1)$, where $2^n - 1$ is prime.	The number $2^3 - 1 = 7$ is prime, so $$2^{3-1}(2^3 - 1) = 4(7) = 28 \quad \text{is perfect.}$$
A natural number is **abundant** if the sum of its proper divisors is greater than the number itself.	$1 + 2 + 3 + 6 + 7 + 14 + 21 = 54 > 42 \leftarrow$ Abundant
A natural number is **deficient** if the sum of its proper divisors is less than the number itself.	$1 + 2 + 4 + 8 = 15 < 16 \leftarrow$ Deficient
Two natural numbers are **amicable,** or **friendly,** if each equals the sum of the other's proper divisors.	The smallest amicable pair is 220 and 284. Proper divisors of 220: 1, 2, 4, 5, 10, 11, 20, 22, 44, 55, 110 Proper divisors of 284: 1, 2, 4, 71, 142 $$1 + 2 + 4 + 5 + 10 + 11 + 20 + 22 + 44 + 55 + 110 = 284$$ $$1 + 2 + 4 + 71 + 142 = 220$$
Goldbach's conjecture (which is not proved) states that every even number greater than 2 can be written as the sum of two prime numbers.	$12 = 5 + 7 \qquad 46 = 3 + 43$ Goldbach's conjecture
Twin primes are two primes that differ by 2.	17 and 19 29 and 31 Twin primes
Fermat's Last Theorem (proved in the 1990s) states that there are no triples of natural numbers (a, b, c) that satisfy the equation $a^n + b^n = c^n$ for any natural number $n \geq 3$.	$2^3 + 6^3 = 8 + 216 = 224$, but 224 is not a perfect cube.

Concepts	Examples

5.4 Greatest Common Factor and Least Common Multiple

The **greatest common factor (GCF)** of a group of natural numbers is the largest natural number that is a factor of all the numbers in the group.

Prime factors method:

$$450 = 2 \cdot 3^2 \cdot 5^2$$

$$660 = 2^2 \cdot 3 \cdot 5 \cdot 11$$

$$\text{GCF} = 2 \cdot 3 \cdot 5 = 30$$

Dividing by prime factors method:

$$
\begin{array}{r|rr}
2 & 450 & 660 \\ \hline
3 & 225 & 330 \\ \hline
5 & 75 & 110 \\ \hline
  & 15 & 22
\end{array}
$$

GCF = 2 · 3 · 5 = 30

Euclidean algorithm:

Prime factors method:

$$450 = 2 \cdot 3^2 \cdot 5^2$$

$$660 = 2^2 \cdot 3 \cdot 5 \cdot 11$$

$$\text{LCM} = 2^2 \cdot 3^2 \cdot 5^2 \cdot 11 = 9900$$

The **least common multiple (LCM)** of a group of natural numbers is the smallest natural number that is a multiple of all the numbers in the group.

Dividing by prime factors method:

$$
\begin{array}{r|rr}
2 & 450 & 660 \\ \hline
2 & 225 & 330 \\ \hline
3 & 225 & 165 \\ \hline
3 & 75 & 55 \\ \hline
5 & 25 & 55 \\ \hline
  & 5 & 11
\end{array}
$$

LCM = 2 · 2 · 3 · 3 · 5 · 5 · 11 = 9900

Formula:

$$\text{LCM} = \frac{450 \cdot 660}{\text{GCF of 450 and 660}} = \frac{297{,}000}{30} = 9900$$

5.5 The Fibonacci Sequence and the Golden Ratio

The **Fibonacci sequence** begins with two 1s, and each succeeding term is the sum of the preceding two terms.

1, 1, 2, 3, 5, 8, 13, 21, 34, 55, 89, 144, 233, 377, . . .

Concepts	Examples
The **golden ratio,** $$\frac{1 + \sqrt{5}}{2},$$ arises in many ways. One is as the limit of the ratio of adjacent terms in the Fibonacci sequence.	The ratios (to three decimal places), $\frac{1}{1} = 1.000$, $\frac{2}{1} = 2.000$, $\frac{3}{2} = 1.500$, $\frac{5}{3} \approx 1.667$, $\frac{8}{5} = 1.600, \dots$ are approaching $\dfrac{1 + \sqrt{5}}{2} \approx 1.618.$

CHAPTER 5   TEST

In Exercises 1–6, decide whether each statement is true *or* false.

1. For all natural numbers n, 1 is a factor of n, and n is a multiple of n.

2. If a natural number is not perfect, then it must be abundant.

3. If a natural number is divisible by 9, then it must also be divisible by 3.

4. If p and q are different primes, 1 is their greatest common factor, and pq is their least common multiple.

5. No two prime numbers differ by 1.

6. There are infinitely many prime numbers.

7. Use divisibility tests to determine whether the number

$$540,487,608$$

is divisible by each of the following.

(a) 2   (b) 3   (c) 4
(d) 5   (e) 6   (f) 8
(g) 9   (h) 10   (i) 12

8. Decide whether each number is prime, composite, or neither.

(a) 91   (b) 101   (c) 1

9. Give the prime factorization of 2970.

10. In your own words state the fundamental theorem of arithmetic.

11. Decide whether each number is perfect, deficient, or abundant.

(a) 18   (b) 32   (c) 28

12. Which of the following statements is false?
  A. There are no known odd perfect numbers.
  B. Every even perfect number must end in 8 or 26.
  C. Goldbach's conjecture for the number 12 is illustrated by the equation $12 = 7 + 5$.

13. Give a pair of twin primes between 60 and 80.

14. Find the greatest common factor of 99, 135, and 216.

15. Find the least common multiple of 91 and 154.

16. *Day Off for Fast-food Workers* Both Katherine and Josh work at a fast-food outlet. Katherine has every sixth day off, and Josh has every fourth day off. If they are both off on Wednesday of this week, what will be the day of the week that they are next off together?

17. The twenty-first Fibonacci number is 10,946 and the twenty-second Fibonacci number is 17,711. What is the twenty-third Fibonacci number?

18. Make a conjecture about the next equation in the following list, and verify it.

$$8 - (1 + 1 + 2 + 3) = 1$$
$$13 - (1 + 2 + 3 + 5) = 2$$
$$21 - (2 + 3 + 5 + 8) = 3$$
$$34 - (3 + 5 + 8 + 13) = 5$$

19. Choose the correct completion of this statement: If p is a prime number, then $2^p - 1$ is _____ prime.
  A. never   **B.** sometimes   **C.** always

20. Determine the eighth term of a Fibonacci-type sequence with first term 1 and second term 4.

21. Choose any term after the first in the sequence described in **Exercise 20.** Square it. Multiply the two terms on either side of it. Subtract the smaller result from the larger. Now repeat the process with a different term. Make a conjecture about what this process will yield for any term of the sequence.

22. Which one of the following is the *exact* value of the golden ratio?

  A. $\dfrac{1 + \sqrt{5}}{2}$ **B.** $\dfrac{1 - \sqrt{5}}{2}$ **C.** 1.6   **D.** 1.618

The Real Numbers and Their Representations

6

Unsettled Weather Ahead
weather.g
Friday, May 23, 2014

Western Cutoff Low Brings Unsettled Weather to the Area

L Unsettled Moisture

Today
79°
Rain Chance
40%
Afternoon

Saturday
77°
Rain Chance
60%

Sun
8:
Rain Ch
35°

Unsettled Weather
Expected into Next Wee

@NWSKansasCity

US National Weather
Service Pleasant Hill

In the March 12, 2014, issue of the *New Orleans Times Picayune*, columnist Jarvis DeBerry wrote the following in an article titled "Old Math or Common Core Math, Which Troubles You More?"

After a February board meeting for my alma mater's student newspaper, I told some students that I began Washington University in the engineering school. One asked if my previous focus on math and science ever proves useful in journalism. I joked: "Only when a colleague needs help figuring out the percent something has increased." Another board member who, like me, graduated from WashU and worked in journalism, responded with something close to awe: "You can do percentages? I mean, seriously?"

In the development of the real numbers (the topic of this chapter), the unit number 1 is the place at which everything starts. (0 showed up much later in our number system.) The concept of percent has become a standard by which portions of one whole thing are described.

Percent means "per one hundred," and the symbol % is used to represent percent. Thus,

1% means one one-hundredth,   or $\dfrac{1}{100}$,   or   0.01.

One hundred percent, or 100%, means 1 whole thing.

As consumers, we are faced with the use of percent on a daily basis: advertisements for sale items, interest on loans and savings, poll numbers, chance of precipitation in daily weathercasts, and so on. Occupations that otherwise may not require formal mathematics often require the basic concept of percent.

- Retail managers marking up an item to sell might be required to find a given percent of the wholesale cost.

- The same retailer may need to use a percent to determine how much to subtract from the usual selling price to mark an item that is on sale.

- Teachers assigning grades may need to find a percent of a total number of points.

- A manager in a publishing company may need to determine the percent change of sales from one edition of a text to the next, or the percent of sales that a particular title captures in its market.

Some people, such as DeBerry, have a natural talent—or a learned ability—for determining percents, while others don't have a clue. Those who are proficient use many different methods to find simple percents. For example, if you are asked to find

20% of 50,

you might mentally calculate using one of the following methods.

1. You think, "Well, 20% means $\frac{1}{5}$, and to find $\frac{1}{5}$ of something I divide by 5, so 50 divided by 5 is 10. The answer is 10."

2. You think, "20% is twice 10%, and to find 10% of something I move the decimal point one place to the left. So 10% of 50 is 5.0, or just 5, and I simply double 5 to get 10. The answer is 10."

For those who don't think this way, there is the tried-and-true method of multiplying 50 by 0.20.

One whole dollar ($1.00) is the basic monetary unit in the United States. One one-hundredth of a dollar is a penny, or one cent. Notice the correlation between this concept and that of percent. One cent is represented $0.01, or just $.01. *Then how do we represent 99 cents?* The answer is **$.99.** But so many times we see signs such as the one here from Wendy's, indicating a price of **.99¢.** Because ¢ is a symbol for "cents," this posted price actually means that the spicy nuggets sell for less than one penny. Think about it. *Do you understand why?*

If you don't have the knack for computing percents using shortcuts, there are sound mathematical procedures for working with this concept. This chapter introduces the real number system, the operations of arithmetic with real numbers, and selected applications of fractions, decimals, and percents in occupations and trades.

6.1   REAL NUMBERS, ORDER, AND ABSOLUTE VALUE

OBJECTIVES

1 Represent a number on a number line.

2 Identify a number as positive, negative, or zero.

3 Identify a number as belonging to one or more sets of numbers.

4 Given two numbers *a* and *b*, determine whether $a = b$, $a < b$, or $a > b$.

5 Given a number *a*, determine its additive inverse and absolute value.

6 Interpret signed numbers in tables of economic and occupations data.

Sets of Real Numbers

The mathematician Leopold Kronecker (1823–1891) once made the statement, "God made the integers, all the rest is the work of man." The *natural numbers* are those numbers with which we count discrete objects. By including 0 in the set, we obtain the set of *whole numbers*.

NATURAL NUMBERS

$\{1, 2, 3, 4, \ldots\}$ is the set of **natural numbers.**

WHOLE NUMBERS

$\{0, 1, 2, 3, \ldots\}$ is the set of **whole numbers.**

These numbers, along with many others, can be represented on **number lines** like the one pictured in **Figure 1.** We draw a number line by locating any point on the line and labeling it 0. This is the **origin.** Choose any point to the right of 0 and label it 1. The distance between 0 and 1 gives a unit of measure used to locate other points, as shown in **Figure 1.** The numbers labeled and those continuing in the same way to the right correspond to the set of whole numbers.

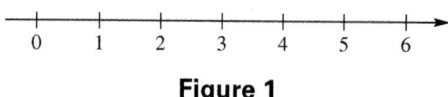

Figure 1

All the whole numbers starting with 1 are located to the right of 0 on the number line. But numbers may also be placed to the left of 0. These numbers, written $-1, -2, -3,$ and so on, are shown in **Figure 2.** (The negative sign is used to show that the numbers are located to the *left* of 0.)

Figure 2

The numbers to the *left* of 0 are **negative numbers.** The numbers to the *right* of 0 are **positive numbers.** Positive numbers and negative numbers are called **signed numbers.** The number 0 itself is neither positive nor negative.

There are many practical applications of negative numbers.

- Temperatures may fall below zero. The lowest temperature ever recorded in meteorological records was $-128.6°F$ at Vostok, Antarctica, on July 22, 1983.

- Altitudes below sea level can be represented by negative numbers. The shore surrounding the Dead Sea is 1312 feet below sea level, written -1312 feet.

The Origins of Zero The Mayan Indians of Mexico and Central America had one of the earliest numeration systems that included a symbol for zero. The very early Babylonians had a positional system, but they placed only a space between "digits" to indicate a missing power. When the Greeks absorbed Babylonian astronomy, they used the letter omicron, o, of their alphabet or ō to represent "no power," or "zero." The Greek numeration system was gradually replaced by the Roman numeration system.

The original Hindu word for zero was *sunya,* meaning "void." The Arabs adopted this word as *sifr,* or "vacant." The word *sifr* passed into Latin as *zephirum,* which over the years became *zevero, zepiro,* and finally, *zero.*

The natural numbers, their negatives, and zero make up the set of *integers.*

INTEGERS

$\{\ldots, -3, -2, -1, 0, 1, 2, 3, \ldots\}$ is the set of **integers.**

Not all numbers are integers. For example, $\frac{1}{2}$ is a number *halfway* between the integers 0 and 1. Several numbers that are not integers are *graphed* in **Figure 3.** The **graph** of a number is a point on the number line representing that number. Think of the graph of a set of numbers as a "picture" of the set. All the numbers indicated in **Figure 3** can be written as quotients of integers and are examples of *rational numbers.* An integer, such as 2, is also a rational number. This is true because $2 = \frac{2}{1}$.

Figure 3

RATIONAL NUMBERS

$\{x \mid x \text{ is a quotient of two integers, with denominator not equal to } 0\}$ is the set of **rational numbers.**

(Read the part in the braces as "the set of all numbers x such that x is a quotient of two integers, with denominator not equal to 0.")

The set symbolism used in the definition of rational numbers,

$$\{x \mid x \textbf{ has a certain property}\},$$

is called **set-builder notation.** This notation is convenient to use when it is not possible, or practical, to list all the elements of the set.

There are other numbers on the number line that are not rational. The first such number ever to be discovered was $\sqrt{2}$. The Pythagorean theorem, named for the Greek mathematician Pythagoras and covered in more detail in **Chapter 9,** says that in a right triangle, the length of the side opposite the right angle (the hypotenuse) is equal to the square root of the sum of the squares of the two perpendicular sides (the legs). In **Figure 4(a),** this is symbolized

$$c = \sqrt{a^2 + b^2}.$$

A right triangle having both legs a and b of length 1 is placed on a number line as shown in **Figure 4(b).** By the Pythagorean theorem, the length of the hypotenuse c is

$$c = \sqrt{1^2 + 1^2}$$

$$c = \sqrt{1 + 1}$$

$$c = \sqrt{2}.$$

(a)

(b)

Figure 4

Figure 4(b) also shows an arc of a circle, centered at 0 with radius $\sqrt{2}$, intersecting the number line at point P. The coordinate of P is $\sqrt{2}$. The Greeks discovered that this number cannot be expressed as a quotient of integers—it is *irrational*.

IRRATIONAL NUMBERS

$\{x \mid x$ is a number on the number line that is not rational$\}$ is the set of **irrational numbers.**

Irrational numbers include $\sqrt{3}$, $\sqrt{7}$, $-\sqrt{10}$, and π, which is the ratio of the distance around a circle (its *circumference*) to the distance across it (its *diameter*). All numbers that can be represented by points on the number line (the union of the sets of rational and irrational numbers) are called *real numbers*.

REAL NUMBERS

$\{x \mid x$ is a number that can be represented by a point on the number line$\}$ is the set of **real numbers.**

Real numbers can be written as decimal numbers. Any rational number can be written as a decimal that will either come to an end (terminate) or repeat in a fixed "block" of digits. For example,

$$\frac{2}{5} = 0.4 \quad \text{and} \quad \frac{27}{100} = 0.27 \quad \text{are terminating decimals.}$$

$$\frac{1}{3} = 0.3333\ldots \quad \text{and} \quad \frac{3}{11} = 0.27272727\ldots \quad \text{are repeating decimals.}$$

The decimal representation of an irrational number neither terminates nor repeats. Decimal representations of rational and irrational numbers will be discussed further later in this chapter.

Figure 5 illustrates two ways to represent the relationships among the various sets of real numbers.

(a)   (b)

Figure 5

The TI-83/84 Plus calculator will convert a decimal to a fraction. See **Example 1(d).**

EXAMPLE 1 Identifying Elements of a Set of Numbers

List the numbers in the set that belong to each set of numbers.

$$\left\{-5, -\frac{2}{3}, 0, \sqrt{2}, \frac{13}{4}, 5, 5.8\right\}$$

(a) natural numbers **(b)** whole numbers **(c)** integers

(d) rational numbers **(e)** irrational numbers **(f)** real numbers

Solution

(a) The only natural number in the set is 5.

(b) The whole numbers consist of the natural numbers and 0, so the elements of the set that are whole numbers are 0 and 5.

(c) The integers in the set are -5, 0, and 5.

(d) The rational numbers are -5, $-\frac{2}{3}$, 0, $\frac{13}{4}$, 5, and 5.8, because each of these numbers *can* be written as the quotient of two integers. For example, $5.8 = \frac{58}{10} = \frac{29}{5}$.

(e) The only irrational number in the set is $\sqrt{2}$.

(f) All the numbers in the set are real numbers. ∎

Order in the Real Numbers

Suppose that a and b represent two real numbers. If their graphs on the number line are the same point, then a **is equal to** b. If the graph of a lies to the left of b, then a **is less than** b, and if the graph of a lies to the right of b, then a **is greater than** b. The **law of trichotomy** says that for two numbers a and b, one and only one of the following is true.

$$a = b, \quad a < b, \quad \text{or} \quad a > b$$

When read from left to right, the inequality $a < b$ is read "a is less than b."

$$7 < 8 \qquad \text{7 is less than 8.}$$

The inequality $a > b$ means "a is greater than b."

$$8 > 2 \qquad \text{8 is greater than 2.}$$

Notice that the symbol always points to the lesser number.

$$\text{Lesser number} \longrightarrow \quad 8 < 15$$

The symbol ≤, read from left to right, means "is less than or equal to."

$$5 \leq 9 \qquad \text{5 is less than or equal to 9.}$$

This statement is true because $5 < 9$ is true. *If either the $<$ part or the $=$ part is true, then the inequality $\leq$ is true.* Also, $8 \leq 8$ is true because $8 = 8$ is true. But it is not true that $13 \leq 9$ because neither $13 < 9$ nor $13 = 9$ is true.

The symbol ≥ means "is greater than or equal to."

$$9 \geq 5 \qquad \text{9 is greater than or equal to 5.}$$

This statement is true because $9 > 5$ is true.

The calculator returns a 1 for each of these statements of inequality, signifying that each is true.

$7 < 8$ \
$8 > 2$ \
$5 \leq 9$

The symbol for equality, =, was first introduced by the Englishman **Robert Recorde** in his 1557 algebra text *The Whetstone of Witte*. He used two parallel line segments, because, he claimed, no two things can be more equal.

The symbols for order relationships, $<$ and $>$, were first used by **Thomas Harriot** (1560–1621), another Englishman. These symbols were not immediately adopted by other mathematicians.

EXAMPLE 2 Comparing Real Numbers

Determine whether each statement is *true* or *false*.

(a) $6 \neq 6$ **(b)** $5 < 19$ **(c)** $15 \leq 20$ **(d)** $25 \geq 30$ **(e)** $12 \geq 12$

Solution

(a) The statement $6 \neq 6$ is false because 6 *is equal to* 6.

(b) Because 5 is indeed less than 19, this statement is true.

(c) The statement $15 \leq 20$ is true because $15 < 20$.

(d) Both $25 > 30$ and $25 = 30$ are false, so $25 \geq 30$ is false.

(e) Because $12 = 12$, the statement $12 \geq 12$ is true. ∎

The inequalities in **Example 2(a) and (d)** are false, as signified by the 0. The statement in **Example 2(e)** is true.

Additive Inverses and Absolute Value

For any nonzero real number x, there is exactly one number on the number line the same distance from 0 as x but on the opposite side of 0. In **Figure 6,** the numbers 3 and -3 are the same distance from 0 but are on opposite sides of 0. Thus, 3 and -3 are called **additive inverses, negatives,** or **opposites** of each other.

Figure 6

The additive inverse of the number 0 is 0 itself. This makes 0 the only real number that is its own additive inverse. Other additive inverses occur in distinct pairs. For example, 4 and -4 are additive inverses, as are 6 and -6. Several pairs of additive inverses are shown in **Figure 7.**

The TI-83/84 Plus distinguishes between the negative symbol ($^-$) and the operation of subtraction.

Figure 7

The additive inverse of a number can be indicated by writing the symbol $-$ in front of the number. With this symbol, the additive inverse of 7 is written -7. The additive inverse of -4 is written $-(-4)$ and can be read "the opposite of -4" or "the negative of -4." **Figure 7** suggests that 4 is an additive inverse of -4. A number can have only one additive inverse, so the symbols 4 and $-(-4)$ must represent the same number, which means that

$$-(-4) = 4.$$

DOUBLE NEGATIVE RULE

For any real number x, the following is true.

$$-(-x) = x$$

Table 1

Number	Additive Inverse
-4	$-(-4)$ or 4
0	0
19	-19
$-\frac{2}{3}$	$\frac{2}{3}$

Table 1 shows several numbers and their additive inverses. An important property of additive inverses will be studied later in this chapter:

$$a + (-a) = (-a) + a = 0, \quad \text{for all real numbers } a.$$

As mentioned above, additive inverses are numbers that are the same distance from 0 (but in opposite directions) on the number line. See **Figure 7** on the previous page. This idea can also be expressed by saying that a number and its additive inverse have the same *absolute value*. The **absolute value** of a real number can be defined as the undirected distance between 0 and the number on the number line.

The symbol for the absolute value of the number x is $|x|$, read **"the absolute value of x."** For example, the distance between 0 and 2 on the number line is 2 units, so

$$|2| = 2.$$

Because the distance between 0 and -2 on the number line is also 2 units,

$$|-2| = 2.$$

Absolute value is a measure of undirected distance, so ***the absolute value of a number is never negative.*** Because 0 is a distance of 0 units from 0, $|0| = 0.$

FORMAL DEFINITION OF ABSOLUTE VALUE

For any real number x, the absolute value of x is defined as follows.

$$|x| = \begin{cases} x & \text{if } x \geq 0 \\ -x & \text{if } x < 0 \end{cases}$$

If x is a positive number or 0, then its absolute value is x itself. For example, because 8 is a positive number, $|8| = 8$. By the second part of the definition, ***if x is a negative number, then its absolute value is the additive inverse of x.*** For example, if $x = -9$, then $|-9| = -(-9) = 9$, since the additive inverse of -9 is 9.

The formal definition of absolute value can be confusing if it is not read carefully. The "$-x$" in the second part of the definition *does not* represent a negative number. Since x is negative in the second part, $-x$ represents the opposite of a negative number, which is a positive number.

EXAMPLE 3 Using Absolute Value

Simplify by finding the absolute value.

(a) $|5|$ **(b)** $|-5|$ **(c)** $-|5|$

(d) $-|-14|$ **(e)** $|8-2|$ **(f)** $-|8-2|$

Solution

(a) $|5| = 5$ **(b)** $|-5| = -(-5) = 5$

(c) $-|5| = -(5) = -5$ **(d)** $-|-14| = -(14) = -14$

(e) $|8-2| = |6| = 6$ **(f)** $-|8-2| = -|6| = -6$ ∎

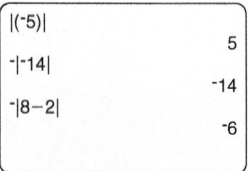

This screen supports the results of **Example 3(b), (d), and (f).**

Example 3(e) shows that absolute value bars also serve as grouping symbols. ***Perform any operations that appear inside absolute value symbols before finding the absolute value.***

Applications of Real Numbers

EXAMPLE 4 Interpreting Signed Numbers in a Table

The consumer price index (CPI) measures the average change in prices of goods and services purchased by urban consumers in the United States. **Table 2** shows the percent change in the CPI for selected categories of goods and services from 2009 to 2010 and from 2010 to 2011. Use the table to answer each question.

Table 2

Category	Change from 2009 to 2010	Change from 2010 to 2011
Appliances	−4.5	−1.2
Education	4.4	4.2
Gasoline	18.4	26.4
Housing	−0.4	1.3
Medical care	3.4	3.0

Source: U.S. Bureau of Labor Statistics.

(a) Which category in which years represents the greatest percent decrease?

(b) Which category in which years represents the least change?

Solution

(a) We must find the negative number with the greatest absolute value. The number that satisfies this condition is −4.5, so the greatest percent decrease was shown by appliances from 2009 to 2010.

(b) We must find the number (either positive, negative, or zero) with the least absolute value. From 2009 to 2010, housing showed the least change, a decrease of 0.4 percent. ∎

In the next example, we see how the need for certain occupations during the upcoming years is changing, some for better and some for worse.

EXAMPLE 5 Comparing Occupational Rates of Change

Table 3 shows the total rates of change projected to occur in demand for some of the fastest-growing and some of the most rapidly-declining occupations from 2012 to 2022.

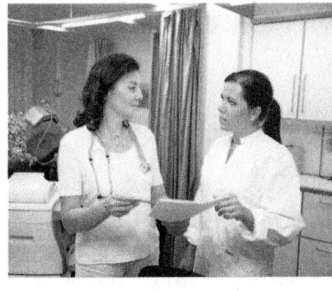

Table 3

Occupation (2012–2022)	Total Rate of Change (in percent)
Interpreters and translators	46.1
Personal care aides	48.8
Physicians' assistants	38.4
Word processors and typists	−25.1
Postal service clerks	−31.8
Locomotive firers	−42.0

Source: Bureau of Labor Statistics.

Which occupation in **Table 3** on the preceding page is expected to see

(a) the greatest change?   **(b)** the least change?

Solution

(a) We want the greatest change, without regard to whether the change is an increase or a decrease. Look for the number with the greatest absolute value. That number is for personal care aides:

$$|48.8| = 48.8.$$

(b) Using similar reasoning, the least change is for word processors and typists:

$$|-25.1| = 25.1.$$ ∎

6.1   EXERCISES

Give a number that satisfies the given condition.

1. An integer between 4.5 and 5.5

2. A rational number between 2.8 and 2.9

3. A whole number that is not positive and is less than 1

4. A whole number greater than 4.5

5. An irrational number that is between $\sqrt{13}$ and $\sqrt{15}$

6. A real number that is neither negative nor positive

Decide whether each statement is true *or* false.

7. Every natural number is positive.

8. Every whole number is positive.

9. Every integer is a rational number.

10. Every rational number is a real number.

List all numbers from each set that are **(a)** *natural numbers;* **(b)** *whole numbers;* **(c)** *integers;* **(d)** *rational numbers;* **(e)** *irrational numbers;* **(f)** *real numbers.*

11. $\left\{ -9, -\sqrt{7}, -1\frac{1}{4}, -\frac{3}{5}, 0, \sqrt{5}, 3, 5.9, 7 \right\}$

12. $\left\{ -5.3, -5, -\sqrt{3}, -1, -\frac{1}{9}, 0, 1.2, 1.8, 3, \sqrt{11} \right\}$

Use an integer or decimal to express each number in bold-face print representing a change or measurement in each of the following.

13. *U.S. Population*   Between July 1, 2011, and July 1, 2012, the population of the United States increased by approximately **2,259,000.** (*Source:* U.S. Census Bureau.)

14. *Number of Movie Screens*   Between 2011 and 2012, the number of movie screens in the United States increased by **209.** (*Source:* Motion Picture Association of America.)

15. *World Series Attendance*   From 2011 to 2012, attendance at the first game of the World Series went from 46,406 to 42,982, a decrease of **3424.** (*Source:* Major League Baseball.)

16. *Number of U. S. Banks*   In 1935, there were 15,295 banks in the United States. By 2012, the number was 7083, representing a decrease of **8212.** (*Source:* Federal Deposit Insurance Corporation.)

17. *Dow Jones Average*   On Friday, August 23, 2013, the Dow Jones Industrial Average (DJIA) closed at 15,010.51. On the previous day, it had closed at 14,963.74. Thus, on Friday it closed up **46.77** points. (*Source: The Washington Post.*)

18. *NASDAQ*   On Tuesday, August 27, 2013, the NASDAQ closed at 3578.52. On the previous day, it had closed at 3657.57. Thus, on Tuesday it closed down **79.05** points. (*Source: The Washington Post.*)

19. *Height of Mt. Arenal in Costa Rica*   The height of Mt. Arenal, an active volcano in Costa Rica, is **5436** feet above sea level. (*Source: The New York Times Almanac.*)

20. *Elevation of New Orleans*   The city of New Orleans, devastated by Hurricane Katrina in 2005, lies **8** feet below sea level. (*Source:* U.S. Geological Survey, *Elevations and Distances in the United States.*)

21. *Melting Point of Fluorine*   The melting point of fluorine gas is **220°** below 0° Celsius.

22. *Boiling Point of Chlorine*   The boiling point of chlorine is approximately **30°** below 0° Fahrenheit.

Depths and Heights of Seas and Mountains *The chart gives selected depths and heights of bodies of water and mountains.*

Bodies of Water	Average Depth in Feet (as a negative number)	Mountains	Altitude in Feet (as a positive number)
Pacific Ocean	−14,040	McKinley	20,237
South China Sea	−4802	Point Success	14,164
Gulf of California	−2375	Matlalcueyetl	14,636
Caribbean Sea	−8448	Ranier	14,416
Indian Ocean	−12,800	Steele	16,642

Source: The World Almanac and Book of Facts.

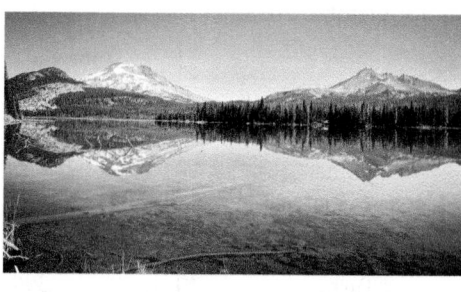

23. List the bodies of water in order, starting with the deepest and ending with the shallowest.

24. List the mountains in order, starting with the lowest and ending with the highest.

25. *True or false:* The absolute value of the depth of the Pacific Ocean is greater than the absolute value of the depth of the Indian Ocean.

26. *True or false:* The absolute value of the depth of the Gulf of California is greater than the absolute value of the depth of the Caribbean Sea.

Graph each group of numbers on a number line.

27. $-2, -6, -4, 3, 4$

28. $-5, -3, -2, 0, 4$

29. $\frac{1}{4}, 2\frac{1}{2}, -3\frac{4}{5}, -4, -1\frac{5}{8}$

30. $5\frac{1}{4}, 4\frac{5}{9}, -2\frac{1}{3}, 0, -3\frac{2}{5}$

31. Match each expression in Column I with its value in Column II. Some choices in Column II may not be used.

I	II
(a) $|-7|$	**A.** 7
(b) $-(-7)$	**B.** -7
(c) $-|-7|$	**C.** neither A nor B
(d) $-|-(-7)|$	**D.** both A and B

32. Fill in the blanks with the correct values: The opposite of -2 is ____, while the absolute value of -2 is ____. The additive inverse of -2 is ____, while the additive inverse of the absolute value of -2 is ____.

Find **(a)** *the additive inverse (or opposite) of each number and* **(b)** *the absolute value of each number.*

33. -2

34. -8

35. 6

36. 11

37. $7 - 4$

38. $8 - 3$

39. $7 - 7$

40. $3 - 3$

Select the lesser of the two given numbers.

41. $-12, -4$

42. $-9, -14$

43. $-8, -1$

44. $-15, -16$

45. $3, |-4|$

46. $5, |-2|$

47. $|-3|, |-4|$

48. $|-8|, |-9|$

49. $-|-6|, -|-4|$

50. $-|-2|, -|-3|$

51. $|5 - 3|, |6 - 2|$

52. $|7 - 2|, |8 - 1|$

Decide whether each statement is true *or* false.

53. $6 > -(-2)$

54. $-8 > -(-2)$

55. $-4 \le -(-5)$

56. $-6 \le -(-3)$

57. $|-6| < |-9|$

58. $|-12| < |-20|$

59. $-|8| > |-9|$

60. $-|12| > |-15|$

61. $-|-5| \ge -|-9|$

62. $-|-12| \le -|-15|$

63. $|6 - 5| \ge |6 - 2|$

64. $|13 - 8| \le |7 - 4|$

65. ***Population Change*** The table shows the percent change in population from 2000 to 2012 for selected metropolitan areas.

Metropolitan Area	Percent Change
Las Vegas	45.4
San Francisco	8.0
Chicago	4.7
New Orleans	−8.3
Phoenix	33.1
Detroit	−3.6

Source: U. S. Census Bureau.

(a) Which metropolitan area had the greatest percent change in population? What was this change? Was it an increase or a decrease?

(b) Which metropolitan area had the least change in population? What was this change? Was it an increase or a decrease?

66. *Trade Balance*   The table gives the net trade balance, in millions of dollars, for selected U.S. trade partners for October 2013.

Country	Trade Balance (in millions of dollars)
India	−1967
China	−28,862
The Netherlands	2325
France	−1630
Turkey	396

Source: U.S. Census Bureau.

A negative balance means that imports to the United States exceeded exports from the United States. A positive balance means that exports exceeded imports.

(a) Which country had the greatest discrepancy between exports and imports? Explain.

(b) Which country had the least discrepancy between exports and imports? Explain.

(c) Which two countries were closest in their trade balance figures?

67. *CPI Data*   Refer to **Table 2** in **Example 4.** Of the data for 2009 to 2010, which of the categories Appliances or Housing shows the greater change (without regard to sign)?

68. *Change in Occupations*   Refer to **Table 3** in **Example 5.** Did the demand for physicians' assistants or for postal service clerks show the lesser change (without regard to sign)?

6.2	**OPERATIONS, PROPERTIES, AND APPLICATIONS OF REAL NUMBERS**

OBJECTIVES

1 Perform the operations of addition, subtraction, multiplication, and division of signed numbers.

2 Apply the rules for order of operations.

3 Identify and apply properties of addition and multiplication of real numbers.

4 Determine change in investment and meteorological data using subtraction and absolute value.

Operations on Real Numbers

The result of adding two numbers is called their **sum.** The numbers being added are called **addends** (or **terms**).

ADDING REAL NUMBERS

Like Signs   Add two numbers with the *same* sign by adding their absolute values. The sign of the sum (either + or −) is the same as the sign of the two addends.

Unlike Signs   Add two numbers with *different* signs by subtracting the lesser absolute value from the greater to find the absolute value of the sum. The sum is positive if the positive number has the greater absolute value. The sum is negative if the negative number has the greater absolute value.

For example, to add −12 and −8, first find their absolute values.

$$|-12| = 12 \quad \text{and} \quad |-8| = 8$$

−12 and −8 have the *same* sign, so add their absolute values: $12 + 8 = 20$. Give the sum the sign of the two numbers. Because both numbers are negative, the sum is negative and

$$-12 + (-8) = -20.$$

Find $-17 + 11$ by subtracting the absolute values, because these numbers have different signs.

$$|-17| = 17 \quad \text{and} \quad |11| = 11$$
$$17 - 11 = 6$$

Give the result the sign of the number with the larger absolute value.

$$-17 + 11 = -6$$

Negative because $|-17| > |11|$

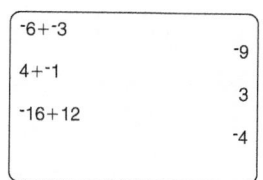

The calculator supports the results of
Example 1(a), (c), and (e).

EXAMPLE 1 Adding Signed Numbers

Find each sum.

(a) $-6 + (-3)$ **(b)** $-12 + (-4)$ **(c)** $4 + (-1)$

(d) $-9 + 16$ **(e)** $-16 + 12$ **(f)** $-4 + 4$

Solution

(a) $-6 + (-3) = -(6 + 3) = -9$

(b) $-12 + (-4) = -(12 + 4) = -16$

(c) $4 + (-1) = 3$

(d) $-9 + 16 = 7$

(e) $-16 + 12 = -4$

(f) $-4 + 4 = 0$ The sum of additive inverses is 0.   ∎

The result of subtracting two numbers is called their **difference.** In $a - b$, a is called the **minuend,** and b is called the **subtrahend.** Compare the two statements below.

$$7 - 5 = 2 \quad \text{and} \quad 7 + (-5) = 2$$

In a similar way,

$$9 - 3 = 9 + (-3).$$

That is, to subtract 3 from 9, add the additive inverse of 3 to 9. These examples suggest the following rule for subtraction.

DEFINITION OF SUBTRACTION

For all real numbers a and b,

$$a - b = a + (-b).$$

(Change the sign of the subtrahend and add.)

EXAMPLE 2 Subtracting Signed Numbers

Find each difference.

(a) $6 - 8$ **(b)** $-12 - 4$ **(c)** $-10 - (-7)$ **(d)** $15 - (-3)$

Solution

Change to addition.

Change sign of the subtrahend and add.

(a) $6 - 8 = 6 + (-8) = -2$

Change to addition.

Sign is changed.

(b) $-12 - 4 = -12 + (-4) = -16$

(c) $-10 - (-7) = -10 + [-(-7)]$ This step can be omitted.

$$= -10 + 7$$

$$= -3$$

(d) $15 - (-3) = 15 + 3 = 18$ ∎

Practical Arithmetic From the time of Egyptian and Babylonian merchants, practical aspects of arithmetic complemented mystical (or "Pythagorean") tendencies. This was certainly true in the time of **Adam Riese** (1489–1559), a "reckon master" influential when commerce was growing in Northern Europe. He championed new methods of reckoning using Hindu-Arabic numerals and quill pens. (The Roman methods then in common use moved counters on a ruled board.) Riese thus fulfilled Fibonacci's efforts 300 years earlier to supplant Roman numerals and methods.

The result of multiplying two numbers is called their **product.** The two numbers being multiplied are called **factors.**

Any rules for multiplication with negative real numbers should be consistent with the usual rules for multiplication of positive real numbers and zero. Observe the pattern of products below.

$$4 \cdot 5 = 20$$
$$4 \cdot 4 = 16$$
$$4 \cdot 3 = 12$$
$$4 \cdot 2 = 8$$
$$4 \cdot 1 = 4$$
$$4 \cdot 0 = 0$$
$$4 \cdot (-1) = ?$$

Products decrease by 4 in each line.

What number must be assigned as the product $4 \cdot (-1)$ so that the pattern is maintained? The numbers just to the left of the equality symbols decrease by 1 each time, and the products to the right decrease by 4 each time. To maintain the pattern, the number to the right in the bottom equation must be 4 less than 0, which is -4, so

$$4 \cdot (-1) = -4.$$

The pattern continues with

$$4 \cdot (-2) = -8$$
$$4 \cdot (-3) = -12$$
$$4 \cdot (-4) = -16,$$

and so on. In the same way,

$$-4 \cdot 2 = -8$$
$$-4 \cdot 3 = -12$$
$$-4 \cdot 4 = -16,$$

and so on. A similar observation can be made about the product of two negative real numbers. Look at the pattern that follows.

$$-5 \cdot 4 = -20$$
$$-5 \cdot 3 = -15$$
$$-5 \cdot 2 = -10$$
$$-5 \cdot 1 = -5$$
$$-5 \cdot 0 = 0$$
$$-5 \cdot (-1) = ?$$

Products increase by 5 in each line.

The numbers just to the left of the equality symbols decrease by 1 each time. The products on the right increase by 5 each time. To maintain the pattern, the product $-5 \cdot (-1)$ must be 5 more than 0, so it seems reasonable for the following to be true.

$$-5 \cdot (-1) = 5$$

Continuing this pattern gives the following.

$$-5 \cdot (-2) = 10$$
$$-5 \cdot (-3) = 15$$
$$-5 \cdot (-4) = 20$$
$$\vdots$$

$$(+) \cdot (+) = +$$
$$(-) \cdot (-) = +$$
$$(+) \cdot (-) = -$$
$$(-) \cdot (+) = -$$

MULTIPLYING REAL NUMBERS

Like Signs Multiply two numbers with the *same* sign by multiplying their absolute values to find the absolute value of the product. The product is positive.

Unlike Signs Multiply two numbers with *different* signs by multiplying their absolute values to find the absolute value of the product. The product is negative.

EXAMPLE 3 Multiplying Signed Numbers

Find each product.

(a) $-9 \cdot 7$ **(b)** $14 \cdot (-5)$ **(c)** $-8 \cdot (-4)$

Solution

(a) $-9 \cdot 7 = -63$ **(b)** $14 \cdot (-5) = -70$ **(c)** $-8 \cdot (-4) = 32$ ∎

```
-9*7
            -63
14*-5
            -70
-8*-4
             32
```

The symbol (∗) represents multiplication on this screen. The display supports the results of **Example 3.**

The result of dividing two numbers is called their **quotient.** In the quotient $a \div b$ (or $\frac{a}{b}$), where $b \neq 0$, a is called the **dividend** (or **numerator**), and b is called the **divisor** (or **denominator**). For real numbers a, b, and c,

$$\text{if} \quad \frac{a}{b} = c, \quad \text{then} \quad a = b \cdot c.$$

To illustrate this, consider the quotient $\frac{10}{-2}$. The value of this quotient is obtained by asking, "What number multiplied by -2 gives 10?" From our discussion of multiplication, the answer to this question must be "-5." Therefore,

$$\frac{10}{-2} = -5, \quad \text{because} \quad 10 = -2 \cdot (-5).$$

Similarly,

$$\frac{-10}{2} = -5 \quad \text{and} \quad \frac{-10}{-2} = 5.$$

These facts, along with the fact that the quotient of two positive numbers is positive, lead to the following rules for division.

$$(+)/(+) = +$$
$$(-)/(-) = +$$
$$(+)/(-) = -$$
$$(-)/(+) = -$$

DIVIDING REAL NUMBERS

Like Signs Divide two numbers with the *same* sign by dividing their absolute values to find the absolute value of the quotient. The quotient is positive.

Unlike Signs Divide two numbers with *different* signs by dividing their absolute values to find the absolute value of the quotient. The quotient is negative.

EXAMPLE 4 Dividing Signed Numbers

Find each quotient.

(a) $\dfrac{15}{-5}$ **(b)** $\dfrac{-100}{-25}$ **(c)** $\dfrac{-60}{3}$

Solution

(a) $\dfrac{15}{-5} = -3$ **(b)** $\dfrac{-100}{-25} = 4$ **(c)** $\dfrac{-60}{3} = -20$

This is true because $-5 \cdot (-3) = 15.$ ∎

```
15/-5
             -3
-100/-25
              4
-60/3
            -20
```

The division operation is represented by a slash (/). This screen supports the results of **Example 4.**

If 0 is divided by a nonzero number, the quotient is 0.

$$\frac{0}{a} = 0, \quad \text{for } a \neq 0$$

This is true because $a \cdot 0 = 0$. However, we cannot divide by 0. There is a good reason for this. Whenever a division is performed, we want to obtain one and only one quotient. Now consider this division problem.

$$\frac{7}{0} = ?$$

We must ask ourselves,

"What number multiplied by 0 gives 7?"

There is no such number because the product of 0 and any number is zero. Now consider this quotient.

$$\frac{0}{0} = ?$$

There are infinitely many answers to the question, "What number multiplied by 0 gives 0?" Division by 0 does not yield a *unique* quotient, and thus it is not permitted.

```
ERR:DIVIDE BY 0
1 Quit
2: Goto
```

Dividing by zero leads to this message on the TI-83/84 Plus.

DIVISION INVOLVING ZERO

$\dfrac{a}{0}$ **is undefined for all** a. $\dfrac{0}{a} = 0$ **for all nonzero** a.

Order of Operations

Given an expression such as

$$5 + 2 \cdot 3,$$

should 5 and 2 be added first, or should 2 and 3 be multiplied first? When an expression involves more than one operation, we use the following rules for **order of operations.**

```
5+2*3
```

What result does the calculator give? The order of operations determines the answer. (See **Example 5(a)**.)

ORDER OF OPERATIONS

If parentheses or square brackets are present:

Step 1   Work separately above and below any **fraction bar.**

Step 2   Use the rules below within each set of **parentheses or square brackets.** Start with the innermost set and work outward.

If no parentheses or brackets are present:

Step 1   Apply any **exponents.**

Step 2   Do any **multiplications or divisions** in the order in which they occur, working from left to right.

Step 3   Do any **additions or subtractions** in the order in which they occur, working from left to right.

The sentence **"Please excuse my dear Aunt Sally"** is often used to help us remember the rules for order of operations. The letters **P, E, M, D, A, S** are the first letters of the words of the sentence, and they stand for *parentheses, exponents, multiply, divide, add, subtract* (*Remember also that M and D have equal priority, as do A and S. Operations with equal priority are performed in order from left to right.*)

When evaluating an exponential expression that involves a negative sign, be aware that $(-a)^n$ and $-a^n$ do not necessarily represent the same quantity. For example, if $a = 2$ and $n = 6$, then

$$(-2)^6 = (-2)(-2)(-2)(-2)(-2)(-2) = 64 \qquad \text{The base is } -2.$$

while

$$-2^6 = -(2 \cdot 2 \cdot 2 \cdot 2 \cdot 2 \cdot 2) = -64. \qquad \text{The base is } 2.$$

EXAMPLE 5   Using the Order of Operations

Use the order of operations to simplify each expression.

(a) $5 + 2 \cdot 3$

(b) $4 \cdot 3^2 + 7 - (2 + 8)$

(c) $\dfrac{2(8 - 12) - 11(4)}{5(-2) - 3}$

(d) -6^4

(e) $(-6)^4$

(f) $(-8)(-3) - [4 - (3 - 6)]$

Solution   *Be careful! Multiply first.*

(a) $5 + 2 \cdot 3 = 5 + 6$ Multiply.

$\qquad\qquad\quad = 11$ Add.

(b) $4 \cdot 3^2 + 7 - (2 + 8) = 4 \cdot 3^2 + 7 - 10$ Work within parentheses first.

3^2 means $3 \cdot 3$, not $3 \cdot 2$.

$\qquad\qquad\qquad\qquad = 4 \cdot 9 + 7 - 10$ Apply the exponent.

$\qquad\qquad\qquad\qquad = 36 + 7 - 10$ Multiply.

$\qquad\qquad\qquad\qquad = 43 - 10$ Add.

$\qquad\qquad\qquad\qquad = 33$ Subtract.

(c) $\dfrac{2(8 - 12) - 11(4)}{5(-2) - 3} = \dfrac{2(-4) - 11(4)}{5(-2) - 3}$ Work separately above and below fraction bar.

$\qquad\qquad\qquad\qquad = \dfrac{-8 - 44}{-10 - 3}$ Multiply.

$\qquad\qquad\qquad\qquad = \dfrac{-52}{-13}$ Subtract.

$\qquad\qquad\qquad\qquad = 4$ Divide.

(d) $-6^4 = -(6 \cdot 6 \cdot 6 \cdot 6) = -1296$

The base is 6, not -6.

(e) $(-6)^4 = (-6)(-6)(-6)(-6) = 1296$

The base is -6 here.

(f) $-8(-3) - [4 - (3 - 6)] = -8(-3) - [4 - (-3)]$ Work within parentheses.

Start here. $= -8(-3) - [4 + 3]$ Definition of subtraction

$\qquad\qquad\qquad\qquad = -8(-3) - 7$ Work within brackets.

$\qquad\qquad\qquad\qquad = 24 - 7$ Multiply.

$\qquad\qquad\qquad\qquad = 17$ Subtract.   ■

Properties of Addition and Multiplication of Real Numbers

PROPERTIES OF ADDITION AND MULTIPLICATION

For real numbers a, b, and c, the following properties hold.

Closure Properties	$a + b$ **and** ab **are real numbers.**
Commutative Properties	$a + b = b + a \qquad ab = ba$
Associative Properties	$(a + b) + c = a + (b + c)$
	$(ab)c = a(bc)$
Identity Properties	There is a real number 0 such that
	$a + 0 = a$ and $0 + a = a.$
	There is a real number 1 such that
	$a \cdot 1 = a$ and $1 \cdot a = a.$
Inverse Properties	For each real number a, there is a single real number $-a$ such that
	$a + (-a) = 0$ and $(-a) + a = 0.$
	For each nonzero real number a, there is a single real number $\frac{1}{a}$ such that
	$a \cdot \dfrac{1}{a} = 1$ and $\dfrac{1}{a} \cdot a = 1.$
Distributive Property of Multiplication with Respect to Addition	$a(b + c) = ab + ac$
	$(b + c)a = ba + ca$

- The set of real numbers is said to be **closed** with respect to the operations of addition and multiplication. This means that the sum of two real numbers and the product of two real numbers are themselves real numbers.

- The **commutative** properties state that two real numbers may be added or multiplied in either order without affecting the result.

- The **associative** properties allow us to group terms or factors in any manner we wish without affecting the result.

- The number 0 is the **identity element for addition.** Adding 0 to a real number will always yield.

- The number 1 is the **identity element for multiplication.** Multiplying a real number by 1 will always yield that real number.

- Each real number a has an **additive inverse,** $-a$, such that the sum of a and its additive inverse is the additive identity element 0.

- Each nonzero real number a has a **multiplicative inverse,** or **reciprocal,** $\frac{1}{a}$, such that the product of a and its multiplicative inverse is the multiplicative identity element 1.

- The **distributive** property allows us to change certain products to sums and certain sums to products.

EXAMPLE 6 Identifying Properties of Addition and Multiplication

Identify the property illustrated in each statement.

(a) $5 + 7$ is a real number.   **(b)** $5 + (6 + 8) = (5 + 6) + 8$

(c) $8 + 0 = 8$ **(d)** $-4\left(-\dfrac{1}{4}\right) = 1$

(e) $4 + (3 + 9) = 4 + (9 + 3)$ **(f)** $5(x + y) = 5x + 5y$

Solution

(a) The statement that the sum of two real numbers is also a real number is an example of the *closure property of addition*.

(b) Because the grouping of the terms is different on the two sides of the equation, this illustrates the *associative property of addition*.

(c) Adding 0 to a number yields the number itself. This is an example of the *identity property of addition*.

(d) Multiplying a number by its reciprocal yields 1, and this illustrates the *inverse property of multiplication*.

(e) The order of the addends (terms) 3 and 9 is different, so this is justified by the *commutative property of addition*.

(f) The factor 5 is distributed to the terms x and y. This is an example of the *distributive property of multiplication with respect to addition*.   ■

Applications of Signed Numbers

Problem-Solving Strategy

When problems deal with gains and losses, the gains may be interpreted as positive numbers and the losses as negative numbers. The phrases "in the black" (for making money) and "in the red" (for losing money) go back to the days when bookkeepers used black ink to represent gains and red ink to represent losses.

Also, temperatures above 0° are positive, and those below 0° are negative. Altitudes above sea level are considered positive, and those below sea level are considered negative.

We must sometimes express a change from one number (quantity, measure, etc.) to another. For example, if the high temperature in New Orleans was 54°F yesterday and the high today is 68°F, we interpret this as an increase of 14°. The high temperature today is *greater than* it was yesterday, so there is an *increase*, represented by a *positive* number. That number can be found mathematically.

Subtract 54 from 68 to obtain 14.

If the opposite situation had occurred, similar reasoning would say that there was a *decrease*, which would be represented by a *negative* number.

Subtract 68 from 54 to obtain −14.

In this example, both measures are positive. However, if one or both of the measures are negative, determining the amount of change may not be as easy. We can mathematically define the magnitude (or amount) of change from one to the other by taking the absolute value of their difference. ***Because opposites have the same absolute value, the order in which we subtract does not matter.***

DETERMINING CHANGE FROM *a* TO *b*

Suppose that *a* and *b* are real numbers. The amount (without regard to sign) of change *from a to b* is given by

$$|a - b|, \quad \text{or, equivalently,} \quad |b - a|.$$

The change is interpreted to be a **positive change** if $a < b$, while it is a **negative change** if $a > b$. If $a = b$, there is no change.

EXAMPLE 7 Interpreting Change from a Table

Suppose that you are an employee of a fund management company and you come across the results shown in **Figure 8** in a trade publication. Amounts are rounded to the nearest percent.

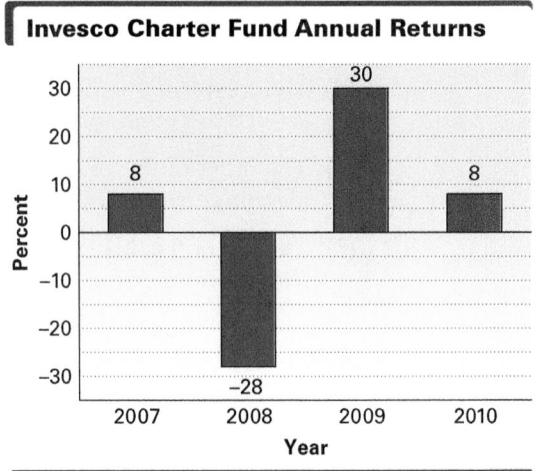

Invesco Charter Fund Annual Returns

Source: Morningstar, Invesco.

Figure 8

Illustrate by subtraction and absolute value how to determine the change in percent of annual returns from **(a)** 2007 to 2008 and **(b)** 2008 to 2009.

Solution

(a) From 2007 to 2008, the annual return went from 8 percent to −28 percent. This is a decrease, so our answer will be *negative*. The amount of the decrease is

$$|8 - (-28)| = |8 + 28| = |36| = 36.$$

(Note that we could have subtracted in the order $-28 - 8 = -36$, which has the same absolute value as 36.) The change from 2007 to 2008 is

$$- 36 \text{ percent.}$$

The negative sign indicates a decrease.   36 is the absolute value of the difference of the two amounts.

(b) To find the change from 2008 to 2009, which by inspection is an increase, find the absolute value of the difference of the two amounts in either order, and interpret it as a *positive* amount.

$$|-28 - 30| = |-58| = 58 \quad \text{or} \quad |30 - (-28)| = |58| = 58$$

The change from 2008 to 2009 is +58 percent.

The + sign is understood if not specifically indicated.

EXAMPLE 8 Interpreting Temperature Change from a Map

The daily highs for selected cities during a particularly cold two-day period in Minnesota are shown in **Figure 9.** Determine the change in temperature from Monday to Tuesday for each city listed.

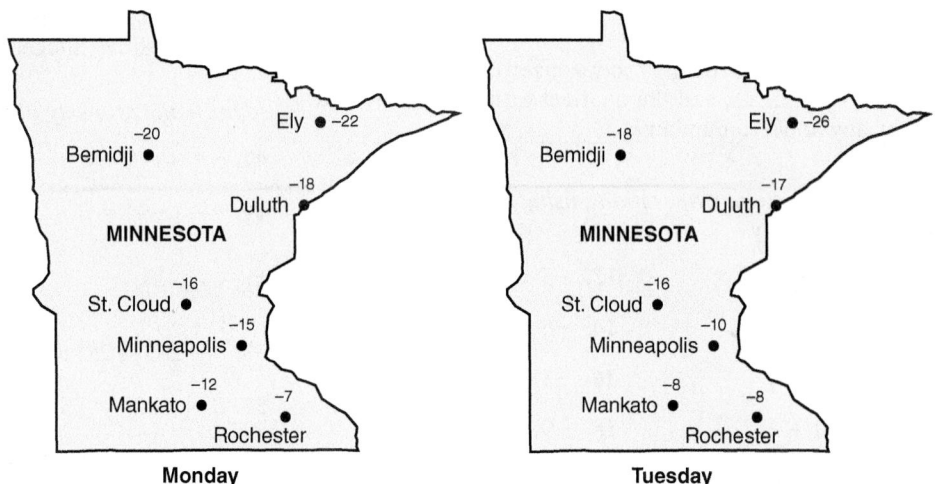

Figure 9

Solution

In each case we determine the sign of the change by observation. If the temperature on Tuesday *is greater than* that on Monday, the change is *positive*. If Tuesday's temperature *is less than* that on Monday, the change is *negative*. Equal temperatures indicate *no change*.

In Ely, the high temperature was less on Tuesday than on Monday because $-26 < -22$, so the change is negative. The amount is

$$|-26 - (-22)| = |-26 + 22| = |-4| = 4.$$

Thus the change is -4 degrees.

In Bemidji, the high temperature went from -20 to -18, which is an increase. Subtracting these temperatures in either order and taking the absolute value gives

$$|-20 - (-18)| = |-20 + 18| = |-2| = 2.$$

Thus, the change is $+2$ degrees. The other changes can be found similarly.

Duluth: +1 degree   St. Cloud: no change

Minneapolis: +5 degrees   Mankato: +4 degrees

Rochester: −1 degree

6.2 EXERCISES

Complete each statement and give an example.

1. The sum of two positive numbers is a _____ number.

2. The sum of two negative numbers is a _____ number.

3. The sum of a positive number and a negative number is negative if the negative number has the _____ absolute value.

4. The sum of a positive number and a negative number is positive if the positive number has the _____ absolute value.

5. The difference between two positive numbers is negative if _____.

6. The difference between two negative numbers is negative if _____.

7. The sum of a positive number and a negative number is 0 if the numbers are _____ .

8. The product of two numbers with the same sign is _____ .

9. The product of two numbers with different signs is _____ .

10. The quotient formed by any nonzero number divided by 0 is _____ , and the quotient formed by 0 divided by any nonzero number is _____ .

Perform the indicated operations, using the order of operations as necessary.

11. $-12 + (-8)$ **12.** $-5 + (-2)$

13. $12 + (-16)$ **14.** $-6 + 17$

15. $-12 - (-1)$ **16.** $-3 - (-8)$

17. $-5 + 11 + 3$ **18.** $-9 + 16 + 5$

19. $12 - (-3) - (-5)$ **20.** $15 - (-6) - (-8)$

21. $(-12)(-2)$ **22.** $(-3)(-5)$

23. $9(-12)(-4)(-1)(3)$ **24.** $-5(-17)(2)(-2)(4)$

25. $\dfrac{-18}{-3}$ **26.** $\dfrac{-100}{-50}$

27. $\dfrac{36}{-6}$ **28.** $\dfrac{52}{-13}$

29. $\dfrac{0}{12}$ **30.** $\dfrac{0}{-7}$

31. $-6 + [5 - (3 + 2)]$ **32.** $-8[4 + (7 - 8)]$

33. $-4 - 3(-2) + 5^2$ **34.** $-6 - 5(-8) + 3^2$

35. $\dfrac{2(-5) + (-3)(-2^2)}{-3^2 + 9}$ **36.** $\dfrac{3(-4) + (-5)(-2)}{2^3 - 2 + (-6)}$

37. $\dfrac{(-8 + 6) \cdot (-5)}{-5 - 5}$ **38.** $\dfrac{(-10 + 4) \cdot (-3)}{-7 - 2}$

39. $-8(-2) - [(4^2) + (7 - 3)]$

40. $-7(-3) - [2^3 - (3 - 4)]$

41. $\dfrac{(-6 + 3) \cdot (-4)}{-5 - 1} - \dfrac{(-9 + 6) \cdot (-3)}{-4 + 3}$

42. $\dfrac{2(-5 + 3)}{-2^2} - \dfrac{(-3^2 + 2)(3)}{3 - (-4)}$

43. $-\dfrac{1}{4}[3(-5) + 7(-5) + 1(-2)]$

44. $\dfrac{5 - 3\left(\dfrac{-5 - 9}{-7}\right) - 6}{-9 - 11 + 3 \cdot 7}$

45. Which of the following expressions are undefined?

  A. $\dfrac{8}{0}$ **B.** $\dfrac{9}{6 - 6}$ **C.** $\dfrac{4 - 4}{5 - 5}$ **D.** $\dfrac{0}{-1}$

46. If you have no money in your pocket and you divide it equally among your three siblings, how much does each get? Use this situation to explain division of zero by a positive integer.

Identify the property illustrated by each statement.

47. $6 + 9 = 9 + 6$ **48.** $8 \cdot 4 = 4 \cdot 8$

49. $9 + (-9) = 0$ **50.** $12 + 0 = 12$

51. $9 \cdot 1 = 9$ **52.** $\left(\dfrac{1}{-3}\right) \cdot (-3) = 1$

53. $0 + 283 = 283$ **54.** $(3 \cdot 5) \cdot 4 = 4 \cdot (3 \cdot 5)$

55. $6 \cdot (4 \cdot 2) = (6 \cdot 4) \cdot 2$ **56.** $0 = -8 + 8$

57. $19 \cdot 12$ is a real number.

58. $19 + 12$ is a real number.

59. $7 + (2 + 5) = (7 + 2) + 5$

60. $2 \cdot (4 + 3) = 2 \cdot 4 + 2 \cdot 3$

61. $9 \cdot 6 + 9 \cdot 8 = 9 \cdot (6 + 8)$

Provide short answers in Exercises 62–66.

62. One of the authors received an email message from an old friend, Frank Capek. Frank said that his grandson had to evaluate

$$9 + 15 \div 3.$$

Frank and his wife, Barbara, said that the answer is 8, but the grandson said that the correct answer is 14. The grandson's reasoning is "There is a rule called the Order of Process so that you proceed from right to left rather than from left to right."

(a) What is the correct answer?

(b) Is his grandson's reasoning correct? Explain.

63. The following conversation actually took place between one of the authors of this text and his son, Jack, when Jack was four years old.

DADDY: "Jack, what is $3 + 0$?"
JACK: "3"
DADDY: "Jack, what is $4 + 0$?"
JACK: "4 ... and Daddy, *string* plus zero equals *string!*"

What property of addition of real numbers did Jack recognize?

64. Many everyday activities are commutative. The order in which they occur does not affect the outcome. For example, "putting on your shirt" and "putting on your pants" are commutative operations. Decide whether the given activities are commutative.

(a) putting on your shoes; putting on your socks

(b) getting dressed; taking a shower

(c) combing your hair; brushing your teeth

65. Many everyday occurrences can be thought of as operations that have opposites or inverses. For example, the inverse operation for "going to sleep" is "waking up." For each of the given activities, specify its inverse activity.

(a) cleaning up your room

(b) earning money

(c) increasing the volume on your MP3 player

66. The distributive property holds for multiplication with respect to addition. Does the distributive property hold for addition with respect to multiplication? That is, is

$$a + (b \cdot c) = (a + b) \cdot (a + c)$$

true for all values of a, b, and c? (*Hint:* Let $a = 2$, $b = 3$, and $c = 4$.)

Each expression in Exercises 67–74 is equal to either 81 *or* −81. *Decide which of these is the correct value in each case.*

67. -3^4 **68.** $-(3^4)$ **69.** $(-3)^4$

70. $-(-3^4)$ **71.** $-(-3)^4$ **72.** $[-(-3)]^4$

73. $-[-(-3)]^4$ **74.** $-[-(-3^4)]$

75. *S&P 500 Index Fund* The graph shows annual returns (to the nearest percent) for Class A shares of the Invesco S&P 500 Index Fund from 2009 to 2013. Use subtraction and absolute value to determine the change in returns from one year to the next. Give your answer as both a signed number (in percent) and a word description.

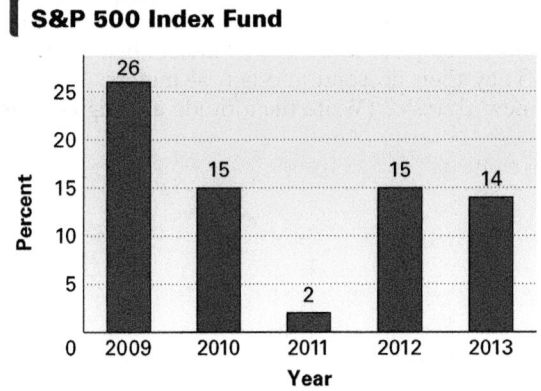

(a) 2009 to 2010   **(b)** 2010 to 2011

(c) 2011 to 2012   **(d)** 2012 to 2013

76. *Company Profits and Losses* The graph shows profits and losses for a private company for the years 2009 through 2013. Use subtraction and absolute value to determine the change in profit or loss from one year to the next. Give your answer as both a signed number (in thousands of dollars) and a word description.

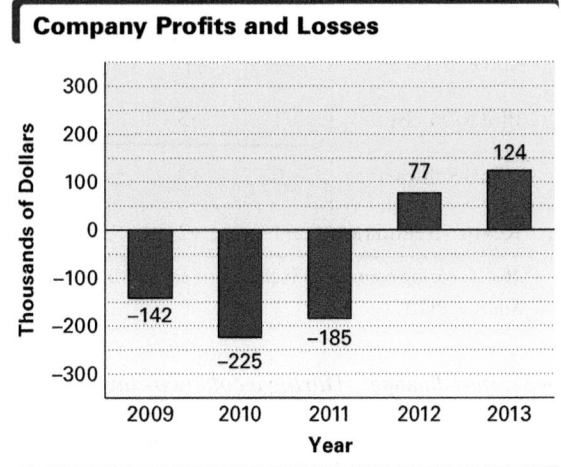

(a) 2009 to 2010   **(b)** 2010 to 2011

(c) 2011 to 2012   **(d)** 2012 to 2013

Heights of Mountains and Depths of Trenches The table shows the heights of some selected mountains and the depths of some selected ocean trenches.

Mountain	Height (in feet)	Trench	Depth (in feet, as a negative number)
Foraker	17,400	Philippine	−32,995
Wilson	14,246	Cayman	−24,721
Pikes Peak	14,110	Java	−23,376

Source: World Almanac and Book of Facts.

Use the information given to answer Exercises 77–82.

77. What is the difference between the height of Mt. Foraker and the depth of the Philippine Trench?

78. What is the difference between the height of Pikes Peak and the depth of the Java Trench?

79. How much deeper is the Cayman Trench than the Java Trench?

80. How much deeper is the Philippine Trench than the Cayman Trench?

81. How much higher is Mt. Wilson than Pikes Peak?

82. If Mt. Wilson and Pikes Peak were stacked one on top of the other, how much higher would they be than Mt. Foraker?

Golf Scores The table gives scores above or below par (that is, above or below the score "standard") for selected golfers during the 2013 PGA Tour Championship. Write a signed number that represents the total score for the four rounds (above or below par) for each golfer.

	Golfer	Round 1	Round 2	Round 3	Round 4
83.	Steve Stricker	−4	+1*	−2	−5
84.	Phil Mickelson	+1	−3	0	−2
85.	Charl Schwartzel	−2	+9	+7	−4
86.	Kevin Streelman	−1	+2	+4	−3

*Golf scoring commonly includes a + sign with a score over par.
Source: PGA.

Temperature Change During a cold two-day period in North Dakota, the daily highs for selected cities were as shown in the figure. Determine the change in temperature from Thursday to Friday for each city listed. *All temperatures in Exercises 87–96 are in degrees Fahrenheit.*

Thursday

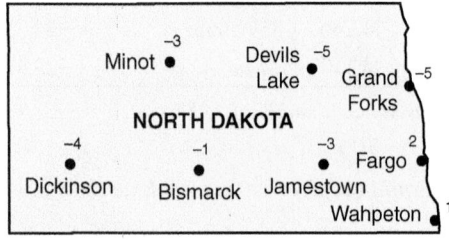

Friday

87. Dickinson

88. Minot

89. Bismarck

90. Devils Lake

91. Jamestown

92. Grand Forks

93. Fargo

94. Wahpeton

95. *24-Hour Temperature Change* Television weather forecasters often show maps indicating how the current temperature compares to that of 24 hours earlier. Refer to the map for Thursday used in **Exercises 87–94,** and imagine that the temperatures listed indicated the change in temperature compared to 24 hours earlier. Use the table to determine the temperature in each city 24 hours earlier. (When no sign is shown on the map, + is understood.)

City	Current Temperature	Temperature 24 Hours Earlier
Dickinson	34	
Minot	28	
Bismarck	30	
Devils Lake	32	
Jamestown	35	
Grand Forks	31	
Fargo	34	
Wahpeton	36	

96. *24-Hour Temperature Change* Repeat **Exercise 95** for the Friday map used in **Exercises 87–94.**

97. *Breaching of Humpback Whales* Humpback whale researchers Mark and Debbie noticed that one of their favorite whales, "Pineapple," breached 15 feet above the surface of the ocean while her mate cruised 12 feet below the surface. What is the difference between these two levels?

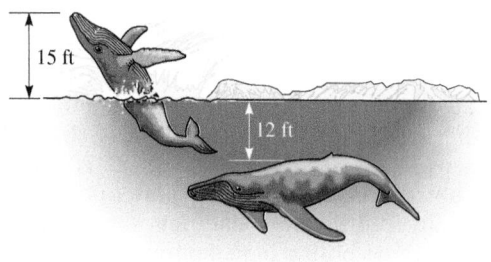

98. *Altitude of Hikers* The surface, or rim, of a canyon is at altitude 0. On a hike down into the canyon, a party of hikers stop for a rest at 130 meters below the surface. They then descend another 54 meters. What is their new altitude? (Write the altitude as a signed number.)

99. *Birth Date of a Greek Mathematician* A certain Greek mathematician was born in 428 B.C. Her father was born 41 years earlier. In what year was her father born?

100. *Birth Date of a Roman Philosopher* A certain Roman philosopher was born in 325 B.C. Her mother was born 35 years earlier. In what year was her mother born?

101. *Student Loans* In 2005, undergraduate college students had an average of $4906 in student loans. This average increased by $788 by 2010 and then dropped $154 by 2012. What was the average amount of such loans in 2012? (*Source:* The College Board.)

102. *Entertainment Expenditures* Among entertainment expenditures, the average annual spending per U.S. household on fees and admissions was $526 in 2001. This amount increased $80 by 2006 and then decreased $12 by 2011. What was the average household expenditure for fees and admissions in 2011? (*Source:* U.S. Bureau of Labor Statistics.)

103. *Record Low Temperatures* The lowest temperature ever recorded in Illinois was −36°F. The lowest temperature ever recorded in Utah was 33°F lower than Illinois's record low. What is the record low temperature in Utah? (*Source:* National Climatic Data Center.)

104. *Record Low Temperatures* The lowest temperature ever recorded in South Carolina was −19°F. The lowest temperature ever recorded in Wisconsin was 36°F lower than South Carolina's record low. What is the record low temperature in Wisconsin? (*Source:* National Climatic Data Center.)

105. *Temperature Extremes* The lowest temperature ever recorded in Arkansas was −29°F. The highest temperature ever recorded there was 149°F more than the lowest. What is this highest temperature? (*Source:* National Climatic Data Center.)

106. *Drastic Temperature Change* On January 23, 1943, the temperature rose 49°F in two minutes in Spearfish, South Dakota. If the starting temperature was −4°F, what was the temperature two minutes later? (*Source:* National Climatic Data Center.)

6.3 RATIONAL NUMBERS AND DECIMAL REPRESENTATION

OBJECTIVES

1. Define and identify rational numbers.
2. Write a rational number in lowest terms.
3. Add, subtract, multiply, and divide rational numbers in fraction form.
4. Solve a carpentry problem using operations with fractions.
5. Apply the density property and find arithmetic mean.
6. Convert a rational number in fraction form to a decimal number.
7. Convert a terminating or repeating decimal to a rational number in fraction form.

Definition and the Fundamental Property

Recall from **Section 6.1** that quotients of integers are called **rational numbers.** Think of the rational numbers as being made up of all the fractions (quotients of integers with denominator not equal to zero) and all the integers. Any integer can be written as a quotient of two integers.

For example, the integer 9 can be written as the quotient

$$\frac{9}{1}, \quad \text{or} \quad \frac{18}{2}, \quad \text{or} \quad \frac{27}{3}, \quad \text{and so on.}$$

Also, −5 can be expressed as a quotient of integers as

$$\frac{-5}{1}, \quad \text{or} \quad \frac{-10}{2}, \quad \text{and so on.}$$

(How can the integer 0 be written as a quotient of integers?)

RATIONAL NUMBERS

Rational numbers $= \{x \mid x \text{ is a quotient of two integers, with denominator not } 0\}$

A rational number is in **lowest terms** if the greatest common factor of the numerator (top number) and the denominator (bottom number) is 1. Rational numbers are written in lowest terms using the following property.

FUNDAMENTAL PROPERTY OF RATIONAL NUMBERS

If a, b, and k are integers with $b \neq 0$ and $k \neq 0$, then the following is true.

$$\frac{a \cdot k}{b \cdot k} = \frac{a}{b}$$

The calculator gives 36/54 in lowest terms, as illustrated in **Example 1.**

EXAMPLE 1 Writing a Fraction in Lowest Terms

Write $\frac{36}{54}$ in lowest terms.

Solution

The greatest common factor of 36 and 54 is 18.

$$\frac{36}{54} = \frac{2 \cdot 18}{3 \cdot 18} = \frac{2}{3}$$

Use the fundamental property with $k = 18$.

In **Example 1,** we see that $\frac{36}{54} = \frac{2}{3}$. If we multiply the numerator of the fraction on the left by the denominator of the fraction on the right, we obtain $36 \cdot 3 = 108$. If we multiply the denominator of the fraction on the left by the numerator of the fraction on the right, we obtain $54 \cdot 2 = 108$. The result is the same in both cases.

One way of determining whether two fractions are equal is to perform this test. If the product of the **"extremes"** (36 and 3 in this case) equals the product of the **"means"** (54 and 2), the fractions are equal. This is the **cross-product test.**

CROSS-PRODUCT TEST FOR EQUALITY OF RATIONAL NUMBERS

For rational numbers $\frac{a}{b}$ and $\frac{c}{d}$, where $b \neq 0$, $d \neq 0$, the following is true.

$$\frac{a}{b} = \frac{c}{d} \quad \text{if and only if} \quad a \cdot d = b \cdot c$$

Operations with Rational Numbers

The operation of addition of rational numbers can be illustrated by the sketches in **Figure 10.** The rectangle at the top left is divided into three equal portions, with one of the portions in color. The rectangle at the top right is divided into five equal parts, with two of them in color.

The total of the areas in color is represented by the sum

$$\frac{1}{3} + \frac{2}{5}.$$

To evaluate this sum, the areas in color must be redrawn in terms of a common unit. Since the least common multiple of 3 and 5 is 15, redraw both rectangles with 15 parts. See **Figure 11.** In the figure, 11 of the small rectangles are in color, so

$$\frac{1}{3} + \frac{2}{5} = \frac{5}{15} + \frac{6}{15} = \frac{11}{15}.$$

Figure 10

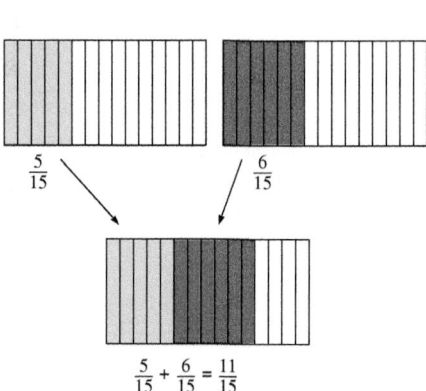

Figure 11

ADDING AND SUBTRACTING RATIONAL NUMBERS

If $\frac{a}{b}$ and $\frac{c}{d}$ are rational numbers, then the following are true.

$$\frac{a}{b} + \frac{c}{d} = \frac{ad + bc}{bd} \quad \text{and} \quad \frac{a}{b} - \frac{c}{d} = \frac{ad - bc}{bd}$$

This formal definition is seldom used in practice. We usually first rewrite the fractions with the least common multiple of their denominators, called the **least common denominator (LCD)**.

EXAMPLE 2   Adding and Subtracting Rational Numbers

Perform each operation.

(a) $\dfrac{2}{15} + \dfrac{1}{10}$ **(b)** $\dfrac{173}{180} - \dfrac{69}{1200}$

Solution

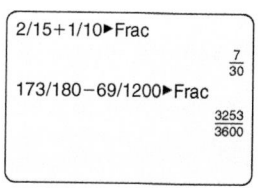

The results of **Example 2** are illustrated in this screen.

(a) Since $30 \div 15 = 2$, $\dfrac{2}{15} = \dfrac{2 \cdot 2}{15 \cdot 2} = \dfrac{4}{30}$

and since $30 \div 10 = 3$, $\dfrac{1}{10} = \dfrac{1 \cdot 3}{10 \cdot 3} = \dfrac{3}{30}.$

> The LCD is 30.

Thus, $\dfrac{2}{15} + \dfrac{1}{10} = \dfrac{4}{30} + \dfrac{3}{30} = \dfrac{7}{30}.$

(b) The least common multiple of 180 and 1200 is 3600.

$$\frac{173}{180} - \frac{69}{1200} = \frac{3460}{3600} - \frac{207}{3600} = \frac{3460 - 207}{3600} = \frac{3253}{3600}$$

Fractions that are greater than 1 may be expressed in **mixed number** form.

The mixed number form of $\dfrac{3}{2}$ is $1\dfrac{1}{2}.$

It is understood that the whole number part and the fraction part of a mixed number are added (even though no addition symbol is shown).

EXAMPLE 3   Conversions Involving Mixed Numbers

Perform each conversion.

(a) $2\dfrac{5}{8}$ to a fraction   **(b)** $\dfrac{86}{5}$ to a mixed number

Solution

(a) $2\dfrac{5}{8} = 2 + \dfrac{5}{8}$ The addition is understood.

$= \dfrac{16}{8} + \dfrac{5}{8}$ Write 2 as a fraction with denominator 8.

$= \dfrac{21}{8}$ Add the fractions.

A shortcut for writing $2\frac{5}{8}$ as a fraction leads to the same result. We multiply the denominator (8) by the whole number part (2) and add the numerator (5) to find the numerator of the mixed number.

$$(8 \times 2) + 5 = \mathbf{21}$$

Then use the original denominator of the fraction part (8) as the denominator.

$$2\frac{5}{8} = \frac{\mathbf{21}}{\mathbf{8}}$$

(b) To convert $\frac{86}{5}$ to a mixed number, we use long division. The quotient is the whole number part of the mixed number. The remainder is the numerator of the fraction part, while the divisor is the denominator.

$$
\begin{array}{r}
17 \quad \leftarrow \text{ Whole number part}\\
\text{Denominator of the fraction} \rightarrow 5\overline{)86}\\
\underline{5}\\
36\\
\underline{35}\\
1 \quad \leftarrow \text{ Numerator of the fraction}
\end{array}
$$

Thus $\dfrac{86}{5} = 17\dfrac{1}{5}$. ∎

MULTIPLYING RATIONAL NUMBERS

If $\frac{a}{b}$ and $\frac{c}{d}$ are rational numbers, then the following is true.

$$\frac{a}{b} \cdot \frac{c}{d} = \frac{ac}{bd}$$

EXAMPLE 4 Multiplying Rational Numbers

Find each product. If it is greater than 1, write as a mixed number.

(a) $\dfrac{3}{4} \cdot \dfrac{7}{10}$ **(b)** $\dfrac{5}{18} \cdot \dfrac{3}{10}$ **(c)** $2\dfrac{1}{3} \cdot 1\dfrac{1}{2}$

Solution

(a) $\dfrac{3}{4} \cdot \dfrac{7}{10} = \dfrac{3 \cdot 7}{4 \cdot 10} = \dfrac{21}{40}$

(b) $\dfrac{5}{18} \cdot \dfrac{3}{10} = \dfrac{5 \cdot 3}{18 \cdot 10} = \dfrac{15}{180} = \dfrac{1 \cdot 15}{12 \cdot 15} = \dfrac{1}{12}$

To illustrate the results of **Example 4(a) and (b),** we use parentheses around the fraction factors.

In practice, a multiplication problem such as this is often solved by using slash marks to indicate that common factors have been divided out of the numerator and denominator.

$$\frac{\overset{1}{\cancel{5}}}{\underset{6}{\cancel{18}}} \cdot \frac{\overset{1}{\cancel{3}}}{\underset{2}{\cancel{10}}} = \frac{1}{6} \cdot \frac{1}{2} \qquad \begin{array}{l}\text{3 is divided out of 3 and 18.}\\ \text{5 is divided out of 5 and 10.}\end{array}$$

$$= \frac{1}{12}$$

(c) $2\dfrac{1}{3} \cdot 1\dfrac{1}{2} = \dfrac{7}{3} \cdot \dfrac{3}{2}$ Convert mixed numbers to fractions.

$\qquad\qquad = \dfrac{7}{3} \cdot \dfrac{\overset{1}{3}}{2}$ Divide out the common factor 3.
$\qquad\qquad\qquad \underset{1}{}$

$\qquad\qquad = \dfrac{7}{2}$ Multiply the fractions.

$\qquad\qquad = 3\dfrac{1}{2}$ Write as a mixed number.

■

A fraction bar indicates the operation of division. The multiplicative inverse of the nonzero number b is $\dfrac{1}{b}$. We define division using the multiplicative inverse.

DEFINITION OF DIVISION

If a and b are real numbers, where $b \neq 0$, then the following is true.

$$\frac{a}{b} = a \cdot \frac{1}{b}$$

You probably have heard the rule, "To divide fractions, invert the divisor and multiply." To illustrate this rule, suppose that you have $\dfrac{7}{8}$ of a gallon of milk and you wish to find how many quarts you have. A quart is $\dfrac{1}{4}$ of a gallon, so you must ask yourself, "*How many $\dfrac{1}{4}$s are there in $\dfrac{7}{8}$?*" This would be interpreted as

$$\frac{7}{8} \div \frac{1}{4}, \quad \text{or} \quad \frac{\dfrac{7}{8}}{\dfrac{1}{4}}.$$

The fundamental property of rational numbers can be extended to rational number values of a, b, and k.

$$\frac{a}{b} = \frac{a \cdot k}{b \cdot k} = \frac{\dfrac{7}{8} \cdot 4}{\dfrac{1}{4} \cdot 4} = \frac{\dfrac{7}{8} \cdot 4}{1} = \frac{7}{8} \cdot \frac{4}{1} \quad \text{Let } a = \tfrac{7}{8},\, b = \tfrac{1}{4},\, \text{and } k = 4 \left(\text{the reciprocal of } b = \tfrac{1}{4}\right).$$

To divide $\dfrac{7}{8}$ by $\dfrac{1}{4}$ is equivalent to multiplying $\dfrac{7}{8}$ by the reciprocal, $\dfrac{4}{1}$.

$$\frac{7}{8} \cdot \frac{4}{1} = \frac{28}{8} = \frac{7}{2} \quad \text{Multiply and reduce to lowest terms.}$$

Thus there are $\dfrac{7}{2}$, or $3\dfrac{1}{2}$, quarts in $\dfrac{7}{8}$ gallon.

DIVIDING RATIONAL NUMBERS

If $\dfrac{a}{b}$ and $\dfrac{c}{d}$ are rational numbers, where $\dfrac{c}{d} \neq 0$, then the following is true.

$$\frac{a}{b} \div \frac{c}{d} = \frac{a}{b} \cdot \frac{d}{c} = \frac{ad}{bc}$$

Early U.S. cents and **half cents** used fractions to denote their denominations. The half cent used $\frac{1}{200}$ and the cent used $\frac{1}{100}$. (See **Exercise 28** for a photo of an interesting error coin.)

The coins shown here were part of the collection of Louis E. Eliasberg, Sr. **Louis Eliasberg** was the only person ever to assemble a complete collection of United States coins. The Eliasberg gold coins were auctioned in 1982, while the copper, nickel, and silver coins were auctioned in two sales in 1996 and 1997. The half cent pictured sold for $506,000 and the cent sold for $27,500. The cent shown in **Exercise 28** went for a mere $2970.

EXAMPLE 5 Dividing Rational Numbers

Find each quotient.

(a) $\dfrac{3}{5} \div \dfrac{7}{15}$ **(b)** $\dfrac{-4}{7} \div \dfrac{3}{14}$ **(c)** $\dfrac{2}{9} \div 4$ **(d)** $-9 \div \dfrac{3}{5}$

Solution

This screen supports the results in
Example 4(b) and (c).

(a) $\dfrac{3}{5} \div \dfrac{7}{15} = \dfrac{3}{5} \cdot \dfrac{15}{7} = \dfrac{45}{35} = \dfrac{9 \cdot 5}{7 \cdot 5} = \dfrac{9}{7}$

(b) $\dfrac{-4}{7} \div \dfrac{3}{14} = \dfrac{-4}{7} \cdot \dfrac{14}{3} = \dfrac{-56}{21} = \dfrac{-8 \cdot 7}{3 \cdot 7} = \dfrac{-8}{3} = -\dfrac{8}{3}$ $\dfrac{-a}{b}, \dfrac{a}{-b},$ and $-\dfrac{a}{b}$ are all equal.

(c) $\dfrac{2}{9} \div 4 = \dfrac{2}{9} \div \dfrac{4}{1} = \dfrac{2}{9} \cdot \dfrac{1}{4} = \dfrac{\overset{1}{2}}{9} \cdot \dfrac{1}{\underset{2}{4}} = \dfrac{1}{18}$

(d) $-9 \div \dfrac{3}{5} = \dfrac{\overset{-3}{-9}}{1} \cdot \dfrac{5}{\underset{1}{3}} = -15$ ∎

EXAMPLE 6 Applying Operations with Fractions to Carpentry

A carpenter has a board 72 inches long that he must cut into 10 pieces of equal length. This will require 9 cuts. See **Figure 12.**

(a) If each cut causes a waste of $\dfrac{3}{16}$ inch, how many inches of actual board will remain after the cuts?

(b) What will be the length of each of the resulting pieces?

Figure 12

Solution

(a) We start with 72 inches and must subtract $\dfrac{3}{16}$ nine times.

Rather than writing out each of these, we represent the amount subtracted by $9\left(\dfrac{3}{16}\right)$.

$$72 - 9\left(\dfrac{3}{16}\right) = 72 - \left(\dfrac{9}{1} \cdot \dfrac{3}{16}\right) \qquad 9 = \dfrac{9}{1}$$

$$= 72 - \dfrac{27}{16} \qquad \text{Multiply the fractions.}$$

$$= \dfrac{1152}{16} - \dfrac{27}{16} \qquad \text{Use a common denominator.}$$

$$= \dfrac{1125}{16} \qquad \text{Subtract fractions.}$$

$$= 70\dfrac{5}{16} \qquad \text{Write as a mixed number.}$$

Thus $70\dfrac{5}{16}$ inches of actual board will remain.

Benjamin Banneker (1731–1806) spent the first half of his life tending a farm in Maryland. He gained a reputation locally for his mechanical skills and his ability in mathematical problem solving. In 1772 he acquired astronomy books from a neighbor and devoted himself to learning astronomy, observing the skies, and making calculations. In 1789 Banneker joined the team that surveyed what is now the District of Columbia.

Banneker published almanacs yearly from 1792 to 1802. He sent a copy of his first almanac to **Thomas Jefferson,** along with an impassioned letter against slavery. Jefferson subsequently championed the cause of this early African-American mathematician.

(b) The $70\frac{5}{16}$, or $\frac{1125}{16}$, inches of board from part (a) will be divided into 10 pieces of equal length.

$$\frac{1125}{16} \div 10 = \frac{1125}{16} \cdot \frac{1}{10} \qquad \text{Definition of division}$$

$$= \frac{\overset{225}{\cancel{1125}}}{16} \cdot \frac{1}{\underset{2}{\cancel{10}}} \qquad \text{Divide out the common factor 5.}$$

$$= \frac{225}{32} \qquad \text{Multiply.}$$

$$= 7\frac{1}{32} \qquad \text{Convert to a mixed number.}$$

Each piece will measure $7\frac{1}{32}$ inches. ∎

Density and the Arithmetic Mean

There is no integer between two consecutive integers, such as 3 and 4. However, a rational number can always be found between any two distinct rational numbers. For this reason, the set of rational numbers is said to be *dense.*

DENSITY PROPERTY OF THE RATIONAL NUMBERS

If r and t are distinct rational numbers, with $r < t$, then there exists a rational number s such that

$$r < s < t.$$

Repeated applications of the density property lead to the following conclusion.

> *There are infinitely many rational numbers between two distinct rational numbers.*

One example of a rational number that is between two distinct rational numbers is the *arithmetic mean* of the two numbers. To find the **arithmetic mean,** or **average,** of n numbers, we add the numbers and then divide the sum by n. For two numbers, the number that lies halfway between them is their average.

Table 4

Academic Year	Amount of Tuition and Fees
2007–08	$21,427
2008–09	22,036
2009–10	21,908
2010–11	22,771
2011–12	23,479

Source: National Center for Education Statistics.

EXAMPLE 7 Finding an Arithmetic Mean (Average)

Table 4 shows the average amount of tuition and fees at private 4-year institutions for five academic years. What is the average cost for this period?

Solution

To find this average, divide the sum of the amounts by the number of amounts, 5.

$$\frac{21{,}427 + 22{,}036 + 21{,}908 + 22{,}771 + 23{,}479}{5} = \frac{111{,}621}{5}$$

$$= 22{,}324\frac{1}{5}$$

The average amount for the period is $22,324 (rounded to the nearest dollar). ∎

EXAMPLE 8 Finding a Measurement in a Socket Wrench Set

A carpenter owns a socket wrench set that has measurements in the English system. As is the custom in carpentry, measurements are given in half-, quarter-, eighth-, and sixteenth-inches. He finds that his $\frac{3}{8}$-inch socket is just a bit too small for his job, while his $\frac{1}{2}$-inch socket is just a bit too large. He suspects that he will need to use the socket with the measure that is halfway between these (their arithmetic mean, or average). What measure socket must he use?

Solution

The carpenter needs to find the average of $\frac{3}{8}$ and $\frac{1}{2}$. To do this, find their sum and divide by 2.

$$\frac{3}{8} + \frac{1}{2} = \frac{3}{8} + \frac{4}{8} \qquad \text{Find a common denominator.}$$

$$= \frac{7}{8} \qquad \text{Add the numerators, and keep the same denominator.}$$

Now divide $\frac{7}{8}$ by 2.

$$\frac{7}{8} \div 2 = \frac{7}{8} \cdot \frac{1}{2} \qquad \text{Definition of division}$$

$$= \frac{7}{16} \qquad \text{Multiply the numerators and multiply the denominators.}$$

He must use the $\frac{7}{16}$-inch socket. ∎

Simon Stevin (1548–1620) worked as a bookkeeper in Belgium and became an engineer in the Netherlands army. He is usually given credit for the development of **decimals.**

Decimal Form of Rational Numbers

Rational numbers can be expressed as decimals. Decimal numerals have place values that are powers of 10. The place values are as shown here.

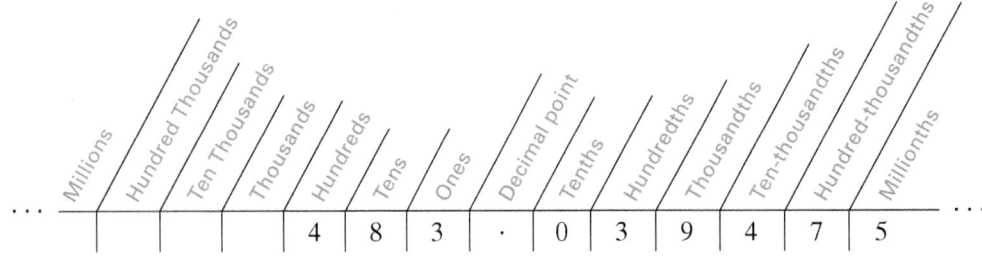

The decimal numeral 483.039475 is read "four hundred eighty-three and thirty-nine thousand, four hundred seventy-five millionths."

A rational number in the form $\frac{a}{b}$ can be expressed as a decimal most easily by entering it into a calculator. For example, to write $\frac{3}{8}$ as a decimal, enter 3, then enter the operation of division, then enter 8. Press the equals key to find the following equivalence.

$$\frac{3}{8} = 0.375$$

$$\begin{array}{r} 0.375 \\ 8\overline{)3.000} \\ \underline{24} \\ 60 \\ \underline{56} \\ 40 \\ \underline{40} \\ 0 \end{array} \qquad \begin{array}{r} 0.3636\ldots \\ 11\overline{)4.00000\ldots} \\ \underline{33} \\ 70 \\ \underline{66} \\ 40 \\ \underline{33} \\ 70 \\ \underline{66} \\ 40 \\ \ddots \end{array}$$

2/3
         .6666666667

While 2/3 has a repeating decimal representation ($2/3 = 0.\overline{6}$), the calculator rounds off in the final decimal place displayed.

5/11
         .4545454545
1/3
         .3333333333
5/6
         .8333333333

Although only ten decimal digits are shown, all three fractions have decimals that repeat endlessly.

This same result may be obtained by long division, as shown in the margin. By this result, the rational number $\frac{3}{8}$ is the same as the decimal 0.375. A decimal such as 0.375, which stops, is called a **terminating decimal.**

$$\frac{1}{4} = 0.25, \quad \frac{7}{10} = 0.7, \quad \text{and} \quad \frac{89}{1000} = 0.089 \qquad \text{Examples of terminating decimals}$$

Not all rational numbers can be represented by terminating decimals. For example, convert $\frac{4}{11}$ into a decimal by dividing 11 into 4 using a calculator. The display shows

$$0.3636363636, \quad \text{or perhaps} \quad 0.363636364.$$

However, the long division process shown in the margin indicates that we will actually get $0.3636\ldots$, with the digits 36 repeating over and over indefinitely. To indicate this, we write a bar (called a *vinculum*) over the "block" of digits that repeats.

$$\frac{4}{11} = 0.\overline{36} \qquad 0.\overline{36} \text{ means } 0.3636\ldots.$$

A decimal such as $0.\overline{36}$, which continues indefinitely, is called a **repeating decimal.**

$$\frac{5}{11} = 0.\overline{45}, \quad \frac{1}{3} = 0.\overline{3}, \quad \text{and} \quad \frac{5}{6} = 0.8\overline{3} \qquad \text{Examples of repeating decimals}$$

While we distinguish between *terminating* and *repeating* decimals in this text, some mathematicians prefer to consider all rational numbers as repeating decimals. This can be justified by thinking this way: If the division process leads to a remainder of 0, then zeros repeat without end in the decimal form. For example, we can consider the decimal form of $\frac{3}{4}$ as follows.

$$\frac{3}{4} = 0.75\overline{0}$$

By considering the possible remainders that may be obtained when converting a quotient of integers to a decimal, we can draw an important conclusion about the decimal form of rational numbers. If the remainder is never zero, the division will produce a repeating decimal. This happens because each step of the division process must produce a remainder that is less than the divisor. Since the number of different possible remainders is less than the divisor, the remainders must eventually begin to repeat. This makes the digits of the quotient repeat, producing a repeating decimal.

DECIMAL REPRESENTATION OF RATIONAL NUMBERS

Any rational number can be expressed as either a terminating decimal or a repeating decimal.

To determine whether the decimal form of a quotient of integers will terminate or repeat, we use the following rule. Justification of this rule is based on the fact that the prime factors of 10 are 2 and 5, and the decimal system uses ten as its base.

CRITERIA FOR TERMINATING AND REPEATING DECIMALS

A rational number $\frac{a}{b}$ in *lowest terms* results in a **terminating decimal** if the only prime factor of the denominator is 2 or 5 (or both).

A rational number $\frac{a}{b}$ in *lowest terms* results in a **repeating decimal** if a prime other than 2 or 5 appears in the prime factorization of the denominator.

To find a baseball player's batting average, we divide the number of hits by the number of at-bats. A surprising paradox exists concerning averages. It is possible for Player A to have a higher batting average than Player B in each of two successive years, yet for the two-year period, Player B can have a higher total batting average. Look at the chart for Boston Red Sox players Mike Lowell and Jacoby Ellsbury.

Year	Mike Lowell	Jacoby Ellsbury
2007	$\frac{191}{589} = .324$	$\frac{41}{116} = .353$
2008	$\frac{115}{419} = .274$	$\frac{155}{554} = .280$
Two-year total	$\frac{306}{1008} = .304$	$\frac{196}{670} = .293$

In both individual years, Ellsbury had a higher average, but for the two-year period, Lowell had the higher average. This is an example of **Simpson's paradox** from statistics. (The authors thank Carol Merrigan for researching this information.)

EXAMPLE 9 Determining Whether a Decimal Terminates or Repeats

Determine whether the decimal form terminates or repeats.

(a) $\frac{7}{8}$ **(b)** $\frac{13}{150}$ **(c)** $\frac{6}{75}$

Solution

(a) The rational number $\frac{7}{8}$ is in lowest terms. Its denominator is 8, and since 8 factors as 2^3, the decimal form will terminate. No primes other than 2 or 5 divide the denominator.

(b) The rational number $\frac{13}{150}$ is in lowest terms with denominator

$$150 = 2 \cdot 3 \cdot 5^2.$$

Because **3** appears as a prime factor of the denominator, the decimal form will repeat.

(c) First write the rational number $\frac{6}{75}$ in lowest terms.

$$\frac{6}{75} = \frac{2}{25} \qquad \text{Denominator is 25.}$$

Because $25 = 5^2$, the decimal form will terminate. ∎

We have seen that a rational number will be represented by either a terminating or a repeating decimal. Must a terminating decimal or a repeating decimal represent a rational number? The answer is *yes*. For example, the terminating decimal 0.6 represents a rational number.

$$0.6 = \frac{6}{10} = \frac{3}{5}$$

EXAMPLE 10 Writing Decimals as Quotients of Integers

Write each decimal as a quotient of integers.

(a) 0.437 **(b)** 8.2 **(c)** $0.\overline{85}$

Solution

The results of **Example 10(a) and (b)** are supported in this screen.

(a) $0.437 = \frac{437}{1000}$ Read as "four hundred thirty-seven thousandths" and then write as a fraction.

(b) $8.2 = 8 + \frac{2}{10} = \frac{82}{10} = \frac{41}{5}$ Read as a decimal, write as a sum, and then add.

(c) To convert a repeating decimal to a quotient of integers, we use some simple algebra.

Step 1 Let $x = 0.\overline{85}$, so $x = 0.858585\ldots$.

Step 2 Multiply both sides of the equation $x = 0.858585\ldots$ by 100. (Use 100 since there are **two** digits in the part that repeats, and $100 = 10^2$.)

$$x = 0.858585\ldots$$

$$100x = 100(0.858585\ldots)$$

$$100x = 85.858585\ldots$$

$1 = 0.99999999$

Terminating or Repeating? One of the most baffling truths of elementary mathematics is the following:

$$1 = 0.9999\ldots.$$

Most people believe that $0.\overline{9}$ has to be less than 1, but this is not the case. The following argument shows why. Let $x = 0.9999\ldots$. Then

$$10x = 9.9999\ldots$$
$$\underline{x = 0.9999\ldots}$$
$$9x = 9 \qquad \text{Subtract.}$$
$$x = 1. \qquad \text{Divide.}$$

Therefore, $1 = 0.9999\ldots$. Similarly, it can be shown that any terminating decimal can be represented as a repeating decimal with an endless string of 9s. For example, $0.5 = 0.49999\ldots$ and $2.6 = 2.59999\ldots$. This is a way of justifying that any rational number may be represented as a repeating decimal.

Step 3 Subtract the expressions in Step 1 from the final expressions in Step 2.

$$100x = 85.858585\ldots \qquad \text{(Recall that } x = 1x \text{ and}$$
$$\underline{x = 0.858585\ldots} \qquad 100x - x = 99x.)$$
$$99x = 85 \qquad\qquad \text{Subtract.}$$

Step 4 Solve the equation $99x = 85$ by dividing both sides by 99.

$$99x = 85$$
$$\frac{99x}{99} = \frac{85}{99} \qquad \text{Divide by 99.}$$
$$x = \frac{85}{99} \qquad \frac{99x}{99} = x$$
$$0.\overline{85} = \frac{85}{99} \qquad x = 0.\overline{85}$$

When checking with a calculator, remember that the calculator will show only a finite number of decimal places and may round off in the final decimal place shown. ∎

FOR FURTHER THOUGHT

The Influence of Spanish Coinage on Stock Prices

Until August 28, 2000, when decimalization of the U.S. stock market began, market prices were reported with fractions having denominators that were powers of 2, such as $17\frac{3}{4}$ and $112\frac{5}{8}$. Did you ever wonder why this was done?

During the early years of the United States, prior to the minting of its own coinage, the Spanish eight-reales coin, also known as the Spanish milled dollar, circulated freely in the states. Its fractional parts, the four reales, two reales, and one real, were known as **pieces of eight** and were described as such in pirate and treasure lore. When the New York Stock Exchange was founded in 1792, it chose to use the Spanish milled dollar as its price basis, rather than the decimal base proposed by Thomas Jefferson that same year. All prices on the U.S. stock markets are now reported in decimals. (*Source:* "Stock price tables go to decimal listings," *The Times Picayune*, June 27, 2000.)

For Group or Individual Investigation

Consider this: Have you ever heard this old cheer? "Two bits, four bits, six bits, a dollar. All for the (home team), stand up and holler." The term **two bits** refers to 25 cents. Discuss how this cheer is based on the Spanish eight-reales coin.

6.3 EXERCISES

Basic Concepts of Fractions *Complete each of the following, based on the discussion in this section.*

1. A number that can be represented as a quotient of integers with denominator not 0 is called a(n) _____.

2. In the fraction $\frac{7}{13}$, _____ is the numerator and _____ is the denominator.

3. A number of the type in **Exercise 1** is in lowest terms if its numerator and denominator have _____ as their greatest common factor.

4. The fundamental property of rational numbers allows us to write $\frac{18}{27}$ as the equivalent $\frac{2}{3}$ because there is a common factor of _____ in the numerator and the denominator.

5. The fractions $\frac{13}{27}$ and $\frac{221}{459}$ are equivalent because the product of the extremes, 13 and _____, is equal to the product of the means, 27 and _____. Both products are _____.

6. In the mixed number $3\frac{1}{7}$ there is a(n) _____ sign understood between the whole number part and the fraction part.

7. To divide $\frac{7}{12}$ by $\frac{3}{4}$, we multiply _____ by the reciprocal of the divisor. That reciprocal is _____.

8. The rational numbers exhibit the density property, which says that between any two distinct rational numbers there exists _____.

9. The integers do not exhibit the density property. For example, between 5 and _____ there is no other integer.

10. A rational number will have a decimal representation that will show one of two patterns: It will _____ or it will _____.

Choose the expression(s) that is (are) equivalent to the given rational number.

11. $\frac{4}{8}$

   A. $\frac{1}{2}$ **B.** $\frac{8}{4}$ **C.** 0.5   **D.** $0.5\overline{0}$ **E.** $0.\overline{55}$

12. $\frac{2}{3}$

   A. 0.67   **B.** $0.\overline{6}$ **C.** $\frac{20}{30}$ **D.** 0.666...   **E.** 0.6

13. $\frac{5}{9}$

   A. 0.56   **B.** 0.55   **C.** $0.\overline{5}$ **D.** $\frac{9}{5}$ **E.** $1\frac{4}{5}$

14. $\frac{1}{4}$

   A. 0.25   **B.** $0.24\overline{9}$ **C.** $\frac{25}{100}$ **D.** 4   **E.** $\frac{10}{400}$

Write each fraction in lowest terms.

15. $\frac{16}{48}$ 16. $\frac{21}{28}$ 17. $-\frac{15}{35}$ 18. $-\frac{8}{48}$

Write each fraction in three other ways.

19. $\frac{3}{8}$ 20. $\frac{9}{10}$

21. $-\frac{5}{7}$ 22. $-\frac{7}{12}$

23. *Fractional Parts* Write a fraction in lowest terms that represents the portion of each figure that is in color.

(a)   (b)

(c)   (d)

24. *Fractional Parts* Write a fraction in lowest terms that represents the region described in parts (a)–(d).

(a) the dots in the rectangle as a part of the dots in the entire figure

(b) the dots in the triangle as a part of the dots in the entire figure

(c) the dots in the rectangle as a part of the dots in the union of the triangle and the rectangle

(d) the dots in the intersection of the triangle and the rectangle as a part of the dots in the union of the triangle and the rectangle

25. Fractional Parts Refer to the figure for **Exercise 24**, and write a description of the region that is represented by the fraction $\frac{1}{12}$.

26. Batting Averages In a softball league, Paul got 8 hits in 20 at-bats, and Josh got 12 hits in 30 at-bats. Which player (if either) had the higher batting average?

27. Batting Averages After ten games, the following statistics were obtained.

Player	At-bats	Hits	Home Runs
Anne	40	9	2
Christine	36	12	3
Leah	11	5	1
Otis	16	8	0
Carol	20	10	2

Answer using estimation skills as necessary.

(a) Which player got a hit in exactly $\frac{1}{3}$ of his or her at-bats?

(b) Which player got a hit in just less than $\frac{1}{2}$ of his or her at-bats?

(c) Which player got a home run in just less than $\frac{1}{10}$ of his or her at-bats?

(d) Which player got a hit in just less than $\frac{1}{4}$ of his or her at-bats?

(e) Which two players got hits in exactly the same fractional parts of their at-bats? What was the fractional part, reduced to lowest terms?

28. Error Coin Refer to the margin note discussing the use of common fractions on early U.S. copper coinage. The photo here shows an error near the bottom that occurred on an 1802 large cent. Discuss the error and how it represents a mathematical impossibility.

Perform the indicated operations and express answers in lowest terms. Use the order of operations as necessary.

29. $\frac{3}{8} + \frac{1}{8}$ **30.** $\frac{7}{9} + \frac{1}{9}$ **31.** $\frac{5}{16} + \frac{7}{12}$

32. $\frac{1}{15} + \frac{7}{18}$ **33.** $\frac{2}{3} - \frac{7}{8}$ **34.** $\frac{13}{20} - \frac{5}{12}$

35. $\frac{5}{8} - \frac{3}{14}$ **36.** $\frac{19}{15} - \frac{7}{12}$ **37.** $\frac{3}{4} \cdot \frac{9}{5}$

38. $\frac{3}{8} \cdot \frac{2}{7}$ **39.** $-\frac{2}{3} \cdot \left(-\frac{5}{8}\right)$ **40.** $-\frac{2}{4} \cdot \frac{3}{9}$

41. $\frac{5}{12} \div \frac{15}{4}$ **42.** $\frac{15}{16} \div \frac{30}{8}$

43. $-\frac{9}{16} \div \left(-\frac{3}{8}\right)$ **44.** $-\frac{3}{8} \div \left(-\frac{5}{4}\right)$

45. $\left(\frac{1}{3} \div \frac{1}{2}\right) + \frac{5}{6}$ **46.** $\frac{2}{5} \div \left(-\frac{4}{5} \div \frac{3}{10}\right)$

Convert each mixed number to a fraction, and convert each fraction to a mixed number.

47. $4\frac{1}{3}$ **48.** $3\frac{7}{8}$ **49.** $2\frac{9}{10}$

50. $\frac{18}{5}$ **51.** $\frac{27}{4}$ **52.** $\frac{19}{3}$

Perform each operation and express your answer as a mixed number.

53. $3\frac{1}{4} + 2\frac{7}{8}$ **54.** $6\frac{1}{5} - 2\frac{7}{15}$

55. $-4\frac{7}{8} \cdot 3\frac{2}{3}$ **56.** $-4\frac{1}{6} \div 1\frac{2}{3}$

Carpenter Calculations *Carpentry applications often require calculations involving fractions and mixed numbers with denominators of 2, 4, 8, and 16. Perform each of the following, and express each answer as a mixed number.*

57. $\frac{9}{16} + 2\left(\frac{5}{8}\right) - \frac{1}{2}$ **58.** $\frac{5}{16} + 3\left(\frac{3}{8}\right) - \frac{1}{4}$

59. $9\left(2\frac{1}{2}\right) + 3\left(5\frac{1}{8}\right)$ **60.** $8\left(4\frac{1}{4}\right) - 3\left(7\frac{1}{2}\right)$

61. $5\left(\frac{1}{16}\right) + 3\left(2\frac{1}{2}\right) - \frac{7}{16}$ **62.** $8\left(\frac{3}{16}\right) + 2\left(6\frac{1}{4}\right) - \frac{13}{16}$

63. $4\left[3\left(\frac{1}{8}\right) + 2\left(\frac{7}{16}\right)\right] - 2\left(\frac{1}{2} - \frac{1}{16}\right)$

64. $6\left[2\left(\frac{5}{8}\right) + 3\left(\frac{3}{16}\right)\right] - 3\left(\frac{3}{8} - \frac{3}{16}\right)$

Solve each problem.

65. *Socket Wrench Measurements* A hardware store sells a 22-piece socket wrench set. The measure of the largest socket is $\frac{3}{4}$ in., while the measure of the smallest socket is $\frac{3}{16}$ in. What is the difference between these measures?

66. *TV Guide* First published in 1953, the digest-sized *TV Guide* has changed to a "full-sized" magazine, as shown in the figure. What is the difference in their heights? (*Source: TV Guide.*)

67. *Desk Height* The diagram appears in a woodworker's book. Find the height of the desk to the top of the writing surface.

68. *Legs of a Desk* The desk in **Exercise 67** has four legs, each of which consists of three individual pieces. What is the total length of these twelve pieces?

69. *Golf Tees* The Pride Golf Tee Company, the only U.S. manufacturer of wooden golf tees, has created the Professional Tee system shown in the figure. (*Source: The Gazette.*)

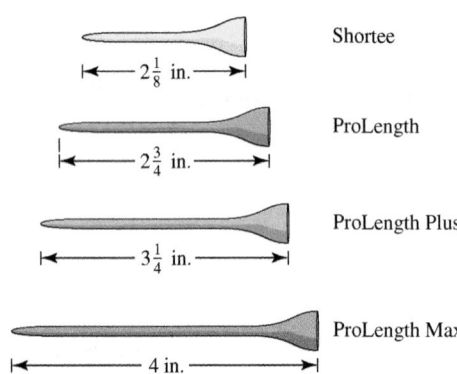

(a) Find the difference between the lengths of the ProLength Plus and the once-standard Shortee.

(b) The ProLength Max tee is the longest tee allowed by the U.S. Golf Association's Rules of Golf. How much longer is the ProLength Max than the Shortee?

70. *Recipe for Grits* The following chart appears on a package of Quaker® Quick Grits.

	Microwave	Stove Top		
Servings	**1**	**1**	**4**	**6**
Water	$\frac{3}{4}$ cup	1 cup	3 cups	4 cups
Grits	3 Tbsp	3 Tbsp	$\frac{3}{4}$ cup	1 cup
Salt (optional)	dash	dash	$\frac{1}{4}$ tsp	$\frac{1}{2}$ tsp

(a) How many cups of water would be needed for 6 microwave servings?

(b) How many cups of grits would be needed for 5 stove-top servings? (*Hint:* 5 is halfway between 4 and 6.)

71. *Cuts on a Board* A board is 48 in. long. It must be divided into four pieces of equal length, and each cut will cause a waste of $\frac{3}{16}$ in. How long will each piece be after the cuts are made?

72. *Cuts on a Board* A board is 72 in. long. It must be divided into six pieces of equal length, and each cut will cause a waste of $\frac{1}{8}$ in. How long will each piece be after the cuts are made?

73. Cake Recipe A cake recipe calls for $1\frac{3}{4}$ cups of sugar. A caterer has $15\frac{1}{2}$ cups of sugar on hand. How many cakes can he make?

74. Fabric It takes $2\frac{1}{4}$ yd of fabric to cover a chair of a particular design. How many chairs can be covered with $23\frac{2}{3}$ yd of fabric?

75. Fabric It takes $2\frac{3}{8}$ yd of fabric to make a costume for a school play. How much fabric would be needed for seven costumes?

76. Cookie Recipe A cookie recipe calls for $2\frac{2}{3}$ cups of sugar. How much sugar would be needed to make four batches of cookies?

77. Public 4-Year Institution Costs The table shows the average amount of tuition and fees at public 4-year institutions for in-state students for five academic years. What is the average cost for this period (rounded to the nearest dollar)? (*Source:* National Center for Education Statistics.)

Academic Year	Amount of Tuition and Fees
2007–08	$5943
2008–09	6312
2009–10	6695
2010–11	7136
2011–12	7701

78. Public 2-Year Institution Costs The table shows the average amount of tuition and fees at public 2-year institutions for in-state students for five academic years. What is the average cost for this period (rounded to the nearest dollar)? (*Source:* National Center for Education Statistics.)

Academic Year	Amount of Tuition and Fees
2007–08	$2061
2008–09	2136
2009–10	2285
2010–11	2439
2011–12	2647

Find the rational number halfway between the two given rational numbers.

79. $\frac{1}{2}, \frac{3}{4}$

80. $\frac{1}{3}, \frac{5}{12}$

81. $\frac{3}{5}, \frac{2}{3}$

82. $\frac{7}{12}, \frac{5}{8}$

83. $-\frac{2}{3}, -\frac{5}{6}$

84. $-\frac{5}{16}, -\frac{5}{2}$

*Use the method of **Example 9** to decide whether each rational number would yield a repeating or a terminating decimal. (Hint: Write in lowest terms before trying to decide.)*

85. $\frac{8}{15}$ **86.** $\frac{8}{35}$ **87.** $\frac{13}{125}$

88. $\frac{3}{24}$ **89.** $\frac{22}{55}$ **90.** $\frac{24}{75}$

Convert each rational number into either a repeating or a terminating decimal. Use a calculator if your instructor so allows.

91. $\frac{3}{4}$ **92.** $\frac{7}{8}$

93. $\frac{3}{16}$ **94.** $\frac{9}{32}$

95. $\frac{3}{11}$ **96.** $\frac{9}{11}$

97. $\frac{2}{7}$ **98.** $\frac{11}{15}$

Convert each decimal into a quotient of integers, written in lowest terms.

99. 0.4 **100.** 0.9

101. 0.85 **102.** 0.105

103. 0.934 **104.** 0.7984

105. $0.\overline{67}$ **106.** $0.\overline{53}$

107. $0.0\overline{42}$ **108.** $0.0\overline{86}$

109. $0.0\overline{1}$ **110.** $0.1\overline{2}$

111. Hard to Believe? Follow through on all parts of this exercise in order.

(a) Find the decimal for $\frac{1}{3}$.

(b) Find the decimal for $\frac{2}{3}$.

(c) By adding the decimal expressions obtained in parts (a) and (b), obtain a decimal expression for $\frac{1}{3} + \frac{2}{3} = \frac{3}{3} = 1$.

(d) State your result. Read the margin note on terminating and repeating decimals in this section, which refers to this idea.

112. Hard to Believe? It is a fact that $\frac{1}{3} = 0.333\ldots$. Multiply both sides of this equation by 3. Does your answer bother you? See the margin note on terminating and repeating decimals in this section.

6.4 IRRATIONAL NUMBERS AND DECIMAL REPRESENTATION

OBJECTIVES

1 Understand how irrational numbers differ from rational numbers in their decimal representations.

2 Follow the proof that $\sqrt{2}$ is an irrational number.

3 Use a calculator to find square roots.

4 Apply the product and quotient rules for square roots.

5 Rationalize a denominator.

6 Understand the relevance of the irrational numbers π, ϕ, and e in mathematics.

Definition and Basic Concepts

Every rational number has a decimal form that terminates or repeats, and every repeating or terminating decimal represents a rational number. However,

$$0.102001000200001000002\ldots$$

does not terminate and does not repeat. (It is true that there is a pattern in this decimal, but no single block of digits repeats indefinitely.)*

IRRATIONAL NUMBERS

Irrational numbers = $\{x \mid x$ is a number represented by a nonrepeating, nonterminating decimal$\}$

As the name implies, an irrational number cannot be represented as a quotient of integers.

The decimal number mentioned at the top of this page is an irrational number. Other irrational numbers include $\sqrt{2}$, $\frac{1 + \sqrt{5}}{2}$ (ϕ, from **Section 5.5**), π (the ratio of the circumference of a circle to its diameter), and e (a constant *approximately equal to* 2.71828). There are infinitely many irrational numbers.

Irrationality of $\sqrt{2}$ and Proof by Contradiction

Figure 13 illustrates how a point with coordinate $\sqrt{2}$ can be located on a number line. (This was first mentioned in **Section 6.1**.)

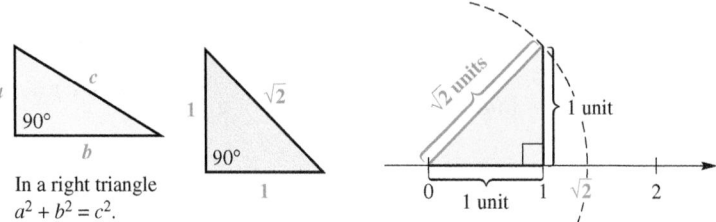

In a right triangle $a^2 + b^2 = c^2$.

Figure 13

The proof that $\sqrt{2}$ is irrational is a classic example of a **proof by contradiction.** We begin by assuming that $\sqrt{2}$ is rational, which leads to a contradiction, or absurdity. The method is also called **reductio ad absurdum** (Latin for "reduce to the absurd"). In order to understand the proof, we consider three preliminary facts:

1. When a rational number is written in lowest terms, the greatest common factor of the numerator and denominator is 1.

2. If an integer is even, then it has 2 as a factor and may be written in the form $2k$, where k is an integer.

3. If a perfect square is even, then its square root is even.

The irrational number $\sqrt{2}$ was discovered by the Pythagoreans in about 500 B.C. This discovery was a great setback to their philosophy that everything is based on the whole numbers. The Pythagoreans kept their findings secret, and legend has it that members of the group who divulged this discovery were sent out to sea, and, according to Proclus (410–485), "perished in a shipwreck, to a man."

---

*In this section, we will assume that the digits of a number such as this continue indefinitely in the pattern established. The next few digits would be 000000100000002, and so on.

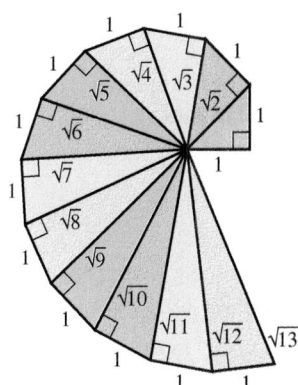

An interesting way to represent the lengths corresponding to $\sqrt{2}$, $\sqrt{3}$, $\sqrt{4}$, $\sqrt{5}$, and so on, is shown in the figure. Use the **Pythagorean theorem** to verify the lengths in the figure.

THEOREM

Statement: $\sqrt{2}$ is an irrational number.

Proof: Assume that $\sqrt{2}$ is a rational number. Then by definition,

$$\sqrt{2} = \frac{p}{q}, \quad \text{for some integers } p \text{ and } q.$$

Furthermore, assume that $\frac{p}{q}$ is the form of $\sqrt{2}$ that is written in lowest terms, so the greatest common factor of p and q is 1.

$$2 = \frac{p^2}{q^2} \quad \text{Square both sides of the equation.}$$

$$2q^2 = p^2 \quad \text{Multiply by } q^2.$$

The last equation, $2q^2 = p^2$, indicates that 2 is a factor of p^2. So p^2 is even, and thus p is even. Since p is even, it may be written in the form $2k$, where k is an integer.

Now, substitute $2k$ for p in the last equation and simplify.

$$2q^2 = (2k)^2 \quad \text{Let } p = 2k.$$

$$2q^2 = 4k^2 \quad (2k)^2 = 2k \cdot 2k = 4k^2$$

$$q^2 = 2k^2 \quad \text{Divide by 2.}$$

Since q^2 has 2 as a factor, q^2 must be even, and thus q must be even. This leads to a contradiction: p and q cannot both be even because they would then have a common factor of 2. It was assumed that their greatest common factor is 1. The original assumption that $\sqrt{2}$ is rational has led to a contradiction, so $\sqrt{2}$ is irrational. ∎

Operations with Square Roots

In everyday mathematical work, nearly all of our calculations deal with rational numbers, usually in decimal form. However, we must sometimes perform operations with irrational numbers. ***Recall that $\sqrt{a}$, for $a \geq 0$, is the nonnegative number whose square is a. That is, $(\sqrt{a})^2 = a$.***

$$\sqrt{2}, \quad \sqrt{3}, \quad \text{and} \quad \sqrt{13} \quad \text{Examples of square roots that are irrational}$$

$$\sqrt{4} = 2, \quad \sqrt{36} = 6, \quad \text{and} \quad \sqrt{100} = 10 \quad \text{Examples of square roots that are rational}$$

If n is a positive integer that is not the square of an integer, then $\sqrt{n}$ is an irrational number.

A calculator with a square root key can give approximations of square roots of numbers that are not perfect squares. We use the $\approx$ symbol to indicate "is approximately equal to." Sometimes, for convenience, the $=$ symbol is used even if the statement is actually one of approximation, such as $\pi = 3.14$.

EXAMPLE 1 Using a Calculator to Approximate Square Roots

Use a calculator to verify the following approximations.

(a) $\sqrt{2} \approx 1.414213562$ **(b)** $\sqrt{6} \approx 2.449489743$ **(c)** $\sqrt{1949} \approx 44.14748011$

Solution

Use a calculator, such as the ones found on today's smartphones, to verify these approximations. Depending on the model, fewer or more digits may be displayed, and because of different rounding procedures, final digits may differ slightly. ∎

EXAMPLE 2   Applying a Formula for Pipe Flow

The following formula gives the number N of smaller pipes of diameter d that are necessary to supply the same total flow as one larger pipe of diameter D.

$$N = \sqrt{\left(\dfrac{D}{d}\right)^5}$$

This formula takes into account the extra friction caused by the smaller pipes. Use this formula to determine the number of $\frac{1}{2}$-inch pipes that will provide the same flow as one $1\frac{1}{2}$-inch pipe. (*Source:* Saunders, Hal M., and Robert A. Carman. *Mathematics for the Trades—A Guided Approach.* Pearson, 2015.)

Solution

Let $d = \frac{1}{2}$ and $D = 1\frac{1}{2} = \frac{3}{2}$ in the formula.

$$N = \sqrt{\left(\dfrac{\frac{3}{2}}{\frac{1}{2}}\right)^5} \qquad d = \tfrac{1}{2}, D = \tfrac{3}{2}$$

$$= \sqrt{3^5} \qquad \tfrac{3}{2} \div \tfrac{1}{2} = \tfrac{3}{2} \cdot \tfrac{2}{1} = 3$$

$$= \sqrt{243} \qquad 3^5 = 243$$

$$= 15.59 \qquad \text{Approximate with a calculator.}$$

In this case the answer must be a whole number, so we round 15.59 up to 16. A total of 16 pipes measuring $\frac{1}{2}$ inch will be needed. ■

We will now look at some simple operations with square roots. Notice that

$$\sqrt{4} \cdot \sqrt{9} = 2 \cdot 3 = 6$$

and

$$\sqrt{4 \cdot 9} = \sqrt{36} = 6.$$

Thus, $\sqrt{4} \cdot \sqrt{9} = \sqrt{4 \cdot 9}$. This is a particular case of the following rule.

PRODUCT RULE FOR SQUARE ROOTS

For nonnegative real numbers a and b, the following is true.

$$\boldsymbol{\sqrt{a} \cdot \sqrt{b} = \sqrt{a \cdot b}}$$

Just as every rational number $\frac{a}{b}$ can be written in *lowest terms* (by using the fundamental property of rational numbers), every square root radical has a *simplified form*.

CONDITIONS FOR A SIMPLIFIED SQUARE ROOT RADICAL

A square root radical is in **simplified form** if the following three conditions are met.

1. The number under the radical (**radicand**) has no factor (except 1) that is a perfect square.

2. The radicand has no fractions.

3. No denominator contains a radical.

Tsu Ch'ung-chih (about A.D. 500), the Chinese mathematician honored on the above stamp, investigated the digits of π. **Aryabhata**, his Indian contemporary, gave 3.1416 as the value.

EXAMPLE 3 **Simplifying a Square Root Radical (Product Rule)**

Simplify $\sqrt{27}$.

Solution

Since 9 is a factor of 27, and 9 is a perfect square, $\sqrt{27}$ is not in simplified form. The first condition for simplified form is not met. We simplify as follows.

$$\sqrt{27} = \sqrt{9 \cdot 3}$$

$\boxed{\text{Simplified form}}$ $= \sqrt{9} \cdot \sqrt{3}$ Use the product rule.

$= 3\sqrt{3}$ $\sqrt{9} = 3$ because $3^2 = 9$.   ∎

Expressions such as $\sqrt{27}$ and $3\sqrt{3}$ represent the *exact value* of the square root of 27. If we use the square root key of a calculator, we find

$$\sqrt{27} \approx 5.196152423.$$

If we find $\sqrt{3}$ and then multiply the result by 3, we obtain

$$3\sqrt{3} \approx 3(1.732050808) \approx 5.196152423.$$

These approximations are the same, as we would expect. The work in **Example 3** provides the mathematical justification that they are indeed equal.

QUOTIENT RULE FOR SQUARE ROOTS

For nonnegative real numbers a and positive real numbers b, the following is true.

$$\frac{\sqrt{a}}{\sqrt{b}} = \sqrt{\frac{a}{b}}$$

EXAMPLE 4 **Simplifying Square Root Radicals (Quotient Rule)**

Simplify each radical.

(a) $\sqrt{\dfrac{25}{9}}$ **(b)** $\sqrt{\dfrac{3}{4}}$ **(c)** $\sqrt{\dfrac{1}{2}}$

Solution

(a) The radicand contains a fraction, so the radical expression is not simplified.

$$\sqrt{\frac{25}{9}} = \frac{\sqrt{25}}{\sqrt{9}} = \frac{5}{3}$$ Use the quotient rule.

(b) $\sqrt{\dfrac{3}{4}} = \dfrac{\sqrt{3}}{\sqrt{4}} = \dfrac{\sqrt{3}}{2}$ Use the quotient rule.

(c) $\sqrt{\dfrac{1}{2}} = \dfrac{\sqrt{1}}{\sqrt{2}} = \dfrac{1}{\sqrt{2}}$ $\boxed{\text{This is not yet simplified.}}$

Condition 3 for simplified form is not met. To find an equivalent expression with no radical in the denominator, we **rationalize the denominator.**

Carl Gauss Square roots of negative numbers were called **imaginary numbers** by early mathematicians. Eventually the symbol *i* came to represent the **imaginary unit** $\sqrt{-1}$, and numbers of the form *a* + *bi*, where *a* and *b* are real numbers, were named **complex numbers.**

In about 1831, **Carl Gauss** was able to show that numbers of the form *a* + *bi* can be represented as points on the plane just as real numbers are. He shared this contribution with **Robert Argand,** a bookkeeper in Paris, who wrote an essay on the geometry of the complex numbers in 1806. This went unnoticed at the time.

The complex number *i* has the property that its whole number powers repeat in a cycle, with four values.

$$i^0 = 1 \quad i^1 = i \quad i^2 = -1 \quad i^3 = -i$$

The pattern continues on and on this way.

To rationalize the denominator here, we multiply $\frac{1}{\sqrt{2}}$ by $\frac{\sqrt{2}}{\sqrt{2}}$, which is a form of 1, the identity element for multiplication.

$$\frac{1}{\sqrt{2}} = \frac{1}{\sqrt{2}} \cdot \frac{\sqrt{2}}{\sqrt{2}} = \frac{\sqrt{2}}{2} \qquad \sqrt{2} \cdot \sqrt{2} = 2$$

This is the simplified form of $\sqrt{\frac{1}{2}}$.

Is $\sqrt{4} + \sqrt{9} = \sqrt{4 + 9}$ a true statement? The answer is *no*, because

$$\sqrt{4} + \sqrt{9} = 2 + 3 = 5, \quad \text{while} \quad \sqrt{4 + 9} = \sqrt{13}, \quad \text{and} \quad 5 \neq \sqrt{13}.$$

Square root radicals may be combined, however, if they have the same radicand. Such radicals are called **like radicals.** We add (and subtract) like radicals using the distributive property.

EXAMPLE 5 **Adding and Subtracting Square Root Radicals**

Add or subtract as indicated.

(a) $3\sqrt{6} + 4\sqrt{6}$ **(b)** $\sqrt{18} - \sqrt{32}$

Solution

(a) Since both terms contain $\sqrt{6}$, they are like radicals, and may be combined.

$$3\sqrt{6} + 4\sqrt{6} = (3 + 4)\sqrt{6} \qquad \text{Distributive property}$$

$$= 7\sqrt{6} \qquad \text{Add.}$$

(b) If we simplify $\sqrt{18}$ and $\sqrt{32}$, then this operation can be performed.

$$\sqrt{18} - \sqrt{32} = \sqrt{9 \cdot 2} - \sqrt{16 \cdot 2} \qquad \text{Factor so that perfect squares are in the radicands.}$$

$$= \sqrt{9} \cdot \sqrt{2} - \sqrt{16} \cdot \sqrt{2} \qquad \text{Product rule}$$

$$= 3\sqrt{2} - 4\sqrt{2} \qquad \text{Take square roots.}$$

$$= (3 - 4)\sqrt{2} \qquad \text{Distributive property}$$

$$= -1\sqrt{2} \qquad \text{Subtract.}$$

$$= -\sqrt{2} \qquad -1 \cdot a = -a$$

Like radicals may be added or subtracted by adding or subtracting their coefficients (the numbers by which they are multiplied) and keeping the same radical.

Examples: $9\sqrt{7} + 8\sqrt{7} = 17\sqrt{7}$ (because $9 + 8 = 17$)

$4\sqrt{3} - 12\sqrt{3} = -8\sqrt{3}$ (because $4 - 12 = -8$)

The Irrational Numbers π, ϕ, and e

Figure 14 shows approximations for three important irrational numbers. The first, $\boldsymbol{\pi}$, represents the ratio of the circumference of a circle to its diameter. The second, $\boldsymbol{\phi}$, is the Golden Ratio. Its exact value is $\frac{1 + \sqrt{5}}{2}$. The third is $\boldsymbol{e}$, a fundamental number in our universe. It is the base of the *natural exponential* and *natural logarithmic* functions. The letter *e* was chosen to honor Leonhard Euler, who published extensive research on the number in 1746.

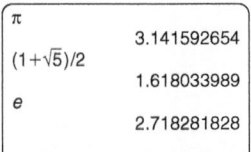

π	
	3.141592654
$(1+\sqrt{5})/2$	
	1.618033989
e	
	2.718281828

Figure 14

This poem, dedicated to **Archimedes** ("the immortal Syracusan"), allows us to learn the first 31 digits of the decimal representation of π. By replacing each word with the number of letters it contains, with a decimal point following the initial 3, the decimal is found. The poem was written by A. C. Orr, and it appeared in the *Literary Digest* in 1906.

> *Now I, even I, would celebrate*
> *In rhymes unapt, the great*
> *Immortal Syracusan, rivaled nevermore,*
> *Who in his wondrous lore*
> *Passed on before,*
> *Left men his guidance*
> *How to circles mensurate.*

Pi (π)

$$\pi \approx 3.14159265358979323846264338327 9$$

The computation of the digits of π has fascinated mathematicians since ancient times. Archimedes was the first to explore it extensively. As of August 5, 2014, its value had been computed to 12 trillion decimal places. Some of today's foremost researchers of the digits of π are Yasumasa Kanada, Gregory and David Chudnovsky, and the team of Alexander J. Yee and Shigeru Kondo.

A History of π, by Petr Beckmann, is a classic that is now in its third edition. Numerous Web sites, including the following, are devoted to the history and methods of computation of pi.

www.joyofpi.com/

www.math.utah.edu/~alfeld/Archimedes/Archimedes.html

www.super-computing.org/

www.pbs.org/wgbh/nova/sciencenow/3210/04.html

www.numberworld.org/misc_runs/pi-5t/details.html

One of the methods of computing pi involves the topic of *infinite series.*

EXAMPLE 6 Computing the Digits of Pi Using an Infinite Series

It is shown in higher mathematics that the *infinite series*

$$1 - \frac{1}{3} + \frac{1}{5} - \frac{1}{7} + \frac{1}{9} + \ldots \text{ "converges" to } \frac{\pi}{4}.$$

That is, as more and more terms are considered, its value becomes closer and closer to $\frac{\pi}{4}$. With a calculator, approximate the value of pi using twenty-one terms of this series.

Solution

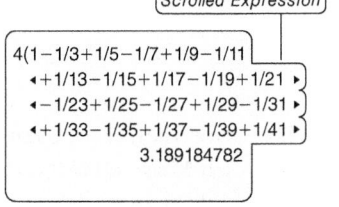

Figure 15

Figure 15 shows the necessary calculation on the TI-83/84 Plus calculator. The sum of the first twenty-one terms is multiplied by 4, to obtain the approximation

$$3.189184782.$$

This series converges slowly. Although this is correct only to the first decimal place, better approximations are obtained using more terms of the series. ∎

A rectangle that satisfies the condition that the ratio of its length to its width is equal to the ratio of the sum of its length and width to its length is called a **Golden Rectangle.** See **Figure 16.** This ratio is called the **Golden Ratio.** Its exact value is the irrational number $\frac{1 + \sqrt{5}}{2}$. It is represented by the Greek letter ϕ (phi).

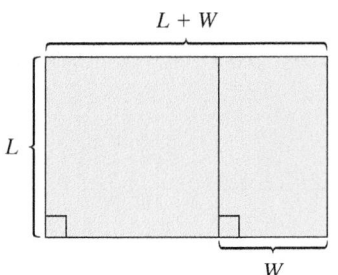

In a golden rectangle,

$$\frac{L + W}{L} = \frac{L}{W}.$$

Figure 16

Phi (ϕ)

$$\phi = \frac{1 + \sqrt{5}}{2} \approx 1.618033988749894848204586834365$$

In 1767 **J. H. Lambert** proved that π is irrational (and thus its decimal will never terminate and never repeat). Nevertheless, the 1897 Indiana state legislature considered a bill that would have *legislated* the value of π. In one part of the bill, the value was stated to be 4, and in another part, 3.2. Amazingly, the bill passed the House, but the Senate postponed action on the bill indefinitely.

Two books on phi are *The Divine Proportion, A Study in Mathematical Beauty,* by H. E. Huntley, and the more recent *The Golden Ratio,* by Mario Livio. Web sites devoted to this irrational number include the following.

www.mcs.surrey.ac.uk/Personal/R.Knott/Fibonacci/

www.goldennumber.net/

www.mathforum.org/dr.math/faq/faq.golden.ratio.html

www.geom.uiuc.edu/~demo5337/s97b/art.htm

EXAMPLE 7 Computing the Digits of Phi Using the Fibonacci Sequence

The first twelve terms of the Fibonacci sequence are

$$1, 1, 2, 3, 5, 8, 13, 21, 34, 55, 89, 144.$$

Each term after the first two terms is obtained by adding the two previous terms. Thus, the thirteenth term is $89 + 144 = 233$. As one goes farther out in the sequence, the ratio of a term to its predecessor gets closer to ϕ. How far out must one go in order to approximate ϕ so that the first five decimal places agree?

Solution

After 144, the next three Fibonacci numbers are 233, 377, and 610. **Figure 17** shows that $\frac{610}{377} \approx 1.618037135$, which agrees with ϕ to the fifth decimal place. ∎

The irrational number e is a fundamental constant in mathematics.

> *e*
>
> $e \approx 2.718281828459045235360287471353$

Because of its nature, e is less well understood by the layperson than π (or even ϕ, for that matter). The 1994 book *e: The Story of a Number,* by Eli Maor, attempted to rectify this situation. The following Web sites also give information on e.

www.mathforum.org/dr.math/faq/faq.e.html

www-groups.dcs.st-and.ac.uk/~history/HistTopics/e.html

http://antwrp.gsfc.nasa.gov/htmltest/gifcity/e.1mil

www.math.toronto.edu/mathnet/answers/ereal.html

Example 8 illustrates another infinite series, this one converging to e.

EXAMPLE 8 Computing the Digits of e Using an Infinite Series

The infinite series

$$2 + \frac{1}{1 \cdot 2} + \frac{1}{1 \cdot 2 \cdot 3} + \frac{1}{1 \cdot 2 \cdot 3 \cdot 4} + \ldots \text{ converges to } e.$$

Use a calculator to approximate e using the first seven terms of this series.

Solution

Figure 18 shows the sum of the first seven terms. (The denominators have all been multiplied out.) The sum is 2.718253968, which agrees with e to four decimal places. This series converges more rapidly than the one for π in **Example 6.** ∎

233/144
     1.618055556
377/233
     1.618025751
610/377
     1.618037135

Figure 17

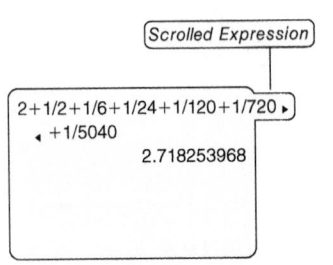

Scrolled Expression

2+1/2+1/6+1/24+1/120+1/720 ▸
◂ +1/5040
     2.718253968

Figure 18

6.4 EXERCISES

Identify each number as rational *or* irrational.

1. $\frac{4}{9}$ **2.** $\frac{7}{8}$ **3.** $\sqrt{10}$ **4.** $\sqrt{14}$

5. 1.618   **6.** 2.718   **7.** $0.\overline{41}$ **8.** $0.\overline{32}$

9. π **10.** e **11.** 3.14159   **12.** $\frac{22}{7}$

13. 0.878778777877778 . . .   **14.** $\frac{1 + \sqrt{5}}{2}$

In Exercises 15 and 16, work parts (a) and (b) in order.

15. **(a)** Find the sum.   0.272772777277772 . . .

$+0.616116111611116 . . .$

(b) Based on the result of part (a), we can conclude that the sum of two _____ numbers may be a(n) _____ number.

16. **(a)** Find the sum.   0.010110111011110 . . .

$+0.252552555255552 . . .$

(b) Based on the result of part (a), we can conclude that the sum of two _____ numbers may be a(n) _____ number.

Use a calculator to find a rational decimal approximation for each irrational number.

17. $\sqrt{39}$ **18.** $\sqrt{44}$ **19.** $\sqrt{15.1}$ **20.** $\sqrt{33.6}$

21. $\sqrt{884}$ **22.** $\sqrt{643}$ **23.** $\sqrt{\frac{9}{8}}$ **24.** $\sqrt{\frac{6}{5}}$

25. *Plumbing*   Use the formula from **Example 2,**

$$N = \sqrt{\left(\frac{D}{d}\right)^5},$$

to find the number of $\frac{3}{4}$-inch pipes that would be necessary to provide the same total flow as a single $1\frac{1}{2}$-inch pipe.

26. *Plumbing*   Use the formula from **Example 2** to find the number of $\frac{5}{8}$-inch pipes that would be necessary to provide the same total flow as a single 2-inch pipe.

Solve each problem. Use a calculator as necessary, and give approximations to the nearest tenth unless specified otherwise.

27. *Allied Health*   Body surface area (BSA) is used in the allied health field to calculate proper dosages of drugs based on a patient's height and weight. The formula

$$\text{BSA} = \sqrt{\frac{\text{weight in kg} \times \text{height in cm}}{3600}}$$

will give the patient's BSA in square meters. (*Source: Saunders, Hal M., and Robert A. Carman. Mathematics for the Trades—A Guided Approach, Tenth Edition. Pearson, 2015.*) What is the BSA for a person who weighs 100 kilograms and is 200 centimeters tall?

28. *Allied Health*   Use the formula from **Exercise 27** to find the BSA of a person who weighs 94 kilograms and is 190 centimeters tall.

29. *Diagonal of a Box*   The length of the diagonal of a box is given by

$$D = \sqrt{L^2 + W^2 + H^2},$$

where *L*, *W*, and *H* are the length, width, and height of the box. Find the length of the diagonal, *D*, of a box that is 4 feet long, 3 feet wide, and 2 feet high.

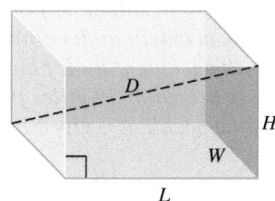

30. *Distance to the Horizon*   A meteorologist provided this answer to one of the readers of his newspaper column, a 6-foot man who lives 150 feet above the ground.

> *To find the distance to the horizon in miles, take the square root of the height of your view and multiply that result by 1.224. That will give you the number of miles to the horizon.*

Assuming the viewer's eyes are 6 feet above his floor, the total height from the ground is $150 + 6 = 156$ feet. How far can he see to the horizon?

31. *Period of a Pendulum*   The period of a pendulum, in seconds, depends on its length, *L*, in feet, and is given by the formula

$$P = 2\pi\sqrt{\frac{L}{32}}.$$

If a pendulum is 5.1 feet long, what is its period? Use 3.14 for π.

32. *Radius of an Aluminum Can*   The radius of the circular top or bottom of an aluminum can with surface area *S* in square cm and height *h* in cm is given by

$$r = \frac{-h + \sqrt{h^2 + 0.64S}}{2}.$$

What radius should be used to make a can with height 12 cm and surface area 400 square cm?

33. *Electronics Formula* The formula

$$I = \sqrt{\frac{2P}{L}}$$

relates the coefficient of self-induction L (in henrys), the energy P stored in an electronic circuit (in joules), and the current I (in amps). Find the value of I if $P = 120$ joules and $L = 80$ henrys.

34. *Law of Tensions* In the study of sound, one version of the law of tensions is

$$f_1 = f_2\sqrt{\frac{F_1}{F_2}}.$$

Find f_1 to the nearest unit if $F_1 = 300$, $F_2 = 60$, and $f_2 = 260$.

Accident Reconstruction *Police sometimes use the following procedure to estimate the speed at which a car was traveling at the time of an accident. A police officer drives the car involved in the accident under conditions similar to those during which the accident took place and then skids to a stop. If the car is driven at 30 miles per hour, then the speed at the time of the accident is given by*

$$s = 30\sqrt{\frac{a}{p}}.$$

Here, a is the length of the skid marks left at the time of the accident, and p is the length of the skid marks in the police test. Find s, to the nearest unit, for the following values of a and p.

35. $a = 862$ feet; $p = 156$ feet

36. $a = 382$ feet; $p = 96$ feet

37. $a = 84$ feet; $p = 26$ feet

38. $a = 90$ feet; $p = 35$ feet

39. *Area of the Bermuda Triangle* **Heron's formula** gives a method of finding the area of a triangle if the lengths of its sides are known. Suppose that a, b, and c are the lengths of the sides. Let s denote one-half of the perimeter of the triangle (called the **semiperimeter**); that is,

$$s = \frac{1}{2}(a + b + c).$$

Then the area $\mathcal{A}$ of the triangle is given by

$$\mathcal{A} = \sqrt{s(s-a)(s-b)(s-c)}.$$

Find the area of the Bermuda Triangle, if the "sides" of this triangle measure approximately 850 miles, 925 miles, and 1300 miles. Give your answer to the nearest thousand square miles.

40. *Area Enclosed by the Vietnam Veterans' Memorial* The Vietnam Veterans' Memorial in Washington, D.C., is in the shape of an unenclosed isosceles triangle with equal sides of length 246.75 feet. If the triangle were enclosed, the third side would have length 438.14 feet. Use Heron's formula from the previous exercise to find the area of this enclosure to the nearest hundred square feet. (*Source:* Information pamphlet obtained at the Vietnam Veterans' Memorial.)

41. *Perfect Triangles* A **perfect triangle** is a triangle whose sides have whole number lengths and whose area is numerically equal to its perimeter. Use Heron's formula to show that the triangle with sides of length 9, 10, and 17 is perfect.

42. *Heron Triangles* A **Heron triangle** is a triangle having integer sides and area. Use Heron's formula to show that each of the following is a Heron triangle.

(a) $a = 11$, $b = 13$, $c = 20$

(b) $a = 13$, $b = 14$, $c = 15$

(c) $a = 7$, $b = 15$, $c = 20$

*Use the methods of **Examples 3 and 4** to simplify each expression. Then, use a calculator to approximate both the given expression and the simplified expression. (Both should be the same.)*

43. $\sqrt{50}$ **44.** $\sqrt{32}$ **45.** $\sqrt{75}$

46. $\sqrt{150}$ **47.** $\sqrt{288}$ **48.** $\sqrt{200}$

49. $\dfrac{5}{\sqrt{6}}$ **50.** $\dfrac{3}{\sqrt{2}}$

51. $\sqrt{\dfrac{7}{4}}$ **52.** $\sqrt{\dfrac{8}{9}}$

53. $\sqrt{\dfrac{7}{3}}$ **54.** $\sqrt{\dfrac{14}{5}}$

*Use the method of **Example 5** to perform the indicated operations.*

55. $\sqrt{17} + 2\sqrt{17}$ **56.** $3\sqrt{19} + \sqrt{19}$

57. $5\sqrt{7} - \sqrt{7}$ **58.** $3\sqrt{27} - \sqrt{27}$

59. $3\sqrt{18} + \sqrt{2}$ **60.** $2\sqrt{48} - \sqrt{3}$

61. $-\sqrt{12} + \sqrt{75}$ **62.** $2\sqrt{27} - \sqrt{300}$

Irrational Investigations *Exercises 63–78 deal with the irrational numbers* π, φ, e, *and* $\sqrt{3}$. *Use a calculator or computer as necessary.*

63. Move one matchstick to make the equation approximately true. (*Source:* www.joyofpi.com)

64. Find the square root of $\frac{2143}{22}$ using a calculator. Then find the square root of that result. Compare your result to the decimal given for π in the margin note. What do you notice?

65. Use a calculator to find the first eight digits in the decimal for $\frac{355}{113}$. Compare the result to the decimal for π given in the text. What do you notice?

66. You may have seen the statements

"Use $\frac{22}{7}$ for π"   and   "Use 3.14 for π."

Since $\frac{22}{7}$ is the quotient of two integers, and 3.14 is a terminating decimal, do these statements suggest that π is rational?

67. In the Bible (I Kings 7:23), a verse describes a circular pool at King Solomon's temple, about 1000 B.C. The pool is said to be ten cubits across, "and a line of 30 cubits did compass it round about." What value of π does this imply?

68. The ancient Egyptians used a method for finding the area of a circle that is equivalent to a value of 3.1605 for π. Write this decimal as a mixed number.

69. The computation of π has fascinated mathematicians and others for centuries. In the nineteenth century, the British mathematician William Shanks spent many years of his life calculating π to 707 decimal places. It turned out that only the first 527 were correct. Use an Internet search to find the 528th decimal digit of π (following the whole number part 3).

70. A **mnemonic device** is a scheme whereby one is able to recall facts by memorizing something completely unrelated to the facts. One way of learning the first few digits of the decimal for π is to memorize a sentence (or several sentences) and count the letters in each word of the sentence. For example,

"See, I know a digit,"

will give the first 5 digits of π: "See" has 3 letters, "I" has 1 letter, "know" has 4 letters, "a" has 1 letter, and "digit" has 5 letters. So the first five digits are 3.1415.

Verify that the following mnemonic devices work.

(a) "May I have a large container of coffee?"

(b) "See, I have a rhyme assisting my feeble brain, its tasks ofttimes resisting."

(c) "How I want a drink, alcoholic of course, after the heavy lectures involving quantum mechanics."

71. In the second season of the original *Star Trek* series, the episode "Wolf in the Fold" told the story of an alien entity that had taken over the computer of the starship *Enterprise*. To drive the entity out of the computer, Mr. Spock gave the alien the compulsory directive to compute π to the last digit. Explain why this strategy proved successful.

72. *Northern Exposure* ran between 1990 and 1995 on the CBS network. In the episode "Nothing's Perfect," the local disc jockey Chris Stevens meets and develops a relationship with a mathematician after accidentally running over her dog. Her area of research is computation of the decimal digits of pi. She mentions that a string of eight 8s appears in the decimal relatively early in the expansion. Use an Internet search to determine the position at which this string appears.

73. Use a calculator to find the decimal approximations for

$$\phi = \frac{1 + \sqrt{5}}{2} \quad \text{and its \textbf{conjugate,}} \quad \frac{1 - \sqrt{5}}{2}.$$

Comment on the similarities and differences in the two decimals.

74. In some literature, the Golden Ratio is defined to be the reciprocal of

$$\frac{1 + \sqrt{5}}{2}, \quad \text{which is} \quad \frac{2}{1 + \sqrt{5}}.$$

Use a calculator to find a decimal approximation for $\frac{2}{1 + \sqrt{5}}$, and compare it to φ as defined in this text. What do you observe?

75. Near the end of the 2008 movie *Harold & Kumar Escape from Guantanamo Bay*, Kumar (Kal Penn), recites a poem dealing with the square root of 3, written by the late David Feinberg. The text of the poem can be found on the Internet by searching

"David Feinberg Square Root of 3."

There are references to irrational numbers, integers, an approximation for the square root of 3, and the product rule for square root radicals. Why would Kumar prefer the 3 to be a 9?

76. See **Exercise 75.** What is the decimal approximation for $\sqrt{3}$ (to 4 decimal places) given in Feinberg's poem?

77. An approximation for e is

$$2.718281828.$$

A student noticed that there seems to be a repetition of four digits in this number (1, 8, 2, 8) and concluded that e is rational, because repeating decimals represent rational numbers. Was the student correct? Why or why not?

78. Use a calculator with an exponential key to find values for the following:

$$(1.1)^{10}, \quad (1.01)^{100}, \quad (1.001)^{1000},$$

$$(1.0001)^{10,000}, \quad \text{and} \quad (1.00001)^{100,000}.$$

Compare your results to the approximation given for e in this section. What do you find?

Roots Other Than Square Roots *The concept of square (second) root can be extended to* **cube (third) root, fourth root,** *and so on. For example,*

$$\sqrt[3]{8} = 2 \quad because \quad 2^3 = 8,$$

$$\sqrt[3]{1000} = 10 \quad because \quad 10^3 = 1000,$$

$$\sqrt[4]{81} = 3 \quad because \quad 3^4 = 81, \quad and\ so\ on.$$

If $n \geq 2$ and a is a nonnegative number, then $\sqrt[n]{a}$ represents the nonnegative number whose nth power is a.

Find each root.

79. $\sqrt[3]{64}$ **80.** $\sqrt[3]{125}$

81. $\sqrt[3]{343}$ **82.** $\sqrt[3]{729}$

83. $\sqrt[3]{216}$ **84.** $\sqrt[3]{512}$

85. $\sqrt[4]{1}$ **86.** $\sqrt[4]{16}$

87. $\sqrt[4]{256}$ **88.** $\sqrt[4]{625}$

89. $\sqrt[4]{4096}$ **90.** $\sqrt[4]{2401}$

Use a calculator to approximate each root. (Hint: To find the fourth root, find the square root of the square root.)

91. $\sqrt[3]{43}$ **92.** $\sqrt[3]{87}$

93. $\sqrt[3]{198}$ **94.** $\sqrt[4]{2107}$

95. $\sqrt[4]{10,265.2}$ **96.** $\sqrt[4]{863.5}$

97. $\sqrt[4]{968.1}$ **98.** $\sqrt[4]{12,966.4}$

6.5   APPLICATIONS OF DECIMALS AND PERCENTS

OBJECTIVES

1 Perform operations of arithmetic with decimal numbers.

2 Round whole numbers and decimals to a given place value.

3 Perform computations using percent.

4 Convert among forms of fractions, decimals, and percents.

5 Find percent increase and percent decrease.

6 Apply formulas involving fractions and decimals from the allied health industry.

Operations with Decimals

Because calculators have, for the most part, replaced paper-and-pencil methods for operations with decimals and percent, we will only briefly mention these latter methods. *We strongly suggest that the work in this section be done with a calculator at hand.*

ADDITION AND SUBTRACTION OF DECIMALS

To add or subtract decimal numbers, line up the decimal points in a column and perform the operation.

EXAMPLE 1   Adding and Subtracting Decimal Numbers

Find each of the following.

(a) $0.46 + 3.9 + 12.58$ **(b)** $12.1 - 8.723$

Solution

(a)   0.46   Line up decimal points.
       3.90   Attach a zero as a placeholder.
    +12.58
      ‾‾‾‾‾
     16.94   ← Sum

(b)   12.100   Attach zeros.
    −8.723
    ‾‾‾‾‾‾
     3.377   ← Difference

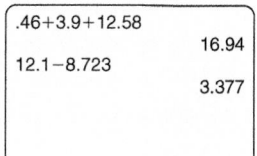

This screen supports the results in
Example 1.

Recall that when two numbers are multiplied, the numbers are **factors** and the answer is the **product.** When two numbers are divided, the number being divided is the **dividend,** the number doing the dividing is the **divisor,** and the answer is the **quotient.**

MULTIPLICATION AND DIVISION OF DECIMALS

Multiplication To multiply decimals, multiply in the same manner as integers are multiplied. The number of decimal places to the right of the decimal point in the product is the *sum* of the numbers of places to the right of the decimal points in the factors.

Division To divide decimals, move the decimal point to the right the same number of places in the divisor and the dividend so as to obtain a whole number in the divisor. Divide in the same manner as integers are divided. The number of decimal places to the right of the decimal point in the quotient is the same as the number of places to the right of the decimal in the dividend.

EXAMPLE 2 Multiplying and Dividing Decimal Numbers

Find each of the following.

(a) 4.613×2.52 **(b)** $65.175 \div 8.25$

Solution

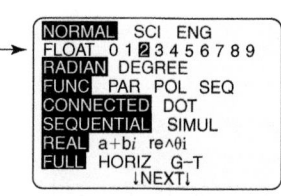

Here the calculator is set to round the answer to two decimal places.

(a)

$$
\begin{array}{r}
4.613 \quad \leftarrow 3 \text{ decimal places} \\
\times \quad 2.52 \quad \leftarrow 2 \text{ decimal places} \\
\hline
9226 \\
23065 \\
9226 \\
\hline
11.62476 \quad \leftarrow 3 + 2 = 5 \text{ decimal places}
\end{array}
$$

(b)

$$8.25\overline{)65.175} \rightarrow$$

$$
\begin{array}{r}
7.9 \\
825\overline{)6517.5} \\
5775 \\
\hline
7425 \\
7425 \\
\hline
0
\end{array}
$$

Bring the decimal point straight up in the answer.

Rounding Methods

To round, or approximate, a whole number or a decimal number to a given place value, use the following procedure. (You may wish to refer to the diagram in **Section 6.3** that describes place values determined by powers of 10.)

RULES FOR ROUNDING

Whole Numbers

Step 1 Locate the **place** to which the whole number is being rounded.

Step 2 Look at the next **digit to the right** of the place to which the number is being rounded.

Step 3A If the digit to the right is **less than 5,** replace it and all digits following it with zeros. Do not change the digit in the place to which the number is being rounded.

Step 3B If the digit to the right is **5 or greater,** replace it and all digits following it with zeros, but also add 1 to the digit in the place to which the number is being rounded. (If adding 1 to a 9, replace the 9 with 0 and add 1 to the next digit to the left. If that next digit is also 9, repeat this procedure; and so on, to the left.)

"**Technology** pervades the world outside school. There is no question that students will be expected to use calculators in other settings; this technology is now part of our culture . . . students no longer have the same need to perform these [paper-and-pencil] procedures with large numbers of lengthy expressions that they might have had in the past without ready access to technology."

From *Computation, Calculators, and Common Sense (A Position Paper of the National Council of Teachers of Mathematics).*

> **RULES FOR ROUNDING**
>
> **Decimal Numbers**
>
> *Steps 1 and 2 are the same as for whole numbers.*
>
> *Step 3A* If the digit to the right is **less than 5,** drop all digits to the right of the place to which the number is being rounded. Do not change the digit in the place to which it is being rounded.
>
> *Step 3B* If the digit to the right is **5 or greater,** drop it and all digits following it, but also add 1 to the digit in the place to which the number is being rounded. (When adding 1 to a 9, use the same procedure as for whole numbers.)
>
> *Note:* Some disciplines have guidelines specifying that in certain cases, a *downward* roundoff is made. We will not investigate these.

EXAMPLE 3 Rounding Numbers

Round to the place values indicated.

(a) 0.9175 to the nearest tenth, hundredth, and thousandth

(b) 1358 to the nearest thousand, hundred, and ten

Solution

(a) Round 0.9175 as follows: 0.9 to the nearest tenth,
0.92 to the nearest hundredth,
0.918 to the nearest thousandth.

(b) Round 1358 as follows: 1000 to the nearest thousand,
1400 to the nearest hundred,
1360 to the nearest ten. ∎

0.9175	
	0.92

The calculator rounds 0.9175 to the nearest hundredth.

0.9175	
	0.918

The calculator rounds 0.9175 *up* to 0.918.

Percent

The word **percent** means **"per hundred."** The symbol % represents "percent."

> **PERCENT**
>
> $$1\% = \frac{1}{100} = 0.01$$

EXAMPLE 4 Converting Percents to Decimals

Convert each percent to a decimal.

(a) 98%   **(b)** 3.4%   **(c)** 0.2%   **(d)** 150%

Solution

(a) $98\% = 98(1\%) = 98(0.01) = 0.98$

(b) $3.4\% = 3.4(1\%) = 3.4(0.01) = 0.034$

(c) $0.2\% = 0.2(1\%) = 0.2(0.01) = 0.002$

(d) $150\% = 150(1\%) = 150(0.01) = 1.5$ ∎

EXAMPLE 5 Converting Decimals to Percents

Convert each decimal to a percent.

(a) 0.13   **(b)** 0.532   **(c)** 2.3   **(d)** 0.07

Solution

Reverse the procedure used in **Example 4.**

(a) $0.13 = 13(0.01) = 13(1\%) = 13\%$

(b) $0.532 = 53.2(0.01) = 53.2(1\%) = 53.2\%$

(c) $2.3 = 230(0.01) = 230(1\%) = 230\%$

(d) $0.07 = 7(0.01) = 7(1\%) = 7\%$ ∎

Examples 4 and 5 suggest the following shortcut methods for converting.

CONVERTING BETWEEN DECIMALS AND PERCENTS

To convert a percent to a decimal, drop the percent symbol (%) and move the decimal point two places to the left, inserting zeros as placeholders if necessary.

To convert a decimal to a percent, move the decimal point two places to the right, inserting zeros as placeholders if necessary, and attach the percent symbol (%).

EXAMPLE 6 Converting Fractions to Percents

Convert each fraction to a percent.

(a) $\dfrac{3}{5}$ **(b)** $\dfrac{14}{25}$ **(c)** $2\dfrac{7}{10}$

Solution

(a) First write $\frac{3}{5}$ as a decimal. Dividing 3 by 5 gives $\frac{3}{5} = 0.6 = 60\%$.

(b) $\dfrac{14}{25} = \dfrac{14 \cdot 4}{25 \cdot 4} = \dfrac{56}{100} = 0.56 = 56\%$

(c) $2\dfrac{7}{10} = 2.7 = 270\%$ ∎

CONVERTING A FRACTION TO A PERCENT

To convert a fraction to a percent, convert the fraction to a decimal, and then convert the decimal to a percent.

The percent symbol, %, probably evolved from a symbol introduced in an Italian manuscript of 1425. Instead of "per 100," "P 100," or "P cento," which were common at that time, the author used "P$\overset{R}{}$." By about 1650 the $\overset{R}{}$ had become $\frac{0}{0}$, so "per $\frac{0}{0}$" was often used. Finally the "per" was dropped, leaving $\frac{0}{0}$ or %.

(*Source: Historical Topics for the Mathematics Classroom,* the Thirty-first Yearbook of the National Council of Teachers of Mathematics, 1969.)

In the following examples involving percents, three methods are shown. They illustrate some basic ideas of solving equations. The second method in each case involves using cross-products. The third method involves the percent key of a basic calculator. (Keystrokes may vary among models.)

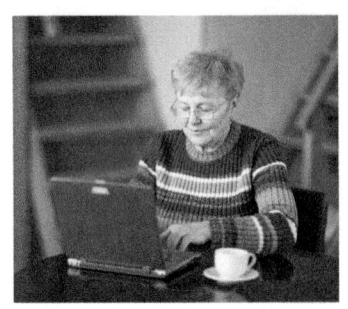

EXAMPLE 7 Finding a Percent of a Number

A publisher requires that an author reduce the page count in her next edition by 18%. The current edition has 250 pages. How many pages must the author cut from her book?

Solution

This problem can be reworded as follows: Find 18% of 250.

Method 1   The key word "of" translates as "times."

$$18\%(250) = 0.18(250) = 45$$

Method 2   Think "18 is to 100 as what (x) is to 250?" This translates as follows.

$$\frac{18}{100} = \frac{x}{250}$$

$$100x = 18 \cdot 250 \qquad \frac{a}{b} = \frac{c}{d} \text{ leads to } ad = bc.$$

$$x = \frac{18 \cdot 250}{100} \qquad \text{Divide by 100.}$$

$$x = 45 \qquad \text{Simplify.}$$

Method 3   Use the percent key on a calculator with the following keystrokes.

$\boxed{2}\ \boxed{5}\ \boxed{0}\ \boxed{\times}\ \boxed{1}\ \boxed{8}\ \boxed{\%}$ 　　　**45**　⎯ Final display

Thus, 18% of 250 is 45. The author must reduce her page count by 45 pages. ■

EXAMPLE 8 Finding What Percent One Number Is of Another

A kindergarten teacher has submitted 6 of the required 50 class preparations to the principal of her school. What percent of her requirement has she completed?

Solution

This problem can be reworded as follows: What percent of 50 is 6?

Method 1   Let the phrase "what percent" be represented by $x \cdot 1\%$ or $0.01x$. Again the word "of" translates as "times," while "is" translates as "equals."

$$0.01x \cdot 50 = 6$$

$$0.50x = 6 \qquad \text{Multiply on the left side.}$$

$$50x = 600 \qquad \text{Multiply by 100 to clear decimals.}$$

$$x = 12 \qquad \text{Divide by 50.}$$

Method 2   Think "What (x) is to 100 as 6 is to 50?"

$$\frac{x}{100} = \frac{6}{50}$$

$$50x = 600 \qquad \text{Cross-products}$$

$$x = 12 \qquad \text{Divide by 50.}$$

Method 3   Use the following keystrokes on a calculator.

$\boxed{6}\ \boxed{\div}\ \boxed{5}\ \boxed{0}\ \boxed{\%}$ 　　　**12**　⎯ Final display

Thus, 6 is 12% of 50. She has completed 12% of her requirement. ■

WHEN Will I Ever USE This ?

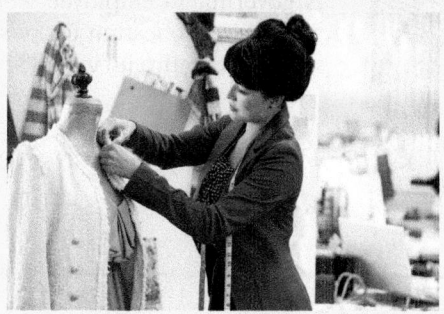

Cynthia (not her real name) had graduated in fashion merchandising and worked for eight years in an upscale women's clothing store in New Orleans. She decided to leave her position to go back to school with the goal of becoming a veterinarian.

Her curriculum required a course in college algebra, and Cynthia finished with the highest average in her class. Along the way she realized something that would have saved her a lot of time in her previous job. One day her instructor (one of the authors) made an offhand comment about percent increase. He said something like this:

If you want to mark up an item by a given percent, such as 15%, all you need to do is multiply the original price by 1.15. That's your final amount.

After class, she approached him and admitted that when she marked up items for retail sale, as her first step she would find the amount of markup on her calculator, and then in a separate step add it to the wholesale cost of the item.

For example, if the cost was $25.80, she would calculate **15% of $25.80** on her calculator in the first step, to obtain **$3.87**. Then in her second step, she would add

$$\textbf{\$3.87} + \$25.80 \quad \text{to obtain} \quad \$29.67. \leftarrow \text{Selling price}$$

She only now realized that the selling price could be obtained in a single step by multiplying

$$\$25.80 \cdot 1.15 \quad \text{to obtain} \quad \$29.67. \leftarrow \text{Selling price}$$

She realized that she could have saved time had she known this procedure.

The reason that this method works can be explained by the identity property of multiplication and the distributive property. The explanation below uses 15%, but any percent could be used with the same result.

Suppose that C represents the wholesale cost of an item. Then $0.15C$ represents 15% of C, the amount of the markup. The selling price S is found by adding wholesale cost to the amount of markup.

$$S = C + 0.15C \qquad \text{Selling price = wholesale cost + markup}$$
$$S = 1C + 0.15C \qquad \text{Identity property of multiplication}$$
$$S = (1 + 0.15)C \qquad \text{Distributive property}$$
$$S = 1.15C \qquad 1 + 0.15 = 1.15$$

A similar situation holds if a discount is to be applied. For example, to mark an item down 25%, just subtract from 100% to get 75%, and then multiply the original amount by 0.75. The result is the discounted price.

Cynthia went on to get her doctor's degree in veterinary medicine and open her own practice in the New Orleans area.

EXAMPLE 9 Finding a Number That Is a Given Percent of a Given Number

A government employee working for the county judicial system chooses 5% of a jury pool to question for possible service. This amounts to 38 people. What is the size of the entire jury pool?

Solution

This problem can be reworded as follows: 38 is 5% of what number?

Method 1 $38 = 0.05x$ Let x represent the number.

$$x = \frac{38}{0.05}$$ Divide by 0.05.

$$x = 760$$ Simplify.

Method 2   Think "38 is to what number (x) as 5 is to 100?"

$$\frac{38}{x} = \frac{5}{100}$$

$$5x = 3800$$ Cross-products

$$x = 760$$ Divide by 5.

Method 3   Use the following keystrokes on a calculator.

[3] [8] [÷] [5] [%]   **760**   Final display

Each method shows us that 38 is 5% of 760. There are 760 in the jury pool.   ∎

   Consumers often encounter figures in the media that involve **percent change,** which includes **percent increase** and **percent decrease.** The following guidelines are helpful in understanding these concepts.

FINDING PERCENT INCREASE OR DECREASE

1. To find the **percent increase from a to b,** where $b > a$, subtract a from b, and divide this result by a. Convert to a percent.

   Example: The percent increase from 4 to 7 is $\frac{7-4}{4} = \frac{3}{4} = 75\%$.

2. To find the **percent decrease from a to b,** where $b < a$, subtract b from a, and divide this result by a. Convert to a percent.

   Example: The percent decrease from 8 to 6 is $\frac{8-6}{8} = \frac{2}{8} = \frac{1}{4} = 25\%$.

EXAMPLE 10 Solving Problems about Percent Change

Solve each problem involving percent change.

(a) An electronics store marked up a laptop computer from the store's cost of $1200 to a selling price of $1464. What was the percent markup?

(b) The enrollment in a community college declined from 12,750 during one school year to 11,350 the following year. Find the percent decrease to the nearest tenth of a percent.

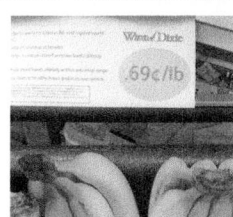

Solution

(a) "Markup" is a name for an increase. Let x = the percent increase (as a decimal).

$$\text{percent increase} = \frac{\text{amount of increase}}{\text{original amount}}$$

Subtract to find the amount of increase.

$$x = \frac{1464 - 1200}{1200} \qquad \text{Substitute the given values.}$$

Use the original cost.

$$x = \frac{264}{1200}$$

$$x = 0.22 \qquad \text{Use a calculator.}$$

The computer was marked up 22%.

(b) Let x = the percent decrease (as a decimal).

$$\text{percent decrease} = \frac{\text{amount of decrease}}{\text{original amount}}$$

Subtract to find the amount of decrease.

$$x = \frac{12{,}750 - 11{,}350}{12{,}750} \qquad \text{Substitute the given values.}$$

Use the original enrollment.

$$x = \frac{1400}{12{,}750}$$

$$x \approx 0.110 \qquad \text{Use a calculator.}$$

The college enrollment decreased by about 11.0%. ◼

When calculating a percent increase or a percent decrease, use the original number (before the increase or decrease) as the base. A common error is to use the final number (*after* the increase or decrease) in the denominator of the fraction. Applications of decimal numbers sometimes involve formulas.

▌EXAMPLE 11   Determining a Child's Body Surface Area

If a child weighs k kilograms, then the child's body surface area S in square meters (m²) is determined by the following formula.

$$S = \frac{4k + 7}{k + 90}$$

What is the body surface area of a child who weighs 40 pounds? *(Source:* Hegstad, Lorrie N., and Wilma Hayek. *Essential Drug Dosage Calculations, 4th ed.* Prentice Hall, 2001.)

Solution

Tables and Web sites for conversion between the metric and English systems are readily available. Using www.metric-conversions.org, we find that 40 pounds is approximately 18.144 kilograms. Use this value for k in the formula.

$$S = \frac{4(\mathbf{18.144}) + 7}{\mathbf{18.144} + 90} \qquad \text{Let } k = 18.144 \text{ in the formula.}$$

$$S = 0.74 \qquad \text{Use a calculator. Round to the nearest hundredth.}$$

The body surface area is approximately 0.74 m². ◼

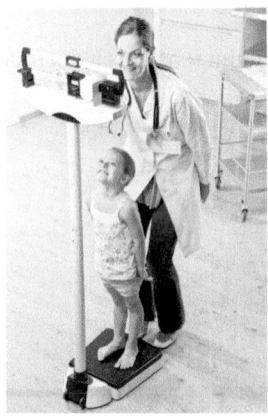

EXAMPLE 12 Determining a Child's Dose of a Drug

If D represents the usual adult dose of a drug, the corresponding child's dose C is calculated by the following formula.

$$C = \frac{\text{body surface area in square meters}}{1.7} \times D$$

Determine the appropriate dose for a child weighing 40 pounds if the usual adult dose is 50 milligrams. (*Source*: Hegstad, Lorrie N., and Wilma Hayek. *Essential Drug Dosage Calculations*, 4th ed. Prentice Hall, 2001.)

Solution

From **Example 11,** the body surface area of a child weighing 40 pounds is 0.74 m². Apply the formula for the child's dose.

$$C = \frac{\mathbf{0.74}}{1.7} \times \mathbf{50} \qquad \text{Body surface area = 0.74, } D = 50.$$

$$C = 22 \qquad \text{Use a calculator. Round to the nearest unit.}$$

The child's dose is 22 milligrams. ∎

6.5 EXERCISES

Concepts of Percent   *Decide whether each statement is* true *or* false.

1. 300% of 12 is 36.

2. 25% of a quantity is the same as $\frac{1}{4}$ of that quantity.

3. To find 50% of a quantity, we may simply divide the quantity by 2.

4. A soccer team that has won 12 games and lost 8 games has a winning percentage of 60%.

5. If 70% is the lowest passing grade on a quiz that has 50 items of equal value, then answering at least 35 items correctly will assure you of a passing grade.

6. 30 is more than 40% of 120.

7. .99¢ = 99 cents

8. If an item usually costs $70.00 and it is discounted 10%, then the discount price is $7.00.

Calculate each of the following using either a calculator or paper-and-pencil methods, as directed by your instructor.

9. 8.53 + 2.785

10. 9.358 + 7.2137

11. 8.74 − 12.955

12. 2.41 − 3.997

13. 25.7 × 0.032

14. 45.1 × 8.344

15. 1019.825 ÷ 21.47

16. −262.563 ÷ 125.03

17. $\dfrac{118.5}{1.45 + 2.3}$

18. 2.45(1.2 + 3.4 − 5.6)

Personal Finance   *Solve each problem.*

19. Andrew has $48.35 in his checking account. He uses his debit card to make purchases of $35.99 and $20.00, which overdraws his account. His bank charges his account an overdraft fee of $28.50. He then deposits his paycheck for $66.27 from his part-time job at Arby's. What is the balance in his account?

20. Kayla has $37.60 in her checking account. She uses her debit card to make purchases of $25.99 and $19.34, which overdraws her account. Her bank charges her account an overdraft fee of $25.00. She then deposits her paycheck for $58.66 from her part-time job at Subway. What is the balance in her account?

21. Ahmad owes $382.45 on his Visa account. He returns two items costing $25.10 and $34.50 for credit. Then he makes purchases of $45.00 and $98.17.

(a) How much should his payment be if he wants to pay off the balance on the account?

(b) Instead of paying off the balance, he makes a payment of $300 and then incurs a finance charge of $24.66. What is the balance on his account?

22. Sabrina owes $237.59 on her MasterCard account. She returns one item costing $47.25 for credit and then makes two purchases of $12.39 and $20.00.

(a) How much should her payment be if she wants to pay off the balance on the account?

(b) Instead of paying off the balance, she makes a payment of $75.00 and incurs a finance charge of $32.06. What is the balance on her account?

23. *Bank Account Balance* In August, Kimberly began with a bank account balance of $904.89. Her withdrawals and deposits for August are given below:

Withdrawals	Deposits
$35.84	$85.00
$26.14	$120.76
$3.12	$205.00
$21.46	

Assuming no other transactions, what was her account balance at the end of August?

24. *Bank Account Balance* In September, David began with a bank account balance of $904.89. His withdrawals and deposits for September are given below:

Withdrawals	Deposits
$41.29	$80.59
$13.66	$276.13
$84.40	$550.00
$93.00	

Assuming no other transactions, what was his account balance at the end of September?

Rounding *Round each number to the place value indicated. For example, in part (a) of Exercise 25, round 54,793 to the nearest ten thousand. (Hint: Always round from the original number.)*

25. 54,793

(a) ten thousand (b) thousand

(c) hundred (d) ten

26. 453,258

(a) hundred thousand (b) thousand

(c) hundred (d) ten

27. 0.892451

(a) hundred-thousandth

(b) ten-thousandth

(c) thousandth

(d) hundredth

(e) tenth

(f) one or unit

28. 22.483956

(a) hundred-thousandth

(b) ten-thousandth

(c) thousandth

(d) hundredth

(e) tenth

(f) ten

Use the concept of percent in Exercises 29–32.

29. Match the fractions in Group II with their equivalent percents in Group I.

I		II	
(a) 25%	(b) 10%	A. $\frac{1}{3}$	B. $\frac{1}{50}$
(c) 2%	(d) 20%	C. $\frac{3}{4}$	D. $\frac{1}{10}$
(e) 75%	(f) $33\frac{1}{3}\%$	E. $\frac{1}{4}$	F. $\frac{1}{5}$

30. Fill in each blank with the correct numerical response.

(a) 5% means _____ in every 100.

(b) 25% means 6 in every _____.

(c) 200% means _____ for every 4.

(d) 0.5% means _____ in every 100.

(e) _____ % means 12 for every 2.

31. The figures in **Exercise 23** of **Section 6.3** are reproduced here. Express the fractional parts represented by the shaded areas as percents.

(a)

(b)

(c)

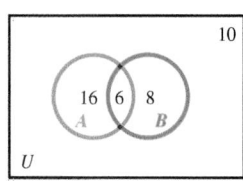

(d)

32. The Venn diagram shows the numbers of elements in the four regions formed.

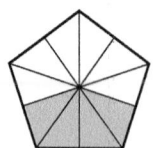

(a) What percent of the elements in the universe are in $A \cap B$?

(b) What percent of the elements in the universe are in A but not in B?

(c) What percent of the elements in $A \cup B$ are in $A \cap B$?

(d) What percent of the elements in the universe are in neither A nor B?

Convert each decimal to a percent.

33. 0.42   **34.** 0.87   **35.** 0.365

36. 0.792   **37.** 0.008   **38.** 0.0093

39. 2.1   **40.** 8.9

Convert each percent to a decimal.

41. 96%   **42.** 23%   **43.** 5.46%

44. 2.99%   **45.** 0.3%   **46.** 0.6%

47. 400%   **48.** 260%   **49.** $\frac{1}{2}$%

50. $\frac{2}{5}$%   **51.** $3\frac{1}{2}$%   **52.** $8\frac{3}{4}$%

Convert each fraction to a percent.

53. $\frac{1}{5}$ **54.** $\frac{2}{5}$ **55.** $\frac{1}{100}$ **56.** $\frac{1}{50}$

57. $\frac{3}{8}$ **58.** $\frac{5}{6}$ **59.** $\frac{3}{2}$ **60.** $\frac{7}{4}$

61. Explain the difference between $\frac{1}{2}$ of a quantity and $\frac{1}{2}$% of the quantity.

62. Explain the difference between 9% and .9%.

Work each problem involving percent.

63. What is 26% of 480?

64. What is 38% of 12?

65. What is 10.5% of 28?

66. What is 48.6% of 19?

67. What percent of 30 is 45?

68. What percent of 48 is 20?

69. 25% of what number is 150?

70. 12% of what number is 3600?

71. 0.392 is what percent of 28?

72. 78.84 is what percent of 292?

Solve each problem involving percent increase or decrease.

73. *Percent Increase* After one year on the job, Grady got a raise from $10.50 per hour to $11.34 per hour. What was the percent increase in his hourly wage?

74. *Percent Discount* Clayton bought a ticket to a rock concert at a discount. The regular price of the ticket was $70.00, but he paid only $59.50. What was the percent discount?

75. *Percent Decrease* Between 2000 and 2012, the estimated population of Toledo, Ohio, declined from 313,619 to 284,012. What was the percent decrease to the nearest tenth? (*Source:* U.S. Census Bureau.)

76. *Percent Increase* Between 2000 and 2012, the estimated population of Oklahoma City, Oklahoma, grew from 506,132 to 599,199. What was the percent increase to the nearest tenth? (*Source:* U.S. Census Bureau.)

77. *Percent Discount* The DVD of the Original Broadway production of the musical *Memphis* was available at www.amazon.com for $16.22. The list price of this DVD was $17.98. To the nearest tenth, what was the percent discount? (*Source:* www.amazon.com)

78. *Percent Discount* The Blu-ray of the movie *Django Unchained* had a list price of $39.99 and was for sale at www.amazon.com at $14.99. To the nearest tenth, what was the percent discount? (*Source:* www.amazon.com)

79. Value of 1916-D Mercury Dime The 1916 Mercury dime minted in Denver is quite rare. In 1979 its value in Extremely Fine condition was $625. The 2014 value had increased to $6200. What was the percent increase in the value of this coin from 1979 to 2014? (*Sources: A Guide Book of United States Coins; Coin World Coin Values.*)

80. Value of 1903-O Morgan Dollar In 1963, the value of a 1903 Morgan dollar minted in New Orleans in typical Uncirculated condition was $1500. Due to a discovery of a large hoard of these dollars late that year, the value plummeted. Its value in 2014 was $650. What was the percent decrease in its value from 1963 to 2014? (*Sources: A Guide Book of United States Coins; Coin World Coin Values.*)

Gasoline Prices *The line graph shows the average price, adjusted for inflation, that Americans paid for a gallon of gasoline for selected years between 1958 and 2008. Use this information in Exercises 81 and 82.*

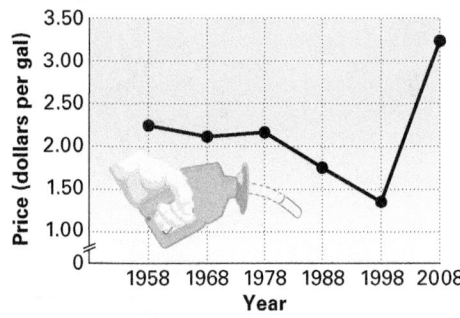

Average Gasoline Prices

Source: www.inflationdata.com

81. By what percent did prices increase from 1998 to 2008?

82. By what percent did prices decrease from 1978 to 1988?

Business Earnings Report *An article in the March 1, 2014, business section of* The Gazette *covered various facets of the earnings report of a major corporation. Answer each of the following questions about a particular phase of the report. Round to the nearest tenth if applicable.*

83. In 2013 profit fell from $1.56 billion to $1.23 billion. What was the percent decrease in profit?

84. Sales rose 2.3% to $8.7 billion. What were the sales prior to this rise?

85. Profit in one division dropped 24% to $680 million. What was the profit prior to this drop?

86. Shares of the company closed on one recent day at $17.98 per share, down $1.19. What percent decrease did this represent?

Use mental techniques to answer the questions in Exercises 87–92. Try to avoid using paper and pencil or a calculator.

87. Allowance Increase Carly's allowance was raised from $4.00 per week to $5.00 per week. What was the percent of the increase?

 A. 25%   **B.** 20%   **C.** 50%   **D.** 30%

88. Boat Purchase and Sale Susan bought a boat five years ago for $5000 and sold it this year for $2000. What percent of her original purchase did she lose on the sale?

 A. 40%   **B.** 50%   **C.** 20%   **D.** 60%

89. Population of Alabama A 2012 report indicated that the population of Alabama was 4,822,023, with 26.0% represented by African Americans. What is the best estimate of the African American population in Alabama? (*Source:* U.S. Census Bureau.)

 A. 500,000   **B.** 1,500,000
 C. 1,250,000   **D.** 750,000

90. Population of Hawaii A 2012 report indicated that the population of Hawaii was 1,392,313, with 19.4% of the population being of two or more races. What is the best estimate of this racial demographic population of Hawaii? (*Source:* U.S. Census Bureau.)

 A. 280,000   **B.** 300,000   **C.** 21,400   **D.** 24,000

91. Discount and Markup Suppose that an item regularly costs $100.00 and is discounted 20%. If it is then marked up 20%, is the resulting price $100.00? If not, what is it?

92. Computing a Tip Suppose that you have decided that you will always tip 20% when dining in restaurants. By what whole number should you divide the bill to find the amount of the tip?

Body Surface Area *Use the formula for determining a child's body surface area*

$$S = \frac{4k + 7}{k + 90}$$

in **Example 11** *to work Exercises 93–96. Round to the nearest hundredth.*

93. Find the body surface area *S* in square meters of a child who weighs 20 kilograms.

94. Find the body surface area *S* in square meters of a child who weighs 26 kilograms.

95. Find the body surface area *S* in square meters of a child who weighs 20 pounds. (Use *k* = 9.07.)

96. Find the body surface area *S* in square meters of a child who weighs 26 pounds. (Use *k* = 11.79.)

Child's Medication Dosage Use the formula for determining a child's dose of a drug

$$C = \frac{\text{body surface area in square meters}}{1.7} \times D$$

in *Example 12* to work Exercises 97–100. Round to the nearest unit.

97. If the usual adult dose D of a drug is 250 mg, what is the child's dose for a child weighing 20 kilograms? (*Hint:* Use the result of **Exercise 93.**)

98. If the usual adult dose D of a drug is 250 mg, what is the child's dose for a child weighing 26 kilograms? (*Hint:* Use the result of **Exercise 94.**)

99. If the usual adult dose D of a drug is 500 mg, what is the child's dose for a child weighing 20 pounds? (*Hint:* Use the result of **Exercise 95.**)

100. If the usual adult dose D of a drug is 500 mg, what is the child's dose for a child weighing 26 pounds? (*Hint:* Use the result of **Exercise 96.**)

Metabolic Units One way to measure a person's cardio fitness is to calculate how many METs, or metabolic units, he or she can reach at peak exertion. One MET is the amount of energy used when sitting quietly. To calculate ideal METs, we can use one of the following formulas.

$$\text{MET} = 14.7 - \text{age} \cdot 0.13$$

$$\text{MET} = 14.7 - \text{age} \cdot 0.11$$

(*Source: New England Journal of Medicine.*)

101. A 40-year-old woman wishes to find her ideal MET.

  (a) Write the expression using her age.

  (b) Calculate her ideal MET.

  (c) Researchers recommend that people reach about 85% of their MET when exercising. Calculate 85% of the ideal MET from part (b). Then refer to the following table. What activity can the woman do that is approximately this value?

Activity	METs	Activity	METs
Golf (with cart)	2.5	Skiing (water or downhill)	6.8
Walking (3 mph)	3.3	Swimming	7.0
Mowing lawn (power mower)	4.5	Walking (5 mph)	8.0
Ballroom or square dancing	5.5	Jogging	10.2

Source: Harvard School of Public Health.

102. Repeat **Exercise 101** for a 55-year-old man.

Exercises 103–106 are based on formulas found in Auto Math Handbook: Mathematical Calculations, Theory, and Formulas for Automotive Enthusiasts, *by John Lawlor (1991, HP Books).*

103. *Blood Alcohol Concentration* The blood alcohol concentration (BAC) of a person who has been drinking is given by the formula

$$\text{BAC} = \frac{(\text{ounces} \times \text{percent alcohol} \times 0.075)}{\text{body weight in lb}}$$
$$- (\text{hours of drinking} \times 0.015).$$

Suppose a policeman stops a 190-pound man who, in two hours, has ingested four 12-ounce beers, each having a 3.2% alcohol content. The formula would then read

$$\text{BAC} = \frac{[(4 \times 12) \times 3.2 \times 0.075]}{190} - (2 \times 0.015).$$

(a) Find this BAC.

(b) Find the BAC for a 135-pound woman who, in three hours, has drunk three 12-ounce beers, each having a 4.0% alcohol content.

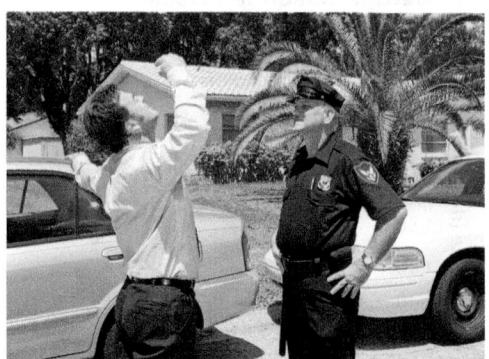

104. *Approximate Automobile Speed* The approximate speed of an automobile in miles per hour (mph) can be found in terms of the engine's revolutions per minute (rpm), the tire diameter in inches, and the overall gear ratio by the following formula.

$$\text{mph} = \frac{\text{rpm} \times \text{tire diameter}}{\text{gear ratio} \times 336}$$

If a certain automobile has an rpm of 5600, a tire diameter of 26 inches, and a gear ratio of 3.12, what is its approximate speed (mph)?

105. *Engine Horsepower* Horsepower can be found from mean effective pressure (mep) in pounds per square inch, engine displacement in cubic inches, and revolutions per minute (rpm) using the following formula.

$$\text{Horsepower} = \frac{\text{mep} \times \text{displacement} \times \text{rpm}}{792,000}$$

An engine has displacement of 302 cubic inches and indicated mep of 195 pounds per square inch at 4000 rpm. What is its approximate horsepower?

106. Torque Approximation To determine the torque at a given value of rpm, the following formula applies.

$$\text{Torque} = \frac{5252 \times \text{horsepower}}{\text{rpm}}$$

If the horsepower of a certain vehicle is 400 at 4500 rpm, what is the approximate torque?

Win-Loss Record *Exercises 107 and 108 deal with winning percentage in the standings of sports teams.*

107. At the end of the regular 2013 Major League Baseball season, the standings of the East Division of the American League were as shown. Winning percentage is commonly expressed as a decimal rounded to the nearest thousandth. To find the winning percentage of a team, divide the number of wins (W) by the total number of games played (W + L). Find the winning percentage of each team.

(a) Boston   (b) Tampa Bay

(c) New York Yankees   (d) Toronto

Team	W	L	Pct.
Boston	97	65	
Tampa Bay	92	71	
Baltimore	85	77	.525
New York Yankees	85	77	
Toronto	74	88	

Source: World Almanac and Book of Facts.

108. Repeat **Exercise 107** for the following standings for the East Division of the National League.

(a) Washington   (b) New York Mets

(c) Philadelphia   (d) Miami

Team	W	L	Pct.
Atlanta	96	66	.593
Washington	86	76	
New York Mets	74	88	
Philadelphia	73	89	
Miami	62	100	

Source: World Almanac and Book of Facts.

Tipping Procedure *It is customary in our society to "tip" the wait staff when dining in restaurants. One common rate for tipping is 15%. A quick way of figuring a tip that will give a close approximation of 15% follows.*

Step 1 *Round off the bill to the nearest dollar.*

Step 2 *Find 10% of this amount by moving the decimal point one place to the left.*

Step 3 *Take half of the amount obtained in Step 2 and add it to the result of Step 2.*

These steps will give approximately 15% of the bill. The amount obtained in Step 3 is 5%, and

$$10\% + 5\% = 15\%.$$

Use the method above to find an approximation of 15% for each restaurant bill.

109. $29.57   **110.** $38.32

111. $5.15   **112.** $7.89

For Excellent Service *Suppose that you get extremely good service and decide to tip 20%. You can use the first two steps listed earlier and then, in Step 3, double the amount you obtained in Step 2. Use this method to find an approximation of 20% for each restaurant bill.*

113. $59.96   **114.** $40.24

115. $180.43   **116.** $199.86

Postage Stamp Pricing *Refer to the margin note on decimal point abuse. At one time, the United States Postal Service sold rolls of 33-cent stamps that featured fruit berries. One such stamp is suggested on the left. On the right is a photo of the pricing information found on the cellophane wrapper of such a roll.*

0 775700 0

100 STAMPS PSA
.33¢ ea. TOTAL $33.00
FRUIT BERRIES
ITEM 7757
BCA

117. Look at the second line of the pricing information. According to the price listed *per stamp*, how many stamps should you be able to purchase for one cent?

118. The total price listed is the amount the Postal Service actually charges. If you were to multiply the listed price *per stamp* by the number of stamps, what should the total price be?

Pricing of Pie and Coffee *The photos here were taken at a flea market near Natchez, Mississippi. The handwritten signs indicate that a piece of pie costs .10¢ and a cup of coffee ("ffee") costs .5¢. Assuming these are the actual prices, answer the questions in Exercises 119–122.*

119. How much will 10 pieces of pie and 10 cups of coffee cost?

120. How much will 20 pieces of pie and 10 cups of coffee cost?

121. How many pieces of pie can you get for $1.00?

122. How many cups of coffee can you get for $1.00?

123. *Producer Percent* In the 1967 movie *The Producers*, Leo Bloom (Gene Wilder) and Max Bialystock (Zero Mostel) scheme to make a fortune by overfinancing what they think will be a Broadway flop. After enumerating the percent of profits all of Max's little old ladies have been offered in the production, reality sets in. Watch the movie to see what percent of the profits was sold.

124. *Willy Wonka and Percent* There are several appearances of percent in the 1971 movie *Willy Wonka and the Chocolate Factory*. In one of them, upon preparing a mixture in his laboratory, Willy Wonka (Gene Wilder) states an impossible percent analysis as he drinks his latest concoction. Watch the movie to see what percent the ingredients total up to be.

CHAPTER 6 SUMMARY

KEY TERMS

6.1
natural numbers
whole numbers
number line
origin
negative numbers
positive numbers
signed numbers
integers
graph
rational numbers
irrational numbers
real numbers
additive inverses
   (negatives, opposites)
absolute value

6.2
sum
addends (terms)
difference
minuend
subtrahend
product
factors
quotient
dividend (numerator)
divisor (denominator)
positive change
negative change

6.3
extremes
means
cross-product test
   (for equality of fractions)
least common denominator
   (LCD)
mixed number
arithmetic mean (average)
terminating decimal
repeating decimal

6.4
irrational number
radicand
like radicals
Golden Rectangle
Golden Ratio

6.5
factors
product
dividend
divisor
quotient
percent

NEW SYMBOLS

$\{x \mid x \text{ has a certain property}\}$	set-builder notation
%	percent
¢	cents
$a = b$	a is equal to b
$a < b$	a is less than b
$a \leq b$	a is less than or equal to b

$a > b$	a is greater than b
$a \geq b$	a is greater than or equal to b
$|x|$	absolute value of x
π	irrational number $\pi \approx 3.14159$
ϕ	irrational number $\phi \approx 1.618$
e	irrational number $e \approx 2.71828$

TEST YOUR WORD POWER

See how well you have learned the vocabulary in this chapter.

1. The **absolute value** of a real number is
  A. the same as the opposite of the number in all cases.
  B. the same as the number itself in all cases.
  C. never zero.
  D. its undirected distance from zero on the number line.

2. The **sum** of two numbers is the result obtained by
  A. addition.   **B.** subtraction.
  C. multiplication.   **D.** division.

3. The **identity element for multiplication** is
  A. 0.   **B.** 1.   **C.** –1.   **D.** –*a*, for the real number *a*.

4. An example of an **irrational number** is
  A. ϕ.   **B.** *e*.
  C. π.   **D.** all of these.

5. An example of a rational number that has a **terminating decimal** representation is
  A. $\dfrac{1}{3}$.   **B.** $\dfrac{1}{7}$.   **C.** $\dfrac{1}{2}$.   **D.** $\dfrac{1}{9}$.

6. The irrational number π represents
  A. the circumference of a circle divided by its radius.
  B. the radius of a circle divided by its diameter.
  C. the diameter of a circle divided by its radius.
  D. the circumference of a circle divided by its diameter.

ANSWERS
  1. D **2.** A **3.** B **4.** D **5.** C **6.** D

QUICK REVIEW

Concepts	*Examples*

6.1 Real Numbers, Order, and Absolute Value

Sets of Numbers

Natural Numbers $\{1, 2, 3, 4, \dots\}$

Whole Numbers $\{0, 1, 2, 3, 4, \dots\}$

Integers $\{\dots, -2, -1, 0, 1, 2, \dots\}$

Rational Numbers
$\{x \mid x$ is a quotient of two integers, with denominator not equal to $0\}$

Irrational Numbers
$\{x \mid x$ is a number on the number line that is not rational$\}$

Real Numbers
$\{x \mid x$ is a number that can be represented by a point on the number line$\}$

Order in the Real Numbers
Suppose that *a* and *b* are real numbers.

$a = b$ if they are represented by the same point on the number line.

$a < b$ if the graph of *a* lies to the left of the graph of *b*.

$a > b$ if the graph of *a* lies to the right of the graph of *b*.

Additive Inverse
The additive inverse of *a* is $-a$. For all *a*,
$$a + (-a) = (-a) + a = 0.$$

Absolute Value
$$|x| = \begin{cases} x & \text{if } x \geq 0 \\ -x & \text{if } x < 0 \end{cases}$$

Examples:

10, 25, 143   *Natural numbers*

0, 8, 47   *Whole numbers*

$-22, -7, 0, 4, 9$ *Integers*

$-\dfrac{2}{3}, -0.14, 0, \dfrac{15}{8},$
$6, 0.33333 \dots, \sqrt{4}$ *Rational numbers*

$-\sqrt{22}, \sqrt{3}, \pi$ *Irrational numbers*

$-3, -\dfrac{2}{7}, 0.7, \pi, \sqrt{11}$ *Real numbers*

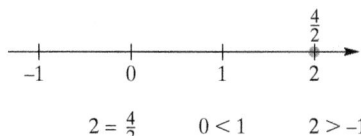

$2 = \frac{4}{2}$ $0 < 1$ $2 > -1$

$-(-5) = 5$ $-\left(-\dfrac{2}{3}\right) = \dfrac{2}{3}$

$5 + (-5) = 0$

$|-1| = 1$ $|0| = 0$ $|2| = 2$

Concepts	*Examples*

6.2 Operations, Properties, and Applications of Real Numbers

Addition

Like Signs: Add the absolute values. The sum has the same sign as the given numbers.

Unlike Signs: Find the absolute values of the numbers, and subtract the lesser absolute value from the greater. The sum has the same sign as the number with the greater absolute value.

Add.

$$9 + 4 = 13$$
$$-8 + (-5) = -13$$
$$7 + (-12) = -5$$
$$-5 + 13 = 8$$

Subtraction

For all real numbers a and b,

$$a - b = a + (-b).$$

Subtract.

$$-3 - 4 = -3 + (-4) = -7$$
$$-2 - (-6) = -2 + 6 = 4$$
$$13 - (-8) = 13 + 8 = 21$$

Multiplication and Division

Like Signs: The product or quotient of two numbers with like signs is positive.

Unlike Signs: The product or quotient of two numbers with different signs is negative.

Multiply or divide.

$$6 \cdot 5 = 30 \quad -7(-8) = 56 \quad \frac{20}{4} = 5 \quad \frac{-24}{-6} = 4$$

$$-6(5) = -30 \quad 6(-5) = -30$$

$$\frac{-18}{9} = -2 \quad \frac{49}{-7} = -7$$

Division Involving 0

$\dfrac{a}{0}$ is undefined for all a. $\dfrac{0}{a} = 0$ for all nonzero a.

$\dfrac{5}{0}$ is undefined. $\dfrac{0}{5} = 0$

Order of Operations

If parentheses or square brackets are present:

Step 1 Work separately above and below any fraction bar.

Step 2 Use the rules below within each set of parentheses or square brackets. Start with the innermost set and work outward.

If no parentheses or brackets are present:

Step 1 Apply any exponents.

Step 2 Do any multiplications or divisions in the order in which they occur, working from left to right.

Step 3 Do any additions or subtractions in the order in which they occur, working from left to right.

Simplify.

$$(-6)[2^2 - (3 + 4)] + 3$$

$= (-6)[2^2 - 7] + 3$ Work inside the innermost parentheses.

$= (-6)[4 - 7] + 3$ Work inside the brackets.

$= (-6)[-3] + 3$

$= 18 + 3$ Multiply.

$= 21$ Add.

Properties of Real Numbers

If a and b are real numbers, then

Closure Properties

$a + b$ and ab are real numbers.

$3 + 4$ and $3 \cdot 4$ are real numbers.

Commutative Properties

$$a + b = b + a$$
$$ab = ba$$

$$7 + (-1) = -1 + 7$$
$$5(-3) = (-3)5$$

Associative Properties

$$(a + b) + c = a + (b + c)$$
$$(ab)c = a(bc)$$

$$(3 + 4) + 8 = 3 + (4 + 8)$$
$$[-2(6)]4 = -2[(6)4]$$

Concepts	Examples

Identity Properties

$$a + 0 = a \qquad 0 + a = a$$
$$a \cdot 1 = a \qquad 1 \cdot a = a$$

$$-7 + 0 = -7 \quad 0 + (-7) = -7$$
$$9 \cdot 1 = 9 \qquad 1 \cdot 9 = 9$$

Inverse Properties

$$a + (-a) = 0 \qquad -a + a = 0$$
$$a \cdot \frac{1}{a} = 1 \qquad \frac{1}{a} \cdot a = 1 \quad (a \neq 0)$$

$$7 + (-7) = 0 \qquad -7 + 7 = 0$$
$$-2\left(-\frac{1}{2}\right) = 1 \quad -\frac{1}{2}(-2) = 1$$

Distributive Property

$$a(b + c) = ab + ac$$
$$(b + c)a = ba + ca$$

$$5(4 + 2) = 5(4) + 5(2)$$
$$(4 + 2)5 = 4(5) + 2(5)$$

6.3 Rational Numbers and Decimal Representation

Fundamental Property of Rational Numbers

$$\frac{a \cdot k}{b \cdot k} = \frac{a}{b} \quad (b \neq 0, k \neq 0)$$

Write $\frac{8}{12}$ in lowest terms.

$$\frac{8}{12} = \frac{2 \cdot 4}{3 \cdot 4} = \frac{2}{3}$$

Cross-Product Test for Equality of Rational Numbers

$$\frac{a}{b} = \frac{c}{d} \text{ if and only if } a \cdot d = b \cdot c \quad (b \neq 0, d \neq 0)$$

Is $\frac{25}{36} = \frac{5}{6}$ a true statement?

$$25 \cdot 6 = 150 \quad \text{and} \quad 36 \cdot 5 = 180$$

Because $150 \neq 180$, the statement is false.

Adding and Subtracting Rational Numbers

$$\frac{a}{b} + \frac{c}{d} = \frac{ad + bc}{bd} \quad \text{and} \quad \frac{a}{b} - \frac{c}{d} = \frac{ad - bc}{bd}$$

In practice, we usually find the least common denominator to add and subtract fractions.

Add or subtract.

$$\frac{2}{5} + \frac{7}{5} = \frac{2 + 7}{5} = \frac{9}{5}, \text{ or } 1\frac{4}{5}$$

$$\frac{2}{3} - \frac{1}{2} = \frac{4}{6} - \frac{3}{6} \quad \text{6 is the LCD.}$$

$$= \frac{1}{6}$$

Multiplying and Dividing Rational Numbers

$$\frac{a}{b} \cdot \frac{c}{d} = \frac{ac}{bd} \quad (b \neq 0, d \neq 0)$$

$$\frac{a}{b} \div \frac{c}{d} = \frac{a}{b} \cdot \frac{d}{c} = \frac{ad}{bc} \quad (b \neq 0, c \neq 0, d \neq 0)$$

Multiply or divide.

$$\frac{4}{3} \cdot \frac{5}{6} = \frac{20}{18} = \frac{10}{9}, \text{ or } 1\frac{1}{9}$$

$$\frac{6}{5} \div \frac{1}{4} = \frac{6}{5} \cdot \frac{4}{1} = \frac{24}{5}, \text{ or } 4\frac{4}{5}$$

Density Property of the Rational Numbers

If r and t are distinct rational numbers, with $r < t$, then there exists a rational number s such that

$$r < s < t.$$

Find the average, or mean, of $\frac{2}{3}$ and $\frac{3}{4}$.

$$\frac{2}{3} + \frac{3}{4} = \frac{8 + 9}{12} = \frac{17}{12} \quad \text{Add.}$$

$$\frac{1}{2} \cdot \frac{17}{12} = \frac{17}{24} \quad \text{Find half of the sum.}$$
$$\leftarrow \text{Average of } \tfrac{2}{3} \text{ and } \tfrac{3}{4}$$

The decimal representation of a rational number will either terminate or will repeat indefinitely in a "block" of digits.

$$\frac{2}{3} = 0.\overline{6}, \text{ or } 0.666\ldots \qquad \frac{3}{16} = 0.1875$$

Concepts	*Examples*

6.4 Irrational Numbers and Decimal Representation

Decimal Representation
The decimal for an irrational number neither terminates nor repeats.

$$\sqrt{2}, \quad \sqrt{10}, \quad 0.10110111011110\ldots$$

Approximations
Approximations for irrational numbers (for example, square roots of whole numbers that are not perfect squares) can be found with a calculator.

$$\sqrt{2} \approx 1.414213562 \qquad \sqrt{10} \approx 3.16227766$$

Product and Quotient Rules for Square Roots

$$\sqrt{a} \cdot \sqrt{b} = \sqrt{a \cdot b} \quad (a \geq 0, b \geq 0)$$

$$\frac{\sqrt{a}}{\sqrt{b}} = \sqrt{\frac{a}{b}} \quad (a \geq 0, b > 0)$$

Simplify.

$$\sqrt{54} = \sqrt{9 \cdot 6} = \sqrt{9} \cdot \sqrt{6} = 3\sqrt{6}$$

$$\frac{\sqrt{36}}{\sqrt{4}} = \sqrt{\frac{36}{4}} = \sqrt{9} = 3$$

Conditions Necessary for the Simplified Form of a Square Root Radical

1. The number under the radical (radicand) has no factor (except 1) that is a perfect square.

2. The radicand has no fractions.

3. No denominator contains a radical.

Simplify.

$$\sqrt{\frac{5}{6}} = \frac{\sqrt{5}}{\sqrt{6}} = \frac{\sqrt{5} \cdot \sqrt{6}}{\sqrt{6} \cdot \sqrt{6}} = \frac{\sqrt{30}}{6}$$

Three Important Irrational Numbers

$$\pi \approx 3.14159265358979323846264338327 9$$

$$\phi = \frac{1 + \sqrt{5}}{2} \approx 1.61803398874989484820458683436 5$$

$$e \approx 2.71828182845904523536028747135 3$$

The rational number $\frac{355}{113}$ gives an excellent approximation for the irrational number π.

The Golden Ratio ϕ appears throughout nature.

The irrational number e is important in higher mathematics.

6.5 Applications of Decimals and Percents

Addition and Subtraction of Decimals
To add or subtract decimal numbers, line up the decimal points in a column and perform the operation.

Add or subtract.

$1.2 + 36.158 + 9.26$	$93.86 - 42.9142$
$\begin{array}{r} 1.200 \\ 36.158 \\ 9.260 \\ \hline 46.618 \end{array}$	$\begin{array}{r} 93.8600 \\ -\ 42.9142 \\ \hline 50.9458 \end{array}$

Concepts	Examples

Multiplication and Division of Decimals

Multiplication To multiply decimals, multiply in the same manner as integers are multiplied. The number of decimal places to the right of the decimal point in the product is the *sum* of the numbers of places to the right of the decimal points in the factors.

Division To divide decimals, move the decimal point to the right the same number of places in the divisor and the dividend so as to obtain a whole number in the divisor. Divide in the same manner as integers are divided. The number of decimal places to the right of the decimal point in the quotient is the same as the number of places to the right of the decimal point in the dividend.

Multiply or divide.

51.6×2.3

$$\begin{array}{r} 51.6 \\ 2.3 \\ \hline 1548 \\ 1032 \\ \hline 118.68 \end{array}$$

$35.38 \div 6.1$

$$\begin{array}{r} 5.8 \\ 61\overline{)353.8} \\ 305 \\ \hline 488 \\ 488 \\ \hline 0 \end{array}$$

Rules for Rounding
See pages 307–308.

Round 745.2935 to the given place value.

hundreds: 700

ones or units: 745

tenths: 745.3

thousandths: 745.294

Percent
The word **percent** means "per hundred." The symbol % represents "percent."

$$1\% = \frac{1}{100} = 0.01$$

Converting between Decimals and Percents
To convert a percent to a decimal, drop the percent symbol and move the decimal point two places to the left, inserting zeros as placeholders if necessary.

Convert 0.8% to a decimal.

$$0.8\% = 0.008$$

To convert a decimal to a percent, move the decimal point two places to the right, inserting zeros as placeholders if necessary, and attach the percent symbol.

Convert 0.8 to a percent.

$$0.8 = 0.80 = 80\%$$

Converting a Fraction to a Percent
To convert a fraction to a percent, convert the fraction to a decimal, and then convert the decimal to a percent.

Convert $\frac{11}{4}$ to a percent.

$$\frac{11}{4} = 2\frac{3}{4} = 2.75 = 275\%$$

Finding Percent Increase or Decrease
To find the percent increase from a to b, where $b > a$, subtract a from b, and divide this result by a. Convert to a percent.

To find the percent decrease from a to b, where $b < a$, subtract b from a, and divide this result by a. Convert to a percent.

The sales of a textbook decreased from $3,500,000 in its third edition to $2,975,000 in its fourth edition. What was the percent decrease?

$$\text{Percent decrease} = \frac{\$3,500,000 - \$2,975,000}{\$3,500,000}$$

$$= \frac{\$525,000}{\$3,500,000}$$

$$= 0.15$$

The percent decrease was 15%.

CHAPTER 6	**TEST**

1. Consider $\{-4, -\sqrt{5}, -\frac{3}{2}, -0.5, 0, \sqrt{3}, 4.1, 12\}$. List the elements of the set that belong to each of the following.

   (a) natural numbers

   (b) whole numbers

   (c) integers

   (d) rational numbers

   (e) irrational numbers

   (f) real numbers

2. Match each set in (a)–(d) with the correct set-builder notation description in A–D.

   (a) $\{\ldots, -4, -3, -2, -1\}$

   (b) $\{3, 4, 5, 6, \ldots\}$

   (c) $\{1, 2, 3, 4, \ldots\}$

   (d) $\{-12, \ldots, -2, -1, 0, 1, 2, \ldots, 12\}$

   A. $\{x \mid x$ is an integer with absolute value less than or equal to 12$\}$

   B. $\{x \mid x$ is an integer greater than 2.5$\}$

   C. $\{x \mid x$ is a negative integer$\}$

   D. $\{x \mid x$ is a positive integer$\}$

3. Decide whether each statement is *true* or *false*.

   (a) The absolute value of a number must be positive.

   (b) $|-7| = -(-7)$

   (c) $\frac{2}{5}$ is an example of a real number that is not an integer.

   (d) Every real number is either positive or negative.

Perform the indicated operations. Use the order of operations as necessary.

4. $6^2 - 4(9 - 1)$

5. $\dfrac{(-8 + 3) - (5 + 10)}{7 - 9}$

6. $(-3)(-2) - [5 + (8 - 10)]$

7. $5(-6) - (3 - 8)^2 + 12$

8. **Temperature Extremes** The record high temperature in the United States was 134° Fahrenheit, recorded at Death Valley, California, in 1913. The record low was -80°F, at Prospect Creek, Alaska, in 1971. How much greater was the highest temperature than the lowest temperature? (*Source: The World Almanac and Book of Facts.*)

9. **Altitude of a Plane** The surface of the Dead Sea has altitude 1299 ft below sea level. A pilot is flying 80 ft above that surface. How much altitude must she gain to clear a 3852-ft pass by 225 ft? (*Source: The World Almanac and Book of Facts.*)

10. Match each statement in (a)–(f) with the property that justifies it in A–F.

    (a) $7 \cdot (8 \cdot 5) = (7 \cdot 8) \cdot 5$

    (b) $3x + 3y = 3(x + y)$

    (c) $8 \cdot 1 = 1 \cdot 8 = 8$

    (d) $7 + (6 + 9) = (6 + 9) + 7$

    (e) $9 + (-9) = -9 + 9 = 0$

    (f) $5 \cdot 8$ is a real number.

    A. Distributive property

    B. Identity property

    C. Closure property

    D. Commutative property

    E. Associative property

    F. Inverse property

11. **Basketball Shot Statistics** Six players on the local high school basketball team had shooting statistics as shown in the table below. Answer each question, using estimation skills as necessary.

Player	Field Goal Attempts	Field Goals Made
Ed	40	13
Jack	10	4
Chuck	20	8
Ben	6	4
Charlie	7	2
Jason	7	6

   (a) Which players made more than half of their attempts?

   (b) Which players made just less than $\frac{1}{3}$ of their attempts?

   (c) Which player made exactly $\frac{2}{3}$ of his attempts?

   (d) Which two players made the same fractional parts of their attempts? What was the fractional part, reduced to lowest terms?

   (e) Which player made the greatest fractional part of his attempts?

Perform each operation. Write your answer in lowest terms.

12. $\dfrac{3}{16} + \dfrac{1}{2}$

13. $\dfrac{9}{20} - \dfrac{3}{32}$

14. $\dfrac{3}{8} \cdot \left(-\dfrac{16}{15}\right)$

15. $\dfrac{7}{9} \div 1\dfrac{3}{4}$

16. *Foreign-born Population* Approximately 40 million people living in the United States in 2010 were born in other countries. The graph gives the fractional number for each region of birth for these people.

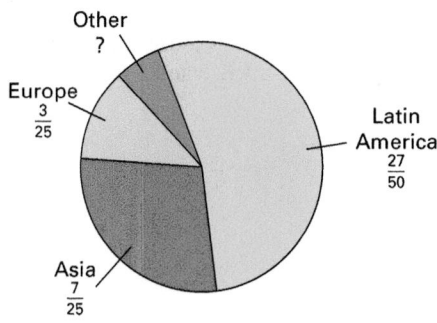

U.S. Foreign-Born Population by Region of Birth

Other ?

Europe $\dfrac{3}{25}$

Latin America $\dfrac{27}{50}$

Asia $\dfrac{7}{25}$

Source: U.S. Census Bureau.

(a) What fractional part of the U.S. foreign-born population was from a region other than the ones specified?

(b) What fractional part of the foreign-born population was from Latin America or Asia?

(c) About how many people (in millions) were born in Europe?

17. Convert each rational number into a repeating or terminating decimal. Use a calculator if your instructor so allows.

(a) $\dfrac{9}{20}$

(b) $\dfrac{5}{12}$

18. Convert each decimal into a quotient of integers, reduced to lowest terms.

(a) 0.72

(b) $0.\overline{58}$

19. Identify each number as rational or irrational.

(a) $\sqrt{10}$

(b) $\sqrt{16}$

(c) 0.01

(d) $0.\overline{01}$

(e) 0.0101101110 . . .

(f) π

For each of the following, (a) use a calculator to find a decimal approximation and (b) simplify the radical according to the guidelines in this chapter.

20. $\sqrt{150}$

21. $\dfrac{13}{\sqrt{7}}$

22. $2\sqrt{32} - 5\sqrt{128}$

23. *Rate of Return on an Investment* If an investment of P dollars grows to A dollars in two years, the annual rate of return on the investment is given by

$$r = \dfrac{\sqrt{A} - \sqrt{P}}{\sqrt{P}}.$$

What is the rate if an investment of $50,000 grows to $58,320?

24. Work each of the following using either a calculator or paper-and-pencil methods, as directed by your instructor.

(a) 4.6 + 9.21

(b) $12 - 3.725 - 8.59$

(c) 86(0.45)

(d) $236.439 \div (-9.73)$

25. Round 346.0449 to the given place values.

(a) tens

(b) hundredths

(c) thousandths

26. *Sale Price* A dress that originally sold for $100.00 is discounted 40% for a sale. Then the owner decides to offer an additional 10% off of the sale price. What is the final price of the dress?

27. Consider the figure.

(a) What percent of the total number of shapes are circles?

(b) What percent of the total number of shapes are not stars?

28. *Sales of Books* Use estimation techniques to answer the following: In 2013, Carol sold $300,000 worth of books. In 2014, she sold $900,000. Her 2014 sales were _____ of her 2013 sales.

A. 30%   **B.** $33\dfrac{1}{3}$%   **C.** 3%   **D.** 300%

29. *Creature Comforts* From a list of "everyday items" often taken for granted, adults were asked to indicate those items they wouldn't want to live without. Complete the results shown in the table if 2400 adults were surveyed.

Item	Percent That Wouldn't Want to Live Without	Number That Wouldn't Want to Live Without
Toilet paper	69%	
Zipper	42%	
Frozen food		384
Self-stick note pads		144

(Other items included tape, hairspray, pantyhose, paper clips, and Velcro.)

Source: Market Facts for Kleenex Cottonelle.

30. *Child's Drug Dosage* If D represents the usual adult dose of a drug, the corresponding child's dose C is calculated by the following formula.

$$C = \frac{\text{body surface area in square meters}}{1.7} \times D$$

Determine the appropriate dose for a child with body surface area 0.85 m^2 if the usual adult dose is 150 mg.

The Basic Concepts of Algebra

7

I've never had to use algebra in real life.

Most algebra teachers have heard something like this at one time or another. Those who have uttered it likely do use algebra but don't realize it.

Consider the little word *per*, which is interpreted "as compared to." The concept of percent, covered in Chapter 6, refers to a comparison to 100. When we shop for a new car, we are often interested in its miles-per-gallon rating, which can be symbolized mi/gal or mpg. The slash indicates division, as does the "p" in mpg. Both indicate a *ratio* of miles to gallons, also called a *rate*.

Suppose that a manufacturer says that a hybrid car has a rating of 39 mpg—that is, 39 miles compared to 1 gallon of gas.

Can this car travel 468 miles on one tank of gas from your home to your lake cabin and back?

One way to answer this question is to use a *proportion,* which is a statement that two ratios are equal. Suppose that we

let x represent the number of gallons that the tank holds.

We can now write an *equation.*

$$\frac{39 \text{ miles}}{1 \text{ gallon}} = \frac{468 \text{ miles}}{x \text{ gallons}}$$

As we will see in this chapter, we solve this equation by applying some basic rules of algebra, one being that for this statement to be true, the product 39 times x must equal the product 1 times 468.

$$\frac{39}{1} = \frac{468}{x}$$

$$39 \cdot x = 1 \cdot 468$$

$$39x = 468$$

To find the value of x, we use a property of algebra that allows us to multiply or divide each side of an equation by the same number without affecting the number or numbers that make the equation true. Here we divide each side by 39.

$$\frac{39x}{39} = \frac{468}{39}$$

$$x = 12$$

We also need to consider the size of the tank of the car we will be driving. If the tank holds 12 gallons (or more) when full, we won't need to fill up along the way if we leave with a full tank.

You might say,

"I could have done that problem a lot more easily by just dividing 468 by 39 at the beginning."

In this case, you have a good understanding of rates, or ratios. You are also probably one of those people who has a knack for computing percents. *And you just used algebra even if you did not realize it.* But not all proportion problems are as simple as this one, and general rules are necessary when the problem involves data that are too involved for you to solve "in your head." (For example, see Example 6 in Section 7.3, where a proportion is used to estimate the number of fish in a lake.)

The word *algebra* has its roots in a ninth-century work by Mohammad ibn Mūsā al-Khowārizmī titled *Hisab al-jabr w'al muqualbalah,* which translates as

"the science of transposition and cancellation."

From Latin versions of this text, **al-jabr** became the broad term covering the art of equation solving. In the opener for Chapter 8, we continue this discussion of rates.

7.1   LINEAR EQUATIONS

OBJECTIVES

1 Solve a linear equation.

2 Identify a linear equation as a conditional equation, an identity, or a contradiction.

3 Solve a literal equation or a formula for a specified variable.

4 Use a linear model in an application.

Algebra dates back to the Babylonians of 2000 B.C. The Egyptians also worked problems in algebra, but the problems were not as complex as those of the Babylonians. In about the sixth century, the Hindus developed methods for solving problems involving interest, discounts, and partnerships.

Many Hindu and Greek works on mathematics were preserved only because Moslem scholars from about 750 to 1250 made translations of them. For example, **Mohammad ibn Mūsā al-Khowārizmī** wrote books on algebra and on the Hindu numeration system (the one we use) that had tremendous influence in Western Europe. His name is remembered today in the word *algorithm*.

Solving Linear Equations

An **algebraic expression** involves only the basic operations of addition, subtraction, multiplication, division (except by 0), raising to powers, and taking roots on any collection of variables and numbers.

$$8x + 9, \quad \sqrt{y} + 4, \quad \text{and} \quad \frac{x^3 y^8}{z} \quad \text{Examples of algebraic expressions}$$

An **equation** is a statement that two algebraic expressions are equal. A *linear equation in one variable* involves only real numbers and one variable.

$$x + 1 = -2, \quad x - 3 = 5, \quad \text{and} \quad 2x + 5 = 10 \quad \text{Examples of linear equations}$$

LINEAR EQUATION IN ONE VARIABLE

An equation in the variable x is a **linear equation** if it can be written in the form

$$Ax + B = C,$$

where A, B, and C are real numbers, with $A \neq 0$.

A linear equation in one variable is also called a **first-degree equation,** because the greatest power on the variable is one.

If the variable in an equation is replaced by a real number that makes the statement true, then that number is a **solution** of the equation. For example, 8 is a solution of the equation

$$x - 3 = 5,$$

because replacing x with 8 gives a true statement. An equation is solved by finding its **solution set,** the set of all solutions. The solution set of the equation $x - 3 = 5$ is $\{8\}$.

Equivalent equations are equations with the same solution set. Equations generally are solved by starting with a given equation and producing a series of simpler equivalent equations. For example,

$$8x + 1 = 17, \quad 8x = 16, \quad \text{and} \quad x = 2 \quad \text{Equivalent equations}$$

are equivalent equations because each has the same solution set, {2}. We use the addition and multiplication properties of equality to produce equivalent equations.

ADDITION PROPERTY OF EQUALITY

For all real numbers A, B, and C, the equations

$$A = B \quad \text{and} \quad A + C = B + C$$

are equivalent. (The same number may be added to both sides of an equation without changing the solution set.)

algebrista, algebra In Spain under Moslem rule, the word **algebrista** referred to the person who restored (reset) broken bones. Signs outside barber shops read *Algebrista y Sangrador* (bonesetter and bloodletter). Such services were part of the barber's trade. The traditional red-and-white striped barber pole symbolizes blood and bandages.

MULTIPLICATION PROPERTY OF EQUALITY

For all real numbers A, B, and C, where $C \neq 0$, the equations

$$A = B \quad \text{and} \quad AC = BC$$

are equivalent. (Both sides of an equation may be multiplied by the same non-zero number without changing the solution set.)

Because subtraction and division are defined in terms of addition and multiplication, respectively, we are able to subtract the same number from both sides of the equation and divide both sides by the same nonzero number without affecting the solution set.

The following steps can be used to solve a linear equation in one variable.

SOLVING A LINEAR EQUATION IN ONE VARIABLE

Step 1 **Clear fractions.** Eliminate any fractions by multiplying both sides of the equation by a common denominator.

Step 2 **Simplify each side separately.** Use the distributive property to clear parentheses, and combine like terms as needed.

Step 3 **Isolate the variable terms on one side.** Use the addition property of equality to transform the equation so that all terms with variables are on one side and all numbers are on the other.

Step 4 **Transform so that the coefficient of the variable is 1.** Use the multiplication property of equality to obtain an equation with only the variable (with coefficient 1) on one side.

Step 5 **Check.** Substitute the solution into the original equation.

EXAMPLE 1 Using the Distributive Property to Solve a Linear Equation

Solve $2(x - 5) + 3x = x + 6$.

Solution

Step 1 Because there are no fractions in this equation, Step 1 does not apply.

Step 2 Use the distributive property to simplify and combine terms on the left.

$$2(x - 5) + 3x = x + 6$$
$$2x - 10 + 3x = x + 6 \quad \text{Distributive property}$$
$$5x - 10 = x + 6 \quad \text{Combine like terms.}$$

Step 3 Next, use the addition property of equality.

$$5x - 10 + 10 = x + 6 + 10 \quad \text{Add 10.}$$
$$5x = x + 16 \quad \text{Combine like terms.}$$
$$5x - x = x + 16 - x \quad \text{Subtract } x.$$
$$4x = 16 \quad \text{Combine like terms.}$$

The problem-solving strategy of guessing and checking, discussed in **Chapter 1,** was actually used by the early Egyptians in equation solving. This method, called the **Rule of False Position,** involved making an initial guess at the solution of an equation, and then following up with an adjustment in the likely event that the guess was incorrect. For example (using our modern notation), if the equation

$$6x + 2x = 32$$

was to be solved, an initial guess might have been $x = 3$. Substituting 3 for x gives

$$6(3) + 2(3) \overset{?}{=} 32$$
$$18 + 6 \overset{?}{=} 32$$
$$24 = 32. \quad \textbf{False}$$

The guess, 3, gives a value (24) that is smaller than the desired value (32). Since 24 is $\frac{3}{4}$ of 32, the guess, 3, is $\frac{3}{4}$ of the actual solution. The actual solution, therefore, must be 4, since 3 is $\frac{3}{4}$ of 4.

Use the methods explained in this section to verify this result.

Step 4   Use the multiplication property of equality to isolate x on the left.

$$\frac{4x}{4} = \frac{16}{4} \qquad \text{Divide by 4.}$$

$$x = 4 \qquad \text{Simplify.}$$

Step 5   *Check* by substituting 4 for x in the original equation.

$$2(x - 5) + 3x = x + 6 \qquad \text{Original equation}$$
$$2(4 - 5) + 3(4) \overset{?}{=} 4 + 6 \qquad \text{Let } x = 4.$$
$$2(-1) + 3(4) \overset{?}{=} 10 \qquad \text{Work inside the parentheses on the left, and add on the right.}$$
$$-2 + 12 \overset{?}{=} 10 \qquad \text{Multiply.}$$
$$10 = 10 \quad \checkmark \quad \text{True}$$

A true statement indicates that $\{4\}$ is the solution set.   ∎

EXAMPLE 2   Solving a Linear Equation with Fractions

Solve $\dfrac{x + 7}{6} + \dfrac{2x - 8}{2} = -4.$

Solution

Step 1
$$6\left(\frac{x + 7}{6} + \frac{2x - 8}{2}\right) = 6(-4) \qquad \begin{array}{l}\text{Multiply each side by the least}\\\text{common denominator (LCD),}\\\text{6, to eliminate the fractions.}\end{array}$$

Step 2
$$6\left(\frac{x + 7}{6}\right) + 6\left(\frac{2x - 8}{2}\right) = 6(-4) \qquad \text{Distributive property}$$

Multiply each term by 6.

$$x + 7 + 3(2x - 8) = -24 \qquad \text{Multiply.}$$
$$x + 7 + 6x - 24 = -24 \qquad \text{Distributive property}$$
$$7x - 17 = -24 \qquad \text{Combine like terms.}$$

Step 3
$$7x - 17 + 17 = -24 + 17 \qquad \text{Add 17.}$$
$$7x = -7 \qquad \text{Combine like terms.}$$

Step 4
$$\frac{7x}{7} = \frac{-7}{7} \qquad \text{Divide by 7.}$$
$$x = -1 \qquad \text{Simplify.}$$

Step 5   *Check:*
$$\frac{x + 7}{6} + \frac{2x - 8}{2} = -4 \qquad \text{Original equation}$$
$$\frac{-1 + 7}{6} + \frac{2(-1) - 8}{2} \overset{?}{=} -4 \qquad \text{Let } x = -1.$$
$$\frac{6}{6} + \frac{-10}{2} \overset{?}{=} -4 \qquad \text{Simplify each fraction.}$$
$$1 - 5 \overset{?}{=} -4$$
$$-4 = -4 \quad \checkmark \qquad \text{True}$$

The solution -1 checks, so the solution set is $\{-1\}$.   ∎

EXAMPLE 3 Solving a Linear Equation with Decimals

Solve $0.06x + 0.09(15 - x) = 0.07(15)$.

Solution

Because each decimal number is in hundredths, multiply both sides of the equation by 100. This is done by moving the decimal points two places to the right.

$$0.06x + 0.09(15 - x) = 0.07(15) \qquad \text{Original equation}$$

$$0.06x + 0.09(15 - x) = 0.07(15) \qquad \text{Multiply each term by 100.}$$

$$6x + 9(15 - x) = 7(15)$$

$$6x + 9(15) - 9x = 105 \qquad \text{Distributive property; multiply.}$$

$$6x + 135 - 9x = 105 \qquad \text{Multiply.}$$

$$-3x + 135 = 105 \qquad \text{Combine like terms.}$$

$$-3x + 135 - 135 = 105 - 135 \qquad \text{Subtract 135.}$$

$$-3x = -30 \qquad \text{Combine like terms.}$$

$$\frac{-3x}{-3} = \frac{-30}{-3} \qquad \text{Divide by } -3.$$

$$x = 10 \qquad \text{Simplify.}$$

Check to verify that the solution set is $\{10\}$.

Special Kinds of Linear Equations

The preceding equations had solution sets containing one element. For example,

$$2(x - 5) + 3x = x + 6 \quad \text{has solution set} \quad \{4\}.$$

Some equations have no solutions. Others have an infinite number of solutions.

EXAMPLE 4 Recognizing Conditional Equations, Identities, and Contradictions

Sofia Kovalevskaya (1850–1891) was the most widely known Russian mathematician in the late nineteenth century. She did most of her work in the theory of **differential equations**—equations invaluable for expressing rates of change. For example, in biology, the rate of growth of a population, say of microbes, can be precisely stated by differential equations.

Kovalevskaya studied privately because public lectures were not open to women. She eventually received a degree (1874) from the University of Göttingen, Germany. In 1884 she became a lecturer at the University of Stockholm and later was appointed professor of higher mathematics.

Solve each equation. Decide whether it is a *conditional equation*, an *identity*, or a *contradiction*.

(a) $5x - 9 = 4(x - 3)$ **(b)** $5x - 15 = 5(x - 3)$ **(c)** $5x - 15 = 5(x - 4)$

Solution

(a)

$$5x - 9 = 4(x - 3)$$

$$5x - 9 = 4x - 12 \qquad \text{Distributive property}$$

$$5x - 9 - 4x = 4x - 12 - 4x \qquad \text{Subtract } 4x.$$

$$x - 9 = -12 \qquad \text{Combine like terms.}$$

$$x - 9 + 9 = -12 + 9 \qquad \text{Add 9.}$$

$$x = -3 \qquad \text{Solution set } \{-3\}$$

The solution set has one element, so $5x - 9 = 4(x - 3)$ is a **conditional equation.**

François Viète (1540–1603) was a lawyer at the court of Henry IV of France and studied equations. Viète simplified the notation of algebra and was among the first to use letters to represent numbers.

(b) $5x - 15 = 5(x - 3)$

$\quad$ $5x - 15 = 5x - 15$ $\quad$ Distributive property

$\quad\quad\quad$ $0 = 0$ $\quad\quad$ Subtract 5x and add 15.

The final line, $0 = 0$, indicates that the solution set is {all real numbers}, and the equation $5x - 15 = 5(x - 3)$ is an **identity.** (*Note:* The first step yielded $5x - 15 = 5x - 15$, which is true for all values of x, implying an identity there.)

(c) $\quad\quad$ $5x - 15 = 5(x - 4)$

$\quad\quad\quad$ $5x - 15 = 5x - 20$ $\quad\quad$ Distributive property

$\quad$ $5x - 15 - 5x = 5x - 20 - 5x$ $\quad$ Subtract 5x.

$\quad\quad\quad\quad$ $-15 = -20$ $\quad\quad\quad$ False

Because the result, $-15 = -20$, is *false*, the equation has no solution. The solution set is $\varnothing$, and the equation is a **contradiction.** ∎

Table 1 summarizes this discussion.

Table 1   Types of Equations

Type of Equation	Number of Solutions	Indication When Solving
Conditional	One	Final line is x = a number. (See **Example 4(a)**.)
Identity	Infinite; solution set {all real numbers}	Final line is true, such as $0 = 0$. (See **Example 4(b)**.)
Contradiction	None; solution set $\varnothing$	Final line is false, such as $-15 = -20$. (See **Example 4(c)**.)

Literal Equations and Formulas

An equation involving *variables* (or letters), such as $cx + d = e$, is called a **literal equation.** The most useful examples of literal equations are *formulas*. The solution of a problem in algebra often depends on the use of a mathematical statement or **formula** in which more than one letter is used to express a relationship.

$$d = rt, \quad I = prt, \quad \text{and} \quad S = \frac{A}{5T} + \frac{d}{20} \quad \text{Examples of formulas}$$

In some cases, a formula must be solved for one of its variables. This process is called **solving for a specified variable.** The steps used are similar to those used in solving linear equations.

When you are solving for a specified variable, the key is to treat that variable as if it were the only one. Treat all other variables like numbers (constants).

SOLVING FOR A SPECIFIED VARIABLE

Step 1 If the equation contains fractions, multiply both sides by the LCD to clear the fractions.

Step 2 Transform so that all terms with the specified variable are on one side and all terms without that variable are on the other side.

Step 3 Divide each side by the factor that is the coefficient of the specified variable.

EXAMPLE 5 Solving for a Specified Variable

To determine how much welded parts shrink in groove joints, the formula

$$S = \frac{A}{5T} + \frac{d}{20}$$

is used. Here, S represents transverse shrinkage, A represents the cross-sectional area of the weld in square millimeters, T is the thickness of the plates in millimeters, and d is the root opening in millimeters. (*Source:* Saunders, Hal M., and Robert A. Carman. *Mathematics for the Trades—A Guided Approach*, 10th ed. Pearson, 2015.) Solve this welding formula for d.

Solution

$$S = \frac{A}{5T} + \frac{d}{20} \qquad \text{Given formula}$$

$$20T \cdot S = 20T\left(\frac{A}{5T} + \frac{d}{20}\right) \qquad \text{Multiply by the LCD of the fractions, } 20T.$$

$$20TS = 20T\left(\frac{A}{5T}\right) + 20T\left(\frac{d}{20}\right) \qquad \text{Distributive property}$$

$$20TS = 4A + Td \qquad \text{Multiply and simplify.}$$

$$20TS - 4A = Td \qquad \text{Subtract } 4A.$$

$$\frac{20TS - 4A}{T} = d \qquad \text{Divide by } T. \qquad ■$$

Models

An equation or an inequality that expresses a relationship among various quantities is an example of a **mathematical model.** The relationship between the Fahrenheit and Celsius temperature scales is an example of a *linear model.*

EXAMPLE 6 Using the Formulas for Fahrenheit and Celsius

In the Fahrenheit temperature scale, water freezes at 32 degrees and boils at 212 degrees. The equivalent measures for the Celsius scale are 0 degrees and 100 degrees. In **Chapter 8** we will justify the formula

$$F = \frac{9}{5}C + 32$$

for converting Celsius C to Fahrenheit F.

(a) Find the Fahrenheit temperature that corresponds to 30 degrees Celsius.

(b) Solve the formula for C.

Solution

(a) Let $C = 30$ in the formula.

$$F = \frac{9}{5}(30) + 32 \qquad \text{Let } C = 30.$$

$$F = 54 + 32 \qquad \text{Multiply.}$$

$$F = 86 \qquad \text{Add.}$$

The Celsius temperature 30 degrees corresponds to 86 degrees Fahrenheit.

The Axioms of Equality When we solve an equation, we must make sure that it remains "balanced"—that is, any operation that is performed on one side of the equation must also be performed on the other side in order to ensure that the set of solutions remains the same.

Underlying the rules for solving equations are four axioms of equality, listed below. For all real numbers a, b, and c, the following are true.

1. **Reflexive axiom**
   $a = a$

2. **Symmetric axiom**
   If $a = b$, then $b = a$.

3. **Transitive axiom**
   If $a = b$ and $b = c$, then $a = c$.

4. **Substitution axiom**
   If $a = b$, then a may replace b in any statement without affecting the truth or falsity of the statement.

A relation, such as equality, that satisfies the first three of these axioms (reflexive, symmetric, and transitive), is called an *equivalence relation.*

(b)
$$F = \frac{9}{5}C + 32 \qquad \text{Given formula}$$

$$F - 32 = \frac{9}{5}C \qquad \text{Subtract 32.}$$

$$\frac{5}{9}(F - 32) = \frac{5}{9}\left(\frac{9}{5}C\right) \qquad \text{Multiply by } \frac{5}{9}.$$

$$\frac{5}{9}(F - 32) = C \qquad \text{Simplify on the right.}$$

$$C = \frac{5}{9}(F - 32) \qquad \text{Rewrite.}$$

This final line is the form of the equation to convert Fahrenheit to Celsius. ■

7.1   EXERCISES

Solve each equation.

1. $7x + 8 = 1$

2. $5x - 4 = 21$

3. $8 - 8x = -16$

4. $9 - 2x = 15$

5. $7x - 5x + 15 = x + 8$

6. $2x + 4 - x = 4x - 5$

7. $12x + 15x - 9 + 5 = -3x - 4$

8. $-4x + 5x - 8 + 4 = 6x - 4$

9. $2(x + 3) = -4(x + 1)$

10. $4(x - 9) = 8(x + 3)$

11. $3(2x + 1) - 2(x - 2) = 5$

12. $4(x - 2) + 2(x + 3) = 6$

13. $2x + 3(x - 4) = 2(x - 3)$

14. $6x - 3(5x + 2) = 4(1 - x)$

15. $6x - 4(3 - 2x) = 5(x - 4) - 10$

16. $-2x - 3(4 - 2x) = 2(x - 3) + 2$

17. $-[2x - (5x + 2)] = 2 + (2x + 7)$

18. $-[6x - (4x + 8)] = 9 + (6x + 3)$

19. $-3x + 6 - 5(x - 1) = -(2x - 4) - 5x + 5$

20. $4(x + 2) - 8x - 5 = -3x + 9 - 2(x + 6)$

21. $\dfrac{3x}{4} + \dfrac{5x}{2} = 13$

22. $\dfrac{8x}{3} - \dfrac{2x}{4} = -13$

23. $\dfrac{x - 8}{5} + \dfrac{8}{5} = -\dfrac{x}{3}$

24. $\dfrac{2x - 3}{7} + \dfrac{3}{7} = -\dfrac{x}{3}$

25. $\dfrac{3x + 7}{6} + \dfrac{x + 7}{6} = \dfrac{x + 6}{4}$

26. $\dfrac{2x + 5}{5} = \dfrac{3x + 1}{2} + \dfrac{-x + 7}{2}$

27. $0.05x + 0.12(x + 5000) = 940$

28. $0.09x + 0.13(x + 300) = 61$

29. $0.02(50) + 0.08x = 0.04(50 + x)$

30. $0.20(14{,}000) + 0.14x = 0.18(14{,}000 + x)$

31. $0.05x + 0.10(200 - x) = 0.45x$

32. $0.08x + 0.12(260 - x) = 0.48x$

Decide whether each equation is conditional, an identity, or a contradiction. Give the solution set.

33. $-2x + 5x - 9 = 3(x - 4) - 5$

34. $-6x + 2x - 11 = -2(2x - 3) + 4$

35. $6x + 2(x - 2) = 9x + 4$

36. $-4(x + 2) = -3(x + 5) - x$

37. $-11x + 4(x - 3) + 6x = 4x - 12$

38. $3x - 5(x + 4) + 9 = -11 + 15x$

39. $7[2 - (3 + 4x)] - 2x = -9 + 2(1 - 15x)$

40. $4[6 - (1 + 2x)] + 10x = 2(10 - 3x) + 8x$

Formulas from Trades and Occupations *The formulas in Exercises 41–50 are found in various trades and occupations. Solve each formula for the specified variable. (Sources: Saunders, Hal M., and Robert A. Carman. Mathematics for the Trades—A Guided Approach, 10th ed. Pearson, 2015; Timmons, Daniel L., and Catherine W. Johnson. Math Skills for Allied Health Careers. Pearson, 2008.)*

41. $p = \dfrac{wA}{150}$;   for A (allied health)

42. $p = \dfrac{mA}{150}$;   for m (allied health)

43. $\text{ACH} = \dfrac{60\ell}{v}$;   for ℓ (energy efficiency)

44. $\text{HP} = \dfrac{tr}{5252}$;   for r (automotive)

45. $\ell = a + b + \dfrac{1}{2}t$;   for t (sheet metal)

46. $r = c + h + \dfrac{1}{4}s$;   for s (forestry)

47. $r_1 x = r_2(\ell + x)$;   for ℓ (electrical)

48. $v = (21.78 - 0.101a)h$;   for a (allied health)

49. $\ell = -h^2 + 2rh$;   for r (sheet metal)

50. $r = \dfrac{d^2 n}{2.5}$;   for n (automotive)

Mathematical Formulas *Solve each formula for the specified variable.*

51. $d = rt$;   for t (distance)

52. $I = prt$;   for r (simple interest)

53. $\mathcal{A} = bh$;   for b (area of a parallelogram)

54. $P = 2L + 2W$;   for L (perimeter of a rectangle)

55. $P = a + b + c$;   for a (perimeter of a triangle)

56. $V = LWH$;   for W (volume of a rectangular solid)

57. $\mathcal{A} = \dfrac{1}{2}bh$;   for b (area of a triangle)

58. $C = 2\pi r$;   for r (circumference of a circle)

59. $S = 2\pi rh + 2\pi r^2$;   for h
(surface area of a right circular cylinder)

60. $\mathcal{A} = \dfrac{1}{2}h(B + b)$;   for B (area of a trapezoid)

61. $V = \dfrac{1}{3}\pi r^2 h$;   for h (volume of a cone)

62. $V = \dfrac{1}{3}Bh$;   for h (volume of a right pyramid)

Use the formulas in **Example 6** *to make the following degree conversions.*

63. 15 degrees Celsius to Fahrenheit

64. 25 degrees Celsius to Fahrenheit

65. −20 degrees Celsius to Fahrenheit

66. −40 degrees Celsius to Fahrenheit

67. 41 degrees Fahrenheit to Celsius

68. 59 degrees Fahrenheit to Celsius

69. −13 degrees Fahrenheit to Celsius

70. −40 degrees Fahrenheit to Celsius

Model for Contaminant Flow If a range hood removes contaminants at a flow rate of F liters of air per second, then the percent P of contaminants that are also removed from the surrounding air can be modeled by

$$P = 1.06F + 7.18,$$

where F is between and inclusive of 10 and 75. (Source: Rezvan, R. L., "Effectiveness of Local Ventilation in Removing Simulated Pollutants from Point Sources," 65–75. In *Proceedings of the Third International Conference on Indoor Air Quality and Climate*, 1984.)

71. What flow rate F, to the nearest unit, must a range hood have to remove 50% of the contaminants from the air?

72. Repeat **Exercise 71** for 60%.

73. To the nearest hundredth percent, what are the minimum and maximum values for P in this model?

74. Solve the formula for F.

| 7.2 | **APPLICATIONS OF LINEAR EQUATIONS** |

OBJECTIVES

1. Translate verbal expressions involving the operations of arithmetic into symbolic mathematical expressions.
2. Solve applications to find unknown numbers.
3. Solve applications involving mixture and simple interest.
4. Solve applications involving different denominations of money.
5. Solve applications involving motion.

Translating Words into Symbols

There are key words and phrases that translate into mathematical expressions involving addition, subtraction, multiplication, and division. The ability to make these translations is important when solving applications.

TRANSLATING FROM WORDS TO MATHEMATICAL EXPRESSIONS

Verbal Expression	Mathematical Expression (where x and y are numbers)
Addition	
The **sum** of a number and 7	$x + 7$
6 **more than** a number	$x + 6$
3 **plus** a number	$3 + x$
24 **added to** a number	$x + 24$
A number **increased by** 5	$x + 5$
The **sum** of two numbers	$x + y$
Subtraction	
2 **less than** a number	$x - 2$
12 **minus** a number	$12 - x$
A number **decreased by** 12	$x - 12$
The **difference between** two numbers	$x - y$
A number **subtracted from** 10	$10 - x$
Multiplication	
16 **times** a number	$16x$
A number **multiplied by** 6	$6x$
$\frac{2}{3}$ **of** a number (as applied to fractions and percent)	$\frac{2}{3}x$
Twice (2 times) a number	$2x$
Triple (3 times) a number	$3x$
The **product** of two numbers	xy
Division	
The **quotient** of 8 and a number	$\frac{8}{x}$ $(x \neq 0)$
A number **divided by** 13	$\frac{x}{13}$
The **ratio** of two numbers or the **quotient** of two numbers	$\frac{x}{y}$ $(y \neq 0)$

The equality symbol, $=$, is often indicated by the word *is.* In fact, because equal mathematical expressions represent different names for the same number, words that indicate the idea of "sameness" translate as $=$. For example,

If the product of a number and 12 is decreased by 7, the result is 105

translates to the mathematical equation

$12x - 7 = 105,$

where x represents the unknown number. Note that $7 - 12x = 105$ is incorrect because subtraction is not commutative.

Guidelines for Applications

To solve applied problems, the following six steps are helpful.

SOLVING AN APPLIED PROBLEM

Step 1 **Read** the problem carefully until you understand what is given and what is to be found.

Step 2 **Assign a variable** to represent the unknown value, using diagrams or tables as needed. Write down what the variable represents. If necessary, express any other unknown values in terms of the variable.

Step 3 **Write an equation** using the variable expression(s).

Step 4 **Solve** the equation.

Step 5 **State the answer.** Does it seem reasonable?

Step 6 **Check** the answer in the words of the *original* problem.

Finding Unknown Quantities

Problem-Solving Strategy

A common type of problem involves finding two quantities when the sum of the quantities is known. Choose a variable to represent one of the unknowns, and then represent the other quantity in terms of the same variable, using information from the problem. Then write an equation based on the words of the problem.

EXAMPLE 1 Finding Numbers of Strikeouts

Two outstanding major league pitchers in recent years are Yu Darvish and Max Scherzer. In 2013, they combined for a total of 517 strikeouts. Darvish had 37 more strikeouts than Scherzer. How many strikeouts did each pitcher have? (*Source:* www.mlb.com)

Solution

Step 1 **Read** the problem. We are asked to find the number of strikeouts each pitcher had.

Step 2 **Assign a variable** to represent the number of strikeouts for one of the men.

Let s = the number of strikeouts for Scherzer.

We must also find the number of strikeouts for Darvish. Because he had 37 more strikeouts than Scherzer,

$s + 37$ = the number of strikeouts for Darvish.

Step 3 **Write an equation.** The sum of the numbers of strikeouts is 517.

Scherzer's strikeouts	+	Darvish's strikeouts	=	Total
s	+	$(s + 37)$	=	517

Step 4   **Solve** the equation.

$$s + (s + 37) = 517$$

$$2s + 37 = 517 \qquad \text{Combine like terms.}$$

$$2s + 37 - 37 = 517 - 37 \qquad \text{Subtract 37.}$$

$$2s = 480 \qquad \text{Combine like terms.}$$

$$\frac{2s}{2} = \frac{480}{2} \qquad \text{Divide by 2.}$$

Don't stop here.

$$s = 240$$

Step 5   **State the answer.** We let *s* represent the number of strikeouts for Scherzer, so Scherzer had 240. Then the number of strikeouts for Darvish is

$$s + 37 = 240 + 37 = 277. \qquad \text{Be sure to find the second answer.}$$

Step 6   **Check.** 277 is 37 more than 240, and the sum of 240 and 277 is 517. ■

EXAMPLE 2 Finding Lengths of Pieces of Wood

A carpenter is working on a project that calls for three pieces of wood. The longest piece must be twice the length of the middle-sized piece, and the shortest piece must be 10 inches shorter than the middle-sized piece. If the three pieces are to be cut from a board 70 inches long, how long must each piece be?

Solution

Step 1   **Read** the problem. Three lengths must be found.

Step 2   **Assign a variable.** Because the middle-sized piece appears in both comparisons, let *x* represent the length, in inches, of the middle-sized piece.

$$x = \text{the length of the middle-sized piece,}$$

$$2x = \text{the length of the longest piece, and}$$

$$x - 10 = \text{the length of the shortest piece. See } \textbf{Figure 1.}$$

2x   x   x – 10

Figure 1

Step 3   **Write an equation.**

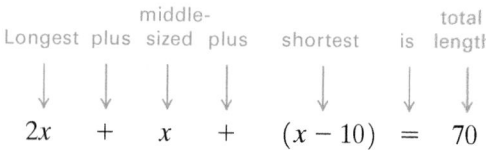

$$2x \quad + \quad x \quad + \quad (x - 10) \quad = \quad 70$$

Step 4   **Solve.**

$$4x - 10 = 70 \qquad \text{Combine like terms.}$$

$$4x - 10 + 10 = 70 + 10 \qquad \text{Add 10.}$$

$$4x = 80 \qquad \text{Combine like terms.}$$

$$\frac{4x}{4} = \frac{80}{4} \qquad \text{Divide by 4.}$$

$$x = 20$$

Step 5   **State the answer.** The middle-sized piece is 20 inches long, the longest piece is 2(20) = 40 inches long, and the shortest piece is 20 − 10 = 10 inches long.

Step 6   **Check.** The sum of the lengths is 70 inches. All conditions of the problem are satisfied. ■

Problems involving age have been around since antiquity. The *Greek Anthology* gives the only information known about the life of the mathematician **Diophantus:**

Diophantus passed $\frac{1}{6}$ of his life in childhood, $\frac{1}{12}$ in youth, and $\frac{1}{7}$ more as a bachelor. Five years after his marriage was born a son who died 4 years before his father, at $\frac{1}{2}$ his father's final age.

Try to write an equation and solve it to show that Diophantus was 84 years old when he died.

Mixture and Interest Problems

Problem-Solving Strategy

Percents often are used in problems involving mixing different concentrations of a substance or different interest rates. In each case, to get the amount of pure substance or the interest, we multiply.

MIXTURE PROBLEMS	**INTEREST PROBLEMS (ANNUAL)**
base × rate (%) = percentage	principal × rate (%) = interest
$b \times r = p$	$P \times r = I$

In an equation, the percent should be written as a decimal.

EXAMPLE 3   Using Percents in Applications

Use percents in each of the following.

(a) A nurse has 40 liters of a 35% alcohol solution. How much pure alcohol does that solution contain?

(b) If $1300 is invested for one year at 2% simple interest, how much interest is earned in one year?

Solution

(a)   40   ×   0.35   =   14 liters   **(b)** $1300   ×   0.02   = $26

  35% = 0.35   2% = 0.02

Amount of   Rate of   Amount of   Principal   Interest   Interest
solution   concentration   pure alcohol   rate   earned

Problem-Solving Strategy

Creating a table makes it easier to set up an equation for a problem, which is usually the most difficult step.

EXAMPLE 4   Solving a Mixture Problem

A pharmacist must combine 8 liters of a 40% acid solution with some 70% solution to obtain a 50% solution. How much of the 70% solution should be used?

Solution

Step 1 **Read** the problem. We must find the amount of 70% solution to be used.

Step 2 **Assign a variable.** Let x = the number of liters of 70% solution to be used. The information in the problem is illustrated in **Figure 2.**

After combining

From 70%
From 40%

8 L   Unknown   (8 + x) L
          number of liters, x

Figure 2

Use the given information to complete the table.

Percent (as a decimal)	Number of Liters	Liters of Pure Acid
40% = 0.40	8	0.40(8) = 3.2
70% = 0.70	x	0.70x
50% = 0.50	8 + x	0.50(8 + x)

Sum must equal

The numbers in the right column were found by multiplying the strengths and the numbers of liters. The number of liters of pure acid in the 40% solution plus the number of liters of pure acid in the 70% solution must equal the number of liters of pure acid in the 50% solution.

Step 3 **Write an equation.**

$$3.2 + 0.70x = 0.50(8 + x)$$

Step 4 **Solve.**

$$3.2 + 0.70x = 4 + 0.50x \qquad \text{Distributive property}$$

$$32 + 7x = 40 + 5x \qquad \text{Multiply by 10 to clear decimals.}$$

$$2x = 8 \qquad \text{Subtract 32 and 5x.}$$

$$x = 4 \qquad \text{Divide by 2.}$$

Step 5 **State the answer.** The pharmacist should use 4 liters of the 70% solution.

Step 6 **Check.** 8 liters of 40% solution plus 4 liters of 70% solution is

$$8(0.40) + 4(0.70) = 6 \text{ liters}$$

of acid. Similarly, 8 + 4 or 12 liters of 50% solution has

$$12(0.50) = 6 \text{ liters}$$

of acid in the mixture. The total amount of pure acid is 6 liters both before and after mixing, so the answer checks. ∎

EXAMPLE 5 Solving an Investment Problem

After winning the state lottery, Theo has $40,000 to invest. He will put part of the money in an account paying 4% interest and the remainder into stocks paying 6% interest. His accountant tells him that the total annual income from these investments should be $2040. How much should he invest at each rate?

Solution

Step 1 **Read** the problem again. We must find the two amounts.

Step 2 **Assign a variable.**

Let x = the amount to invest at 4%.

Then 40,000 − x = the amount to invest at 6%.

The formula for interest is $I = prt$. Here the time, t, is 1 year.

Rate (as a decimal)	Principal	Interest
4% = 0.04	x	0.04x
6% = 0.06	40,000 − x	0.06(40,000 − x)
	40,000	2040

← Totals

Step 3   **Write an equation.** The last column of the table gives the equation.

Interest at 4%	plus	interest at 6%	is	total interest.
↓	↓	↓	↓	↓
$0.04x$	$+$	$0.06(40{,}000 - x)$	$=$	2040

Step 4   **Solve.** $0.04x + 0.06(40{,}000) - 0.06x = 2040$ Distributive property

$$4x + 6(40{,}000) - 6x = 204{,}000$$ Multiply by 100.

$$-2x + 240{,}000 = 204{,}000$$ Combine like terms.

$$-2x = -36{,}000$$ Subtract 240,000.

$$x = 18{,}000$$ Divide by −2.

Step 5   **State the answer.** Theo should invest $18,000 at 4%. At 6%, he should invest $40,000 − $18,000 = $22,000.

Step 6   **Check** by finding the annual interest at each rate.

$$0.04(\$18{,}000) = \$720 \quad \text{and} \quad 0.06(\$22{,}000) = \$1320$$

$$\$720 + \$1320 = \$2040, \quad \text{as required.} \qquad \blacksquare$$

Monetary Denomination Problems

> **Problem-Solving Strategy**
>
> Problems that involve money are similar to mixture and investment problems.
>
> **MONEY DENOMINATION PROBLEMS**
> **Number × Value of one = Total value**
>
> For example, if a jar contains 37 quarters, the monetary value of the coins is
>
> $$37 \quad \times \quad \$0.25 \quad = \quad \$9.25.$$
> $$\uparrow \qquad\qquad \uparrow \qquad\qquad \uparrow$$
> Number of coins   Denomination   Monetary value

EXAMPLE 6 **Solving a Monetary Denomination Problem**

A group of 25 coins consisting of nickels and quarters has a value of $5.65. How many of each denomination does the group contain?

Solution

Step 1   **Read** the problem. We must find the number of each denomination.

Step 2   **Assign a variable.**

Let $x =$ the number of nickels.

Then $25 - x =$ the number of quarters.

Denomination	Number of Coins	Value
$0.05	x	$0.05x$
$0.25	$25 - x$	$0.25(25 - x)$
	25	5.65

Sum must equal

Step 3   **Write an equation.** The last column of the table gives the following.

$$0.05x + 0.25(25 - x) = 5.65$$

Step 4 **Solve.** $5x + 25(25 - x) = 565$ Multiply by 100.

$5x + 625 - 25x = 565$ Distributive property

$-20x = -60$ Subtract 625. Combine like terms.

$x = 3$ Divide by -20.

Step 5 **State the answer.** The cashier has 3 nickels and $25 - 3 = $ **22** quarters.

Step 6 **Check.** There are $3 + 22 = 25$ coins, and the value of the coins is

$$\$0.05(3) + \$0.25(22) = \$5.65, \quad \text{as required.} \qquad \blacksquare$$

Motion Problems

If an automobile travels at an average rate of 50 miles per hour for two hours, then it travels $50 \times 2 = 100$ miles. This is an example of the basic relationship

distance = rate × time.

This is given by the formula $d = rt$. By solving, in turn, for r and t, we obtain two other equivalent forms of the formula. The three forms are given below.

DISTANCE, RATE, TIME RELATIONSHIP

$$d = rt \qquad r = \frac{d}{t} \qquad t = \frac{d}{r}$$

EXAMPLE 7   Using the Distance, Rate, Time Relationship

Use a formula relating distance, rate, and time in each of the following.

(a) The speed of sound is 1088 feet per second at sea level at 32°F. Under these conditions, how far does sound travel in 5 seconds?

(b) The winner of the first Indianapolis 500 race (in 1911) was Ray Harroun, driving a Marmon Wasp at an average speed of 74.59 miles per hour. How long did it take for him to complete the 500-mile course? (*Source: The Universal Almanac.*)

(c) At the 2012 Olympic Games, Lithuanian swimmer Ruta Meilutyte won the women's 100-m breast stroke, swimming the event in 65.47 seconds. What was her rate? (*Source:* www.olympic.org)

Solution

(a) $1088 \quad \times \quad 5 \quad = \quad 5440$ feet

            Rate   ×   Time   =   Distance

(b) To complete the 500 miles, it took Harroun

Distance $\longrightarrow \dfrac{500}{74.59} = 6.70$ hours   (rounded). $\longleftarrow$ Time
Rate $\longrightarrow$

Here, we found time given rate and distance, using $t = \frac{d}{r}$. To convert 0.70 hour to minutes, multiply by 60 to get $0.70(60) = 42$ minutes. The race took him 6 hours, 42 minutes to complete.

(c)   Rate $= \dfrac{\text{Distance}}{\text{Time}} \longrightarrow \dfrac{100}{65.47} = 1.53$ meters per second (rounded) $\blacksquare$

Can we average averages? A car travels from *A* to *B* at 40 miles per hour and returns at 60 miles per hour. What is its rate for the entire trip?

The correct answer is not 50 miles per hour, as you might expect. Remembering the distance, rate, time relationship and letting *x* = the distance between *A* and *B*, we can simplify a complex fraction to find the correct answer.

$$\begin{aligned}
\text{Average rate for} \atop \text{entire trip} &= \frac{\text{Total distance}}{\text{Total time}} \\
&= \frac{x + x}{\dfrac{x}{40} + \dfrac{x}{60}} \\
&= \frac{2x}{\dfrac{3x}{120} + \dfrac{2x}{120}} \\
&= \frac{2x}{\dfrac{5x}{120}} \\
&= 2x \cdot \frac{120}{5x} \\
&= 48
\end{aligned}$$

The average rate for the entire trip is 48 miles per hour.

Problem-Solving Strategy

Motion problems use the distance formula,

$$d = rt.$$

In this formula, ***when rate (or speed) is given in miles per hour, time must be given in hours.*** To solve such problems, ***draw a sketch*** to illustrate what is happening in the problem, and ***make a table*** to summarize the given information.

Step 2 in our problem-solving steps involves assigning a variable. In most cases, we assign the variable to the unknown quantity that we are directed to find. However, in some cases, like the following one in **Example 8,** it is easier to assign the variable to a different quantity and then later in the process use its value to find the final answer. Knowing when to do this comes from experience in problem solving, and the way to gain experience is to solve lots of problems.

EXAMPLE 8 Solving a Motion Problem

Greg can bike from home to work in $\frac{3}{4}$ hour. By bus, the trip takes $\frac{1}{4}$ hour. If the bus travels 20 mph faster than Greg rides his bike, how far is it to his workplace?

Solution

Step 1 **Read** the problem. We must find the distance between Greg's home and his workplace.

Step 2 **Assign a variable.** Although the problem asks for a distance, it is easier here to let *x* be his speed when he rides his bike to work. Then the speed of the bus is $x + 20$.

$$d = rt = x \cdot \frac{3}{4} = \frac{3}{4}x, \quad \text{Distance of trip by bike}$$

and

$$d = rt = (x + 20) \cdot \frac{1}{4} = \frac{1}{4}(x + 20) \quad \text{Distance of trip by bus}$$

We summarize this information in a table.

	Rate	Time	Distance
Bike	x	$\frac{3}{4}$	$\frac{3}{4}x$
Bus	$x + 20$	$\frac{1}{4}$	$\frac{1}{4}(x + 20)$

Same distance

Step 3 **Write an equation.** The key to setting up the correct equation is to recognize that the distance is the *same* in both cases. See **Figure 3.**

Figure 3

$$\frac{3}{4}x = \frac{1}{4}(x + 20) \quad \text{The distance is the same.}$$

Step 4 **Solve.** $\quad 4\left(\dfrac{3}{4}x\right) = 4\left(\dfrac{1}{4}\right)(x + 20)$ $\quad$ Multiply by 4.

$$3x = x + 20 \quad\quad \text{Multiply.}$$

$$2x = 20 \quad\quad \text{Subtract } x.$$

$$x = 10 \quad\quad \text{Divide by 2.}$$

Step 5 **State the answer.** The required distance is given by $d = rt$.

$$d = \frac{3}{4}x = \frac{3}{4}(10) = \frac{30}{4} = 7.5 \text{ miles} \quad \text{Distance by bike}$$

Step 6 **Check** by finding the distance by bus.

$$d = \frac{1}{4}(x + 20) = \frac{1}{4}(10 + 20) = \frac{30}{4} = 7.5 \text{ miles} \quad \text{Distance by bus}$$

This yields the same result. It is 7.5 miles to Greg's workplace. ∎

7.2 EXERCISES

Decide whether each of the following translates into an expression or an equation.

1. the product of a number and 6

2. 39% of a number

3. $\frac{2}{3}$ of a number is 36.

4. 9 is 5 more than a number.

5. the ratio of a number and 24

6. 48 divided by a number is 12.

Translate each verbal phrase into a mathematical expression. Use x to represent the unknown number.

7. a number decreased by 12

8. 7 more than a number

9. the product of 6 less than a number and 4 more than the number

10. the quotient of a number and 9

11. the ratio of 25 and a nonzero number

12. $\frac{6}{7}$ of a number

Unknown Numbers *Let x represent the number, write an equation for the sentence, and then solve.*

13. If 2 is added to five times a number, the result is equal to 5 more than four times the number. Find the number.

14. If four times a number is added to 8, the result is three times the number added to 5. Find the number.

15. If 2 is subtracted from a number and this difference is tripled, the result is 6 more than the number. Find the number.

16. If 3 is added to a number and this sum is doubled, the result is 2 more than the number. Find the number.

17. The sum of three times a number and 7 more than the number is the same as the difference between −11 and twice the number. What is the number?

18. If 4 is added to twice a number and this sum is multiplied by 2, the result is the same as if the number is multiplied by 3 and 4 is added to the product. What is the number?

*Use the methods of **Examples 1 and 2** or your own method to solve each problem.*

19. ***Concert Revenues*** Madonna and Bruce Springsteen had the two top-grossing North American concert tours for 2012, together generating $427 million in ticket sales. If Bruce Springsteen took in $29 million less than Madonna, how much did each tour generate? (*Source:* www.billboard.com)

20. **Automobile Sales** The Toyota Camry and the Honda Accord were the top-selling passenger cars in the United States in 2012. Honda Accord sales were 75 thousand less than Toyota Camry sales, and 735 thousand of these two cars were sold. How many of each model of car were sold? (*Source:* www.goodcarbadcar.net)

21. **NBA Record** In the 2012–2013 NBA regular season, the Miami Heat won two more than four times as many games as they lost. The Heat played 82 games. How many wins and losses did the team have? (*Source:* www.nba.com)

22. **MLB Record** In the 2013 Major League Baseball season, the Tampa Bay Rays won 50 fewer than twice as many games as they lost. They played 163 regular season games. How many wins and losses did the team have? (*Source:* www.mlb.com)

23. **U.S. Senate** During the 113th Congress, the U.S. Senate had a total of 98 Democrats and Republicans. There were 6 fewer Republicans than Democrats. How many Democrats and Republicans were there in the Senate? (*Source: World Almanac and Book of Facts.*)

24. **U.S. House of Representatives** The total number of Democrats and Republicans in the U.S. House of Representatives during the 113th Congress was 432. There were 32 fewer Democrats than Republicans. How many members of each party were there? (*Source: World Almanac and Book of Facts.*)

25. **Submarine Sandwich** Nagaraj has a party-length sandwich that is 59 inches long and is to be cut into three pieces. The middle piece will be 5 inches longer than the shortest piece, and the shortest piece will be 9 inches shorter than the longest piece. How long will the pieces be?

26. **Office Manager Duties** In one week, an office manager booked 55 tickets, divided among three airlines. He booked 7 more tickets on American Airlines than on United Airlines. On Southwest Airlines, he booked 4 more than twice as many tickets as on United. How many tickets did he book on each airline?

27. **U.S. Olympic Medals** China earned a total of 88 medals at the 2012 Olympics. The number of gold medals was 15 more than the number of bronze medals. The number of bronze medals was 4 less than the number of silver medals. How many of each kind of medal did China earn? (*Source: World Almanac and Book of Facts.*)

28. **Textbook Editor Duties** A textbook editor spent $7\frac{1}{2}$ hours making telephone calls, writing e-mails, and attending meetings. She spent twice as much time attending meetings as making calls, and $\frac{1}{2}$ hour longer writing e-mails than making calls. How many hours did she spend on each task?

*Use basic formulas, as in **Example 3**, to solve each problem.*

29. **Acid Mixture** How much pure acid is in 500 milliliters of a 14% acid solution?

30. **Alcohol Mixture** How much pure alcohol is in 300 liters of a 30% alcohol solution?

31. **Interest Earned** If $10,000 is invested for 1 year at 2.5% simple interest, how much interest is earned?

32. **Interest Earned** If $50,000 is invested at 3% simple interest for 2 years, how much interest is earned?

33. **Monetary Value of Coins** What is the monetary amount of 497 nickels?

34. **Monetary Value of Coins** What is the monetary amount of 89 half-dollars?

*Use the method of **Example 4** or your own method to solve each problem.*

35. **Alcohol Mixture** In a chemistry class, 12 liters of a 12% alcohol solution must be mixed with a 20% solution to get a 14% solution. How many liters of the 20% solution are needed?

Strength	Liters of Solution	Liters of Alcohol
12%	12	
20%		
14%		

36. **Alcohol Mixture** How many liters of a 10% alcohol solution must be mixed with 40 liters of a 50% solution to get a 40% solution?

37. **Antifreeze Mixture** A car radiator needs a 40% antifreeze solution. The radiator now holds 20 liters of a 20% solution. How many liters of this should be drained and replaced with 100% antifreeze to get the desired strength?

38. **Chemical Mixture** A tank holds 80 liters of a chemical solution. Currently, the solution has a strength of 30%. How much of this should be drained and replaced with a 70% solution to get a final strength of 40%?

39. **Insecticide Mixture** How much water must be added to 3 gallons of a 4% insecticide solution to reduce the concentration to 3%? (*Hint:* Water is 0% insecticide.)

40. **Alcohol Mixture in First Aid Spray** A medicated first aid spray on the market is 78% alcohol by volume. If the manufacturer has 50 liters of the spray containing 70% alcohol, how much pure alcohol should be added so that the final mixture is the required 78% alcohol? (*Hint:* Pure alcohol is 100% alcohol.)

*Use the method of **Example 5** or your own method to solve each problem. Assume all rates and amounts are annual.*

41. Investments at Different Rates John earned $12,000 last year by giving tennis lessons. He invested part at 3% simple interest and the rest at 4%. He earned a total of $440 in interest. How much did he invest at each rate?

Rate (as a Decimal)	Principal	Interest in One Year
0.03		
0.04		
	12,000	440

42. Investments at Different Rates Kim won $60,000 on a slot machine in Las Vegas. She invested part at 2% simple interest and the rest at 3%. She earned a total of $1600 in interest. How much was invested at each rate?

43. Investments at Different Rates Derrick invested some money at 4.5% simple interest and $1000 less than twice this amount at 3%. His total income from the interest was $1020. How much was invested at each rate?

44. Investments at Different Rates Laquenia invested some money at 3.5% simple interest, and $5000 more than 3 times this amount at 4%. She earned $1440 in interest. How much did she invest at each rate?

*Use the method of **Example 6** or your own method to solve each problem.*

45. Coin Mixture Carlos has a box of coins that he uses when playing poker with his friends. The box currently contains 44 coins, consisting of pennies, dimes, and quarters. The number of pennies is equal to the number of dimes, and the total value is $4.37. How many of each denomination of coin does he have in the box?

Denomination	Number of Coins	Value
0.01	x	$0.01x$
	x	
0.25		
	44	4.37

Totals

46. Coin Mixture Kathy found some coins while looking under her sofa pillows. There were equal numbers of nickels and quarters, and twice as many half-dollars as quarters. If she found $2.60 in all, how many of each denomination of coin did she find?

47. Attendance at a School Play For opening night of a school production of *Death of a Salesman*, 410 tickets were sold. Students paid $3 each, while nonstudents paid $7 each. If a total of $1650 was collected, how many students and how many nonstudents attended?

48. Attendance at a Concert A total of 1100 people attended a James Taylor concert. Floor tickets cost $40 each, while balcony tickets cost $28 each. If a total of $41,600 was collected, how many of each type of ticket were sold?

49. Attendance at a Sporting Event At the local minor league hockey arena home games, Row 1 seats cost $35 each, and Row 2 seats cost $30 each. The 105 seats in these rows were sold out for the season. The total receipts for them were $3420. How many of each type of seat were sold?

50. Coin Mixture In the nineteenth century, the United States minted two-cent and three-cent pieces. Frances Steib has three times as many three-cent pieces as two-cent pieces, and the face value of these coins is $1.76. How many of each denomination does she have?

Use the formula $d = rt$ in Exercises 51–54.

51. Distance between Cities A small plane traveled from Warsaw to Rome, averaging 164 miles per hour. The trip took two hours. What is the distance from Warsaw to Rome?

52. Distance between Cities A driver averaged 53 miles per hour and took 10 hours to travel from Memphis to Chicago. What is the distance between Memphis and Chicago?

53. Distance Traveled Suppose that an automobile averages 55 miles per hour, and travels for 30 minutes. Is the distance traveled

$$55 \cdot 30 = 1650 \text{ miles}?$$

If not, give the correct distance.

54. Average Speed Which of the following choices is the best *estimate* for the average speed of a trip of 350 miles that lasted 6.8 hours?

A. 50 miles per hour   **B.** 30 miles per hour

C. 60 miles per hour   **D.** 40 miles per hour

*Use the method of **Example 8** or your own method to solve each problem.*

55. Distance Traveled to Work When Glen drives his car to work, the trip takes 30 minutes. When he rides the bus, it takes 45 minutes. The average speed of the bus is 12 miles per hour less than his speed when driving. Find the distance he travels to work.

56. *Distance Traveled to School* Theresa can get to school in 15 minutes if she rides her bike. It takes her 45 minutes if she walks. Her speed when walking is 10 miles per hour slower than her speed when riding. How far does she travel to school?

57. *Travel Times of Trains* A train leaves Little Rock, Arkansas, and travels north at 85 kilometers per hour. Another train leaves at the same time and travels south at 95 kilometers per hour. How long will it take before they are 315 kilometers apart?

	Rate	Time	Distance
First train	85	*t*	
Second train			

58. *Travel Times of Steamers* Two steamers leave a port on a river at the same time, traveling in opposite directions. Each is traveling 22 miles per hour. How long will it take for them to be 110 miles apart?

	Rate	Time	Distance
First steamer	22	*t*	
Second steamer			

59. *Travel Times of Commuters* Nancy and Mark commute to work, traveling in opposite directions. Nancy leaves the house at 9:00 A.M. and averages 35 miles per hour. Mark leaves at 9:15 A.M. and averages 40 miles per hour. At what time will they be 140 miles apart?

60. *Travel Times of Bicyclers* Jeff leaves his house on his bicycle at 7:30 A.M. and averages 5 miles per hour. His wife, Joan, leaves at 8:00 A.M., following the same path and averaging 8 miles per hour. At what time will Joan catch up with Jeff?

61. *Time Traveled by a Pleasure Boat* A pleasure boat on the Mississippi River traveled from New Roads, Louisiana, to New Orleans with a stop at White Castle. On the first part of the trip, the boat traveled at an average speed of 10 miles per hour. From White Castle to New Orleans the average speed was 15 miles per hour. The entire trip covered 100 miles. How long did the entire trip take if the two parts each took the same number of hours?

62. *Time Traveled on a Visit* Steve leaves Nashville to visit his cousin David in Napa, 80 miles away. He travels at an average speed of 50 miles per hour. One-half hour later David leaves to visit Steve, traveling at an average speed of 60 miles per hour. How long after David leaves will they meet?

Automobile Racing In Exercises 63–66, find the time. Use a calculator and round your answers to the nearest thousandth. (*Source:* The World Almanac and Book of Facts.)

	Event and Year	Participant	Distance	Rate
63.	Indianapolis 500, 2013	Tony Kanaan (Chevrolet)	500 miles	187.433 mph
64.	Daytona 500, 2014	Dale Earnhardt, Jr. (Chevrolet)	500 miles	145.290 mph
65.	Indianapolis 500, 1980	Johnny Rutherford (Hy-Gain McLaren/Goodyear)	255 miles*	148.725 mph
66.	Indianapolis 500, 1975	Bobby Unser (Jorgensen Eagle)	435 miles*	149.213 mph

*rain-shortened

Olympic Results In Exercises 67–70, find the rate. Use a calculator and round answers to the nearest hundredth. All events were at the 2012 Olympics. (*Source:* www.olympic.org)

	Event	Participant	Distance	Time
67.	200-m run, Women	Allyson Felix, USA	200 meters	21.88 seconds
68.	400-m run, Women	Sanya Richards-Ross, USA	400 meters	49.55 seconds
69.	200-m run, Men	Usain Bolt, Jamaica	200 meters	19.32 seconds
70.	110-m hurdles, Men	Aries Merritt, USA	110 meters	12.92 seconds

7.3   RATIO, PROPORTION, AND VARIATION

OBJECTIVES

1 Write a comparison of two quantities as a ratio.

2 Find unit price.

3 Solve proportions using equation-solving methods.

4 Write proportions in applications from nursing and biological field studies and solve them.

5 Determine the constant of variation in direct, inverse, joint, and combined variation, and solve variation applications.

Writing Ratios

One of the most frequently used mathematical concepts in everyday life is *ratio*. A baseball player's batting average is actually a ratio. The slope, or pitch, of a roof on a building may be expressed as a ratio. A percent is a ratio (a comparison to 100). Ratios provide a way of comparing two numbers or quantities.

> **RATIO**
>
> A **ratio** is a comparison of two quantities expressed as a quotient. The ratio of the number a to the number b is written in any of the following ways.
>
> $$a \text{ to } b, \qquad \frac{a}{b}, \qquad a\!:\!b$$

When ratios are used in comparing units of measure, the units should be the same.

EXAMPLE 1   Writing Ratios

Write a ratio for each word phrase.

(a) 5 hours to 3 hours   **(b)** 6 hours to 3 days

Solution

(a) The ratio of 5 hr to 3 hr is

$$\frac{5 \text{ hr}}{3 \text{ hr}} = \frac{5}{3}.$$ The ratio is 5 to 3.

(b) To find the ratio of 6 hr to 3 days, first convert 3 days to hours.

$$3 \text{ days} = 3 \text{ days} \cdot \frac{24 \text{ hr}}{1 \text{ day}} = 72 \text{ hr}$$

The ratio of 6 hr to 3 days is found as follows.

$$\frac{6 \text{ hr}}{3 \text{ days}} = \frac{6 \text{ hr}}{72 \text{ hr}} = \frac{6}{72} = \frac{1}{12}$$ The ratio is 1 to 12. ∎

Unit Pricing

Ratios can be applied in unit pricing, to see which size of an item offered in different sizes has the best price per unit.

EXAMPLE 2   Finding Price per Unit

A supermarket charges the following for a jar of extra crunchy peanut butter.

Peanut Butter

Size	Price
18-oz	$1.78
28-oz	$2.97
40-oz	$3.98

Which size is the best buy? That is, which size has the lowest unit price?

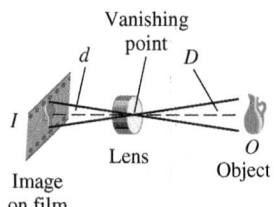

Vanishing point

d   *D*

I   Lens   *O*

Image on film   Object

When you look a long way down a straight road or railroad track, it seems to narrow as it vanishes in the distance. The point where the sides seem to touch is called the **vanishing point.**

The same thing occurs in the lens of a camera, as shown in the figure. Suppose *I* represents the length of the image, *O* the length of the object, *d* the distance from the lens to the film, and *D* the distance from the lens to the object. These four quantities are related by the following proportion.

$$\frac{\text{Image length}}{\text{Object length}} = \frac{\text{Image distance}}{\text{Object distance}}$$

or

$$\frac{I}{O} = \frac{d}{D}$$

Given the length of the image on the film and its distance from the lens, the length of the object determines the distance the lens must be from the object.

Solution

Write ratios comparing the price for each size jar to the number of units (ounces) per jar. Then divide to obtain the price per unit (ounce). The results in **Table 2** are rounded to the nearest thousandth.

Table 2

Size	Unit Cost (dollars per ounce)	
18-oz	$\dfrac{\$1.78}{18} = \$0.099$	← —— The best buy
28-oz	$\dfrac{\$2.97}{28} = \$0.106$	
40-oz	$\dfrac{\$3.98}{40} = \$0.100$	

Because the 18-oz size produces the lowest unit cost, it is the best buy. Thus, buying the largest size does not always provide the best buy. ∎

Solving Proportions

PROPORTION

A **proportion** is a statement that two ratios are equal.

For example, $\dfrac{3}{4} = \dfrac{15}{20}$ Proportion

is a proportion that says the ratios $\frac{3}{4}$ and $\frac{15}{20}$ are equal. In the proportion

$$\frac{a}{b} = \frac{c}{d} \quad (b, d \neq 0),$$

a, *b*, *c*, and *d* are the **terms** of the proportion. The *a* and *d* terms are called the **extremes,** and the *b* and *c* terms are called the **means.** We read the proportion $\frac{a}{b} = \frac{c}{d}$ as "*a* is to *b* as *c* is to *d*." Multiply each side of this proportion by the common denominator, *bd*.

$$bd \cdot \frac{a}{b} = bd \cdot \frac{c}{d} \qquad \text{Multiply each side by } bd.$$

$$\frac{b}{b}(d \cdot a) = \frac{d}{d}(b \cdot c) \qquad \text{Associative and commutative properties}$$

$$ad = bc \qquad \text{Commutative and identity properties}$$

We can also find the products *ad* and *bc* by multiplying diagonally.

$$\frac{a}{b} = \frac{c}{d}$$

bc

ad

For this reason, *ad* and *bc* are called **cross products** of the proportion.

CROSS PRODUCTS

If $\dfrac{a}{b} = \dfrac{c}{d}$, then the cross products of the proportion, *ad* and *bc*, are equal.

Also, if $ad = bc$, then $\dfrac{a}{b} = \dfrac{c}{d}$ (where $b \neq 0$, $d \neq 0$).

For a proportion to be true, the product of the extremes must equal the product of the means. If $\frac{a}{c} = \frac{b}{d}$, then $ad = cb$, or $ad = bc$. This means that these two corresponding proportions are equivalent.

$$\frac{a}{b} = \frac{c}{d} \quad \text{can also be written as} \quad \frac{a}{c} = \frac{b}{d}.$$

Sometimes one form is more convenient to work with than the other.

EXAMPLE 3   Solving a Proportion

Solve the proportion $\dfrac{x}{63} = \dfrac{5}{9}$.

Solution

$$\frac{x}{63} = \frac{5}{9}$$

$9x = 63 \cdot 5$ Set the cross products equal.

$9x = 315$ Multiply.

$x = 35$ Divide by 9.

The solution set is $\{35\}$.   ■

EXAMPLE 4   Solving an Equation Using Cross Products

Solve $\dfrac{x-2}{5} = \dfrac{x+1}{3}$.

Solution

Find the cross products, and set them equal to each other.

$3(x-2) = 5(x+1)$ Cross products

Be sure to use parentheses.

$3x - 6 = 5x + 5$ Distributive property

$3x = 5x + 11$ Add 6.

$-2x = 11$ Subtract 5x.

$x = -\dfrac{11}{2}$ Divide by −2.

The solution set is $\left\{-\frac{11}{2}\right\}$.   ■

We now consider a proportion problem that occurs in the allied health field.

EXAMPLE 5   Using a Proportion to Determine Proper Dosage of a Drug

Nurses use proportions to determine the amount of a drug to administer when the dose is measured in milligrams (mg), but the drug is packaged in a diluted form in milliliters (mL). For example, to find the number of milliliters of fluid needed to administer 300 mg of a drug that comes packaged as 120 mg in 2 mL of fluid, a nurse sets up the proportion

$$\frac{120 \text{ mg}}{2 \text{ mL}} = \frac{300 \text{ mg}}{x \text{ mL}},$$

where x represents the amount to administer in milliliters. (*Source:* Hoyles, Celia, Richard Noss, and Stefano Pozzi. "Proportional Reasoning in Nursing Practice." *Journal for Research in Mathematics Education,* 32, 1, 4–27.)

(a) Solve the proportion above.

(b) Determine the correct dose if 120 mg of Amikacin is packaged as 100 mg in 2-mL vials.

Solution

(a) We must solve the following proportion.

$$\frac{120}{2} = \frac{300}{x}$$

$$120x = 2 \cdot 300 \qquad \text{Cross products}$$

$$120x = 600 \qquad \text{Multiply.}$$

$$x = 5 \qquad \text{Divide by 120.}$$

Thus, 5 milliliters of fluid are needed.

(b) Let x represent the correct dose. Set up the proportion as in part (a).

$$\frac{100 \text{ mg}}{2 \text{ mL}} = \frac{120 \text{ mg}}{x \text{ mL}} \qquad \text{Set up the ratios consistently.}$$

Now solve for x.

$$\frac{100}{2} = \frac{120}{x}$$

$$100x = 240 \qquad \text{Cross products}$$

$$x = 2.4 \qquad \text{Divide by 100.}$$

Thus, 2.4 milliliters are needed.   ■

Researchers use sampling to make predictions about populations. In the biological sciences, populations of birds, fish, and other wildlife species are made using proportions. The mathematics of how reliable these predictions are (confidence intervals) is a topic for statistics courses, and the internet provides information about this topic. See, for example, http://www.pivotalresearch.ca/resources-sample-calc.php. In the next example, we show how a proportion is used in sampling.

EXAMPLE 6 **Using a Proportion to Approximate the Number of Fish in a Lake**

To estimate a population, biologists obtain a sample of fish in a lake and mark each specimen with a harmless tag. Later they return, get a similar sample of fish from the same areas of the lake, and determine the proportion of previously tagged fish in the new sample. The total fish population is estimated by assuming that the proportion of tagged fish in the new sample is the same as the proportion of tagged fish in the entire lake.

Suppose biologists tag 300 fish on May 1. When they return on June 1 and take a new sample of 400 fish, they discover that 5 of the 400 were previously tagged. Estimate the number of fish in the lake.

Solution

Let x represent the number of fish in the lake. Set up and solve a proportion.

Tagged fish on May 1 $\longrightarrow \dfrac{300}{x} = \dfrac{5}{400} \longleftarrow$ Tagged fish in the June 1 sample
Total fish in the lake $\longrightarrow \quad\quad\quad\longleftarrow$ Total number in the June 1 sample

$$5x = 120{,}000 \qquad \text{Cross products}$$

$$x = 24{,}000 \qquad \text{Divide by 5.}$$

Based on this sampling procedure, there are about 24,000 fish in the lake. ∎

Direct Variation

Table 3

Number of Gallons	Cost of This Number of Gallons
1	$3.50
2	$7.00
3	$10.50
4	$14.00
5	$17.50

Suppose that the cost of gasoline is $3.50 per gallon, and you decide to buy 5 gallons. **Table 3** shows the relationship between the number of gallons you pump and the price shown on the gas pump for that number of gallons. There is a distinct relationship between the number of gallons and the total cost.

Suppose that we let x represent the number of gallons pumped and let y represent the price in dollars for that number of gallons. Then the relationship between x and y is given by the equation

$$y = 3.50x,$$

or

$$\frac{y}{x} = 3.50.$$

This relationship is an example of **direct variation.** Here the quotient $\frac{y}{x}$ is always 3.50, and it is the **constant of variation.**

> **DIRECT VARIATION**
>
> **y varies directly as x,** or **y is directly proportional to x,** if there exists a non-zero constant k such that
>
> $$y = kx, \quad \text{or, equivalently,} \quad \frac{y}{x} = k.$$
>
> The constant k is the **constant of variation.**

In direct variation where $k > 0$, as x increases, y increases, and similarly as x decreases, y decreases.

SOLVING A VARIATION PROBLEM

Step 1 Write the variation equation.

Step 2 Substitute the initial values and solve for k.

Step 3 Rewrite the variation equation with the value of k from Step 2.

Step 4 Substitute the remaining values, solve for the unknown, and find the required answer.

EXAMPLE 7 Solving a Direct Variation Problem

Hooke's law for an elastic spring states that the distance a spring stretches is directly proportional to the force applied. If a force of 150 pounds stretches a certain spring 8 centimeters, how much will a force of 400 pounds stretch the spring?

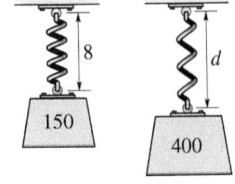

Figure 4

Solution

Step 1 See **Figure 4.** If d is the distance the spring stretches, and f is the force applied, then $d = kf$ for some constant k.

$$d = kf \qquad \text{Variation equation}$$

Step 2 Substitute $d = 8$ and $f = 150$, and solve for k.

$$8 = k \cdot 150 \qquad \text{Let } d = 8 \text{ and } f = 150.$$

$$k = \frac{8}{150} \qquad \text{Divide by 150 and interchange sides.}$$

$$k = \frac{4}{75} \qquad \text{Lowest terms}$$

Step 3 Thus $d = \frac{4}{75}f$.

Step 4 Now let $f = 400$.

$$d = \frac{4}{75}(400) \qquad \text{Let } f = 400.$$

$$d = \frac{64}{3} \qquad \text{Multiply and simplify.}$$

The spring will stretch $21\frac{1}{3}$ centimeters if a force of 400 pounds is applied. ■

In some cases, one quantity will vary directly as a power of another.

DIRECT VARIATION AS A POWER

y varies directly as the nth power of x if there exists a nonzero real number k such that

$$y = kx^n.$$

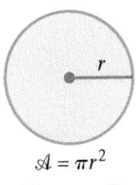

$\mathcal{A} = \pi r^2$

Figure 5

An example of direct variation as a power involves the area of a circle. See **Figure 5.** The formula for the area of a circle is $\mathcal{A} = \pi r^2$. Here, π is the constant of variation, and the area $\mathcal{A}$ varies directly as the square of the radius r.

EXAMPLE 8 Solving a Direct Variation Problem

The distance a body falls from rest varies directly as the square of the time it falls (here we disregard air resistance). If a skydiver falls 64 feet in 2 seconds, how far will she fall in 8 seconds?

Solution

Step 1 If d represents the distance the skydiver falls, and t represents the time it takes to fall, then for some constant k, $d = kt^2$.

Step 2 To find the value of k, use the fact that the skydiver falls 64 feet in 2 seconds.

$$d = kt^2 \qquad \text{Formula}$$
$$64 = k(2)^2 \qquad \text{Let } d = 64 \text{ and } t = 2.$$
$$k = 16 \qquad \text{Evaluate } k.$$

Step 3 With this result, the variation equation can be written.

$$d = 16t^2$$

Step 4 Now let $t = 8$ to find the number of feet the skydiver will fall in 8 seconds.

$$d = 16t^2$$
$$= 16(8)^2$$
$$= 1024 \qquad 8^2 = 8 \cdot 8 = 64$$

The skydiver will fall 1024 feet in 8 seconds. ■

Inverse Variation

Another type of variation is *inverse variation*. **With inverse variation, for $k > 0$, as one variable increases, the other variable decreases.**

For example, in a closed space, volume decreases as pressure increases, which can be illustrated by a trash compactor. See the figure at the side. As the compactor presses down, the pressure on the trash increases, and in turn, the trash occupies a smaller space.

As pressure on trash increases, volume of trash decreases.

Bill Veeck was the owner of several major league baseball teams in the 1950s and 1960s. He was known to often sit in the stands and enjoy games with his paying customers. Here is a quotation attributed to him:

*I have discovered in 20 years of moving around a ballpark, that the knowledge of the game is usually in **inverse proportion** to the price of the seats.*

INVERSE VARIATION

y* varies inversely as *x if there exists a nonzero real number k such that

$$y = \frac{k}{x}, \quad \text{or, equivalently,} \quad xy = k.$$

Also, ***y* varies inversely as the *n*th power of *x*** if there exists a nonzero real number k such that

$$y = \frac{k}{x^n}.$$

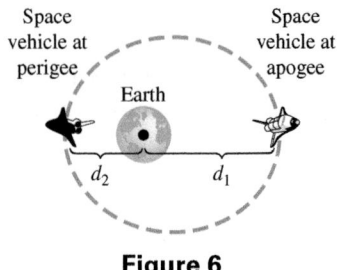

Space vehicle at perigee

Space vehicle at apogee

Earth

d_2 d_1

Figure 6

Johann Kepler (1571–1630) established the importance of the **ellipse** in 1609, when he discovered that the orbits of the planets around the sun were elliptical, not circular.

Halley's comet, which has been studied since 467 B.C., has an elliptical orbit that is long and narrow, with one axis much longer than the other. This comet was named for the British astronomer and mathematician **Edmund Halley** (1656–1742), who predicted its return after observing it in 1682. The comet appears regularly every 76 years.

EXAMPLE 9 Solving an Inverse Variation Problem

The weight of an object above Earth varies inversely as the square of its distance from the center of Earth. A space vehicle in an elliptical orbit has a maximum distance from the center of Earth (apogee) of 6700 miles. Its minimum distance from the center of Earth (perigee) is 4090 miles. See **Figure 6** (not to scale). If an astronaut in the vehicle weighs 57 pounds at its apogee, what does the astronaut weigh at the perigee?

Solution

If w is the weight and d is the distance from the center of Earth, then the variation equation is

$$w = \frac{k}{d^2}, \quad \text{for some constant } k.$$

At the apogee the astronaut weighs 57 pounds and the distance from the center of Earth is 6700 miles. Use these values to find k.

$$57 = \frac{k}{(6700)^2} \qquad \text{Let } w = 57 \text{ and } d = 6700.$$

$$k = 57(6700)^2 \qquad \text{Multiply by } (6700)^2. \text{ Rewrite.}$$

Then the weight at the perigee with $d = 4090$ miles is

$$w = \frac{57(6700)^2}{(4090)^2} \approx 153 \text{ pounds.} \qquad \text{Use a calculator.} \qquad ■$$

Joint and Combined Variation

If one variable varies as the product of several other variables (perhaps raised to powers), the first variable is said to be in **joint variation** as the others.

EXAMPLE 10 Solving a Joint Variation Problem

The strength of a rectangular beam varies jointly as its width and the square of its depth. If the strength of a beam 2 inches wide by 10 inches deep is 1000 pounds per square inch, what is the strength of a beam 4 inches wide and 8 inches deep?

Solution

If S represents the strength, w the width, and d the depth, then, for some constant k, the variation equation is $S = kwd^2$.

$$S = kwd^2 \qquad \boxed{10^2 = 10 \cdot 10 = 100}$$

$$1000 = k \cdot 2 \cdot 10^2 \qquad \text{Let } S = 1000, w = 2, \text{ and } d = 10.$$

$$1000 = 200k \qquad \text{Apply the exponent. Multiply.}$$

$$k = 5 \qquad \text{Divide by 200. Rewrite.}$$

Thus, $S = 5wd^2$. Find S for $w = 4$ and $d = 8$ by substitution.

$$S = 5 \cdot 4 \cdot 8^2 \qquad \text{Let } w = 4 \text{ and } d = 8.$$

$$S = 1280$$

The strength of the beam is 1280 pounds per square inch. ■

Combined variation involves combinations of direct and inverse variation.

EXAMPLE 11 Solving a Combined Variation Problem

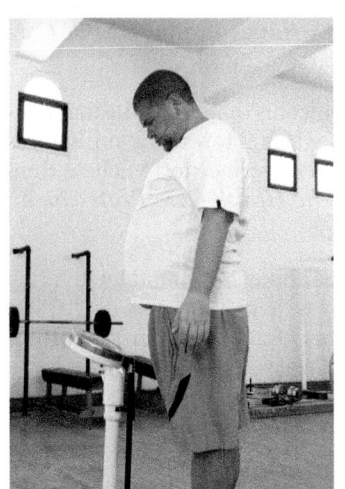

Body mass index, or BMI, is used by physicians to assess a person's level of fatness. BMI varies directly as an individual's weight in pounds and inversely as the square of the individual's height in inches. A person who weighs 118 lb and is 64 in. tall has a BMI of 20.25. (BMI is usually rounded to the nearest whole number.) (*Source: Washington Post.*)

Grady weighs 200 pounds and is 6 feet, 2 inches tall. Find his BMI.

Solution

Let B represent the BMI, w the weight, and h the height. Use the given information to determine k.

$$B = \frac{kw}{h^2}$$ ← BMI varies directly as the weight.
                          ← BMI varies inversely as the square of the height.

$$20.25 = \frac{k(118)}{64^2}$$ Let $B = 20.25$, $w = 118$, and $h = 64$.

$$k = \frac{20.25(64^2)}{118}$$ Multiply by 64^2. Divide by 118.

$$k \approx 703$$ Use a calculator.

Use $k = 703$, $w = 200$, and $h = (6 \times 12) + 2 = 74$ to find B, Grady's BMI.

$$B = \frac{703(200)}{74^2} \approx 25.68 \approx 26$$ Nearest whole number   ∎

7.3 EXERCISES

Determine the ratio and write it in lowest terms.

1. 50 feet to 80 feet

2. 12 miles to 36 miles

3. 17 dollars to 68 dollars

4. 600 people to 500 people

5. 288 inches to 12 feet

6. 60 inches to 2 yards

7. 5 days to 40 hours

8. 75 minutes to 4 hours

Merchandise Pricing *A supermarket was surveyed to find the prices charged for items in various sizes. Find the best buy (based on price per unit) for each item.*

9. Granulated Sugar

Size	Price
4-lb	$1.79
10-lb	$4.29

10. Ground Coffee

Size	Price
15-oz	$3.43
34.5-oz	$6.98

11. Salad Dressing

Size	Price
16-oz	$2.44
32-oz	$2.98
48-oz	$4.95

12. Black Pepper

Size	Price
2-oz	$2.23
4-oz	$2.49
8-oz	$6.59

13. Vegetable Oil

Size	Price
16-oz	$1.66
32-oz	$2.59
64-oz	$4.29
128-oz	$6.49

14. Mouthwash

Size	Price
8.5-oz	$0.99
16.9-oz	$1.87
33.8-oz	$2.49
50.7-oz	$2.99

15. Tomato Ketchup

Size	Price
14-oz	$1.39
24-oz	$1.55
36-oz	$1.78
64-oz	$3.99

16. Grape Jelly

Size	Price
12-oz	$1.05
18-oz	$1.73
32-oz	$1.84
48-oz	$2.88

Solve each equation.

17. $\dfrac{x}{4} = \dfrac{175}{20}$

18. $\dfrac{x}{8} = \dfrac{49}{56}$

19. $\dfrac{3x-2}{5} = \dfrac{6x-5}{11}$

20. $\dfrac{5+x}{3} = \dfrac{x+7}{5}$

21. $\dfrac{3x+1}{7} = \dfrac{2x-3}{6}$

22. $\dfrac{2x+7}{3} = \dfrac{x-1}{4}$

Drug Dosage Calculations Work the following problems involving drug dosages.

23. A physician orders 37.5 milligrams of Cylert (permoline). It is available in 18.75-milligram tablets. How many tablets should the nurse administer? (*Source:* Hegstad, Lorrie N., and Wilma Hayek. *Essential Drug Dosage Calculations,* 4th ed. Prentice Hall, 2001.)

24. K-Tab (potassium chloride) is available in 750-milligram (0.75-gram) tablets. A physician orders that 1.5 grams of K-Tab should be given with meals. How many tablets should the nurse administer with each meal? (*Source:* Hegstad, Lorrie N., and Wilma Hayek. *Essential Drug Dosage Calculations,* 4th ed. Prentice Hall, 2001.)

25. A patient's order is 40 milligrams of codeine phosphate. Available in stock is 50 milligrams in 1 milliliter of liquid. How many milliliters should be administered? (*Source:* Timmons, Daniel L., and Catherine W. Johnson. *Math Skills for Allied Health Careers.* Pearson Prentice Hall, 2008.)

26. A nurse is asked to administer 200 milligrams of fluconazole to a patient. There is a stock solution that provides 40 milligrams per milliliter. How much of the solution should be given to the patient? (*Source:* Timmons, Daniel L., and Catherine W. Johnson. *Math Skills for Allied Health Careers.* Pearson Prentice Hall, 2008.)

27. A doctor prescribed ampicillin for a child who weighs 9.1 kilograms. The label on the box recommends a daily dosage of 100 milligrams per kilogram of weight. How much ampicillin should the child receive per day? (*Source:* Timmons, Daniel L., and Catherine W. Johnson. *Math Skills for Allied Health Careers.* Pearson Prentice Hall, 2008.)

28. An order is for 250 milligrams of a drug given orally. You have scored tablets in 100-milligram dosages. How many tablets should you give? (*Source:* Lesmeister, Michele Benjamin. *Math Basics for the Health Care Professional,* 4th ed. Pearson, 2014.)

29. A drug label notes that the client's medicine has 250 milligrams in 5 milliliters of syrup. How many milliliters would deliver 375 milligrams of medicine? (*Source:* Lesmeister, Michele Benjamin. *Math Basics for the Health Care Professional,* 4th ed. Pearson, 2014.)

30. A physician orders 50 milligrams of hydroxyzine pamoate by mouth every 12 hours. Each teaspoonful contains 25 milligrams. How many teaspoons should be administered every 12 hours? (*Source:* Lesmeister, Michele Benjamin. *Math Basics for the Health Care Professional,* 4th ed. Pearson, 2014.)

31. A label for lorazepam indicates that each milliliter contains 4 milligrams of the drug. How many milligrams are in 3 milliliters? (*Source:* Lesmeister, Michele Benjamin. *Math Basics for the Health Care Professional,* 4th ed. Pearson, 2014.)

32. Flow rate in milliliters per hour F is found by dividing volume in millilters V by time in hours t. A doctor has prescribed 750 milligrams of ampicillin in 125 milliliters to infuse (to be given) over 45 minutes. What is the infusion rate in milliliters per hour? (*Source:* Lesmeister, Michele Benjamin. *Math Basics for the Health Care Professional,* 4th ed. Pearson, 2014.)

Solve each problem involving proportions.

33. *Price of Gasoline* If 6 gallons of premium unleaded gasoline cost $17.82, how much would it cost to completely fill a 15-gallon tank?

34. *Sales Tax* If the sales tax on a $16.00 DVD is $1.40, how much would the sales tax be on a $120.00 Blu-ray disc player?

35. *Tagging Fish for a Population Estimate* Louisiana biologists tagged 250 fish in the oxbow lake False River on October 5. On a later date they found 7 tagged fish in a sample of 350. Estimate the total number of fish in False River to the nearest hundred.

36. *Tagging Fish for a Population Estimate* On May 13 researchers at Spirit Lake tagged 420 fish. When they returned a few weeks later, their sample of 500 fish contained 9 that were tagged. Give an approximation of the fish population in Spirit Lake to the nearest hundred.

37. *Distance between Cities* The distance between Singapore and Tokyo is 3300 miles. On a certain wall map, this distance is represented by 11 inches. The actual distance between Mexico City and Cairo is 7700 miles. How far apart are they on the same map?

38. *Distance between Cities* A wall map of the United States has a distance of 8.5 inches between Memphis and Denver, two cities that are actually 1040 miles apart. The actual distance between St. Louis and Des Moines is 333 miles. How far apart are St. Louis and Des Moines on this map?

39. *Distance between Cities* On a world globe, the distance between Capetown and Bangkok, two cities that are actually 10,080 kilometers apart, is 12.4 inches. The actual distance between Moscow and Berlin is 1610 kilometers. How far apart are Moscow and Berlin on this globe?

40. *Distance between Cities* On a world globe, the distance between Rio de Janeiro and Hong Kong, two cities that are actually 17,615 kilometers apart, is 21.5 inches. The actual distance between Paris and Stockholm is 1605 kilometers. How far apart are Paris and Stockholm on this globe?

41. *Cleaning Mixture* According to the directions on a bottle of Armstrong® Concentrated Floor Cleaner, for routine cleaning, $\frac{1}{4}$ cup of cleaner should be mixed with 1 gallon of warm water. How much cleaner should be mixed with $10\frac{1}{2}$ gallons of water?

42. *Cleaning Mixture* See **Exercise 41.** The directions also specify that for extra-strength cleaning, $\frac{1}{2}$ cup of cleaner should be used for each gallon of water. How much cleaner should be mixed with $15\frac{1}{2}$ gallons of water?

Solve each problem involving variation.

43. *Force Required to Compress a Spring* The force required to compress a spring varies directly as the change in the length of the spring. If a force of 12 pounds is required to compress a certain spring 3 inches, how much force is required to compress the spring 5 inches?

44. *Interest on an Investment* The interest earned on an investment varies directly as the rate of interest. If the interest is $48 when the interest rate is 5%, find the interest when the rate is 4.2%.

45. *Weight of a Moose* The weight of an object on the moon varies directly as the weight of the object on Earth. According to *Guinness World Records*, "Shad," a goat, weighs 352 pounds. Shad would weigh about 59 pounds on the moon. A bull moose weighing 1800 pounds was shot in Canada. How much would the moose have weighed on the moon?

46. *Voyage in a Paddleboat* According to *Guinness World Records*, the longest recorded voyage in a paddle boat is 2226 miles in 103 days by the foot power of two boaters down the Mississippi River. Assuming a constant rate, how far would they have gone if they had traveled 120 days? (Distance varies directly as time.)

47. *Exchange Rate (Dollars and Euros)* The euro is the common currency used by most European countries, including Italy. On a recent day, the exchange rate between euros and U.S. dollars was 1 euro to $1.4294. Ashley went to Rome and exchanged her U.S. currency for euros, receiving 300 euros. How much in U.S. dollars did she exchange?

48. *Exchange Rate (U.S. and Mexico)* If 8 U.S. dollars can be exchanged for 103.0 Mexican pesos, how many pesos, to the nearest hundredth, can be obtained for $65?

49. *Pressure Exerted by a Liquid* The pressure exerted by a certain liquid at a given point varies directly as the depth of the point beneath the surface of the liquid. The pressure at a depth of 10 feet is 50 pounds per square inch. What is the pressure at a depth of 20 feet?

50. *Pressure of a Gas in a Container* If the volume is constant, the pressure of a gas in a container varies directly as the temperature. (Temperature must be measured in *kelvins* (K), a unit of measurement used in physics.) If the pressure is 5 pounds per square inch at a temperature of 200 K, what is the pressure at a temperature of 300 K?

51. *Falling Body* For a body falling freely from rest (disregarding air resistance), the distance the body falls varies directly as the square of the time. If an object is dropped from the top of a tower 400 feet high and hits the ground in 5 seconds, how far did it fall in the first 3 seconds?

52. *Illumination from a Light Source* The illumination produced by a light source varies inversely as the square of the distance from the source. If the illumination produced 4 feet from a light source is 75 foot-candles, find the illumination produced 9 feet from the same source.

53. *Skidding Car* The force needed to keep a car from skidding on a curve varies inversely as the radius of the curve and jointly as the weight of the car and the square of the rate (speed). If 242 pounds of force keep a 2000-pound car from skidding on a curve of radius 500 feet at 30 miles per hour, what force would keep the same car from skidding on a curve of radius 750 feet at 50 miles per hour?

54. Load Supported by a Column The maximum load that a cylindrical column with a circular cross section can hold varies directly as the fourth power of the diameter of the cross section and inversely as the square of the height. A 9-meter column 1 meter in diameter will support 8 metric tons. How many metric tons can be supported by a column 12 meters high and $\frac{2}{3}$ meter in diameter?

BMI Formula *Use the formula*

$$B = \frac{kw}{h^2}$$

from **Example 11** *to find the BMI of a man with the given weight and height. Round to the nearest whole number.*

55. weight: 180 pounds
height: 72 inches

56. weight: 195 pounds
height: 68 inches

57. weight: 260 pounds
height: 66 inches

58. weight: 140 pounds   height: 64 inches

Fish Weight-Estimation *Girth is the distance around the body of a fish.*

59. The weight of a trout varies jointly as its length and the square of its girth. One angler caught a trout that weighed 10.5 pounds and measured 26 inches long with an 18-inch girth. Find the weight of a trout that is 22 inches long with a 15-inch girth.

60. The weight of a bass varies jointly as its girth and the square of its length. A prize-winning bass weighed in at 22.7 pounds and measured 36 inches long with a 21-inch girth. How much would a bass 28 inches long with an 18-inch girth weigh?

Consumer Price Index *The consumer price index (CPI), issued by the U.S. Bureau of Labor Statistics, provides a means of determining the purchasing power of the U.S. dollar from one year to the next. Using the period from 1982 to 1984 as a measure of 100.0, the CPI for selected years from 1999 to 2011 is shown here.*

Year	Consumer Price Index
1999	166.6
2001	177.1
2003	184.0
2005	195.3
2007	207.3
2009	214.5
2011	224.9

Source: Bureau of Labor Statistics.

To use the CPI to predict a price in a particular year, we can set up a proportion and compare it with a known price in another year, as follows.

$$\frac{\text{Price in year } A}{\text{Index in year } A} = \frac{\text{Price in year } B}{\text{Index in year } B}$$

Use the CPI figures in the table to find the amount that would be charged for using the same amount of electricity that cost $225 in 1999. Give your answer to the nearest dollar.

61. in 2001   **62.** in 2003   **63.** in 2007   **64.** in 2011

Work each problem from the world of television and film.

65. The Andy Griffith Show In an episode of *The Andy Griffith show*, Andy told Opie (Ron Howard) that there were 400 needy boys in their county, which calculated to be $1\frac{1}{2}$ boys per square mile. What was the area of their county?

66. Mean Girls In the movie *Mean Girls*, Regina George (Rachel McAdams) tells Cady (Lindsay Lohan) that her candy bar has 120 calories and 48 of them are from fat. If her candy bar has 180 calories, how many would be from fat?

7.4   LINEAR INEQUALITIES

OBJECTIVES

1 Graph an interval on a number line.

2 Solve a linear inequality using the addition and multiplication properties of inequality.

3 Solve an application that leads to a linear inequality.

Number Lines and Interval Notation

Inequalities are algebraic expressions related by any of these symbols.

$<$ "is less than" $\leq$ "is less than or equal to"

$>$ "is greater than" $\geq$ "is greater than or equal to"

Unless otherwise specified, we solve an inequality by finding all real number solutions for it. For example, the solution set of $x \leq 2$ includes *all real numbers* that are less than or equal to 2, not just the *integers* less than or equal to 2.

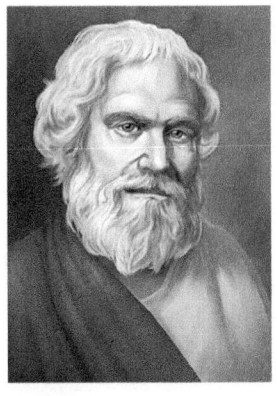

Archimedes, one of the greatest mathematicians of antiquity, was born in the Greek city of Syracuse about 287 B.C.

A colorful story about Archimedes relates his reaction to one of his discoveries. While taking a bath, he noticed that an immersed object, if heavier than a fluid, "will, if placed in it, descend to the bottom of the fluid, and the solid will, when weighed in the fluid, be lighter than its true weight by the weight of the fluid displaced." This discovery so excited him that he ran through the streets shouting "Eureka!" ("I have found it!") without bothering to clothe himself.

Archimedes met his death at age 75 during the pillage of Syracuse. He was using a sand tray to draw geometric figures when a Roman soldier came upon him. He ordered the soldier to move clear of his "circles," and the soldier obliged by killing him.

We show the solution set of this inequality by graphing the real numbers satisfying $x \leq 2$. We do this by placing a square bracket at 2 on a number line and drawing an arrow from the bracket to the left (to show that all numbers less than 2 are also part of the graph).* See **Figure 7.**

Figure 7

The set of numbers less than or equal to 2 is an example of an **interval** on the number line. To write intervals, we use **interval notation.** For example, using this notation, the interval of all numbers less than or equal to 2 is written as $(-\infty, 2]$. Interval notation often uses the **infinity symbol,** ∞. The **negative infinity symbol,** $-\infty$, does not indicate a number. It is used to show that the interval includes all real numbers less than 2. As on the number line, the square bracket indicates that 2 is part of the solution. *A parenthesis is always used next to the infinity symbol.*

The set of real numbers is written in interval notation as $(-\infty, \infty)$. Examples of other sets written in interval notation are shown in **Table 4.** In these intervals, assume that $a < b$.

Table 4

Type of Interval	Set-Builder Notation	Interval Notation	Graph
Open interval	$\{x \mid a < x < b\}$	(a, b)	
Closed interval	$\{x \mid a \leq x \leq b\}$	$[a, b]$	
Half-open (or half-closed) interval	$\{x \mid a \leq x < b\}$	$[a, b)$	
	$\{x \mid a < x \leq b\}$	$(a, b]$	
Disjoint interval	$\{x \mid x < a \text{ or } x > b\}$	$(-\infty, a) \cup (b, \infty)$	
	$\{x \mid x > a\}$	(a, ∞)	
	$\{x \mid x \geq a\}$	$[a, \infty)$	
Infinite interval	$\{x \mid x < a\}$	$(-\infty, a)$	
	$\{x \mid x \leq a\}$	$(-\infty, a]$	
	$\{x \mid x \text{ is a real number}\}$	$(-\infty, \infty)$	

*Some texts use solid circles rather than square brackets to indicate that the end point is included on a number line graph. Open circles are also used to indicate noninclusion, in place of the parentheses whose use is described in **Example 1(a).**

Bernard Bolzano (1781–1848) was an early exponent of rigor and precision in mathematics. Many early results in such areas as calculus were produced by the masters in the field. These masters knew what they were doing and produced accurate results. However, their sloppy arguments caused trouble in the hands of the less gifted. The work of Bolzano and others helped put mathematics on a strong footing.

EXAMPLE 1 **Graphing Intervals Written in Interval Notation on a Number Line**

Write each inequality in interval notation, and graph the interval.

(a) $x > -5$ **(b)** $-1 \le x < 3$

Solution

(a) The statement $x > -5$ says that x can be any number greater than -5 but cannot be -5. The interval is written $(-5, \infty)$. Place a parenthesis at -5 and draw an arrow to the right, as shown in **Figure 8**. The parenthesis indicates that -5 is not part of the graph.

Figure 8

(b) The statement $-1 \le x < 3$ is read "-1 is less than or equal to x *and* x is less than 3." Thus, we want the set of numbers that are *between* -1 and 3, with -1 included and 3 excluded. In interval notation, we write $[-1, 3)$, using a square bracket at -1 because -1 is part of the graph, and a parenthesis at 3 because 3 is not part of the graph. The graph is shown in **Figure 9.**

Figure 9

Addition Property of Inequality

LINEAR INEQUALITY IN ONE VARIABLE

A **linear inequality in one variable** can be written in the form

$$Ax + B < C,$$

where A, B, and C are real numbers, with $A \ne 0$. (The symbol $<$ may be replaced by $>$, $\le$, or $\ge$.)

Just as we can add the same quantity to both sides of an *equation,* we can do the same for an *inequality.* This is the **addition property of inequality.**

ADDITION PROPERTY OF INEQUALITY

For any real number expressions A, B, and C, the inequalities

$$A < B \quad \text{and} \quad A + C < B + C$$

have the same solutions. (The same number may be added to each side of an inequality without changing the solutions.)

The same number may also be *subtracted* from each side of an inequality.

Amalie ("Emmy") Noether (1882–1935) was an outstanding mathematician in the field of **abstract algebra.** She studied and worked in Germany at a time when it was very difficult for a woman to do so. At the University of Erlangen in 1900, Noether was one of only two women. Although she could attend classes, professors could and did deny her the right to take the exams for their courses. Not until 1904 was Noether allowed to officially register. She completed her doctorate four years later.

In 1916 Emmy Noether went to Göttingen to work with David Hilbert on the general theory of relativity. But even with Hilbert's backing and prestige, it was three years before the faculty voted to make Noether a *Privatdozent,* the lowest rank in the faculty. In 1922 Noether was made an unofficial professor (or assistant). She received no pay for this post, although she was given a small stipend to lecture in algebra.

EXAMPLE 2 Using the Addition Property of Inequality

Solve $7 + 3x > 2x - 5$.

Solution

Follow the same general procedure as in solving linear equations.

$$7 + 3x > 2x - 5$$
$$7 + 3x - 2x > 2x - 5 - 2x \qquad \text{Subtract } 2x.$$
$$7 + x > -5 \qquad \text{Combine like terms.}$$
$$7 + x - 7 > -5 - 7 \qquad \text{Subtract 7.}$$
$$x > -12 \qquad \text{Combine like terms.}$$

The solution set is $(-12, \infty)$. Its graph is shown in **Figure 10.**

Figure 10

Multiplication Property of Inequality

The addition property of inequality cannot be used to solve inequalities such as

$$4x \geq 28.$$

These inequalities require the *multiplication property of inequality.* To see how this property works, we look at some examples.

Multiply each side of the true inequality $3 < 7$ by the positive number 2. The result is $6 < 14$, which is a true statement. However, if we multiply by -2, we obtain $-6 < -14$, which is *false.*

In solving inequalities, when multiplying both sides by a negative number, we must reverse the direction of the inequality symbol to maintain the truth value of the statement. In summary, the **multiplication property of inequality** has two parts.

MULTIPLICATION PROPERTY OF INEQUALITY

Let A, B, and C be real number expressions, with $C \neq 0$.

  1. If C is *positive,* then the inequalities

$$A < B \quad \text{and} \quad AC < BC \qquad \text{Here } C \text{ is positive.}$$

  have the same solutions.

  2. If C is *negative,* then the inequalities

$$A < B \quad \text{and} \quad AC > BC \qquad \text{Here } C \text{ is negative.}$$

  have the same solutions.

(Each side of an inequality may be multiplied by the same positive number without changing the solutions. ***If the multiplier is negative, we must reverse the direction of the inequality symbol.***)

The multiplication property of inequality also permits *division* of each side of an inequality by the same nonzero number. In **Example 3** that follows, notice how the inequality symbol is reversed *only* for part (b), where both sides of the inequality are divided by a negative number.

EXAMPLE 3 Using the Multiplication Property of Inequality

Solve each inequality and graph the solution set.

(a) $3x < -18$ **(b)** $-4x \geq 8$

Solution

(a)
$$3x < -18$$

> 3 is a positive number, so the inequality symbol does not change.

$$\frac{3x}{3} < \frac{-18}{3} \quad \text{Divide by 3, a } \textit{positive} \text{ number.}$$

$$x < -6$$

The solution set is $(-\infty, -6)$. The graph is shown in **Figure 11**.

Figure 11

(b)
$$-4x \geq 8$$

$$\frac{-4x}{-4} \leq \frac{8}{-4} \quad \begin{array}{l}\text{Divide by } -4, \text{ a } \textit{negative} \text{ number.}\\ \text{Reverse the inequality symbol.}\end{array}$$

> Reverse the inequality when multiplying or dividing by a negative number.

$$x \leq -2$$

The solution set $(-\infty, -2]$ is graphed in **Figure 12**.

Figure 12

Solving Linear Inequalities

SOLVING A LINEAR INEQUALITY IN ONE VARIABLE

Step 1 **Simplify each side separately.** Use the distributive property to clear parentheses and combine like terms on each side as needed.

Step 2 **Isolate the variable terms on one side.** Use the addition property of inequality to get all terms with variables on one side of the inequality and all numbers on the other side.

Step 3 **Isolate the variable.** Use the multiplication property of inequality to change the inequality in the variable x to the form

$$x < k, \quad x > k, \quad x \leq k, \quad \text{or} \quad x \geq k, \quad \text{where } k \text{ is a number.}$$

Remember: Reverse the direction of the inequality symbol only when multiplying or dividing each side of an inequality by a negative number.

EXAMPLE 4 Solving a Linear Inequality

Solve $5(x - 3) - 7x \geq 4(x - 3) + 9$. Give the solution set in interval form, and then graph.

Solution

Step 1
$$5(x - 3) - 7x \geq 4(x - 3) + 9$$

$$5x - 15 - 7x \geq 4x - 12 + 9 \qquad \text{Distributive property}$$

$$-2x - 15 \geq 4x - 3 \qquad \text{Combine like terms.}$$

Step 2
$$-2x - 15 - 4x \geq 4x - 3 - 4x \qquad \begin{array}{l}\text{Use the addition property of}\\\text{inequality and subtract } 4x.\end{array}$$

$$-6x - 15 \geq -3$$

$$-6x - 15 + 15 \geq -3 + 15 \qquad \text{Add 15.}$$

$$-6x \geq 12 \qquad \text{Combine like terms.}$$

Step 3
$$\frac{-6x}{-6} \leq \frac{12}{-6} \qquad \begin{array}{l}\text{Use the multiplication property of inequality. Divide}\\\text{by } -6, \text{ a } \textit{negative} \text{ number. Reverse the symbol.}\end{array}$$

$$x \leq -2$$

The solution set is $(-\infty, -2]$. Its graph is shown in **Figure 13.**

Figure 13

In Step 3 of **Example 4** we used the property that says the following.

> ***Multiplying or dividing an inequality by a negative number***
> ***requires reversing the direction of the inequality symbol.***

In that step, we divided both sides of $-6x \geq 12$ by -6, and changed $\geq$ to $\leq$. Note that if it had been $6x \geq -12$, we would have divided by 6 and the symbol would NOT have been reversed. The fact that the sign of -12 is negative is irrelevant when applying this rule for solving inequalities.

Applications

Problem-Solving Strategy

The table gives some of the more common phrases that suggest inequality, along with examples and translations.

Phrase	Example	Inequality
Is greater than	A number *is greater than* 4.	$x > 4$
Is less than	A number *is less than* -12.	$x < -12$
Is at least	A number *is at least* 6.	$x \geq 6$
Is at most	A number *is at most* 8.	$x \leq 8$

WHEN Will I Ever USE This ?

Have you ever wondered what grade you will need on a test in order to keep a certain average in a course? Knowing how to interpret your teacher's grading system and your past scores in an inequality enables you to do this. For example, suppose that you are about to take your fourth test. Your previous scores (each out of 100) are 86, 88, and 78, and you want to keep an average of at least 80. To find the average of four scores, you must add them and divide by 4. Furthermore, this average must be *greater than or equal to* 80. You can apply the same six problem-solving steps from **Section 7.2,** changing Step 3 to "Write an inequality" rather than "Write an equation."

Step 1 **Read** the problem again.

Step 2 **Assign a variable.** Let $x =$ your score on your fourth test.

Step 3 **Write an inequality.** To find your average after 4 tests, add the test scores and divide by 4.

$$\underset{\text{Average}}{\underbrace{\frac{86 + 88 + 78 + x}{4}}} \underset{\substack{\text{is at}\\\text{least 80.}}}{\geq} 80$$

Step 4 **Solve.**

$$\frac{252 + x}{4} \geq 80 \qquad \text{Add the known scores.}$$

$$4\left(\frac{252 + x}{4}\right) \geq 4(80) \qquad \begin{array}{l}\text{Multiply by 4 to}\\\text{clear the fraction.}\end{array}$$

$$252 + x \geq 320$$

$$252 + x - 252 \geq 320 - 252 \qquad \text{Subtract 252.}$$

$$x \geq 68 \qquad \text{Combine like terms.}$$

Step 5 **State the answer.** You must score 68 or more on the fourth test to have an average of *at least* 80.

Step 6 **Check.** Determine whether this minimum score of 68 gives an average of 80.

$$\frac{86 + 88 + 78 + 68}{4} = \frac{320}{4} = 80 \quad \checkmark$$

EXAMPLE 5   Comparing Rate Plans for a Rental Truck

Newlyweds Bryce and Lauren need to rent a truck for one day to move their belongings to their new home. They can rent a truck of the size they need from We're Outta Here for $59.95 per day with a mileage charge of $0.28 per mile, or from Moving On Out for $64.95 per day plus $0.25 per mile. They are not sure how many miles they will need to drive during their move. After how many miles will the Moving On Out rental be a better deal than the one from We're Outta Here?

Solution

For the Moving On Out rental to be a better deal, its price must be less than that of We're Outta Here. Let x represent the number of miles traveled. Then

$$59.95 + 0.28x \quad \text{represents the price for We're Outta Here,}$$

and

$$64.95 + 0.25x \quad \text{represents the price for Moving On Out.}$$

We must solve the following inequality.

Price for Moving On Out		Price for We're Outta Here	
$64.95 + 0.25x$	$<$	$59.95 + 0.28x$	
$6495 + 25x$	$<$	$5995 + 28x$	Multiply by 100.
$25x - 28x$	$<$	$5995 - 6495$	Subtract 28x and 6495.
$-3x$	$<$	-500	Subtract.
x	$>$	$166.\overline{6}$	Divide by −3. Reverse the inequality symbol.

The price for Moving On Out *will be less than* that of We're Outta Here when the number of miles traveled *is greater than* about 167 miles. To make their decision, Bryce and Lauren need to determine the number of miles they plan to drive and compare it to 167 miles. ∎

Three-Part Inequalities

Inequalities that say that one number is *between* two other numbers are **three-part inequalities.** For example,

$$-3 < 5 < 7 \quad \text{says that 5 is between −3 and 7.}$$

For some applications, it is necessary to work with an inequality such as

$$3 < x + 2 < 8, \quad \text{where } x + 2 \text{ is between 3 and 8.}$$

To solve this inequality, we subtract 2 from each of the three parts.

$$3 - 2 < x + 2 - 2 < 8 - 2 \quad \text{Subtract 2 from each part.}$$
$$1 < \quad x \quad < 6 \quad \text{Simplify.}$$

The idea is to use "is less than" to get the inequality in the form

> The symbols must point in the same direction and toward the lesser number.

a number $< x <$ **another number.**

EXAMPLE 6 Solving a Three-Part Inequality

Solve $4 \le 3x - 5 < 6$. Give the solution set in interval form, and then graph.

Solution

$$4 \le \quad 3x - 5 \quad < 6$$
$$4 + 5 \le 3x - 5 + 5 < 6 + 5 \qquad \text{Add 5 to each part.}$$
$$9 \le \quad 3x \quad < 11 \qquad \text{Simplify.}$$

> Remember to divide all three parts by 3.

$$\frac{9}{3} \le \quad \frac{3x}{3} \quad < \frac{11}{3} \qquad \text{Divide each part by 3.}$$
$$3 \le \quad x \quad < \frac{11}{3} \qquad \text{Simplify.}$$

The solution set is $\left[3, \frac{11}{3}\right)$. Its graph is shown in **Figure 14.**

Figure 14

EXAMPLE 7 Interpreting Tolerance Using an Inequality

Suppose a bottle indicates that it contains 32 ounces of a sports drink. It may contain slightly more or less, depending on the **tolerance** allowed by the packager. If the agreed-upon tolerance is 0.25 ounce, then the bottle may contain 0.25 ounce more or 0.25 ounce less and still satisfy the requirement.

(a) Write a three-part inequality to illustrate this last statement. (Assume that equality also holds.) Let x represent the actual amount in the bottle.

(b) Solve the inequality and interpret the solution.

Solution

(a) The difference between x and 32 must be greater than or equal to -0.25 and less than or equal to 0.25. This is written as follows.

$$-0.25 \le \quad x - 32 \quad \le 0.25$$

(b)
$$-0.25 + 32 \le x - 32 + 32 \le 0.25 + 32 \qquad \text{Add 32.}$$
$$31.75 \le \quad x \quad \le 32.25 \qquad \text{Add.}$$

This final inequality indicates that the actual amount in the bottle must be between and inclusive of 31.75 ounces and 32.25 ounces.

7.4 EXERCISES

In Exercises 1–6, match each set in Group I with the correct graph or interval notation in A–F in Group II.

                    I   II

1. $\{x \mid x \le 3\}$ **2.** $\{x \mid x > 3\}$ **A.**   **B.**

3. $\{x \mid x < 3\}$ **4.** $\{x \mid x \ge 3\}$ **C.** $(3, \infty)$ **D.** $(-\infty, 3]$

5. $\{x \mid -3 \le x \le 3\}$ **6.** $\{x \mid -3 < x < 3\}$ **E.** $(-3, 3)$ **F.** $[-3, 3]$

Solve each inequality. Give the solution set in both interval and graph forms.

7. $10x \geq 70$

8. $12x \leq 72$

9. $4x + 1 \geq 21$

10. $5x + 2 \geq 52$

11. $\dfrac{3x - 1}{4} > 5$

12. $\dfrac{5x - 6}{8} < 8$

13. $-4x < 16$

14. $-2x > 10$

15. $-\dfrac{3}{4}x \geq 30$

16. $-1.5x \leq -\dfrac{9}{2}$

17. $-1.3x \geq -5.2$

18. $-2.5x \leq -1.25$

19. $\dfrac{2x - 5}{-4} > 5$

20. $\dfrac{3x - 2}{-5} < 6$

21. $x + 4(2x - 1) \geq x$

22. $x - 2(x - 4) \leq 3x$

23. $-(4 + x) + 2 - 3x < -14$

24. $-(9 + x) - 5 + 4x \geq 4$

25. $-3(x - 6) > 2x - 2$

26. $-2(x + 4) \leq 6x + 16$

27. $\dfrac{2}{3}(3x - 1) \geq \dfrac{3}{2}(2x - 3)$

28. $\dfrac{7}{5}(10x - 1) < \dfrac{2}{3}(6x + 5)$

Solve each inequality. Give the solution set in both interval and graph forms.

29. $-4 < x - 5 < 6$

30. $-1 < x + 1 < 8$

31. $-9 \leq x + 5 \leq 15$

32. $-4 \leq x + 3 \leq 10$

33. $-6 \leq 2x + 4 \leq 16$

34. $-15 < 3x + 6 < -12$

35. $-19 \leq 3x - 5 \leq 1$

36. $-16 < 3x + 2 < -10$

37. $-1 \leq \dfrac{2x - 5}{6} \leq 5$

38. $-3 \leq \dfrac{3x + 1}{4} \leq 3$

39. $4 \leq 5 - 9x < 8$

40. $4 \leq 3 - 2x < 8$

Solve each problem.

41. Truck Rental John and Suzanne needed to rent a truck for a day, so they priced what they needed at two rental firms. Agency A wanted $28 for one day, plus a fee of $0.25 per mile, while Agency B wanted $32 for one day, plus a fee of $0.15 per mile. After how many miles will the deal that Agency B offers be better than that of Agency A?

42. Car Rental Cody and Margaret needed to rent a car for a day, so they checked out two rental firms. Agency X wanted $47 for one day, plus a fee of $0.20 per mile, while Agency Y wanted $38 for one day, plus a fee of $0.35 per mile. After how many miles will the deal that Agency X offers be better than that of Agency Y?

43. Taxicab Fare In a large city, taxicabs charge $3.00 for the first $\frac{1}{5}$ mile and $0.50 for each additional $\frac{1}{5}$ mile. Frank has only $7.50. What is the maximum distance he can travel (not including a tip for the cabbie)?

44. Taxicab Fare Fifteen years ago taxicab fares in the city in **Exercise 43** were $0.90 for the first $\frac{1}{7}$ mile and $0.10 for each additional $\frac{1}{7}$ mile. Based on the information given there and the answer you found, how much farther could Frank have traveled at that time?

45. Grade Average Hollis earned scores of 90 and 82 on his first two tests in English Literature. What score must he make on his third test to keep an average of 84 or greater?

46. Grade Average Beth scored 92 and 96 on her first two tests in Methods in Photography. What score must she make on her third test to keep an average of 90 or greater?

47. Grade Average Pedro has scores of 68, 84, 82, and 76 after four tests. What score must he make on his fifth test to have an average of 80 or greater?

48. Grade Average Luigi has scores of 96, 88, 92, and 90 after four tests. What score must he make on his fifth test to have an average of 90 or greater?

49. Grade Average Katrina has scores of 88, 92, and 78 after three tests. Her final exam counts as two test scores. What score must she make on her final to have an average of 80 or greater?

50. Grade Average Selena has scores of 90, 84, and 96 after three tests. Her final exam counts as two test scores. What score must she make on her final to have an average of 80 or greater?

Tolerance In Exercises 51–54, a container capacity and a tolerance are given. Let x represent the amount in a particular container. Give a three-part inequality that describes the conditions that must be fulfilled to stay within the given tolerance. Then solve the inequality to determine the acceptable limits of the contents of the container.

51. capacity: 18 ounces; tolerance: 0.15 ounces

52. capacity: 22 ounces; tolerance: 0.20 ounces

53. capacity: 52.5 milliliters; tolerance: 0.75 milliliters

54. capacity: 125.8 milliliters; tolerance: 0.50 milliliters

Personal Health *Solve each problem.*

55. A BMI (body mass index) between 19 and 25 is considered healthy. Use the formula

$$BMI = \frac{703 \times (\text{weight in pounds})}{(\text{height in inches})^2}$$

to find the weight range w, to the nearest pound, that gives a healthy BMI (body mass index) for each of the following heights. (*Source:* www.bmi-calculator.net)

(a) 72 inches   **(b)** Your height in inches

56. To achieve the maximum benefit from exercising, the heart rate in beats per minute should be in the target heart rate (THR) zone. For a person aged A, the formula is

$$0.7(220 - A) \le THR \le 0.85(220 - A).$$

(*Source:* Hockey, Robert V. *Physical Fitness: The Pathway to Healthful Living.* Times Mirror/Mosby College Publishing.)

Find THR to the nearest whole number for each age.

(a) 35   **(b)** Your age

Profit/Cost Analysis *A product yields a profit only when the revenue R from selling the product exceeds the cost C of producing it (R and C in dollars). Find the least whole number of units x that must be sold for the business to show a profit for the item described.*

57. Peripheral Visions, Inc. finds that the cost to produce x studio-quality DVDs is

$$C = 20x + 100,$$

and the revenue produced from them is $R = 24x$.

58. Speedy Delivery finds that the cost to make x customer deliveries is

$$C = 3x + 2300,$$

and the revenue produced from them is $R = 5.50x$.

7.5 PROPERTIES OF EXPONENTS AND SCIENTIFIC NOTATION

OBJECTIVES

1 Identify the base and the exponent in an exponential expression, and evaluate exponential expressions with natural number exponents.

2 Interpret the use of zero and negative integer exponents.

3 Apply the product, quotient, power, and special rules for exponents.

4 Convert a number in standard notation to scientific notation and a number in scientific notation to standard notation.

5 Compute with numbers in scientific notation.

Exponents and Exponential Expressions

Exponents are used to write products of repeated factors.

$$\underbrace{3 \cdot 3 \cdot 3 \cdot 3}_{\text{4 factors of 3}} = 3^4. \longleftarrow \text{Exponent}$$

Base

The number 4 shows that 3 appears as a factor four times. The number 4 is the **exponent** and 3 is the **base.** The quantity 3^4 is called an **exponential expression.** Read 3^4 as "3 to the fourth power" or "3 to the fourth." Multiplying out the four 3s gives 81.

$$3^4 = 3 \cdot 3 \cdot 3 \cdot 3 = 81$$

EXPONENTIAL EXPRESSION

If a is a real number and n is a natural number, then the exponential expression a^n is defined as follows.

$$a^n = \underbrace{a \cdot a \cdot a \cdot \ldots \cdot a}_{n \text{ factors of } a}$$

The number a is the *base* and n is the *exponent.*

EXAMPLE 1 Evaluating Exponential Expressions

Evaluate each exponential expression.

(a) 10^2 **(b)** 10^3 **(c)** $(-2)^4$ **(d)** $(-2)^5$ **(e)** 10^1

Solution $10^2 = 10 \cdot 10, \textit{not } 10 \cdot 2.$

(a) $10^2 = 10 \cdot 10 = 100$ Read 10^2 as "10 squared."

(b) $10^3 = 10 \cdot 10 \cdot 10 = 1000$ Read 10^3 as "10 cubed."

(c) $(-2)^4 = (-2)(-2)(-2)(-2) = 16$

(d) $(-2)^5 = (-2)(-2)(-2)(-2)(-2) = -32$

(e) $10^1 = 10$ ■

In the exponential expression $3x^7$, the base of the exponent 7 is x, *not* $3x$.

$$3x^7 = 3 \cdot x \cdot x \cdot x \cdot x \cdot x \cdot x \cdot x \qquad \text{Base is } x.$$

$$(3x)^7 = (3x)(3x)(3x)(3x)(3x)(3x)(3x) \qquad \text{Base is } 3x.$$

For $(-2)^6$, the parentheses around -2 indicate that the base is -2.

$$(-2)^6 = (-2)(-2)(-2)(-2)(-2)(-2) = 64 \qquad \text{Base is } -2.$$

In the expression -2^6, the base is 2, *not* -2. The $-$ sign tells us to find the negative, or additive inverse, of 2^6. It acts as a symbol for the factor -1.

$$-2^6 = -(2 \cdot 2 \cdot 2 \cdot 2 \cdot 2 \cdot 2) = -64 \qquad \text{The base is 2.}$$

Therefore, because $64 \neq -64$, $(-2)^6 \neq -2^6$.

EXAMPLE 2   Evaluating Exponential Expressions

Evaluate each exponential expression.

(a) -10^2 **(b)** -10^4 **(c)** $(-10)^4$

Solution

(a) $-10^2 = -(10 \cdot 10) = -100$ **(b)** $-10^4 = -(10 \cdot 10 \cdot 10 \cdot 10) = -10{,}000$

(c) $(-10)^4 = (-10)(-10)(-10)(-10) = 10{,}000$ ■

The Product Rule

Consider the product $2^5 \cdot 2^3$, which can be simplified as follows.

$$\overbrace{2^5 \cdot 2^3 = (2 \cdot 2 \cdot 2 \cdot 2 \cdot 2)(2 \cdot 2 \cdot 2) = 2^8}^{5 + 3 = 8}$$

This result—products of exponential expressions with the same base are found by adding exponents—is generalized as the **product rule for exponents.**

> **PRODUCT RULE FOR EXPONENTS**
>
> If m and n are natural numbers and a is any real number, then
>
> $$a^m \cdot a^n = a^{m+n}.$$

EXAMPLE 3   Applying the Product Rule

Apply the product rule for exponents in each case.

(a) $10^4 \cdot 10^7$ **(b)** $10^3 \cdot 10$ **(c)** $10^3 \cdot 10^8 \cdot 10^2$

Solution

(a) $10^4 \cdot 10^7 = 10^{4+7} = 10^{11}$ **(b)** $10^3 \cdot 10 = 10^3 \cdot 10^1 = 10^{3+1} = 10^4$

> *Do not make the error of writing*
> $10 \cdot 10 = 100$ *as the base.*

(c) $10^3 \cdot 10^8 \cdot 10^2 = 10^{3+8+2} = 10^{13}$ Product rule extended to three powers   ■

This screen supports the discussion preceding **Example 2.**

$(-2)^6$	
	64
-2^6	
	-64

The term **googol,** meaning 10^{100}, was coined by Professor Edward Kasner of Columbia University. A googol is made up of a 1 with one hundred zeros following it. This number exceeds the estimated number of electrons in the universe, which is 10^{79}.

The Web search engine Google is named after a googol. Sergey Brin, president and cofounder of Google, Inc., was a mathematics major. He chose the name Google to describe the vast reach of this search engine. The term "googling" is now part of the English language.

If a googol isn't big enough for you, try a **googolplex:**

googolplex $= 10^{\text{googol}}$.

Zero and Negative Exponents

We now consider 0 as an exponent. How can we define an expression such as 4^0 so that it is consistent with the product rule? By the product rule, we should have

$$4^2 \cdot 4^0 = 4^{2+0} = 4^2.$$

For the product rule to hold true, 4^0 must equal 1. This leads to the definition of a^0 for any nonzero real number a.

> **ZERO EXPONENT**
>
> If a is any nonzero real number, then $a^0 = 1$.

The expression 0^0 **is undefined.***

EXAMPLE 4 Applying the Definition of Zero Exponent

Evaluate each expression.

(a) 10^0 **(b)** $(-10)^0$ **(c)** -10^0 **(d)** $5^0 + 12^0$

Solution

(a) $10^0 = 1$ **(b)** $(-10)^0 = 1$ The base is -10.

(c) $-10^0 = -(10^0) = -1$ The base is 10.   **(d)** $5^0 + 12^0 = 1 + 1 = 2$ ∎

We now define a negative exponent. Using the product rule again,

$$8^2 \cdot 8^{-2} = 8^{2+(-2)} = 8^0 = 1.$$

This indicates that 8^{-2} is the reciprocal of 8^2. But $\frac{1}{8^2}$ is the reciprocal of 8^2, and a number can have only one reciprocal. Therefore, we conclude that $8^{-2} = \frac{1}{8^2}$.

> **NEGATIVE EXPONENT**
>
> For any natural number n and any nonzero real number a,
>
> $$a^{-n} = \frac{1}{a^n}.$$

With this definition and the ones given earlier, the expression a^n is meaningful for any integer exponent n and any nonzero real number a.

EXAMPLE 5 Applying the Definition of Negative Exponents

Write the following expressions with only positive exponents and simplify.

(a) 2^{-3} **(b)** 3^{-2} **(c)** 10^{-1} **(d)** 10^{-3}

Solution

(a) $2^{-3} = \frac{1}{2^3} = \frac{1}{8}$ **(b)** $3^{-2} = \frac{1}{3^2} = \frac{1}{9}$

(c) $10^{-1} = \frac{1}{10^1} = \frac{1}{10}$ **(d)** $10^{-3} = \frac{1}{10^3} = \frac{1}{1000}$ ∎

---

*In advanced studies, 0^0 is called an *indeterminate form*.

This screen supports the results in parts (b), (c), and (d) of **Example 4.**

EXAMPLE 6 Evaluating Exponential Expressions

Evaluate each expression.

(a) $3^{-1} + 4^{-1}$ **(b)** $5^{-1} - 2^{-1}$ **(c)** $\dfrac{1}{2^{-3}}$ **(d)** $\dfrac{10^{-3}}{10^{-2}}$

Solution

(a) $3^{-1} + 4^{-1} = \dfrac{1}{3} + \dfrac{1}{4} = \dfrac{4}{12} + \dfrac{3}{12} = \dfrac{7}{12}$ $3^{-1} = \frac{1}{3}; \ 4^{-1} = \frac{1}{4}$

(b) $5^{-1} - 2^{-1} = \dfrac{1}{5} - \dfrac{1}{2} = \dfrac{2}{10} - \dfrac{5}{10} = -\dfrac{3}{10}$

(c) $\dfrac{1}{2^{-3}} = \dfrac{1}{\frac{1}{2^3}} = 1 \div \dfrac{1}{2^3} = 1 \cdot \dfrac{2^3}{1} = 2^3 = 8$

> To divide, multiply by the reciprocal of the divisor.

(d) $\dfrac{10^{-3}}{10^{-2}} = \dfrac{\frac{1}{10^3}}{\frac{1}{10^2}} = \dfrac{1}{10^3} \div \dfrac{1}{10^2} = \dfrac{1}{10^3} \cdot \dfrac{10^2}{1} = \dfrac{10^2}{10^3} = \dfrac{100}{1000} = \dfrac{1}{10^1},$ or $\dfrac{1}{10}$ ∎

(calculator screen)

```
3^-1+4^-1▶Frac
                7/12
5^-1-2^-1▶Frac
               -3/10
```

This screen supports the results in parts (a) and (b) of **Example 6.**

The following special rules for negative exponents can be verified using the definition of a negative exponent.

SPECIAL RULES FOR NEGATIVE EXPONENTS

If $a \neq 0$ and $b \neq 0$, then $\dfrac{1}{a^{-n}} = a^n$ and $\dfrac{a^{-n}}{b^{-m}} = \dfrac{b^m}{a^n}.$

The Quotient Rule

A quotient, such as $\dfrac{a^8}{a^3}$, can be simplified in much the same way as a product. (Assume that the denominator is not 0.) Using the definition of an exponent,

$$\frac{a^8}{a^3} = \frac{a \cdot a \cdot a \cdot a \cdot a \cdot a \cdot a \cdot a}{a \cdot a \cdot a} = a \cdot a \cdot a \cdot a \cdot a = a^5.$$

Notice that $8 - 3 = 5$. In the same way,

$$\frac{a^3}{a^8} = \frac{a \cdot a \cdot a}{a \cdot a \cdot a \cdot a \cdot a \cdot a \cdot a \cdot a} = \frac{1}{a^5} = a^{-5}.$$

Here, $3 - 8 = -5$. These examples suggest the **quotient rule for exponents.**

QUOTIENT RULE FOR EXPONENTS

If a is any nonzero real number and m and n are integers, then

$$\frac{a^m}{a^n} = a^{m-n}.$$

EXAMPLE 7 Applying the Quotient Rule

Apply the quotient rule for exponents in each case.

(a) $\dfrac{10^7}{10^2}$ **(b)** $\dfrac{2^{10}}{2^9}$ **(c)** $\dfrac{10^4}{10^6}$

Solution

Numerator exponent

Denominator exponent

(a) $\dfrac{10^7}{10^2} = 10^{7-2} = 10^5$

Subtract.

Use the definition of negative exponent.

(b) $\dfrac{2^{10}}{2^9} = 2^{10-9} = 2^1 = 2$ **(c)** $\dfrac{10^4}{10^6} = 10^{4-6} = 10^{-2} = \dfrac{1}{10^2}$ ∎

EXAMPLE 8 Applying the Quotient Rule

Write each quotient using only positive exponents.

(a) $\dfrac{2^7}{2^{-3}}$ **(b)** $\dfrac{10^{-2}}{10^5}$ **(c)** $\dfrac{10^{-5}}{10^{-2}}$ **(d)** $\dfrac{4}{4^{-1}}$

Solution

Be careful when subtracting a negative number.

(a) $\dfrac{2^7}{2^{-3}} = 2^{7-(-3)} = 2^{10}$ **(b)** $\dfrac{10^{-2}}{10^5} = 10^{-2-5} = 10^{-7} = \dfrac{1}{10^7}$

(c) $\dfrac{10^{-5}}{10^{-2}} = 10^{-5-(-2)} = 10^{-3} = \dfrac{1}{10^3}$ **(d)** $\dfrac{4}{4^{-1}} = \dfrac{4^1}{4^{-1}} = 4^{1-(-1)} = 4^2$ ∎

The Power Rules

The expression $(3^4)^2$ can be simplified as

$$(3^4)^2 = 3^4 \cdot 3^4 = 3^{4+4} = 3^8, \quad \text{where } 4 \cdot 2 = 8.$$

This example suggests the first of the **power rules for exponents.** The other two parts can be demonstrated with similar examples.

POWER RULES FOR EXPONENTS

If a and b are real numbers, and m and n are integers, then

$$(a^m)^n = a^{mn}, \quad (ab)^m = a^m b^m, \quad \text{and} \quad \left(\dfrac{a}{b}\right)^m = \dfrac{a^m}{b^m} \quad (b \neq 0).$$

In the statements of rules for exponents, we always assume that zero never appears to a negative power or to the power zero.

EXAMPLE 9   Applying the Power Rules

Use one or more power rules in each case.

(a) $(10^8)^3$ **(b)** $\left(\dfrac{2}{3}\right)^4$ **(c)** $(3 \cdot 10)^4$ **(d)** $(6 \cdot 10^3)^2$

Solution

(a) $(10^8)^3 = 10^{8 \cdot 3} = 10^{24}$ **(b)** $\left(\dfrac{2}{3}\right)^4 = \dfrac{2^4}{3^4} = \dfrac{16}{81}$

(c) $(3 \cdot 10)^4 = 3^4 \cdot 10^4 = 81 \cdot 10{,}000 = 810{,}000$

(d) $(6 \cdot 10^3)^2 = 6^2 \cdot 10^6 = 36 \cdot 1{,}000{,}000 = 36{,}000{,}000$ ∎

Notice that

$$6^{-3} = \left(\frac{1}{6}\right)^3 = \frac{1}{216} \quad \text{and} \quad \left(\frac{2}{3}\right)^{-2} = \left(\frac{3}{2}\right)^2 = \frac{9}{4}.$$

These are examples of two special rules for negative exponents.

SPECIAL RULES FOR NEGATIVE EXPONENTS

If $a \neq 0$ and $b \neq 0$ and n is an integer, then

$$a^{-n} = \left(\frac{1}{a}\right)^n \quad \text{and} \quad \left(\frac{a}{b}\right)^{-n} = \left(\frac{b}{a}\right)^n.$$

```
(3/7)⁻²►Frac
                    49
                     9
(4/5)⁻³►Frac
                   125
                    64
```

This screen supports results in
Example 10 (b) and (c).

EXAMPLE 10   Applying Special Rules for Negative Exponents

Write each expression with only positive exponents, and then evaluate.

(a) 10^{-2} **(b)** $\left(\dfrac{3}{7}\right)^{-2}$ **(c)** $\left(\dfrac{4}{5}\right)^{-3}$

Solution

(a) $10^{-2} = \left(\dfrac{1}{10}\right)^2 = \dfrac{1}{100}$ **(b)** $\left(\dfrac{3}{7}\right)^{-2} = \left(\dfrac{7}{3}\right)^2 = \dfrac{49}{9}$

(c) $\left(\dfrac{4}{5}\right)^{-3} = \left(\dfrac{5}{4}\right)^3 = \dfrac{125}{64}$ ∎

EXAMPLE 11   Writing Expressions with No Negative Exponents

Simplify each expression so that no negative exponents appear in the final result.

(a) $3^2 \cdot 3^{-5}$ **(b)** $(4^{-2})^{-5}$ **(c)** $(10^{-4})^6$

Solution

(a) $3^2 \cdot 3^{-5} = 3^{2+(-5)} = 3^{-3} = \dfrac{1}{3^3}, \quad \text{or} \quad \dfrac{1}{27}$

(b) $(4^{-2})^{-5} = 4^{-2(-5)} = 4^{10}$ **(c)** $(10^{-4})^6 = 10^{(-4)6} = 10^{-24} = \dfrac{1}{10^{24}}$ ∎

Scientific Notation

Many of the numbers that occur in science are very large or very small. Writing these numbers is simplified by using *scientific notation*.

> **SCIENTIFIC NOTATION**
>
> A number is written in **scientific notation** when it is expressed in the form
>
> $$a \times 10^n, \quad \text{where } 1 \leq |a| < 10, \text{ and } n \text{ is an integer.}$$

Scientific notation requires that the number be written as a product of a number between 1 and 10 (or −1 and −10) and some integer power of 10. (1 and −1 are allowed as values of a, but 10 and −10 are not.) For example,

$$8000 = 8 \cdot 1000 = 8 \cdot 10^3, \quad \text{or} \quad 8 \times 10^3. \longleftarrow \text{Scientific notation}$$

In scientific notation, it is customary to use × instead of a multiplication dot.

The steps involved in writing a number in scientific notation follow. (If the number is negative, ignore the negative sign, go through these steps, and then attach a negative sign to the result.)

> **CONVERTING A POSITIVE NUMBER TO SCIENTIFIC NOTATION**
>
> *Step 1* **Position the decimal point.** Place a caret, ∧, to the right of the first nonzero digit, where the decimal point will be placed.
>
> *Step 2* **Determine the numeral for the exponent.** Count the number of digits from the decimal point to the caret. This number gives the absolute value of the exponent on 10.
>
> *Step 3* **Determine the sign for the exponent.** Decide whether multiplying by 10^n should make the result of Step 1 larger or smaller. The exponent should be positive to make the result larger. It should be negative to make the result smaller.

It is helpful to remember that for $n \geq 1$, $10^{-n} < 1$ and $10^n \geq 10$.

EXAMPLE 12 Converting to Scientific Notation

Convert each number from standard notation to scientific notation.

(a) 8,200,000   **(b)** 0.000072

Solution

(a) Place a caret to the right of the 8 (the first nonzero digit) to mark the new location of the decimal point.

$$8_\wedge 200{,}000$$

Count from the decimal point, which is understood to be after the last 0, to the caret.

$$8_\wedge 200{,}000. \longleftarrow \text{Decimal point}$$

Count 6 places.

Because the number 8.2 is to be made larger, the exponent on 10 is positive.

$$8{,}200{,}000 = 8.2 \times 10^6$$

8200000

8.2ᴇ6

.000072

7.2ᴇ⁻5

If a graphing calculator is set in scientific notation mode, it will give results as shown here. E6 means "times 10^6" and E−5 means "times 10^{-5}". Compare to the results of **Example 12**.

(b) $0.00007_\wedge 2$ Count from left to right.

5 places

The number 7.2 is to be made smaller, so the exponent on 10 is negative.

$$0.000072 = 7.2 \times 10^{-5}$$ ∎

CONVERTING A POSITIVE NUMBER FROM SCIENTIFIC NOTATION TO STANDARD NOTATION

- Multiplying a positive number by a positive power of 10 makes the number larger, so move the decimal point to the right if n is positive in 10^n.

- Multiplying a positive number by a negative power of 10 makes the number smaller, so move the decimal point to the left if n is negative.

- If n is zero, do not move the decimal point.

EXAMPLE 13 Converting from Scientific Notation

Convert each number from scientific notation to standard notation.

(a) 6.93×10^5 **(b)** 4.7×10^{-6} **(c)** -1.083×10^0

Solution

(a) $6.93 \times 10^5 = 6.93000_\wedge$ Attach 0s as necessary.

5 places

The decimal point was moved 5 places to the right.

$$6.93 \times 10^5 = 693{,}000$$

(b) $4.7 \times 10^{-6} = {}_\wedge 000004.7$ Attach 0s as necessary.

6 places

The decimal point was moved 6 places to the left.

$$4.7 \times 10^{-6} = 0.0000047$$

(c) $-1.083 \times 10^0 = -1.083$ ∎

EXAMPLE 14 Using Scientific Notation in Computation

Evaluate $\dfrac{1{,}920{,}000 \times 0.0015}{0.000032 \times 45{,}000}$ using scientific notation.

Solution

$$\frac{1{,}920{,}000 \times 0.0015}{0.000032 \times 45{,}000} = \frac{1.92 \times 10^6 \times 1.5 \times 10^{-3}}{3.2 \times 10^{-5} \times 4.5 \times 10^4}$$ Express all numbers in scientific notation.

$$= \frac{1.92 \times 1.5 \times 10^6 \times 10^{-3}}{3.2 \times 4.5 \times 10^{-5} \times 10^4}$$ Commutative and associative properties.

$$= \frac{1.92 \times 1.5}{3.2 \times 4.5} \times 10^4$$ Product and quotient rules.

Don't stop here. ── $= 0.2 \times 10^4$ Simplify.

$$= (2 \times 10^{-1}) \times 10^4$$ Write 0.2 using scientific notation.

$$= 2 \times 10^3, \quad \text{or} \quad 2000$$ Associative property; product rule; multiply.   ∎

Affordable health care has become a national issue during the past few years. Escalating health care costs affect how people decide which health insurance plans to choose, and business owners must consider these costs as well when providing plans for their employees.

EXAMPLE 15 **Using Scientific Notation to Analyze Rising Health Care Costs**

In 1990, national health care costs in the United States were $724 billion. By 2012, these costs were four times that amount. (*Source:* U.S. Centers for Medicare and Medicaid Services.)

(a) Write the 1990 amount using scientific notation.

(b) What were the costs in 2012?

Solution

(a) 724 billion

$= 724 \times 10^9$ 1 billion $= 1{,}000{,}000{,}000 = 10^9$

$= (7.24 \times 10^2) \times 10^9$ Write 724 in scientific notation.

$= 7.24 \times 10^{11}$ Product rule; $10^2 \cdot 10^9 = 10^{2+9}$

In 1990, the costs were $\$7.24 \times 10^{11}$.

(b) $(7.24 \times 10^{11}) \times 4$ Multiply the result in part (a) by 4.

$= (4 \times 7.24) \times 10^{11}$ Commutative and associative properties.

$= 28.96 \times 10^{11}$ Multiply.

$= (2.896 \times 10^1) \times 10^{11}$ Write 28.96 in scientific notation.

$= 2.896 \times 10^{12}$ Product rule; $10^1 \times 10^{11} = 10^{12}$

Costs in 2012 were about $\$2{,}896{,}000{,}000{,}000$ (almost $3 trillion). ∎

7.5 EXERCISES

Write each of the following as a power of 10. For example, one hundred $= 10^2$.

1. one thousand

2. one hundred thousand

3. one million   **4.** ten million

5. one billion   **6.** one trillion

Evaluate each exponential expression.

7. 5^4 **8.** 10^3

9. $(-2)^5$ **10.** $(-5)^4$

11. -2^3 **12.** -3^2

13. $-(-3)^4$ **14.** $-(-5)^2$

15. 8^{-1} **16.** 9^{-1}

17. 7^{-2} **18.** 4^{-2}

19. -7^{-2} **20.** -16^{-1}

21. $\dfrac{5^{-1}}{4^{-2}}$ **22.** $\dfrac{2^{-3}}{3^{-2}}$

23. $\left(\dfrac{1}{5}\right)^{-3}$ **24.** $\left(\dfrac{1}{2}\right)^{-3}$

25. $\left(\dfrac{4}{5}\right)^{-2}$ **26.** $\left(\dfrac{2}{3}\right)^{-2}$

27. $4^{-1} + 5^{-1}$ **28.** $3^{-1} + 2^{-1}$

29. 12^0 **30.** 8^0

31. $(-4)^0$ **32.** $(-23)^0$

33. $3^0 - 4^0$ **34.** $10^0 - 8^0$

Use the product, quotient, and power rules to simplify each expression. Write answers with only positive exponents.

35. $10^{12} \cdot 10^4$

36. $10^6 \cdot 10^8$

37. $10^{-6} \cdot 10^5$

38. $10^{-9} \cdot 10^8$

39. $\dfrac{5^{16}}{5^{17}}$

40. $\dfrac{3^{12}}{3^{13}}$

41. $\dfrac{10^5}{10^3}$

42. $\dfrac{10^8}{10^5}$

43. $\dfrac{10^{-2}}{10^{-5}}$

44. $\dfrac{10^{-2}}{10^{-6}}$

45. $10^{-8} \cdot 10^6 \cdot 10^3$

46. $10^{-12} \cdot 10^{10} \cdot 10^3$

47. $(5^{-2})^{-1}$

48. $(6^{-1})^{-2}$

49. $\dfrac{(10^{-3})^{-2}}{10^{-5}}$

50. $\dfrac{(10^{-1})^{-5}}{10^{-3}}$

51. $\dfrac{10^8 \cdot 10^4}{10^6 \cdot 10^{12}}$

52. $\dfrac{10^{10} \cdot 10^5}{10^8 \cdot 10^9}$

53. $\dfrac{(6 \times 10^{-2})^2}{(3 \times 10^5)^2}$

54. $\dfrac{(4 \times 10^{-2})^3}{(2 \times 10^3)^3}$

Convert each number from standard notation to scientific notation.

55. 230

56. 46,500

57. 8,100,000,000

58. 7,250,000

59. 1,400,000,000,000

60. 1,300,000,000,000,000

61. 0.02

62. 0.0051

63. 0.5623

64. 0.1234

65. 0.0000044

66. 0.00000099

Convert each number from scientific notation to standard notation.

67. 6.5×10^3

68. 2.317×10^5

69. 2.8×10^7

70. 9.1×10^8

71. 1.5×10^{10}

72. 4.4×10^{11}

73. 4.2×10^{-1}

74. 5.3×10^{-1}

75. 1.52×10^{-2}

76. 1.63×10^{-4}

77. 8.33×10^{-6}

78. 7.51×10^{-6}

Use scientific notation to perform each of the following computations. Leave the answers in scientific notation.

79. $\dfrac{0.002 \times 3900}{0.000013}$

80. $\dfrac{0.009 \times 600}{0.02}$

81. $\dfrac{0.0004 \times 56,000}{0.000112}$

82. $\dfrac{0.018 \times 20,000}{300 \times 0.0004}$

83. $\dfrac{840,000 \times 0.03}{0.00021 \times 600}$

84. $\dfrac{28 \times 0.0045}{140 \times 1500}$

Solve each problem.

85. *U.S. Population* In 2014, the population of the United States was approximately 317.4 million. (*Source:* U.S. Census Bureau.)

  (a) Write the population using scientific notation.

  (b) Write $1 trillion ($1,000,000,000,000) using scientific notation.

  (c) Using the answers from parts (a) and (b), calculate how much each person in the United States would have to contribute in order to make someone a trillionaire. Write this amount in standard notation to the nearest dollar.

86. *National Debt* In 2014, the national debt of the United States was about $17.27 trillion. The U.S. population at that time was approximately 317.4 million. (*Source:* U.S. Census Bureau.)

  (a) Write the population using scientific notation.

  (b) Write the amount of the national debt using scientific notation.

  (c) Using the answers for parts (a) and (b), calculate how much debt this is per American. Write this amount in standard notation to the nearest ten dollars.

87. *Powerball Lottery* In the early years of the Powerball Lottery, a player had to choose five numbers from 1 through 49 and one number from 1 through 42. It can be shown that there are about 8.009×10^7 different ways to do this. Suppose that a group of 2000 people decided to purchase tickets for all these numbers, and each ticket cost $1.00. How much should each person have expected to pay? (*Source:* www.powerball.com)

88. *Population of Monaco*   In 2013, the population of India was about 1.22×10^9, which was 4.0×10^4 times the population of Monaco. What was the population of Monaco? (*Source: World Almanac and Book of Facts.*)

89. *Distance of Uranus from the Sun*   A parsec, a unit of length used in astronomy, is 1.9×10^{13} miles. The mean distance of Uranus from the sun is 1.8×10^7 miles. How many parsecs is Uranus from the sun?

90. *Number of Inches in a Mile*   An inch is approximately 1.57828×10^{-5} mile. Find the reciprocal of this number to determine the number of inches in a mile.

91. *Speed of Light*   The speed of light is approximately 3×10^{10} centimeters per second. How long will it take light to travel 9×10^{12} centimeters?

92. *Rocket from Earth to the Sun*   The average distance from Earth to the sun is 9.3×10^7 miles. How long would it take a rocket, traveling at 2.9×10^3 miles per hour, to reach the sun?

93. *Miles in a Light-Year*   A *light-year* is the distance that light travels in one year. Find the number of miles in a light-year if light travels 1.86×10^5 miles per second.

94. *Time for Light to Travel*   Use the information given in the previous two exercises to find the number of minutes necessary for light from the sun to reach Earth.

95. *Population of Luxembourg*   In 2013, the population of Luxembourg was approximately 5.15×10^5, while the population density was about 516 people per square mile. (*Source: The World Factbook.*)

(a) Write the population density in scientific notation.

(b) To the nearest square mile, what is the area of Luxembourg?

96. *Population of Costa Rica*   In 2013, the population of Costa Rica was approximately 4.696×10^6. The population density was 91.97 people per square kilometer. (*Source: The World Almanac and Book of Facts.*)

(a) Write the population density in scientific notation.

(b) To the nearest hundred square kilometers, what is the area of Costa Rica?

97. *Star Trek Mathematics*   In a television episode of *Star Trek*, Captain Kirk once said that a booster would increase the sound on the bridge of the ship by a factor of "one to the fourth power." Explain his error.

98. *Star Trek Mathematics*   Captain Kirk probably meant to use scientific notation in his statement in **Exercise 97.** What single-word change would accomplish this?

7.6   POLYNOMIALS AND FACTORING

OBJECTIVES

1 Know the basic terminology of polynomials.

2 Add and subtract polynomials.

3 Multiply polynomials.

4 Multiply two binomials using the FOIL method.

5 Find special products of binomials.

6 Factor the greatest common factor from a polynomial.

7 Factor a trinomial using the FOIL method in reverse.

8 Factor a perfect square trinomial and a difference of squares.

Basic Terminology

A **term,** or **monomial,** is defined to be a number, a variable, or a product of numbers and variables. A **polynomial** is a term, or a finite sum or difference of terms, with only nonnegative integer exponents permitted on the variables. If the terms of a polynomial contain only the variable x, then the polynomial is called a **polynomial in x.** (Polynomials in other variables are defined similarly.)

$$5x^3 - 8x^2 + 7x - 4, \quad 9x^5 - 3, \quad 8x^2, \quad \text{and} \quad 6 \qquad \text{Examples of polynomials in } x$$

The expression $9x^2 - 4x - \dfrac{6}{x}$ is not a polynomial because of the presence of $-\dfrac{6}{x}$. The terms of a polynomial cannot have variables in a denominator.

The greatest exponent in a polynomial in one variable is the **degree** of the polynomial. A nonzero constant has degree 0. (The polynomial 0 has no degree.)

$$3x^6 - 5x^2 + 2x + 3 \quad \text{is a polynomial of degree 6.}$$

A polynomial containing exactly three terms is called a **trinomial,** and one containing exactly two terms is a **binomial. Table 5** gives examples.

Table 5

Polynomial	Degree	Type
$9x^4 - 4x^3 + 8x^2$	4	Trinomial
$29x^3 + 8x^2$	3	Binomial
$-10x$	1	Monomial

Addition and Subtraction

Since the variables used in polynomials represent real numbers, a polynomial represents a real number. This means that all the properties of the real numbers hold for polynomials. Here is an application of the distributive property.

$$3x^5 - 7x^5 = (3 - 7)\,x^5 = -4x^5 \quad \text{Combine like terms.}$$

Like terms are terms that have the exact same variable factors. Thus, polynomials are added by adding coefficients of like terms and are subtracted by subtracting coefficients of like terms.

▍EXAMPLE 1 Adding and Subtracting Polynomials

Add or subtract, as indicated.

(a) $(2x^4 - 3x^2 + x) + (4x^4 + 7x^2 + 6x)$

(b) $(-3x^3 - 8x^2 + 4) - (x^3 + 7x^2 - 3)$

(c) $4(x^2 - 3x + 7) - 5(2x^2 - 8x - 4)$

Solution

(a) $(2x^4 - 3x^2 + x) + (4x^4 + 7x^2 + 6x)$

$$= (2 + 4)x^4 + (-3 + 7)x^2 + (1 + 6)x \quad \text{Combine like terms.}$$

$$= 6x^4 + 4x^2 + 7x$$

(b) $(-3x^3 - 8x^2 + 4) - (x^3 + 7x^2 - 3)$

$$= (-3 - 1)x^3 + (-8 - 7)x^2 + [4 - (-3)]$$

$$= -4x^3 - 15x^2 + 7$$

(c) $4(x^2 - 3x + 7) - 5(2x^2 - 8x - 4)$

$$= 4x^2 - 4(3x) + 4(7) - 5(2x^2) - 5(-8x) - 5(-4) \quad \text{Distributive property}$$

$$= 4x^2 - 12x + 28 - 10x^2 + 40x + 20 \quad \text{Associative property}$$

$$= -6x^2 + 28x + 48 \quad \text{Combine like terms.}$$

■

As shown in **Example 1,** polynomials are often written with their terms in **descending powers.** The term of greatest degree is first, the one with the next greatest degree is second, and so on.

Multiplication

The associative and distributive properties, together with the properties of exponents, can also be used to find the product of two polynomials.

$$(3x - 4)(2x^2 - 3x + 5)$$

$$= (3x - 4)(2x^2) - (3x - 4)(3x) + (3x - 4)(5)$$

$$= 3x(2x^2) - 4(2x^2) - 3x(3x) - (-4)(3x) + 3x(5) - 4(5)$$

$$= 6x^3 - 8x^2 - 9x^2 + 12x + 15x - 20$$

$$= 6x^3 - 17x^2 + 27x - 20$$

Such a product can be written vertically, as shown in **Example 2.**

EXAMPLE 2 Multiplying Polynomials Vertically

Multiply $(3x - 4)(2x^2 - 3x + 5)$.

Solution

$$
\begin{array}{r}
2x^2 - 3x + 5 \\
3x - 4 \\
\hline
-8x^2 + 12x - 20 \\
6x^3 - 9x^2 + 15x \\
\hline
6x^3 - 17x^2 + 27x - 20
\end{array}
$$

Multiply each term of the first polynomial by each term of the second.

Be sure to place like terms in columns.

$\longleftarrow -4(2x^2 - 3x + 5)$

$\longleftarrow 3x(2x^2 - 3x + 5)$

Add in columns. ∎

The memory aid "FOIL" is a convenient way to find the product of two binomials. FOIL (for First, Outside, Inside, Last) gives the pairs of terms to be multiplied to get the product, as shown in the next examples.

EXAMPLE 3 Using the FOIL Method

Find each product.

(a) $(6x + 1)(4x - 3)$ **(b)** $(2x + 7)(2x - 7)$ **(c)** $(x^2 - 4)(x^2 + 4)$

Solution

(a) $(6x + 1)(4x - 3)$

$$
\begin{array}{cccc}
\text{F} & \text{O} & \text{I} & \text{L}
\end{array}
$$

$= (6x)(4x) + (6x)(-3) + 1(4x) + 1(-3)$

$= 24x^2 - 18x + 4x - 3$

$= 24x^2 - 14x - 3$ Combine like terms.

(b) $(2x + 7)(2x - 7)$

$= 4x^2 - 14x + 14x - 49$ FOIL method

$= 4x^2 - 49$ Combine like terms.

(c) $(x^2 - 4)(x^2 + 4)$

$= x^4 + 4x^2 - 4x^2 - 16$ FOIL method

$= x^4 - 16$ Combine like terms. ∎

The **special product**

$$(x + y)(x - y) = x^2 - y^2$$

can be used to solve some multiplication problems.

$$51 \times 49 = (50 + 1)(50 - 1)$$
$$= 50^2 - 1^2$$
$$= 2500 - 1$$
$$= 2499$$

$$102 \times 98 = (100 + 2)(100 - 2)$$
$$= 100^2 - 2^2$$
$$= 10{,}000 - 4$$
$$= 9996$$

Once these patterns are recognized, multiplications of this type can be done mentally.

Special Products

As shown in **Examples 3(b) and (c)**, *the product of two binomials of the forms $x + y$ and $x - y$ is always a binomial.* Check that the following is true.

PRODUCT OF THE SUM AND DIFFERENCE OF TWO TERMS

$$(x + y)(x - y) = x^2 - y^2$$

The product $x^2 - y^2$ is called a **difference of two squares.**

The **special product**

$$(x + y)^2 = x^2 + 2xy + y^2$$

can be illustrated geometrically using the diagram shown here. Each side of the large square has length $x + y$, so the area of the square is

$$(x + y)^2.$$

The large square is made up of two smaller squares and two congruent rectangles. The sum of the areas of these figures is

$$x^2 + 2xy + y^2.$$

Since these expressions represent the same quantity, they must be equal, thus giving us the pattern for squaring a binomial.

EXAMPLE 4 Multiplying $(x + y)(x - y)$

Find each product.

(a) $(3x + 1)(3x - 1)$ **(b)** $(5x^3 - 3)(5x^3 + 3)$

(c) $(9x - 11)(9x + 11)$

Solution

(a) Using the pattern discussed earlier, replace x with $3x$ and replace y with 1.

$$(3x + 1)(3x - 1)$$
$$= (3x)^2 - 1^2$$
$$= 9x^2 - 1$$

(b) $(5x^3 - 3)(5x^3 + 3)$ **(c)** $(9x - 11)(9x + 11)$

$$= (5x^3)^2 - 3^2 \qquad\qquad = (9x)^2 - (11)^2$$
$$= 25x^6 - 9 \qquad\qquad = 81x^2 - 121$$

     Squares of binomials are also special products. These are verified by first writing as two factors and then using the FOIL method.

SQUARES OF BINOMIALS

$$(x + y)^2 = x^2 + 2xy + y^2$$
$$(x - y)^2 = x^2 - 2xy + y^2$$

EXAMPLE 5 Squaring Binomials

Find each product.

(a) $(x + 6)^2$ **(b)** $(2x + 5)^2$ **(c)** $(3x - 7)^2$

Solution

(a) $(x + 6)^2 = x^2 + 2(x)(6) + 6^2$

> The square of a binomial has three terms. $(x + y)^2 \neq x^2 + y^2$

$$= x^2 + 12x + 36$$

(b) $(2x + 5)^2$ **(c)** $(3x - 7)^2$

$$= (2x)^2 + 2(2x)(5) + (5)^2 \qquad = (3x)^2 - 2(3x)(7) + (7)^2$$
$$= 4x^2 + 20x + 25 \qquad\qquad\quad = 9x^2 - 42x + 49$$

Factoring

The process of finding polynomials whose product equals a given polynomial is called **factoring.** For example, since

$$4x + 12 = 4(x + 3),$$

both 4 and $x + 3$ are called **factors** of $4x + 12$. Also, $4(x + 3)$ is called a **factored form** of $4x + 12$. A polynomial that cannot be written as a product of two polynomials with integer coefficients is a **prime polynomial.** A polynomial is **factored completely** when it is written as a product of prime polynomials with integer coefficients.

     Factoring is the inverse of multiplying, so a check requires that the product of the factored form yield the original polynomial.

Factoring Out the Greatest Common Factor

When factoring a polynomial, we first look for a monomial that is the greatest common factor (GCF) of all the terms of the polynomial.

$$6x^4 + 9x^3 + 18x^2$$

$$= 3x^2(2x^2) + 3x^2(3x) + 3x^2(6) \quad \text{GCF} = 3x^2$$

$$= 3x^2(2x^2 + 3x + 6)$$

EXAMPLE 6 Factoring Out the Greatest Common Factor

Factor out the greatest common factor from each polynomial.

(a) $9x^5 + x^2$ **(b)** $5x^4 - 10x^3 + 20x^2$

Solution

(a) $9x^5 + x^2 = x^2 \cdot 9x^3 + x^2 \cdot 1$ The greatest common factor is x^2.

$$= x^2(9x^3 + 1)$$

(b) $5x^4 - 10x^3 + 20x^2$ Factoring can always be checked by multiplying

$$= 5x^2(x^2 - 2x + 4)$$ out the factored form.   ■

Factoring Trinomials

Factoring trinomials requires using the FOIL method in reverse.

EXAMPLE 7 Factoring Trinomials

Factor each trinomial.

(a) $4x^2 - 11x + 6$ **(b)** $6x^2 - 7x - 5$

Solution

(a) To factor this polynomial, we must find integers a, b, c, and d such that

$$4x^2 - 11x + 6 = (ax + b)(cx + d).$$

By using FOIL, we see that $ac = 4$ and $bd = 6$. The positive factors of 4 are 4 and 1 or 2 and 2. Since the middle term is negative, we consider only negative factors of 6. The possibilities are -2 and -3 or -1 and -6. Try various arrangements.

$$(2x - 1)(2x - 6) = 4x^2 - 14x + 6 \quad \text{Incorrect}$$

$$(2x - 2)(2x - 3) = 4x^2 - 10x + 6 \quad \text{Incorrect}$$

$$(x - 2)(4x - 3) = 4x^2 - 11x + 6 \quad \text{Correct}$$

The last trial gives the correct factorization.

(b) Again, we try various possibilities. The positive factors of 6 could be 2 and 3 or 1 and 6. As factors of -5 we have only -1 and 5 or -5 and 1.

$$(2x - 5)(3x + 1) = 6x^2 - 13x - 5 \quad \text{Incorrect}$$

$$(3x - 5)(2x + 1) = 6x^2 - 7x - 5 \quad \text{Correct}$$

Thus, $6x^2 - 7x - 5$ factors as $(3x - 5)(2x + 1)$.   ■

PERFECT SQUARE TRINOMIALS

$$x^2 + 2xy + y^2 = (x + y)^2$$
$$x^2 - 2xy + y^2 = (x - y)^2$$

EXAMPLE 8   **Factoring Perfect Square Trinomials**

Factor each polynomial.

(a) $16x^2 - 40x + 25$ **(b)** $169x^2 + 104x + 16$

Solution

(a) First verify that the middle term of the trinomial being factored, $-40x$ here, is twice the product of the two terms in the binomial $4x - 5$.

$$-40x = 2(4x)(-5)$$

Because $16x^2 = (4x)^2$ and $25 = 5^2$, use the second pattern shown above.

$$16x^2 - 40x + 25 = (4x)^2 - 2(4x)(5) + (5)^2$$
$$= (4x - 5)^2$$

(b) $169x^2 + 104x + 16 = (13x + 4)^2$, because $2(13x)(4) = 104x$.   ∎

Factoring Special Binomials

DIFFERENCE OF SQUARES

$$x^2 - y^2 = (x + y)(x - y)$$

EXAMPLE 9   **Factoring Differences of Squares**

Factor each polynomial.

(a) $4x^2 - 9$ **(b)** $256x^4 - 625$ **(c)** $16x^4 - 1$

Solution

(a) $4x^2 - 9$

$$= (2x)^2 - 3^2$$
$$= (2x + 3)(2x - 3) \quad \text{Difference of squares}$$

(b) $256x^4 - 625$

$$= (16x^2)^2 - 25^2$$
$$= (16x^2 + 25)(16x^2 - 25) \quad \text{Difference of squares}$$
$$= (16x^2 + 25)(4x + 5)(4x - 5) \quad \text{Difference of squares}$$

(c) $16x^4 - 1$

$$= (4x^2 + 1)(4x^2 - 1) \quad \text{Difference of squares}$$
$$= (4x^2 + 1)(2x + 1)(2x - 1) \quad \text{Difference of squares}$$

In parts (b) and (c), the sum of squares cannot be factored further.   ∎

7.6 EXERCISES

Find each sum or difference.

1. $(3x^2 - 4x + 5) + (-2x^2 + 3x - 2)$

2. $(4x^3 - 3x^2 + 5) + (-3x^3 - x^2 + 5)$

3. $(12x^2 - 8x + 6) - (3x^2 - 4x + 2)$

4. $(8x^2 - 5x) - (3x^2 - 2x + 4)$

5. $(6x^4 - 3x^2 + x) - (2x^3 + 5x^2 + 4x) + (x^2 - x)$

6. $-(8x^3 + x - 3) + (2x^3 + x^2) - (4x^2 + 3x - 1)$

7. $5(2x^2 - 3x + 7) - 2(6x^2 - x + 12)$

8. $6(3x^2 - 4x + 8) - 3(2x^2 - 3x + 1)$

Find each product.

9. $(x + 3)(x - 8)$

10. $(x - 3)(x - 9)$

11. $(4x - 1)(7x + 2)$

12. $(5x - 6)(3x + 4)$

13. $4x^2(3x^3 - 5x + 1)$

14. $2x^3(x^2 - 4x + 3)$

15. $(2x + 3)(2x - 3)$

16. $(8x - 3)(8x + 3)$

17. $(x + 7)^2$

18. $(x + 9)^2$

19. $(5x - 3)^2$

20. $(6x - 5)^2$

21. $(x + 3)(10x^3 + 4x^2 - 5x + 2)$

22. $(x + 2)(12x^3 - 3x^2 + x + 1)$

Factor the greatest common factor from each polynomial.

23. $12x + 36$

24. $15x + 75$

25. $8x^3 - 4x^2 + 6x$

26. $9x^3 + 12x^2 - 36x$

27. $8x^4 + 6x^3 - 12x^2$

28. $2x^5 - 10x^4 + 16x^3$

Factor each trinomial.

29. $x^2 - 2x - 15$

30. $x^2 + 8x + 12$

31. $x^2 + 2x - 35$

32. $x^2 - 7x + 6$

33. $6x^2 - 48x - 120$

34. $8x^2 - 24x - 320$

35. $3x^3 + 12x^2 + 9x$

36. $9x^4 - 54x^3 + 45x^2$

37. $6x^2 + 5x - 6$

38. $14x^2 + 11x - 15$

39. $5x^2 - 7x - 6$

40. $12x^2 + 11x - 5$

41. $21x^2 - x - 2$

42. $30x^2 + x - 1$

43. $24x^4 + 10x^3 - 4x^2$

44. $18x^5 + 15x^4 - 75x^3$

Factor each perfect square trinomial. It may be necessary to factor out a common factor first.

45. $x^2 - 8x + 16$

46. $x^2 - 12x + 36$

47. $x^2 + 14x + 49$

48. $x^2 + 18x + 81$

49. $9x^2 - 12x + 4$

50. $16x^2 - 40x + 25$

51. $32x^2 - 48x + 18$

52. $20x^2 - 100x + 125$

53. $4x^2 + 28x + 49$

54. $9x^2 - 12x + 4$

Factor each difference of squares.

55. $x^2 - 36$

56. $x^2 - 64$

57. $100 - x^2$

58. $25 - x^2$

59. $9x^2 - 16$

60. $16x^2 - 25$

61. $25x^4 - 9$

62. $36x^4 - 25$

63. $x^4 - 625$

64. $x^4 - 81$

Decide on a factoring method, and then factor the polynomial completely.

65. $13x^3 + 39x^2 + 52x$

66. $8x^2 - 10x - 3$

67. $12x^2 + 16x - 35$

68. $36x^2 + 60x + 25$

69. $4x^2 + 28x + 49$

70. $6x^4 + 7x^2 - 3$

71. $x^8 - 81$

72. $100x^4 - 100$

First factor out the common factor −1, and then factor each trinomial.

73. $-x^2 - 4x + 21$

74. $-x^2 + x + 72$

75. $-3x^2 - x + 4$

76. $-5x^2 + 2x + 16$

77. $-2x^2 - 5x - 2$

78. $-3x^2 + 13x - 4$

QUADRATIC EQUATIONS AND APPLICATIONS

OBJECTIVES

1 Recognize a quadratic equation in standard form.

2 Use the zero-factor property to solve a quadratic equation (when applicable).

3 Use the square root property to solve a quadratic equation (when applicable).

4 Use the quadratic formula to solve a quadratic equation.

5 Solve an application that leads to quadratic equations.

Quadratic Equations and the Zero-Factor Property

We have considered linear equations and inequalities in earlier sections. Now we investigate *second-degree,* or *quadratic,* equations.

QUADRATIC EQUATION

An equation that can be written in the form

$$ax^2 + bx + c = 0 \quad \text{Standard form}$$

where a, b, and c are real numbers, with $a \neq 0$, is a **quadratic equation.** The form of the equation given above is called **standard form.**

One method of solving a quadratic equation depends on the following property.

ZERO-FACTOR PROPERTY

If $ab = 0$, then $a = 0$ or $b = 0$ or both.

Solving a quadratic equation by the zero-factor property requires that the equation be in standard form before factoring.

EXAMPLE 1 Using the Zero-Factor Property

Solve $6x^2 + 7x = 3$.

Solution

$6x^2 + 7x = 3$		Given equation
$6x^2 + 7x - 3 = 0$		Write in standard form.
$(3x - 1)(2x + 3) = 0$		Factor.
$3x - 1 = 0 \quad$ or $\quad 2x + 3 = 0$		Zero-factor property
$3x = 1 \quad$ or $\quad 2x = -3$		Solve each equation.
$x = \dfrac{1}{3} \quad$ or $\quad x = -\dfrac{3}{2}$		Divide.

Check. Substitute $\frac{1}{3}$ and $-\frac{3}{2}$ in the original equation. The solution set is $\left\{\frac{1}{3}, -\frac{3}{2}\right\}$. ∎

The Square Root Property

A quadratic equation of the form $x^2 = k$, $k \geq 0$, can be solved as follows, using factoring and the zero-factor property.

$x^2 = k$		
$x^2 - k = 0$		Subtract k.
$(x + \sqrt{k})(x - \sqrt{k}) = 0$		Factor, using radicals.
$x + \sqrt{k} = 0 \quad$ or $\quad x - \sqrt{k} = 0$		Zero-factor property
$x = -\sqrt{k} \quad$ or $\quad x = \sqrt{k}$		Solve each equation.

Historical Controversy For centuries mathematicians wrestled with finding a formula that could solve **cubic (third-degree) equations.** In sixteenth-century Italy, **Niccolo Tartaglia** had developed a method of solving a cubic equation of the form

$$x^3 + mx = n.$$

Girolamo Cardano begged to know Tartaglia's method, and after he was told, he was sworn to secrecy. Nonetheless, Cardano published Tartaglia's method in his 1545 work *Ars Magna* (although he did give Tartaglia credit).

The formula for finding one real solution of the equation $x^3 + mx = n$ is

$$x = \sqrt[3]{\frac{n}{2} + \sqrt{\left(\frac{n}{2}\right)^2 \left(\frac{m}{3}\right)^3}}$$
$$- \sqrt[3]{-\left(\frac{n}{2}\right) + \sqrt{\left(\frac{n}{2}\right)^2 + \left(\frac{m}{3}\right)^3}}.$$

Show that 2 is a solution of $x^3 + 9x = 26$ using this formula, with $m = 9$ and $n = 26$.

Completing the square, a technique used in deriving the quadratic formula, has important applications in algebra. To transform the expression $x^2 + kx$ into the square of a binomial, we add to it the square of half the coefficient of x.

$$\left[\left(\frac{1}{2}\right)k\right]^2 = \frac{k^2}{4}$$

We then obtain

$$x^2 + kx + \frac{k^2}{4} = \left(x + \frac{k}{2}\right)^2.$$

For example, to make $x^2 + 6x$ the square of a binomial, we add 9, because $9 = \left[\frac{1}{2}(6)\right]^2$. This results in the trinomial $x^2 + 6x + 9$, which is equal to $(x + 3)^2$.

   The Greeks had a method of completing the square geometrically. For example, to complete the square for $x^2 + 6x$, begin with a square of side x. Add three rectangles of width 1 and length x to the right side and the bottom. Each rectangle has area $1x$, or x, so the total area of the figure is now $x^2 + 6x$. To fill in the corner (that is, "complete the square"), we add 9 1-by-1 squares as shown. The new completed square has sides of length $x + 3$ and area

$$(x + 3)^2 = x^2 + 6x + 9.$$

This leads to the **square root property** for solving equations.

SQUARE ROOT PROPERTY

If $k \geq 0$, then the solutions of $x^2 = k$ are $\pm\sqrt{k}$.

If $k > 0$, the equation $x^2 = k$ has two real solutions. If $k = 0$, there is only one solution, 0. If $k < 0$, there are no real solutions. (In this last case, there *are* *complex* solutions. Complex numbers are covered in more extensive algebra texts.)

EXAMPLE 2 Using the Square Root Property

Use the square root property to solve each quadratic equation for real solutions.

(a) $x^2 = 25$ **(b)** $x^2 = 18$ **(c)** $x^2 = -3$ **(d)** $(x - 4)^2 = 12$

Solution

(a) Since $\sqrt{25} = 5$, the solution set of the equation $x^2 = 25$ is $\{5, -5\}$, which may be abbreviated $\{\pm 5\}$.

(b)
$$x^2 = 18$$
$$x = \pm\sqrt{18} \qquad \text{Square root property}$$
$$x = \pm\sqrt{9 \cdot 2} \qquad \text{Factor 18 as } 9 \cdot 2.$$
$$x = \pm\sqrt{9} \cdot \sqrt{2} \qquad \text{Product rule for square roots}$$
$$x = \pm 3\sqrt{2} \qquad \sqrt{9} = 3$$

The solution set is $\left\{\pm 3\sqrt{2}\right\}$.

(c) Because $-3 < 0$, the equation $x^2 = -3$ has no real solutions. The solution set is $\varnothing$.

(d) To solve this equation, we extend the square root property to a binomial base with exponent 2.

$$(x - 4)^2 = 12$$
$$x - 4 = \pm\sqrt{12} \qquad \text{Square root property extended}$$
$$x = 4 \pm \sqrt{12} \qquad \text{Add 4.}$$
$$x = 4 \pm \sqrt{4 \cdot 3} \qquad \text{Factor 12 as } 4 \cdot 3.$$
$$x = 4 \pm 2\sqrt{3} \qquad \sqrt{4 \cdot 3} = 2\sqrt{3}$$

The solution set is $\left\{4 \pm 2\sqrt{3}\right\}$.   ∎

The Quadratic Formula

By *completing the square* (see the margin note at left), we can derive one of the most important formulas in algebra, the *quadratic formula*.

$$ax^2 + bx + c = 0$$

Standard quadratic equation ($a > 0$)

$$x^2 + \frac{b}{a}x + \frac{c}{a} = 0$$

Divide by a.

$$x^2 + \frac{b}{a}x = -\frac{c}{a}$$

Add $-\frac{c}{a}$.

$$x^2 + \frac{b}{a}x + \frac{b^2}{4a^2} = \frac{b^2}{4a^2} - \frac{c}{a}$$

Add $\frac{b^2}{4a^2}$.

$$\left(x + \frac{b}{2a}\right)^2 = \frac{b^2 - 4ac}{4a^2}$$

Factor on the left.
Combine terms on the right.

$$x + \frac{b}{2a} = \pm\sqrt{\frac{b^2 - 4ac}{4a^2}}$$

Square root property

$$x + \frac{b}{2a} = \pm\frac{\sqrt{b^2 - 4ac}}{\sqrt{4a^2}}$$

Quotient rule for square roots

$$x = -\frac{b}{2a} \pm \frac{\sqrt{b^2 - 4ac}}{2a}$$

Subtract $\frac{b}{2a}$.

> Be careful;
> $-b \pm \sqrt{b^2 - 4ac}$ is
> all written over $2a$.

$$x = \frac{-b \pm \sqrt{b^2 - 4ac}}{2a}$$

Combine like terms.
This is also valid for $a < 0$.

QUADRATIC FORMULA

The solutions of $ax^2 + bx + c = 0$, $a \neq 0$, are given by the **quadratic formula.**

$$x = \frac{-b \pm \sqrt{b^2 - 4ac}}{2a}$$

EXAMPLE 3 Using the Quadratic Formula

Solve $x^2 - 4x + 2 = 0$.

Solution

$$x = \frac{-b \pm \sqrt{b^2 - 4ac}}{2a}$$

Quadratic formula

$$x = \frac{-(-4) \pm \sqrt{(-4)^2 - 4(1)(2)}}{2(1)}$$

$a = 1$, $b = -4$, $c = 2$

$$x = \frac{4 \pm \sqrt{16 - 8}}{2}$$

Start to simplify.

$$x = \frac{4 \pm 2\sqrt{2}}{2}$$

$\sqrt{16 - 8} = \sqrt{8} = 2\sqrt{2}$

$$x = \frac{2(2 \pm \sqrt{2})}{2}$$

Factor out 2 in the numerator.

> Factor, and then
> divide out the
> common factor.

$$x = 2 \pm \sqrt{2}$$

Divide out the common factor.

The solution set is $\left\{2 + \sqrt{2},\ 2 - \sqrt{2}\right\}$, abbreviated $\left\{2 \pm \sqrt{2}\right\}$. ∎

A Radical Departure from the Other Methods of Evaluating the Golden Ratio Recall from **Chapter 5** that the golden ratio is found in numerous places in mathematics, art, and nature. In a margin note there, we showed that the *"continued" fraction*

$$1 + \cfrac{1}{1 + \cfrac{1}{1 + \cfrac{1}{1 + \cdots}}}$$

is equal to the golden ratio, $\frac{1 + \sqrt{5}}{2}$. Now consider this *"nested" radical:*

$$\sqrt{1 + \sqrt{1 + \sqrt{1 + \cdots}}}$$

Let *x* represent this radical expression. Because it appears "within itself," we can write

$$x = \sqrt{1 + x}$$
$$x^2 = 1 + x$$
$$x^2 - x - 1 = 0.$$

Using the quadratic formula, with $a = 1$, $b = -1$, and $c = -1$, it can be shown that the positive solution of this equation, and thus the value of the nested radical, is (you guessed it!) the golden ratio.

EXAMPLE 4 **Using the Quadratic Formula**

Solve $2x^2 = x + 4$.

Solution

First write the equation in standard form as $2x^2 - x - 4 = 0$.

$$x = \frac{-(-1) \pm \sqrt{(-1)^2 - 4(2)(-4)}}{2(2)}$$ Quadratic formula with $a = 2$, $b = -1$, $c = -4$

$$x = \frac{1 \pm \sqrt{1 + 32}}{4}$$ Simplify the radicand.

$$x = \frac{1 \pm \sqrt{33}}{4}$$ Add.

The solution set is $\left\{ \frac{1 \pm \sqrt{33}}{4} \right\}$.

Applications

EXAMPLE 5 **Applying a Quadratic Equation**

Two cars left an intersection at the same time, one heading due north, and the other due west. When they were exactly 100 miles apart, the car headed north had gone 20 miles farther than the car headed west. How far had each car traveled?

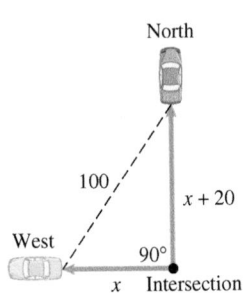

North

West   90°

$x + 20$

x Intersection

100

Figure 15

Solution

Step 1 **Read** the problem carefully.

Step 2 **Assign a variable.** See **Figure 15**.

Let x = the distance traveled by the car headed west.

Then $(x + 20)$ = the distance traveled by the car headed north.

The cars are 100 miles apart. The hypotenuse of the right triangle equals 100.

Step 3 **Write an equation.**

$$c^2 = a^2 + b^2$$ Pythagorean theorem

$$100^2 = x^2 + (x + 20)^2$$ Substitute.

Step 4 **Solve.** $10,000 = x^2 + x^2 + 40x + 400$ Square the binomial.

$$2x^2 + 40x - 9600 = 0$$ Standard form

$$x^2 + 20x - 4800 = 0$$ Divide both sides by 2.

Use the quadratic formula to find x.

$$x = \frac{-20 \pm \sqrt{20^2 - 4(1)(-4800)}}{2(1)}$$ $a = 1$, $b = 20$, $c = -4800$

$$x = \frac{-20 \pm \sqrt{19,600}}{2}$$ Simplify under the radical.

$$x = 60 \quad \text{or} \quad x = -80$$ Use a calculator.

Step 5 **State the answer.**   Distance cannot be negative here, so discard the negative solution. The required distances are 60 miles and $60 + 20 = 80$ miles.

Step 6 **Check.**   Because $60^2 + 80^2 = 100^2$, the answer is correct.

Évariste Galois (1811–1832), as a young Frenchman, agreed to fight a duel. He had been engaged for some time in mathematical research that centered on solving equations by using **group theory.** Now, anticipating the possibility of his death, he summarized the essentials of his discoveries in a letter to a friend. The next day Galois was killed. He was not yet 21 years old when he died.

EXAMPLE 6 Applying a Quadratic Equation

If an object on Earth is projected upward from the top of a 144-foot building with an initial velocity of 112 feet per second, its position (in feet above the ground) is given by

$$s = -16t^2 + 112t + 144,$$

where t is time in seconds after it was projected and air resistance is neglected. How long does it take for the object to hit the ground?

Solution

When the object hits the ground, its distance above the ground is 0. Find t when s is 0.

$$0 = -16t^2 + 112t + 144 \qquad \text{Let } s = 0.$$

$$0 = t^2 - 7t - 9 \qquad \text{Divide both sides by } -16.$$

$$t = \frac{7 \pm \sqrt{49 + 36}}{2} \qquad \text{Quadratic formula}$$

$$t = \frac{7 \pm \sqrt{85}}{2} \qquad \text{Add.} \quad \boxed{\text{This must be rejected.}}$$

$$t \approx 8.1 \quad \text{or} \quad t \approx -1.1 \qquad \text{Use a calculator.}$$

Because it cannot hit the ground before it is projected, discard the negative solution. It will hit the ground about 8.1 seconds after it is projected. ∎

Niels Henrik Abel (1802–1829) of Norway was identified in childhood as a mathematical genius but never received in his lifetime the professional recognition his work deserved. He proved that a general formula for solving **fifth-degree equations** does not exist. The quadratic formula (for equations of degree 2) is well known, and formulas do exist for solving third- and fourth-degree equations. Abel's accomplishment ended a search that had lasted for years.

7.7   EXERCISES

Solve each equation by the zero-factor property.

1. $(x + 3)(x - 9) = 0$

2. $(x + 6)(x + 4) = 0$

3. $(2x - 7)(5x + 1) = 0$

4. $(7x - 3)(6x + 4) = 0$

5. $x(x + 7) = 0$

6. $x(x - 8) = 0$

7. $x^2 - x - 12 = 0$

8. $x^2 + 4x - 5 = 0$

9. $x^2 + 9x + 14 = 0$

10. $x^2 + 3x - 4 = 0$

11. $2x^2 + 3x - 5 = 0$

12. $3x^2 - 5x - 28 = 0$

13. $12x^2 + 4x = 1$

14. $15x^2 + 7x = 2$

15. $(x + 4)(x - 6) = -16$

16. $(x - 1)(3x + 2) = 4x$

Solve each equation for real solutions by using the square root property.

17. $x^2 = 64$

18. $x^2 = 16$

19. $x^2 = 24$

20. $x^2 = 48$

21. $x^2 = -5$

22. $x^2 = -10$

23. $(x - 4)^2 = 9$

24. $(x + 3)^2 = 25$

25. $(4 - x)^2 = 3$

26. $(3 + x)^2 = 11$

27. $(2x - 5)^2 = 13$

28. $(4x + 1)^2 = 19$

Solve each equation for real solutions by the quadratic formula.

29. $x^2 + 3x - 7 = 0$

30. $x^2 + 2x - 5 = 0$

31. $2x^2 = 2x + 1$

32. $9x^2 = 6x + 1$

33. $x^2 - 1 = x$

34. $2x^2 - 5 = 4x$

35. $4x(x + 1) = 1$

36. $4x(x - 1) = 19$

37. $(x + 2)(x - 3) = 1$

38. $(x - 5)(x + 2) = 6$

39. $x^2 - 6x = -14$

40. $x^2 - 2x = -2$

Solve each problem. Use a calculator as necessary, and round approximations to the nearest tenth.

41. Distances Traveled by Ships Two ships leave port at the same time, one heading due south and the other heading due east. Several hours later, they are 170 miles apart. If the ship traveling south travels 70 miles farther than the other, how many miles does each travel?

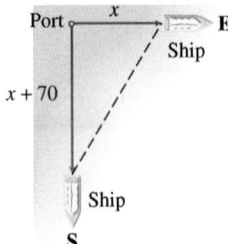

42. Distances Traveled by Ships Two ships leave port at the same time, one heading due north and the other heading due east. Several hours later, they are 20 miles apart. If the ship traveling north travels 4 miles farther than the other, how many miles does each travel?

43. Height of a Kite Paulette is flying a kite that is 30 feet farther above her hand than its horizontal distance from her. The string from her hand to the kite is 150 feet long. How far is the kite above her hand?

44. Leaning Ladder A 13-foot ladder is leaning against a house. The distance from the bottom of the ladder to the house is 7 feet less than the distance from the top of the ladder to the ground. How far is the bottom of the ladder from the house?

45. Length of a Wire Suppose that a wire is attached to a top of a building 400 feet high and is pulled tight. It is attached to the ground 100 feet from the base of the building, as shown in the figure. How long is the wire?

46. Length of a Wire Suppose that a wire is attached to the top of a building 407 feet high and is pulled tight. The length of the wire is twice the distance between the base of the building and the point on the ground where the wire is attached. How long is the wire?

47. Side Lengths of a Triangle Find the lengths of the sides of the right triangle.

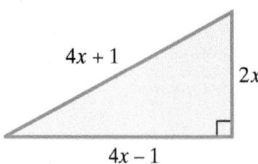

48. Side Lengths of a Triangle Find the lengths of the sides of the right triangle.

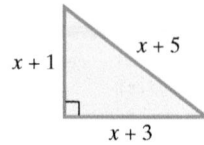

49. Size of a Toy Piece A toy manufacturer needs a piece of plastic in the shape of a right triangle with the longer leg 2 centimeters more than twice as long as the shorter leg, and the hypotenuse 1 centimeter more than the longer leg. How long should the three sides of the triangular piece be?

50. Size of a Developer's Property A developer owns a piece of land enclosed on three sides by streets, giving it the shape of a right triangle. The hypotenuse is 8 meters longer than the longer leg, and the shorter leg is 9 meters shorter than the hypotenuse. Find the lengths of the three sides of the property.

51. Height of a Projectile An object is projected directly upward from the ground. After t seconds its distance in feet above the ground is $s = 144t - 16t^2$.

   (a) After how many seconds will the object be 128 feet above the ground? (*Hint:* Look for a common factor before solving the equation.)

   (b) When does the object strike the ground?

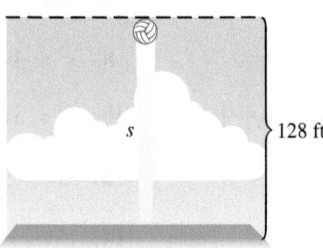

Ground level

52. Height of a Projectile A building is 400 feet high. Suppose that a ball is projected upward from the top, and its position s in feet above the ground is given by the equation

$$s = -16t^2 + 45t + 400,$$

where t is the number of seconds elapsed. How long will it take for the ball to reach a height of 200 feet above the ground?

53. **Height of a Projectile** A high-rise condominium building is 407 feet high. Suppose that a ball is projected upward from the top and its position s in feet above the ground is given by the equation $s = -16t^2 + 75t + 407$, where t is the number of seconds elapsed. How long will it take for the ball to reach a height of 450 feet above the ground?

54. **Height of a Projectile** Refer to the equations in **Exercises 52 and 53.** Suppose that the first sentence in each problem did not give the height. How could you use the equation to determine the height?

55. **Dimensions of a Strip of Flooring around a Rug** Kyle and Marin want to buy a rug for a room that is 15 feet by 20 feet. They want to leave an even strip of flooring uncovered around the edges of the room. How wide a strip will they have if they buy a rug with an area of 234 square feet?

56. **Dimensions of a Border around a Pool** A club swimming pool is 30 feet wide and 40 feet long. The club members want an exposed aggregate border in a strip of uniform width around the pool. They have enough material for 296 square feet. How wide can the strip be?

57. **Dimensions of a Garden** Arif's backyard is 20 meters by 30 meters. He wants to put a flower garden in the middle of the backyard, leaving a strip of grass of uniform width around the flower garden. To be happy, he must have 184 square meters of grass. Under these conditions, what will the length and width of the garden be?

58. **Dimensions of a Piece of Sheet Metal** A rectangular piece of sheet metal has a length that is 4 inches less than twice the width. A square piece 2 inches on a side is cut from each corner. The sides are then turned up to form an uncovered box of volume 256 cubic inches. Find the length and width of the original piece of metal.

CHAPTER 7   SUMMARY

KEY TERMS

7.1
algebraic expression
equation
linear equation
   (first-degree equation)
solution
solution set
equivalent equations
conditional equation
identity
contradiction
literal equation
formula
solving for a specified
   variable
mathematical model

7.3
ratio
proportion
terms (of a proportion)
extremes
means
cross products
   (of a proportion)
direct variation
   (direct proportion)
constant of variation
inverse variation
joint variation
combined variation

7.4
interval
interval notation
linear inequality
three-part inequality
tolerance

7.5
exponent
base
exponential expression
scientific notation

7.6
term (monomial)
polynomial

degree (of a polynomial)
like terms
descending powers
difference of two squares
factoring
factor
factored form
prime polynomial
factored completely

7.7
quadratic equation
standard form
square root property
quadratic formula

NEW SYMBOLS

a to b, $\dfrac{a}{b}$, $a:b$ ratio of a to b

∞, $-\infty$ infinity, negative infinity

$(-\infty, 2], (-3, \infty), (-3, 2]$
   examples of interval notation

a^n a to the nth power

TEST YOUR WORD POWER

See how well you have learned the vocabulary in this chapter.

1. A **solution set** is the set of numbers that
   A. make an expression undefined.
   B. make an equation false.
   C. make an equation true.
   D. make an expression equal to 0.

2. An **inequality** is
   A. a statement that two algebraic expressions are equal.
   B. a point on a number line.
   C. an equation with no solutions.
   D. a statement with algebraic expressions related by $<, \leq, >,$ or $\geq$.

3. A **ratio**
   A. compares two quantities using a quotient.
   B. says that two quotients are equal.
   C. is a product of two quantities.
   D. is a difference between two quantities.

4. A **proportion**
   A. compares two quantities using a quotient.
   B. says that two ratios are equal.
   C. is a product of two quantities.
   D. is a difference between two quantities.

5. A **monomial** is a polynomial with
   A. only one term.
   B. exactly two terms.
   C. exactly three terms.
   D. more than three terms.

6. A **binomial** is a polynomial with
   A. only one term.
   B. exactly two terms.
   C. exactly three terms.
   D. more than three terms.

7. A **trinomial** is a polynomial with
   A. only one term.
   B. exactly two terms.
   C. exactly three terms.
   D. more than three terms.

8. The **FOIL** method is used to
   A. add two binomials.
   B. add two trinomials.
   C. multiply two binomials.
   D. multiply two trinomials.

9. **Factoring** is
   A. a method of multiplying polynomials.
   B. the process of writing a polynomial as a product.
   C. the answer in a multiplication problem.
   D. a way to add the terms of a polynomial.

10. A **quadratic equation** is an equation that can be written in the form
    A. $Ax + B = C$.   B. $ax^2 + bx + c = 0$ $(a \neq 0)$.
    C. $x = k$.   D. $x = k^2$.

ANSWERS
1. C 2. D 3. A 4. B 5. A
6. B 7. C 8. C 9. B 10. B

QUICK REVIEW

Concepts	Examples

7.1 Linear Equations

Addition and Multiplication Properties of Equality

The same number may be added to (or subtracted from) each side of an equation to obtain an equivalent equation.

Similarly, the same nonzero number may be multiplied by or divided into each side of an equation to obtain an equivalent equation.

Solving a Linear Equation in One Variable

Step 1 Clear fractions.

Step 2 Simplify each side separately.

Step 3 Isolate the variable terms on one side.

Step 4 Transform the equation so that the coefficient of the variable is 1.

Solve the equation.

$$4(8 - 3x) = 32 - 8(x + 2)$$

$$32 - 12x = 32 - 8x - 16 \qquad \text{Distributive property}$$

$$32 - 12x = 16 - 8x \qquad \text{Combine like terms.}$$

$$32 - 12x + 12x = 16 - 8x + 12x \qquad \text{Add } 12x.$$

$$32 = 16 + 4x \qquad \text{Combine like terms.}$$

$$32 - 16 = 16 + 4x - 16 \qquad \text{Subtract 16.}$$

$$16 = 4x \qquad \text{Combine like terms.}$$

$$\frac{16}{4} = \frac{4x}{4} \qquad \text{Divide by 4.}$$

$$x = 4 \qquad \text{Interchange sides.}$$

Concepts	Examples

Step 5 Check.

Check: Substitute 4 for x in the original equation.

$$4(8 - 3x) = 32 - 8(x + 2) \quad \text{Original equation}$$
$$4[8 - 3(4)] \overset{?}{=} 32 - 8(4 + 2) \quad \text{Let } x = 4.$$
$$4[8 - 12] \overset{?}{=} 32 - 8(6) \quad \text{Multiply. Add.}$$
$$4[-4] \overset{?}{=} 32 - 48 \quad \text{Subtract. Multiply.}$$
$$-16 = -16 \quad \checkmark \quad \text{True.}$$

The solution set is $\{4\}$.

Solve $A = \dfrac{1}{2}bh$ for h.

Solving for a Specified Variable

Step 1 If the equation contains fractions, multiply both sides by the LCD to clear the fractions.

Step 2 Transform the equation so that all terms with the specified variable are on one side and all terms without that variable are on the other side.

Step 3 Divide each side by the factor that is the coefficient of the specified variable.

$$A = \frac{1}{2}bh$$

$$2A = 2\left(\frac{1}{2}bh\right) \quad \text{Multiply by 2.}$$

$$2A = bh \quad 2 \cdot \frac{1}{2} = 1$$

$$\frac{2A}{b} = h, \quad \text{or} \quad h = \frac{2A}{b} \quad \begin{array}{l}\text{Divide by } b.\\ \text{Interchange sides.}\end{array}$$

7.2 Applications of Linear Equations

Solving an Applied Problem

Step 1 Read the problem.

Step 2 Assign a variable.

Step 3 Write an equation.

Step 4 Solve the equation.

Step 5 State the answer.

Step 6 Check.

How many liters of 30% alcohol solution and 80% alcohol solution must be mixed to obtain 100 L of 50% alcohol solution?

Let x = number of liters of 30% solution.

Then $100 - x$ = number of liters of 80% solution.

Percent (as a decimal)	Liters of Solution	Liters of Pure Alcohol
0.30	x	$0.30x$
0.80	$100 - x$	$0.80(100 - x)$
0.50	100	$0.50(100)$

From the last column of the table, write an equation and solve it.

$$0.30x + 0.80(100 - x) = 0.50(100)$$
$$0.30x + 80 - 0.80x = 50 \quad \text{Distributive property}$$
$$3x + 800 - 8x = 500 \quad \begin{array}{l}\text{Multiply by 10 to}\\ \text{clear decimals.}\end{array}$$
$$-5x + 800 = 500 \quad \text{Combine like terms.}$$
$$-5x = -300 \quad \text{Subtract 800.}$$
$$x = 60 \quad \text{Divide by } -5.$$

60 liters of 30% solution and $100 - 60 = 40$ liters of 80% solution are required.

Concepts	Examples

7.3 Ratio, Proportion, and Variation

Ratio

To write a ratio, express quantities in the same units and write as a quotient.

Write a ratio for the word phrase.

4 feet to 8 inches = 48 inches to 8 inches

$$= \frac{48}{8}$$

$$= \frac{6}{1} \qquad \text{Lowest terms}$$

The ratio is $\frac{6}{1}$.

Proportion

To solve a proportion, use the method of cross products.

Solve the proportion.

$$\frac{x}{12} = \frac{35}{60}$$

$$60x = 12 \cdot 35 \qquad \text{Cross products}$$

$$60x = 420 \qquad \text{Multiply.}$$

$$x = 7 \qquad \text{Divide by 60.}$$

The solution set is $\{7\}$.

Solving Variation Problems

Step 1 Write the variation equation.

$$y = kx \quad \text{or} \quad y = kx^n \qquad \text{Direct variation}$$

$$y = \frac{k}{x} \quad \text{or} \quad y = \frac{k}{x^n} \qquad \text{Inverse variation}$$

Step 2 Find k by substituting the appropriate given values of x and y into the equation.

Step 3 Rewrite the variation equation with the value of k from Step 2.

Step 4 Substitute the remaining values, and solve for the unknown.

The weight of an object y on Earth is directly proportional to the weight x of that same object on the moon. If a 200-pound astronaut weighs 32 pounds on the moon, how much would a dog weighing 8 pounds on the moon weigh on Earth?

$$y = kx \qquad \text{Variation equation (Step 1)}$$

$$200 = k \cdot 32 \qquad \text{Let } y = 200 \text{ and } x = 32, \text{ and solve for } k. \text{ (Step 2)}$$

$$\frac{200}{32} = k$$

$$k = \frac{25}{4} \qquad \frac{200}{32} \text{ in lowest terms is } \frac{25}{4}.$$

Write the variation equation $y = kx$ with $k = \frac{25}{4}$.

$$y = \frac{25}{4}x \qquad \text{(Step 3)}$$

$$y = \frac{25}{4}(8) \qquad \text{Let } x = 8. \text{ (Step 4)}$$

$$y = 50 \qquad \text{Solve for } y.$$

The dog would weigh 50 pounds on Earth.

Concepts	*Examples*

7.4 Linear Inequalities

Solving Linear Inequalities in One Variable

Step 1 Simplify each side of the inequality by clearing parentheses, fractions, and decimals, as needed, and combining like terms.

Step 2 Use the addition property of inequality to get all terms with variables on one side and all terms without variables on the other side.

Step 3 Use the multiplication property of inequality to write the inequality in the form $x < k$ or $x > k$.

If an inequality is multiplied or divided by a negative number, the direction of the inequality symbol must be reversed.

To solve a three-part inequality, work with all three parts at the same time.

Solve $3(x + 2) - 5x \le 12$.

$$3x + 6 - 5x \le 12 \qquad \text{Distributive property}$$
$$-2x + 6 \le 12 \qquad \text{Combine like terms.}$$
$$-2x + 6 - 6 \le 12 - 6 \qquad \text{Subtract 6.}$$
$$-2x \le 6 \qquad \text{Combine like terms.}$$
$$\frac{-2x}{-2} \ge \frac{6}{-2} \qquad \begin{array}{l}\text{Divide by 2.}\\ \text{Change } \le \text{ to } \ge .\end{array}$$
$$x \ge -3$$

The solution set $[-3, \infty)$ is graphed below.

Solve $-4 < 2x + 3 \le 7$.

$$-4 < \quad 2x + 3 \quad \le 7$$
$$-4 - 3 < 2x + 3 - 3 \le 7 - 3 \qquad \text{Subtract 3.}$$
$$-7 < \quad 2x \quad \le 4$$
$$\frac{-7}{2} < \quad \frac{2x}{2} \quad \le \frac{4}{2} \qquad \text{Divide by 2.}$$
$$-\frac{7}{2} < \quad x \quad \le 2$$

The solution set $\left(-\frac{7}{2}, 2\right]$ is graphed below.

7.5 Properties of Exponents and Scientific Notation

Definitions and Rules for Exponents

For all integers m and n and all real numbers a and b, the following rules apply.

Product Rule $\qquad a^m \cdot a^n = a^{m+n}$

Quotient Rule $\qquad \dfrac{a^m}{a^n} = a^{m-n} \quad (a \ne 0)$

Zero Exponent $\qquad a^0 = 1 \quad (a \ne 0)$

Negative Exponent $\qquad a^{-n} = \dfrac{1}{a^n} \quad (a \ne 0)$

Power Rules $\qquad$ (a) $(a^m)^n = a^{mn}$ (b) $(ab)^m = a^m b^m$

$\qquad\qquad\qquad$ (c) $\left(\dfrac{a}{b}\right)^n = \dfrac{a^n}{b^n} \quad (b \ne 0)$

Apply the rules for exponents.

$$3^4 \cdot 3^2 = 3^6$$

$$\frac{2^5}{2^3} = 2^2$$

$$27^0 = 1 \qquad (-5)^0 = 1$$

$$5^{-2} = \frac{1}{5^2}$$

$$(6^3)^4 = 6^{12} \qquad (5 \cdot 2)^4 = 5^4 \cdot 2^4$$

$$\left(\frac{2}{3}\right)^5 = \frac{2^5}{3^5}$$

Concepts	Examples

Special Rules for Negative Exponents

$$\frac{1}{a^{-n}} = a^n \quad (a \neq 0) \qquad \frac{a^{-n}}{b^{-m}} = \frac{b^m}{a^n} \quad (a, b \neq 0)$$

$$a^{-n} = \left(\frac{1}{a}\right)^n \quad (a \neq 0) \qquad \left(\frac{a}{b}\right)^{-n} = \left(\frac{b}{a}\right)^n \quad (a, b \neq 0)$$

$$\frac{1}{10^{-3}} = 10^3 \qquad \frac{10^{-3}}{10^{-4}} = \frac{10^4}{10^3}$$

$$4^{-3} = \left(\frac{1}{4}\right)^3 \qquad \left(\frac{4}{7}\right)^{-2} = \left(\frac{7}{4}\right)^2 = \frac{7^2}{4^2}$$

Scientific Notation

A number is in scientific notation when it is expressed in the form

$$a \times 10^n,$$

where $1 \leq |a| < 10$, and n is an integer.

Write 23,500,000,000 in scientific notation.

$$23{,}500{,}000{,}000 = 2.35 \times 10^{10}$$

Write 4.3×10^{-6} in standard notation.

$$4.3 \times 10^{-6} = 0.0000043$$

7.6 Polynomials and Factoring

Adding and Subtracting Polynomials

Add or subtract polynomials by combining like terms.

Subtract. $(5x^4 + 3x^2) - (7x^4 + x^2 - x)$

$$= 5x^4 + 3x^2 - 7x^4 - x^2 + x$$

$$= -2x^4 + 2x^2 + x$$

Multiplying Polynomials

To multiply two polynomials, multiply each term of one by each term of the other.

Multiply. $(x^3 + 3x)(4x^2 - 5x + 2)$

$$= 4x^5 - 5x^4 + 2x^3 + 12x^3 - 15x^2 + 6x$$

$$= 4x^5 - 5x^4 + 14x^3 - 15x^2 + 6x$$

To multiply two binomials, use the **FOIL** method. Multiply the **First** terms, the **Outer** terms, the **Inner** terms, and the **Last** terms. Then add these products.

$(2x + 3)(x - 7)$

$$= 2x(x) + 2x(-7) + 3x + 3(-7) \quad \text{FOIL method}$$

$$= 2x^2 - 11x - 21 \quad \text{Multiply. Combine like terms.}$$

Special Products

$$(x + y)(x - y) = x^2 - y^2$$

$$(x + y)^2 = x^2 + 2xy + y^2$$

$$(x - y)^2 = x^2 - 2xy + y^2$$

$$(3x + 8)(3x - 8) = 9x^2 - 64$$

$$(5x + 3)^2 = 25x^2 + 30x + 9$$

$$(2x - 1)^2 = 4x^2 - 4x + 1$$

Factoring Out the Greatest Common Factor

Use the distributive property to write the given polynomial as a product of two factors, one of which is the greatest common factor of the terms of the polynomial.

Factor.

$$4x^5 + 12x^3 - 8x^2 \quad \text{GCF} = 4x^2$$

$$= 4x^2(x^3 + 3x - 2) \quad \text{Check by multiplying.}$$

Factoring Trinomials

To factor a trinomial, choose factors of the first term and factors of the last term. Then, place them in a pair of parentheses of this form.

$$(\quad)(\quad)$$

Try various combinations of the factors until the correct product yields the given trinomial.

Factor $15x^2 + 14x - 8$.

The factors of 15 are 5 and 3, and 15 and 1.

The factors of -8 are -4 and 2, 4 and -2, -1 and 8, and 1 and -8.

Various combinations of these factors lead to the following.

$$15x^2 + 14x - 8$$

$$= (5x - 2)(3x + 4) \quad \text{Check by multiplying.}$$

Special Factoring

Use the special products above in reverse to factor a difference of squares or a perfect square trinomial.

Factor.

$4x^2 - 25$	$9x^2 + 6x + 1$	$16x^2 - 56x + 49$
$= (2x)^2 - (5)^2$	$= (3x + 1)^2$	$= (4x - 7)^2$
$= (2x + 5)(2x - 5)$		

Concepts

Examples

7.7 Quadratic Equations and Applications

Quadratic equations can be solved in some cases by using the zero-factor property or the square root property. The quadratic formula can always be used to solve a quadratic equation.

Zero-Factor Property

If $ab = 0$, then $a = 0$ or $b = 0$ or both.

Square Root Property

If $k \geq 0$, then the solutions of $x^2 = k$ are $\pm\sqrt{k}$.

Quadratic Formula

The solutions of $ax^2 + bx + c = 0$, $a \neq 0$, are given by the following formula.

$$x = \frac{-b \pm \sqrt{b^2 - 4ac}}{2a}$$

Solve $3x^2 - 10x - 8 = 0$.

By the zero-factor property:

$(3x + 2)(x - 4) = 0$ Factor.

$3x + 2 = 0$ or $x - 4 = 0$ Set each factor equal to 0.

$x = -\dfrac{2}{3}$ $x = 4$ Solve.

By the quadratic formula:

$a = 3, b = -10, c = -8$

$x = \dfrac{-(-10) \pm \sqrt{(-10)^2 - 4(3)(-8)}}{2(3)}$ Substitute.

$x = \dfrac{10 \pm \sqrt{100 + 96}}{6}$ Perform the operations.

$x = \dfrac{10 \pm \sqrt{196}}{6}$ Add under the radical.

$x = \dfrac{10 \pm 14}{6}$ $\sqrt{196} = 14$

$x = 4$ or $-\dfrac{2}{3}$ Simplify to find two solutions.

The solution set is $\left\{-\dfrac{2}{3}, 4\right\}$.

CHAPTER 7   TEST

Solve each equation.

1. $5x - 3 + 2x = 3(x - 2) + 11$

2. $\dfrac{2x - 1}{3} + \dfrac{x + 1}{4} = \dfrac{43}{12}$

3. Decide whether the equation

$$3x - (2 - x) + 4x = 7x - 2 - (-x)$$

is conditional, an identity, or a contradiction. Give its solution set.

4. Solve for v: $S = vt - 16t^2$.

Solve each application.

5. **Areas of Hawaiian Islands** Three islands in the Hawaiian island chain are Hawaii (the Big Island), Maui, and Kauai. Together, their areas total 5300 square miles. The island of Hawaii is 3293 square miles larger than the island of Maui, and Maui is 177 square miles larger than Kauai. What is the area of each island?

6. *Chemical Mixture* How many liters of a 20% solution of a chemical should Roxanne mix with 10 liters of a 50% solution to obtain a mixture that is 40% chemical?

7. *Speeds of Trains* A passenger train and a freight train leave a town at the same time and travel in opposite directions. Their speeds are 60 mph and 75 mph, respectively. How long will it take for the trains to be 297 miles apart?

8. *Merchandise Pricing* Which is the better buy for processed cheese slices: 16 slices for $4.38 or 12 slices for $3.30?

9. *Drug Dosage* A physician orders 7.5 milligrams daily for Zyprexa (olanzipine). How many 2.5-milligram tablets of this antipsychotic drug should be administered? (*Source:* Giangrasso, Anthony Patrick, and Delores M. Shrimpton. *Ratio & Proportion Dosage Calculations,* 2nd ed. Pearson, 2014.)

10. *Distance between Cities* The distance between Boston and Milwaukee is 1050 miles. On a certain map this distance is represented by 21 inches. On the same map Seattle and Cincinnati are 46 inches apart. What is the actual distance between Seattle and Cincinnati?

11. *Current in a Circuit* The current in a simple electrical circuit is inversely proportional to the resistance. If the current is 80 amps when the resistance is 30 ohms, find the current when the resistance is 12 ohms.

Solve each inequality. Give the solution set in both interval and graph forms.

12. $-4x + 2(x - 3) \geq 4x - (3 + 5x) - 7$

13. $-10 < 3x - 4 \leq 14$

14. *Grade Average* Robert has scores of 83, 76, and 79 on his first three tests in Survey of Mathematics. If he wants an average of at least 80 after his fourth test, what are the possible scores he can make on his fourth test?

Evaluate each exponential expression.

15. $\left(\dfrac{4}{3}\right)^2$

16. $-(-2)^6$

17. $\left(\dfrac{3}{4}\right)^{-3}$

18. $-5^0 + (-5)^0$

Use the properties of exponents to simplify each expression. Write answers with positive exponents only.

19. $\dfrac{(10^{-2})^{-3}}{10^4 \cdot 10^2}$

20. $\dfrac{10^{-4} \cdot 10^{12}}{10^7}$

21. Write each number in standard notation.

  (a) 6.93×10^8 **(b)** 1.25×10^{-7}

22. Use scientific notation to evaluate the following. Leave the answer in scientific notation.

$$\frac{(2,500,000)(0.00003)}{(0.05)(5,000,000)}$$

23. *Time Traveled for a Radio Signal* The mean distance to Earth from Pluto is 4.58×10^9 kilometers. The first U.S. space probe to Pluto transmitted radio signals from Pluto to Earth at the speed of light, 3.00×10^5 kilometers per second. How long (in seconds) did it take for the signals to reach Earth?

Perform the indicated operations.

24. $(3x^3 - 5x^2 + 8x - 2) - (3x^3 - 9x^2 + 2x - 12)$

25. $(5x + 2)(3x - 4)$

26. $(4x^2 - 3)(4x^2 + 3)$

27. $(x + 6)^2$

Factor each polynomial completely.

28. $x^2 + 3x - 28$

29. $2x^2 + 19x + 45$

30. $25x^2 - 49$

31. $x^2 - 18x + 81$

32. $2x^3 - 18x^2 + 40x$

Solve each quadratic equation.

33. $6x^2 + 7x - 3 = 0$

34. $x^2 - 13 = 0$

35. $x^2 - x = 7$

36. *Time an Object Has Descended* The equation

$$s = 16t^2 + 15t$$

gives the distance s in feet an object dropped off a building has descended in t seconds. Find the time t when the object has descended 25 feet. Use a calculator and round the answer to the nearest hundredth.

Graphs, Functions, and Systems of Equations and Inequalities

8

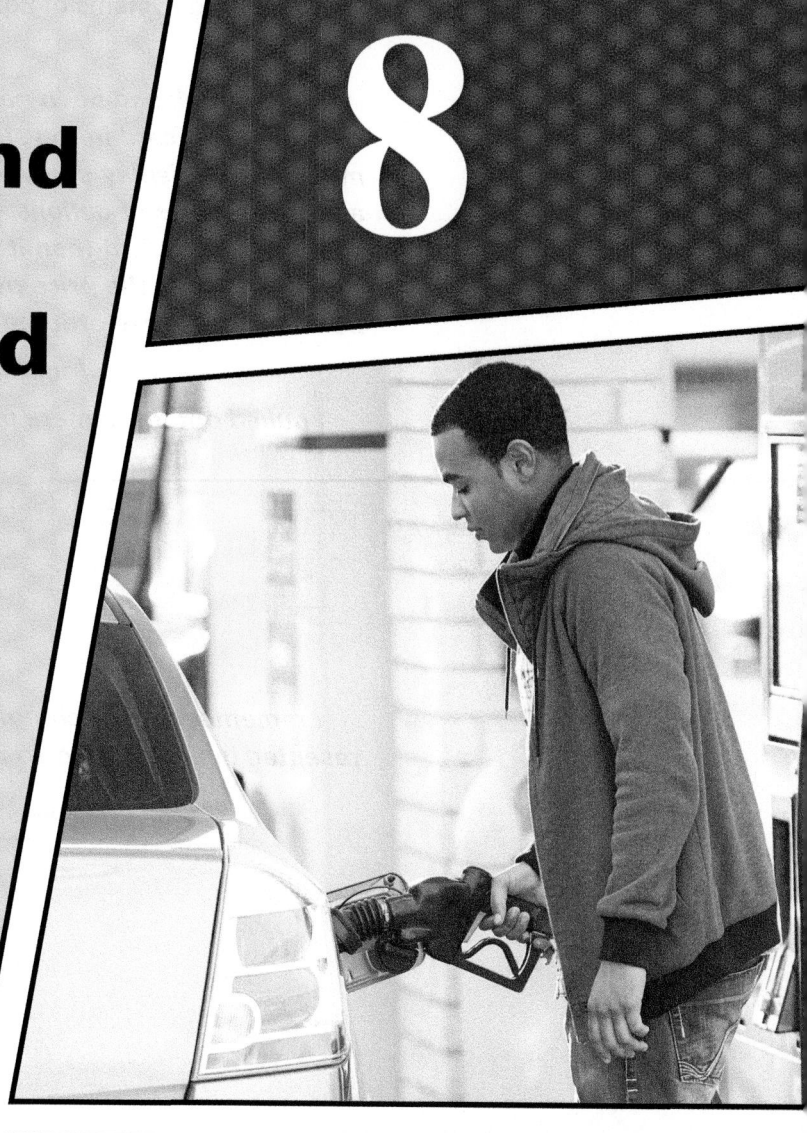

The Day My Algebra Class Finally Made Sense

by Christopher Eric Rogers

I am a first-year college student with aspirations to become a writer while working my way through school delivering pizzas. One of my classes is algebra, which seems to be irrelevant to my major, but it's required for the degree that I want. I've never been a bad math student, but it has never been my favorite subject, and it's always seemed to be totally removed from any everyday experience (except maybe balancing my check book). Until today.

My teacher Mrs. Schmulen was talking about ordered pairs, graphs, functions, lines, slope, intercepts, and other things that I remember hearing about in high school. I never needed them then, and I thought I would never have to hear about them again. And then the proverbial light bulb went on in my head when I least expected it.

My gas tank had been nearly empty for two days and needed filling. I put my debit card in the slot, selected my grade, and started to pump my gas. The display showed two numbers spinning by: the sale price and the number of gallons. Below them was the rate: $3.289, which is basically $3.29. And then it occurred to me that price divided by number of gallons is the price per gallon. These two spinning numbers can be written as those ordered pairs she talked about:

(number of gallons, total price).

I pulled out my camera phone and took some pictures.

I remember Mrs. Schmulen saying that pairs of numbers can be represented in a table, and so when I got home after work I did this:

Number of Gallons	Sale Price
0.000	0.00
2.402	7.90
5.003	16.45
7.251	23.85
9.544	31.39
12.248	40.28
14.865	48.89

She also said that points representing pairs of numbers can be graphed:

These points lie in a straight line. They can be connected to represent other pairs not shown in this table. And I had to stop when the number of gallons was 14.865, because that's all my tank would hold. I vaguely remember that she talked about functions. Is this what she meant by something called a linear function?

What's this? Dividing the price by the number of gallons in every picture gives the price per gallon, which is the slope of this line! (If the price had been almost $4.00 per gallon like it was last week, the line would be steeper. Whoa! Is this what the term "steeper" means when referring to increased price?) This slope is also the constant that shows up in direct variation, *which we covered in an earlier chapter.*

Mrs. Schmulen talked about domain. . . . *and that's what the numbers of gallons represent. There is a smallest value, 0, which showed up when I started, and a largest value, 14.865, because my tank couldn't hold any more. I also had the option of a $6.00 car wash, which I declined. It would have moved all the points upward 6 units and changed the starting point to the ordered pair (0, 6). And that's the y-intercept she talked about.*

My dad says he learns something new every day. As I drove around town during dinner time, this young person realized that he had learned something new from Mrs. Schmulen today. Maybe, when I become a writer, I can write about today's mathematics learning experience.

8.1 THE RECTANGULAR COORDINATE SYSTEM AND CIRCLES

OBJECTIVES

1 Plot ordered pairs in a rectangular coordinate system.

2 Find the distance between two points using the distance formula.

3 Find the midpoint of a segment using the midpoint formula.

4 Find the equation of a circle given the coordinates of the center and the radius.

5 Find the center and radius of a circle given its equation.

6 Apply the midpoint formula and the definition of a circle.

Rectangular Coordinates

Each pair of numbers $(1, 2)$, $(-1, 5)$, and $(3, 7)$ is an example of an **ordered pair**—a pair of numbers written within parentheses in which the positions of the numbers are relevant. The two numbers are the **components** of the ordered pair. Two ordered pairs are **equal** if and only if their first components are equal and their second components are equal.

An ordered pair is graphed using two number lines that intersect at right angles at the zero points, as shown in **Figure 1**. The common zero point is called the **origin**. The horizontal line, the **x-axis,** represents the first number in an ordered pair, and the vertical line, the **y-axis,** represents the second. The x-axis and the y-axis make up a **rectangular** (or **Cartesian**) **coordinate system.** The axes form four **quadrants,** numbered I, II, III, and IV as shown in **Figure 2**. (A point on an axis is not considered to be in any of the four quadrants.)

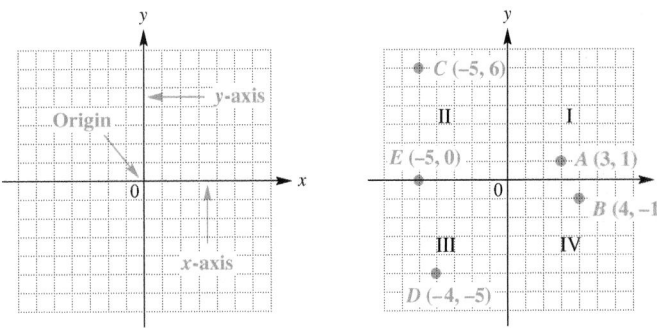

Figure 1   **Figure 2**

We locate, or plot, the point on the graph that corresponds to the ordered pair $(3, 1)$ by moving three units from zero to the right along the x-axis, and then one unit up parallel to the y-axis; this point is labeled A in **Figure 2.** The phrase "the point corresponding to the ordered pair $(3, 1)$" is abbreviated "the point $(3, 1)$." The numbers in an ordered pair are called the **coordinates** of the corresponding point.

An ordered pair may also represent an open interval (introduced in **Chapter 7**). The context of the discussion tells us whether we are discussing points in the Cartesian coordinate system or an open interval on a number line.

Distance Formula

To find the distance between two points, say $(3, -4)$ and $(-5, 3)$, we use the Pythagorean theorem. In **Figure 3,** we see that the vertical line through $(-5, 3)$ and the horizontal line through $(3, -4)$ intersect at the point $(-5, -4)$. Thus, the point $(-5, -4)$ becomes the vertex of the right angle in a right triangle. By the Pythagorean theorem, the square of the length of the hypotenuse, c, in **Figure 3** is equal to the sum of the squares of the lengths of the two legs a and b.

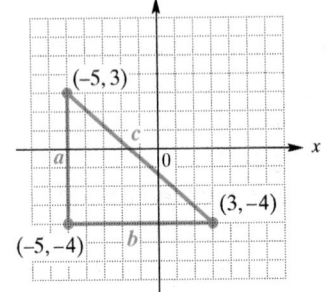

Figure 3

$$c^2 = a^2 + b^2 \qquad \text{Equation of the Pythagorean theorem}$$

The length a is the distance between the endpoints of that leg. Because the x-coordinate of both points is -5, the side is vertical, and we can find a by finding the difference between the y-coordinates. Subtract -4 from 3 to get a positive value of a. Similarly, find b by subtracting -5 from 3.

$$a = 3 - (-4) = 7$$
$$b = 3 - (-5) = 8$$

Use parentheses when subtracting a negative number.

Substitute these values into the equation.

$$c^2 = a^2 + b^2$$
$$c^2 = 7^2 + 8^2 \qquad \text{Let } a = 7 \text{ and } b = 8.$$
$$c^2 = 49 + 64 \qquad \text{Apply the exponents.}$$
$$c^2 = 113 \qquad \text{Add.}$$
$$c = \sqrt{113} \qquad \text{Square root property, } c > 0$$

Therefore, the distance between $(3, -4)$ and $(-5, 3)$ is $\sqrt{113}$.

This result can be generalized. **Figure 4** shows the two different points (x_1, y_1) and (x_2, y_2). We can find a formula for the distance d between these two points.

Double Descartes After the French postal service issued the above stamp in honor of **René Descartes,** sharp eyes noticed that the title of Descartes's most famous book was wrong. Thus a second stamp (see facing page) was issued with the correct title. The book in question, *Discourse on Method,* appeared in 1637. His method was *analysis,* going from self-evident truths step-by-step to more distant and more general truths. One of these truths is his famous statement, "I think, therefore I am."

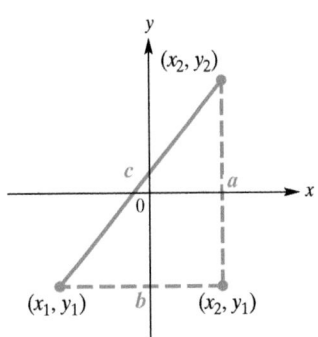

Figure 4

In **Figure 4,** the distance between (x_2, y_2) and (x_2, y_1) is given by $a = y_2 - y_1$, and the distance between (x_1, y_1) and (x_2, y_1) is given by $b = x_2 - x_1$. Thus,

$$c^2 = (x_2 - x_1)^2 + (y_2 - y_1)^2. \quad \text{Pythagorean theorem}$$

Using the square root property, we obtain the **distance formula.** (Here we use d to represent distance.)

DISTANCE FORMULA

The distance d between the points (x_1, y_1) and (x_2, y_2) is given by this formula.

$$d = \sqrt{(x_2 - x_1)^2 + (y_2 - y_1)^2}$$

The small numbers 1 and 2 in the ordered pairs (x_1, y_1) and (x_2, y_2) are called **subscripts.** We read x_1 as **"x sub 1."** Subscripts are used to distinguish between different values of a variable that have a common property.

EXAMPLE 1 Finding the Distance between Two Points

Find the distance between the points $(-3, 5)$ and $(6, 4)$.

Solution

Designating the points as (x_1, y_1) and (x_2, y_2) is arbitrary. Let us choose $(x_1, y_1) = (-3, 5)$ and $(x_2, y_2) = (6, 4)$.

$$d = \sqrt{(x_2 - x_1)^2 + (y_2 - y_1)^2} \quad \text{Distance formula}$$

$$= \sqrt{(6 - (-3))^2 + (4 - 5)^2} \quad x_2 = 6, \ y_2 = 4, \ x_1 = -3, \ y_1 = 5$$

Begin with the x- and y-values of the same point.

$$= \sqrt{9^2 + (-1)^2} \quad \text{Subtract twice.}$$

$$= \sqrt{82} \quad \text{Square and add.} \qquad ■$$

Midpoint Formula

The **midpoint** of a line segment is the point on the segment that is equidistant from both endpoints. Given the coordinates of the two endpoints of a line segment, we can find the coordinates of the midpoint of the segment.

MIDPOINT FORMULA

The coordinates of the midpoint M of the line segment with endpoints (x_1, y_1) and (x_2, y_2) are given by the following formula.

$$M = \left(\frac{x_1 + x_2}{2}, \frac{y_1 + y_2}{2} \right)$$

Thus, the coordinates of the midpoint of a line segment are found by calculating the averages of the x- and y-coordinates of the endpoints.

Descartes wrote his *Geometry* as an application of his method. It was published as an appendix to the *Discourse*. His attempts to unify algebra and geometry influenced the creation of what became coordinate geometry and influenced the development of calculus by Newton and Leibniz in the next generation.

In 1649 Descartes went to Sweden to tutor Queen Christina. She preferred working in the unheated castle in the early morning. Descartes was used to staying in bed until noon. The rigors of the Swedish winter proved too much for him, and he died less than a year later.

EXAMPLE 2 Finding the Midpoint of a Line Segment

Find the coordinates of the midpoint M of the line segment with endpoints $(8, -4)$ and $(-9, 6)$.

Solution

Use the midpoint formula to find the coordinates of M.

$$M = \left(\frac{8 + (-9)}{2}, \frac{-4 + 6}{2}\right) = \left(-\frac{1}{2}, 1\right) \quad \begin{matrix} x_1 = 8,\ x_2 = -9, \\ y_1 = -4,\ y_2 = 6 \end{matrix}$$ ∎

An Application of the Midpoint Formula

EXAMPLE 3 Applying the Midpoint Formula to Data

Figure 5 depicts how a graph might indicate the increase in the revenue generated by fast-food restaurants in the United States from $69.8 billion in 1990 to $164.8 billion in 2010. Use the midpoint formula and the two given points to estimate the revenue from fast-food restaurants in 2000, and compare it to the actual figure of $107.1 billion.

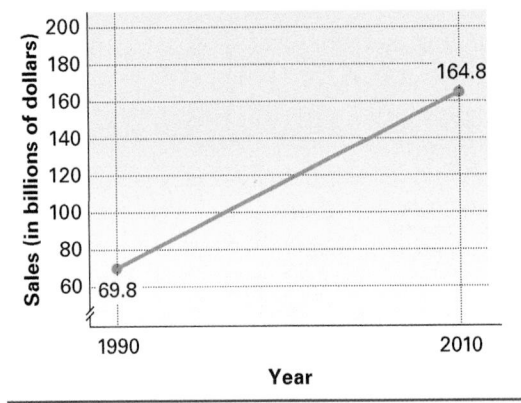

Revenue of Fast-Food Restaurants in U.S.

Source: National Restaurant Association.

Figure 5

Solution

The year 2000 lies halfway between 1990 and 2010, so we must find the coordinates of the midpoint M of the segment that has endpoints

$$(1990, 69.8) \quad \text{and} \quad (2010, 164.8).$$

(Here, the second component is in billions of dollars.)

$$M = \left(\frac{1990 + 2010}{2}, \frac{69.8 + 164.8}{2}\right) = (2000, 117.3) \quad \text{Use the midpoint formula.}$$

Thus, our estimate is $117.3 billion, which is greater than the actual figure of $107.1 billion. (This discrepancy is due to actual revenue with an average increase of $3.73 billion between 1990 and 2000, and then of $5.77 billion between 2000 and 2010. Graphs such as this can sometimes be misleading.) ∎

Circles

An application of the distance formula leads to one of the most familiar shapes in geometry, the circle. A **circle** is the set of all points in a plane that lie a fixed distance from a fixed point. The fixed point is called the **center** and the fixed distance is called the **radius.**

EXAMPLE 4 Finding an Equation of a Circle

Find an equation of the circle with radius 3 and center at $(0, 0)$, and graph the circle.

Solution

If the point (x, y) is on the circle, the distance from (x, y) to the center $(0, 0)$ is 3, as shown in **Figure 6.**

$$\sqrt{(x_2 - x_1)^2 + (y_2 - y_1)^2} = d \quad \text{Distance formula}$$

$$\sqrt{(x - 0)^2 + (y - 0)^2} = 3 \quad x_1 = 0,\, y_1 = 0,\, x_2 = x,\, y_2 = y,\, d = 3$$

$$x^2 + y^2 = 9 \quad \text{Square both sides.}$$

An equation of this circle is $x^2 + y^2 = 9$. It can be graphed by locating all points three units from the origin. ∎

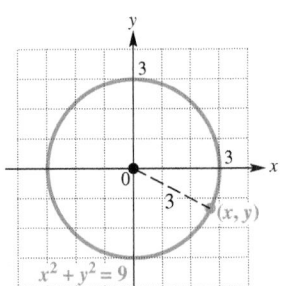

Figure 6

Example 4 can be generalized to obtain the equation of a circle with radius r and center at (h, k). If (x, y) is a point on the circle, the distance from the center (h, k) to the point (x, y) is r. Then by the distance formula,

$$\sqrt{(x - h)^2 + (y - k)^2} = r.$$

Squaring both sides gives the **center-radius form** of the equation of a circle.

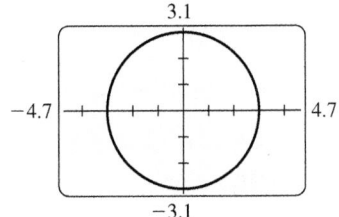

To graph $x^2 + y^2 = 9$, in **Example 4,** we solve for y to obtain

$$y_1 = \sqrt{9 - x^2} \text{ and } y_2 = -\sqrt{9 - x^2}.$$

Then we graph both in a square window.

EQUATION OF A CIRCLE

The equation of a circle of radius r with center at (h, k) is

$$(x - h)^2 + (y - k)^2 = r^2.$$

In particular, a circle of radius r with center at the origin has equation

$$x^2 + y^2 = r^2.$$

In these equations, r^2 will be greater than or equal to 0. If the constant on the right is 0, the graph is a single point. If it is negative, there is no graph.

EXAMPLE 5 Finding an Equation of a Circle and Graphing

Find an equation of the circle that has its center at $(4, -3)$ and radius 5, and graph the circle.

Solution

Use the equation of a circle with $h = 4$, $k = -3$, and $r = 5$.

$$(x - h)^2 + (y - k)^2 = r^2 \quad \text{Center-radius form}$$

$$(x - 4)^2 + [y - (-3)]^2 = 5^2 \quad \text{Substitute.}$$

$$(x - 4)^2 + (y + 3)^2 = 25$$

$$\boxed{\textit{Be careful with signs.}}$$

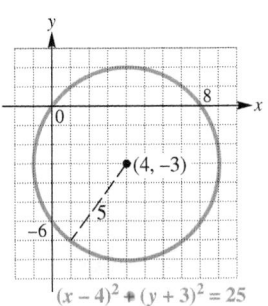

Figure 7

The graph of this circle is shown in **Figure 7.** ∎

In the equation found in **Example 5,** multiplying out $(x - 4)^2$ and $(y + 3)^2$ and then combining like terms gives the following.

$$(x - 4)^2 + (y + 3)^2 = 25$$

$$x^2 - 8x + 16 + y^2 + 6y + 9 = 25$$

$$x^2 + y^2 - 8x + 6y = 0$$

This result suggests that an equation that has both x^2- and y^2-terms with equal coefficients may represent a circle. The next example shows how to determine this, using a method from algebra called **completing the square.**

EXAMPLE 6 Completing the Square and Graphing a Circle

Graph $x^2 + y^2 + 2x + 6y - 15 = 0$.

Solution

Because the equation has x^2- and y^2-terms with equal coefficients, its graph could be that of a circle. To find the center and radius, complete the squares in x and y as follows.

$$x^2 + y^2 + 2x + 6y = 15 \qquad \text{Add 15 to both sides.}$$

$$(x^2 + 2x \quad) + (y^2 + 6y \quad) = 15 \qquad \text{Rewrite in anticipation of completing the square.}$$

$$(x^2 + 2x + 1) + (y^2 + 6y + 9) = 15 + 1 + 9 \qquad \text{Complete the squares in both } x \text{ and } y.$$

$$(x + 1)^2 + (y + 3)^2 = 25 \qquad \text{Factor on the left and add on the right.}$$

The final equation shows that the graph is a circle with center at $(-1, -3)$ and radius 5. The graph is shown in **Figure 8.** ∎

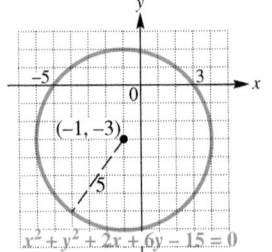

Figure 8

An Application of Circles

EXAMPLE 7 Locating the Epicenter of an Earthquake

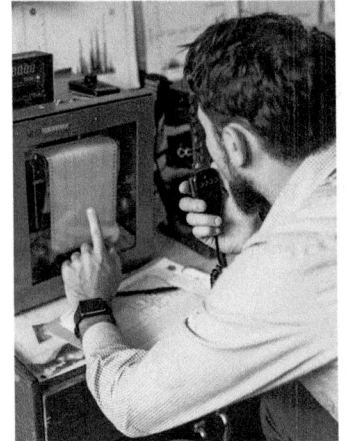

Seismologists can locate the epicenter of an earthquake by determining the intersection of three circles. The radii of these circles represent the distances from the epicenter to each of three receiving stations. The centers of the circles represent the receiving stations.

Suppose receiving stations A, B, and C are located on a coordinate plane at the points $(1, 4)$, $(-3, -1)$, and $(5, 2)$, respectively. Let the distances from the earthquake epicenter to the stations be 2 units, 5 units, and 4 units, respectively. See **Figure 9.** Where on the coordinate plane is the epicenter located?

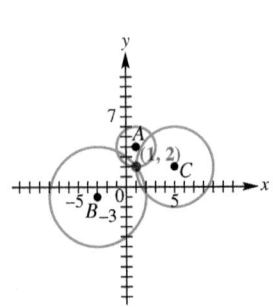

Figure 9

Solution

In **Figure 9,** the epicenter appears to be located at $(1, 2)$. To check this algebraically, determine the equation for each circle, and substitute $x = 1$ and $y = 2$.

Station A:	**Station B:**	**Station C:**
$(x - 1)^2 + (y - 4)^2 = 2^2$	$(x + 3)^2 + (y + 1)^2 = 5^2$	$(x - 5)^2 + (y - 2)^2 = 4^2$
$(1 - 1)^2 + (2 - 4)^2 = 4$	$(1 + 3)^2 + (2 + 1)^2 = 25$	$(1 - 5)^2 + (2 - 2)^2 = 16$
$0 + 4 = 4$	$16 + 9 = 25$	$16 + 0 = 16$
$4 = 4$	$25 = 25$	$16 = 16$

The point $(1, 2)$ does lie on all three graphs. Thus, it must be the epicenter. ∎

FOR FURTHER THOUGHT

Locating Nothing

Phlash Phelps is the morning radio personality on Sirius XM Satellite Radio's *Sixties on Six* Decades

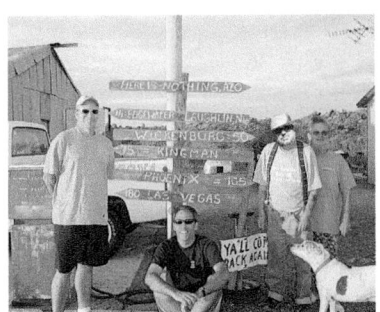

channel. Phlash is an expert on U.S. geography. He loves traveling around the country to strange, out-of-the-way locations. The photo shows Kurt Gilchrist and Phlash (seated) visiting a small Arizona settlement called *Nothing*. (Nothing is so small that it's not named on current maps.) The sign indicates that Nothing is 50 mi from Wickenburg, AZ, 75 mi from Kingman, AZ, 105 mi from Phoenix, AZ, and 180 mi from Las Vegas, NV.

For Group or Individual Investigation

Discuss how the concepts of **Example 7** can be used to locate Nothing, AZ, on a map of the area.

8.1 EXERCISES

Fill in each blank with the correct response.

1. For any value of x, the point $(x, 0)$ lies on the _____ -axis.

2. For any value of y, the point $(0, y)$ lies on the _____ -axis.

3. The circle $x^2 + y^2 = 9$ has the point _____ as its center.

4. The point $(\_\_\_\_, 0)$ is the center of the circle

$$(x - 2)^2 + y^2 = 16.$$

Name the quadrant, if any, in which each point is located.

5. (a) $(1, 6)$
    (b) $(-4, -2)$
    (c) $(-3, 6)$
    (d) $(7, -5)$
    (e) $(-3, 0)$

6. (a) $(-2, -10)$
    (b) $(4, 8)$
    (c) $(-9, 12)$
    (d) $(3, -9)$
    (e) $(0, -8)$

*Locate the following points on the rectangular coordinate system, using a graph similar to **Figure 2**.*

7. $(2, 3)$

8. $(-1, 2)$

9. $(-3, -2)$

10. $(1, -4)$

11. $(0, 5)$

12. $(-2, -4)$

13. $(-2, 4)$

14. $(3, 0)$

15. $(-2, 0)$

16. $(3, -3)$

Find each of the following.

(a) *the distance between the two points in each pair*

(b) *the coordinates of the midpoint of the segment having the points as endpoints*

17. $(3, 4)$ and $(-2, 1)$

18. $(-2, 1)$ and $(3, -2)$

19. $(-2, 4)$ and $(3, -2)$

20. $(1, -5)$ and $(6, 3)$

21. $(-3, 7)$ and $(2, -4)$

22. $(0, 5)$ and $(-3, 12)$

Find each of the following.

(a) *the distance between P and Q*

(b) *the coordinates of the midpoint of the segment joining P and Q*

23.

24.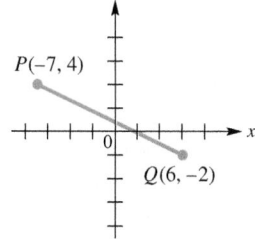

Match each center-radius form of the equation of a circle with the correct graph from choices A–D.

25. $(x - 3)^2 + (y - 2)^2 = 25$

26. $(x - 3)^2 + (y + 2)^2 = 25$

27. $(x + 3)^2 + (y - 2)^2 = 25$

28. $(x + 3)^2 + (y + 2)^2 = 25$

A.

B.

C.

D.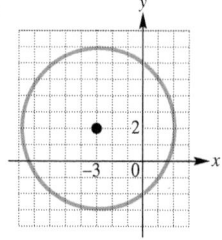

Write an equation of the circle with the given center and radius.

29. $(0, 0); r = 6$

30. $(0, 0); r = 5$

31. $(-1, 3); r = 4$

32. $(2, -2); r = 3$

33. $(0, 4); r = \sqrt{3}$

34. $(-2, 0); r = \sqrt{5}$

Find the center and the radius of each circle.

35. $x^2 + y^2 + 4x + 6y + 9 = 0$

36. $x^2 + y^2 - 8x - 12y + 3 = 0$

37. $x^2 + y^2 + 10x - 14y - 7 = 0$

38. $x^2 + y^2 - 2x + 4y - 4 = 0$

39. $x^2 + y^2 - 4x - 8y + 4 = 0$

40. $x^2 + y^2 + 10x + 8y + 5 = 0$

Graph each circle.

41. $x^2 + y^2 = 36$

42. $x^2 + y^2 = 81$

43. $(x - 2)^2 + y^2 = 36$

44. $x^2 + (y + 3)^2 = 49$

45. $(x + 2)^2 + (y - 5)^2 = 16$

46. $(x - 4)^2 + (y - 3)^2 = 25$

47. $(x + 3)^2 + (y + 2)^2 = 36$

48. $(x - 5)^2 + (y + 4)^2 = 49$

Solve each problem.

49. *Bachelor's Degree Attainment* The graph shows a straight line that approximates the percentage of Americans 25 years old or older who earned bachelor's degrees or higher during the years 1990–2008.

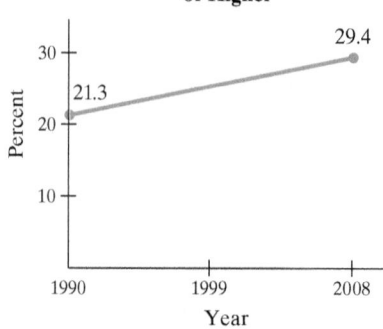

Source: U.S. Census Bureau.

(a) Use the midpoint formula and the two given points to estimate the percent in 1999.

(b) Compare your answer with the actual percent of 25.2.

50. *Temporary Assistance for Needy Families (TANF)* The graph shows an idealized linear relationship for the average monthly payment to needy families in the TANF program. Based on this information, what was the average payment to families in 2004, to the nearest dollar?

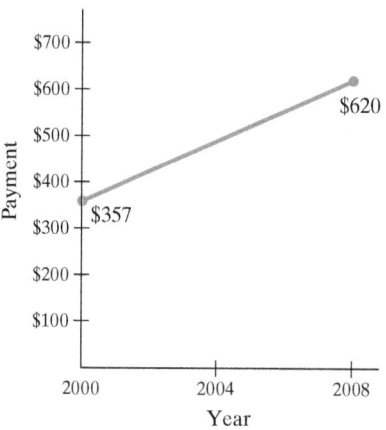

Average Monthly Payment to TANF Program Recipients

Source: Administration for Children and Families; U.S. Census Bureau.

51. *Poverty-Level Income Cutoffs* The table lists how poverty-level income cutoffs (in dollars) for a family of four have changed over time. Use the midpoint formula to approximate the poverty-level cutoff in 2006, to the nearest dollar.

Year	Income (in dollars)
1980	8414
1990	13,359
2000	17,604
2004	19,305
2008	22,025

Source: U.S. Census Bureau.

52. *Public College Enrollment* Enrollments in public colleges for recent years are shown in the table. Use the midpoint formula to estimate the enrollments for each year.

(a) 2002 **(b)** 2006

Year	Enrollment (in thousands)
2000	11,753
2004	12,980
2008	13,972

Source: U.S. Census Bureau.

53. *Drawing a Circle* A circle can be drawn on a piece of posterboard by fastening one end of a string, pulling the string taut with a pencil, and tracing a curve as shown in the figure. Explain why this method works.

54. *Crawfish Racing* This figure shows how the crawfish race is held at the Crawfish Festival in Breaux Bridge, Louisiana. Explain why a circular "race-track" is appropriate for such a race.

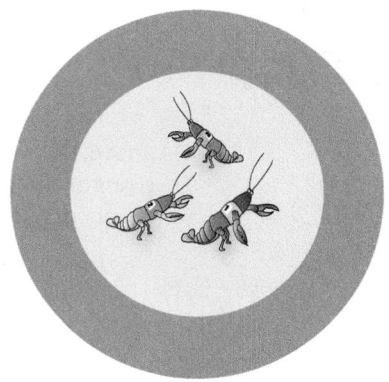

55. *Epicenter of an Earthquake* Three receiving stations record the presence of an earthquake. The locations of the receiving stations and the distances to the epicenter are contained in the following three equations:

$$(x - 2)^2 + (y - 1)^2 = 25,$$
$$(x + 2)^2 + (y - 2)^2 = 16,$$
and $$(x - 1)^2 + (y + 2)^2 = 9.$$

Graph the circles and determine the location of the earthquake epicenter.

56. *Epicenter of an Earthquake* Show algebraically that if three receiving stations at

$$(1, 4), \quad (-6, 0), \quad \text{and} \quad (5, -2)$$

record distances to an earthquake epicenter of 4 units, 5 units, and 10 units, respectively, the epicenter lies at $(-3, 4)$.

8.2   LINES, SLOPE, AND AVERAGE RATE OF CHANGE

OBJECTIVES

1 Determine ordered pairs and graph a linear equation in two variables.

2 Find the x- and y-intercepts of the graph of a linear equation.

3 Find the slope of a nonvertical line given two points on the line.

4 Graph a line given its slope and a point on the line.

5 Determine whether two lines are either parallel or perpendicular to each other by comparing their slopes.

6 Interpret slope as average rate of change.

Linear Equations in Two Variables

Earlier we studied linear equations in a single variable. A solution of such an equation is a real number.

A linear equation in *two* variables will have solutions written as ordered pairs. Equations with two variables will, in general, have an infinite number of solutions. To find ordered pairs that satisfy the equation, select any number for one of the variables, substitute it into the equation for that variable, and then solve for the other variable.

For example, suppose $x = 0$ in the equation $2x + 3y = 6$.

$$2x + 3y = 6 \quad \text{Given equation}$$
$$2(0) + 3y = 6 \quad \text{Let } x = 0.$$
$$0 + 3y = 6 \quad \text{Multiply.}$$
$$3y = 6 \quad \text{Add.}$$
$$y = 2 \quad \text{Divide by 3.}$$

This gives the ordered pair $(0, 2)$. Other ordered pairs satisfying $2x + 3y = 6$ include

$$(6, -2), \quad (3, 0), \quad (-3, 4), \quad \text{and} \quad (9, -4).$$

The equation $2x + 3y = 6$ is graphed by plotting the ordered pairs mentioned above. These are shown in **Figure 10(a)**. The resulting points appear to lie on a straight line. If all the ordered pairs that satisfy the equation $2x + 3y = 6$ were graphed, they would form the straight line shown in **Figure 10(b)**.

The graph of any first-degree equation in two variables is a straight line.

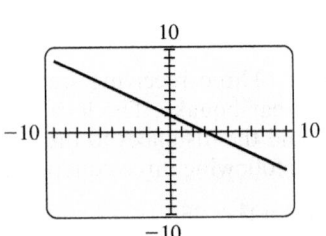

This is a calculator graph of the line shown in **Figure 10(b)**. We must first solve $2x + 3y = 6$ for y to input the equation.

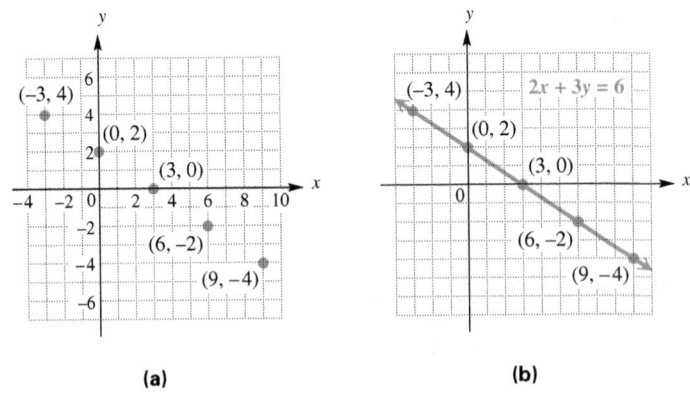

(a)   (b)

Figure 10

LINEAR EQUATION IN TWO VARIABLES

An equation that can be written in the form

$$Ax + By = C \quad \text{(where } A \text{ and } B \text{ are not both } 0\text{)}$$

is a **linear equation in two variables.** This form is called **standard form.**

When we provide answers in standard form, we do so with $A > 0$ (or, if $A = 0$, then with $B > 0$) and with A, B, and C having greatest common factor 1.

Intercepts

Two points that are useful for graphing lines are the x- and y-intercepts. The **x-intercept** is the point (if any) where the line crosses the x-axis, and the **y-intercept** is the point (if any) where the line crosses the y-axis. (*Note:* In many texts, the intercepts are defined as numbers and not as points. However, in this text we will refer to intercepts as points.)

INTERCEPTS FOR GRAPHS OF LINEAR EQUATIONS

- To find the x-intercept, let $y = 0$ and solve for x.
- To find the y-intercept, let $x = 0$ and solve for y.

EXAMPLE 1   **Graphing an Equation Using Intercepts**

Find the x- and y-intercepts of $4x - y = -3$, and graph the equation.

Solution

To find the x-intercept, let $y = 0$.

$$4x - 0 = -3 \quad \text{Let } y = 0.$$
$$4x = -3$$
$$x = -\frac{3}{4} \quad \text{x-intercept is } \left(-\frac{3}{4}, 0\right).$$

To find the y-intercept, let $x = 0$.

$$4(0) - y = -3 \quad \text{Let } x = 0.$$
$$-y = -3$$
$$y = 3 \quad \text{y-intercept is } (0, 3).$$

The intercepts are the two points $\left(-\frac{3}{4}, 0\right)$ and $(0, 3)$. Use these two points to draw the graph, as shown in **Figure 11**. ∎

Figure 11

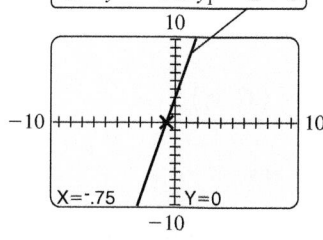

The display at the bottom of the screen supports the fact that $\left(-\frac{3}{4}, 0\right)$, is the x-intercept of the line in **Figure 11**. We could locate the y-intercept similarly.

EXAMPLE 2   **Graphing Lines with a Single Intercept**

Graph each line.

(a) $y = 2$ **(b)** $x = -1$

Solution

(a) Writing the equation $y = 2$ as

$$0x + 1y = 2$$

shows that any value of x, including $x = 0$, gives $y = 2$, making the y-intercept $(0, 2)$. Because y is always 2, there is no value of x corresponding to $y = 0$, so the graph has no x-intercept. The graph, shown in **Figure 12(a),** is a horizontal line.

Figure 12

(b) In this equation, $x = -1$ for all y. No value of y makes $x = 0$. The graph has no y-intercept and thus must be vertical, as shown in **Figure 12(b)**. ∎

Slope

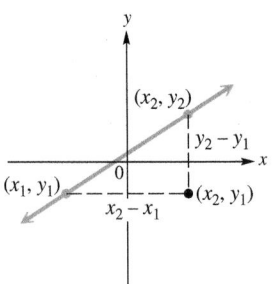

Figure 13

Two distinct points determine a unique line. A line also can be determined by a point on the line and some measure of the "steepness" of the line. One way to measure the steepness of a line is to compare the vertical change in the line (the *rise*) to the horizontal change (the *run*) while moving along the line from one fixed point to another.

Suppose that (x_1, y_1) and (x_2, y_2) are two different points on a line. Then, moving along the line from (x_1, y_1) to (x_2, y_2), the y-value changes from y_1 to y_2, an amount equal to $y_2 - y_1$. As y changes from y_1 to y_2, the value of x changes from x_1 to x_2 by the amount $x_2 - x_1$. See **Figure 13**. The ratio of the change in y to the change in x is called the **slope** of the line. The letter m is used to denote the slope.

SLOPE FORMULA

If $x_1 \neq x_2$, the slope m of the line through the distinct points (x_1, y_1) and (x_2, y_2) is given by the following formula.

$$m = \frac{\text{rise}}{\text{run}} = \frac{\text{change in } y}{\text{change in } x} = \frac{y_2 - y_1}{x_2 - x_1}.$$

▓▓ EXAMPLE 3   Using the Slope Formula

Find the slope of the line that passes through the points $(2, -1)$ and $(-5, 3)$.

Solution

Let $(2, -1) = (x_1, y_1)$ and $(-5, 3) = (x_2, y_2)$, and use the slope formula.

$$m = \frac{y_2 - y_1}{x_2 - x_1} = \frac{3 - (-1)}{-5 - 2} = \frac{4}{-7} = -\frac{4}{7}$$

> Start with the x- and
> y-values of the same point.

See **Figure 14.** Now let $(2, -1) = (x_2, y_2)$ and $(-5, 3) = (x_1, y_1)$.

$$m = \frac{-1 - 3}{2 - (-5)} = \frac{-4}{7} = -\frac{4}{7}$$ The same answer

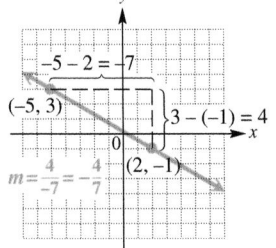

Figure 14

This example suggests that the slope is the same no matter which point is considered first. Using similar triangles from geometry, we can show that the slope is the same for *any* two different points chosen on the line.   ∎

▓▓ EXAMPLE 4   Finding Slopes of Vertical and Horizontal Lines

Find the slope, if possible, of each of the following lines.

(a) $x = -3$ **(b)** $y = 5$

Solution

(a) By inspection, $(-3, 5)$ and $(-3, -4)$ are two points that satisfy the equation $x = -3$. Use these two points to find the slope.

$$m = \frac{-4 - 5}{-3 - (-3)} = \frac{-9}{0}$$ Undefined slope

Division by zero is undefined, so the slope is undefined. (This is why the definition of slope includes the restriction that $x_1 \neq x_2$.)

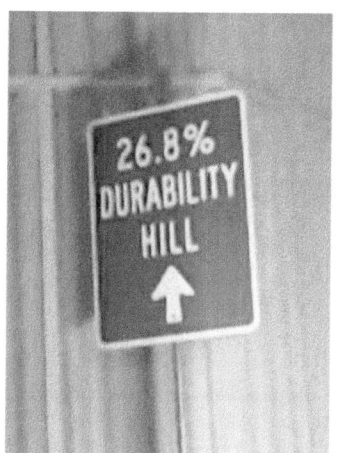

Visitors to Epcot Center at Walt Disney World in Florida love the ride **Test Track.** This sign at the beginning of the ride indicates an upward **slope** of about $\frac{1}{4}$.

(b) Find the slope by selecting two different points on the line, such as $(3, 5)$ and $(-1, 5)$, and by using the definition of slope.

$$m = \frac{5 - 5}{3 - (-1)} = \frac{0}{4} = 0 \quad \text{Slope 0}$$

In **Example 2,** $x = -1$ has a graph that is a vertical line, and $y = 2$ has a graph that is a horizontal line. Generalizing from those results and the results of **Example 4,** we can make the following statements about vertical and horizontal lines.

VERTICAL AND HORIZONTAL LINES

- A vertical line has an equation of the form $x = a$, where a is a real number, and its slope is undefined.

- A horizontal line has an equation of the form $y = b$, where b is a real number, and its slope is 0.

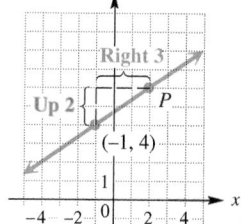

Figure 15

EXAMPLE 5   Graphing a Line Using Slope and a Point

Graph the line that has slope $\frac{2}{3}$ and passes through the point $(-1, 4)$.

Solution

First locate the point $(-1, 4)$ on a graph as shown in **Figure 15.** Then,

$$m = \frac{\text{change in } y}{\text{change in } x} = \frac{2}{3}. \quad \text{Definition of slope}$$

Recall that the geometric interpretation of slope is "rise over run." Move *up* 2 units in the y-direction and then *right* 3 units in the x-direction to locate another point on the graph (labeled P). The line through $(-1, 4)$ and P is the required graph.   ∎

The line graphed in **Figure 14** has a negative slope, $-\frac{4}{7}$, and the line *falls* from left to right. In contrast, the line graphed in **Figure 15** has a positive slope, $\frac{2}{3}$, and it *rises* from left to right. These ideas can be generalized. (**Figure 16** shows lines of positive, negative, zero, and undefined slopes.)

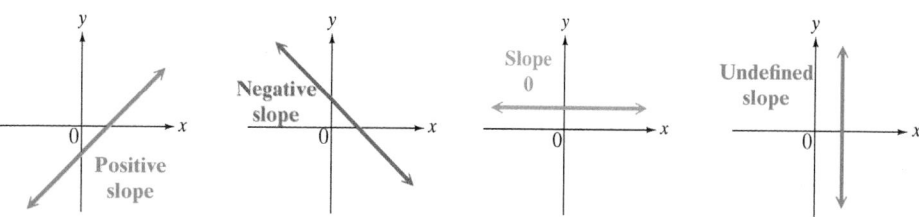

Figure 16

POSITIVE AND NEGATIVE SLOPES

- A line with a positive slope rises from left to right.

- A line with a negative slope falls from left to right.

Parallel and Perpendicular Lines

The slope of a line is a measure of the steepness of the line. **Parallel** lines have equal steepness, and thus their slopes (if defined) also must be equal. Also, lines with the same slope are parallel.

SLOPES OF PARALLEL LINES

- Two nonvertical lines with the same slope are parallel.

- Two nonvertical parallel lines have the same slope.

Furthermore, any two vertical lines are parallel.

Perpendicular lines are lines that meet at right angles. It can be shown that the slopes of perpendicular lines have a product of -1, provided that neither line is vertical. For example, if the slope of a line is $\frac{3}{4}$, then any line perpendicular to it has slope $-\frac{4}{3}$, because $\frac{3}{4}\left(-\frac{4}{3}\right) = -1$.

SLOPES OF PERPENDICULAR LINES

- If neither is vertical, two perpendicular lines have slopes that are negative reciprocals—that is, their product is -1.

- Two lines with slopes that are negative reciprocals are perpendicular.

- Every vertical line is perpendicular to every horizontal line.

EXAMPLE 6 **Determining Whether Two Lines Are Parallel or Perpendicular**

Consider the four lines described below.

$$L_1 \text{ passes through } (-2, 1) \text{ and } (4, 5).$$

$$L_2 \text{ passes through } (3, 0) \text{ and } (0, -2).$$

$$L_3 \text{ passes through } (0, -3) \text{ and } (2, 0).$$

$$L_4 \text{ passes through } (-3, 0) \text{ and } (0, -2).$$

Find the slopes of these lines, and determine which two lines are parallel and which two are perpendicular.

Solution

We apply the slope formula in each case.

$$L_1: \quad m_1 = \frac{5 - 1}{4 - (-2)} = \frac{4}{6} = \frac{2}{3} \qquad L_2: \quad m_2 = \frac{-2 - 0}{0 - 3} = \frac{-2}{-3} = \frac{2}{3}$$

$$L_3: \quad m_3 = \frac{0 - (-3)}{2 - 0} = \frac{3}{2} \qquad L_4: \quad m_4 = \frac{-2 - 0}{0 - (-3)} = -\frac{2}{3}$$

Lines L_1 and L_2 have slope $\frac{2}{3}$, so they are parallel. Lines L_3 and L_4 have slopes that are negative reciprocals $\left(\frac{3}{2}\left(-\frac{2}{3}\right) = -1\right)$, so they are perpendicular. ∎

Average Rate of Change

The slope formula applied to any two points on a line gives the **average rate of change** in y per unit change in x, where the value of y depends on the value of x.

For example, suppose the height of a boy increased from 60 to 68 inches between the ages of 12 and 16, as shown in **Figure 17.** We can find the boy's average growth rate (or average change in height per year).

Change in height y ⟶
Change in age x ⟶ $\dfrac{68 - 60}{16 - 12} = \dfrac{8}{4} = 2$ inches per year

The boy may actually have grown more than 2 inches during some years and less than 2 inches during other years. If we plotted ordered pairs

(age, height)

for those years and drew a line connecting any two of those points, the average rate of change we would find would probably be slightly different from that found above. However, using the data for ages 12 and 16, the boy's *average* change in height was 2 inches per year over these years.

Growth Rate

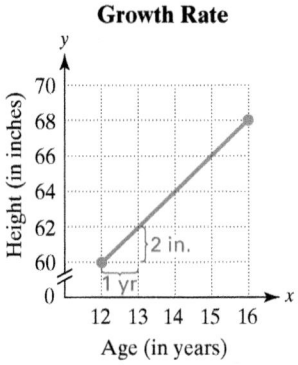

Figure 17

EXAMPLE 7 **Interpreting Slope as Average Rate of Change**

The graph in **Figure 18** shows the number of digital cable TV customers in the United States from 2007 to 2012. Find the average rate of change in the number of customers per year.

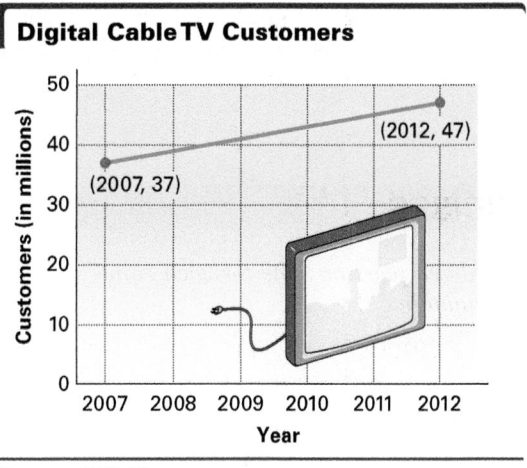

Source: SNL Kagan.

Figure 18

Solution

To determine the average rate of change, we need two pairs of data. From the graph, we have the ordered pairs (2007, 37) and (2012, 47). Use the slope formula.

average rate of change $= \dfrac{47 - 37}{2012 - 2007} = \dfrac{10}{5} = 2$ A positive slope indicates an increase.

This means that the average number of digital TV customers *increased* by 2 million per year from 2007 through 2012. ■

EXAMPLE 8 Interpreting Slope as Average Rate of Change

In 2006, there were 65 million basic cable TV customers in the United States. There were 56 million such customers in 2012. See **Figure 19**. Find the average rate of change in the number of customers per year. (*Source:* SNL Kagan.)

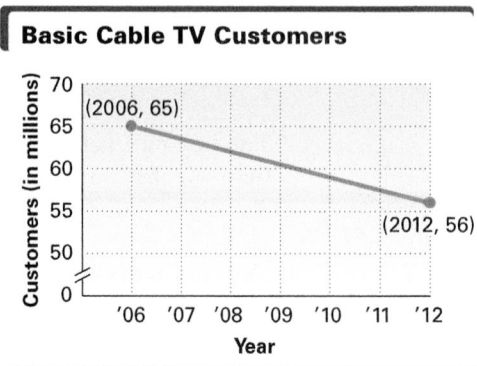

Figure 19

Solution

To use the slope formula, we need two ordered pairs. Here, we let one ordered pair be (2006, 65) and the other be (2012, 56).

$$\text{average rate of change } = \frac{56 - 65}{2012 - 2006} = \frac{-9}{6} = -1.5$$

> A negative slope indicates a decrease.

The graph in **Figure 19** confirms that the line through the ordered pairs falls from left to right and, therefore, has negative slope. Thus, the number of basic cable TV customers *decreased* by an average of 1.5 million customers per year from 2006 through 2012. ∎

8.2 EXERCISES

Complete the given ordered pairs or table for each equation. Then graph the equation.

1. $x - y = 4$; (0,), (,0), (2,), (, −1)

2. $x + y = 5$; (0,), (,0), (2,), (4,)

3. $2x + y = 5$; (0,), (,0), (1,), (,1)

4. $x + 3y = 12$; (0,), (,0), (3,), (,6)

5. $4x + 5y = 20$; (0,), (,0), (3,), (,2)

6. $3x - 4y = 24$; (0,), (,0), (6,), (, −3)

7. $3x + 2y = 8$

x	y
0	
	0
2	
	−2

8. $5x + y = 12$

x	y
0	
	0
	−3
2	

For each equation, give the x-intercept and the y-intercept. Then graph the equation.

9. $3x + 2y = 12$

10. $2x + 5y = 10$

11. $5x + 6y = 10$

12. $x + 3y = 6$

13. $2x - y = 5$

14. $3x - 2y = 4$

15. $x - 3y = 2$

16. $4x - y = -3$

17. $x + y = 0$

18. $2x - y = 0$

19. $3x - y = 0$

20. $x + 4y = 0$

21. $x = 2$

22. $x = -2$

23. $y = 4$

24. $y = -3$

In Exercises 25–32, match the equation with the figure in choices A–D below that most closely resembles its graph.

A.

B.

C.

D.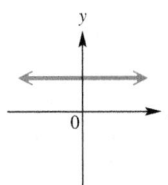

25. $y + 2 = 0$

26. $y + 4 = 0$

27. $x + 3 = 0$

28. $x + 7 = 0$

29. $y - 2 = 0$

30. $y - 4 = 0$

31. $x - 3 = 0$

32. $x - 7 = 0$

33. What is the slope (or pitch) of this roof?

34. What is the slope (or grade) of this hill?

35. Use the coordinates of the indicated points to find the slope of each line.

(a)

(b)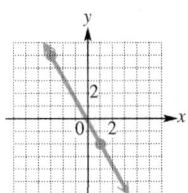

36. Determine whether the slope of the given line in (a)–(d) is *positive, negative, zero,* or *undefined.*

(a)

(b)

(c)

(d)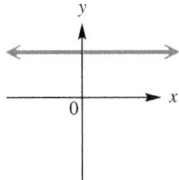

Find the slope of the line through each pair of points by using the slope formula.

37. $(-2, -3)$ and $(-1, 5)$

38. $(-4, 3)$ and $(-3, 4)$

39. $(8, 1)$ and $(2, 6)$

40. $(13, -3)$ and $(5, 6)$

41. $(2, 4)$ and $(-4, 4)$

42. $(-6, 3)$ and $(2, 3)$

43. $(1, 6)$ and $(1, 8)$

44. $(-3, 8)$ and $(-3, 2)$

Graph each line with the given slope and passing through the given point.

45. $m = \frac{1}{2};\ (-3, 2)$

46. $m = \frac{2}{3};\ (0, 1)$

47. $m = -\frac{5}{4};\ (-2, -1)$

48. $m = -\frac{3}{2};\ (-1, -2)$

49. $m = -2;\ (-1, -4)$

50. $m = 3;\ (1, 2)$

51. $m = 0;\ (2, -5)$

52. $m = 0;\ (2, 4)$

53. undefined slope; $(4, 2)$

54. undefined slope; $(-3, 1)$

Determine whether the lines described are parallel, perpendicular, or neither parallel nor perpendicular.

55. L_1 through $(4, 6)$ and $(-8, 7)$, and L_2 through $(7, 4)$ and $(-5, 5)$

56. L_1 through $(9, 15)$ and $(-7, 12)$, and L_2 through $(-4, 8)$ and $(-20, 5)$

57. L_1 through $(2, 0)$ and $(5, 4)$, and L_2 through $(6, 1)$ and $(2, 4)$

58. L_1 through $(1, 2)$ and $(-7, -2)$, and L_2 through $(1, -1)$ and $(5, -9)$

59. L_1 through $(0, 1)$ and $(2, -3)$, and L_2 through $(10, 8)$ and $(5, 3)$

60. L_1 through $(0, -7)$ and $(2, 3)$, and L_2 through $(0, -3)$ and $(1, -2)$

Use the concept of slope to solve each problem.

61. *Steepness of an Upper Deck* The upper deck at U.S. Cellular Field in Chicago has produced, among other complaints, displeasure with its steepness. It has been compared to a ski jump. It is 160 ft from home plate to the front of the upper deck and 250 ft from home plate to the back. The top of the upper deck is 63 ft above the bottom. What is its slope?

62. *Grade (Slope) of a Ramp* When designing the TD Banknorth Garden arena in Boston to replace the old Boston Garden, architects were careful to design the ramps leading up to the entrances so that circus elephants would be able to walk up the ramps. The maximum grade (or slope) that an elephant will walk on is 13%. Suppose that such a ramp were constructed with a horizontal run of 150 ft. What would be the maximum vertical rise the architects could use?

Rate of Change *Find and interpret the average rate of change illustrated in each graph.*

63.

64.

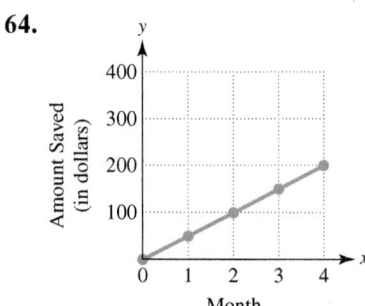

Use the idea of average rate of change to solve each problem.

65. *Biological Sciences Majors* The graph gives the percent of first-time full-time freshmen at four-year colleges and universities who planned to major in biological sciences.

Source: Higher Education Research Institute, UCLA.

(a) Use the given ordered pairs to find the slope of the line.

(b) The slope of the line is _____ .
           (positive/negative)
This means that during the period represented, the percent of freshmen planning to major in the biological sciences _____ .
                        (increased/decreased)

(c) What was the increase in the percent of freshmen *per year* who planned to major in the biological sciences during the period shown?

66. *Business Majors* The graph gives the percent of first-time full-time freshmen at four-year colleges and universities who planned to major in business.

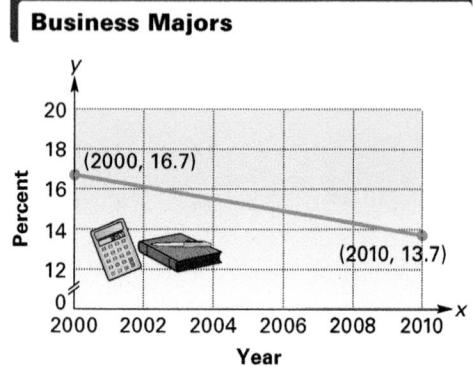

Source: Higher Education Research Institute, UCLA.

(a) Use the given ordered pairs to find the slope of the line.

(b) The slope of the line is _____ .
           (positive/negative)
This means that during the period represented, the percent of freshmen planning to major in business _____ .
                 (increased/decreased)

(c) What was the decrease in the percent of freshmen *per year* who planned to major in business during the period shown?

67. *Wireless Subscribers* The graph shows the number of wireless subscriber connections in millions in the United States for the years 2007 through 2012.

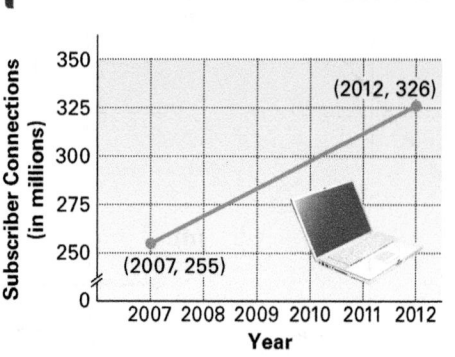

Source: CTIA.

(a) Use the given ordered pairs to find the slope of the line.

(b) Interpret the slope in the context of this problem.

68. *Wireless-Only Households* The graph shows the percent of wireless-only households in the United States for the years 2007 through 2012.

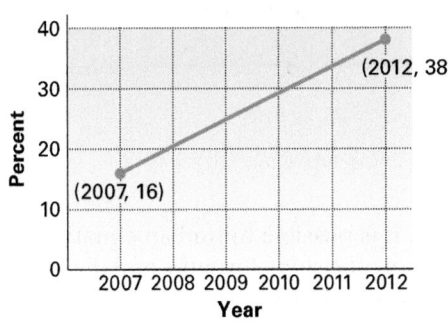

Wireless-Only Households

Source: CTIA.

(a) Use the given ordered pairs to find the slope of the line to the nearest tenth.

(b) Interpret the slope in the context of this problem.

69. *Digital Cameras* In 2010, the number of digital cameras sold in the United States totaled 7246 thousand. In 2013, 1670 thousand were sold. Find and interpret the average rate of change in the number of digital cameras sold per year to the nearest thousand. (*Source:* Consumer Electronics Association.)

70. *Desktop Computers* In 2010, sales of desktop computers in the United States totaled $7390 million. In 2013, sales were $6876 million. Find and interpret the average rate of change in sales of desktop computers per year to the nearest million dollars. (*Source:* Consumer Electronics Association.)

71. *Gasoline Prices* The average price of a gallon of gasoline in 1980 was $1.22. In 2012, the average price was $3.70. Find and interpret the average rate of change in the price of a gallon of gasoline per year to the nearest cent. (*Source:* Energy Information Administration.)

72. *Movie Ticket Prices* The average price of a movie ticket in 1990 was $4.23. In 2012, the average price was $7.96. Find and interpret the average rate of change in the price of a movie ticket per year to the nearest cent. (*Source*: Motion Picture Association of America.)

8.3 EQUATIONS OF LINES

OBJECTIVES

1 Find an equation of a line using point-slope form.

2 Find an equation of a line using slope-intercept form.

3 Use slope-intercept form to sketch the graph of a line from the equation.

4 Find an equation of a line parallel or perpendicular to a given line through a given point.

5 Know how the formulas for the Fahrenheit and Celsius temperature scales are derived.

Point-Slope Form

If the slope of a line and a particular point on a line are known, it is possible to find an equation of the line. Suppose that the slope of a line is m and that (x_1, y_1) is a particular point on the line. Let (x, y) be any other point on the line. Then, by the definition of slope, we have the following.

$$m = \frac{y - y_1}{x - x_1} \qquad \text{Slope formula}$$

$$m(x - x_1) = \frac{y - y_1}{x - x_1}(x - x_1) \qquad \text{Multiply by } x - x_1.$$

$$m(x - x_1) = y - y_1 \qquad \text{Simplify the right side.}$$

Interchanging the sides of this last equation gives the *point-slope form* of the equation of a line.

POINT-SLOPE FORM

The equation of a line through (x_1, y_1) with slope m is written in **point-slope form** as follows.

$$y - y_1 = m(x - x_1)$$

EXAMPLE 1 **Finding an Equation Given the Slope and a Point**

Find the standard form of an equation of the line with slope $\frac{1}{3}$, passing through the point $(-2, 5)$.

Solution

$$y - y_1 = m(x - x_1) \qquad \text{Point-slope form}$$

$$y - 5 = \frac{1}{3}[x - (-2)] \qquad \text{Let } (x_1, y_1) = (-2, 5) \text{ and } m = \frac{1}{3}.$$

> **Substitute carefully.**

$$y - 5 = \frac{1}{3}(x + 2) \qquad \text{Simplify the right side.}$$

$$3y - 15 = x + 2 \qquad \text{Multiply by 3.}$$

$$x - 3y = -17 \qquad \text{Standard form} \qquad \blacksquare$$

If two points on a line are known, it is possible to find an equation of the line. One method is to first find the slope using the slope formula, and then use the slope with one of the given points in the point-slope form.

EXAMPLE 2 **Finding an Equation Given Two Points**

Find the standard form of an equation of the line passing through the points $(-4, 3)$ and $(6, -2)$.

Solution

First find the slope, using the definition.

$$m = \frac{-2 - 3}{6 - (-4)} = \frac{-5}{10} = -\frac{1}{2} \qquad \begin{array}{l} x_1 = -4, \ y_1 = 3, \\ x_2 = 6, \ y_2 = -2 \end{array}$$

Either $(-4, 3)$ or $(6, -2)$ may be used as (x_1, y_1) in the point-slope form of the equation of the line. If $(-4, 3)$ is used, then $x_1 = -4$ and $y_1 = 3$.

$$y - y_1 = m(x - x_1) \qquad \text{Point-slope form}$$

$$y - 3 = -\frac{1}{2}[x - (-4)] \qquad \text{Let } (x_1, y_1) = (-4, 3) \text{ and } m = -\frac{1}{2}.$$

$$y - 3 = -\frac{1}{2}(x + 4) \qquad \text{Definition of subtraction}$$

$$2(y - 3) = -(x + 4) \qquad \text{Multiply by 2.}$$

$$2y - 6 = -x - 4 \qquad \text{Distributive property}$$

$$x + 2y = 2 \qquad \text{Standard form} \qquad \blacksquare$$

Slope-Intercept Form

Suppose that the slope m of a line is known, and the y-intercept of the line has coordinates $(0, b)$. Then we have the following.

$$y - y_1 = m(x - x_1) \qquad \text{Point-slope form}$$

$$y - b = m(x - 0) \qquad \text{Let } (x_1, y_1) = (0, b).$$

$$y - b = mx \qquad \text{Subtract. Multiply.}$$

$$y = mx + b \qquad \text{Add } b \text{ to both sides.}$$

Maria Gaetana Agnesi (1719–1799) did much of her mathematical work in coordinate geometry. She grew up in a scholarly atmosphere. Her father was a mathematician on the faculty at the University of Bologna. In a larger sense she was an heir to the long tradition of Italian mathematicians.

Maria was fluent in several languages by age 13, but she chose mathematics over literature. The curve shown below, called the **witch of Agnesi**, is studied in analytic geometry courses.

$$y = \frac{a^3}{x^2 + a^2}$$

This result is known as the *slope-intercept form* of the equation of the line.

SLOPE-INTERCEPT FORM

The equation of a line with slope m and y-intercept $(0, b)$ is written in **slope-intercept form** as follows.

$$y = mx + b$$

↑   ↑

Slope y-intercept is $(0, b)$.

EXAMPLE 3 Writing an Equation in Slope-Intercept Form

Write each of the following equations in slope-intercept form.

(a) The line $x - 3y = -17$ described in **Example 1**

(b) The line $x + 2y = 2$ described in **Example 2**

Solution

(a) Solve for y to obtain the slope-intercept form.

$$x - 3y = -17$$

$$-3y = -x - 17 \qquad \text{Subtract } x.$$

$$y = \frac{1}{3}x + \frac{17}{3} \qquad \text{Divide by } -3.$$

The slope is $\frac{1}{3}$ and the y-intercept is $\left(0, \frac{17}{3}\right)$.

(b)
$$x + 2y = 2$$

$$2y = -x + 2 \qquad \text{Subtract } x.$$

$$y = -\frac{1}{2}x + 1 \qquad \text{Multiply by } \frac{1}{2}.$$

The slope is $-\frac{1}{2}$ and the y-intercept is $(0, 1)$. ■

If the slope-intercept form of the equation of a line is known, the method of graphing described in **Example 5** of **Section 8.2** can be used to graph the line.

EXAMPLE 4 Graphing a Line Using Slope and y-Intercept

Graph the line with the equation $y = -\frac{2}{3}x + 3$.

Solution

Because the equation is given in slope-intercept form, we can see that the slope is $-\frac{2}{3}$ and the y-intercept is $(0, 3)$. For now, interpret $-\frac{2}{3}$ as $\frac{-2}{3}$. Plot the point $(0, 3)$, and then, using the "rise over run" interpretation of slope, move *down* 2 units (because of the -2 in the numerator of the slope) and to the *right* 3 units (because of the 3 in the denominator). We arrive at the point $(3, 1)$.

Plot the point $(3, 1)$, and join the two points with a line, as shown in **Figure 20**. (We could also have interpreted $-\frac{2}{3}$ as $\frac{2}{-3}$ and obtained a different second point. However, the line would be the same.) ■

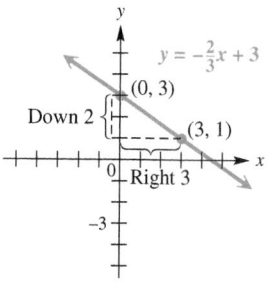

Figure 20

▐▐▐ EXAMPLE 5 Using a Slope Relationship (Parallel Lines)

Find the slope-intercept form of the equation of the line parallel to the graph of $2x + 3y = 6$, passing through the point $(-2, -1)$. Graph both lines.

Solution

The slope of the graph of $2x + 3y = 6$ in **Figure 21** can be found by solving for y.

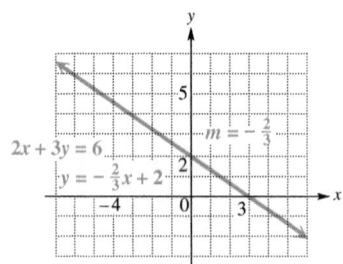

Figure 21

$$2x + 3y = 6$$

$$3y = -2x + 6 \qquad \text{Subtract } 2x.$$

$$y = -\frac{2}{3}x + 2 \qquad \text{Divide by 3.}$$

$$\underset{\text{Slope}}{\uparrow}$$

The slope is given by the coefficient of x, so $m = -\frac{2}{3}$. The line through $(-2, -1)$ and parallel to $2x + 3y = 6$ must have the same slope. To find the required equation, use the point-slope form with $(x_1, y_1) = (-2, -1)$ and $m = -\frac{2}{3}$.

$$y - (-1) = -\frac{2}{3}[x - (-2)] \qquad y_1 = -1, \; m = -\frac{2}{3}, \; x_1 = -2$$

$$y + 1 = -\frac{2}{3}(x + 2) \qquad \text{Definition of subtraction}$$

$$y + 1 = -\frac{2}{3}x - \frac{4}{3} \qquad \text{Distributive property}$$

$$y = -\frac{2}{3}x - \frac{4}{3} - 1 \qquad \text{Subtract 1.}$$

$$y = -\frac{2}{3}x - \frac{7}{3} \qquad \text{Subtract.}$$

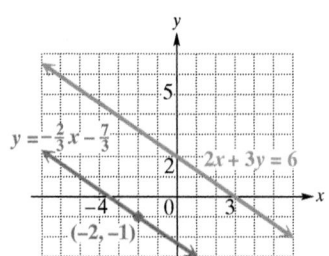

Figure 22

Both lines are shown in **Figure 22**. ▪

▐▐▐ EXAMPLE 6 Using a Slope Relationship (Perpendicular Lines)

Find the slope-intercept form of the equation of the line perpendicular to the graph of $2x + 3y = 6$, passing through the point $(-4, 5)$. Graph both lines.

Solution

In **Example 5** we found that the slope of the line $2x + 3y = 6$ is $-\frac{2}{3}$. A line perpendicular to this line must have a slope that is the negative reciprocal of $-\frac{2}{3}$, which is $\frac{3}{2}$. Use the point $(-4, 5)$ and slope $\frac{3}{2}$ in the point-slope form to obtain the equation of the perpendicular line shown in **Figure 23**.

$$y - 5 = \frac{3}{2}[x - (-4)] \qquad y_1 = 5, \; m = \frac{3}{2}, \; x_1 = -4$$

$$y - 5 = \frac{3}{2}(x + 4) \qquad \text{Definition of subtraction}$$

$$y - 5 = \frac{3}{2}x + 6 \qquad \text{Distributive property}$$

$$y = \frac{3}{2}x + 11 \qquad \text{Add 5.}$$

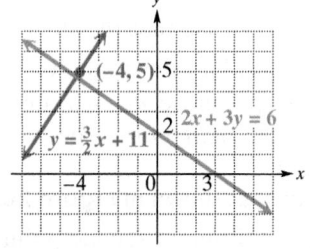

Figure 23

An Application of Linear Equations

One familiar formula that provides exact results gives the relationship between the Celsius and Fahrenheit temperature scales. In **Example 6** of **Section 7.1** we examined the formula for converting Celsius to Fahrenheit. The following example shows how that formula is derived.

EXAMPLE 7 Deriving the Formula for Converting Celsius to Fahrenheit

In the Fahrenheit scale, water freezes at 32 degrees and boils at 212 degrees. In the Celsius scale, water freezes at 0 degrees and boils at 100 degrees. There is an exact linear relationship between these two scales. Use this information to derive the formula for converting Celsius to Fahrenheit.

Solution

For now, we will let x represent the Celsius degree measure and let y represent the Fahrenheit measure. The two ordered pairs

$$(0, 32) \quad \text{and} \quad (100, 212)$$

illustrate a relationship between the two scales. We now find the equation of the line containing these two points. First, find the slope of the line.

$$m = \frac{212 - 32}{100 - 0} \quad \text{Slope formula with } x_1 = 0,$$
$$y_1 = 32, x_2 = 100, y_2 = 212$$

$$m = \frac{180}{100} \quad \text{Subtract.}$$

$$m = \frac{9}{5} \quad \text{Lowest terms}$$

Now, because $(0, 32)$ is the y-intercept, we can substitute into the slope-intercept form to find the equation of the line.

$$y = mx + b \quad \text{Slope-intercept form}$$

$$y = \frac{9}{5}x + 32 \quad m = \tfrac{9}{5}, b = 32$$

Finally, replace x with C and y with F to represent the two scales.

$$F = \frac{9}{5}C + 32 \quad \text{The familiar formula} \qquad \blacksquare$$

8.3 EXERCISES

Match each equation in Group I with the correct description given in Group II.

I	**II**
1. $y = 4x$	**A.** slope $= -2$, through the point $(4, 1)$
2. $y = \dfrac{1}{4}x$	**B.** slope $= -2$, y-intercept $(0, 1)$
3. $y = -2x + 1$	**C.** passing through the points $(0, 0)$ and $(4, 1)$
4. $y - 1 = -2(x - 4)$	**D.** passing through the points $(0, 0)$ and $(1, 4)$

In Exercises 5–12, match each equation with the graph that it most closely resembles in Choices A–H. (Hint: Determining the signs of m and b will help you make your decision.)

5. $y = 2x + 3$

6. $y = -2x + 3$

7. $y = -2x - 3$

8. $y = 2x - 3$

9. $y = 2x$

10. $y = -2x$

11. $y = 3$

12. $y = -3$

A.

B.

C.

D.

E.

F.

G.

H.

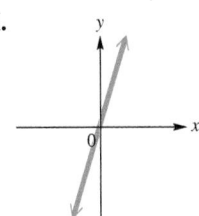

Use the geometric interpretation of slope (rise divided by run) to find the slope of each line. Then, by identifying the y-intercept from the graph, write the slope-intercept form of the equation of the line.

13.

14.

15.

16.

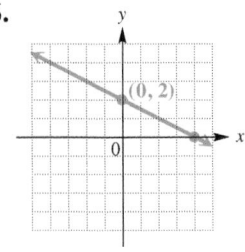

Write the slope-intercept form of the equation of the line satisfying the given conditions.

17. Through $(-2, 4)$; slope $-\frac{3}{4}$

18. Through $(-1, 6)$; slope $-\frac{5}{6}$

19. Through $(5, 8)$; slope -2

20. Through $(12, 10)$; slope 1

21. Through $(-5, 4)$; slope $\frac{1}{2}$

22. Through $(7, -2)$; slope $\frac{1}{4}$

23. x-intercept $(3, 0)$; slope 4

24. x-intercept $(-2, 0)$; slope -5

Write an equation for a line that satisfies the given conditions.

25. Through $(9, 5)$; slope 0

26. Through $(-4, -2)$; slope 0

27. Through $(9, 10)$; undefined slope

28. Through $(-2, 8)$; undefined slope

29. Through $(0.5, 0.2)$; vertical

30. Through $\left(\frac{5}{8}, \frac{2}{9}\right)$; vertical

31. Through $(-7, 8)$; horizontal

32. Through $(2, 7)$; horizontal

Write the equation, in slope-intercept form if possible, of the line passing through the two points.

33. $(3, 4)$ and $(5, 8)$

34. $(5, -2)$ and $(-3, 14)$

35. $(6, 1)$ and $(-2, 5)$

36. $(-3, 6)$ and $(6, 12)$

37. $(2, 5)$ and $(1, 5)$

38. $(-2, 2)$ and $(4, 2)$

39. $(7, 6)$ and $(7, -8)$

40. $(13, 5)$ and $(13, -1)$

41. $(1, -3)$ and $(-1, -3)$

42. $(-4, 6)$ and $(5, 6)$

Find the equation, in slope-intercept form, of the line satisfying the given conditions.

43. $m = 5$; $b = 15$

44. $m = -2$; $b = 12$

45. $m = -\frac{2}{3}$; $b = \frac{4}{5}$

46. $m = -\frac{5}{8}$; $b = -\frac{1}{3}$

47. Slope $\frac{2}{5}$; y-intercept $(0, 5)$

48. Slope $-\frac{3}{4}$; y-intercept $(0, 7)$

For each equation **(a)** *write in slope-intercept form,* **(b)** *give the slope of the line, and* **(c)** *give the y-intercept.*

49. $x + y = 12$ **50.** $x - y = 14$

51. $5x + 2y = 20$ **52.** $6x + 5y = 40$

53. $2x - 3y = 10$ **54.** $4x - 3y = 10$

Write the equation, in slope-intercept form, of the line satisfying the given conditions.

55. Through $(7, 2)$; parallel to $3x - y = 8$

56. Through $(4, 1)$; parallel to $2x + 5y = 10$

57. Through $(-2, -2)$; parallel to $-x + 2y = 10$

58. Through $(-1, 3)$; parallel to $-x + 3y = 12$

59. Through $(8, 5)$; perpendicular to $2x - y = 7$

60. Through $(2, -7)$; perpendicular to $5x + 2y = 18$

61. Through $(-2, 7)$; perpendicular to $x = 9$

62. Through $(8, 4)$; perpendicular to $x = -3$

Celsius and Fahrenheit *Refer to* **Example 7** *to answer Exercises 63–66.*

63. Determine the formula for converting Fahrenheit to Celsius by applying the method of **Example 7** to the points $(32, 0)$ and $(212, 100)$. Give the answer using C and F.

64. Refer to the formula derived in **Example 7** and solve algebraically for C. (See **Section 7.1** if necessary.) Verify that the result is the same as determined in **Exercise 63.**

65. Use either formula to find the temperature at which Celsius and Fahrenheit are equal. (*Hint:* Replace C with F and solve for the single variable.)

66. At what Celsius temperature is the corresponding Fahrenheit temperature numerically double the Celsius temperature?

8.4   LINEAR FUNCTIONS, GRAPHS, AND MODELS

OBJECTIVES

1 Know the meanings of the terms *relation*, *function*, *domain*, *range*, *independent variable*, and *dependent variable*.

2 Use function notation.

3 Identify a linear function and graph it.

4 Perform cost analysis using linear functions.

5 Construct a linear model from a set of data points.

Relations and Functions

In the chapter opener we gave an example of how the number of gallons of gasoline pumped is associated with one and only one total price. This is an example of a *function*, a special case of a *relation*.

RELATION

A **relation** is a set of ordered pairs.

Once again, suppose that it is time to fill up your car's gas tank. At your local station, 89-octane gas is selling for $3.10 per gallon. The final price you pay is determined by the number of gallons you buy multiplied by the price per gallon (in this case, $3.10). **Table 1** on the next page gives ordered pairs to illustrate this situation.

If we let x denote the number of gallons pumped, then the price y in dollars can be found by the linear equation

$$y = 3.10x.$$

Theoretically, there are infinitely many ordered pairs (x, y) that satisfy this equation. We are limited to nonnegative values for x here, since we cannot have a negative number of gallons. There also is a practical maximum value for x in this situation, which varies from one car to another—that value is the capacity of the tank.

Table 1

Number of Gallons Pumped	Price for This Number of Gallons
0	$0.00 = 0($3.10)
1	$3.10 = 1($3.10)
2	$6.20 = 2($3.10)
3	$9.30 = 3($3.10)
4	$12.40 = 4($3.10)

For every number of gallons, there is one and only one sale price. The price charged *depends* on the number of gallons pumped. When there were 0 gallons pumped, the price was 0 dollars. When there were 25.825 gallons pumped, the price was $79.00. If we graph a line segment joining (0, 0) and (25.825, 79.00), what is its slope?

Now look at the prices for Supreme, Plus, Regular, and Diesel. Which fuel was bought? (The answer is on **page 432**.)

In this example, the total price depends on the amount of gasoline pumped. For this reason, price is called the *dependent variable*, and the number of gallons is called the *independent variable*. Generalizing, if the value of the variable y depends on the value of the variable x, then y is the **dependent variable** and x the **independent variable**.

The set of all values taken on by the independent variable is the **domain** of the relation. The set of all dependent variable values that result is the **range** of the relation. As mentioned earlier, a special kind of relation, called a *function*, is important in mathematics and its applications. Three variations of the definition of function are now given.

VARIATIONS OF THE DEFINITION OF FUNCTION

1. A **function** is a relation in which, for each value of the first component of the ordered pairs, there is *exactly one* value of the second component.

2. A **function** is a set of distinct ordered pairs in which no first component is repeated.

3. A **function** is defined by a rule or correspondence that assigns exactly one range value to each distinct domain value.

In a function, there is exactly one value of the dependent variable (the second component) for each value of the independent variable (the first component).

Function Notation

When a function f is defined with a rule or an equation using x and y for the independent and dependent variables, we say "y is a function of x" to emphasize that y depends on x. For a function f, we use the notation

$$y = f(x),$$

called **function notation,** to express this and read $f(x)$ as "**f of x.**" (In this notation the parentheses do not indicate multiplication.) For example, in function f, if $y = 2x - 7$, we write

> Do not read $f(x)$ as "f times x."

$$f(x) = 2x - 7.$$

Note that $f(x)$ is just another name for the dependent variable y. For example, if

$$y = f(x) = 3x - 5,$$

and $x = 2$, then we find y, or $f(2)$, by replacing x with 2.

$$y = f(2)$$
$$y = 3 \cdot 2 - 5 \qquad f(x) = 3x - 5$$
$$y = 1 \qquad \text{Multiply, and then subtract.}$$

The fact that $(2, 1)$ belongs to the function f is written with function notation as

$$f(2) = 1.$$

We read $f(2)$ as "f of 2" or "f at 2."

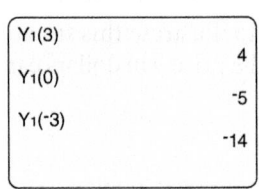

For $Y_1 = 3X - 5$, function notation capability of the TI-83/84 Plus shows the value of Y_1, or f, at 3, 0, and −3.

These ideas and the symbols used to represent them can be explained as follows.

$$y = f(x) = 3x - 5$$

Name of the function

Defining expression

Value of the function

Name of the independent variable

EXAMPLE 1 Using Function Notation

Find the following for the function

$$f(x) = -2x + 3.$$

(a) $f(0)$ **(b)** $f(1)$ **(c)** $f(3)$ **(d)** the value of x for which $f(x) = 7$

(e) Use these results to give four ordered pairs that belong to f.

Solution

(a)
$$f(x) = -2x + 3 \qquad \text{Given function}$$
$$f(0) = -2(0) + 3 \qquad \text{Replace } x \text{ with } 0.$$
$$= 0 + 3 \qquad \text{Multiply.}$$
$$= 3 \qquad \text{Add.}$$

(b) $f(1) = -2(1) + 3$ **(c)** $f(3) = -2(3) + 3$
$$= -2 + 3 \qquad\qquad\qquad = -6 + 3$$
$$= 1 \qquad\qquad\qquad\qquad = -3$$

(d) Replace $f(x)$ with 7 and solve for x.

$$f(x) = -2x + 3 \qquad \text{Given function}$$
$$7 = -2x + 3 \qquad \text{Replace } f(x) \text{ with } 7.$$
$$4 = -2x \qquad \text{Subtract 3.}$$
$$-2 = x \qquad \text{Divide by } -2.$$

Thus, when $x = -2$, $f(x) = f(-2) = 7$.

(e) The results in parts (a)–(d) indicate that these ordered pairs all belong to f.

$$(0, 3), \quad (1, 1), \quad (3, -3), \quad \text{and} \quad (-2, 7) \qquad \blacksquare$$

Linear Functions

In our earlier discussion, we saw that if x represents the number of gallons pumped and 3.10 is the price per gallon, then

$$y = 3.10x$$

is the total price paid. If we decide to also get a car wash for 4 dollars, then a fixed amount is added to the variable amount. In this case,

$$y = 3.10x + 4$$

represents the total cost. This is an example of a linear equation in two variables, where 3.10 is the slope m of the line and $(0, 4)$ is the y-intercept. In the context of functions, it is called a *linear function*.

LINEAR FUNCTION

A function that can be defined by a rule written in the form

$$f(x) = ax + b$$

for real numbers a and b is a **linear function.**

The form $f(x) = ax + b$ defining a linear function is the same as that of the slope-intercept form of the equation of a line with a representing the slope. We know that the graph of $f(x) = ax + b$ will be a line with slope a and y-intercept $(0, b)$.

EXAMPLE 2 **Graphing Linear Functions**

Graph each linear function. Assume that x can be any real number. Give the domain and the range.

(a) $f(x) = -2x + 3$ **(b)** $f(x) = 3$

Solution

(a) One way to graph this function is to locate the y-intercept, $(0, 3)$. From this point, use the slope $-2 = \frac{-2}{1}$ to move down 2 and right 1. This second point is used to obtain the graph in **Figure 24(a).**

Alternatively, we can use the ordered pairs found in **Example 1** to plot the graph. Those ordered pairs are also shown in the table accompanying **Figure 24(a).**

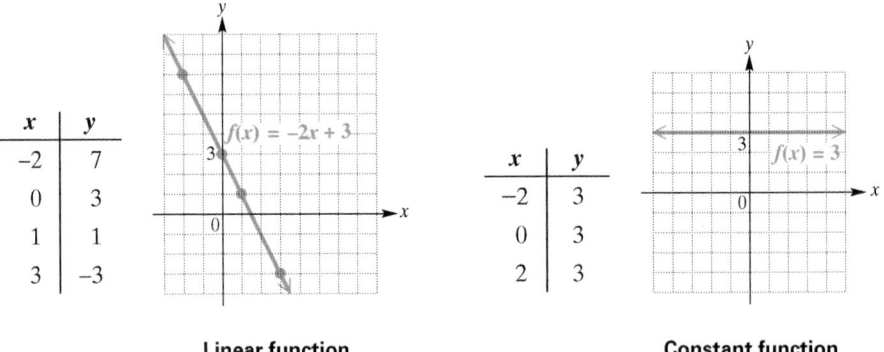

x	y
-2	7
0	3
1	1
3	-3

Linear function
(a)

x	y
-2	3
0	3
2	3

Constant function
(b)

Figure 24

The domain and the range are both $(-\infty, \infty)$.

(b) From the previous section, we know that the graph of $y = 3$ is a horizontal line. Therefore, the graph of $f(x) = 3$ is a horizontal line $(m = 0)$ with y-intercept $(0, 3)$ as shown in **Figure 24(b).** The domain is $(-\infty, \infty)$ and the range is $\{3\}$. ∎

The function defined in **Example 2(b)** and graphed in **Figure 24(b)** is an example of a constant function. A **constant function** is a linear function of the form

$$f(x) = b,$$

where b is a real number.

In applications of linear functions, domain values are often restricted. In the case of the gas-pumping example, x can take on only non-negative values. The size of the tank would also put a restriction on the maximum value of x.

Answer to the Gasoline Pumping question on page 430 Divide the sale amount by the number of gallons to find that the price per gallon is that of diesel fuel.

Linear Models

If an entrepreneur opens a business that specializes in selling a particular product, the goal is to earn a profit. Linear functions can model cost, revenue, and profit.

EXAMPLE 3 Analyzing Cost, Revenue, and Profit

Peripheral Visions, Inc., produces studio-quality DVDs of live concerts. The company places an ad in a trade newsletter. The cost of the ad is $100. Each DVD costs $20 to produce, and the company charges $24 per disk.

(a) Express the cost C as a function of x, the number of DVDs produced and sold.

(b) Express the revenue R as a function of x, the number of DVDs sold.

(c) When will the company break even? That is, for what value of x does revenue equal cost?

(d) Graph the cost and revenue functions on the same coordinate system, and interpret the graph.

Solution

(a) The **fixed cost** is $100, and for each DVD produced, the **variable cost** is $20. The cost C can be expressed as a function of x, the number of DVDs produced.

$$C(x) = 20x + 100 \quad (C \text{ in dollars})$$

(b) Each DVD sells for $24, so the revenue R is given by

$$R(x) = 24x \quad (R \text{ in dollars}).$$

(c) The company will just break even (no profit and no loss) if revenue just equals cost, or $R(x) = C(x)$. Solve this equation for x.

$$R(x) = C(x)$$
$$24x = 20x + 100 \quad \text{Substitute for } R(x) \text{ and } C(x).$$
$$4x = 100 \quad \text{Subtract } 20x.$$
$$x = 25 \quad \text{Divide by 4.}$$

If 25 DVDs are produced and sold, the company will break even.

(d) **Figure 25** shows the graphs of the two functions. (For convenience, we use lines rather than discrete points with whole number y-values.) At the break-even point, we see that when 25 DVDs are produced and sold, both the cost and the revenue are $600. If fewer than 25 DVDs are produced and sold (that is, when $x < 25$), the company loses money. When more than 25 DVDs are produced and sold (that is, when $x > 25$), there is a profit.

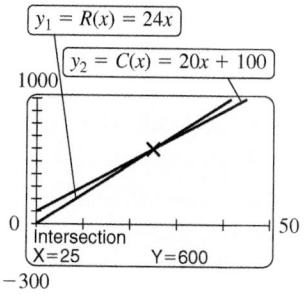

The break-even point is (25, 600), as indicated at the bottom of the screen. The calculator can find the point of intersection of the graphs. Compare with **Figure 25**.

Figure 25

Given data points that lie approximately on a straight line, we can develop a linear function, or **linear model,** to describe the data.

EXAMPLE 4 Modeling Tuition Costs

Average annual tuition and fees for in-state students at public two-year colleges are shown in **Table 2.**

(a) Graph the data. Let $x = 0$ correspond to 2009, $x = 1$ correspond to 2010, and so on. What type of equation might model the data?

(b) Find a linear function f that models the data, using the information for the years 2009 and 2013.

(c) Use the equation from part (b) to approximate the cost of tuition and fees at public two-year colleges in 2014.

Table 2

Year	Cost (in dollars)
2009 ($x = 0$)	2787
2010 ($x = 1$)	2938
2011 ($x = 2$)	3074
2012 ($x = 3$)	3216
2013 ($x = 4$)	3264

Source: The College Board.

Solution

(a) The points are plotted in **Figure 26,** where x corresponds to the year as described, and y represents the cost in dollars. It appears that a linear equation will model the data.

Figure 26

(b) Since the points in **Figure 26** lie approximately on a straight line, we can write a linear equation that models the relationship between year x and cost y. We use the two data points for 2009 and 2013 to find the slope of the line.

$$m = \frac{3264 - 2787}{4 - 0} = \frac{477}{4} = 119.25$$

Start with the x- and y-values of the same point.

Use (0, 2787) and (4, 3264).

The slope 119.25 indicates that the cost of tuition and fees increased by about $119.25 per year from 2009 to 2013. We use this slope, the y-intercept $(0, 2787)$, and the slope-intercept form to write an equation of the line.

$$f(x) = 119.25x + 2787$$

(c) The value $x = 5$ corresponds to the year 2014.

$$f(x) = 119.25x + 2787 \qquad \text{Equation from part (b)}$$
$$f(5) = 119.25(5) + 2787 \qquad \text{Substitute 5 for } x.$$
$$f(5) \approx 3383 \qquad \text{Multiply and then add.}$$

According to this model, average tuition and fees for in-state students at public two-year colleges in 2014 were about $3383. ■

In **Example 4,** if we had chosen a different pair of data points, we would have found a slightly different equation. However, all such equations should yield similar results, because the data points are approximately linear.

8.4   EXERCISES

Choose from the following list of responses for Exercise 1–6. Each choice is used once and only once.

function	dependent	domain	range
line	horizontal	constant	linear
independent	set of ordered pairs		

1. A relation is a _____ .

2. The set of all first components in a relation is the _____ of the relation. Each one is a value of the _____ variable.

3. The set of all second components in a relation is the _____ of the relation. Each one is a value of the _____ variable.

4. A relation in which each first component is paired with one and only one second component is a(n) _____ .

5. $f(x) = 3x + 6$ is an example of a(n) _____ function. Its graph is a(n) _____ .

6. $f(x) = 6$ is an example of a(n) _____ function. Its graph is a(n) _____ line.

Let $f(x) = 2x + 3$ and $g(x) = x^2 - 2$. Find each function value.

7. $f(1)$ 8. $f(4)$ 9. $g(2)$

10. $g(0)$ 11. $g(-1)$ 12. $g(-3)$

13. $f(-8)$ 14. $f(-5)$ 15. $f(0)$

16. $g(0)$ 17. $f\left(-\dfrac{3}{2}\right)$ 18. $g\left(\sqrt{2}\right)$

Sketch the graph of each linear function. Give the domain and range.

19. $f(x) = -2x + 5$ 20. $f(x) = 4x - 1$

21. $f(x) = \dfrac{1}{2}x + 2$ 22. $f(x) = -\dfrac{1}{4}x + 1$

23. $f(x) = 2x$ 24. $f(x) = -3x$

25. $f(x) = 5$ 26. $f(x) = -4$

Find the value of x for which $f(x) = 10$.

27. $f(x) = 3x - 2$ 28. $f(x) = 4x + 6$

29. $f(x) = \dfrac{1}{2}x + 2$ 30. $f(x) = \dfrac{1}{4}x - 8$

Cost and Revenue Models   *In Exercises 31–34, do the following.*

  (a) *Express the cost C as a function of x, where x represents the quantity of items as given.*

  (b) *Express the revenue R as a function of x.*

  (c) *Determine the value of x for which revenue equals cost.*

  (d) *Graph the equations*

$$y = C(x) \quad and \quad y = R(x)$$

  on the same axes, and interpret the graph.

31. Perian stuffs envelopes for extra income during her spare time. Her initial cost to obtain the necessary information for the job was $200.00. Each envelope costs $0.02 and she gets paid $0.04 per envelope stuffed. Let x represent the number of envelopes stuffed.

32. Bart runs a copying service in his home. He paid $3500 for the copier and a lifetime service contract. Each sheet of paper he uses costs $0.01, and he gets paid $0.05 per copy he makes. Let x represent the number of copies he makes.

33. Frank operates a delivery service in a southern city. His start-up costs amounted to $2300. He estimates that it costs him (in terms of gasoline, wear and tear on his car, etc.) $3.00 per delivery. He charges $5.50 per delivery. Let x represent the number of deliveries he makes.

34. Jane bakes cakes and sells them at Louisiana parish fairs. Her initial cost for the Pointe Coupee Parish fair this year was $40.00. She figures that each cake costs $2.50 to make, and she charges $6.50 per cake. Let x represent the number of cakes sold. (Assume that there were no cakes left over.)

Solve each problem.

35. *Tuition Costs* Average annual tuition and fees for in-state students at public four-year colleges are shown in the table for selected years and graphed as ordered pairs of points, where $x = 0$ represents 2005, $x = 1$ represents 2006, and so on, and $f(x)$ represents the cost in dollars.

Tuition and Fees

Year	Cost (in dollars)
2005	5492
2006	5804
2007	6191
2008	6591
2009	7050
2010	7605

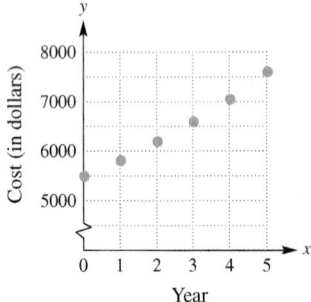

Source: Trends in College Pricing 2010, The College Board.

(a) Use the points from the years 2005 and 2010 to find a linear function f that models the data.

(b) Use the function from part (a) to estimate the cost of tuition and fees, to the nearest dollar, at public four-year colleges in 2012.

36. *Tuition Costs* Average annual tuition and fees for private four-year colleges are shown in the table.

Tuition and Fees

Year	Cost (in dollars)
1996	12,881
1998	13,973
2000	15,470
2002	16,826
2004	18,604
2006	20,517
2008	22,449

Source: Annual Survey of Colleges, The College Board.

Let $x = 0$ represent 1996, $x = 2$ represent 1998, and so on, and let $f(x)$ represent the cost in dollars.

(a) Use the information for the years 1996 and 2008 to find a linear function f that models the data.

(b) Use the function from part (a) to estimate the cost in 2007. Compare the estimate to the actual 2007 cost of $21,979.

37. *High School Graduates* The percentage of the U.S. population 25 years and older with at least a high school diploma is shown in the table for selected years.

High School Graduates

Year	Percent
1950	34.3
1960	41.1
1970	52.3
1980	66.5
1990	77.6
2000	84.1
2005	85.2

Source: U.S. Census Bureau.

Let $x = 0$ represent 1950, $x = 10$ represent 1960, and so on.

(a) Use the data for 1950 and 2000 to find a linear function f that models the data.

(b) Use the function from part (a) to approximate the percentage, to the nearest tenth, of the U.S. population 25 years and older who were at least high school graduates in 1995.

38. *Nuclear Waste* The table gives the heavy metal nuclear waste (in thousands of metric tons) from spent reactor fuel stored temporarily at reactor sites, awaiting permanent storage. (*Source:* "Burial of Radioactive Nuclear Waste under the Seabed," *Scientific American,* January 1998, p. 62.)

Heavy Metal Nuclear Waste

Year x	Waste y
1995	32
2000	42
2010	61
2020*	76

*Estimate by the U.S. Department of Energy.

Let $x = 0$ represent 1995, $x = 5$ represent 2000, and so on.

(a) Use $(0, 32)$ and $(25, 76)$ to find the equation of a line that approximates the other ordered pairs. Use the form $f(x) = ax + b$.

(b) Use the equation from part (a) to estimate the amount of nuclear waste in 2018.

39. *Distances and Velocities of Galaxies*   The table lists the distances (in megaparsecs; 1 megaparsec = 3.085 × 10^{24} cm, and 1 megaparsec = 3.26 million light-years) and velocities (in kilometers per second) of four galaxies moving rapidly away from Earth.

Galaxy	Distance	Velocity
Virgo	15	1600
Ursa Minor	200	15,000
Corona Borealis	290	24,000
Bootes	520	40,000

Source: Acker, A., and C. Jaschek, *Astronomical Methods and Calculations,* John Wiley and Sons. Karttunen, H. (editor), *Fundamental Astronomy,* Springer-Verlag.

(a) Find a linear function of the form

$$f(x) = ax$$

that models these data using $(520, 40{,}000)$ and $(0, 0)$. Round a to the nearest tenth.

(b) Use the function from part (a) to predict the velocity of a galaxy 400 megaparsecs from Earth.

40. *Forensic Studies*   Forensic scientists use the lengths of the tibia (t), a bone from the ankle to the knee, and the femur (r), the bone from the knee to the hip socket, to calculate the height of a person. A person's height (h) is determined from the lengths of these bones using functions defined by the following formulas. All measurements are in centimeters.

For men:	*For women:*
$h(r) = 69.09 + 2.24r$	$h(r) = 61.41 + 2.32r$
or $h(t) = 81.69 + 2.39t$	or $h(t) = 72.57 + 2.53t$

(a) Find the height of a man with a femur measuring 56 centimeters.

(b) Find the height of a man with a tibia measuring 40 centimeters.

(c) Find the height of a woman with a femur measuring 50 centimeters.

(d) Find the height of a woman with a tibia measuring 36 centimeters.

41. *Limo Fares*   A limo driver charges $2.50 per mile.

(a) Complete the table with the correct response for the price $f(x)$ she charges for a trip of x miles.

x	$f(x)$
0	
1	
2	
3	

(b) The linear function that gives a rule for the amount charged is $f(x) =$ ____.

(c) Graph this function for the domain $\{0, 1, 2, 3\}$.

42. *Cost to Mail a Package*   A package weighing x pounds costs $f(x)$ dollars to mail to a given location, where

$$f(x) = 2.75x.$$

(a) Evaluate $f(3)$.

(b) Describe what 3 and the value $f(3)$ mean in part (a), making use of the terms *independent variable* and *dependent variable.*

(c) How much would it cost to mail a 5-lb package? Write the answer using function notation.

43. *Speeding Fines*   Speeding fines are determined by

$$f(x) = 10(x - 65) + 50, \quad x > 65,$$

where $f(x)$ is the cost, in dollars, of the fine if a person is caught driving x miles per hour.

(a) Radar clocked a driver at 76 mph. How much was the fine?

(b) While balancing his checkbook, Johnny ran across a canceled check that his wife Gwen had written to the Department of Motor Vehicles for a speeding fine. The check was written for $100. How fast was Gwen driving?

(c) At what whole number speed are tickets first given?

(d) For what speeds is the fine greater than $200?

44. *Expansion and Contraction of Gases*   In 1787, Jacques Charles noticed that gases expand when heated and contract when cooled. Suppose that a particular gas follows the model

$$f(x) = \frac{5}{3}x + 455,$$

where x is temperature in degrees Celsius and $f(x)$ is volume in cubic centimeters. (*Source:* Bushaw, D., et al., *A Sourcebook of Applications of School Mathematics,* MAA, 1980. Reprinted with permission.)

(a) Find the volume when the temperature is 27°C.

(b) What is the temperature when the volume is 605 cubic centimeters?

8.5 QUADRATIC FUNCTIONS, GRAPHS, AND MODELS

OBJECTIVES

1 Know the meanings of the terms *quadratic function, parabola, axis of symmetry (axis),* and *vertex.*

2 Graph a quadratic function of the form $f(x) = a(x - h)^2 + k$.

3 Find the coordinates of the vertex of the graph of a quadratic function.

4 Find a maximum or minimum in an application of a quadratic function.

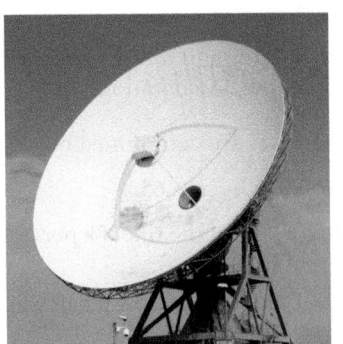

A parabolic dish

Quadratic Functions and Parabolas

We now look at *quadratic functions,* those defined by second-degree polynomials.

QUADRATIC FUNCTION

A function f is a **quadratic function** if it can be defined as follows.

$$f(x) = ax^2 + bx + c,$$

where a, b, and c are real numbers, with $a \neq 0$.

The simplest quadratic function f is $f(x) = x^2$. Plotting the points in the table below and drawing a smooth curve through them gives the graph in **Figure 27**. This graph is called a **parabola.**

Parabolas are symmetric about a line (the y-axis in **Figure 27**). The line of symmetry for a parabola is called the **axis of symmetry** (or simply **axis**) of the parabola. The point where the axis intersects the parabola is the **vertex** of the parabola. The vertex is the lowest (or highest) point of a vertical parabola.

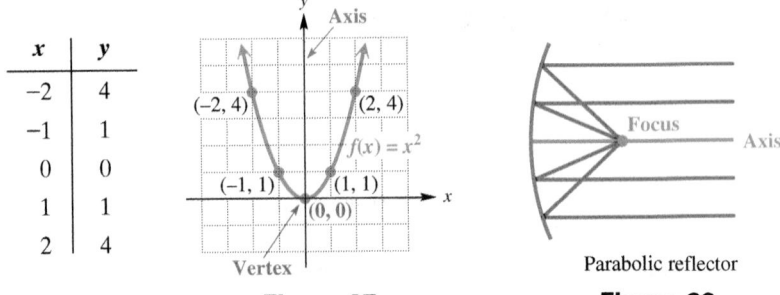

x	y
-2	4
-1	1
0	0
1	1
2	4

Figure 27   **Figure 28**

The *focus* of a parabola is a point on its axis that determines the curvature. See **Figure 28.** When the parabolic reflector of a solar oven is aimed at the sun, the light rays bounce off the reflector and collect at the focus, creating intense heat at that point.

Graphs of Quadratic Functions

The first example shows how the constant a affects the graph of a function of the form $g(x) = ax^2$.

EXAMPLE 1 Graphing Quadratic Functions ($g(x) = ax^2$)

Graph each function. Compare with the graph of $f(x) = x^2$.

(a) $g(x) = -x^2$ **(b)** $g(x) = \dfrac{1}{2}x^2$

Solution

(a) For a given value of x, the corresponding value of $g(x) = -x^2$ will be the negative of what it was for $f(x) = x^2$. See the table of values on the next page.

The graph of $g(x) = -x^2$ is the same shape as that of $f(x) = x^2$ but opens downward, as in **Figure 29.**

In general, the graph of $f(x) = ax^2 + bx + c$
opens downward whenever $a < 0$.

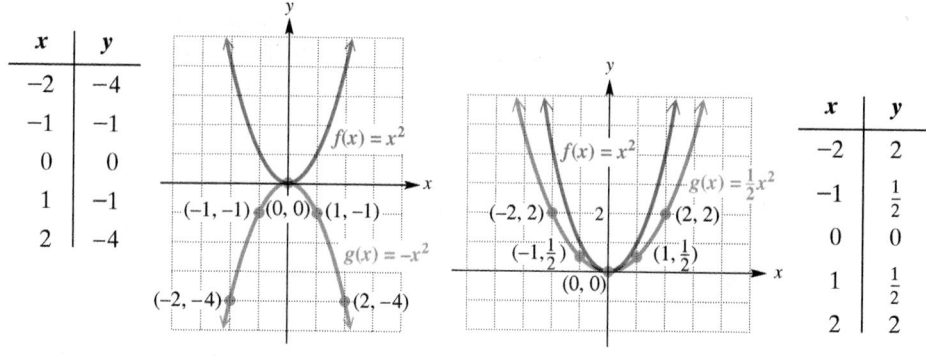

x	y
-2	-4
-1	-1
0	0
1	-1
2	-4

x	y
-2	2
-1	$\frac{1}{2}$
0	0
1	$\frac{1}{2}$
2	2

Figure 29   **Figure 30**

The screen illustrates the three graphs considered in **Example 1** and **Figures 29** and **30.**

(b) Choose a value of x, and then find $g(x)$. The coefficient $\frac{1}{2}$ will cause the resulting value of $g(x)$ to be less than that of $f(x) = x^2$, making the parabola wider than the graph of $f(x) = x^2$. See **Figure 30.**

In both parabolas of this example, the axis is the vertical line $x = 0$, and the vertex is the origin $(0, 0)$. ∎

Vertical and horizontal shifts of the graph of $(x) = x^2$ are called **translations.**

EXAMPLE 2 Graphing a Quadratic Function (Vertical Shift)

Graph $g(x) = x^2 - 4$. Compare with the graph of $f(x) = x^2$.

Solution

By comparing the tables of values for $g(x) = x^2 - 4$ and $f(x) = x^2$ shown with **Figure 31,** we can see that for corresponding x-values, the y-values of g are each 4 less than those for f. This leads to a *vertical shift*. Thus, the graph of

$$g(x) = x^2 - 4$$

is the same as that of $f(x) = x^2$, but translated 4 units down. See **Figure 31.** The vertex of this parabola (here the lowest point) is at $(0, -4)$. The axis of the parabola is the vertical line $x = 0$.

Compare with **Figure 31.**

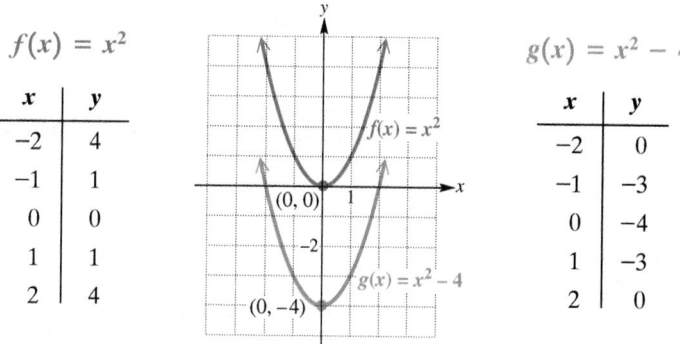

$f(x) = x^2$

x	y
-2	4
-1	1
0	0
1	1
2	4

$g(x) = x^2 - 4$

x	y
-2	0
-1	-3
0	-4
1	-3
2	0

Figure 31 ∎

EXAMPLE 3 Graphing a Quadratic Function (Horizontal Shift)

Graph $g(x) = (x - 4)^2$. Compare with the graph of $f(x) = x^2$.

Solution

Comparing the tables of values shown with **Figure 32** reveals that the graph of $g(x) = (x - 4)^2$ is the same as that of $f(x) = x^2$, but translated 4 units to the right. This is a *horizontal shift*. The vertex is at $(4, 0)$. As shown in **Figure 32,** the axis of this parabola is the vertical line $x = 4$.

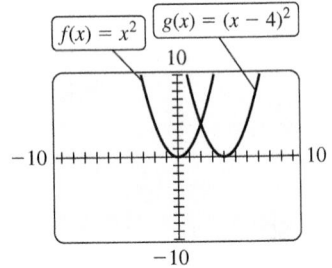

Compare with **Figure 32.**

$f(x) = x^2$

x	y
-2	4
-1	1
0	0
1	1
2	4

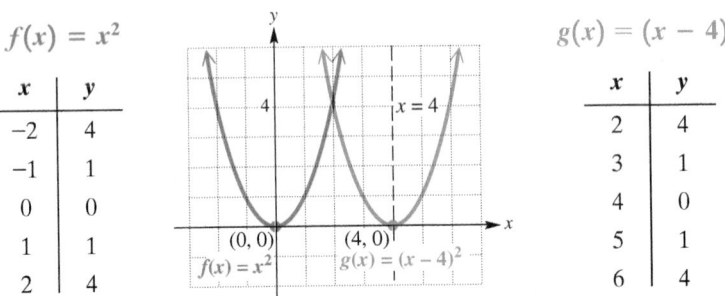

$g(x) = (x - 4)^2$

x	y
2	4
3	1
4	0
5	1
6	4

Figure 32

Errors frequently occur when horizontal shifts are involved. To determine the direction and magnitude of horizontal shifts, find the value of x that would cause the expression $x - h$ to equal 0. For example, in comparison to the graph of $y = x^2$, the graph of

$$f(x) = (x - 5)^2 \text{ would be shifted 5 units to the } right,$$

because $x = +5$ would cause $x - 5$ to equal 0. On the other hand, the graph of

$$f(x) = (x + 4)^2 \text{ would be shifted 4 units to the } left,$$

because $x = -4$ would cause $x + 4$ to equal 0.

GENERAL PRINCIPLES FOR GRAPHS OF QUADRATIC FUNCTIONS

1. The graph of the quadratic function
$$f(x) = a(x - h)^2 + k, \quad a \neq 0,$$
   is a parabola with vertex (h, k) and with the vertical line $x = h$ as axis.

2. The graph opens upward if a is positive and downward if a is negative.

3. The graph is wider than that of $y = x^2$ if $0 < |a| < 1$.
   The graph is narrower than that of $y = x^2$ if $|a| > 1$.

The trajectory of a shell fired from a cannon is a **parabola.** To reach the maximum range with a cannon, it is shown in calculus that the muzzle must be set at 45°. If the muzzle is elevated above 45°, the shell goes too high and falls too soon. If the muzzle is set below 45°, the shell is rapidly pulled to Earth by gravity.

EXAMPLE 4 Graphing a Quadratic Function Using General Principles

Graph $f(x) = -2(x + 3)^2 + 4$.

Solution

The parabola opens downward (because $a < 0$), and it is narrower than the graph of $f(x) = x^2$, since $a = -2$, and $|-2| > 1$. It has vertex at $(-3, 4)$, as shown in **Figure 33** on the next page. To complete the graph, we plotted the additional ordered pairs $(-4, 2)$ and $(-2, 2)$.

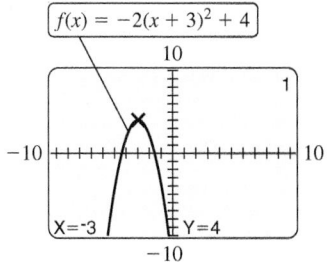

Compare with **Figure 33**. The vertex is $(-3, 4)$.

x	y
−4	2
−3	4
−2	2

Figure 33

Vertex of a Parabola

When the equation of a parabola is given in the form $f(x) = ax^2 + bx + c$, we can determine the vertex in two ways.

1. By completing the square (**Example 5**)

2. By using a formula that can be derived by completing the square (**Example 6**)

EXAMPLE 5 Finding the Vertex by Completing the Square

Find the vertex of the graph of $f(x) = x^2 - 4x + 5$.

Solution

To find the vertex, we need to express $x^2 - 4x + 5$ in the form $(x - h)^2 + k$. This is done by completing the square. (See **Chapter 7**.)

$$y = x^2 - 4x + 5 \qquad \text{Replace } f(x) \text{ with } y.$$

$$y - 5 = x^2 - 4x \qquad \text{Transform so that the constant term is on the left.}$$

$$y - 5 + 4 = x^2 - 4x + 4 \qquad \text{Half of } -4 \text{ is } -2; \ (-2)^2 = 4. \text{ Add 4 to both sides.}$$

$$y - 1 = (x - 2)^2 \qquad \text{Combine terms on the left, and factor on the right.}$$

$$y = (x - 2)^2 + 1 \qquad \text{Add 1 to both sides.}$$

Now write the original equation as $f(x) = (x - 2)^2 + 1$. As shown earlier, the vertex of this parabola is $(2, 1)$.

A formula for the vertex of the graph of a quadratic function can be found by completing the square for the general form of the equation $y = ax^2 + bx + c$. Using this process, we arrive at the following.

$$y = a\left[x - \underbrace{\left(-\frac{b}{2a}\right)}_{h}\right]^2 + \underbrace{\frac{4ac - b^2}{4a}}_{k} \qquad \begin{array}{l}\text{Write addition as subtraction} \\ \text{of the opposite in the brackets.}\end{array}$$

The final equation shows that the vertex (h, k) can be expressed in terms of a, b, and c. It is not necessary to memorize the expression for k, because it can be obtained by replacing x with $-\frac{b}{2a}$.

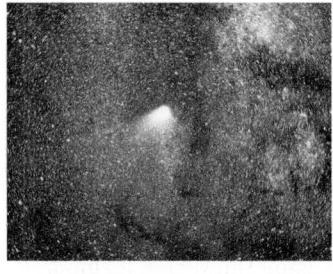

Johann Kepler (1571–1630) established the importance of a curve called an **ellipse** in 1609, when he discovered that the orbits of the planets around the sun were elliptical, not circular. The orbit of Halley's comet, shown here, also is elliptical.

See **For Further Thought** at the end of this section for more on ellipses.

VERTEX FORMULA

The vertex of the graph of $f(x) = ax^2 + bx + c \ (a \neq 0)$ has these coordinates.

$$\left(-\frac{b}{2a}, \ f\left(-\frac{b}{2a}\right)\right)$$

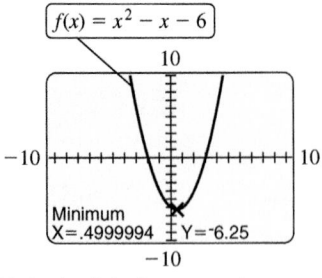

Notice the slight discrepancy when we instruct the calculator to find the vertex (a *minimum* here). This reinforces the fact that *we must understand the concepts and not totally rely on technology!*

EXAMPLE 6 Finding the Vertex Using the Formula

Use the vertex formula to find the vertex of the graph of the function

$$f(x) = x^2 - x - 6.$$

Solution

For $f(x) = x^2 - x - 6$, or $1x^2 - 1x - 6$, the values are $a = 1$, $b = -1$, and $c = -6$. The x-coordinate of the vertex of the parabola is given by

$$-\frac{b}{2a} = -\frac{(-1)}{2(1)} = \frac{1}{2}.$$

The y-coordinate is $f\left(-\frac{b}{2a}\right) = f\left(\frac{1}{2}\right)$.

$$f\left(\frac{1}{2}\right) = \left(\frac{1}{2}\right)^2 - \frac{1}{2} - 6 = \frac{1}{4} - \frac{1}{2} - 6 = -\frac{25}{4}$$

Finally, the vertex is $\left(\frac{1}{2}, -\frac{25}{4}\right)$. ∎

General Graphing Guidelines

We now examine a general approach to graphing quadratic functions using intercepts and the vertex.

GRAPHING A QUADRATIC FUNCTION $f(x) = ax^2 + bx + c$

Step 1 **Decide whether the graph opens upward or downward.** Determine whether the graph opens upward (if $a > 0$) or opens downward (if $a < 0$) to aid in the graphing process.

Step 2 **Find the vertex.** Find the vertex either by using the formula or by completing the square.

Step 3 **Find the y-intercept.** Find the y-intercept by evaluating $f(0)$.

Step 4 **Find the x-intercepts.** Find the x-intercepts, if any, by solving $f(x) = 0$.

Step 5 **Complete the graph.** Find and plot additional points as needed, using the symmetry about the axis.

Galileo Galilei (1564–1642) died in the year Newton was born. His work was important in Newton's development of calculus. The idea of **function** is implicit in Galileo's analysis of the parabolic path of a projectile, where height and range are functions (in our terms) of the angle of elevation and the initial velocity.

According to legend, Galileo dropped objects of different weights from the tower of Pisa to disprove the Aristotelian view that heavier objects fall faster than lighter objects. He developed a formula for freely falling objects that is described by

$$d = 16t^2,$$

where *d* is the distance in feet that a given object falls (discounting air resistance) in a given time *t*, in seconds, regardless of weight.

EXAMPLE 7 Graphing a Quadratic Function Using General Guidelines

Graph the quadratic function $f(x) = x^2 - x - 6$.

Solution

Step 1 From the equation, $a = 1 > 0$, so the graph of the function opens upward.

Step 2 The vertex, $\left(\frac{1}{2}, -\frac{25}{4}\right)$, was found in **Example 6** using the vertex formula.

Step 3 To find the y-intercept, evaluate $f(0)$.

$$f(x) = x^2 - x - 6$$

$$f(0) = 0^2 - 0 - 6 \quad \text{Let } x = 0.$$

$$f(0) = -6 \qquad \text{Simplify.}$$

The y-intercept is $(0, -6)$.

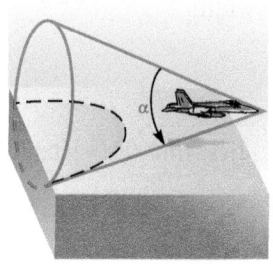

A sonic boom is a loud explosive sound caused by the shock wave that accompanies an aircraft traveling at supersonic speed. The sonic boom shock wave has the shape of a cone, and it intersects the ground in one branch of a curve known as a **hyperbola.** Everyone located along the hyperbolic curve on the ground hears the sound at the same time.

See **For Further Thought** on the next page for more on hyperbolas.

Step 4 Find any x-intercepts. Because the vertex $\left(\frac{1}{2}, -\frac{25}{4}\right)$ is in quadrant IV and the graph opens upward, there will be two x-intercepts. To find them, let $f(x) = 0$ and solve.

$$f(x) = x^2 - x - 6$$
$$0 = x^2 - x - 6 \qquad \text{Let } (x) = 0.$$
$$0 = (x - 3)(x + 2) \qquad \text{Factor.}$$
$$x - 3 = 0 \quad \text{or} \quad x + 2 = 0 \qquad \text{Zero-factor property (Section 7.7)}$$
$$x = 3 \quad \text{or} \qquad x = -2 \qquad \text{Solve for } x.$$

The x-intercepts are $(3, 0)$ and $(-2, 0)$.

Step 5 Plot the points found so far, and plot any additional points as needed. The symmetry of the graph is helpful here. The graph is shown in **Figure 34.**

x	y
-2	0
-1	-4
0	-6
$\frac{1}{2}$	$-\frac{25}{4}$
2	-4
3	0

Figure 34

A Model for Optimization

As we have seen, the vertex of a vertical parabola is either the highest or the lowest point of the parabola. The y-value of the vertex gives the maximum or minimum value of y, while the x-value tells where that maximum or minimum occurs. Often a model can be constructed so that y can be *optimized*.

Problem-Solving Strategy

We often want to know the least or greatest value of some quantity. When that quantity can be expressed using a quadratic function $f(x) = ax^2 + bx + c$, as in the next example, the vertex can be used to find the desired value.

EXAMPLE 8 Finding a Maximum Area

A farmer has 120 feet of fencing. He wants to put a fence around three sides of a rectangular plot of land, with the side of a barn forming the fourth side. Find the maximum area he can enclose. What dimensions give this area?

Solution

Figure 35 shows the enclosed area. Let x represent the width. Then, because there are 120 feet of fencing, we can represent the length in terms of x as follows.

$$x + x + \text{length} = 120 \qquad \text{Sum of the three fenced sides is 120 feet.}$$
$$2x + \text{length} = 120 \qquad \text{Combine terms.}$$
$$\text{length} = 120 - 2x \qquad \text{Subtract } 2x.$$

Figure 35

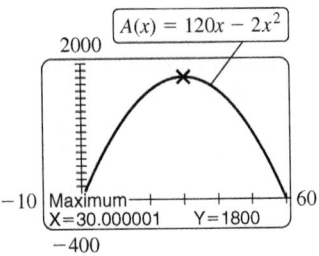

The vertex is (30, 1800), supporting the analytic result in **Example 8.**

The area $\mathscr{A}(x)$ is modeled by the product of the length and width.

$$\mathscr{A}(x) = (120 - 2x)x$$
$$= 120x - 2x^2$$

To make $120x - 2x^2$ (and thus the area) as large as possible, first find the vertex of the graph of the function $\mathscr{A}(x) = 120x - 2x^2$.

$$\mathscr{A}(x) = -2x^2 + 120x \qquad \text{Standard form}$$

Here we have $a = -2$ and $b = 120$. The x-coordinate of the vertex is

$$-\frac{b}{2a} = -\frac{120}{2(-2)} = 30.$$

The vertex of the parabola is (30, 1800). The vertex is a maximum point (since $a = -2 < 0$), so the maximum area that the farmer can enclose is

$$\mathscr{A}(30) = -2(30)^2 + 120(30) = 1800 \quad \text{square feet.}$$

The farmer can enclose a maximum area of 1800 square feet, when the width of the plot is 30 feet and the length is $120 - 2(30) = 60$ feet. ∎

> *Be careful when interpreting the meanings of the coordinates of the vertex in problems involving maximum or minimum values.* Read the problem carefully to determine whether you are asked to find the value of the independent variable, the value of the dependent variable (that is, the function value), or both.

FOR FURTHER THOUGHT

The Conic Sections

The circle, introduced in the first section of this chapter, the parabola, the ellipse, and the hyperbola are known as **conic sections.** As seen in **Figure 36,** each of these geometric shapes can be obtained when a plane and an infinite cone (made up of two *nappes*) intersect.

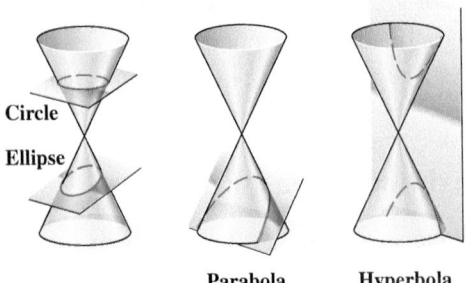

Figure 36

The Greek geometer Apollonius (c. 225 B.C.) was also an astronomer, and his classic work *Conic Sections* thoroughly investigated these figures. Apollonius is responsible for the names "ellipse," "parabola," and "hyperbola." The margin notes in this section show some ways that these figures appear in the world around us.

For Group or Individual Investigation

1. The terms "ellipse," "parabola," and "hyperbola" are similar to the terms "ellipsis," "parable," and "hyperbole." What do these latter three terms mean? You might want to investigate the similarities between the mathematical terminology and these language-related terms.

2. Identify some places in the world around you where conic sections are encountered.

3. The accompanying photo shows how an ellipse can be drawn using tacks and string. Have a class member volunteer to go to the board and, using string and chalk, modify the method to draw a circle. Then have two class members work together to draw an ellipse. (*Hint:* Press hard!)

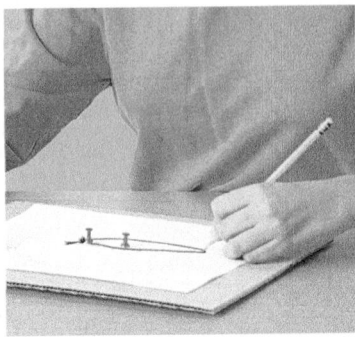

8.5   EXERCISES

In Exercises 1–6, match each equation with the figure in A–F that most closely resembles its graph.

A.   **B.**   **C.**

D.   **E.**   **F.**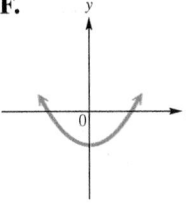

1. $f(x) = x^2 - 5$ **2.** $f(x) = -x^2 + 4$

3. $f(x) = (x - 1)^2$ **4.** $f(x) = (x + 1)^2$

5. $f(x) = (x - 1)^2 + 1$ **6.** $f(x) = (x + 1)^2 + 1$

Identify the vertex of the graph of each quadratic function.

7. $f(x) = -3x^2$ **8.** $f(x) = -0.5x^2$

9. $f(x) = x^2 + 4$ **10.** $f(x) = x^2 - 4$

11. $f(x) = (x - 1)^2$ **12.** $f(x) = (x + 3)^2$

13. $f(x) = (x + 3)^2 - 4$ **14.** $f(x) = (x - 5)^2 - 8$

For each quadratic function, tell whether the graph opens upward or downward, and tell whether the graph is wider than, narrower than, or the same as the graph of $f(x) = x^2$.

15. $f(x) = -2x^2$ **16.** $f(x) = -3x^2 + 1$

17. $f(x) = 0.5x^2$ **18.** $f(x) = \frac{2}{3}x^2 - 4$

Sketch the graph of each quadratic function using the methods described in this section. Indicate the vertex and two additional points on each graph.

19. $f(x) = 3x^2$ **20.** $f(x) = -2x^2$

21. $f(x) = -\frac{1}{4}x^2$ **22.** $f(x) = \frac{1}{3}x^2$

23. $f(x) = x^2 - 1$ **24.** $f(x) = x^2 + 3$

25. $f(x) = -x^2 + 2$ **26.** $f(x) = -x^2 - 4$

27. $f(x) = 2x^2 - 2$ **28.** $f(x) = -3x^2 + 1$

29. $f(x) = (x - 4)^2$ **30.** $f(x) = (x - 3)^2$

31. $f(x) = 3(x + 1)^2$ **32.** $f(x) = -2(x + 1)^2$

33. $f(x) = (x + 1)^2 - 2$ **34.** $f(x) = (x - 2)^2 + 3$

Sketch the graph of each quadratic function. Indicate the coordinates of the vertex of the graph.

35. $f(x) = x^2 + 8x + 14$ **36.** $f(x) = x^2 + 10x + 23$

37. $f(x) = x^2 + 2x - 4$ **38.** $f(x) = 3x^2 - 9x + 8$

39. $f(x) = -2x^2 + 4x + 5$ **40.** $f(x) = -5x^2 - 10x + 2$

Solve each problem.

41. *Dimensions of an Exercise Run*   Steve has 100 meters of fencing material to enclose a rectangular exercise run for his dog. What width will give the enclosure the maximum area? What is the enclosed area?

42. *Dimensions of a Parking Lot*   Morgan's Department Store wants to construct a rectangular parking lot on land bordered on one side by a highway. It has 280 feet of fencing that is to be used to fence off the other three sides. What should be the dimensions of the lot if the enclosed area is to be a maximum? What is the maximum area?

43. *Height of a Projected Object*   If an object on Earth is projected upward with an initial velocity of 32 feet per second, then its height after x seconds is given by

$$f(x) = -16x^2 + 32x.$$

Find the maximum height attained by the object and the number of seconds it takes to hit the ground.

44. *Height of a Projected Object*   A projectile on Earth is fired straight upward so that its distance (in feet) above the ground x seconds after firing is given by

$$f(x) = -16x^2 + 400x.$$

Find the maximum height it reaches and the number of seconds it takes to reach that height.

45. *Height of a Projected Object*   If air resistance is neglected, a projectile on Earth shot straight upward with an initial velocity of 40 meters per second will be at a height s (in meters) given by the function

$$f(x) = -4.9x^2 + 40x,$$

where x is the number of seconds elapsed after projection. After how many seconds will it reach its maximum height, and what is this maximum height? Round your answers to the nearest tenth.

46. *Height of a Projected Object* A space robot is projected from the moon with its height (in feet) given by

$$f(x) = -0.0013x^2 + 1.727x,$$

where x is time in seconds. Find the maximum height the robot can reach and the time it takes to get there. Round answers to the nearest tenth.

47. *Automobile Stopping Distance* Selected values of the stopping distance y (in feet) of a car traveling x mph are given in the table.

Speed x (in mph)	Stopping Distance y (in feet)
20	46
30	87
40	140
50	240
60	282
70	371

Source: National Safety Institute Student Workbook.

The quadratic function

$$y = f(x) = 0.056057x^2 + 1.06657x$$

is one model of the data. Find and interpret $f(45)$.

48. *Path of an Object on a Planet* When an object moves under the influence of constant force (without air resistance), its path is parabolic. This is the path of a ball thrown near the surface of a planet or other celestial object. Suppose two balls are simultaneously thrown upward at a 45° angle on two different planets. If their initial velocities are both 30 mph, then their rectangular coordinates (in feet) can be determined by the function

$$f(x) = x - \frac{g}{1922}x^2,$$

where g is the acceleration due to gravity. The value of g will vary with the mass and size of the planet. (*Source:* Zeilik, M., S. Gregory, and E. Smith, *Introductory Astronomy and Astrophysics*, Saunders College Publishers.)

On Earth, $g = 32.2$, and on Mars, $g = 12.6$. Find the two equations, and determine the difference in the horizontal distances traveled by the two balls.

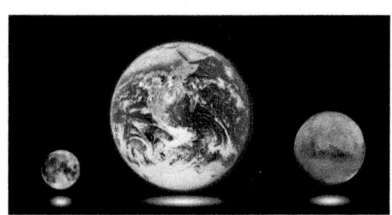

8.6 EXPONENTIAL AND LOGARITHMIC FUNCTIONS, GRAPHS, AND MODELS

OBJECTIVES

1 Know the meanings of the terms *exponential function, horizontal asymptote, logarithmic function,* and *vertical asymptote.*

2 Find powers of the number *e* using a calculator.

3 Use the compound interest formulas.

4 Find the natural logarithm of a number using a calculator.

5 Use doubling time and half-life in applications of exponential growth and decay.

Exponential Functions and Applications

In this section we introduce two new types of functions: *exponential* and *logarithmic.*

EXPONENTIAL FUNCTION

An **exponential function with base b,** where $b > 0$ and $b \neq 1$, is a function f of the following form.

$$f(x) = b^x, \quad \text{where } x \text{ is any real number}$$

Notice that in the definition of exponential function, the base b is restricted to positive numbers, with b ≠ 1.

Thus far, we have defined only integer exponents. In the definition of exponential function, we allow x to take on any real number value. By using methods not discussed in this text, expressions such as

$$2^{9/7}, \quad \left(\frac{1}{2}\right)^{1.5}, \quad \text{and} \quad 10^{\sqrt{3}}$$

can be approximated. A scientific or graphing calculator is capable of determining approximations for these numbers.

The graphs of $f(x) = 2^x$, $g(x) = \left(\frac{1}{2}\right)^x$, and $h(x) = 10^x$ are shown in **Figure 37.** In each case, a table of selected points is given. The points are joined with a smooth curve. For each graph, the curve approaches but does not intersect the x-axis. For this reason, the x-axis is called the **horizontal asymptote** of the graph.

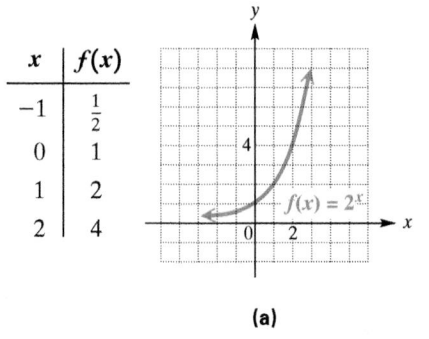

x	$f(x)$
-1	$\frac{1}{2}$
0	1
1	2
2	4

(a)

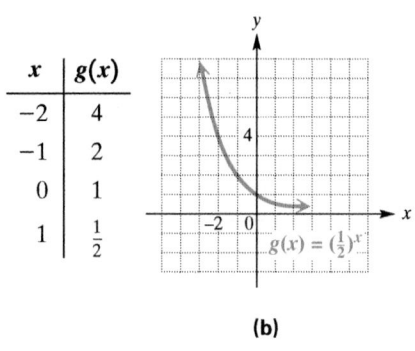

x	$g(x)$
-2	4
-1	2
0	1
1	$\frac{1}{2}$

(b)

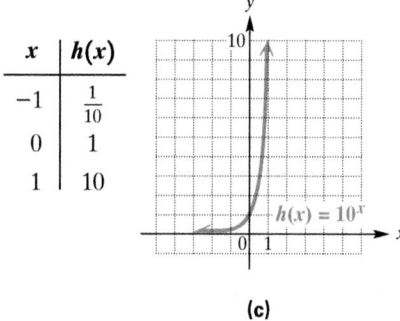

x	$h(x)$
-1	$\frac{1}{10}$
0	1
1	10

(c)

Figure 37

CHARACTERISTICS OF THE GRAPH OF $f(x) = b^x$

1. The graph always will contain the point $(0, 1)$, because $b^0 = 1$.

2. When $b > 1$, the graph will *rise* from left to right (as in **Figures 37(a) and (c)** above, with $b = 2$ and $b = 10$).

   When $0 < b < 1$, the graph will *fall* from left to right (as in **Figure 37(b)**, with $b = \frac{1}{2}$).

3. The x-axis is the horizontal asymptote.

4. The domain is $(-\infty, \infty)$ and the range is $(0, \infty)$.

The **natural exponential function** has the base e. (See **Section 6.4.**) The number e is named after Leonhard Euler (1707–1783) and is approximately 2.718281828. It is an irrational number. As n gets larger without bound,

$$\left(1 + \frac{1}{n}\right)^n \text{ approaches } e.$$

This is expressed as follows.

$$\text{As } n \to \infty, \quad \left(1 + \frac{1}{n}\right)^n \to e \approx 2.718281828.$$

See **Table 3.**

Table 3

n	Approximate Value of $\left(1 + \frac{1}{n}\right)^n$
1	2
100	2.70481
1000	2.71692
10,000	2.71815
1,000,000	2.71828

$2^{9/7}$	
	2.438027308
$(1/2)^{1.5}$	
	.3535533906
$10^{\sqrt{3}}$	
	53.95737429

Compare with the discussion in the text.

X	Y_1
1	2
10	2.5937
100	2.7048
1000	2.7169
10000	2.7181
100000	2.7183
1E6	2.7183

$Y_1 = (1+1/X)^\wedge(X)$

This table shows selected values for $Y_1 = \left(1 + \frac{1}{X}\right)^X$. Compare with **Table 3.**

Powers of e can be approximated on a scientific or graphing calculator. Some powers of e obtained on a calculator are

$$e^{-2} \approx 0.1353352832, \quad e^{1.3} \approx 3.669296668, \quad e^4 \approx 54.59815003.$$

The graph of the function $f(x) = e^x$ is shown in **Figure 38.**

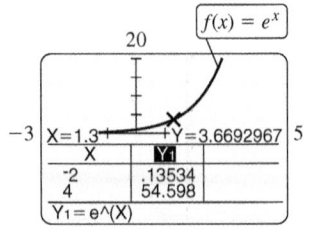

The values for e^{-2}, $e^{1.3}$, and e^4 are approximated in this split-screen graph of $f(x) = e^x$.

x	y
-1	≈ 0.37
0	1
1	≈ 2.72

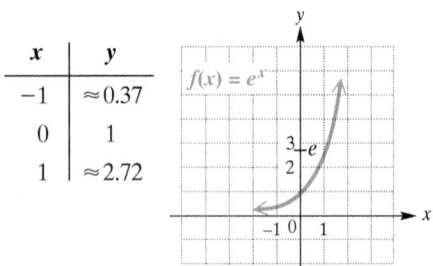

Figure 38

A real-life application of exponential functions occurs in the computation of **compound interest.**

COMPOUND INTEREST FORMULA

Suppose that a principal of P dollars is invested at an annual interest rate r (in percent, expressed as a decimal), compounded n times per year. Then the amount A accumulated after t years is given by the following formula.

$$A = P\left(1 + \frac{r}{n}\right)^{nt}$$

EXAMPLE 1 Applying the Compound Interest Formula

Suppose that $1000 is invested at an annual rate of 2%, compounded quarterly (four times per year). Find the total amount in the account after ten years if no withdrawals are made.

Solution

$$A = P\left(1 + \frac{r}{n}\right)^{nt} \qquad \text{Compound interest formula}$$

$$A = 1000\left(1 + \frac{0.02}{4}\right)^{4 \cdot 10} \qquad P = 1000, \, r = 0.02, \, n = 4, \, t = 10$$

$$A = 1000\,(1.005)^{40} \qquad \text{Simplify.}$$

$$A \approx 1000\,(1.22079) \qquad \text{Evaluate } 1.005^{40} \text{ with a calculator.}$$

$\approx$ means "is approximately equal to."

$$A = 1220.79 \qquad \text{To the nearest cent}$$

There would be $1220.79 in the account at the end of ten years. ∎

The compounding formula given earlier applies if the financial institution compounds interest for a finite number of compounding periods annually. Theoretically, the number of compounding periods per year can get larger and larger (quarterly, monthly, daily, etc.), and if n is allowed to approach infinity, we say that interest is compounded *continuously*. The formula for **continuous compounding** involves the number e.

CONTINUOUS COMPOUND INTEREST FORMULA

Suppose that a principal of P dollars is invested at an annual interest rate r (in percent, expressed as a decimal), compounded continuously. Then the amount A accumulated after t years is given by the following formula.

$$A = Pe^{rt}$$

EXAMPLE 2 Applying the Continuous Compound Interest Formula

Suppose that $5000 is invested at an annual rate of 2.5%, compounded continuously. Find the total amount in the account after four years if no withdrawals are made.

Solution

$A = Pe^{rt}$	Continuous compound interest formula
$A = 5000e^{0.025(4)}$	$P = 5000, r = 0.025, t = 4$
$A = 5000\,e^{0.1}$	Simplify.
$A \approx 5000\,(1.10517)$	Use the e^x key on a calculator.
$A = 5525.85$	To the nearest cent

There will be $5525.85 in the account after four years.   ∎

The continuous compound interest formula is an example of an **exponential growth function.** In situations involving growth or decay of a quantity, the amount or number present at time t can often be approximated by a function of the form

$$A(t) = A_0 e^{kt},$$

If $k > 0$, there is exponential *growth.*
If $k < 0$, there is exponential *decay.*

where A_0 represents the amount or number present at time $t = 0$, and k is a constant.

Logarithmic Functions and Applications

Consider the statement

$$2^3 = 8.$$

Here 3 is the exponent (or power) to which the base 2 must be raised in order to obtain 8. The exponent 3 is called the base-2 **logarithm** of 8, and this is written

$$3 = \log_2 8.$$

In general, we have the following relationship.

DEFINITION OF $\log_b x$

For $b > 0, b \neq 1$:

If $b^y = x,$ then $y = \log_b x.$

Here $\log_b x$ is the exponent to which b must be raised in order to obtain x.

A variation of **exponential growth** is found in the legend of a Persian king, who wanted to please his executive officer, the Grand Vizier, with a gift of his choice. The Grand Vizier explained that he would like to be able to use his chessboard to accumulate wheat. A single grain of wheat would be received for the first square on the board, two grains would be received for the second square, four grains for the third, and so on, doubling the number of grains for each of the 64 squares on the board. As unlikely as it may seem, the number of grains would total 18.5 quintillion!

Table 4 illustrates the relationship between exponential equations and logarithmic equations.

Table 4

Exponential Equation	Logarithmic Equation
$3^4 = 81$	$4 = \log_3 81$
$10^5 = 100{,}000$	$5 = \log_{10} 100{,}000$
$\left(\frac{1}{2}\right)^{-4} = 16$	$-4 = \log_{1/2} 16$
$10^0 = 1$	$0 = \log_{10} 1$
$4^{-3} = \frac{1}{64}$	$-3 = \log_4 \frac{1}{64}$

> A logarithm is an exponent.

The concept of inverse functions (studied in more advanced algebra courses) leads us to the definition of a second new function.

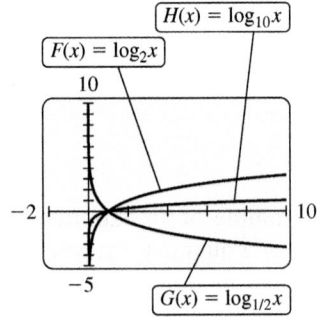

Compare with **Figure 39**. Graphs of logarithmic functions with bases other than 10 and e are obtained with the use of the **change-of-base rule:**

$$\log_a x = \frac{\log x}{\log a} = \frac{\ln x}{\ln a}.$$

Alternatively, they can be drawn by using the capability that allows the user to obtain the graph of the inverse.

Note that log x denotes $\log_{10} x$ and ln x denotes $\log_e x$.

LOGARITHMIC FUNCTION

A **logarithmic function with base b,** where $b > 0$ and $b \neq 1$, is a function g of the following form.

$$g(x) = \log_b x, \quad \text{where } x > 0$$

The graph of the function $g(x) = \log_b x$ can be found by interchanging the roles of x and y in the function $f(x) = b^x$. Geometrically, this is accomplished by reflecting the graph of $f(x) = b^x$ about the line $y = x$.

The graphs of

$$F(x) = \log_2 x, \quad G(x) = \log_{1/2} x, \quad \text{and} \quad H(x) = \log_{10} x$$

are shown in **Figure 39**. The points in each table were obtained by interchanging the roles of x and y in the tables of points given in **Figure 37**. The points are joined with a smooth curve, typical of the graphs of logarithmic functions. For each graph, the curve approaches but does not intersect the y-axis. Thus, the y-axis is called the **vertical asymptote** of the graph.

Figure 39

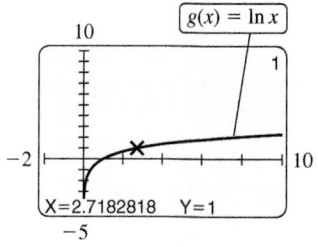

Notice that when

$$x = e \approx 2.7182818,$$
$$y = \ln e = 1.$$

CHARACTERISTICS OF THE GRAPH OF $g(x) = \log_b x$

1. The graph will always contain the point $(1, 0)$, because $\log_b 1 = 0$.

2. When $b > 1$, the graph will *rise* from left to right, from the fourth quadrant to the first (as in **Figure 39(a) and (c),** with $b = 2$ and $b = 10$).

   When $0 < b < 1$, the graph will *fall* from left to right, from the first quadrant to the fourth (as in **Figure 39(b),** with $b = \frac{1}{2}$).

3. The y-axis is the vertical asymptote.

4. The domain is $(0, \infty)$ and the range is $(-\infty, \infty)$.

An important logarithmic function is the function with base e. If we interchange the roles of x and y in the graph of

$$f(x) = e^x \quad \textbf{(Figure 38),}$$

we obtain the graph of $g(x) = \log_e x$. The special symbol for the base-e logarithm of x is $\ln x$. That is,

$$\textbf{ln } x = \log_e x.$$

Figure 40 shows the graph of $g(x) = \ln x$, which is called the **natural logarithmic function.**

The number _e_ is named in honor of Leonhard Euler (1707–1783), the prolific Swiss mathematician. The value of _e_ can be expressed as an **infinite series.**

$$e = 1 + \frac{1}{1} + \frac{1}{1 \cdot 2}$$
$$+ \frac{1}{1 \cdot 2 \cdot 3}$$
$$+ \frac{1}{1 \cdot 2 \cdot 3 \cdot 4} + \cdots$$

It can also be expressed using a **continued fraction.**

$$e = 2 + \cfrac{1}{1 + \cfrac{1}{2 + \cfrac{2}{3 + \cfrac{3}{4 + \cfrac{4}{\ddots}}}}}$$

x	y
≈ 0.37	-1
1	0
≈ 2.72	1

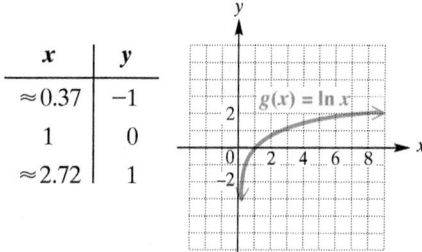

Figure 40

The expression $\ln e^k$ is the unique exponent to which the base e must be raised in order to obtain e^k. Thus, for all real numbers k,

$$\textbf{ln } e^k = k. \quad \text{This will be used in applications to follow.}$$

The expression **log x,** which does not indicate a base, is understood to be the base ten, or **common logarithm,** of x. Common logarithms were devised hundreds of years ago to assist scientists in performing involved calculations. They are still used in some modern applications, such as measurement of earthquakes on the Richter scale, and the measure of acidity or alkalinity of substances in chemistry (pH).

Exponential Models

If an amount of money is left on deposit and not touched, the amount of time it takes for the money to double at a particular interest rate is the **doubling time.**

EXAMPLE 3 Finding the Time for an Amount to Double

Suppose that a certain amount P is invested at an annual rate of 3.5%, compounded continuously. How long will it take for the amount to double?

Solution

We must find the value of t in the continuous compound interest formula that will make A equal to $2P$ (because we want the initial investment, P, to double).

$A = Pe^{rt}$ Continuous compound interest formula

$2P = Pe^{0.035t}$ Substitute $2P$ for A and 0.035 for r.

$2 = e^{0.035t}$ Divide both sides by P.

$\ln 2 = \ln e^{0.035t}$ Take the natural logarithm of both sides.

$\ln 2 = 0.035t$ Use the fact that $\ln e^k = k$.

$t = \dfrac{\ln 2}{0.035}$ Divide both sides by 0.035.

A calculator shows that $\ln 2 \approx 0.6931471806$. Dividing this by 0.035 gives

$$t \approx 19.8$$

to the nearest tenth. Therefore, it will take about 19.8 years for any initial investment P to double under the given conditions.   ■

Further Applications

EXAMPLE 4 Modeling Population Growth

According to the U.S. Census Bureau, the world population reached 6 billion people in 1999 and was growing exponentially. By the end of 2010, the population had grown to 6.947 billion. The projected world population (in billions of people) x years after 2010 is given by the function

$$f(x) = 6.947e^{0.00745x}.$$

(a) Based on this model, what will the world population be in 2020?

(b) Based on this model, in what year will the world population reach 8 billion?

Solution

(a) Since $x = 0$ represents the year 2010, in 2020 the value of x will be $2020 - 2010 = 10$. We find $f(x)$ when x is 10.

$f(x) = 6.947e^{0.00745x}$ Given function

$f(10) = 6.947e^{0.00745(10)}$ Let $x = 10$.

≈ 7.484 Use a calculator.

According to this model, the population will be 7.484 billion in 2020.

(b) $f(x) = 6.947e^{0.00745x}$ Given function

$8 = 6.947e^{0.00745x}$ Let $f(x) = 8$.

$\dfrac{8}{6.947} = e^{0.00745x}$ Divide by 6.947.

$$\ln\left(\frac{8}{6.947}\right) = \ln\ e^{0.00745x} \quad \text{Take natural logarithms on both sides.}$$

$$\ln\left(\frac{8}{6.947}\right) = 0.00745x \quad \text{In } e^x = x$$

$$x = \frac{\ln\left(\frac{8}{6.947}\right)}{0.00745} \quad \text{Divide by 0.00745; rewrite.}$$

$$x \approx 18.9 \quad \text{Use a calculator.}$$

According to this model, the world population will reach 8 billion about 19 years after 2010, or in 2029.   ■

Radioactive materials disintegrate according to exponential decay functions. The **half-life** of a substance that decays exponentially is the amount of time that it takes for the amount to decay to half its initial value.

EXAMPLE 5 Carbon-14 Dating

Carbon-14 is a radioactive form of carbon that is found in all living plants and animals. After a plant or animal dies, the radiocarbon disintegrates. Scientists determine the age of the remains by comparing the amount of carbon-14 present with the amount found in living plants and animals. The amount of carbon-14 present after x years is modeled by the exponential function

$$f(x) = A_0 e^{-0.0001216x},$$

where A_0 represents the initial amount.

(a) What is the half-life of carbon-14?

(b) If an initial sample contains 1 gram of carbon-14, how much will be left after 10,000 years?

Solution

(a) To find the half-life, let $f(x) = \frac{1}{2}A_0$ in the equation.

$$\frac{1}{2}A_0 = A_0 e^{-0.0001216x} \quad \text{Let } f(x) = \frac{1}{2}A_0.$$

$$\frac{1}{2} = e^{-0.0001216x} \quad \text{Divide by } A_0.$$

$$\ln\left(\frac{1}{2}\right) = -0.0001216x \quad \text{Take natural logarithms on both sides.}$$

$$x \approx 5700 \quad \text{Use a calculator.}$$

The half-life of carbon-14 is about 5700 years.

(b) Evaluate $f(x)$ for $x = 10{,}000$ and $y_0 = 1$.

$$f(10{,}000) = 1e^{-0.0001216(10{,}000)} \approx 0.30 \quad \text{Use a calculator.}$$

There will be about 0.30 gram remaining.   ■

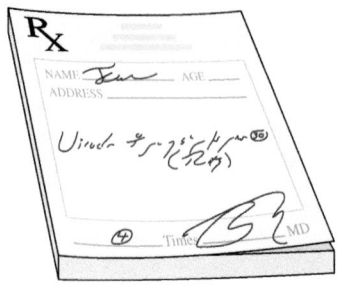

EXAMPLE 6 Determining a Time Interval

The concentration of a drug injected into the bloodstream decreases with time. The intervals of time T, in hours, at which the drug should be administered are given by

$$T = \frac{1}{k} \ln \frac{C_2}{C_1},$$

where k is a constant determined by the drug in use, C_2 is the concentration at which the drug is harmful, and C_1 is the concentration below which the drug is ineffective. (*Source:* Horelick, Brindell, and Sinan Koont, "Applications of Calculus to Medicine: Prescribing Safe and Effective Dosage, *UMAP Module 202.*)

For a certain drug, $k = \frac{1}{3}$, $C_2 = 5$, and $C_1 = 2$. How often should the drug be administered? Round down to the nearest hour.

Solution

$$T = \frac{1}{k} \ln \frac{C_2}{C_1}$$

$$T = \frac{1}{\frac{1}{3}} \ln \frac{5}{2} \qquad \text{Let } k = \frac{1}{3}, \ C_2 = 5, \text{ and } C_1 = 2 \text{ in the formula.}$$

$$T = 3 \ln 2.5$$

$$T = 2.75 \qquad \text{Use a calculator, and round to the nearest hundredth.}$$

Round the value of T down to the nearest hour to find that the drug should be administered every 2 hours. ∎

WHEN Will I Ever USE This ?

When destructive earthquakes occur around the world, news agencies report their magnitudes using the Richter scale. The scale was devised by Charles F. Richter in 1935 at the California Institute of Technology. It is a base-ten logarithmic scale, which means that each unit increase in the measure represents a 10-fold increase in intensity. For example, an earthquake measuring 6.0 on this scale releases ten times as much energy as one that measures 5.0.

> How can we determine the comparative energy release
> between two earthquakes?
>
> Suppose that we hear on a cable news network that an earthquake measuring 5.7 occurred in southern California, followed by an aftershock that measured 5.4. *How do these compare?* Because these measures are exponents on the base 10, we evaluate the quotient $\frac{10^{5.7}}{10^{5.4}}$. Logarithms are exponents, so they follow the same rules as other exponents. We subtract the exponents to get $10^{0.3}$. Use a calculator (if you have a smartphone, there's one there) to raise 10 to the power 0.3 and obtain approximately 1.995, which is very close to 2. This means that the earthquake was about twice as powerful as its aftershock.
>
> Verify that the 9.1 earthquake that caused the tsunami that devastated Japan in 2010 was about 250 times as powerful as the 6.7 Northridge earthquake that struck the Los Angeles area in 1994.

8.6 EXERCISES

To the student: The number of digits shown for calculator approximations in the exercises will vary depending on the model of calculator used.

Fill in each blank with the correct response.

1. For an exponential function $f(x) = a^x$, if $a > 1$, the graph _____ from left to right. If $0 < a < 1$, the (rises/falls)
   graph _____ from left to right. (rises/falls)

2. The y-intercept of the graph of $f(x) = a^x$ is _____.

3. The graph of the exponential function $f(x) = a^x$ _____ have an x-intercept. (does/does not)

4. The point $(2, \_\_\_)$ is on the graph of $f(x) = 4^x$.

5. For a logarithmic function $g(x) = \log_a x$, if $a > 1$, the graph _____ from left to right. If $0 < a < 1$, the (rises/falls)
   graph _____ from left to right. (rises/falls)

6. The x-intercept of the graph of $y = \log_a x$ is _____.

7. The graph of the logarithmic function $g(x) = \log_a x$ _____ have a y-intercept. (does/does not)

8. The point $(100, \_\_\_)$ lies on the graph of $g(x) = \log_{10} x$.

Use a calculator to find an approximation for each number. Give as many digits as the calculator displays.

9. $9^{3/7}$

10. $14^{2/7}$

11. $(0.83)^{-1.2}$

12. $(0.97)^{3.4}$

13. $\left(\sqrt{6}\right)^{\sqrt{5}}$

14. $\left(\sqrt{7}\right)^{\sqrt{3}}$

15. $\left(\frac{1}{3}\right)^{9.8}$

16. $\left(\frac{2}{5}\right)^{8.1}$

Sketch the graph of each function.

17. $f(x) = 3^x$

18. $f(x) = 5^x$

19. $f(x) = \left(\frac{1}{4}\right)^x$

20. $f(x) = \left(\frac{1}{3}\right)^x$

Use a calculator to approximate each number. Give as many digits as the calculator displays.

21. e^3

22. e^4

23. e^{-4}

24. e^{-3}

In Exercises 25–28, rewrite the exponential equation as a logarithmic equation. In Exercises 29–32, rewrite the logarithmic equation as an exponential equation.

25. $4^2 = 16$

26. $5^3 = 125$

27. $\left(\frac{2}{3}\right)^{-3} = \frac{27}{8}$

28. $\left(\frac{1}{10}\right)^{-4} = 10{,}000$

29. $5 = \log_2 32$

30. $3 = \log_4 64$

31. $1 = \log_3 3$

32. $0 = \log_{12} 1$

Use a calculator to approximate each number. Give as many digits as the calculator displays.

33. $\ln 4$

34. $\ln 6$

35. $\ln 0.35$

36. $\ln 2.45$

Sketch the graph of each function. (Hint: Use the graphs of the exponential functions in Exercises 17–20 to help.)

37. $g(x) = \log_3 x$

38. $g(x) = \log_5 x$

39. $g(x) = \log_{1/4} x$

40. $g(x) = \log_{1/3} x$

Investment *Determine the amount of money that will be accumulated in an account that pays compound interest, given the initial principal in each of the following.*

41. $20,000 invested at 3% annual interest for 4 years compounded **(a)** annually; **(b)** semiannually.

42. $35,000 invested at 2.2% annual interest for 3 years compounded **(a)** annually; **(b)** quarterly.

43. $27,500 invested at 2.95% annual interest for 5 years compounded **(a)** daily ($n = 365$); **(b)** continuously.

44. $15,800 invested at 1.6% annual interest for 6.5 years compounded **(a)** quarterly; **(b)** continuously.

Comparing Investment Plans *In Exercises 45 and 46, decide which of the two plans will provide a better yield. (Interest rates stated are annual rates.)*

45. *Plan A:* $40,000 invested for 3 years at 1.5%, compounded quarterly

Plan B: $40,000 invested for 3 years at 1.4%, compounded continuously

46. *Plan A:* $50,000 invested for 10 years at 1.75%, compounded daily ($n = 365$)

Plan B: $50,000 invested for 10 years at 1.7%, compounded continuously

47. ***Comparing Investments*** Ronnie wants to invest $60,000 in a pension plan. One investment offers 7% compounded quarterly. Another offers 6.75% compounded continuously.

(a) Which investment will earn more interest in 5 years?

(b) How much more will the better plan earn?

48. ***Growth of an Account*** If Ronnie (see **Exercise 47**) chooses the plan with continuous compounding, how long will it take for his $60,000 to grow to $80,000?

Solve each problem.

49. ***Doubling Time*** Find the doubling time of an investment earning 2.5% annual interest if interest is compounded continuously.

50. ***Tripling Time*** Find the time it would take the investment in **Exercise 49** to triple.

51. ***Growth of an Account*** How long will it take an investment of $1000 to grow to $1500, if interest is compounded continuously at 3% annually?

52. ***Growth of an Account*** What annual interest rate is required for an investment of $1000 to grow to $1200 in 4 years, if interest is compounded continuously?

53. ***World Population Growth*** As seen in **Example 4,** the world population in billions closely fits the exponential function

$$f(x) = 6.947e^{0.00745x},$$

where x is the number of years after 2010.

(a) Predict the population in 2018.

(b) Predict when the population will reach 8.5 billion.

54. ***Atmospheric Pressure*** The atmospheric pressure (in millibars) at a given altitude x (in meters) is approximated by the function

$$f(x) = 1013e^{-0.0001341x}.$$

Give answers to the nearest unit.

(a) Predict the atmospheric pressure at 1500 meters.

(b) Predict the atmospheric pressure at 11,000 meters.

55. ***Carbon-14 Dating*** Suppose an Egyptian mummy is discovered in which the amount of carbon-14 present is only about one-third the amount found in living human beings. About how long ago did the Egyptian die?

56. ***Carbon-14 Dating*** A sample from a refuse deposit near the Strait of Magellan had 60% of the carbon-14 of a contemporary living sample. How old was the sample?

57. ***Decay of Lead*** A sample of 500 grams of radioactive lead-210 decays to polonium-210 according to the function

$$f(x) = 500e^{-0.032x},$$

where x is time in years. Find the amount of the sample remaining after

(a) 4 years   **(b)** 8 years

(c) 20 years   **(d)** Find the half-life.

58. ***Decay of Plutonium*** Repeat **Exercise 57** for 500 grams of plutonium-241, which decays according to this function, where x is time in years.

$$f(x) = A_0e^{-0.053x}$$

59. ***Decay of Radium*** Find the half-life of radium-226, which decays according to this function, where x is time in years.

$$f(x) = A_0 e^{-0.00043x}$$

60. ***Decay of Iodine*** How long will it take any quantity of iodine-131 to decay to 25% of its initial amount, given that it decays according to this function, where x is time in days?

$$f(x) = A_0 e^{-0.087x}$$

Time Intervals for Drugs *Use the formula given in **Example 6** to determine how often the drug with the given values should be administered. Round down to the nearest hour.*

61. $k = \dfrac{1}{4}$, $C_2 = 6$, $C_1 = 2$ **62.** $k = \dfrac{1}{2}$, $C_2 = 4$, $C_1 = 2$

Climate Change *In 1990 a major scientific periodical published an article dealing with the problem of climate change. The article was accompanied by a graph that illustrated two possible scenarios.*

(a) *The change might be modeled by an exponential function of the form*

$$f(x) = (1.046 \times 10^{-38})(1.0444^x).$$

(b) *The change might be modeled by a linear function of the form*

$$g(x) = 0.009x - 17.67.$$

In both cases, x represents the year, and the function value represents the increase in degrees Celsius. Use these functions to approximate the increase in temperature for each of the following years.

63. 2000   **64.** 2010

65. 2020   **66.** 2040

8.7   SYSTEMS OF LINEAR EQUATIONS

OBJECTIVES

1 Know the meaning of *system of linear equations.*

2 Identify the solution of a system of linear equations from a graph, and classify the system.

3 Solve a system of two linear equations in two variables using the elimination method.

4 Solve a system of two linear equations in two variables using the substitution method.

Linear Systems

In recent years, the number of Americans aged 7 and over participating in hiking has increased, while the number participating in fishing has decreased. These trends can be seen in the graph in **Figure 41.** The two straight-line graphs intersect at the time when the two sports had the *same* number of participants.

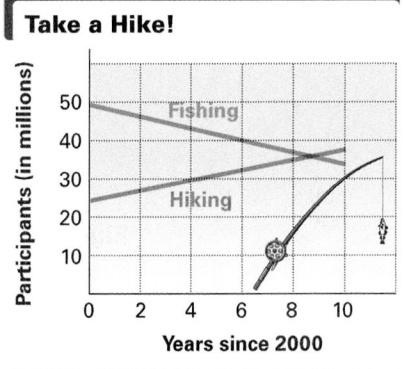

Take a Hike!

Source: National Sporting Goods Association.

Figure 41

$-1.34x + y = 24.3$ Linear system

$1.55x + y = 49.3$ of equations

(Here, $x = 0$ represents 2000, $x = 1$ represents 2001, and so on. y represents millions of participants.)

As shown beside **Figure 41,** we can use a linear equation to model the graph of the number of people who hiked (red graph) and another linear equation to model the graph of the number of people who fished (blue graph).

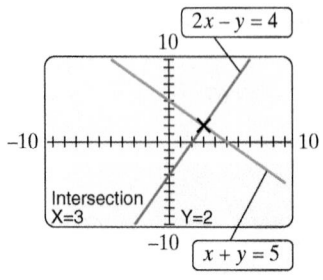

A graphing calculator supports our statement that (3, 2) is the solution of the system

$$x + y = 5$$
$$2x - y = 4.$$

Such a set of equations is a **system of linear equations.** The point where the graphs in **Figure 41** intersect is a solution of each of the individual equations. It is also the solution of the system of linear equations.

In **Figure 42,** the two linear equations $x + y = 5$ and $2x - y = 4$ are graphed in the same coordinate system. Notice that they intersect at the point $(3, 2)$. Because $(3, 2)$ is the only ordered pair that satisfies both equations at the same time, we say that $\{(3, 2)\}$ is the solution set of the system

$$x + y = 5$$
$$2x - y = 4.$$

Because the graph of a linear equation in two variables is a line, there are three possibilities for the number of solutions in the solution set of a linear system.

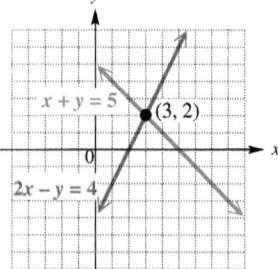

Figure 42

GRAPHS OF A LINEAR SYSTEM IN TWO VARIABLES (THE THREE POSSIBILITIES)

1. The two graphs intersect in a single point. The coordinates of this point give the only solution of the system. In this case, the system is **consistent** and the equations are **independent.** This is the most common case. See **Figure 43(a).**

2. The graphs are parallel lines. In this case, the system is **inconsistent** and the equations are **independent.** That is, there is no solution common to both equations of the system, and the solution set is $\varnothing$. See **Figure 43(b).**

3. The graphs are the same line. In this case, the system is **consistent** and the equations are **dependent,** because any solution of one equation of the system is also a solution of the other. The solution set is an infinite set of ordered pairs representing the points on the line. See **Figure 43(c).**

Figure 43

Elimination Method

In most cases, we cannot rely on graphing to solve systems, so we use algebraic methods. The **elimination method** involves combining the two equations of the system in such a way that one variable is eliminated. This is done using the following rule.

If $a = b$ **and** $c = d$, **then** $a + c = b + d.$

The solution of **systems of equations** of graphs more complicated than straight lines is the principle behind the **mattang,** a stick chart used by the people of the Marshall Islands in the Pacific. A mattang is made of roots tied together with coconut fibers, and it shows the wave patterns found when approaching an island.

SOLVING LINEAR SYSTEMS BY ELIMINATION

Step 1 **Write both equations in standard form $Ax + By = C$.**

Step 2 **Make the coefficients of one pair of variable terms opposite.** Multiply one or both equations by appropriate numbers so that the sum of the coefficients of either x or y is zero.

Step 3 **Add the new equations to eliminate a variable.** The sum should be an equation with just one variable.

Step 4 **Solve** the equation from Step 3.

Step 5 **Find the other value.** Substitute the result of Step 4 into either of the given equations, and solve for the other variable.

Step 6 **Find the solution set.** Check the solution in both of the given equations. Then write the solution set.

EXAMPLE 1 Solving a System by Elimination

Solve the system.

$$5x - 2y = 4 \quad \text{(1)}$$
$$2x + 3y = 13 \quad \text{(2)}$$

Solution

Step 1 Both equations are already in standard form.

Step 2 Our goal is to add the two equations so that one of the variables is eliminated. To eliminate the variable x, we must first transform one or both equations so that the coefficients of x are opposites. Then, when we combine the equations, the term with x will have a coefficient of 0, and we will be able to solve for y. We begin by multiplying equation (1) by 2 and equation (2) by -5.

$$10x - 4y = 8 \quad \text{2 times each side of equation (1)}$$
$$-10x - 15y = -65 \quad \text{−5 times each side of equation (2)}$$

Step 3 Now add the two equations to eliminate x.

$$\begin{array}{r} 10x - 4y = 8 \\ \underline{-10x - 15y = -65} \\ -19y = -57 \end{array} \quad \text{Add.}$$

Step 4 Solve the equation from Step 3 to get $y = 3$. (Divide by -19.)

Step 5 To find x, we substitute 3 for y in either of the original equations.

$$2x + 3y = 13 \quad \text{We use equation (2).}$$
$$2x + 3(3) = 13 \quad \text{Let } y = 3.$$
$$2x + 9 = 13 \quad \text{Multiply.}$$
$$2x = 4 \quad \text{Subtract 9.}$$
$$x = 2 \quad \text{Divide by 2.}$$

Step 6 The solution appears to be $(2, 3)$. To check, substitute 2 for x and 3 for y in both of the original equations.

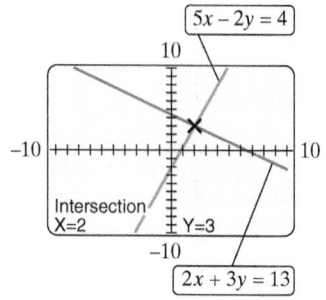

The solution in **Example 1** is supported by a graphing calculator. We solve each equation for *y*, graph them both, and find the point of intersection of the two lines: (2, 3).

Check:

$5x - 2y = 4$ (1)	$2x + 3y = 13$ (2)
$5(2) - 2(3) \stackrel{?}{=} 4$	$2(2) + 3(3) \stackrel{?}{=} 13$
$10 - 6 \stackrel{?}{=} 4$	$4 + 9 \stackrel{?}{=} 13$
$4 = 4$ ✓ True	$13 = 13$ ✓ True

The solution set is $\{(2, 3)\}$. ∎

Substitution Method

Linear systems can also be solved by the **substitution method.**

SOLVING LINEAR SYSTEMS BY SUBSTITUTION

Step 1 **Solve for one variable in terms of the other.** Solve one of the equations for either variable. (If one of the variables has coefficient 1 or −1, choose it, since the substitution method is usually easier this way.)

Step 2 **Substitute** for that variable in the other equation. The result should be an equation with just one variable.

Step 3 **Solve** the equation from Step 2.

Step 4 **Find the other value.** Substitute the result from Step 3 into the equation from Step 1 to find the value of the other variable.

Step 5 **Find the solution set.** Check the solution in both of the given equations. Then write the solution set.

▮▮▮ EXAMPLE 2 Solving a System by Substitution

Solve the system.

$$3x + 2y = 13 \quad \text{(1)}$$
$$4x - y = -1 \quad \text{(2)}$$

Solution

Step 1 First solve one of the equations for either *x* or *y*. Because the coefficient of *y* in equation (2) is −1, we choose to solve for *y* in equation (2).

$$-y = -1 - 4x \qquad \text{Equation (2) rearranged}$$
$$y = 1 + 4x \qquad \text{Multiply by −1.}$$

Step 2 Substitute $1 + 4x$ for *y* in equation (1) to obtain an equation in *x*.

$$3x + 2y = 13 \quad \text{(1)}$$
$$3x + 2(1 + 4x) = 13 \qquad \text{Let } y = 1 + 4x.$$

Step 3 Solve for *x* in the equation just obtained.

$$3x + 2 + 8x = 13 \qquad \text{Distributive property}$$
$$11x = 11 \qquad \text{Combine terms; subtract 2.}$$
$$x = 1 \qquad \text{Divide by 11.}$$

Step 4 Now solve for *y*. Because $y = 1 + 4x$, we find that $y = 1 + 4(1) = 5$.

Step 5 Check to see that the ordered pair $(1, 5)$ satisfies both of the original equations. The solution set is $\{(1, 5)\}$. ∎

EXAMPLE 3 Solving Systems of Special Cases

Solve each system.

(a) $3x - 2y = 4$ (1)

$-6x + 4y = 7$ (2)

(b) $-4x + y = 2$ (3)

$8x - 2y = -4$ (4)

Solution

(a) Eliminate x by multiplying both sides of equation (1) by 2 and then adding.

$$\begin{array}{rl} 6x - 4y = 8 & \text{2 times equation (1)} \\ -6x + 4y = 7 & \text{(2)} \\ \hline 0 = 15 & \text{False} \end{array}$$

Both variables were eliminated here, leaving the false statement $0 = 15$, indicating that these two equations have no solutions in common. The system is inconsistent, with the empty set $\varnothing$ as the solution set.

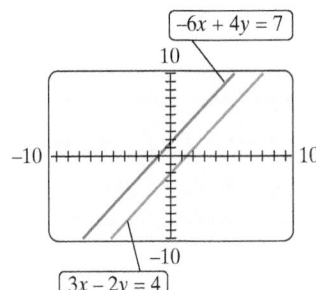

The graphs of the equations in
Example 3(a) are parallel. There are
no solutions.

(b) Eliminate x by multiplying both sides of equation (3) by 2 and then adding the result to equation (4).

$$\begin{array}{rl} -8x + 2y = 4 & \text{2 times equation (3)} \\ 8x - 2y = -4 & \text{(4)} \\ \hline 0 = 0 & \text{True} \end{array}$$

This true statement, $0 = 0$, indicates that a solution of one equation is also a solution of the other, so the solution set is an infinite set of ordered pairs. The two equations are dependent.

We write the solution set of a system of dependent equations as a set of ordered pairs by expressing x in terms of y as follows. Choose either equation and solve for x. We arbitrarily choose equation (3).

$$-4x + y = 2 \qquad \text{(3)}$$

$$x = \frac{2 - y}{-4}$$

$$x = \frac{y - 2}{4} \qquad \text{Multiply by } \tfrac{-1}{-1}.$$

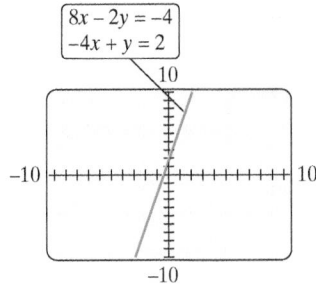

The graphs of the equations in
Example 3(b) coincide. We see only
one line. There are infinitely many
solutions.

The solution set can be written as

$$\left\{ \left(\frac{y - 2}{4}, y \right) \right\}.$$

By selecting values for y and calculating the corresponding values for x, individual ordered pairs of the solution set can be found. For example,

$$\text{if } y = -2, \quad \text{then } x = \frac{-2 - 2}{4} = -1$$

and the ordered pair $(-1, -2)$ is a solution. ■

8.7 EXERCISES

Fill in the blanks with the correct responses.

1. If $(3, -6)$ is a solution of a linear system in two variables, then substituting _____ for x and _____ for y leads to true statements in *both* equations.

2. A solution of a system of independent linear equations in two variables is a(n) _____ _____ of numbers.

3. Which ordered pair could possibly be a solution of the graphed system of equations? Why?

A. $(3, 3)$

B. $(-3, 3)$

C. $(-3, -3)$

D. $(3, -3)$

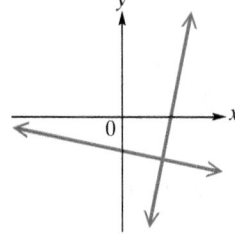

4. Which ordered pair could possibly be a solution of the graphed system of equations? Why?

A. $(3, 0)$

B. $(-3, 0)$

C. $(0, 3)$

D. $(0, -3)$

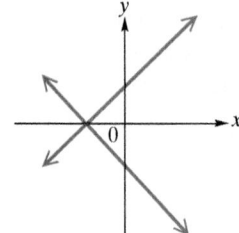

Decide whether the ordered pair is a solution of the given system.

5. $x + y = 6; \quad (5, 1)$
   $x - y = 4$

6. $x - y = 17; \quad (8, -9)$
   $x + y = -1$

7. $2x - y = 8; \quad (5, 2)$
   $3x + 2y = 20$

8. $3x - 5y = -12; \quad (-1, 2)$
   $x - y = 1$

Match each system in Exercises 9–12 with the correct graph in A–D below.

9. $x + y = 6$
   $x - y = 0$

10. $x + y = -6$
    $x - y = 0$

11. $x + y = 0$
    $x - y = -6$

12. $x + y = 0$
    $x - y = 6$

A.

B.

C.

D.

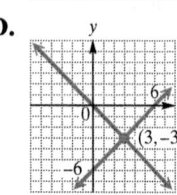

Solve each system by graphing.

13. $x + y = 4$
    $2x - y = 2$

14. $x + y = -5$
    $-2x + y = 1$

Solve each system by elimination.

15. $2x - 5y = 11$
    $3x + y = 8$

16. $-2x + 3y = 1$
    $-4x + y = -3$

17. $3x + 4y = -6$
    $5x + 3y = 1$

18. $4x + 3y = 1$
    $3x + 2y = 2$

19. $3x + 3y = 0$
    $4x + 2y = 3$

20. $8x + 4y = 0$
    $4x - 2y = 2$

21. $\quad 7x + 2y = 6$
    $-14x - 4y = -12$

22. $x - 4y = 2$
    $4x - 16y = 8$

23. $5x - 5y = 3$
    $x - y = 12$

24. $\quad 2x - 3y = 7$
    $-4x + 6y = 14$

25. $\dfrac{x}{2} + \dfrac{y}{3} = -\dfrac{1}{3}$
    $\dfrac{x}{2} + 2y = -7$

26. $\dfrac{x}{5} + y = -\dfrac{12}{5}$
    $\dfrac{x}{10} + \dfrac{y}{3} = -\dfrac{11}{30}$

Solve each system by substitution.

27. $4x + y = 6$
    $y = 2x$

28. $2x - y = 6$
    $y = 5x$

29. $\quad 3x - 4y = -22$
    $-3x + y = 0$

30. $-3x + y = -5$
    $x + 2y = 0$

31. $-x - 4y = -14$
    $2x = y + 1$

32. $-3x - 5y = -17$
    $4x = y - 8$

33. $5x - 4y = 9$
    $3 - 2y = -x$

34. $6x - y = -9$
    $4 + 7x = -y$

35. $x = 3y + 5$
    $y = \dfrac{2}{3}x$

36. $x = 6y - 2$
    $y = \dfrac{4}{3}x$

37. $\dfrac{1}{2}x + \dfrac{1}{3}y = 3$
    $y = 3x$

38. $\dfrac{1}{4}x - \dfrac{1}{5}y = 9$
    $y = 5x$

Outdoor Recreation *Use the graph given at the beginning of this section (repeated here) to work Exercises 39–42.*

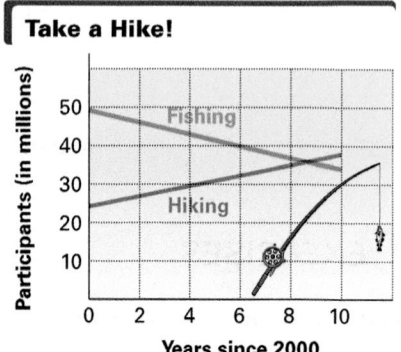

Source: National Sporting Goods Association.

39. Which sport was more popular in 2010?

40. Estimate the year in which participation in the two sports was the same. About how many Americans participated in each sport during that year?

41. If $x = 0$ represents 2000 and $x = 10$ represents 2010, the number of participants y (in millions) in the two sports can be modeled by the linear equations in the following system.

$$-1.34x + y = 24.3 \quad \text{Hiking}$$
$$1.55x + y = 49.3 \quad \text{Fishing}$$

Solve this system. Express values as decimals rounded to the nearest tenth. Write the solution as an ordered pair of the form (year, participants).

42. Interpret the answer for **Exercise 41,** rounding down for the year. How does it compare to the estimate from **Exercise 40?**

AIDS and Race *The graph in the next column shows a comparison of the number of African Americans and the number of Whites living with AIDS in the United States during 1993–2000. Use this graph to work Exercises 43–46.*

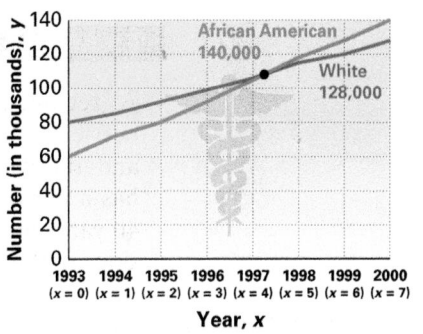

People Living with AIDS

Source: U.S. Centers for Disease Control.

43. Use the points $(0, 60)$ and $(7, 140)$ to find an equation for a line approximating the data for the graph in blue. Write it in standard form.

44. Repeat **Exercise 43,** using the points $(0, 80)$ and $(7, 128)$ for the graph in red.

45. Solve the system formed by the two equations in **Exercises 43 and 44.**

46. Describe how the solution is related to the graph.

8.8 APPLICATIONS OF LINEAR SYSTEMS

OBJECTIVES

1 Solve an application involving a rectangular area using a system of linear equations.

2 Solve an application involving different ticket prices using a system of linear equations.

3 Solve a mixture problem involving percent concentrations using a system of linear equations.

4 Solve a motion problem using a system of linear equations.

Introduction

Problems like the one in the margin on the next page, which comes from a Hindu work that dates back to about A.D. 850, have been around for thousands of years. It can be solved by using a system of equations. In this section we illustrate some strategies for solving applications using systems. The following steps, based on the six-step problem-solving method first introduced in **Chapter 7,** give a strategy for solving problems using more than one variable.

SOLVING AN APPLIED PROBLEM BY WRITING A SYSTEM OF EQUATIONS

Step 1 **Read** the problem carefully until you understand what is given and what is to be found.

Step 2 **Assign variables** to represent the unknown values, using diagrams or tables as needed. *Write down* what each variable represents.

Step 3 **Write a system of equations** that relates the unknowns.

Step 4 **Solve** the system of equations.

Step 5 **State the answer** to the problem. Does it seem reasonable?

Step 6 **Check** the answer in the words of the original problem.

The mixed price of 9 citrons [a lemonlike fruit shown in the photo] and 7 fragrant wood apples is 107; again, the mixed price of 7 citrons and 9 fragrant wood apples is 101. O you arithmetician, tell me quickly the price of a citron and the price of a wood apple here, having distinctly separated those prices well.

*The answer is on **page 467.***

Figure 44

Applications

EXAMPLE 1 Solving a Perimeter Problem

A rectangular soccer field may have a width between 50 and 100 yards and a length between 50 and 100 yards. Suppose that one particular field has a perimeter of 320 yards. Its length measures 40 yards more than its width. What are the dimensions of this field?

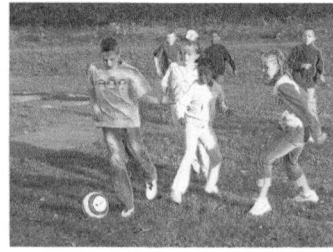

Solution

Step 1 **Read** the problem again. We are asked to find the dimensions of the field.

Step 2 **Assign variables.**

Let L = the length and W = the width.

Step 3 **Write a system of equations.** Because the perimeter is 320 yards, we find one equation by using the perimeter formula.

$$2L + 2W = 320$$

Because the length is 40 yards more than the width, we have

$$L = W + 40.$$

See **Figure 44.** We now have a system to solve.

$$2L + 2W = 320 \quad \text{(1)}$$

$$L = W + 40 \quad \text{(2)}$$

Step 4 **Solve** the system of equations. Since equation (2) is solved for L, we can substitute $W + 40$ for L in equation (1) and solve for W.

$$2L + 2W = 320 \quad \text{(1)}$$

$$2(W + 40) + 2W = 320 \quad \text{\small $L = W + 40$}$$

$$2W + 80 + 2W = 320 \quad \text{\small Distributive property}$$

$$4W + 80 = 320 \quad \text{\small Combine like terms.}$$

$$4W = 240 \quad \text{\small Subtract 80.}$$

$$W = 60 \quad \text{\small Divide by 4.}$$

Let $W = 60$ in the equation $L = W + 40$ to find L.

$$L = 60 + 40 = 100$$

Step 5 **State the answer.** The length is 100 yards, and the width is 60 yards. Both dimensions are within the ranges given in the problem.

Step 6 **Check.** The answer is correct, because the perimeter of this soccer field is

$$2(100) + 2(60) = 320 \text{ yards,}$$

and the length, 100 yards, is indeed 40 yards more than the width, because

$$100 - 40 = 60.$$ ∎

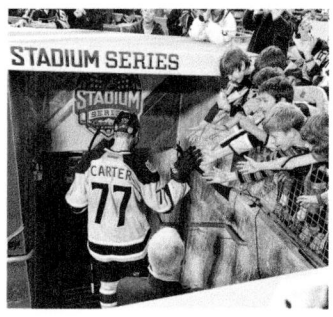

EXAMPLE 2 Solving a Problem about Ticket Prices

For the 2010–2011 National Hockey League and National Basketball Association seasons, two hockey tickets and one basketball ticket purchased at their average prices would have cost $156.16. One hockey ticket and two basketball tickets would have cost $149.57. What were the average ticket prices for the two sports? (*Source:* Team Marketing Report, Chicago.)

Solution

Step 1 **Read** the problem again. There are two unknowns.

Step 2 **Assign variables.**

Let h = the average price for a hockey ticket

and b = the average price for a basketball ticket.

Step 3 **Write a system of equations.** Because two hockey tickets and one basketball ticket cost a total of $156.16, one equation for the system is as follows.

$$2h + b = 156.16$$

By similar reasoning, we can write a second equation.

$$h + 2b = 149.57$$

Therefore, the system is as follows.

$$2h + b = 156.16 \quad \text{(1)}$$
$$h + 2b = 149.57 \quad \text{(2)}$$

Step 4 **Solve** the system of equations. We eliminate h.

$$
\begin{aligned}
2h + b &= 156.16 \quad &\text{(1)}\\
\underline{-2h - 4b} &= \underline{-299.14} \quad &\text{Multiply each side of (2) by −2.}\\
-3b &= -142.98 \quad &\text{Add.}\\
b &= 47.66 \quad &\text{Divide by −3.}
\end{aligned}
$$

To find the value of h, let $b = 47.66$ in equation (2).

$$
\begin{aligned}
h + 2b &= 149.57 \quad &\text{(2)}\\
h + 2(47.66) &= 149.57 \quad &\text{Let } b = 47.66.\\
h + 95.32 &= 149.57 \quad &\text{Multiply.}\\
h &= 54.25 \quad &\text{Subtract 95.32.}
\end{aligned}
$$

Step 5 **State the answer.** The average price for one basketball ticket was $47.66. For one hockey ticket, the average price was $54.25.

Step 6 **Check** that these values satisfy the conditions stated in the problem.

$$2(\$54.25) + \$47.66 = \$156.16, \quad \text{as required.}$$
$$\$54.25 + 2(\$47.66) = \$149.57, \quad \text{as required.}$$ ∎

We solved mixture problems earlier using one variable. Another approach is to use two variables and a system of equations.

EXAMPLE 3 Solving a Mixture Problem

How many ounces each of 5% hydrochloric acid and 20% hydrochloric acid must be combined to get 10 oz of solution that is 12.5% hydrochloric acid?

Solution

Step 1 **Read** the problem. Two solutions of different strengths are being mixed together to get a specific amount of a solution with an "in-between" strength.

Step 2 **Assign variables.** Let x represent the number of ounces of 5% solution and y represent the number of ounces of 20% solution.

Percent (as a decimal)	Ounces of Solution	Ounces of Pure Acid
5% = 0.05	x	$0.05x$
20% = 0.20	y	$0.20y$
12.5% = 0.125	10	0.125(10)

Summarize the information from the problem in a table.

Figure 45 also illustrates what is happening in the problem.

Ounces of solution

Ounces of pure acid

Figure 45

Step 3 **Write a system of equations.** When x ounces of 5% solution and y ounces of 20% solution are combined, the total number of ounces is 10.

$$x + y = 10 \quad \text{(1)}$$

The ounces of pure acid in the 5% solution $(0.05x)$ plus the ounces of pure acid in the 20% solution $(0.20y)$ should equal the total ounces of pure acid in the mixture, which is 0.125(10), or 1.25.

$$0.05x + 0.20y = 1.25 \quad \text{(2)}$$

Notice that these equations can be quickly determined by reading down in the table or using the labels in **Figure 45.**

Step 4 **Solve** the system of equations (1) and (2). We eliminate x.

$$
\begin{array}{rl}
5x + 20y = 125 & \text{Multiply each side of (2) by 100.} \\
\underline{-5x - 5y = -50} & \text{Multiply each side of (1) by −5.} \\
15y = 75 & \text{Add.} \\
y = 5 & \text{Divide by 15.}
\end{array}
$$

Because $y = 5$ and $x + y = 10$, x is also 5.

Step 5 **State the answer.** The desired mixture will require 5 ounces of the 5% solution and 5 ounces of the 20% solution.

Step 6 **Check** that these values satisfy both equations of the system. ■

François Viète, a mathematician of sixteenth-century France, contributed significantly to the evolution of **mathematical symbols.** Before his time, different symbols were often used for different powers of a quantity. Viète used the same letter with a description of the power and the coefficient. According to Howard Eves in *An Introduction to the History of Mathematics*, Viète would have written

$$5BA^2 - 2CA + A^3 = D$$

as

B5 in *A* quad − *C* plano 2 in

A + *A* cub aequatur *D* solido.

EXAMPLE 4 Solving a Motion Problem

Two executives in cities 400 miles apart leave at the same time to drive to a business meeting at a location on the line between their cities. They meet after 4 hours. Find the speed of each car if one car travels 20 miles per hour faster than the other.

Solution

Step 1 **Read** the problem carefully.

Step 2 **Assign variables.**

$$\text{Let } x = \text{the speed of the faster car,}$$
$$\text{and } y = \text{the speed of the slower car.}$$

We use the formula $d = rt$. Each car travels for 4 hours. See the table.

	r	t	d	
Faster car	x	4	$4x$	Find d from $d = rt$.
Slower car	y	4	$4y$	

Sketch what is happening in the problem. See **Figure 46.**

Figure 46

Step 3 **Write two equations.** The total distance traveled by both cars is 400 miles.

$$4x + 4y = 400 \quad \text{(1)}$$

The faster car goes 20 miles per hour faster than the slower car.

$$x = 20 + y \quad \text{(2)}$$

Step 4 **Solve** this system of equations by substitution.

$$4x + 4y = 400 \quad \text{(1)}$$
$$x = 20 + y \quad \text{(2)}$$

Replace x with $20 + y$ in equation (1) and solve for y.

$$4(20 + y) + 4y = 400 \quad \text{Let } x = 20 + y.$$
$$80 + 4y + 4y = 400 \quad \text{Distributive property}$$
$$80 + 8y = 400 \quad \text{Combine like terms.}$$
$$8y = 320 \quad \text{Subtract 80.}$$
$$y = 40 \quad \text{Divide by 8.}$$

Because $x = 20 + y$ and $y = 40$, $x = 20 + 40 = 60$.

Step 5 **State the answer.** The speeds are 40 miles per hour and 60 miles per hour.

Step 6 **Check.** Because each car travels for 4 hours, the total distance traveled is

$$4(60) + 4(40) = 240 + 160 = 400 \text{ miles,} \quad \text{as required.} \quad \blacksquare$$

Solution to the Citron/Wood Apple problem Let c represent the price of a single citron, and w represent the price of a wood apple. The system to solve is

$$9c + 7w = 107$$
$$7c + 9w = 101.$$

We find that the prices are 8 for a citron and 5 for a wood apple.

8.8 EXERCISES

Solve each problem by using a system of equations.

1. ***Win–Loss Record*** During the 2013 major league baseball regular season, the St. Louis Cardinals played 162 games and won the Central Division of the National League. They won 32 more games than they lost. What was their win–loss record that year?

2013 MLB Final Regular Season Standings, National League Central

Team	W	L
St. Louis	—	—
Pittsburgh	94	68
Cincinnati	90	72
Milwaukee	74	88
Chicago Cubs	66	96

Source: www.mlb.com

2. ***Win–Loss Record*** During the 2013 major league baseball season, the Houston Astros played 162 games. They lost 60 more games than they won. What was their win–loss record that year?

2013 MLB Final Regular Season Standings, American League West

Team	W	L
Oakland	96	66
Texas	91	72
L. A. Angels	78	84
Seattle	71	91
Houston	—	—

Source: www.mlb.com

3. ***Dimensions of a Basketball Court*** LeBron and Yao found that the width of their basketball court was 44 feet less than the length. If the perimeter was 288 feet, what were the length and the width of their court?

4. ***Dimensions of a Tennis Court*** Venus and Serena measured a tennis court and found that it was 42 feet longer than it was wide. It had a perimeter of 228 feet. What were the length and the width of the tennis court?

5. ***Cost of Clay*** For his art class, Bryce bought 2 kilograms of dark clay and 3 kilograms of light clay, paying $22 for the clay. He later needed 1 kilogram of dark clay and 2 kilograms of light clay, costing $13 altogether. What was the cost per kilogram for each type of clay?

6. ***Cost of Art Supplies*** For an art project, Nicole bought 8 sheets of colored paper and 3 marker pens for $6.50. She later needed 2 sheets of colored paper and 2 marker pens. These items cost $3.00. Find the cost of 1 marker pen and the cost of 1 sheet of colored paper.

7. ***Dimensions of a Square and a Triangle*** The side of a square is 4 centimeters longer than the side of an equilateral triangle. The perimeter of the square is 24 centimeters more than the perimeter of the triangle. Find the length of a side of the square and the length of a side of the triangle.

8. ***Dimensions of a Rectangle*** The length of a rectangle is 7 feet more than the width. If the length were decreased by 3 feet and the width were increased by 2 feet, the perimeter would be 32 feet. Find the length and width of the original rectangle.

9. ***Coffee Prices*** At a business meeting at Panera Bread, the bill (without tax) for two cappuccinos and three cafe mochas was $17.15. At another table, the bill for one cappuccino and two cafe mochas was $10.37. How much did each type of beverage cost? (*Source:* Panera Bread.)

10. ***Ticket Prices*** Tickets to a concert at Lake Sumter Community College cost $5 for general admission or $4 with a student ID. If 184 people paid to see the concert and $812 was collected, how many of each type of ticket were sold?

11. *Top-Grossing Concerts* Two of the top-grossing North American concert tours in 2012 were Madonna, and Bruce Springsteen and the E Street Band. Based on average ticket prices, it cost a total of $1300 to buy six tickets for Madonna and five tickets for a Springsteen concert. Three tickets for Madonna and four for Springsteen cost a total of $788. How much did an average ticket cost for each tour? (*Source:* www.businessinsider.com)

12. *Top-Grossing Concerts* Two other top-grossing North American concert tours in 2012 were Cirque du Soleil and Coldplay. Based on average ticket prices, it cost a total of $1099 to buy eight tickets for Cirque du Soleil and three tickets for Coldplay. Four tickets for Cirque du Soleil and five tickets for Coldplay cost $833. How much did an average ticket cost for each tour? (*Source:* www.businessinsider.com)

13. *Travel Costs* New York City and Washington, D.C., were the two most expensive U.S. cities for business travel in 2011. On the basis of the average total costs per day for each city (which include a hotel room, car rental, and three meals), 2 days in New York and 3 days in Washington cost $2936, while 4 days in New York and 2 days in Washington cost $3616. What was the average cost per day in each city? (*Source: Business Travel News.*)

14. *Disc Prices* In 2012, the movie *Hugo* was available in both DVD and Blu-ray formats. The price for 3 DVDs and 2 Blu-ray discs was $77.86, while the price for 2 DVDs and 3 Blu-ray discs was $84.39. How much did each format cost? (*Source:* www.amazon.com)

15. *Fortune 500 Companies* The two biggest Fortune 500 companies in 2011 were Wal-Mart and ExxonMobil. ExxonMobil's revenue was $67 billion less than that of Wal-Mart. Total revenue for the two companies was $777 billion. What was the revenue for each company? (*Source: Fortune* magazine.)

16. *Imports and Exports* In 2010, U.S. exports to Canada were $86 billion more than U.S. exports to Mexico. Together, exports to these two countries totaled $412 billion. How much were exports to each country? (*Source:* U.S. Department of Commerce.)

Fan Cost Index The Fan Cost Index (FCI) represents the cost of four average-price tickets, four small soft drinks, two small beers, four hot dogs, parking for one car, two game programs, and two souvenir caps to a sporting event. (*Source:* www.teammarketing.com)

Use the concept of FCI in Exercises 17 and 18.

17. For the 2010–2011 season, the FCI prices for the National Hockey League (NHL) and the National Basketball Association (NBA) totaled $601.53. The hockey FCI was $25.83 more than that of basketball. What were the FCIs for these sports?

18. For the 2011 baseball and 2010–11 football seasons, the FCI prices for Major League Baseball (MLB) and the National Football League (NFL) totaled $617.89. The football FCI was $223.19 more than that of baseball. What were the FCIs for these sports?

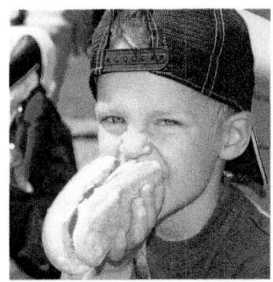

Formulas The formulas $p = br$ (*percentage = base × rate*) and $I = prt$ (*simple interest = principal × rate × time*) are used in the applications in Exercises 23–32. To prepare to use these formulas, work Exercises 19–22.

19. If a container of liquid contains 120 ounces of solution, what is the number of ounces of pure acid if the given solution contains the following acid concentrations?

(a) 10% (b) 25%

(c) 40% (d) 50%

20. If $50,000 is invested in an account paying simple annual interest, how much interest will be earned during the first year at the following rates?

(a) 0.5% (b) 1%

(c) 1.25% (d) 2.5%

21. If a pound of ham costs $4.29, give an expression for the cost of *x* pounds.

22. If a ticket to the movie *Annie* costs $12 and *y* tickets are sold, give an expression for the amount collected.

23. *Acid Mixture* How many liters each of 15% acid and 33% acid should be mixed to obtain 40 liters of 21% acid?

Kind of Solution	Liters of Solution	Amount of Pure Acid
0.15	x	
0.33	y	
0.21	40	

24. *Alcohol Mixture* How many gallons each of 25% alcohol and 35% alcohol should be mixed to obtain 20 gallons of 32% alcohol?

25. *Antifreeze Mixture* A truck radiator holds 18 liters of fluid. How much pure antifreeze must be added to a mixture that is 4% antifreeze in order to fill the radiator with a mixture that is 20% antifreeze?

26. *Acid Mixture* Pure acid is to be added to a 10% acid solution to obtain 27 liters of a 20% acid solution. What amounts of each should be used?

27. *Fruit Drink Mixture* A popular fruit drink is made by mixing fruit juices. Such a mixture with 50% juice is to be mixed with another mixture that is 30% juice to get 200 liters of a mixture that is 45% juice. How much of each should be used?

Kind of Juice	Number of Liters	Amount of Pure Juice
0.50	x	$0.50x$
0.30	y	
0.45		

28. *Candy Mixture* Erin plans to mix pecan clusters that sell for $3.60 per pound with chocolate truffles that sell for $7.20 per pound to get a mixture that she can sell in Valentine boxes for $4.95 per pound. How much of the $3.60 clusters and how much of the $7.20 truffles should she use to create 80 pounds of the mix?

29. *Candy Mixture* A grocer plans to mix candy that sells for $1.20 per pound with candy that sells for $2.40 per pound to get a mixture that he plans to sell for $1.65 per pound. How much of the $1.20 and $2.40 candy should he use if he wants 160 pounds of the mix?

30. *Candy Mixture* How many pounds of candy that sells for $0.75 per pound must be mixed with candy that sells for $1.25 per pound to obtain 9 pounds of a mixture that should sell for $0.96 per pound? (*Source: The Bill Cosby Show.*)

31. *Investment Mix* José must invest a total of $15,000 in two accounts, one paying 4% simple annual interest, and the other paying 3%. If he wants to earn $550 annual interest, how much should he invest at each rate?

Principal	Rate	Interest
x	0.04	
y	0.03	
15,000		

32. *Investment Mix* A total of $3000 is invested, part at 2% simple interest and part at 4%. If the total annual return from the two investments is $100, how much is invested at each rate?

Formulas *The formula $d = rt$ (distance = rate × time) is used in the applications in Exercises 35–38. To prepare to use this formula, work Exercises 33 and 34.*

33. If the speed of a boat in still water is 10 mph, and the speed of the current of a river is x mph, what is the speed of the boat in each situation?

  (a) going upstream (that is, against the current, which slows the boat down)

  (b) going downstream (that is, with the current, which speeds the boat up)

34. If the speed of a killer whale is 25 mph and the whale swims for y hours, give an expression for the number of miles the whale travels.

35. *Speeds of Trains* A train travels 150 miles in the same time that a plane covers 400 miles. If the speed of the plane is 20 miles per hour less than 3 times the speed of the train, find both speeds.

36. *Speeds of Trains* A freight train and an express train leave towns 390 miles apart at the same time, traveling toward one another. The freight train travels 30 mph slower than the express train. They pass one another 3 hours later. What are their speeds?

37. *Speeds of Boat and Current* In his motorboat, Tran travels upstream at top speed to his favorite fishing spot, a distance of 36 miles, in 2 hours. Returning, he finds that the trip downstream, still at top speed, takes only 1.5 hours. Find the speed of Tran's boat and the speed of the current.

38. *Speeds of Snow Speeder and Wind* Braving blizzard conditions on the planet Hoth, Luke Skywalker sets out at top speed in his snow speeder for a rebel base 2400 km away. He travels into a steady headwind and makes the trip in 2.4 hours. Returning, he finds that the trip back, still at top speed but now with a tailwind, takes only 2 hours. Find the top speed of Luke's snow speeder and the speed of the wind.

8.9   LINEAR INEQUALITIES, SYSTEMS, AND LINEAR PROGRAMMING

OBJECTIVES

1 Graph a linear inequality in two variables.

2 Graph a system of linear inequalities in two variables.

3 Apply linear programming to maximize or minimize a value.

Linear Inequalities in Two Variables

Linear inequalities with one variable were graphed on number lines in **Chapter 7.** We graph linear inequalities in two variables in a rectangular coordinate system.

LINEAR INEQUALITY IN TWO VARIABLES

An inequality that can be written as

$$Ax + By < C \quad \text{or} \quad Ax + By > C,$$

where A, B, and C are real numbers and A and B are not both 0, is a **linear inequality in two variables.** The symbols $\leq$ and $\geq$ may replace $<$ and $>$ in this definition.

A line divides the plane into three regions: the line itself and the two half-planes on either side of the line. Recall that the graphs of linear inequalities in one variable are *intervals* on the number line that may include an endpoint. The graphs of linear inequalities in two variables are *regions* in the real number plane and may include a *boundary line*. The **boundary line** for the inequality $Ax + By < C$ or $Ax + By > C$ is the graph of the *equation* $Ax + By = C$.

To graph a linear inequality, we follow these steps.

GRAPHING A LINEAR INEQUALITY

Step 1   **Draw the boundary.**   Draw the graph of the straight line that is the boundary. Make the line solid if the inequality involves $\leq$ or $\geq$. Make the line dashed if the inequality involves $<$ or $>$.

Step 2   **Choose a test point.**   Choose any point not on the line as a test point.

Step 3   **Shade the appropriate region.**   Shade the region that includes the test point if it satisfies the original inequality. Otherwise, shade the region on the other side of the boundary line.

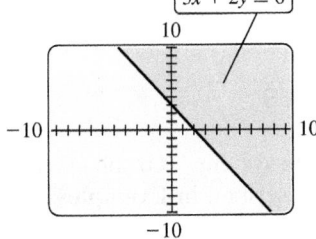

The TI-83/84 Plus allows us to shade the appropriate region for an inequality. Compare with **Figure 47.**

EXAMPLE 1   Graphing a Linear Inequality

Graph $3x + 2y \geq 6$.

Solution

First graph the straight line $3x + 2y = 6$. The graph of this line, the boundary of the graph of the inequality, is shown in **Figure 47.**

The graph of the inequality $3x + 2y \geq 6$ includes the points of the line $3x + 2y = 6$, and either the points *above* the line $3x + 2y = 6$ or the points *below* that line. To decide which, select any point not on the line $3x + 2y = 6$ as a test point. The origin, $(0, 0)$, often is a good choice. Substitute the values from $(0, 0)$ for x and y in the linear inequality $3x + 2y \geq 6$.

$$3(0) + 2(0) \overset{?}{\geq} 6$$

$$0 \geq 6 \quad \text{False}$$

Because the result is false, $(0, 0)$ does not satisfy the inequality, and so the solution set includes all points on the other side of the line, shaded in **Figure 47.** ∎

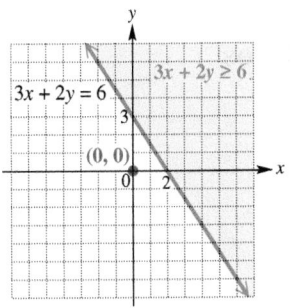

Figure 47

EXAMPLE 2 Graphing a Linear Inequality

Graph $x - 3y > 4$.

Solution

First graph the boundary line, $x - 3y = 4$. The graph is shown in **Figure 48.** The points of the boundary line do not belong to the inequality $x - 3y > 4$ (since the inequality symbol is $>$ and not $\geq$). For this reason, the line is dashed. To decide which side of the line is the graph of the solution set, choose any point that is not on the line—say $(1, 2)$. Substitute 1 for x and 2 for y in the original inequality.

$$1 - 3(2) \overset{?}{>} 4$$

$$-5 > 4 \quad \text{False}$$

Because of this false result, the solution set lies on the side of the boundary line that does *not* contain the test point $(1, 2)$. The solution set, graphed in **Figure 48,** includes only those points in the shaded region (not those on the line).

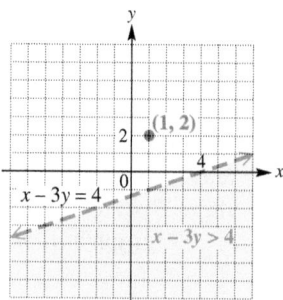

Figure 48

Systems of Inequalities

Systems of inequalities with two variables may be solved by graphing. A system of linear inequalities consists of two or more such inequalities, and the solution set of such a system consists of all points that make all the inequalities true at the same time.

GRAPHING A SYSTEM OF LINEAR INEQUALITIES

Step 1 **Graph each inequality in the same coordinate system.** Graph each inequality in the system, using the method described in **Examples 1 and 2.**

Step 2 **Find the intersection of the regions of solutions.** Indicate the intersection of the regions of solutions of the individual inequalities. This is the solution set of the system.

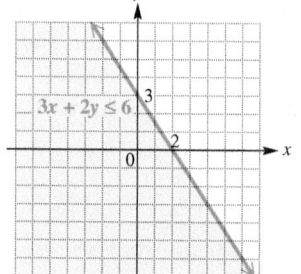

Figure 49

EXAMPLE 3 Graphing a System of Inequalities

Graph the solution set of the linear system.

$$3x + 2y \leq 6$$

$$2x - 5y \geq 10$$

Solution

To graph $3x + 2y \leq 6$, graph $3x + 2y = 6$ as a solid line. Since $(0, 0)$ makes the inequality *true*, shade the region containing $(0, 0)$, as shown in **Figure 49.**

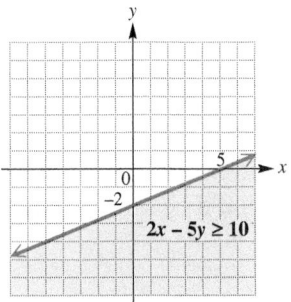

Figure 50

Now graph $2x - 5y \geq 10$. The solid-line boundary is the graph of $2x - 5y = 10$. Since $(0, 0)$ makes the inequality *false*, shade the region that does not contain $(0, 0)$, as shown in **Figure 50.**

The solution set of the system is given by the intersection (overlap) of the regions of the graphs in **Figures 49 and 50.** The solution set is the shaded region in **Figure 51,** and includes portions of the two boundary lines.

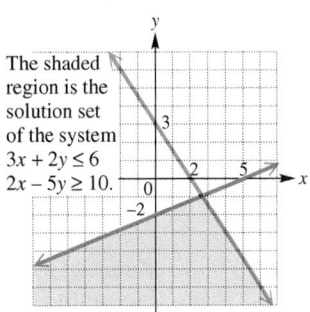

Figure 51

In practice, we usually do all the work in one coordinate system.

▓▓▓EXAMPLE 4 Graphing a System of Inequalities

Graph the solution set of the linear system.

$$2x + 3y \geq 12$$
$$7x + 4y \geq 28$$
$$y \leq 6$$
$$x \leq 5$$

Solution

Graph the four inequalities in one coordinate system, and shade the region common to all four as shown in **Figure 52.** As shown, the boundary lines are all solid. ■

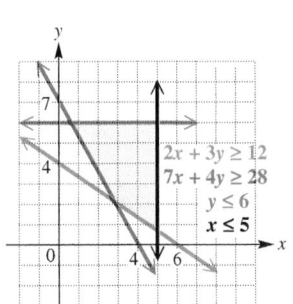

Figure 52

Linear Programming

One important application of mathematics to business and social science is **linear programming.** Linear programming is used to find an optimum value—for example, minimum cost or maximum profit. Procedures for solving linear programming problems were developed in 1947 by George Dantzig, while he was working on a problem of allocating supplies for the Air Force in a way that minimized total cost.

To solve a linear programming problem in general, use the following steps. (The italicized terms are defined in **Example 5.**)

George B. Dantzig (1914–2005) of Stanford University was one of the key people behind **operations research** (OR). As a management science, OR is not a single discipline. It draws from mathematics, probability theory, statistics, and economics. The name given to this "multiplex" shows its historical origins in World War II, when operations of a military nature called forth the efforts of many scientists to research their fields for applications to the war effort and to solve tactical problems.

SOLVING A LINEAR PROGRAMMING PROBLEM

Step 1 Write all necessary *constraints* and the *objective function.*

Step 2 Graph the *region of feasible solutions.*

Step 3 Identify all *vertices.*

Step 4 Find the value of the *objective function* at each *vertex.*

Step 5 The solution is given by the vertex producing the optimum value of the *objective function.*

EXAMPLE 5 Maximizing Rescue Efforts

Earthquake victims in China need medical supplies and bottled water. Each medical kit measures 1 cubic foot and weighs 10 pounds. Each container of water is also 1 cubic foot and weighs 20 pounds. The plane can carry only 80,000 pounds with a total volume of 6000 cubic feet. Each medical kit will aid 6 people, and each container of water will serve 10 people. How many of each should be sent in order to maximize the number of people aided?

Solution

Step 1 We translate the statements of the problem into symbols as follows.

Let x = the number of medical kits to be sent,

and y = the number of containers of water to be sent.

Because negative values of x and y are not valid for this problem, these two inequalities must be satisfied.

$$x \geq 0$$

$$y \geq 0$$

Each medical kit and each container of water will occupy 1 cubic foot of space, and there is a maximum of 6000 cubic feet available.

$$1x + 1y \leq 6000$$

$$\text{or} \quad x + y \leq 6000$$

Each medical kit weighs 10 pounds, and each water container weighs 20 pounds. The total weight cannot exceed 80,000 pounds.

$$10x + 20y \leq 80{,}000$$

$$\text{or, equivalently,} \quad x + 2y \leq 8000 \quad \text{Divide by 10.}$$

The four inequalities in color form a system of linear inequalities.

$$x \geq 0$$

$$y \geq 0$$

$$x + y \leq 6000$$

$$x + 2y \leq 8000$$

These are the **constraints** on the variables in this application.

Because each medical kit will aid 6 victims and each container of water will serve 10 victims, the total number of victims served is represented by the following **objective function.**

Number of victims served = $6x + 10y$ Multiply the number of items by the number of victims served and add.

Step 2 The maximum number of victims served, subject to these constraints, is found by sketching the graph of the solution set of the system. See **Figure 53.** The only feasible values of x and y are those that satisfy all constraints. These values correspond to points that lie on the boundary or in the shaded region, which is called the **region of feasible solutions.**

Step 3 The problem may now be stated as follows: Find values of x and y in the region of feasible solutions as shown in **Figure 53** that will produce the maximum possible value of $6x + 10y$. It can be shown that any optimum value (maximum or minimum) will always occur at a **vertex** (or **corner point**) of the region of feasible solutions.

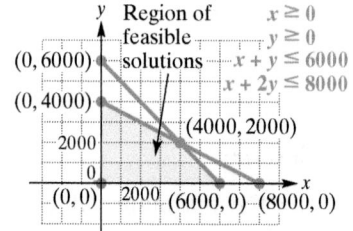

Figure 53

Step 4 Locate the point (x, y) that gives the maximum value by checking the coordinates of the vertices, shown in **Figure 53** and in **Table 5**. Find the number of victims served that corresponds to each coordinate pair.

Table 5

Point	Number of Victims Served = 6x + 10y
$(0, 0)$	$6(0) + 10(0) = 0$
$(0, 4000)$	$6(0) + 10(4000) = 40{,}000$
$(4000, 2000)$	$6(4000) + 10(2000) = 44{,}000$
$(6000, 0)$	$6(6000) + 10(0) = 36{,}000$

Points are from Figure 53.

44,000 is the maximum number.

Step 5 Choose the vertex that gives the maximum number. The maximum number of victims served is 44,000, when 4000 medical kits and 2000 containers of water are sent. ∎

8.9   EXERCISES

In Exercises 1–4, match each system of inequalities with the correct graph from choices A–D.

1. $x \geq 5$
$\quad y \leq -3$

2. $x \leq 5$
$\quad y \geq -3$

3. $x > 5$
$\quad y < -3$

4. $x < 5$
$\quad y > -3$

A.

B.

C.

D.

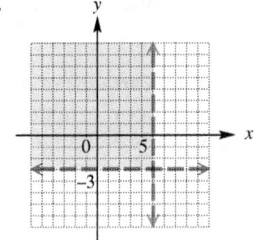

Graph each linear inequality.

5. $x + y \leq 2$

6. $x - y \geq -3$

7. $4x - y \leq 5$

8. $3x + y \geq 6$

9. $x + 3y \geq -2$

10. $x + 2y \leq -5$

11. $4x + 6y \leq -3$

12. $2x - 4y \leq 3$

13. $4x - 3y < 12$

14. $5x + 3y > 15$

15. $y > -x$

16. $y < x$

Graph each system of inequalities.

17. $x + y \leq 1$
$\qquad x \geq 0$

18. $3x - 4y \leq 6$
$\qquad\quad y \geq 1$

19. $2x - \ y \geq 1$
$\quad 3x + 2y \geq 6$

20. $x + 3y \geq 6$
$\quad 3x - 4y \leq 12$

21. $x + y > -5$
$\quad x - y \leq 3$

22. $6x - 4y < 8$
$\quad x + 2y \geq 4$

Exercises 23 and 24 show regions of feasible solutions. Find the maximum and minimum values of the given objective functions.

23. $3x + 5y$

24. $40x + 75y$

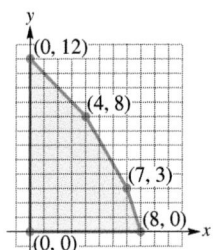

Use graphical methods to find values of x and y that satisfy the given conditions. (It may be necessary to solve a system of equations in order to find vertices.) Find the value of the maximum or minimum of the objective function, as directed.

25.
$x \geq 0$

$y \geq 0$

$2x + 3y \leq 6$

$4x + y \leq 6$

Maximize $5x + 2y$.

26.
$x \geq 0$

$y \geq 0$

$x + y \leq 10$

$5x + 2y \geq 20$

$y \geq \dfrac{1}{2}x$

Minimize $x + 3y$.

27.
$x \geq 2$

$y \geq 5$

$3x - y \geq 12$

$x + y \leq 15$

Minimize $2x + y$.

28.
$x \geq 10$

$y \geq 20$

$2x + 3y \leq 100$

$5x + 4y \leq 200$

Maximize $x + 3y$.

Solve each linear programming problem.

29. Refrigerator Shipping Costs A manufacturer of refrigerators must ship at least 100 refrigerators to its two West Coast warehouses. Each warehouse holds a maximum of 100 refrigerators. Warehouse A holds 25 refrigerators already, while warehouse B has 20 on hand. It costs $12 to ship a refrigerator to warehouse A and $10 to ship one to warehouse B. How many refrigerators should be shipped to each warehouse to minimize cost? What is the minimum cost?

30. Gasoline and Fuel Oil Costs A manufacturing process requires that oil refineries manufacture at least 2 gallons of gasoline for each gallon of fuel oil. To meet the winter demand for fuel oil, at least 3 million gallons a day must be produced. The demand for gasoline is no more than 6.4 million gallons per day. If the price of gasoline is $2.90 per gallon and the price of fuel oil is $3.50 per gallon, how much of each should be produced to maximize revenue?

31. Vitamin Pill Costs Robin takes vitamin pills. Each day, she must have at least 16 units of vitamin A, at least 5 units of vitamin B_1, and at least 20 units of vitamin C. She can choose between red pills costing 10¢ each that contain 8 units of A, 1 of B_1, and 2 of C; and blue pills that cost 20¢ each and contain 2 units of A, 1 of B_1, and 7 of C. How many of each pill should she take in order to minimize her cost and yet fulfill her daily requirements?

32. Food Supplement Costs Renee requires two food supplements, I and II. She can get these supplements from two different products, A and B. Product A provides 3 grams per serving of supplement I, and 2 grams per serving of supplement II. Product B provides 2 grams per serving of supplement I, and 4 grams per serving of supplement II. Her dietician has recommended that she include at least 15 grams of each supplement in her daily diet. If product A costs $0.25 per serving and product B costs $0.40 per serving, how can she satisfy her requirements most economically?

33. Cake and Cookie Production A bakery makes both cakes and cookies. Each batch of cakes requires two hours in the oven and three hours in the decorating room. Each batch of cookies needs one and a half hours in the oven and two-thirds of an hour in the decorating room. The oven is available no more than 15 hours a day, while the decorating room can be used no more than 13 hours a day. How many batches of cakes and cookies should the bakery make in order to maximize profits if cookies produce a profit of $20 per batch and cakes produce a profit of $30 per batch?

34. Media Production The Smartski Company makes two products: DVD recorders and MP3 players. Each DVD recorder gives a profit of $3, while each MP3 player gives a profit of $7. The company must manufacture at least 1 DVD recorder per day to satisfy one of its customers, but no more than 5 because of production problems. Also, the number of MP3 players produced cannot exceed 6 per day. As a further requirement, the number of DVD recorders cannot exceed the number of MP3 players. How many of each should the company manufacture per day in order to obtain the maximum profit?

35. Aid to Earthquake Victims If each medical kit could aid 4 people instead of 6, how would the results in **Example 5** change?

CHAPTER 8   SUMMARY

KEY TERMS

8.1

ordered pair
components
equal ordered pairs
origin
x-axis
y-axis
rectangular (Cartesian)
  coordinate system
quadrants
coordinates
midpoint
circle
center
radius

8.2

linear equation in two
  variables

standard form
x-intercept
y-intercept
slope
parallel
perpendicular
average rate of change

8.3

point-slope form
slope-intercept form

8.4

relation
dependent variable
independent variable
function
function notation
linear function
constant function

8.5

quadratic function
parabola
axis of symmetry (axis)
vertex

8.6

exponential function
horizontal asymptote
natural exponential function
compound interest
continuous compounding
exponential growth function
logarithm
logarithmic function
vertical asymptote
natural logarithmic function
common logarithm
doubling time
half-life

8.7

system of linear equations
consistent system
independent equations
inconsistent system
dependent equations
elimination method
substitution method

8.9

linear inequality in two
  variables
boundary line
linear programming
constraints
objective function
region of feasible solutions
vertex (corner point)

NEW SYMBOLS

(a, b) ordered pair

x_1 a specific value of the variable x
      (read "x-sub-one")

m slope

$f(x)$ function f of x (read "f of x" or "f at x")

$\log_a x$ logarithm of x with base a

e a constant, approximately 2.718281828

$\ln x$ natural (base e) logarithm of x

$\log x$ common (base ten) logarithm of x

TEST YOUR WORD POWER

See how well you have learned the vocabulary in this chapter.

1. An **ordered pair** is a pair of numbers written
  A. in numerical order between brackets.
  B. between parentheses or brackets.
  C. between parentheses in which order is important.
  D. between parentheses in which order does not matter.

2. A **linear equation in two variables** is an equation that can be written in the form
  A. $Ax + By < C.$ **B.** $ax = b.$
  C. $y = x^2.$ **D.** $Ax + By = C.$

3. An **intercept** is
  A. the point where the x-axis and the y-axis intersect.
  B. a pair of numbers written between parentheses in which order matters.
  C. one of the four regions determined by a rectangular coordinate system.
  D. a point where a graph intersects the x-axis or the y-axis.

4. The **slope** of a line is
  A. the measure of the run over the rise of the line.
  B. the distance between two points on the line.
  C. the ratio of the change in y to the change in x along the line.
  D. the horizontal change compared to the vertical change of two points on the line.

5. A **relation** is
  A. a set of ordered pairs.
  B. the ratio of the change in y to the change in x along a line.
  C. the set of all possible values of the independent variable.
  D. all the second components of a set of ordered pairs.

6. A **function** is
  A. the numbers in an ordered pair.
  B. a set of ordered pairs in which each distinct x-value corresponds to exactly one y-value.
  C. a pair of numbers written between parentheses in which order matters.
  D. the set of all ordered pairs that satisfy an equation.

7. The **domain** of a function is
  A. the set of all possible values of the dependent variable y.
  B. a set of ordered pairs.
  C. the difference between the x-values.
  D. the set of all possible values of the independent variable x.

8. The **range** of a function is
  A. the set of all possible values of the dependent variable y.
  B. a set of ordered pairs.
  C. the difference between the y-values.
  D. the set of all possible values of the independent variable x.

9. The **vertex** of a parabola is
  A. the point where the graph intersects the y-axis.
  B. the point where the graph intersects the x-axis.
  C. the lowest point on a parabola that opens up or the highest point on a parabola that opens down.
  D. the origin.

10. A **system of linear equations** consists of
  A. linear equations with second-degree variables.
  B. linear equations that have an infinite number of solutions.
  C. linear equations that are to be solved at the same time.
  D. linear inequalities that are to be solved at the same time.

ANSWERS
1. C **2.** D **3.** D **4.** C **5.** A
6. B **7.** D **8.** A **9.** C **10.** C

QUICK REVIEW

Concepts	*Examples*
8.1 **The Rectangular Coordinate System and Circles**	
Ordered Pairs Plot the ordered pair $(-3, 4)$ by starting at the origin, moving 3 units to the left, and then moving 4 units up.	Plot the point $(-3, 4)$. 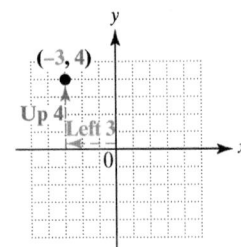
Distance Formula The distance d between the points (x_1, y_1) and (x_2, y_2) is given by the following formula. $$d = \sqrt{(x_2 - x_1)^2 + (y_2 - y_1)^2}$$	Find the distance between $(3, -2)$ and $(-1, 1)$. $$\sqrt{(-1 - 3)^2 + [1 - (-2)]^2}$$ $$= \sqrt{(-4)^2 + 3^2}$$ $$= \sqrt{16 + 9}$$ $$= \sqrt{25}$$ $$= 5$$
Midpoint Formula The coordinates of the midpoint M of the line segment with endpoints (x_1, y_1) and (x_2, y_2) are given by the following formula. $$M = \left(\frac{x_1 + x_2}{2}, \frac{y_1 + y_2}{2} \right)$$	Find the midpoint of the segment with endpoints $(4, -7)$ and $(-10, -13)$. $$\left(\frac{4 + (-10)}{2}, \frac{-7 + (-13)}{2} \right) = (-3, -10)$$

Concepts	*Examples*

Circle

A circle with radius r and center at (h, k) has an equation of the following form.

$$(x - h)^2 + (y - k)^2 = r^2$$

A circle of radius r and center at the origin has an equation of the following form.

$$x^2 + y^2 = r^2$$

Graph $(x + 2)^2 + (y - 3)^2 = 25$.

This equation can be written $[x - (-2)]^2 + (y - 3)^2 = 5^2$. It is a circle with center at $(-2, 3)$ and radius 5.

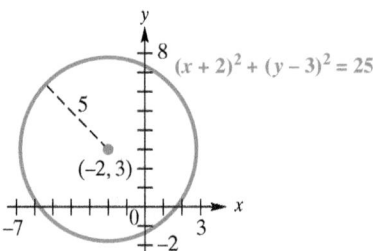

8.2 Lines, Slope, and Average Rate of Change

Linear Equation in Two Variables

An equation that can be written in the from

$$Ax + By = C \quad \text{(where } A \text{ and } B \text{ are not both 0)}$$

is a linear equation in two variables.

The intercepts are helpful when graphing a linear equation in two variables.

Graph the linear equation $x - 2y = 4$ using the intercepts.

x	y
0	-2
4	0

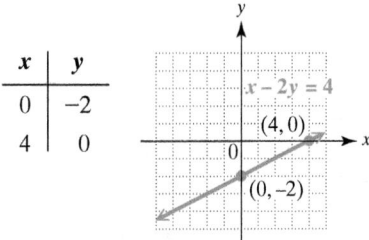

Slope

If $x_1 \neq x_2$, then the slope m of the line through (x_1, y_1) and (x_2, y_2) is given by the following formula.

$$\text{slope } m = \frac{\textbf{rise}}{\textbf{run}} = \frac{\textbf{change in } y}{\textbf{change in } x} = \frac{y_2 - y_1}{x_2 - x_1}$$

Find the slope of the graph of $2x + 3y = 12$.
    Use the intercepts $(6, 0)$ and $(0, 4)$ and the slope formula.

$$m = \frac{4 - 0}{0 - 6} = \frac{4}{-6} = -\frac{2}{3} \quad \begin{matrix} (x_1, y_1) = (6, 0) \\ (x_2, y_2) = (0, 4) \end{matrix}$$

Special Cases of Slope

A horizontal line has slope 0.

A vertical line has undefined slope.

The graph of the line $y = -5$ has slope $m = 0$.

The graph of the line $x = 3$ has undefined slope.

Slopes of Parallel and Perpendicular Lines

Parallel lines have equal slopes.

The lines $y = 2x + 3$ and $4x - 2y = 6$ are **parallel**. Both have slope 2.

$$
\begin{array}{c|c}
y = 2x + 3 & 4x - 2y = 6 \\
 & -2y = -4x + 6 \\
 & y = 2x - 3
\end{array}
$$

Perpendicular lines, neither of which is vertical, have slopes that are negative reciprocals (with a product of -1).

The lines $y = 3x - 1$ and $x + 3y = 4$ are **perpendicular**. Their slopes are negative reciprocals.

$$
\begin{array}{c|c}
y = 3x - 1 & x + 3y = 4 \\
 & 3y = -x + 4 \\
 & y = -\dfrac{1}{3}x + \dfrac{4}{3}
\end{array}
$$

Concepts	*Examples*

Average Rate of Change

To find the average rate of change from (x_1, y_1) to (x_2, y_2), find the slope of the line containing them.

Find the average rate of change from year 0 to year 3.

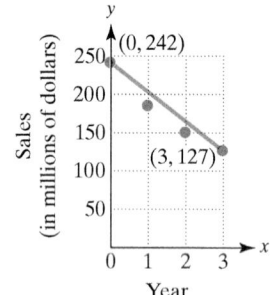

$$m = \frac{127 - 242}{3 - 0} = \frac{-115}{3} = -38\frac{1}{3}$$

From year 0 to year 3, the sales *decreased* by an average of $38\frac{1}{3}$ million dollars per year.

8.3 Equations of Lines

Point-Slope Form

The equation of a line through (x_1, y_1) with slope m is written in point-slope form as follows.

$$y - y_1 = m(x - x_1)$$

Find the standard form of the equation of the line with slope 3, passing through $(4, 1)$.

$$y - 1 = 3(x - 4) \qquad \text{\small } m = 3,\ x_1 = 4,\ y_1 = 1$$

$$y - 1 = 3x - 12 \qquad \text{\small Distributive property}$$

$$11 = 3x - y \qquad \text{\small Subtract } y \text{ and add 12.}$$

$$3x - y = 11 \qquad \text{\small Rewrite.}$$

Slope-Intercept Form

The equation of a line with slope m and y-intercept $(0, b)$ is written in slope-intercept form as follows.

$$y = mx + b$$

Find the standard form of the equation of the line passing through $(0, 5)$ and $(2, 9)$.

The y-intercept is $(0, 5)$, so $b = 5$. The slope is

$$m = \frac{9 - 5}{2 - 0} = \frac{4}{2} = 2,$$

so the slope-intercept form is $y = 2x + 5$.

$$y = 2x + 5$$

$$-5 = 2x - y \qquad \text{\small Subtract } y \text{ and 5.}$$

$$2x - y = -5 \qquad \text{\small Rewrite.}$$

8.4 Linear Functions, Graphs, and Models

Relations and Functions

A relation is a set of ordered pairs.

A function is a relation in which, for each value of the first component of the ordered pairs, there is *exactly* one value of the second component.

Represent the relation $\{(0, 1), (1, 1), (2, 1), (3, 1)\}$ as a table of values and as a graph.

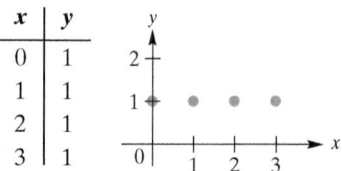

x	y
0	1
1	1
2	1
3	1

This is a function because each independent variable value (from the domain) is paired with one and only one dependent variable value (from the range).

Concepts	*Examples*

Function Notation

For a function f, the symbol $f(x)$ is used to represent the dependent variable associated with the independent variable x.

Find $f(-2)$ if $f(x) = -3x + 6$.
$$f(-2) = -3(-2) + 6$$
$$= 12$$

Linear Function

A function that can be written in the form
$$f(x) = ax + b$$
for real numbers a and b is a linear function.

Graph $f(x) = 2x - 5$.

x	$f(x)$
0	-5
3	1
-1	-7

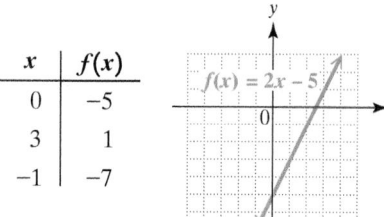

8.5 Quadratic Functions, Graphs, and Models

Graphs of Quadratic Functions

The graph of the quadratic function
$$f(x) = a(x - h)^2 + k \quad (\text{where } a \neq 0)$$
is a parabola with vertex at (h, k) and with the vertical line $x = h$ as axis of symmetry.

- The graph opens upward if a is positive and downward if a is negative.
- The graph is wider than the graph of $y = x^2$ if $0 < |a| < 1$ and narrower if $|a| > 1$.

Graph $f(x) = -(x + 3)^2 + 1$.

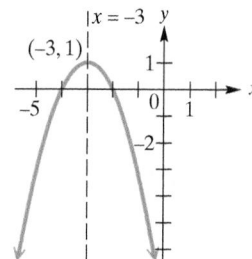

The graph opens down because $a < 0$.

Vertex: $(-3, 1)$

Axis of symmetry: $x = -3$

Vertex Formula

The vertex of the graph of $f(x) = ax^2 + bx + c$ (where $a \neq 0$) has coordinates as follows.
$$\left(-\frac{b}{2a}, f\left(-\frac{b}{2a}\right) \right)$$

Graph $f(x) = x^2 + 4x + 3$.

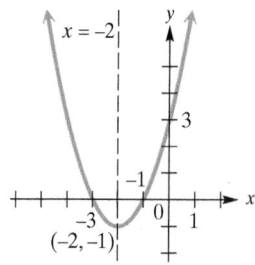

Graphing a Quadratic Function

Step 1   Determine whether the graphs opens up or down.

Step 2   Find the vertex.

Step 3   Find the y-intercept.

Step 4   Find the x-intercept(s), if any.

Step 5   Find and plot additional points as needed.

The graph opens up because $a > 0$.

Vertex: $(-2, -1)$

The solutions of $x^2 + 4x + 3 = 0$ are -1 and -3, so the x-intercepts are $(-1, 0)$ and $(-3, 0)$.

$f(0) = 3$, so the y-intercept is $(0, 3)$.

Axis of symmetry: $x = -2$

Concepts	Examples

8.6 Exponential and Logarithmic Functions, Graphs, and Models

Exponential Functions

For $a > 0$, $a \neq 1$, $f(x) = a^x$ is the exponential function with base a.

Graph of $f(x) = a^x$
1. The graph contains the point $(0, 1)$.
2. When $a > 1$, the graph rises from left to right.
   When $0 < a < 1$, the graph falls from left to right.
3. The x-axis is an asymptote.
4. The domain is $(-\infty, \infty)$ and the range is $(0, \infty)$.

Logarithmic Functions

$y = \log_b x$ means $x = b^y$.

For $b > 0$, $b \neq 1$, $\log_b b = 1$ and $\log_b 1 = 0$.

For $b > 0$, $b \neq 1$, $x > 0$, $g(x) = \log_b x$ is the logarithmic function with base b.

Graph of $g(x) = \log_b x$
1. The graph contains the point $(1, 0)$.
2. When $b > 1$, the graph rises from left to right.
   When $0 < b < 1$, the graph falls from left to right.
3. The y-axis is an asymptote.
4. The domain is $(0, \infty)$ and the range is $(-\infty, \infty)$.

$f(x) = 3^x$ is the exponential function with base 3.

x	y
-1	$\frac{1}{3}$
0	1
1	3

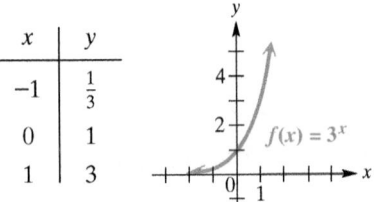

$y = \log_2 x$ means $x = 2^y$.

$$\log_3 3 = 1 \qquad \log_5 1 = 0$$

$g(x) = \log_3 x$ is the logarithmic function with base 3.

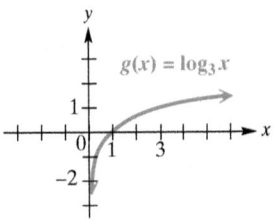

8.7 Systems of Linear Equations

Solving a Linear System by Elimination

Step 1 Write both equations in standard form.

Step 2 Make the coefficients of one pair of variable terms opposites.

Step 3 Add the new equations. The sum should be an equation with just one variable.

Step 4 Solve the equation from Step 3.

Step 5 Find the value of the other variable by substituting the result from Step 4 into either of the original equations.

Step 6 Check the ordered-pair solution in *both* of the *original* equations. Then write the solution set.

Solve by elimination.

$$5x + y = 2 \qquad (1)$$
$$2x - 3y = 11 \qquad (2)$$

To eliminate y, multiply equation (1) by 3, and add the result to equation (2).

$$15x + 3y = 6 \qquad \text{3 times equation (1)}$$
$$\underline{2x - 3y = 11} \qquad (2)$$
$$17x \qquad = 17 \qquad \text{Add.}$$
$$x = 1 \qquad \text{Divide by 17.}$$

Let $x = 1$ in equation (1), and solve for y.

$$5(1) + y = 2$$
$$y = -3$$

Check to verify that $\{(1, -3)\}$ is the solution set.

Concepts	*Examples*
Solving a Linear System by Substitution	Solve by substitution.
Step 1 Solve one of the equations for either variable.	$$4x - y = 7 \quad \text{(1)}$$ $$3x + 2y = 30 \quad \text{(2)}$$
Step 2 Substitute for that variable in the other equation. The result should be an equation with just one variable.	Solve for y in equation (1). $$y = 4x - 7$$
Step 3 Solve the equation from Step 2.	Substitute $4x - 7$ for y in equation (2), and solve for x.
Step 4 Find the value of the other variable by substituting the result from Step 3 into the equation from Step 1.	$$3x + 2y = 30 \quad \text{(2)}$$ $$3x + 2(4x - 7) = 30 \quad \text{Let } y = 4x - 7.$$ $$3x + 8x - 14 = 30 \quad \text{Distributive property}$$
Step 5 Check the ordered-pair solution in *both* of the *original* equations. Then write the solution set.	$$11x - 14 = 30 \quad \text{Combine like terms.}$$ $$11x = 44 \quad \text{Add 14.}$$ $$x = 4 \quad \text{Divide by 11.}$$
	Substitute 4 for x in the equation $y = 4x - 7$ to find y. $$y = 4(4) - 7$$ $$y = 9$$
	Check to verify that $\{(4, 9)\}$ is the solution set.
[8.8] Applications of Linear Systems	
Problem-Solving Method	The perimeter of a rectangle is 18 ft. The length is 3 ft more than twice the width. What are the dimensions of the rectangle?
Step 1 Read the problem carefully.	Let x represent the length and y represent the width. From the perimeter formula, one equation is $2x + 2y = 18$. From the problem, another equation is $x = 2y + 3$. We must solve the following system.
Step 2 Assign variables.	
Step 3 Write a system of equations that relates the unknowns.	$$2x + 2y = 18 \quad \text{(1)}$$ $$x = 2y + 3 \quad \text{(2)}$$
Step 4 Solve the system.	Substitute $2y + 3$ for x in equation (1).
Step 5 State the answer.	$$2x + 2y = 18 \quad \text{(1)}$$ $$2(2y + 3) + 2y = 18 \quad \text{Let } x = 2y + 3.$$ $$4y + 6 + 2y = 18 \quad \text{Distributive property}$$
Step 6 Check.	$$6y = 12 \quad \text{Combine like terms. Subtract.}$$ $$y = 2 \quad \text{Divide by 6.}$$
	Because $y = 2$, $$x = 2(2) + 3 = 7.$$
	Check that the length of the rectangle is 7 ft and the width is 2 ft.

Concepts	Examples

8.9 Linear Inequalities, Systems, and Linear Programming

Graphing a Linear Inequality

Step 1 Graph the line that is the boundary of the region. Make it solid if the inequality is $\leq$ or $\geq$, because of the equality portion of the symbol. Make it dashed if the inequality is $<$ or $>$.

Step 2 Use any point not on the line as a test point. Substitute for x and y in the inequality. If the result is true, shade the region of the line containing the test point. If the result is false, shade the other region.

Graph $2x + y \leq 5$.

Graph the line $2x + y = 5$.

Make it solid because of the equality portion of the symbol $\leq$.

Use $(0, 0)$ as a test point.

$$2x + y \leq 5$$
$$2(0) + 0 \overset{?}{\leq} 5$$
$$0 \leq 5 \quad \text{True}$$

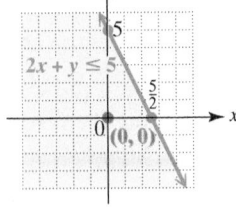

Shade the side of the line containing $(0, 0)$.

Solving a Linear Programming Problem
Write the objective function and all constraints, graph the feasible region, identify all vertex points (corner points), and find the value of the objective function at each vertex point. Choose the required maximum or minimum value accordingly.

Find the maximum value of the objective function

$$8x + 12y$$

for the given constraints.

$$x \geq 0$$
$$y \geq 0$$
$$x + 2y \leq 14$$
$$3x + 4y \leq 36$$

The region of feasible solutions is given here.

Vertex Point	Value of $8x + 12y$
$(0, 0)$	0
$(0, 7)$	84
$(12, 0)$	96
$(8, 3)$	100 ← Maximum

The objective function is maximized at 100 for

$$x = 8 \quad \text{and} \quad y = 3.$$

CHAPTER 8   TEST

1. Find the distance between the points $(-3, 5)$ and $(2, 1)$.

2. Find an equation of the circle whose center has coordinates $(-1, 2)$, with radius 3. Sketch its graph.

3. *Restaurant Revenue*   Total revenue of full-service restaurants in the United States increased from $117.8 billion in 1998 to $184.2 billion in 2010. Use the midpoint formula to estimate the total revenue for 2004, and compare this to the actual figure of $156.9 billion. (*Source:* National Restaurant Association.)

4. Find the x- and y-intercepts of the graph of

$$3x - 2y = 8,$$

and graph the equation.

5. Find the slope of the line passing through the points $(6, 4)$ and $(-1, 2)$.

6. Find the slope-intercept form of the equation of the line described.

    (a) passing through the point $(-1, 3)$, with slope $-\frac{2}{5}$

    (b) passing through the point $(-7, 2)$ and perpendicular to $y = 2x$

    (c) the line through $(-2, 3)$ and $(6, -1)$

7. Which one of the following has a positive slope and a negative y-coordinate for its y-intercept?

    A.   **B.**

    C.   **D.**

8. *Life Expectancy*   The table shows life expectancy at birth, in years, for selected years from 1943 to 2003.

Year	Life Expectancy at Birth (in years)
1943	63.3
1953	68.8
1963	69.9
1973	71.4
1983	74.6
1993	75.5
2003	77.6

Source: Centers for Disease Control and Prevention.

    (a) Use the information given for the years 1943 and 2003, letting $x = 0$ represent 1943 and $x = 60$ represent 2003. Let y represent life expectancy in years. Use these two years to write an equation that models life expectancy.

    (b) Use the equation from part (a) to estimate life expectancy in 2013.

9. *Cellular Phone Subscribers*   In 2006, there were 233 million cellular phone subscribers in the United States. By 2010, this number had risen to 303 million. What was the average rate of change per year during this period? Interpret this number.

10. *Library Fines*   It costs a borrower $0.05 per day for an overdue book, plus a flat $0.50 charge for all books borrowed. Let x represent the number of days the book is overdue, and let y represent the total fine to the tardy user.

    (a) Write an equation in the form

$$y = mx + b$$

    for this situation.

    (b) Give three ordered pairs with x-values of 1, 5, and 10 that satisfy the equation.

11. Write the slope-intercept form of the equation of the line by observing the graph.

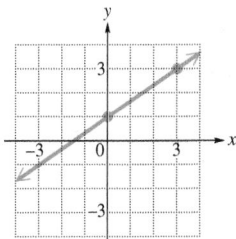

12. Find each of the following for

$$f(x) = -4x + 7.$$

    (a) $f(3)$

    (b) the value of x for which $f(x) = -1$

13. *Calculator Production*   If the cost to produce x units of calculators is

$$C(x) = 50x + 5000 \text{ dollars,}$$

and the revenue is

$$R(x) = 60x \text{ dollars,}$$

find the number of units of calculators that must be produced in order to break even. What is the revenue at the break-even point?

14. Graph the following quadratic function.

$$f(x) = -(x + 3)^2 + 4$$

Give the equation of its axis of symmetry and the coordinates of its vertex.

15. *Dimensions of a Parking Lot* Kirkwood Community College wants to construct a rectangular parking lot on land bordered on one side by a highway. It has 320 ft of fencing with which to fence off the other three sides. What should be the dimensions of the lot if the enclosed area is to be a maximum? What is this maximum area?

16. Use a scientific calculator to find an approximation of each of the following. The number of digits shown will vary depending on the model of calculator used.

(a) $5.1^{4.7}$ **(b)** $e^{-1.85}$ **(c)** $\ln 23.56$

17. *Investment* Suppose that $12,000 is invested in an account that pays 2% annual interest, and it is left untouched for 3 years. How much will be in the account in each of the following cases?

(a) Interest is compounded quarterly (four times per year).

(b) Interest is compounded continuously.

18. *Decay of Plutonium-241* Suppose that the amount, in grams, of plutonium-241 present in a given sample is determined by the function

$$f(x) = 2.00e^{-0.053x},$$

where x is measured in years. Find the amount present in the sample after the given number of years.

(a) 4   **(b)** 10   **(c)** 20

(d) What was the initial amount present?

Solve each system by using elimination, substitution, or a combination of the two methods.

19. $2x + 3y = 2$
$3x - 4y = 20$

20. $x + 3y = 7$
$-2x - 6y = -7$

Solve each problem by using a system of equations.

21. *Ticket Prices* In a recent year, four Red Sox tickets and four Yankees tickets purchased at their average prices cost $420.84, while two Red Sox tickets and six Yankees tickets cost $417.74. Find the average ticket price for a Red Sox ticket and for a Yankees ticket. (*Source:* Team Marketing Report.)

22. *Candy Mixture* Sweet's Candy Store is offering a special mix for Valentine's Day. Ms. Sweet will mix some $6-per-lb nuts with some $3-per-lb chocolate candy to get 100 lb of mix, which she will sell at $3.90 per lb. How many pounds of each should she use?

23. Graph the solution set of the system of inequalities.

$$x + y \le 6$$
$$2x - y \ge 3$$

24. *Profit from Farm Animals* Callie raises only pigs and geese. She wants to raise no more than 16 animals, with no more than 12 geese. She spends $50 to raise a pig and $20 to raise a goose. She has $500 available for this purpose. Find the maximum profit she can make if she makes a profit of $80 per goose and $40 per pig. Indicate how many pigs and geese she should raise to achieve this maximum.

Geometry

9

Programmers of video games, flight simulators, and other virtual reality applications use software programs to render objects in their virtual world in three dimensions. The software can track the location of objects in the "world" and then show only the ones in the part of the world where the user is looking.

Some of the concepts from this chapter are foundational to the rendering process involved in such applications.

9.1   POINTS, LINES, PLANES, AND ANGLES

The Geometry of Euclid

Let no one unversed in geometry enter here.
  —Motto over the door of Plato's Academy

To the ancient Greeks, mathematics meant geometry above all—a rigid kind of geometry from a modern-day point of view. The Greeks studied the properties of figures identical in shape and size (congruent figures) as well as figures identical in shape but not necessarily in size (similar figures). They absorbed ideas about area and volume from the Egyptians and Babylonians and established general formulas. The Greeks were the first to insist that statements in geometry be given rigorous proof.

The most basic ideas of geometry are **point, line,** and **plane.** In fact, it is not really possible to define them with other words. Euclid defined a point as "that which has no part," but this definition is vague. He defined a line as "that which has breadthless length." Again, this definition is vague. Based on our experience, however, we know what Euclid meant. The drawings that we use for points are dots. Lines have properties of no thickness and no width, and they extend indefinitely in two directions.

Euclid's definition of a plane, "a surface which lies evenly with the straight lines on itself," is represented by a flat surface, such as a tabletop or a page in a book.

Euclid's *Elements* as translated by Billingsley appeared in 1570 and was the first English-language translation of the text—the most influential geometry text ever written.

Unfortunately, no copy of *Elements* exists that dates back to the time of Euclid (circa 300 B.C.), and most current translations are based on a revision of the work prepared by Theon of Alexandria.

Points, Lines, and Planes

There are certain universally accepted conventions and symbols used to represent points, lines, and planes. A capital letter usually represents a point. A line may be named by two capital letters representing points that lie on the line, or by a single (usually lowercase) letter, such as ℓ. Subscripts are sometimes used to distinguish one line from another when a lowercase letter is used. For example, ℓ_1 and ℓ_2 would represent two distinct lines. A plane may be named by three capital letters representing points that lie in the plane, or by a letter of the Greek alphabet, such as α (alpha), β (beta), or γ (gamma).

Figure 1 depicts a plane that may be represented either as α or as plane *ADE*. Contained in the plane is the line *DE* (or, equivalently, line *ED*), which is also labeled ℓ in the figure.

Selecting any point on a line divides the line into three parts: the point itself, and two **half-lines,** one on each side of the point. For example, point *A* divides the line shown in **Figure 2** into three parts, *A* itself and two half-lines. Point *A* belongs to neither half-line. As the figure suggests, each half-line extends indefinitely in the direction opposite the other half-line.

Figure 1

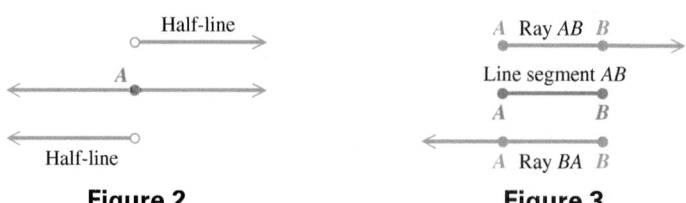

Figure 2

Figure 3

Including an initial point with a half-line gives a **ray.** A ray is named with two letters, one for the initial point of the ray, and one for another point contained in the half-line. In **Figure 3** ray *AB* has initial point *A* and extends in the direction of *B*. On the other hand, ray *BA* has *B* as its initial point and extends in the direction of *A*.

Given any three points that are not in a straight line, a plane can be passed through the points. That is why **camera tripods** have three legs—no matter how irregular the surface, the tips of the three legs determine a plane. A camera support with four legs would wobble unless all four legs were carefully extended just the right amount.

A **line segment** includes both endpoints and is named by its endpoints. **Figure 3** shows line segment AB, which may also be designated as line segment BA.

Table 1 shows these figures along with the symbols used to represent them.

Table 1

Name	Figure	Symbol
Line AB or line BA		$\overleftrightarrow{AB}$ or $\overleftrightarrow{BA}$
Half-line AB		$\overrightarrow{AB}$
Half-line BA		$\overleftarrow{BA}$
Ray AB		$\overrightarrow{AB}$
Ray BA		$\overleftarrow{BA}$
Segment AB or segment BA		$\overline{AB}$ or $\overline{BA}$

For a line, the symbol above the two letters shows two arrowheads, indicating that the line extends indefinitely in both directions. For half-lines and rays, only one arrowhead is used because these extend in only one direction. An open circle is used for a half-line to show that the endpoint is not included, while a solid circle is used for a ray to indicate the inclusion of the endpoint. Since a segment includes both endpoints and does not extend in either direction, solid circles are used to indicate endpoints of line segments.

The geometric definitions of "parallel" and "intersecting" apply to two or more lines or planes. (See **Figure 4.**) **Parallel lines** lie in the same plane and never meet, no matter how far they are extended. However, **intersecting lines** do meet.

If two distinct lines intersect, they intersect in one and only one point.

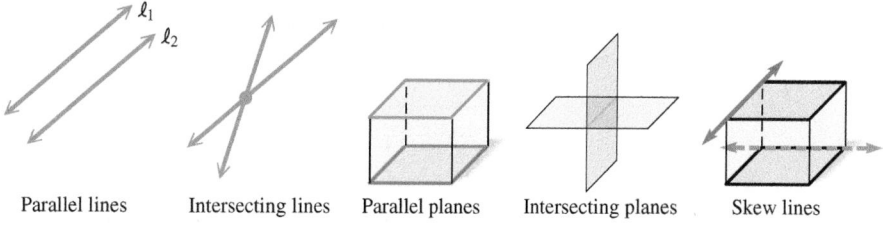

Parallel lines   Intersecting lines   Parallel planes   Intersecting planes   Skew lines

Figure 4

We use the symbol $\parallel$ to denote parallelism. If ℓ_1 and ℓ_2 are parallel lines, as in **Figure 4,** then this may be indicated as

$$\ell_1 \parallel \ell_2.$$

Parallel planes also never meet, no matter how far they are extended. Two distinct **intersecting planes** form a straight line, the one and only line they have in common. **Skew lines** do not lie in a common plane, so they are neither parallel nor intersecting.

Angles are the key to the study of **geodesy,** the measurement of distances on the earth's surface.

Angles

An **angle** is the union of two rays that have a common endpoint. See **Figure 5.** The angle is formed by points on the rays themselves, and no other points. In **Figure 5,** point X is *not* a point on the angle. (It is said to be in the *interior* of the angle.)

Figure 5

The rays forming an angle are its **sides.** The common endpoint of the rays is the **vertex** of the angle. There are two standard ways of naming angles using letters. If no confusion will result, an angle can be named with the letter marking its vertex. Using this method, the angles in **Figure 5** can be named, respectively, angle B, angle E, and angle K.

Angles also can be named with three letters: the first letter names a point on one side of the angle; the middle letter names the vertex; the third names a point on the other side of the angle. In this system, the angles in the figure can be named angle ABC, angle DEF, and angle JKL. The symbol for representing an angle is $\angle$. Rather than writing "angle ABC," we may write "$\angle ABC$."

An angle can be associated with an amount of rotation. For example, in **Figure 6(a),** we let $\overrightarrow{BA}$ first coincide with $\overrightarrow{BC}$—as though they were the same ray. We then rotate $\overrightarrow{BA}$ (the endpoint remains fixed) in a counterclockwise direction to form $\angle ABC$.

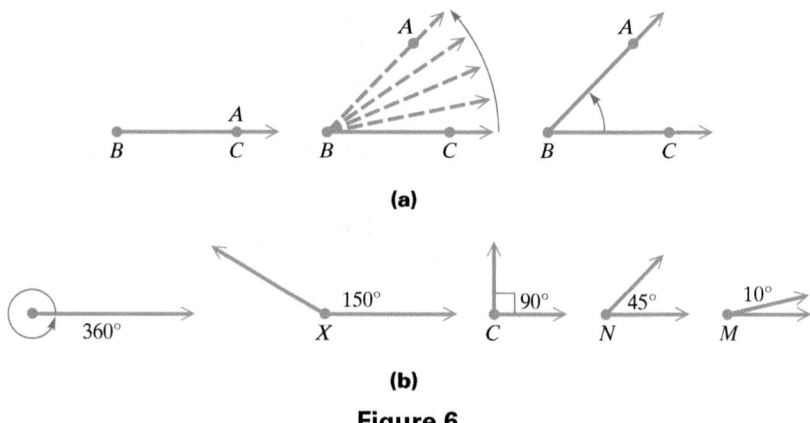

(a)

(b)

Figure 6

Why 360? The use of the number 360 goes back to the Babylonian culture. There are several theories regarding why 360 was chosen for the number of degrees in a complete rotation around a circle. One says that 360 was chosen because it is close to the number of days in a year and because it is conveniently divisible by 2, 3, 4, 5, 6, 8, 9, 10, 12, and other numbers.

Angles are measured by the amount of rotation, using a system that dates back to the Babylonians. Babylonian astronomers chose the number 360 to represent a complete rotation of a ray back onto itself. **One degree,** written $1°$, is defined to be $\frac{1}{360}$ of a complete rotation. **Figure 6(b)** shows angles of various degree measures.

Angles are classified and named with reference to their degree measures. An angle whose measure is between $0°$ and $90°$ is an **acute angle.** Angles M and N in **Figure 6(b)** are acute. An angle that measures $90°$ is a **right angle.** Angle C in the figure is a right angle. The squared symbol $\llcorner$ at the vertex denotes a right angle. Angles that measure more than $90°$ but less than $180°$ are said to be **obtuse angles** (angle X, for example). An angle that measures $180°$ is a **straight angle.** Its sides form a straight line.

A **protractor** is a tool used to measure angles. **Figure 7** shows a protractor measuring an angle whose measure is 135°.

To use a protractor, position the hole (or dot) of the protractor on the vertex of the angle. With the 0-degree measure on the protractor placed on one side of the angle, the other side will show the degree measure of the angle.

Figure 7

When two lines intersect to form right angles, they are called **perpendicular lines.** In **Figure 8,** the sides of ∡*NMP* have been extended to form another angle, ∡*RMQ*. The pair ∡*NMP* and ∡*RMQ* are called **vertical angles.** Another pair of vertical angles have been formed at the same time. They are ∡*NMQ* and ∡*PMR*.

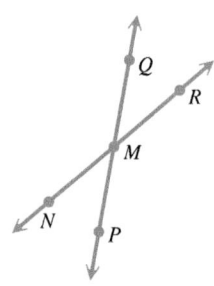

Figure 8

PROPERTY OF VERTICAL ANGLES

Vertical angles have equal measures.

EXAMPLE 1 Finding Angle Measures

Find the measure of each marked angle in the given figure.

(a) Figure 9   **(b) Figure 10**

Solution

(a) Because the marked angles are vertical angles, they have the same measure.

$$4x + 19 = 6x - 5 \qquad \text{Set measures equal.}$$
$$4x + 19 - 4x = 6x - 5 - 4x \qquad \text{Subtract } 4x.$$
$$19 = 2x - 5 \qquad \text{Combine like terms.}$$
$$19 + 5 = 2x - 5 + 5 \qquad \text{Add 5.}$$
$$24 = 2x \qquad \text{Add.}$$

Don't stop here. $\quad 12 = x \qquad$ Divide by 2.

Since $x = 12$, one angle has measure $4(12) + 19 = 67$ degrees. The other has the same measure, because $6(12) - 5 = 67$ as well. Each angle measures 67°.

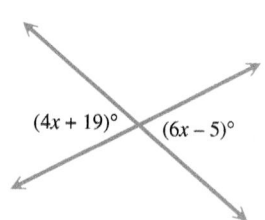

Figure 9

(b) The measures of the marked angles must add to 180°. They form a straight angle.

$$(3x - 30) + 4x = 180 \qquad \text{The angle sum is 180.}$$
$$7x - 30 = 180 \qquad \text{Combine like terms.}$$
$$7x - 30 + 30 = 180 + 30 \qquad \text{Add 30.}$$
$$7x = 210 \qquad \text{Add.}$$

Don't stop here. $\quad x = 30 \qquad$ Divide by 7.

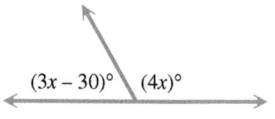

Figure 10

To find the measures of the angles, replace x with 30 in the two expressions.

$$3x - 30 = 3(30) - 30 = 90 - 30 = 60$$
$$4x = 4(30) = 120$$

The two angle measures are 60° and 120°. ∎

If the sum of the measures of two acute angles is 90°, the angles are said to be **complementary,** and each is called the *complement* of the other. For example, angles measuring 40° and 50° are complementary angles, because

$$40° + 50° = 90°.$$

If two angles have a sum of 180°, they are **supplementary.** The *supplement* of an angle whose measure is 40° is an angle whose measure is 140°, because

$$40° + 140° = 180°.$$

If x represents the degree measure of an angle, 90 − x represents the measure of its complement, and 180 − x represents the measure of its supplement.

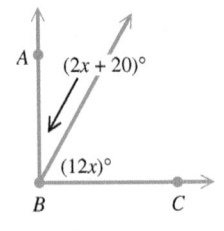

Figure 11

EXAMPLE 2 Finding Angle Measures

Find the measures of the angles in **Figure 11,** given that $\angle ABC$ is a right angle.

Solution

The sum of the measures of the two acute angles is 90° (that is, they are complementary), because they form a right angle.

$$
\begin{array}{ll}
(2x + 20) + 12x = 90 & \text{The angle measures sum to 90°.} \\
14x + 20 = 90 & \text{Combine like terms.} \\
14x = 70 & \text{Subtract 20.} \\
x = 5 & \text{Divide by 14.}
\end{array}
$$

The value of x is 5. Therefore, replace x with 5 in the two expressions.

$$2x + 20 = 2(5) + 20 = 30$$
$$12x = 12(5) = 60$$

The measures of the two angles are 30° and 60°. ∎

EXAMPLE 3 Using Complementary and Supplementary Angles

The supplement of an angle measures 10° more than three times its complement. Find the measure of the angle.

Solution

Let $\qquad x =$ the degree measure of the angle.

Then $\qquad 180 - x =$ the degree measure of its supplement,

and $\qquad 90 - x =$ the degree measure of its complement.

$$
\begin{array}{ll}
180 - x = 10 + 270 - 3x & \text{Distributive property} \\
180 - x = 280 - 3x & \text{Combine like terms.} \\
2x = 100 & \text{Add 3x. Subtract 180.} \\
x = 50 & \text{Divide by 2.}
\end{array}
$$

The angle measures 50°. Because its supplement (130°) is 10° more than three times its complement (40°) (that is, $130 = 10 + 3(40)$ is true), the answer checks. ∎

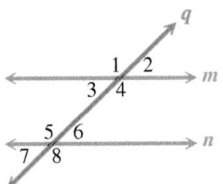

Figure 12

Figure 12 shows parallel lines m and n. When a line q intersects two parallel lines, q is a **transversal.** In **Figure 12,** the transversal intersecting the parallel lines forms eight angles, indicated by numbers. Angles 1 through 8 in the figure possess some special properties regarding their degree measures, as shown in **Table 2.**

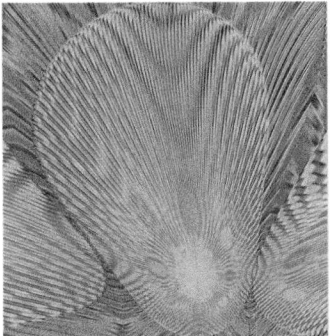

A set of parallel lines with equidistant spacing intersects an identical set, but at a small angle. The result is a **moiré pattern,** named after the fabric *moiré* ("watered") *silk.* Moiré patterns are related to **periodic functions,** which describe regular recurring phenomena (wave patterns such as heartbeats or business cycles). Moirés thus apply to the study of electromagnetic, sound, and water waves, to crystal structure, and to other wave phenomena.

Table 2

Name	Figure	Rule
Alternate interior angles		Angle measures are equal.
Alternate exterior angles		Angle measures are equal.
Interior angles on same side of transversal		Angle measures add to 180°.
Corresponding angles		Angle measures are equal.

The converses of the above also are true. That is, if alternate interior angles are equal, then the lines are parallel. Similar results are valid for alternate exterior angles, interior angles on the same side of a transversal, and corresponding angles.

EXAMPLE 4 **Finding Angle Measures**

Find the measure of each marked angle in **Figure 13,** given that lines m and n are parallel.

Solution

The marked angles are alternate exterior angles, which are equal.

$$3x + 2 = 5x - 40 \quad \text{Set angle measures equal.}$$
$$42 = 2x \quad \text{Subtract 3x. Add 40.}$$
$$21 = x \quad \text{Divide by 2.}$$

Don't stop here.

Thus, $3x + 2 = 3 \cdot 21 + 2 = 65$ and $5x - 40 = 5 \cdot 21 - 40 = 65$.

So both angles measure 65°.

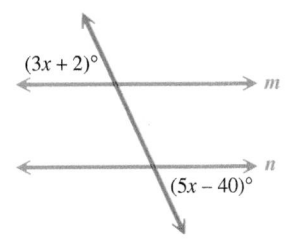

Figure 13

$(3x + 2)°$

m

n

$(5x - 40)°$

9.1 EXERCISES

Fill in each blank with the correct response.

1. The sum of the measures of two complementary angles is _____ degrees.

2. The sum of the measures of two supplementary angles is _____ degrees.

3. The measures of two vertical angles are _____.
   (equal/not equal)

4. The measures of _____ right angles add up to the measure of a straight angle.

Decide whether each statement is true *or* false.

5. A line segment has two endpoints.

6. A ray has one endpoint.

7. If *A* and *B* are distinct points on a line, then ray *AB* and ray *BA* represent the same set of points.

8. If two lines intersect, they lie in the same plane.

9. If two lines are parallel, they lie in the same plane.

10. If two lines are neither parallel nor intersecting, they cannot lie in the same plane.

11. If two lines do not intersect, they must be parallel.

12. There is no angle that is its own complement.

13. Segment *AB* and segment *BA* represent the same set of points.

14. There is no angle whose complement and supplement are the same.

15. There is no angle that is its own supplement.

16. The use of the degree as a unit of measure of an angle goes back to the Egyptians.

Exercises 17–24 name portions of the line shown. For each exercise, **(a)** *give the symbol that represents the portion of the line named, and* **(b)** *draw a figure showing just the portion named, including all labeled points.*

17. line segment *AB*

18. ray *BC*

19. ray *CB*

20. line segment *AD*

21. half-line *BC*

22. half-line *AD*

23. ray *BA*

24. line segment *CA*

Match each symbol in Group I with the symbol in Group II that names the same set of points, based on the figure.

I		**II**	
25. $\overleftrightarrow{PQ}$	26. $\overrightarrow{QR}$	**A.** $\overset{\circ\!\to}{QS}$	**B.** $\overrightarrow{RQ}$
27. $\overrightarrow{QR}$	28. $\overleftrightarrow{PQ}$	**C.** $\overset{\circ}{SR}$	**D.** $\overrightarrow{QS}$
29. $\overrightarrow{RP}$	30. $\overrightarrow{SQ}$	**E.** $\overset{\circ}{SP}$	**F.** $\overrightarrow{QP}$
31. $\overleftrightarrow{PS}$	32. $\overset{\circ\!\to}{PS}$	**G.** $\overleftrightarrow{RS}$	**H.** none of these

Lines, rays, half-lines, and segments may be considered sets of points. The **intersection** *(symbolized ∩) of two sets is composed of all elements common to both sets, while the* **union** *(symbolized ∪) of two sets is composed of all elements found in at least one of the two sets.*

Based on the figure below, specify each of the sets given in Exercises 33–40 in a simpler way.

33. $\overleftrightarrow{MN} \cup \overset{\to}{NO}$

34. $\overleftrightarrow{MN} \cap \overset{\to}{NO}$

35. $\overrightarrow{NP} \cap \overrightarrow{OM}$

36. $\overleftrightarrow{MO} \cup \overrightarrow{OM}$

37. $\overset{\circ\!\to}{OP} \cap O$

38. $\overset{\circ\!\to}{OP} \cup O$

39. $\overrightarrow{NP} \cap \overset{\to}{OP}$

40. $\overleftrightarrow{NP} \cup \overset{\circ\!\to}{OP}$

Give the measure of the complement of each angle.

41. 28°

42. 32°

43. 89°

44. 45°

45. $x°$

46. $(90 - x)°$

Give the measure of the supplement of each angle.

47. 132°

48. 105°

49. 26°

50. 90°

51. $y°$

52. $(180 - y)°$

Complementary and Supplementary Angles *Solve each problem.*

53. If the supplement of an angle is 40° more than twice its complement, what is the measure of the angle?

54. If an angle measures 15° less than twice its complement, what is the measure of the angle?

55. Half the supplement of an angle is 12° less than twice the complement of the angle. Find the measure of the angle.

56. The supplement of an angle measures 25° more than twice its complement. Find the measure of the angle.

Name all pairs of vertical angles in each figure.

57.

58.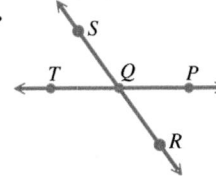

59. In **Exercise 57,** if ∡*ABE* has a measure of 52°, find the measures of the following angles.

(a) ∡*CBD* (b) ∡*CBE*

60. In **Exercise 58,** if ∡*SQP* has a measure of 126°, find the measures of the following angles.

(a) ∡*TQR* (b) ∡*PQR*

Find the measure of each marked angle.

61.

62.

63.

64.

65.

66.

67.

68.

In Exercises 69–72, assume that lines m and n are parallel, and find the measure of each marked angle.

69.

70.

71.

72.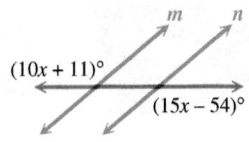

73. The sketch shows parallel lines *m* and *n* cut by a transversal *q*. Complete the steps to prove that alternate exterior angles have the same measure.

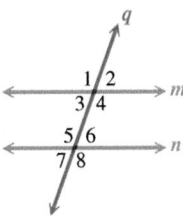

(a) Measure of ∡2 = measure of ∡ _____ , since they are vertical angles.

(b) Measure of ∡3 = measure of ∡ _____ , since they are alternate interior angles.

(c) Measure of ∡6 = measure of ∡ _____ , since they are vertical angles.

(d) By the results of parts (a), (b), and (c), the measure of ∡2 must equal the measure of ∡ _____ , showing that alternate _____ angles have equal measures.

74. Use the sketch to find the measure of each numbered angle. Assume that *m* ∥ *n*.

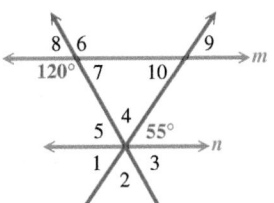

75. Complete these steps in the proof that vertical angles have equal measures. In this exercise, m (∡*x*) means "the measure of the angle *x*." Use the figure at the right.

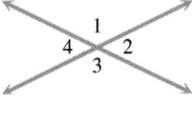

(a) m(∡1) + m(∡2) = _____ °

(b) m(∡2) + m(∡3) = _____ °

(c) Subtract the equation in part (b) from the equation in part (a) to get [m(∡1) + m(∡2)] − [m(∡2) + m(∡3)] = _____ ° − _____ °.

(d) m(∡1) + m(∡2) − m(∡2) − m(∡3) = _____ °

(e) m(∡1) − m(∡3) = _____ °

(f) m(∡1) = m(∡ _____)

9.2 CURVES, POLYGONS, CIRCLES, AND GEOMETRIC CONSTRUCTIONS

OBJECTIVES

1 Classify curves.
2 Identify and classify triangles and quadrilaterals.
3 Learn the vocabulary of circles.
4 Perform geometric constructions.

Curves

The term *curve* is used for describing figures in the plane.

> **SIMPLE CURVE AND CLOSED CURVE**
>
> A **simple curve** can be drawn without lifting the pencil from the paper and without passing through any point twice.
>
> A **closed curve** has its starting and ending points the same and is drawn without lifting the pencil from the paper.

Convex

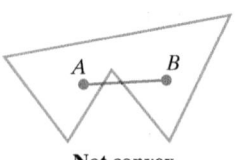

Not convex

Figure 15

Some examples are shown in **Figure 14.**

Simple; closed   Simple; not closed   Not simple; closed   Not simple; not closed

Figure 14

A simple closed figure is said to be **convex** if, for any two points A and B inside the figure, the line segment AB (that is, $\overleftrightarrow{AB}$) is always completely inside the figure. **Figure 15** shows a convex figure and one that is not convex.

Among the most common types of curves in mathematics are those that are both simple and closed, and perhaps the most important of these are *polygons.* A **polygon** is a simple closed curve made up only of straight line segments. The line segments are the *sides,* and the points at which the sides meet are the *vertices* (singular: *vertex*).

Polygons are classified according to the number of line segments used as sides. **Table 3** gives the special names. ***In general, if a polygon has n sides, and no particular value of n is specified, it is called an n-gon.***

Some examples of polygons are shown in **Figure 16.** A polygon may or may not be convex. Polygons with all sides equal and all angles equal are **regular polygons.**

Table 3 Classification of Polygons According to Number of Sides

Number of Sides	Name
3	triangle
4	quadrilateral
5	pentagon
6	hexagon
7	heptagon
8	octagon
9	nonagon
10	decagon

Convex   Not convex

Polygons are simple closed curves made up of straight line segments.

Regular polygons have equal sides and equal angles.

Figure 16

The puzzle game above comes from China, where it has been a popular amusement for centuries. Each figure above is a **tangram.** Any tangram is composed of the same set of seven tans (the pieces making up the figure).

Mathematicians have described various properties of tangrams. While each tan is convex, only 13 convex tangrams are possible. All others, like the figure on the left, are not convex.

Triangles and Quadrilaterals

Triangles are classified by measures of angles as well as by number of equal sides, as shown in the following box. (Notice that tick marks are used in the bottom three figures to show how side lengths are related.)

TYPES OF TRIANGLES

	All Angles Acute	*One Right Angle*	*One Obtuse Angle*
Angles	Acute triangle	Right triangle	Obtuse triangle
	All Sides Equal	*Two Sides Equal*	*No Sides Equal*
Sides	Equilateral triangle	Isosceles triangle	Scalene triangle

Quadrilaterals are classified by sides and angles. An important distinction involving quadrilaterals is whether one or more pairs of sides are parallel.

TYPES OF QUADRILATERALS

Sample Figure	*Definition*
Trapezoid	A **trapezoid** is a quadrilateral with one pair of parallel sides.
Parallelogram	A **parallelogram** is a quadrilateral with two pairs of parallel sides.
Rectangle	A **rectangle** is a parallelogram with a right angle (and consequently, four right angles).
Square	A **square** is a rectangle with all sides having equal length.
Rhombus	A **rhombus** is a parallelogram with all sides having equal length.

An important property of triangles that was first proved by the Greek geometers deals with the sum of the measures of the angles of any triangle.

ANGLE SUM OF A TRIANGLE

The sum of the measures of the interior angles of any triangle is 180°.

While it is not an actual proof, a rather convincing argument for the truth of this statement can be given using any size triangle cut from a piece of paper. Tear each corner from the triangle, as suggested in **Figure 17(a).** You should be able to rearrange the pieces so that the three angles form a straight angle, as shown in **Figure 17(b).**

(a)   (b)

Figure 17

▌▌EXAMPLE 1   Finding Angle Measures in a Triangle

Find the measure of each angle in the triangle of **Figure 18.**

Figure 18

Solution

By the angle sum relationship, the three angle measures must add up to 180°.

$$x + (x + 20) + (210 - 3x) = 180 \qquad \text{Sum is 180.}$$
$$-x + 230 = 180 \qquad \text{Combine like terms.}$$
$$-x = -50 \qquad \text{Subtract 230.}$$

> There are two more values to find.

$$x = 50 \qquad \text{Divide by } -1.$$

Because $x = 50$,

$$x + 20 = 50 + 20 = 70 \quad \text{and} \quad 210 - 3x = 210 - 3(50) = 60.$$

The three angles measure 50°, 70°, and 60°. Because $50° + 70° + 60° = 180°$, the answers satisfy the angle sum relationship. ∎

In the triangle shown in **Figure 19,** angles 1, 2, and 3 are **interior angles,** while angles 4, 5, and 6 are **exterior angles** of the triangle. Using the fact that the sum of the angle measures of any triangle is 180°, and the fact that a straight angle also measures 180°, the following property may be deduced.

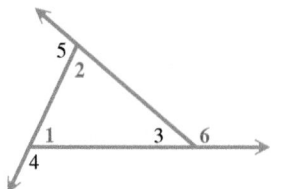

Figure 19

EXTERIOR ANGLE MEASURE

The measure of an exterior angle of a triangle is equal to the sum of the measures of the two opposite interior angles.

In **Figure 19,** the measure of angle 6 is equal to the sum of the measures of angles 1 and 2. Two other such statements can be made.

EXAMPLE 2 Finding Interior and Exterior Angle Measures

Find the measures of interior angles A, B, and C of the triangle in **Figure 20**, and the measure of exterior angle BCD.

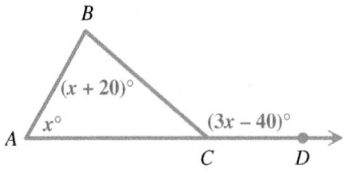

Figure 20

Solution

By the property concerning exterior angles, the sum of the measures of interior angles A and B must equal the measure of angle BCD.

$$x + (x + 20) = 3x - 40$$

$$2x + 20 = 3x - 40 \qquad \text{Combine like terms.}$$

$$-x = -60 \qquad \text{Subtract 3}x\text{. Subtract 20.}$$

$$x = 60 \qquad \text{Divide by } -1.$$

Because the value of x is 60, we have the following.

> m(angle A) denotes the measure of angle A.

$\text{m}(\text{Interior angle } A) = 60°$

$\text{m}(\text{Interior angle } B) = (60 + 20)° = 80°$

$\text{m}(\text{Interior angle } C) = 180° - (60° + 80°) = 40°$

$\text{m}(\text{Exterior angle } BCD) = [3(60) - 40]° = 140°$ ■

Circles

A circle is a simple closed curve defined as follows.

CIRCLE

A **circle** is a set of points in a plane, each of which is the same distance from a fixed point.

A circle may be physically constructed with a compass, where the spike leg remains fixed and the other leg swings around to construct the circle. A string may also be used to draw a circle. For example, loop a piece of chalk on one end of a piece of string. Hold the other end in a fixed position on a chalkboard, and pull the string taut. Then swing the chalk end around to draw a circle.

A circle, along with several lines and segments, is shown in **Figure 21**. The points P, Q, and R lie on the circle. Each lies the same distance from point O, which is the **center** of the circle. (It is the "fixed point" referred to in the definition.) $\overline{OP}$, $\overline{OQ}$, and $\overline{OR}$ are segments whose endpoints are the center and a point on the circle. Each is a **radius** of the circle (plural: *radii*). $\overline{PQ}$ is a segment whose endpoints both lie on the circle and is an example of a **chord**. The segment $\overleftrightarrow{PR}$ is a chord that passes through the center and is a **diameter** of the circle. Notice that the measure of a diameter is twice that of a radius. A diameter such as $\overleftrightarrow{PR}$ in **Figure 21** divides a circle into two parts of equal size, each of which is a **semicircle**.

Figure 21

Figure 21 (repeated)

Thales is credited with the first proof of the **inscribed angle theorem.** Legend records that he studied for a time in Egypt and then introduced geometry to Greece, where he attempted to apply the principles of Greek logic to his newly learned subject.

In **Figure 21,** $\overleftrightarrow{RT}$ is a line that touches (intersects) the circle in only one point, R, and is a **tangent** to the circle. R is the point of tangency. $\overleftrightarrow{PQ}$, which intersects the circle in two points, is a **secant** line. (What is the distinction between a chord and a secant?)

The portion of the circle shown in red in **Figure 21** is an **arc** of the circle. It consists of two endpoints (P and Q) and all points on the circle "between" these endpoints. The colored portion is arc PQ (or QP), denoted in symbols as $\overparen{PQ}$ (or $\overparen{QP}$). An angle such as QPR, which has its vertex P on the circle and its sides $\overrightarrow{PQ}$ and $\overrightarrow{PR}$, is said to be **inscribed** in the circle, and it **intercepts** arc QR.

The Greeks were the first to insist that all propositions, or **theorems,** about geometry be given rigorous proofs before being accepted. One of the theorems receiving such a proof was this one.

INSCRIBED ANGLE

Any angle inscribed in a circle has degree measure half of that of its intercepted arc.

Figure 22(a) states this theorem symbolically. For example, if *arc PR* measures $80°$, then inscribed angle PQR measures $\left(\frac{80}{2}\right)° = 40°$. A special case of this theorem is indicated in **Figure 22(b)**. *Any angle inscribed in a semicircle is a right angle.*

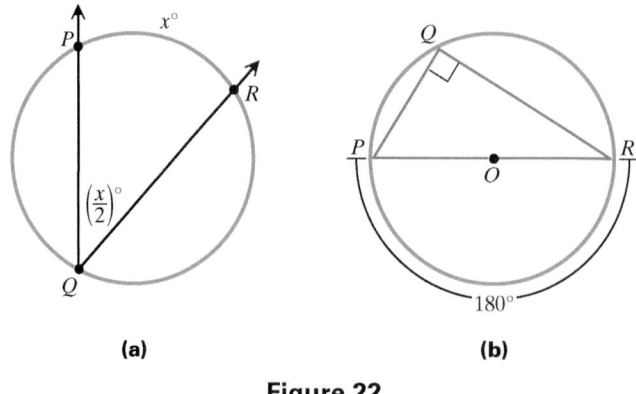

(a)   (b)

Figure 22

Geometric Constructions

A **compass** may be used to:
1. Swing a circular arc with given center and radius.
2. Reproduce a given length. (The Greeks used "collapsing" compasses, which would not allow distances to be copied directly. But Proposition II from Book I of Euclid's *Elements* provides a construction for transferring distances using a collapsing compass. Thus for our purposes, we will use a "fixed" compass.)

To the Greeks, geometry was the highest expression of mathematics. It is no surprise then that they required **geometric constructions** to have abstract beauty. This was achieved by allowing only a minimal set of tools: a compass (also called compasses, or a pair of compasses) for drawing circles and arcs of circles, and an unmarked straightedge for drawing straight line segments.

Here are three basic constructions. Their justifications are based on the *congruence properties* of **Section 9.3.**

Perpendicular Bisector **Construct the perpendicular bisector of a given line segment.**

Let the segment have endpoints A and B. Adjust the compass for any radius greater than half the length of AB. Place the point of the compass at A and draw an arc; then draw another arc of the same size at B. The line drawn through the points of intersection of these two arcs is the desired perpendicular bisector. See **Figure 23.**

Figure 23

In his first effort as a director, Mel Gibson starred in the 1993 movie *The Man Without a Face.* As disfigured former teacher Justin McLeod, he tutors teenager Chuck Norstadt (portrayed by Nick Stahl). McLeod explains to Norstadt how to find the center of a circle using any three points on the circle as he sketches the diagram on a windowpane. His explanation is based on the fact that the **perpendicular bisector** of any chord of a circle passes through the center of the circle. See the figure.

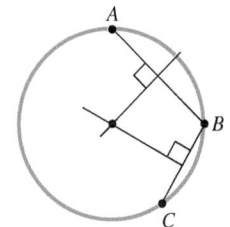

Perpendicular to a Line **Construct a perpendicular from a point off a line to the line.**

1. Let A be the point, r the line. Place the point of the compass at A and draw an arc, cutting r in two points.

2. Swing arcs of equal radius from each of the two points on r that were constructed in (1). The line drawn through the intersection of the two arcs and point A is perpendicular to r. See **Figure 24**.

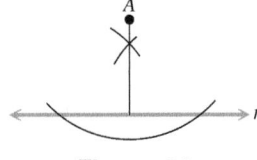

Figure 24

Copied Angle **Copy an angle.**

1. In order to copy an angle ABC on line r, place the point of the compass at B and draw an arc. Then place the point of the compass on r' at some point P and draw the same arc, as in **Figure 25**.

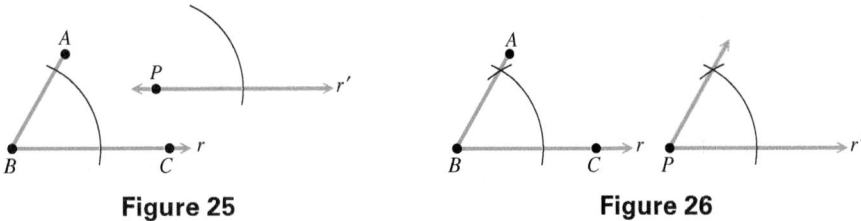

Figure 25 **Figure 26**

2. Measure, with your compass, the distance between the points where the arc intersects the angle, and transfer this distance, as shown in **Figure 26**. Use a straightedge to join P to the point of intersection. The angle is now copied.

There are other basic constructions that can be found in books on plane geometry.

9.2 EXERCISES

Fill in each blank with the correct response.

1. A segment joining two points on a circle is called a(n) _____.

2. A segment joining the center of a circle and a point on the circle is called a(n) _____.

3. A regular triangle is called a(n) _____ triangle.

4. A chord that contains the center of a circle is called a(n) _____.

Decide whether each statement is true *or* false.

5. A rhombus is an example of a regular polygon.

6. If a triangle is isosceles, then it is not scalene.

7. A triangle can have more than one obtuse angle.

8. A square is both a rectangle and a parallelogram.

9. A square must be a rhombus.

10. A rhombus must be a square.

11. In your own words, explain the distinction between a chord and a secant.

12. What common traffic sign in the United States is in the shape of an octagon?

Identify each curve as simple, closed, both, *or* neither.

13.

14.

15.

16.

17.

18.

19.

20.

Decide whether each figure is convex *or* not convex.

21.

22.

23.

24.

25.

26.

Classify each triangle as acute, right, *or* obtuse. *Also classify each as* equilateral, isosceles, *or* scalene.

27.

28.

29.

30.

31.

32.

33.

34.

35.

36.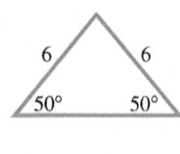

37. Give a definition of *isosceles right triangle.*

38. Can a triangle be both right and obtuse?

Find the measure of each angle in triangle ABC.

39.

40.

41.

42.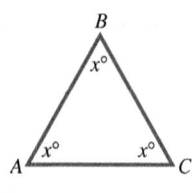

43. Angle Measures In triangle ABC, angles A and B have the same measure, while the measure of angle C is 15 degrees larger than the measure of each of A and B. What are the measures of the three angles?

44. Angle Measures In triangle ABC, the measure of angle A is 3 degrees more than the measure of angle B. The measure of angle B is the same as the measure of angle C. Find the measure of each angle.

In each triangle, find the measure of exterior angle BCD.

45.

46.

47. Find the sum, in degrees, of the six labeled angles. (*Source: Mathematics Teacher*)

48. In $\triangle ABC$ shown, D is some interior point, and x is the measure of $\angle C$, in degrees. Find x. (*Source: Mathematics Teacher*)

49. Using the points, segments, and lines in the figure, list all parts of the circle.

(a) center

(b) radii

(c) diameters

(d) chords

(e) secants

(f) tangents

50. In the classic 1939 movie *The Wizard of Oz,* the Scarecrow, upon getting a brain, says the following:

"The sum of the square roots of any two sides of an isosceles triangle is equal to the square root of the remaining side."

Give an example to show that his statement is incorrect.

In Exercises 51 and 52, construct the perpendicular bisector of segment PQ.

51.

52.

In Exercises 53 and 54, construct a perpendicular from P to the line r.

53.

54.

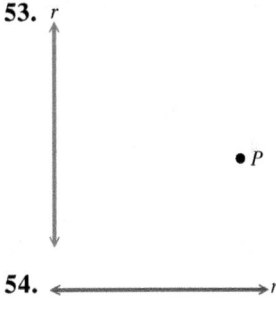

In Exercises 55 and 56, construct a perpendicular through the line r at P.

55.

56.

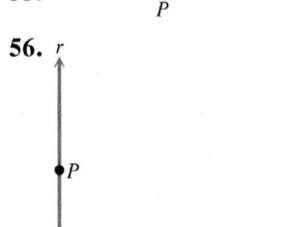

In Exercises 57 and 58, copy the given angle.

57.   **58.**

59. Investigate Proposition II of Book I of Euclid's *Elements*, and explain why the construction it provides enables us to use a "fixed" compass without guilt.

60. Use a software program to duplicate any of the constructions in **Exercises 51–58.** Print your results and show your instructor. There are some excellent free programs (www.geogebra.org, for example) available online.

OBJECTIVES

1 Recognize congruent triangles.

2 Determine similar triangles.

3 Learn and apply the Pythagorean theorem.

Congruent Triangles

Triangles that are both the same size and the same shape are **congruent triangles.** Informally speaking, if two triangles are congruent, then it is possible to pick up one of them and place it on top of the other so that they coincide exactly. As an everyday example of congruent triangles, consider the triangular supports for a child's swing set, machine-produced with exactly the same dimensions each time.

We use the symbol $\triangle$ to designate triangles. **Figure 27** illustrates two congruent triangles, $\triangle ABC$ and $\triangle DEF$. The symbol $\cong$ denotes congruence, so

$$\triangle ABC \cong \triangle DEF.$$

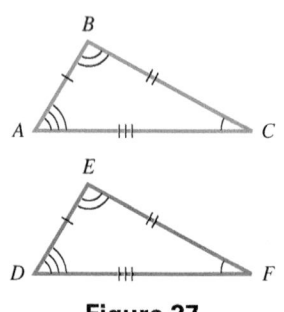

Figure 27

Notice how the angles and sides are marked to indicate which angles are congruent and which sides are congruent. (Using precise terminology, we refer to angles or sides as being *congruent,* while the *measures* of congruent angles or congruent sides are *equal.* We will often use the terms "equal angles" and "equal sides" to describe angles of equal measure and sides of equal measure.)

In geometry the following properties are used to prove that two triangles are congruent.

CONGRUENCE PROPERTIES

Side-Angle-Side (SAS)   If two sides and the included angle of one triangle are equal, respectively, to two sides and the included angle of a second triangle, then the triangles are congruent.

Angle-Side-Angle (ASA)   If two angles and the included side of one triangle are equal, respectively, to two angles and the included side of a second triangle, then the triangles are congruent.

Side-Side-Side (SSS)   If three sides of one triangle are equal, respectively, to three sides of a second triangle, then the triangles are congruent.

EXAMPLE 1 **Proving Congruence**

Refer to **Figure 28.**

Given: $CE = ED$

    $AE = EB$

Prove: $\triangle ACE \cong \triangle BDE$

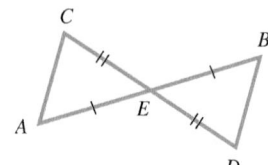

Figure 28

PROOF	STATEMENTS	REASONS
	1. $CE = ED$	**1.** Given
	2. $AE = EB$	**2.** Given
	3. $\measuredangle CEA = \measuredangle DEB$	**3.** Vertical angles are equal.
	4. $\triangle ACE \cong \triangle BDE$	**4.** SAS congruence property

EXAMPLE 2 Proving Congruence

Refer to **Figure 29.**

Given: $\angle ADB = \angle CBD$

$\angle ABD = \angle CDB$

Prove: $\triangle ADB \cong \triangle CBD$

Figure 29

PROOF

STATEMENTS	REASONS
1. $\angle ADB = \angle CBD$	**1.** Given
2. $\angle ABD = \angle CDB$	**2.** Given
3. $DB = DB$	**3.** Reflexive property (a quantity is equal to itself)
4. $\triangle ADB \cong \triangle CBD$	**4.** ASA congruence property

EXAMPLE 3 Proving Congruence

Refer to **Figure 30.**

Given: $AD = CD$

$AB = CB$

Prove: $\triangle ABD \cong \triangle CBD$

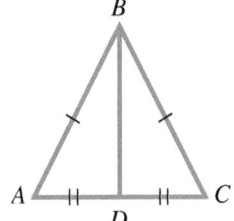

Figure 30

PROOF

STATEMENTS	REASONS
1. $AD = CD$	**1.** Given
2. $AB = CB$	**2.** Given
3. $BD = BD$	**3.** Reflexive property
4. $\triangle ABD \cong \triangle CBD$	**4.** SSS congruence property

Isosceles triangles (**Example 3** and **Figure 31**) have several important features.

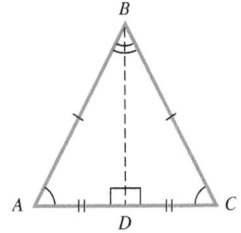

Figure 31

IMPORTANT STATEMENTS ABOUT ISOSCELES TRIANGLES

If $\triangle ABC$ is an isosceles triangle with $AB = CB$, and if D is the midpoint of the base AC (that is, $AD = DC$), then the following properties hold.

1. The base angles A and C are equal.

2. Angles ABD and CBD are equal.

3. Angles ADB and CDB are both right angles.

Similar Triangles

Similar triangles are pairs of triangles that are exactly the same shape but not necessarily the same size. **Figure 32** shows three pairs of similar triangles. (*Note:* The triangles do not need to be oriented in the same fashion in order to be similar.)

Figure 32

Suppose that a correspondence between two triangles *ABC* and *DEF* is set up.

∡*A* corresponds to ∡*D*   side *AB* corresponds to side *DE*

∡*B* corresponds to ∡*E*   side *BC* corresponds to side *EF*

∡*C* corresponds to ∡*F*   side *AC* corresponds to side *DF*

For triangle *ABC* to be similar to triangle *DEF*, these conditions must hold.

1. Corresponding angles must have the same measure.

2. The ratios of the corresponding sides must be constant. That is, the corresponding sides are proportional.

By showing that either of these conditions holds in a pair of triangles, we may conclude that the triangles are similar.

EXAMPLE 4 Verifying Similarity

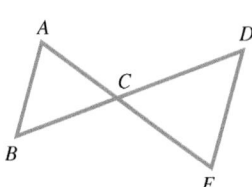

Figure 33

In **Figure 33**, $\overset{\leftrightarrow}{AB}$ is parallel to $\overset{\leftrightarrow}{ED}$. Verify that △*ABC* is similar to △*EDC*.

Solution

Because $\overset{\leftrightarrow}{AB}$ is parallel to $\overset{\leftrightarrow}{ED}$, the transversal $\overset{\leftrightarrow}{BD}$ forms equal alternate interior angles *ABC* and *EDC*. Also, transversal $\overset{\leftrightarrow}{AE}$ forms equal alternate interior angles *BAC* and *DEC*. We know that ∡*ACB* = ∡*ECD*, because they are vertical angles. Because the corresponding angles have the same measures in triangles *ABC* and *EDC*, the triangles are similar. ∎

Once we have shown that two angles of one triangle are equal to the two corresponding angles of a second triangle, it is not necessary to show the same for the third angle. In any triangle the sum of the angles equals 180°, so the measures of the remaining angles *must* be equal. This leads to the following property.

ANGLE-ANGLE (AA) SIMILARITY PROPERTY

If the measures of two angles of one triangle are equal to those of two corresponding angles of a second triangle, then the two triangles are similar.

EXAMPLE 5 Finding Side Lengths in Similar Triangles

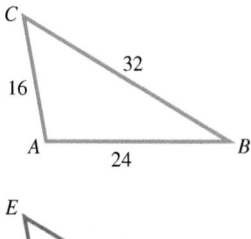

Figure 34

In **Figure 34,** △*EDF* is similar to △*CAB*. Find the unknown side lengths in △*EDF*.

Solution

Side *DF* of the small triangle corresponds to side *AB* of the larger one, and sides *DE* and *AC* correspond. The fact that similar triangles have corresponding sides in proportion leads to the following equation.

$$\frac{8}{16} \underset{\times}{=} \frac{DF}{24}$$

Using algebra, set the two cross products equal. (As an alternative method of solution, multiply both sides by 48, the least common multiple of 16 and 24.)

$$8(24) = 16DF \quad \text{Cross products are equal.}$$

$$192 = 16DF \quad \text{Multiply.}$$

$$12 = DF \quad \text{Divide by 16.}$$

Side *DF* has length 12.

Side *EF* corresponds to side *CB*. This leads to another proportion.

$$\frac{8}{16} = \frac{EF}{32}$$

$$\frac{1}{2} = \frac{EF}{32} \qquad \frac{8}{16} = \frac{1}{2}$$

$$EF = 16 \qquad \text{Multiply by 32.}$$

Side *EF* has length 16.   ■

EXAMPLE 6   Finding Unknown Measures in Similar Triangles

Find the measures of the unknown parts of the similar triangles *STU* and *ZXY* in **Figure 35**.

Figure 35

Solution

Here angles *X* and *T* correspond, as do angles *Y* and *U*, and angles *Z* and *S*. Since angles *Z* and *S* correspond and since angle *S* is 52°, angle *Z* also must be 52°. The sum of the angles of any triangle is 180°. In the larger triangle, *X* = 71° and *Z* = 52°.

$$X + Y + Z = 180 \qquad \text{The angle sum is 180°.}$$

$$\mathbf{71} + Y + \mathbf{52} = 180 \qquad \text{Substitute, and solve for } Y.$$

$$123 + Y = 180 \qquad \text{Add.}$$

$$Y = 57 \qquad \text{Subtract 123.}$$

Angle *Y* measures 57°. Because angles *Y* and *U* correspond, *U* = 57° also.

Now find the unknown sides. Sides *SU* and *ZY* correspond, as do *TS* and *XZ*, and *TU* and *XY*, leading to the following proportions.

$\dfrac{SU}{ZY} = \dfrac{TS}{XZ}$	$\dfrac{XY}{TU} = \dfrac{ZY}{SU}$ Write the proportions.
$\dfrac{48}{144} = \dfrac{TS}{126}$	$\dfrac{XY}{40} = \dfrac{144}{48}$ Substitute.
$\dfrac{1}{3} = \dfrac{TS}{126}$	$\dfrac{XY}{40} = \dfrac{3}{1}$ Lowest terms
$3TS = 126$	$XY = 120$ Cross products are equal.
$TS = 42$	Solve.

Side *TS* has length 42, and side *XY* has length 120.   ■

The Pythagorean Theorem

In a right triangle, the side opposite the right angle (the longest side) is the **hypotenuse.** The other two sides, which are perpendicular, are the **legs.**

Our knowledge of the mathematics of the Babylonians of Mesopotamia is based largely on archaeological discoveries of thousands of clay tablets. On the tablet labeled **Plimpton 322,** there are several columns of inscriptions that represent numbers. In one portion of the tablet (not shown here), the far right column is simply one that serves to number the lines, but two other columns represent values of hypotenuses and legs of right triangles with integer-valued sides.

   Thus, it seems that while the famous theorem relating right-triangle side lengths is named for the Greek Pythagoras, the relationship was known more than 1000 years prior to his time.

> ### PYTHAGOREAN THEOREM
>
> If the two legs of a right triangle have lengths *a* and *b*, and the hypotenuse has length *c*, then
>
> $$a^2 + b^2 = c^2.$$
>
> That is, the sum of the squares of the lengths of the legs is equal to the square of the hypotenuse.

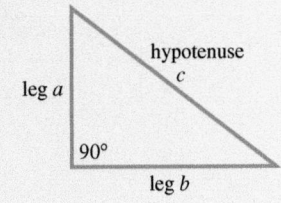

Pythagoras did not actually discover the theorem that was named after him. There is evidence that the Babylonians knew the concept quite well.

Figure 36 illustrates the theorem by using a tile pattern. The side of the square along the hypotenuse measures 5 units. Those along the legs measure 3 and 4 units. If $a = 3$, $b = 4$, and $c = 5$, the equation of the Pythagorean theorem is satisfied.

$$a^2 + b^2 = c^2 \qquad \text{Pythagorean theorem}$$
$$3^2 + 4^2 = 5^2 \qquad \text{Substitute.}$$
$$9 + 16 = 25 \qquad \text{Square.}$$
$$25 = 25 \ \checkmark \qquad \text{Add.}$$

Figure 36

The natural numbers 3, 4, and 5 form the **Pythagorean triple** (3, 4, 5) because they satisfy the equation of the Pythagorean theorem. There are infinitely many such triples.

WHEN Will I Ever USE This ?

Suppose you work for the Department of Forestry and have been called in to cut down a diseased tree at a summer camp. The tree is quite tall and is in an area surrounded by cabins. You measure the distance from the base of the tree to the nearby cabins, and you find that the cabins will be safe if the tree falls within 140 feet of its base.

Is it safe to cut the tree at ground level? If not, how high up the trunk must you cut to guarantee that the tip of the tree will hit the ground within the safe zone?

Assume that the tree stays "hinged" at the location of the cut.

In early afternoon, you find that a 72-inch fence post casts an 18-inch. shadow at the same time the diseased tree casts a 50-foot shadow. See **Figure 37**.

Let y be the height of the tree. Solve the proportion.

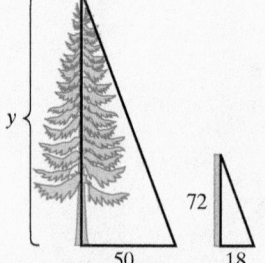

$$\frac{y}{50} = \frac{72}{18}$$

$$\frac{y}{50} = 4 \qquad \text{Reduce: } \frac{72}{18} = \frac{4}{1}.$$

$$y = 200 \qquad \text{Multiply by 50.}$$

Figure 37

Since the tree is 200 feet tall, you cannot cut it at ground level. Refer to **Figure 38**.

Let z be the height above the ground at which to cut. We can use the Pythagorean theorem to find z.

Figure 38

$$z^2 + 140^2 = (200 - z)^2$$

$$z^2 + 19{,}600 = 40{,}000 - 400z + z^2 \qquad \text{FOIL method from \textbf{Chapter 8}}$$

$$19{,}600 = 40{,}000 - 400z \qquad \text{Subtract } z^2.$$

$$400z = 20{,}400 \qquad \text{Add } 400z \text{ and subtract } 19{,}600.$$

$$z = 51 \qquad \text{Divide by 400.}$$

You need to cut the tree 51 feet above the ground.

EXAMPLE 7 **Using the Pythagorean Theorem**

Find the length a in the right triangle shown in **Figure 39.**

Solution

$$a^2 + b^2 = c^2 \qquad \text{Pythagorean theorem}$$

$$a^2 + 36^2 = 39^2 \qquad b = 36,\ c = 39$$

$$a^2 + 1296 = 1521 \qquad \text{Square.}$$

$$a^2 = 225 \qquad \text{Subtract 1296 from both sides.}$$

$$a = 15 \qquad \text{Choose the positive square root, because } a > 0.$$

Verify that $(15, 36, 39)$ is a Pythagorean triple as a check. ■

Figure 39

The statement of the Pythagorean theorem is an *if . . . then* statement. If the antecedent (the statement following the word "if") and the consequent (the statement following the word "then") are interchanged, the new statement is the *converse* of the original. Although the converse of a true statement may not be true, the *converse* of the Pythagorean theorem *is* also a true statement and can be used to determine whether a triangle is a right triangle, given the lengths of the three sides.

CONVERSE OF THE PYTHAGOREAN THEOREM

If a triangle has sides of lengths a, b, and c, where c is the length of the longest side, and if $a^2 + b^2 = c^2$, then the triangle is a right triangle.

EXAMPLE 8 **Applying the Converse of the Pythagorean Theorem**

Jonathan has been contracted to complete an unfinished 8-foot-by-12-foot laundry room in an existing house. He finds that the previous contractor built the floor so that the length of its diagonal is 14 feet, 8 inches. Is the floor "squared off" properly?

Solution

Because 14 feet, 8 inches $= 14\frac{2}{3}$ feet, he must check to see whether the following statement is true.

$$8^2 + 12^2 \stackrel{?}{=} \left(14\frac{2}{3}\right)^2 \qquad a^2 + b^2 = c^2$$

$$8^2 + 12^2 \stackrel{?}{=} \left(\frac{44}{3}\right)^2 \qquad 14\frac{2}{3} = \frac{44}{3}$$

$$208 \stackrel{?}{=} \frac{1936}{9} \qquad \text{Simplify.}$$

$$208 \neq 215\frac{1}{9} \qquad \text{The two values are not equal.}$$

He needs to fix the problem, since the diagonal, which measures 14 feet, 8 inches, should actually measure $\sqrt{208} \approx 14.4 \approx 14$ feet, 5 inches. ■

Following **Hurricane Katrina** in August 2005, the pine trees of southeastern Louisiana provided thousands of examples of **right triangles.** See the photo.

Suppose the vertical distance from the base of a broken tree to the point of the break is 55 inches. The length of the broken part is 144 inches. How far along the ground is it from the base of the tree to the point where the broken part touches the ground?

FOR FURTHER THOUGHT

Proving the Pythagorean Theorem

The Pythagorean theorem has probably been proved in more different ways than any theorem in mathematics. A book titled *The Pythagorean Proposition,* by Elisha Scott Loomis, was first published in 1927. It contained more than 250 different proofs of the theorem.

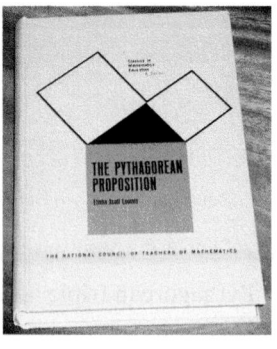

One of the most popular proofs of the theorem follows. This proof requires two formulas for area. The area $\mathscr{A}$ of a square is given by

$$\mathscr{A} = s^2,$$

where s is the length of a side of the square. The area $\mathscr{A}$ of a triangle is given by

$$\mathscr{A} = \frac{1}{2}bh,$$

where b is the base of the triangle and h is the height corresponding to that base.

For Group or Individual Investigation

In the figure given in the next column, the area of the large square must always be the same.

It is made up of four right triangles and a smaller square.

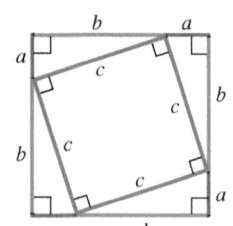

(a) The length of a side of the large square is _____, so its area is (_____)^2, or _____.

(b) The area of the large square can also be found by obtaining the sum of the areas of the four right triangles and the smaller square. The area of each right triangle is _____, so the sum of the areas of the four right triangles is _____. The area of the smaller square is _____.

(c) The sum of the areas of the four right triangles and the smaller square is _____.

(d) Since the areas in (a) and (c) represent the area of the same figure, the expressions there must be equal. Setting them equal to each other, we obtain

_____ = _____.

(e) Subtract $2ab$ from each side of the equation in (d) to obtain the desired result:

_____ = _____.

9.3 EXERCISES

*In Exercises 1–6, provide a STATEMENTS/REASONS proof similar to the ones in **Examples 1–3**.*

1. Given: $AC = BD$; $AD = BC$
Prove: $\triangle ABD \cong \triangle BAC$

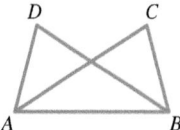

2. Given: $AC = BC$; D is the midpoint of AB.
Prove: $\triangle ADC \cong \triangle BDC$

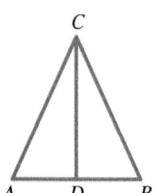

3. Given: $\angle BAC = \angle DAC$; $\angle BCA = \angle DCA$
Prove: $\triangle ABC \cong \triangle ADC$.

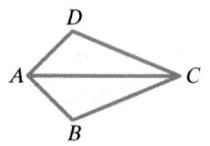

4. Given: $BC = BA$; $\angle 1 = \angle 2$
Prove: $\triangle DBC \cong \triangle DBA$

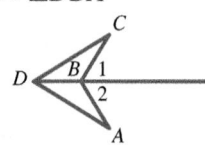

5. Given: $\overleftrightarrow{DB}$ is perpendicular to $\overleftrightarrow{AC}$; $AB = BC$
Prove: $\triangle ABD \cong \triangle CBD$

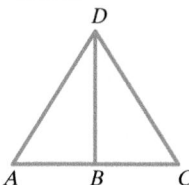

6. Given: $BO = OE$; $\overleftrightarrow{OB}$ is perpendicular to $\overleftrightarrow{AC}$;
$\overleftrightarrow{OE}$ is perpendicular to $\overleftrightarrow{DF}$
Prove: $\triangle AOB \cong \triangle FOE$.

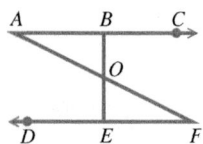

Exercises 7–10 refer to the given figure, which includes an isosceles triangle with AB = BC.

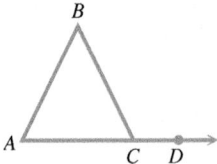

7. What is the measure of ∡BCD if ∡B measures 40°?

8. If ∡C measures 52°, what is the measure of ∡B ?

9. If ∡B measures 46°, then ∡A measures _____ and ∡C measures _____.

10. What is the measure of ∡B if ∡BCD measures 100°?

Write a short explanation for each of the following.

11. Explain why all equilateral triangles must be similar.

12. Explain how this figure demonstrates why the Congruence Properties just before **Example 1** did *not* include a Side-Side-Angle (SSA) property.

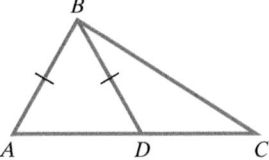

Name the corresponding angles and the corresponding sides for each of the following pairs of similar triangles.

13.

14.

15.

16.

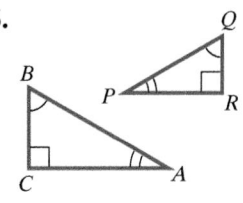

Find all unknown angle measures in each pair of similar triangles.

17.

18. **19.**

20. **21.**

22.

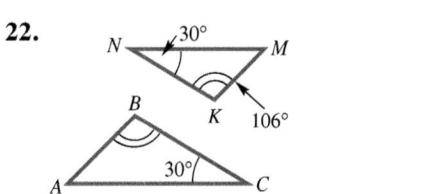

Find the unknown side lengths in each pair of similar triangles.

23. **24.**

25.

26.

27.

28.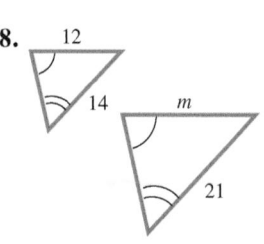

In each diagram, there are two similar triangles. Find the unknown measurement in each. (Hint: In the figure for Exercise 29, the side of length 150 *in the smaller triangle corresponds to a side of length*

$$150 + 180 = 330$$

in the larger triangle.)

29.

30.

31.

32.

33.

34.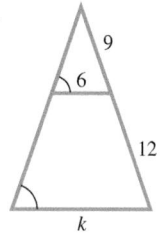

Solve each problem.

35. *Height of a Tree* A tree casts a shadow 45 m long. At the same time, the shadow cast by a vertical 4-m stick is 3 m long. Find the height of the tree.

36. *Height of a Tower* A forest fire lookout tower casts a shadow 80 ft long at the same time that the shadow of a 9-ft truck is 5 ft long. Find the height of the tower.

37. *Lengths of Sides of a Photograph* On a photograph of a triangular piece of land, the lengths of the three sides are 4 cm, 5 cm, and 7 cm, respectively. The shortest side of the actual piece of land is 200 m long. Find the lengths of the other two sides.

38. *Height of a Lighthouse Keeper* The Santa Cruz lighthouse is 14 m tall and casts a shadow 28 m long at 7 P.M. At the same time, the shadow of the lighthouse keeper is 3.5 m long. How tall is she?

39. *Height of a Building* A house is 15 ft tall. Its shadow is 40 ft long at the same time the shadow of a nearby building is 300 ft long. Find the height of the building.

40. *Height of the World's Tallest Human* Robert Wadlow was the tallest human being ever recorded. When a 6-ft stick cast a shadow 24 in., Robert would cast a shadow 35.7 in. How tall was he?

When proportional relationships are expressed graphically, similar triangles result. In Exercises 41 and 42, use similar triangles to answer the question.

41. *Feeding an Army* A cake recipe that serves 6 calls for $1\frac{1}{2}$ cups of flour. How many cups of flour will be needed if the chef must serve 40 people?

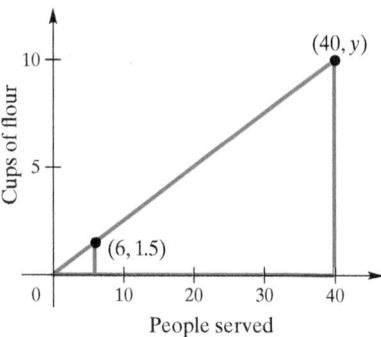

42. *How Much Herbicide?* A landscape maintenance service is spraying for weed control. Eight ounces of the chemical being used treats 500 square feet of lawn. How many ounces of the chemical will be needed for treating 3250 square feet of lawn?

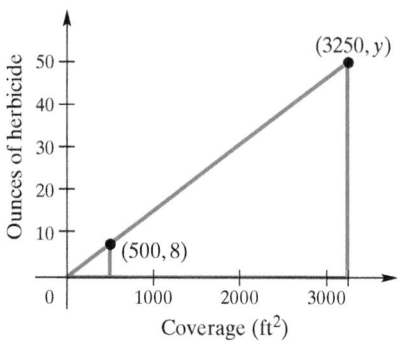

In Exercises 43–50, a and b represent the two legs of a right triangle, and c represents the hypotenuse. Find the lengths of the unknown sides.

43.
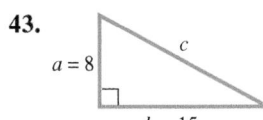
$a = 8$, c, $b = 15$

44.
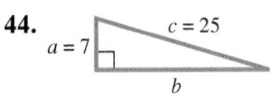
$a = 7$, $c = 25$, b

45.
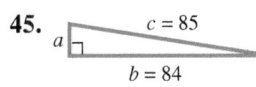
a, $c = 85$, $b = 84$

46.
$a = 11$, $c = 61$, b

47. $a = 14$ m; $b = 48$ m

48. $a = 28$ km; $c = 100$ km

49. $b = 21$ in.; $c = 29$ in.

50. $b = 120$ ft; $c = 169$ ft

51. Refer to **Exercise 50** in **Section 9.2.** Correct the Scarecrow's statement, using language similar to his.

52. Show that if $a^2 + b^2 = c^2$, then it is not necessarily true that $a + b = c$.

There are various formulas that will generate Pythagorean triples. For example, if we choose positive integers r and s, with r > s, then the set of equations

$$a = r^2 - s^2, \quad b = 2rs, \quad c = r^2 + s^2$$

generates a Pythagorean triple (a, b, c). Use the values of r and s given in each of Exercises 53–56 to generate a Pythagorean triple using this method.

53. $r = 2, s = 1$ **54.** $r = 3, s = 2$

55. $r = 4, s = 3$ **56.** $r = 4, s = 2$

57. Show that the formula given for **Exercises 53–56** actually satisfies $a^2 + b^2 = c^2$.

58. It can be shown that if $(x, x + 1, y)$ is a Pythagorean triple, then so is

$$(3x + 2y + 1, \quad 3x + 2y + 2, \quad 4x + 3y + 2).$$

Use this idea to find three more Pythagorean triples, starting with (3, 4, 5). *(Hint:* Here, $x = 3$ and $y = 5$.)

If m is an odd positive integer greater than 1, then

$$\left(m, \frac{m^2 - 1}{2}, \frac{m^2 + 1}{2} \right)$$

is a Pythagorean triple. Use this to find the Pythagorean triple generated by each value of m in Exercises 59–62.

59. $m = 3$ **60.** $m = 5$

61. $m = 7$ **62.** $m = 9$

63. Show that the expressions in the directions for **Exercises 59–62** actually satisfy $a^2 + b^2 = c^2$.

64. Show why $(6, 8, 10)$ is the only Pythagorean triple consisting of consecutive even numbers.

For any integer n greater than 1,

$$(2n, \ n^2 - 1, \ n^2 + 1)$$

is a Pythagorean triple. Use this pattern to find the Pythagorean triple generated by each value of n in Exercises 65–68.

65. $n = 2$ **66.** $n = 3$

67. $n = 4$ **68.** $n = 5$

69. Show that the expressions in the directions for **Exercises 65–68** actually satisfy $a^2 + b^2 = c^2$.

70. Can an isosceles right triangle have sides with integer lengths? Why or why not?

Solve each problem. (You may wish to review quadratic equations from algebra.)

71. *Side Length of a Triangle*   The hypotenuse of a right triangle is 1 m more than the longer leg, and the shorter leg is 7 m. Find the length of the longer leg.

72. *Side Lengths of a Triangle*   The hypotenuse of a right triangle is 3 cm more than twice the shorter leg, and the longer leg is 3 cm less than three times the shorter leg. Find the lengths of the three sides of the triangle.

73. *Height of a Tree*   At a point on the ground 24 ft from the base of a tree, the distance to the top of the tree is 6 ft less than twice the height of the tree. Find the height of the tree.

74. *Dimensions of a Rectangle*   The length of a rectangle is 2 in. less than twice the width. The diagonal is 5 in. Find the length and width of the rectangle.

75. *Height of a Break in Bamboo*   (Problem of the broken bamboo, from the Chinese work *Arithmetic in Nine Sections*, 1261) There is a bamboo 10 ft high, the upper end of which, being broken, reaches the ground 3 ft from the stem. Find the height of the break.

76. *Depth of a Pond* (Adapted from *Arithmetic in Nine Sections*) There grows in the middle of a circular pond 10 ft in diameter a reed that projects 1 ft out of the water. When it is drawn down, it just reaches the edge of the pond. How deep is the water?

Squaring Off a Floor under Construction *Imagine that you are a carpenter building the floor of a rectangular room. What must the diagonal of the room measure if your floor is to be squared off properly, given the dimensions in Exercises 77–80? Give your answer to the nearest inch.*

77. 12 ft by 15 ft   **78.** 14 ft by 20 ft

79. 16 ft by 24 ft   **80.** 20 ft by 32 ft

81. *Proof of the Pythagorean Theorem by Similar Triangles* In the figure, right triangles *ABC*, *CBD*, and *ACD* are similar. This may be used to prove the Pythagorean theorem. Fill in the blanks with the appropriate responses.

(a) By proportion, we have $\frac{c}{b} =$ ____ $/j$.

(b) By proportion, we also have $\frac{c}{a} = a/$ ____ .

(c) From part (a), $b^2 =$ ____ .

(d) From part (b), $a^2 =$ ____ .

(e) From the results of parts (c) and (d) and factoring, $a^2 + b^2 = c($ ____ $)$. Since ____ $= c$, it follows that _____ .

82. *Animated Proof of the Pythagorean Theorem* Go to

www.davis-inc.com/pythagor/proof2.html

to view an animation that provides a proof of the Pythagorean theorem.

*Exercises 83–90 require ingenuity, but all can be solved using the concepts presented so far in this chapter.**

83. *Value of a Measure in a Triangle*
In right triangle *ABC*, if

$$AD = DB + 8,$$

what is the value of *CD*?

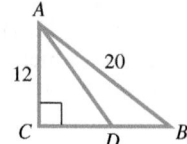

84. *Angle Measure in a Triangle* (A segment that *bisects* an angle divides the angle into two equal angles.) In the figure, angle *A* measures 50°. *OB* bisects angle *ABC*, and *OC* bisects angle *ACB*. What is the measure of angle *BOC*?

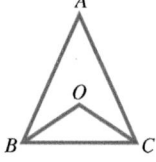

85. *Unknown Length* In triangle *VWZ*, point *X* lies on $\overleftrightarrow{VZ}$ and point *Y* lies on $\overleftrightarrow{WZ}$ with $\overline{XY}$ parallel to $\overline{VW}$. If $VZ = 10$, $XZ = 8$, and $WY = 4$, find the length *ZY*.

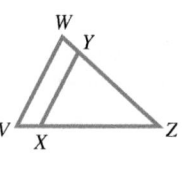

86. *Unknown Length* In right triangle *ABC* with right angle *C*, $BC = 4$ ft and $AC = 3$ ft. Point *R* is on $\overline{BC}$, equidistant from *A* and *B*. Find the length *CR*.

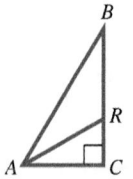

87. *Unknown Angle Measure* In the figure, $\triangle ABC$ has a right angle at *B* and $\measuredangle A = 20°$. If *CD* is the bisector of $\measuredangle ACB$, find $\measuredangle CDB$.

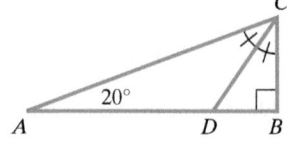

88. *Unknown Length* Triangle *CDE* is equilateral with $DE = 60$ units. *A* is the foot of the perpendicular from *D* to $\overleftrightarrow{CE}$, and *B* is the midpoint of $\overleftrightarrow{DA}$. Find the length *CB*.

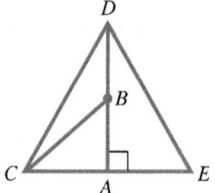

89. *Unknown Angle Sum* The three squares shown in the figure each share a side of $\triangle ABC$. Find the sum

$$\measuredangle EAF + \measuredangle DCJ + \measuredangle GBH.$$

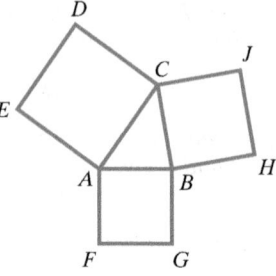

90. *Unknown Length* In the right triangle *ACD* with right angle *C*,

$$AB + AD = BC + DC.$$

If $BC = 8$ and $DC = 10$, find the length *AB*.

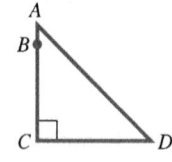

In Exercises 91–93, verify that the following constructions from **Section 9.2** *are valid. Use a STATEMENTS/ REASONS proof.*

91. Perpendicular Bisector

92. Perpendicular to a Line

93. Copied Angle

94. Given a line *m* and a point *A* on *m*, construct a line perpendicular to *m* through *A*. Prove that your construction is valid.

*These and other, similar problems in this chapter have been adapted from *Mathematics Teacher* calendar problems.

9.4 **PERIMETER, AREA, AND CIRCUMFERENCE**

OBJECTIVES

1 Determine the perimeter of a polygon.
2 Determine the areas of polygons and circles.
3 Determine the circumference of a circle.

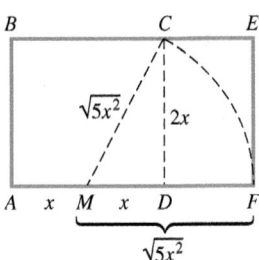

To construct a **golden rectangle,** one in which the ratio of the length to the width is equal to the ratio of the length plus the width to the length, begin with a square $ABCD$. With the point of the compass at M, the midpoint of $\overline{AD}$, swing an arc of radius MC to intersect the extension of $\overline{AD}$ at F. Construct a perpendicular at F, and have it intersect the extension of $\overline{BC}$ at E. $ABEF$ is a golden rectangle with ratio $(1 + \sqrt{5})/2$. (See **Section 5.5** for more on the golden ratio.)

To verify this construction, let $AM = x$, so that $AD = CD = 2x$. Then, by the Pythagorean theorem,

$$MC = \sqrt{x^2 + (2x)^2} = \sqrt{x^2 + 4x^2}$$

$$= \sqrt{5x^2} = x\sqrt{5}.$$

Because CF is an arc of the circle with radius MC, $MF = MC = x\sqrt{5}$. Then the ratio of length AF to width EF is

$$\frac{AF}{EF} = \frac{x + x\sqrt{5}}{2x}$$

$$= \frac{x(1 + \sqrt{5})}{2x}$$

$$= \frac{1 + \sqrt{5}}{2}.$$

Similarly, it can be shown that

$$\frac{AF + EF}{AF} = \frac{1 + \sqrt{5}}{2}.$$

Perimeter of a Polygon

When working with a polygon, we are sometimes required to find its "distance around," or *perimeter*.

PERIMETER

The **perimeter** of any polygon is the sum of the measures of the line segments that form its sides. Perimeter is measured in *linear units*.

The simplest polygon is a triangle. If a triangle has sides of lengths a, b, and c, then to find its perimeter we simply find the sum of a, b, and c, as shown below.

PERIMETER OF A TRIANGLE

The perimeter P of a triangle with sides of lengths a, b, and c is given by the following formula.

$$P = a + b + c$$

$P = a + b + c$

Because a rectangle is made up of two pairs of sides with the two sides in each pair equal in length, the formula for the perimeter of a rectangle may be stated as follows.

PERIMETER OF A RECTANGLE

The perimeter P of a rectangle with length ℓ and width w is given by the following formula.

$$P = 2\ell + 2w, \quad \text{or, equivalently,} \quad P = 2(\ell + w)$$

$P = 2\ell + 2w, \quad \text{or} \quad P = 2(\ell + w)$

EXAMPLE 1 **Using Perimeter to Determine Amount of Fencing**

A plot of land is in the shape of a rectangle. If it has length 50 feet and width 26 feet, how much fencing would be needed to completely enclose the plot?

Solution

We must find the distance around the plot of land.

$$P = 2\ell + 2w \qquad \text{Perimeter formula}$$

$$P = 2(50) + 2(26) \qquad \ell = 50, w = 26$$

$$P = 100 + 52 \qquad \text{Multiply.}$$

$$P = 152 \qquad \text{Add.}$$

The perimeter is 152 feet, so 152 feet of fencing is required. ∎

A square is a rectangle with four sides of equal length. The formula for the perimeter of a square is a special case of the formula for the perimeter of a rectangle.

PERIMETER OF A SQUARE

The perimeter P of a square with all sides of length s is given by the following formula.

$$P = 4s$$

$P = 4s$

Figure 40

EXAMPLE 2 Using the Formula for Perimeter of a Square

A square chess board has perimeter 34 inches. See **Figure 40.** What is the length of each side?

Solution

$$P = 4s \qquad \text{Perimeter formula}$$
$$34 = 4s \qquad P = 34$$
$$s = 8.5 \qquad \text{Divide by 4.}$$

Each side has a measure of 8.5 inches. ∎

EXAMPLE 3 Finding Length and Width of a Rectangle

The length of a basketball court is 6 feet less than twice the width. The perimeter is 288 feet. Find the length and width.

Solution

Step 1 **Read the problem.** We must find the length and width.

Step 2 **Assign a variable.** Let w represent the width. Then $2w - 6$ can represent the length, because the length is 6 less than twice the width. **Figure 41** shows a diagram of the basketball court.

Figure 41

Step 3 **Write an equation.** In the formula $P = 2\ell + 2w$, replace ℓ with $2w - 6$, and replace P with 288, because the perimeter is 288 feet.

$$288 = 2(2w - 6) + 2w$$

Step 4 **Solve the equation.**

$$288 = 2(2w - 6) + 2w$$
$$288 = 4w - 12 + 2w \qquad \text{Distributive property}$$
$$288 = 6w - 12 \qquad \text{Combine like terms.}$$
$$300 = 6w \qquad \text{Add 12.}$$
$$50 = w \qquad \text{Divide by 6.}$$

Step 5 **State the answer.** Because $w = 50$, the width is 50 feet and the length is $2w - 6 = 2(50) - 6 = 94$ feet.

Step 6 **Check.** Because 94 is 6 less than twice 50, and because the perimeter is $2(94) + 2(50) = 288$, the answer is correct. ∎

> **Problem-Solving Strategy**
>
> The six-step method of solving an applied problem from **Section 7.2** can be used to solve problems involving geometric figures, as shown in **Example 3.**

Area of a Polygon

> **AREA**
>
> The amount of plane surface covered by a polygon is its **area.** Area is measured in *square units*.

Metric units will be used extensively in this chapter. Help with the **metric system,** including unit conversion, is available in MyMathLab or at www.pearsonhighered .com/mathstatsresources.

Defining the **area** of a figure requires a basic *unit of area*. One that is commonly used is the *square centimeter,* abbreviated cm^2. One square centimeter, or $1\ cm^2$, is the area of a square one centimeter on a side. In place of $1\ cm^2$, the basic unit of area could be 1 in.^{2}, 1 ft^2, 1 m^2, or any appropriate unit.

As an example, we calculate the area of the rectangle shown in **Figure 42(a).** Using the basic 1-cm^2 unit, **Figure 42(b)** shows that four squares, each 1 cm on a side, can be laid off horizontally while six such squares can be laid off vertically. A total of $4 \cdot 6 = 24$ of the small squares are needed to cover the large rectangle. Thus, the area of the large rectangle is 24 cm^2.

(a)   (b)

Figure 42

We generalize to obtain a formula for the area of a rectangle.

> **AREA OF A RECTANGLE**
>
> The area $\mathscr{A}$ of a rectangle with length ℓ and width w is given by the following formula.
> $$\mathscr{A} = \ell w$$
>
>

The formula for the area of a rectangle $\mathscr{A} = \ell w$ can be used to find formulas for the areas of other figures.

> **AREA OF A SQUARE**
>
> The area $\mathscr{A}$ of a square with all sides of length s is given by the following formula.
> $$\mathscr{A} = s^2$$
>
>

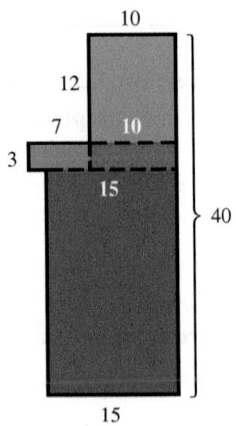

Figure 43

EXAMPLE 4 Using Area to Determine Amount of Carpet

Figure 43 shows the floor plan of a building, made up of various rectangles. If each length given is in meters, how many square meters of carpet would be required to carpet the building?

Solution

The dashed lines in the figure break up the floor area into rectangles. The areas of the various rectangles that result are as follows.

$$10 \text{ m} \cdot 12 \text{ m} = \mathbf{120 \text{ m}^2}, \qquad 3 \text{ m} \cdot 10 \text{ m} = \mathbf{30 \text{ m}^2},$$

$$3 \text{ m} \cdot 7 \text{ m} = \mathbf{21 \text{ m}^2}, \qquad 15 \text{ m} \cdot 25 \text{ m} = \mathbf{375 \text{ m}^2}$$

$$\boxed{40 - 12 - 3 = 25}$$

$$(120 + 30 + 21 + 375) \text{ m}^2 = 546 \text{ m}^2$$

The amount of carpet needed is 546 m². ∎

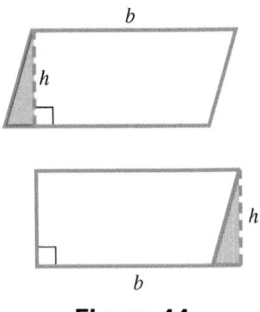

Figure 44

   A **parallelogram** is a four-sided figure with both pairs of opposite sides parallel. Because a parallelogram need not be a rectangle, the formula for the area of a rectangle cannot be used directly for a parallelogram. However, this formula can be used indirectly, as shown in **Figure 44.** Cut off the triangle in color, and slide it to the right end. The resulting figure is a rectangle with the same area as the original parallelogram.

   The *height* of the parallelogram is the perpendicular distance between the top and bottom and is denoted by h in the figure. The width of the rectangle equals the height of the parallelogram, and the length of the rectangle is the base b of the parallelogram, so

$$\mathcal{A} = \text{length} \cdot \text{width} \quad \text{becomes} \quad \mathcal{A} = \text{base} \cdot \text{height}.$$

AREA OF A PARALLELOGRAM

The area $\mathcal{A}$ of a parallelogram with height h and base b is given by the following formula.

$$\mathcal{A} = bh$$

(*Note:* h represents the length of the perpendicular between the parallel sides. If the parallelogram is not a rectangle, then h is not the length of a side.)

$\mathcal{A} = bh$

Figure 45

EXAMPLE 5 Using the Formula for Area of a Parallelogram

Find the area of the parallelogram in **Figure 45.**

Solution

$$\mathcal{A} = bh \qquad \text{Area formula}$$

$$= 15 \text{ cm} \cdot 6 \text{ cm} \qquad b = 15 \text{ cm}, \ h = 6 \text{ cm}$$

$$= 90 \text{ cm}^2 \qquad \text{Multiply.}$$

The area of the parallelogram is 90 cm². ∎

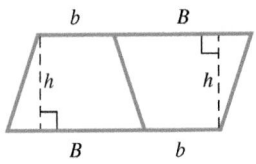

Figure 46

Figure 46 shows how we can find a formula for the area of a trapezoid. Notice that the figure as a whole is a parallelogram. It is made up of two trapezoids, each having height h, shorter base b, and longer base B. The area of the parallelogram is found by multiplying the height h by the base of the parallelogram, $b + B$—that is, $h(b + B)$. Because the area of the parallelogram is twice the area of each trapezoid, the area of each trapezoid is *half* the area of the parallelogram.

AREA OF A TRAPEZOID

The area $\mathcal{A}$ of a trapezoid with parallel bases b and B and height h is given by the following formula.

$$\mathcal{A} = \frac{1}{2}h(b + B)$$

█ EXAMPLE 6 Using the Formula for Area of a Trapezoid

Find the area of the trapezoid in **Figure 47**.

Solution

$$\mathcal{A} = \frac{1}{2}h(B + b) \qquad \text{Area formula}$$

$$= \frac{1}{2}(6\text{ cm})(9\text{ cm} + 3\text{ cm}) \qquad h = 6\text{ cm},\ B = 9\text{ cm},\ b = 3\text{ cm}$$

$$= \frac{1}{2}(6\text{ cm})(12\text{ cm}) \qquad \text{Add.}$$

$$= 36\text{ cm}^2 \qquad \text{Multiply.}$$

Figure 47

The area of the trapezoid is 36 cm^2. ■

The formula for the area of a triangle can be found from the formula for the area of a parallelogram. In **Figure 48,** the triangle with vertices A, B, and C has been combined with another copy of itself, rotated $180°$ about the midpoint of $\overset{\longleftrightarrow}{BC}$, to form a parallelogram. The area of this parallelogram is

$$\mathcal{A} = \text{base} \cdot \text{height}, \quad \text{or} \quad \mathcal{A} = bh.$$

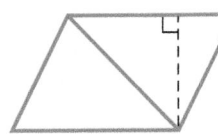

Figure 48

However, the parallelogram has *twice* the area of the triangle, so the area of the triangle is *half* the area of the parallelogram.

AREA OF A TRIANGLE

The area $\mathcal{A}$ of a triangle with height h and base b is given by the following formula.

$$\mathcal{A} = \frac{1}{2}bh$$

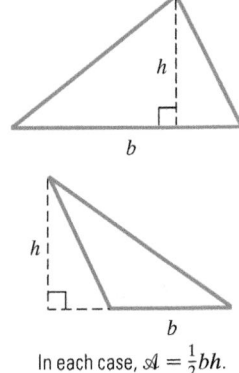

In each case, $\mathcal{A} = \frac{1}{2}bh$.

Figure 49

When applying the formula for the area of a triangle, remember that the height is the perpendicular distance between a vertex and the opposite side (or the extension of that side). See **Figure 49**.

To use the formula for the area of a triangle, $\mathcal{A} = \frac{1}{2}bh$, we must know the height from one of the sides of the triangle to the opposite vertex. Suppose that we know only the lengths of the three sides. Is there a way to determine the area from only this given information?

The answer is yes, and it leads us to the formula known as **Heron's formula.** Heron of Alexandria lived during the second half of the first century A.D., and although the formula is named after him, there is evidence that it was known to Archimedes several centuries earlier.

Let *a, b,* and *c* be lengths of the sides of any triangle. Let

$$s = \frac{1}{2}(a + b + c)$$

represent the **semiperimeter.** Then the area $\mathcal{A}$ of the triangle is given by the formula

$$\mathcal{A} = \sqrt{s(s - a)(s - b)(s - c)}.$$

The Vietnam Veterans Memorial in Washington, D.C., is in the shape of an unenclosed isosceles triangle. The walls form a "V-shape," and each wall measures 246.75 feet. The distance between the ends of the walls is 438.14 feet. Use Heron's formula to show that the area enclosed by the triangular shape is approximately 24,900 ft².

EXAMPLE 7 Finding the Height of a Triangular Sail

The area of a triangular sail of a sailboat is 126 ft². The base of the sail is 12 ft. Find the height of the sail.

Solution

Step 1 **Read the problem.** We must find the height of the triangular sail.

Step 2 **Assign a variable.** Let h = the height of the sail in feet. See **Figure 50.**

Step 3 **Write an equation.** Using the information given in the problem, we substitute 126 ft² for $\mathcal{A}$ and 12 ft for b in the formula for the area of a triangle.

$$\mathcal{A} = \frac{1}{2}bh \qquad \text{Area formula}$$

$$126 \text{ ft}^2 = \frac{1}{2}(12 \text{ ft})h \qquad \mathcal{A} = 126 \text{ ft}^2, \ b = 12 \text{ ft}$$

Step 4 **Solve.** $\qquad 126 \text{ ft}^2 = 6h \text{ ft} \qquad$ Multiply.

$$21 \text{ ft} = h \qquad \text{Divide by 6 ft.}$$

Step 5 **State the answer.** The height of the sail is 21 ft.

Step 6 **Check** to see that the values $\mathcal{A} = 126 \text{ ft}^2$, $b = 12$ ft, and $h = 21$ ft satisfy the formula for the area of a triangle. ∎

Figure 50

Circumference of a Circle

The distance around a circle is its **circumference** (rather than its perimeter). To understand the formula for the circumference of a circle, use a piece of string to measure the distance around a circular object. Then find the object's diameter and divide the circumference by the diameter. The quotient is the same, no matter what the size of the circular object is, and it will be an approximation for the number π.

$$\pi = \frac{\text{circumference}}{\text{diameter}} = \frac{C}{d}, \quad \text{or, alternatively,} \quad C = \pi d$$

Recall that π is not a rational number. **Figure 51** shows that it takes slightly more than three (about 3.14) diameters to make the circumference. In this chapter we will use 3.14 as an approximation for π when one is required.

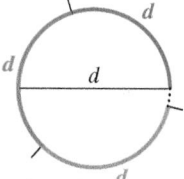

Figure 51

CIRCUMFERENCE OF A CIRCLE

The circumference C of a circle of diameter d is given by the following formula.

$$C = \pi d$$

Also, since $d = 2r$, the circumference C of a circle of radius r is given by the following formula.

$$C = 2\pi r$$

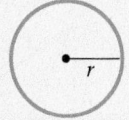

$C = \pi d$

$C = 2\pi r$

On March 8, 2014, Malaysia Airlines Flight 370 (a Boeing 777) disappeared while en route from Malaysia to China. Officials estimated that the plane had about a half-hour of fuel left when satellites received last contact over the Indian Ocean.

If a Boeing 777 can fly 950 km/hr at top speed, and if the plane's flight direction was unknown after its last known location, approximately how large an area should be searched? The answer can be found on the next page.

EXAMPLE 8 Finding the Circumference of a Circle

Find the circumference of each circle described. Use $\pi \approx 3.14$.

(a) A circle with diameter 12.6 centimeters

(b) A circle with radius 1.70 meters

Solution

(a)
$$C = \pi d \qquad \text{Circumference formula}$$
$$\approx (3.14)(12.6 \text{ cm}) \qquad \pi \approx 3.14, \, d = 12.6 \text{ cm}$$
$$= 39.6 \text{ cm} \qquad \text{Multiply.}$$

The circumference is about 39.6 centimeters, rounded to the nearest tenth.

(b)
$$C = 2\pi r \qquad \text{Circumference formula}$$
$$\approx 2(3.14)(1.70 \text{ m}) \qquad \pi \approx 3.14, \, r = 1.70 \text{ m}$$
$$= 10.7 \text{ m} \qquad \text{Multiply.}$$

The circumference is approximately 10.7 meters. ■

Area of a Circle

Start with a circle as shown in **Figure 52(a),** divided into many equal pie-shaped pieces **(sectors).** Rearrange the pieces into an approximate rectangle as shown in **Figure 52(b).** The circle has circumference $2\pi r$, so the "length" of the approximate rectangle is one-half of the circumference, or $\frac{1}{2}(2\pi r) = \pi r$, while its "width" is r. The area of the approximate rectangle is length times width, or $(\pi r)r = \pi r^2$. As we choose smaller and smaller sectors, the figure becomes closer and closer to a rectangle, so its area becomes closer and closer to πr^2.

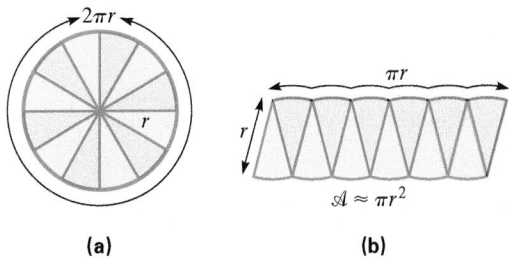

(a)   (b)

Figure 52

AREA OF A CIRCLE

The area $\mathcal{A}$ of a circle with radius r is given by the following formula.

$$\mathcal{A} = \pi r^2$$

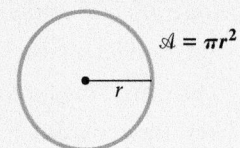

Problem-Solving Strategy

The formula for the area of a circle can be used to determine the best value for your money the next time you purchase a pizza. The next example uses the idea of unit pricing.

EXAMPLE 9 Using Area to Determine Better Value for Pizza

Paw-Paw Johnny's delivers pizza. The price of an 8-inch-diameter pizza is $6.99, and the price of a 16-inch-diameter pizza is $13.98. Which is the better buy?

Solution

To determine which pizza is the better value for the money, we must first find the area of each, and divide the price by the area to determine the price per square inch.

8-inch-diameter pizza area $= \pi(4 \text{ in.})^2 \approx 50.2 \text{ in.}^2$ Radius is $\frac{1}{2}(8 \text{ in.}) = 4 \text{ in.}$

16-inch-diameter pizza area $= \pi(8 \text{ in.})^2 \approx 201 \text{ in.}^2$ Radius is $\frac{1}{2}(16 \text{ in.}) = 8 \text{ in.}$

The price per square inch for the 8-inch pizza is

$$\frac{\$6.99}{50.2} \approx 13.9\,¢,$$

and the price per square inch for the 16-inch pizza is

$$\frac{\$13.98}{201} \approx 7.0\,¢.$$

Therefore, the 16-inch pizza is the better buy, since it costs approximately half as much per square inch. ∎

Solution to Margin Note problem

If the plane travels at full speed of 950 km/hr for half an hour in an unknown direction, then the search area would be a circle centered at the last known location with a radius of

$$r = \frac{950}{2} = 475 \text{ km.}$$

The area of this circle would be

$$\mathcal{A} = \pi(475 \text{ km})^2$$
$$\approx 710{,}000 \text{ km}^2.$$

9.4 EXERCISES

In Exercises 1–5, fill in each blank with the correct response.

1. The perimeter of an equilateral triangle with side length equal to ____ inches is the same as the perimeter of a rectangle with length 20 inches and width 16 inches.

2. A square with area 49 cm² has perimeter ____ cm.

3. If the area of a certain triangle is 40 square inches, and the base measures 8 inches, then the height must measure ____ inches.

4. If the radius of a circle is tripled, then its area is multiplied by a factor of ____.

5. Circumference is to a circle as _____ is to a polygon.

6. **Perimeter or Area?** *Decide whether perimeter or area would be used to solve a problem concerning the measure of the quantity.*

   (a) Sod for a lawn

   (b) Carpeting for a bedroom

   (c) Baseboards for a living room

   (d) Fencing for a yard

   (e) Fertilizer for a garden

   (f) Tile for a bathroom

   (g) Determining the cost of planting rye grass in a lawn for the winter

   (h) Determining the cost of replacing a linoleum floor with a wood floor

Use the formulas of this section to find the area of each figure. In Exercises 17–20, use 3.14 as an approximation for π, and in Exercises 18–20 round to the nearest unit.

7.
6 cm
8 cm

8.
4 cm
4 cm

9.
3 cm
$3\frac{1}{3}$ cm

10.
3 cm
1 cm

11.
2 in.
4 in.
(a parallelogram)

12.
1.5 cm
3 cm
(a parallelogram)

13.
38 mm
22 mm

14.
3 m
5 m

15.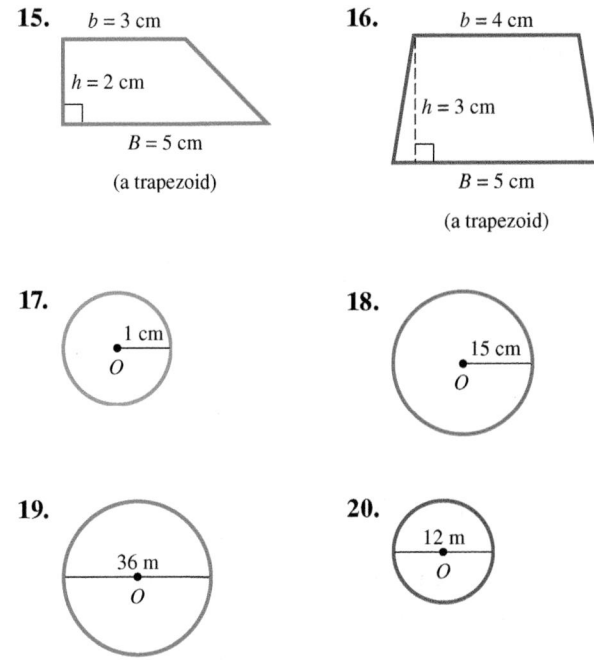

$b = 3$ cm

$h = 2$ cm

$B = 5$ cm

(a trapezoid)

16.

$b = 4$ cm

$h = 3$ cm

$B = 5$ cm

(a trapezoid)

17.

1 cm

O

18.

15 cm

O

19.

36 m

O

20.

12 m

O

Solve each problem.

21. *Window Side Length* A stained-glass window in a church is in the shape of a rhombus. The perimeter of the rhombus is 7 times the length of a side in meters, decreased by 12. Find the length of a side of the window.

22. *Dimensions of a Rectangle* A video rental machine has a rectangular display beside it advertising several movies inside. The display's length is 18 in. more than the width, and the perimeter is 180 in. What are the dimensions of the display?

23. *Dimensions of a Lot* A lot is in the shape of a triangle. One side is 100 ft longer than the shortest side, while the third side is 200 ft longer than the shortest side. The perimeter of the lot is 1200 ft. Find the lengths of the sides of the lot.

24. *Pennant Side Lengths* A wall pennant is in the shape of an isosceles triangle. Each of the two equal sides measures 18 in. more than the third side, and the perimeter of the triangle is 54 in. What are the lengths of the sides of the pennant?

25. *Radius of a Circular Foundation* A hotel is in the shape of a cylinder, with a circular foundation. The circumference of the foundation is 6 times the radius, increased by 14 ft. Find the radius of the circular foundation. (Use 3.14 as an approximation for π.)

26. *Radius of a Circle* If the radius of a certain circle is tripled, with 8.2 cm then added, the result is the circumference of the circle. Find the radius of the circle. (Use 3.14 as an approximation for π.)

27. *Area of Two Lots* The survey plat in the figure below shows two lots that form a trapezoid. The measures of the parallel sides are 115.80 ft and 171.00 ft. The height of the trapezoid is 165.97 ft. Find the combined area of the two lots. Round your answer to the nearest hundredth of a square foot.

28. *Area of a Lot* Lot A in the figure is in the shape of a trapezoid. The parallel sides measure 26.84 ft and 82.05 ft. The height of the trapezoid is 165.97 ft. Find the area of Lot A. Round your answer to the nearest hundredth of a square foot.

29. *Search Area* A search plane carries radar equipment that can detect metal objects (like submarine periscopes or plane wreckage) on the ocean surface up to 15.5 miles away. If the plane completes a circular flight pattern of 471 miles in circumference, how much area will it search? (Use 3.14 as an approximation for π, and round to the nearest 100 mi^2.)

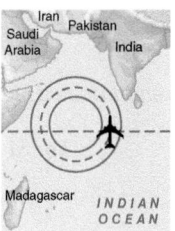

30. *Flight Path* If the search plane from **Exercise 29** needs to search a circular swath with an area of 20,000 square miles, how far will the plane need to fly (in a circle)? (Round to the nearest mile.)

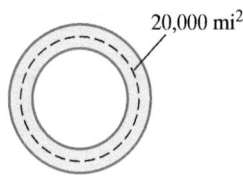

20,000 mi^2

In the chart below, the value of r (radius), d (diameter), C (circumference), or A (area) is given for a particular circle. Find the remaining three values. Leave π in your answers.

	r	*d*	*C*	*A*
31.	6 in.			
32.	9 in.			
33.		10 ft		
34.		40 ft		
35.			12π cm	
36.			18π cm	
37.				100π in.^{2}
38.				256π in.^{2}
39.				$\frac{400}{\pi}$ yd^2
40.			60 m	

Each figure has the perimeter indicated. (Figures are not necessarily to scale.) Find the value of x.

41. $P = 58$

42. $P = 42$

43. $P = 38$

44. $P = 278$

Each figure has the area indicated. Find the value of x.

45. $A = 32.49$

46. $A = 28$

47. $A = 21$

48. $A = 30$

(a trapezoid)

Each circle has the circumference or area indicated. Find the value of x. Use 3.14 as an approximation for π.

49. $C = 37.68$

50. $C = 54.95$

51. $A = 28.26$

52. $A = 18.0864$

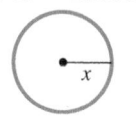

53. Work the parts of this exercise in order, and make a generalization concerning areas of rectangles.

(a) Find the area of a rectangle 4 cm by 5 cm.

(b) Find the area of a rectangle 8 cm by 10 cm.

(c) Find the area of a rectangle 12 cm by 15 cm.

(d) Find the area of a rectangle 16 cm by 20 cm.

(e) The rectangle in part (b) had sides twice as long as the sides of the rectangle in part (a). Divide the larger area by the smaller. Doubling the sides made the area increase _____ times.

(f) To get the rectangle in part (c), each side of the rectangle in part (a) was multiplied by _____. This made the larger area _____ times the size of the smaller area.

(g) To get the rectangle of part (d), each side of the rectangle of part (a) was multiplied by _____. This made the area increase to _____ times what it was originally.

(h) In general, if the length of each side of a rectangle is multiplied by n, the area is multiplied by _____.

54. Use the logic of **Exercise 53** to answer the following: If the height of a triangle is multiplied by n and the base length remains the same, then the area of the triangle is multiplied by _____.

55. Use the logic of **Exercise 53** to answer the following: If the radius of a circle is multiplied by n, then the area of the circle is multiplied by _____.

*Job Cost Use the results of **Exercise 53** to solve each problem.*

56. A ceiling measuring 9 ft by 15 ft can be painted for $60. How much would it cost to paint a ceiling 18 ft by 30 ft?

57. Suppose carpet for a room 10 ft by 12 ft costs $200. Find the cost to carpet a room 20 ft by 24 ft.

58. A carpet cleaner uses 8 oz of shampoo to clean an area 31 ft by 31 ft. How much shampoo would be needed for an area 93 ft by 93 ft?

Total Area as the Sum of Areas *By considering total area as the sum of the areas of all of its parts, we can determine the area of a figure such as those in Exercises 59–62. Find the total area of each figure. Use 3.14 as an approximation for π in Exercises 61 and 62, and round to the nearest hundredth.*

59.

(a parallelogram and a triangle)

[10, 6, 4]

60.

(a triangle, a rectangle, and a parallelogram)

[9, 10, 4, 3]

61.

(a rectangle and two semicircles)

[8, 3, 3]

62.

(a square and four semicircles)

[8, 8, 8, 8]

Area of a Shaded Portion of a Plane Figure *The shaded areas of the figures in Exercises 63–68 may be found by subtracting the area of the unshaded portion from the total area of the figure. Use this approach to find the area of the shaded portion. Use 3.14 as an approximation for π in Exercises 66–68, and round to the nearest hundredth.*

63.

(a triangle within a trapezoid)

[18 ft, 7 ft, 11 ft, 12 ft]

64.

(a trapezoid within a triangle)

[8 cm, 8 cm, 6 cm, 8 cm, 6 cm]

65.

(two congruent triangles within a rectangle)

[48 cm, 48 cm, 74 cm, 36 cm]

66.

(a semicircle within a rectangle)

[21 ft, 23 ft]

67.

(a circle within a square)

[26 m]

68.

(two circles within a circle)

[4 cm]

Pizza Pricing *The following exercises show prices actually charged by Old Town Pizza, a local pizzeria. The dimension is the diameter of the pizza. Find the best buy.*

Menu Item	Prices			
	10-in.	12-in.	14-in.	16-in.
69. Cheese pizza with one topping	$10	$14	$17	$20
70. Cheese pizza with two toppings	$11.50	$15.75	$19	$22.25
71. Choo Choo Chicken	$15	$19	$22	$25
72. Steam Engine + two toppings	$18	$22.50	$26	$29.50

James Garfield's Proof of the Pythagorean Theorem *James A. Garfield, the twentieth president of the United States, provided a proof of the Pythagorean theorem using the figure below. Supply the required information in each of Exercises 73–76, in order, to follow his proof.*

73. Find the area of the trapezoid *WXYZ* using the formula for the area of a trapezoid.

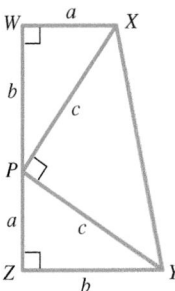

74. Find the area of each of the right triangles *PWX*, *PZY*, and *PXY*.

75. Because the sum of the areas of the three right triangles must equal the area of the trapezoid, set the expression from **Exercise 73** equal to the sum of the three expressions from **Exercise 74.**

76. Simplify the terms of the equation from **Exercise 75** as much as possible. What is the result?

A polygon can be inscribed within a circle or circumscribed about a circle. In the figure, triangle ABC is inscribed within the circle, while square WXYZ is circumscribed about it. These ideas will be used in some of the remaining exercises in this section and later in this chapter.

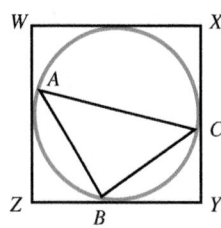

Exercises 77–88 require some ingenuity, but all may be solved using the concepts presented so far in this chapter.

77. *Diameter of a Circle* Given the circle with center O and rectangle $ABCO$, find the diameter of the circle.

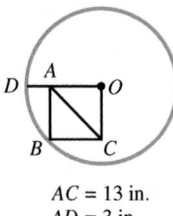

AC = 13 in.
AD = 3 in.

78. *Perimeter of a Triangle* What is the perimeter of $\triangle AEB$ if $AD = 20$ in., $DC = 30$ in., and $AC = 34$ in.?

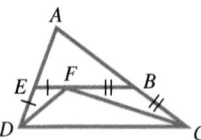

79. *Area of a Square* The area of square $PQRS$ is 1250 square feet. T, U, V, and W are the midpoints of PQ, QR, RS, and SP, respectively. What is the area of square $TUVW$?

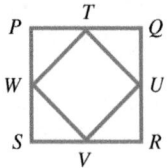

80. *Area of a Quadrilateral* The rectangle $ABCD$ has length twice the width. If P, Q, R, and S are the midpoints of the sides, and the perimeter of $ABCD$ is 96 in., what is the area of quadrilateral $PQRS$?

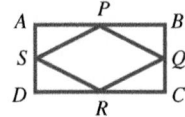

81. *Area of Shaded Region* If the area of $\triangle ACE$ is 10 cm², the area of $\triangle BDE$ is 16 cm², and the area of $\triangle ADE$ is 20 cm², determine the area of the shaded region.

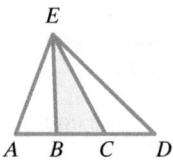

82. *Area of Trapezoid* The three squares have the dimensions indicated in the diagram. What is the area of the shaded trapezoid?

83. *Area of a Shaded Region* Express the area of the shaded region in terms of r, given that the circle is inscribed in the square.

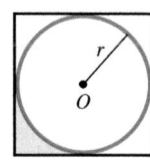

84. *Area of a Pentagon* In the figure, pentagon $PQRST$ is formed by a square and an equilateral triangle such that $PQ = QR = RS = ST = PT$. The perimeter of the pentagon is 80. Find the area of the pentagon.

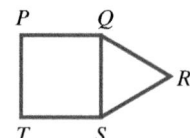

85. *Area of a Quadrilateral* Find the area of quadrilateral $ABCD$ if angles A and C are right angles.

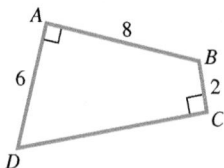

86. *Base Measure of an Isosceles Triangle* An isosceles triangle has a base of 24 and two sides of 13. What other base measure can an isosceles triangle with equal sides of 13 have and still have the same area as the given triangle?

Exercises 87 and 88 refer to the given figure. The center of the circle is O.

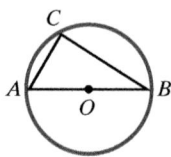

87. *Radius of a Circle* If $\overset{\leftrightarrow}{AC}$ measures 6 in. and $\overset{\leftrightarrow}{BC}$ measures 8 in., what is the radius of the circle?

88. *Lengths of Chords of a Circle* If $\overset{\leftrightarrow}{AB}$ measures 13 cm, and the length of $\overset{\leftrightarrow}{BC}$ is 7 cm more than the length of $\overset{\leftrightarrow}{AC}$, what are the lengths of $\overset{\leftrightarrow}{BC}$ and $\overset{\leftrightarrow}{AC}$?

9.5 | VOLUME AND SURFACE AREA

OBJECTIVES

1 Classify space figures.

2 Calculate surface area and volume of common space figures.

Space Figures

Thus far, this chapter has discussed only **plane figures**—figures that can be drawn completely in the plane of a sheet of paper. However, it takes the three dimensions of space to represent the solid world around us. For example, **Figure 53** shows a "box" (a **rectangular parallelepiped**). The *faces* of a box are rectangles. The faces meet at *edges;* the "corners" are *vertices* (plural of *vertex*—the same word that is used for the "corner" of an angle).

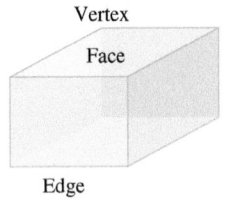

Vertex

Face

Edge

Rectangular parallelepiped (box)

Figure 53

Boxes are one kind of **space figure** belonging to an important group called **polyhedra,** the faces of which are made only of polygons. Perhaps the most interesting polyhedra are the *regular polyhedra.* Recall that a *regular polygon* is a polygon with all sides equal and all angles equal. A regular polyhedron is a space figure, the faces of which are only one kind of regular polygon. It turns out that there are only five different regular polyhedra. They are shown in **Figure 54.** A **tetrahedron** is composed of four equilateral triangles, each three of which meet in a point. Use the figure to verify that there are four faces, four vertices, and six edges.

Polyhedral dice such as the ones shown here are often used in today's role-playing games.

The five regular polyhedra are also known as **Platonic solids,** named for the Greek philosopher Plato. He considered them as "building blocks" of nature and assigned fire to the tetrahedron, earth to the cube, air to the octahedron, and water to the icosahedron. Because the dodecahedron is different from the others due to its pentagonal faces, he assigned to it the cosmos (stars and planets). (*Source:* http://platonicrealms.com/encyclopedia/Platonic-solid) An animated view of the Platonic solids can be found at http://www.wikipedia.org/wiki/Platonic_solid.

The image above is from an Android app (*Dice,* by Teazel.com) that simulates the rolling of polyhedral dice.

Tetrahedron   Hexahedron (cube)   Octahedron   Dodecahedron   Icosahedron

Figure 54

The four remaining regular polyhedra are the **hexahedron,** the **octahedron,** the **dodecahedron,** and the **icosahedron.** The hexahedron, or cube, is composed of six squares, each three of which meet at a point. The octahedron is composed of groups of four regular (i.e., equilateral) triangles meeting at a point. The dodecahedron is formed by groups of three regular pentagons, and the icosahedron is made up of groups of five regular triangles.

Two other types of polyhedra are familiar space figures: pyramids and prisms. **Pyramids** are made of triangular sides and a polygonal base. **Prisms** have two faces in parallel planes; these faces are congruent polygons. The remaining faces of a prism are all parallelograms. (See **Figures 55(a)** and **(b)** on the next page.) By this definition, a box is also a prism.

Figure 55(c) shows space figures made up in part of circles, including *right circular cones* and *right circular cylinders.* It also shows how a circle can generate a *torus,* a doughnut-shaped solid that has interesting topological properties. See **Section 9.7.**

Tetrahedron

Hexahedron (cube)

Octahedron

Dodecahedron

Icosahedron

Patterns such as these may be used to construct three-dimensional models of the **regular polyhedra**. See

http://www.korthalsaltes.com

for some examples.

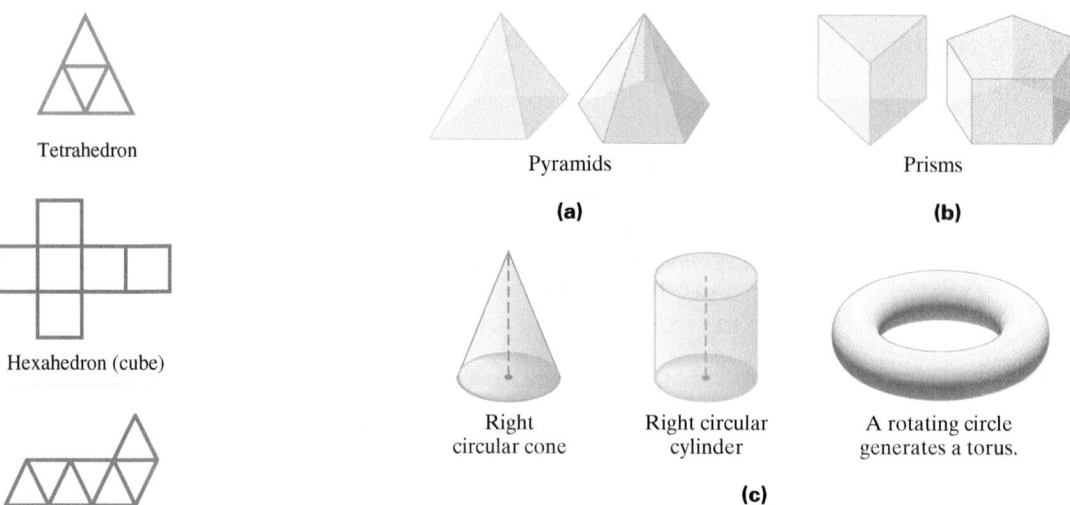

Pyramids

(a)

Prisms

(b)

Right circular cone

Right circular cylinder

A rotating circle generates a torus.

(c)

Figure 55

Volume and Surface Area of Space Figures

While area is a measure of surface covered by a plane figure, **volume** is a measure of capacity of a space figure. Volume is measured in *cubic* units. For example, a cube with edge measuring 1 cm has volume 1 cubic centimeter, which is also written as 1 cm^3, or 1 cc. The **surface area** is the total area that would be covered if the space figure were "peeled" and the peel laid flat. Surface area is measured in *square* units.

VOLUME AND SURFACE AREA OF A BOX

Suppose that a box has length ℓ, width w, and height h. Then the volume V and the surface area S are given by the following formulas.

$$V = \ell wh \quad \text{and} \quad S = 2\ell w + 2\ell h + 2hw$$

If the box is a cube with edge of length s, the formulas are as follows.

$$V = s^3 \quad \text{and} \quad S = 6s^2$$

$V = \ell wh$

$S = 2\ell w + 2\ell h + 2hw$

$V = s^3$

$S = 6s^2$

EXAMPLE 1 Using the Formulas for a Box

Find the volume V and the surface area S of the box shown in **Figure 56**.

Solution

$$V = \ell wh \quad \text{Volume formula}$$
$$= 14 \cdot 7 \cdot 5 \quad \text{Substitute.}$$
$$= 490 \quad \text{Multiply.}$$

Volume is measured in cubic units, so the volume of the box is 490 cubic centimeters, or 490 cm^3.

$w = 7$ cm

$h = 5$ cm

$\ell = 14$ cm

Figure 56

$$S = 2\ell w + 2\ell h + 2hw \qquad \text{Surface area formula}$$
$$= 2(14)(7) + 2(14)(5) + 2(5)(7) \qquad \text{Substitute.}$$
$$= 196 + 140 + 70 \qquad \text{Multiply.}$$
$$= 406 \qquad \text{Add.}$$

Surface areas of space figures are measured in square units, so the surface area of the box is 406 square centimeters, or 406 cm². ∎

A typical tin can is an example of a **right circular cylinder.**

VOLUME AND SURFACE AREA OF A RIGHT CIRCULAR CYLINDER

If a right circular cylinder has height h and the radius of its base is equal to r, then the volume V and the surface area S are given by the following formulas.

$$V = \pi r^2 h$$
$$S = 2\pi r h + 2\pi r^2$$

$$V = \pi r^2 h$$

and $\qquad S = 2\pi r h + 2\pi r^2$

(In the formula for S, the areas of the top and bottom are included.)

EXAMPLE 2 Using the Formulas for a Right Circular Cylinder

In **Figure 57,** the volume of medication in the syringe is 10 mL (which is equivalent to 10 cm³). Find each measure. Use 3.14 as an approximation for π.

(a) the radius of the cylindrical syringe (round to the nearest 0.1 cm)

(b) the surface area of the medication (round to the nearest 0.1 cm²)

Solution

(a)

$$V = \pi r^2 h \qquad \text{Volume formula}$$
$$10 = \pi r^2 (5.0) \qquad V = 10,\ h = 5.0$$
$$\frac{2}{\pi} = r^2 \qquad \text{Divide by } 5.0\pi.$$
$$r = \sqrt{\frac{2}{\pi}} \approx 0.8 \qquad \text{Take the square root and approximate.}$$

The radius is approximately 0.8 cm.

(b)

$$S = 2\pi r h + 2\pi r^2 \qquad \text{Surface area formula}$$
$$= 2\pi(0.8)(5.0) + 2\pi(0.8)^2 \qquad r = 0.8,\ h = 5.0$$
$$= 9.28\pi \qquad \text{Multiply; add.}$$
$$\approx 29.1 \qquad \text{Approximate, using 3.14 for } \pi.$$

The surface area is approximately 29.1 cm². ∎

5.0 cm

Figure 57

The three-dimensional analogue of a circle is a **sphere.** It is defined by replacing the word "plane" with "space" in the definition of a circle (**Section 9.2**).

VOLUME AND SURFACE AREA OF A SPHERE

If a sphere has radius r, then the volume V and the surface area S are given by the following formulas.

$$V = \frac{4}{3}\pi r^3 \quad \text{and} \quad S = 4\pi r^2$$

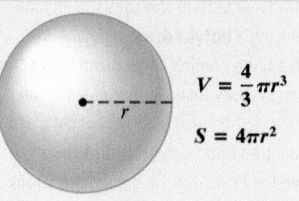

$$V = \frac{4}{3}\pi r^3$$

$$S = 4\pi r^2$$

A cone with circular base having its apex (highest point) directly above the center of its base is a **right circular cone.**

VOLUME AND SURFACE AREA OF A RIGHT CIRCULAR CONE

If a right circular cone has height h and the radius of its circular base is r, then the volume V and the surface area S are given by the following formulas.

$$V = \frac{1}{3}\pi r^2 h$$

$$V = \frac{1}{3}\pi r^2 h$$

$$S = \pi r \sqrt{r^2 + h^2} + \pi r^2$$

and $\quad S = \pi r \sqrt{r^2 + h^2} + \pi r^2$

(In the formula for S, the area of the circular base is included.)

EXAMPLE 3 Comparing Volumes Using Ratios

Figure 58 shows a right circular cone inscribed in a semi-sphere of radius r. What is the ratio of the volume of the cone to the volume of the semi-sphere?

Solution

First, use the formula for the volume of a cone. Note that because the cone is inscribed in the semi-sphere, its height is equal to its radius.

$$V_1 = \text{Volume of the cone} = \frac{1}{3}\pi r^2 h = \frac{1}{3}\pi r^3 \quad \text{Use } h = r.$$

The semi-sphere will have half the volume of a sphere of radius r.

$$V_2 = \text{Volume of the semi-sphere} = \frac{1}{2} \cdot \frac{4}{3}\pi r^3 = \frac{2}{3}\pi r^3$$

Now find the ratio of the first volume to the second.

$$\frac{V_1}{V_2} = \frac{\frac{1}{3}\pi r^3}{\frac{2}{3}\pi r^3} = \frac{1}{2} \qquad \text{The ratio is } \frac{1}{2}.$$

Figure 58

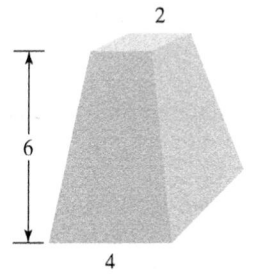

2

6

4

A problem concerning the **frustum of a pyramid** like the one shown above is included in the **Moscow papyrus**, which dates back to about 1850 B.C. Problem 14 in the document reads:

> You are given a truncated pyramid of 6 for the vertical height by 4 on the base by 2 on the top. You are to square this 4, result 16. You are to double 4, result 8. You are to square 2, result 4. You are to add the 16, the 8, and the 4, result 28. You are to take one-third of 6, result 2. You are to take 28 twice, result 56. See, it is 56. You will find it right.

The formula for finding the volume of the frustum of a pyramid with square bases is

$$V = \frac{1}{3}h(B^2 + Bb + b^2),$$

where B is the side length of the lower base, b is the side length of the upper base, and h is the height (or altitude).

A **pyramid** is a space figure having a polygonal base and triangular sides. **Figure 59** shows a pyramid with a square base.

Pyramid

Figure 59

VOLUME OF A PYRAMID

If B represents the area of the base of a pyramid, and h represents the height (that is, the perpendicular distance from the top, or apex, to the base), then the volume V is given by the following formula.

$$V = \frac{1}{3}Bh$$

$V = \frac{1}{3}Bh$

where B is the area of the base

EXAMPLE 4 Using the Volume Formula for a Pyramid

The Great Pyramid at Giza has a square base. When originally constructed, its base measured about 230 meters on a side, and it was about 147 meters high. What was its volume?

Solution

Use the formula for the volume of a pyramid.

$$V = \frac{1}{3}Bh$$

Since the base is square, the area of the base is the square of the side length.

$$V = \frac{1}{3}(230)^2(147) = 2{,}592{,}100 \text{ m}^3$$

9.5 EXERCISES

Decide whether each statement is true *or* false.

1. A cube with volume 125 cubic inches has surface area 150 square inches.

2. A tetrahedron has the same number of faces as vertices.

3. A sphere with a 1-unit radius has three times as many units of surface area as it has units of volume.

4. Each face of an octahedron is an octagon.

5. If you double the length of the edge of a cube, the new cube will have a volume that is four times the volume of the original cube.

6. A dodecahedron can be used as a model for a calendar for a given year, where each face of the dodecahedron contains a calendar for a single month, and there are no faces left over.

Find **(a)** *the volume and* **(b)** *the surface area of each space figure. When necessary, use 3.14 as an approximation for* π*, and round answers to the nearest hundredth.*

7.

$2\frac{1}{4}$ m

4 m

$2\frac{1}{2}$ m

(a box)

8.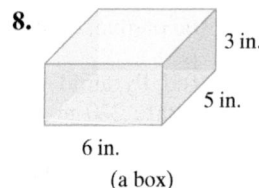

3 in.

5 in.

6 in.

(a box)

9.

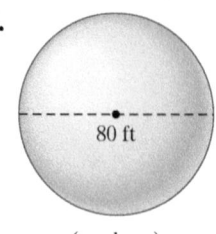

80 ft

(a sphere)

10.

14.8 cm

(a sphere)

11.

5 cm

7 cm

(a right circular cylinder)

12.

12 m

4 m

(a right circular cylinder)

13.

3 m

7 m

(a right circular cone)

14.

6 cm

4 cm

(a right circular cone)

Find the volume of each pyramid. In each case, the base is a rectangle.

15.

$h = 7$ in.

9 in.

8 in.

16.

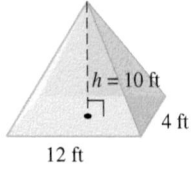

$h = 10$ ft

4 ft

12 ft

Volumes of Common Objects   *Find each volume. Use 3.14 as an approximation for π when necessary.*

17. a coffee can, radius 6.3 cm and height 15.8 cm

18. a soup can, radius 3.2 cm and height 9.5 cm

19. a pork-and-beans can, diameter 7.2 cm and height 10.5 cm

20. a cardboard mailing tube, diameter 2 in. and height 40 in.

21. a coffee mug, diameter 9 cm and height 8 cm

22. a bottle of glue, diameter 3 cm and height 4.3 cm

23. the Red Pyramid at Dahshur, near Cairo—its base is a square 220 m on a side, and its height is 105 m

24. a grain silo in the shape of a right circular cylinder with a base radius of 7 m and a height of 25 m

25. a road construction marker, a cone with height 2 m and base radius $\frac{1}{2}$ m

26. the conical portion of a witch's hat for a Halloween costume, with height 12 in. and base radius 4 in.

In the chart below, the value of r (radius), V (volume), or S (surface area) is given for a particular sphere. Find the remaining two values. Leave π in your answers.

	r	V	S
27.	6 in.		
28.	9 in.		
29.		$\frac{32}{3}\pi$ cm^3	
30.		$\frac{256}{3}\pi$ cm^3	
31.			4π m^2
32.			144π m^2

Solve each problem.

33. Volume or Surface Area?   In order to determine the amount of liquid a spherical tank will hold, would you need to use volume or surface area?

34. Volume or Surface Area?   In order to determine the amount of leather it would take to manufacture a basketball, would you need to use volume or surface area?

35. Irrigation Tank   An irrigation tank is formed of a concrete "box" that is 5 ft wide, 5 ft deep, and 10 ft long, along with two cylindrical sleeves, each 2 ft high and 2.5 ft in diameter. What is the total volume of the tank? (Use 3.14 as an approximation for π, and round to the nearest cubic foot.)

2.5

2

5

10

5

36. Underground Bunker   An underground bunker is to be made of concrete 2 ft thick. It will be semi-spherical with outer radius of 20 feet. How many cubic feet of concrete will be needed to construct the bunker? (Use 3.14 as an approximation for π, and round to the nearest cubic foot.)

18
20

37. Side Length of a Cube One of the three famous construction problems of Greek mathematics required the construction of an edge of a cube with twice the volume of a given cube. If the length of each side of the given cube is x, what would be the length of each side of a cube with twice the original volume?

38. Work through the parts of this exercise in order, and use them to make a generalization concerning volumes of spheres. Leave answers in terms of π.

  (a) Find the volume of a sphere having radius of 1 m.

  (b) Suppose the radius is doubled to 2 m. What is the volume?

  (c) When the radius was doubled, by how many times did the volume increase? (To find out, divide the answer for part (b) by the answer for part (a).)

  (d) Suppose the radius of the sphere from part (a) is tripled to 3 m. What is the volume?

  (e) When the radius was tripled, by how many times did the volume increase?

  (f) In general, if the radius of a sphere is multiplied by n, the volume is multiplied by ____ .

Cost to Fill a Spherical Tank *If a spherical tank 2 m in diameter can be filled with a liquid for $300, find the cost to fill tanks of each diameter.*

39. 6 m   **40.** 8 m   **41.** 10 m

42. Use the logic of **Exercise 38** to answer the following: If the radius of a sphere is multiplied by n, then the surface area of the sphere is multiplied by ____ .

43. Volume Decrease The radius of a sphere is decreased by 30%. By what percent does the volume decrease? Round to the nearest 0.1%.

44. Surface Area Decrease The length of each edge of a cube is decreased by 40%. By what percent does the surface area decrease?

Each of the following figures has the volume indicated. Find the value of x.

45. $V = 60$

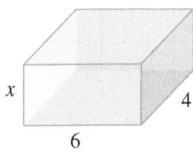

x 4   6
(a box)

46. $V = 450$

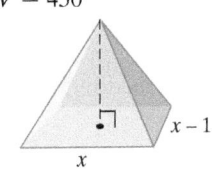

$x - 1$
x
$h = 15$
Base is a rectangle.
(a pyramid)

47. $V = 36\pi$

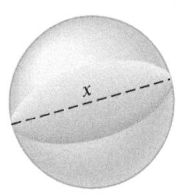

x
(a sphere)

48. $V = 245\pi$

15
x
(a right circular cone)

Exercises 49–58 require some ingenuity, but all can be solved using the concepts presented so far in this chapter.

49. Volume of a Box The areas of the sides of a rectangular box are 30 in.^{2}, 35 in.^{2}, and 42 in.^{2}. What is the volume of the box?

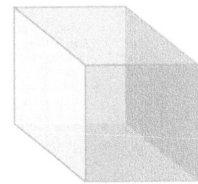

50. Ratio of Volumes Three tennis balls are stacked in a cylindrical container that touches the stack on all sides, on the top, and on the bottom. What is the ratio of the volume filled with tennis balls to the volume of empty space in the container?

51. Equal Area and Volume The inhabitants of Planet Volarea have a unit of distance called a *volar*. The number of square volars in the planet's surface area is the same as the number of cubic volars in the planet's volume. If the diameter of Volarea is 1800 miles, how many miles are in a volar?

52. Change in Volume If the height of a right circular cylinder is halved and the diameter is tripled, how is the volume changed?

h
d

53. Ratio of Areas What is the ratio of the area of the circumscribed square to the area of the inscribed square?

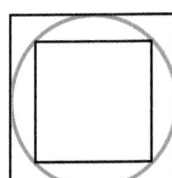

54. _Perimeter of a Square_ Suppose the diameter of the circle shown is 8 in. What is the perimeter of the inscribed square $ABCD$?

55. _Value of a Sum_ In the circle shown with center O, the radius is 6. $QTSR$ is an inscribed square. Find the value of

$$PQ^2 + PT^2 + PR^2 + PS^2.$$

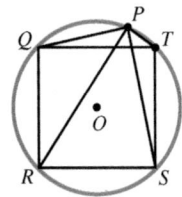

56. _Ratio of Side Lengths_ The square $JOSH$ is inscribed in a semicircle. What is the ratio of x to y?

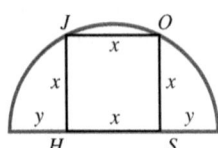

57. _Frustum of a Pyramid_ The feature "When Will I Ever Use This?" on the next page shows an application of the _frustum_ of a pyramid. Use the figure below to help verify the formula for the volume of the frustum of a pyramid with square base. (Note that, in this formula, B and b are the lengths of the sides of the bases, _not_ the areas of the bases.)

$$V = \frac{1}{3}h\left(B^2 + Bb + b^2\right)$$

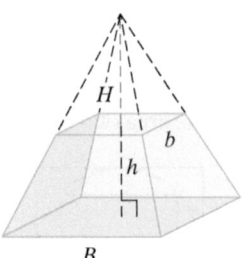

58. _Ratio of Surface Area to Base Area_ The figure shows a pyramid with square base and with height equal to the side length of the base. Find the ratio of the entire surface area to the area of the base.

Euler's Formula _Many crystals and some viruses are constructed in the shapes of regular polyhedra._

Radiolara virus

Leonhard Euler investigated a remarkable relationship among the numbers of faces (F), vertices (V), and edges (E) for the five regular polyhedra. Complete the chart in Exercises 59–63, and then draw a conclusion in Exercise 64.

Polyhedron	Faces (F)	Vertices (V)	Edges (E)	Value of F + V − E
59. Tetrahedron				
60. Hexahedron (cube)				
61. Octahedron				
62. Dodecahedron				
63. Icosahedron				

64. Euler's formula is $F + V - E =$ _____ .

WHEN Will I Ever USE This ?

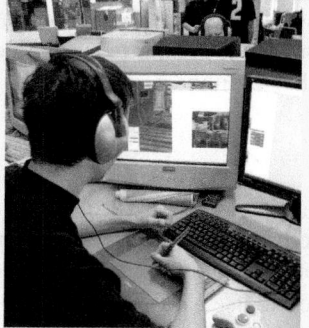

Suppose you are a video game programmer employing digital animation. You have created a "virtual world" with objects placed relatively uniformly throughout. You want the user to be able to navigate around this world and see objects "behind the screen" and within a reasonable visibility range. This "volume of visibility" is the frustum of a square-based pyramid with its apex at the vantage point of the player. (See **Figure 60.**) It is called the *view frustum*. Its *near plane* (the screen) and *far plane* (at the limit of the visible range) are shown in green in the figure. The view frustum contains all objects that are potentially viewable (although some objects may obstruct the player's view of others in the view frustum).

Suppose the screen is square, measuring about $\frac{1}{3}$ meter on a side, and is about 1 meter away from the user's eye. If the range of visibility is 300 meters, what is the volume of the view frustum? If the entire virtual world can be represented by a circular cylinder of radius 1000 meters and height 200 meters, what percentage of the world is contained within a single view frustum?

The view frustum is shown in detail in **Figure 61.** Since it has square bases, its volume is given (see the margin note on **page 531**) by

$$V = \frac{1}{3}h(B^2 + Bb + b^2), \quad \text{Volume formula}$$

Figure 60

where B is the side length of the larger base, and b is the side length of the smaller base. To find B, we use similar triangles.

$$\frac{300}{1} = \frac{B}{\frac{1}{3}} \quad \text{Ratios of corresponding sides are equal.}$$

$$100 = B \quad \text{Multiply using cross products.}$$

We now substitute values for h, B, and b into the formula.

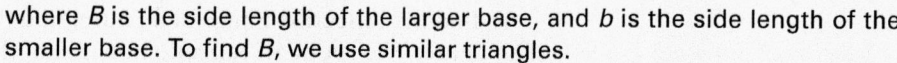

Figure 61

$$V = \frac{1}{3}h(B^2 + Bb + b^2) \quad \text{Volume formula}$$

$$= \frac{1}{3}(299)\left(100^2 + 100\left(\frac{1}{3}\right) + \left(\frac{1}{3}\right)^2\right) \quad h = 299, B = 100, b = \frac{1}{3}$$

$$\approx 1{,}000{,}000 \quad \text{Simplify.}$$

The volume of the view frustum is about 1,000,000 m³.

The volume of the entire virtual world is

$$V = \pi r^2 h \quad \text{Volume of a right circular cylinder}$$

$$= \pi(1000)^2(200) \quad r = 1000, h = 200$$

$$\approx 3.14(1{,}000{,}000)(200) \quad \pi \approx 3.14; \text{ multiply.}$$

$$= 628{,}000{,}000 \quad \text{Multiply.}$$

A single view frustum contains about $\frac{1}{628} \approx 0.16\%$ of the entire virtual world.

The software you are using for rendering three-dimensional objects allows for *frustum culling*, which instructs the graphics hardware to render only the objects in the view frustum, rather than *all* of the objects in the virtual world. This allows for a much more efficient use of memory and processor speed, which lead to shorter loading times and a better player experience.

9.6   TRANSFORMATIONAL GEOMETRY

OBJECTIVES

1 Transform geometric figures by reflection.

2 Transform geometric figures by translation.

3 Transform geometric figures by rotation.

4 Perform size transformations on geometric figures.

In this chapter we have studied concepts of Euclidean geometry. Another branch of geometry, known as **transformational geometry,** investigates how one geometric figure can be transformed into another. In transformational geometry we reflect, rotate, and change the size of figures using concepts that we now discuss.

Reflections

One way to transform one geometric figure into another is by **reflection.** In **Figure 62,** line m is perpendicular to the line segment AA' and bisects this line segment. We call point A' the **reflection image** of point A about line m. Line m is the **line of reflection** for points A and A'. In the figure, we use a dashed line to connect points A and A' to show that these two points are images of each other under this transformation.

Point A' is the reflection image of point A only for line m. If a different line were used, A would have a different reflection image. Think of the reflection image of a point A about a line m as follows:

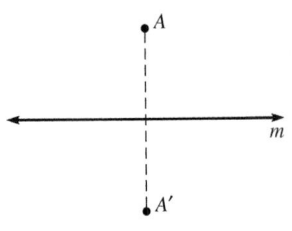

Figure 62

Place a drop of ink at point A, and fold the paper along line m. The spot made by the ink on the other side of m is the reflection image of A. If A' is the image of A about line m, then A is the image of A' about the same line m.

To find the reflection image of a figure, find the reflection image of each point of the figure. The set of all reflection images of the points of the original figure is the reflection image of the figure. **Figure 63** shows several figures (in black) and their reflection images (in color) about the lines shown.

An example of a **reflection.**

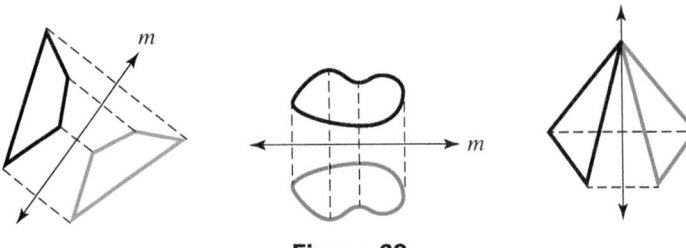

Figure 63

Each point in a plane has exactly one reflection image point with respect to a given line of reflection. Also, each reflection image point has exactly one original point. Thus, two distinct points cannot have the same reflection image. This means there is a *1-to-1 correspondence* between the set of points of the plane and the image points with respect to a given line of reflection. Any operation, such as reflection, in which there is a 1-to-1 correspondence between the points of the plane and their image points is a **transformation.** We call reflection about a line the **reflection transformation.**

If a point A and its image, A', under a certain transformation are the same point, then point A is an **invariant point** of the transformation. The only invariant points of the reflection transformation are the points of the line of reflection.

Three points that lie on the same straight line are **collinear.** In **Figure 64,**

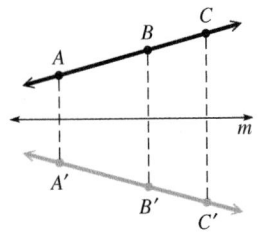

Figure 64

points A, B, and C are collinear,

and it can be shown that the reflection images A', B', and C' are also collinear. Thus, the reflection image of a line is also a line. We express this by saying that **reflection preserves collinearity.**

Figure 65

M. C. Escher (1898–1972) was a Dutch graphic artist, most recognized for spatial illusions, impossible buildings, repeating geometric patterns (tessellations), and his incredible techniques in woodcutting and lithography. He was a humble man who considered himself neither an artist nor a mathematician.

The lithograph pictured here, called *Ascending and Descending,* gives the illusion that the stairs near the top of this building are both ascending and descending simultaneously.

How many kinds of **symmetry** do you see here?

Distance is also preserved by the reflection transformation. Thus, in **Figure 65,** the distance between points A and B, written $|AB|$, is equal to the distance between the reflection images A' and B', or

$$|AB| = |A'B'|.$$

To prove this, we can use the definition of reflection image to verify that

$$|AM| = |MA'|, \quad \text{and} \quad |BN| = |NB'|.$$

Construct segments CB and $C'B'$, each perpendicular to BB'. Note that $CBB'C'$ is a rectangle. Because the opposite sides of a rectangle are equal and parallel, we have

$$|CB| = |C'B'|. \qquad \text{(Side)} \quad \textbf{(1)}$$

Because $CBB'C'$ is a rectangle, we can also say

$$m \measuredangle ACB = m \measuredangle A'C'B' = 90°, \qquad \text{(Angle)} \quad \textbf{(2)}$$

where we use $m \measuredangle ACB$ to represent the measure of angle ACB.

We know $|AM| = |MA'|$ and can show $|CM| = |MC'|$, so that

$$|AC| = |A'C'|. \qquad \text{(Side)} \quad \textbf{(3)}$$

From statements (1), (2), and (3) above, we conclude that in triangles ABC and $A'B'C'$, two sides and the included angle of one are equal in measure to the corresponding two sides and angle of the other and, thus, are congruent by SAS (**Section 9.3**). Corresponding sides of congruent triangles are equal in length, so

$$|AB| = |A'B'|,$$

which is what we wanted to show. Hence, the distance between two points equals the distance between their reflection images, and thus, reflection preserves distance. (The proof we have given is not really complete, because we have tacitly assumed that AB is not parallel to $A'B'$, and that A and B are on the same side of the line of reflection. Some modification would have to be made in the proof above to include these other cases.)

The figures shown in **Figure 66** are their own reflection images about the lines of reflection shown. In this case, the line of reflection is a **line of symmetry** for the figure. **Figure 66(a)** has three lines of symmetry. A circle has every line through its center as a line of symmetry.

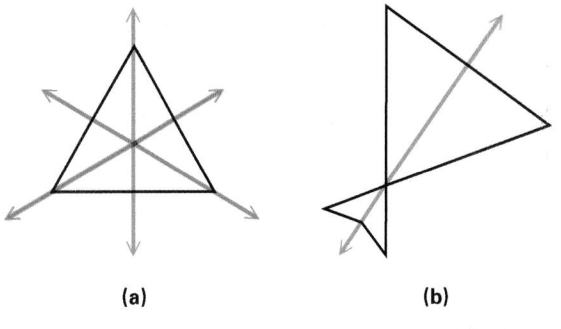

(a)   (b)

Figure 66

Translations and Rotations

We shall use the symbol r_m to represent a reflection about line m, and let us use $r_n \cdot r_m$ to represent a reflection about line m followed by a reflection about line n. We call $r_n \cdot r_m$ the **composition,** or **product,** of the two reflections r_n and r_m. **Figure 67** on the next page shows two examples of the composition of two reflections. In **Figure 67(a),** lines m and n are parallel, whereas they intersect in **Figure 67(b).**

(a)   **(b)**

Figure 67

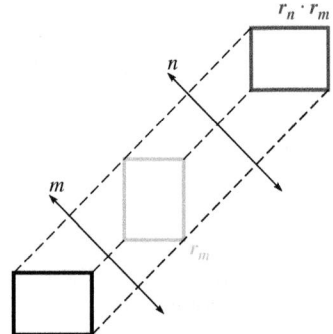

Figure 68

In **Figure 67(a)** both the original figure and its image under the composition of the two reflections appear to be oriented the same way and to have the same "tilt." In fact, it appears that the original figure could be slid along the dashed lines of **Figure 67(a),** with no rotation, so as to cover the image. This composite transformation is a **translation. Figure 68** shows a translation, and the image can be obtained as a composition of two reflections about parallel lines. Check that the distance between a point and its image under a translation is twice the distance between the two parallel lines. The distance between a point and its image under a translation is the **magnitude** of the translation.

A translation of magnitude 0 leaves every point of the plane unchanged and, thus, is the **identity translation.** A translation of magnitude k, followed by a similar translation of magnitude k but of opposite direction, returns a point to its original position, so these two translations are **inverses** of each other. Check that there are no invariant points in a translation of magnitude $k > 0$.

A translation preserves collinearity (three points on the same line have image points that also lie on a line) and distance (the distance between two points is the same as the distance between the images of the points).

In **Figure 67(b),** the original figure could be rotated so as to cover the image. Hence, we call the composition of two reflections about nonparallel lines a **rotation.** The point of intersection of these two nonparallel lines is the **center of rotation.** The black triangle of **Figure 69** was reflected about line m and then reflected about line n, resulting in a rotation with center at B. The dashed lines in color represent the paths of the vertices of the triangle under the rotation. It can be shown that $m \measuredangle ABA'$ is twice as large as $m \measuredangle MBN$. The measure of angle ABA' is the **magnitude** of the rotation.

This **Escher pattern** fills (tiles) the entire plane if we start with one fish, one duck, and one lizard, and then perform repeated translations in opposite directions.

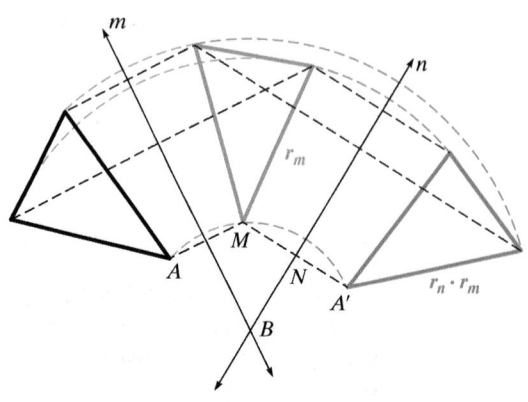

Figure 69

Rotations also preserve collinearity and distance. The identity transformation here is a rotation of 0° or 360°, and rotations of, say, 240° and 120° (or, in general, $x°$ and $360° - x°$, $0 \leq x \leq 360°$) are inverses of each other. The center of rotation is the only invariant point of any rotation except the identity rotation.

We have defined rotations as the composition of two reflections about nonparallel lines of reflection. We can also define a rotation by specifying its center, the angle of rotation, and a direction of rotation, as shown by the following example.

▓▓▓ EXAMPLE 1 Finding an Image under a Rotation

Find the image of a point P under a rotation transformation having center at a point Q and magnitude 135° clockwise.

Solution

To find P', the image of P, first draw angle PQM having measure 135°. Then draw an arc of a circle with center at Q and radius $|PQ|$. The point where this arc intersects side QM is P'. See **Figure 70.**

Figure 70   ▪

Figure 71 shows a rotation transformation having center Q and magnitude 180° clockwise. Point Q bisects the line segment from a point A to its image A', and for this reason this rotation is sometimes called a **point reflection.**

Figure 71

▓▓▓ EXAMPLE 2 Finding Point Reflection Images

Find the point reflection images about point Q for each of the following figures.

(a)   **(b)**

Solution

(a)   **(b)**

The point reflection images are shown in color.   ▪

Let r_m be a reflection about line m, and let T be a translation having nonzero magnitude and a direction parallel to m. Then the composition of T and r_m is a **glide reflection,** as seen in **Figure 72.** Here a reflection followed by a translation is the same as a translation followed by a reflection, so in this case,

$$T \cdot r_m = r_m \cdot T.$$

Because a translation is the composition of *two* reflections, a glide reflection is the composition of *three* reflections. Because it is required that the translation have nonzero magnitude, there is no identity glide transformation.

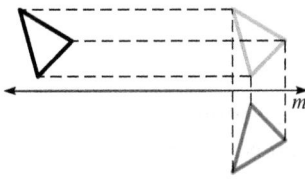

Figure 72

All the transformations of this section discussed so far are **isometries,** or transformations in which the image of a figure has the same size and shape as the original figure. Any isometry is either a reflection or the composition of two or more reflections.

Size Transformations

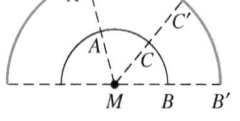

Figure 73

Figure 73 shows a semicircle in black, a point M, and an image semicircle in color. Distance $A'M$ is twice the distance AM and distance $B'M$ is twice the distance BM. In fact, every point of the image semicircle, such as C', was obtained by drawing a line through M and C, and then locating C' such that $|MC'| = 2\,|MC|$.

Such a transformation is a **size transformation** with center M and magnitude 2. We shall assume that a size transformation can have any positive real number k as magnitude. A size transformation having magnitude $k > 1$ is a **dilation,** or **stretch.** A size transformation having magnitude $k < 1$ is a **contraction,** or **shrink.**

EXAMPLE 3 Applying Size Transformations

Apply a size transformation with center M and magnitude $\frac{1}{3}$ to the two pentagons shown in black in **Figure 74.**

Solution

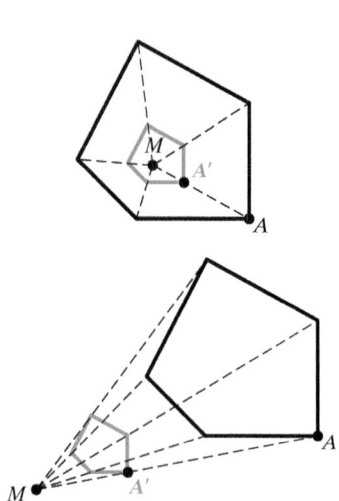

Figure 74

To find the images of these pentagons, we can find the image points of some sample points. For example, if we select point A on each of the original pentagons, we can find the image points by drawing a line through A and M, and locating a point A' such that $|MA'| = \frac{1}{3}|MA|$. By doing this for all points of each of the black pentagons, we get the images shown in color in **Figure 74.** ∎

The identity transformation is a size transformation of magnitude 1, while size transformations of magnitude k and $\frac{1}{k}$, having the same center, are inverses of each other. The only invariant point of a size transformation of magnitude $k \neq 1$ is the center of the transformation.

EXAMPLE 4 Investigating Size Transformations

Does a size transformation **(a)** preserve collinearity? **(b)** preserve distance?

Solution

(a) **Figure 75** shows three collinear points, A, B, and C, and their images under two different size transformations with center at M: one of magnitude 3 and one of magnitude $\frac{1}{3}$. In each case the image points appear to be collinear, and it can be proved that they are, using similar triangles. In fact, the image of a line not through the center of the transformation is a line parallel to the original line.

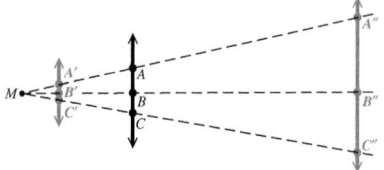

Figure 75

(b) As shown in **Figure 75**, $|AB| \neq |A'B'|$. Thus, a size transformation of magnitude $k \neq 1$ does not preserve distance and is not an isometry.

Transformations are summarized in Table 4 on page 543. ∎

Tessellations

The authors wish to thank Suzanne Alejandre for permission to reprint this article on tessellations, which first appeared at www.mathforum.org/sum95/suzanne/whattess.html.

tessellate (verb), **tessellation** (noun): from Latin *tessera* "a square tablet" or "a die used for gambling." Latin tessera may have been borrowed from Greek *tessares*, meaning "four," since a square tile has four sides. The diminutive of *tessera* was *tessella,* a small, square piece of stone or a cubical tile used in mosaics. Since a mosaic extends over a given area without leaving any region uncovered, the geometric meaning of the word "tessellate" is "to cover the plane with a pattern in such a way as to leave no region uncovered." By extension, space or hyperspace may also be tessellated.

Definition

A dictionary will tell you that the word "tessellate" means to form or arrange small squares in a checkered or mosaic pattern. The word "tessellate" is derived from the Ionic version of the Greek word "tesseres," which in English means "four." The first tilings were made from square tiles.

A regular polygon has 3 or 4 or 5 or more sides and angles, all equal. A **regular tessellation** means a tessellation made up of congruent regular polygons. [Remember: *Regular* means that the sides of the polygon are all the same length. *Congruent* means that the polygons that you put together are all the same size and shape.]

Only three regular polygons tessellate in the Euclidean plane: triangles, squares, or hexagons. We can't show the entire plane, but imagine that these are pieces taken from planes that have been tiled. Here are examples of

a tessellation of triangles

a tessellation of squares

a tessellation of hexagons

When you look at these three samples you can easily notice that the squares are lined up with each other while the triangles and hexagons are not.

Also, if you look at six triangles at a time, they form a hexagon, so the tiling of triangles and the tiling of hexagons are similar and they cannot be formed by directly lining shapes up under each other—a slide (or a glide!) is involved.

You can work out the interior measure of the angles for each of these polygons:

Shape	Angle Measure in Degrees
triangle	60
square	90
pentagon	108
hexagon	120
more than six sides	more than 120 degrees

Since the regular polygons in a tessellation must fill the plane at each vertex, the interior angle must be an exact divisor of 360 degrees. This works for the triangle, square, and hexagon, and you can show working tessellations for these figures. For all the others, the interior angles are not exact divisors of 360 degrees, and, therefore, those figures cannot tile the plane.

Naming Conventions

A tessellation of squares is named "4.4.4.4." Here's how: choose a vertex, and then look at one of the polygons that touches that vertex. How many sides does it have?

Since it's a square, it has four sides, and that's where the first "4" comes from. Now keep going around the vertex in either direction, finding the number of sides of the polygons until you get back to the polygon you started with. How many polygons did you count?

There are four polygons, and each has four sides.

4.4.4.4

For a tessellation of regular congruent hexagons, if you choose a vertex and count the sides of the polygons that touch it, you'll see that there are three polygons and each has six sides, so this tessellation is called "6.6.6":

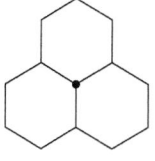

6.6.6

A tessellation of triangles has six polygons surrounding a vertex, and each of them has three sides: "3.3.3.3.3.3."

3.3.3.3.3.3

Semi-regular Tessellations

You can also use a variety of regular polygons to make **semi-regular tessellations.**

A semi-regular tessellation has two properties, which are:

1. It is formed by regular polygons.

2. The arrangement of polygons at every vertex point is identical.

Here are the **eight** semi-regular tessellations:

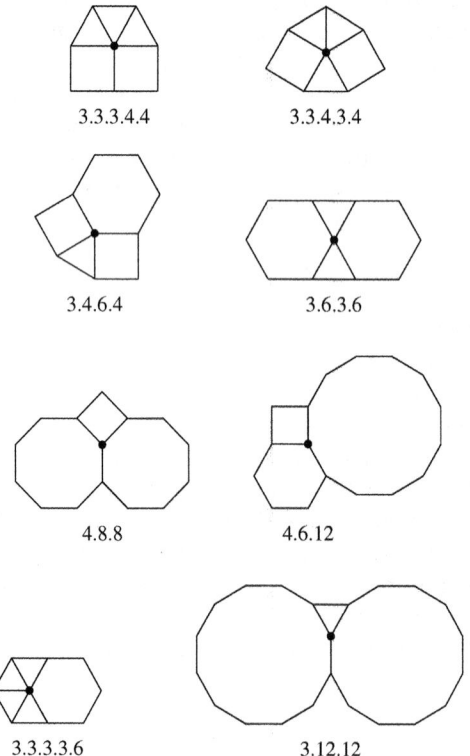

3.3.3.4.4   3.3.4.3.4

3.4.6.4   3.6.3.6

4.8.8   4.6.12

3.3.3.3.6   3.12.12

Interestingly, there are other combinations that seem like they should tile the plane because the arrangements of the regular polygons fill the space around a point. For example:

3.4.3.12   3.4.4.6   5.5.10

If you try tiling the plane with these units of tessellation you will find that they cannot be extended infinitely.

There is an infinite number of tessellations that can be made of patterns that do not have the same combination of angles at every vertex point. There are also tessellations made of polygons that do not share common edges and vertices.

For Group or Individual Investigation

1. Use the naming conventions to name each of these semi-regular tessellations.

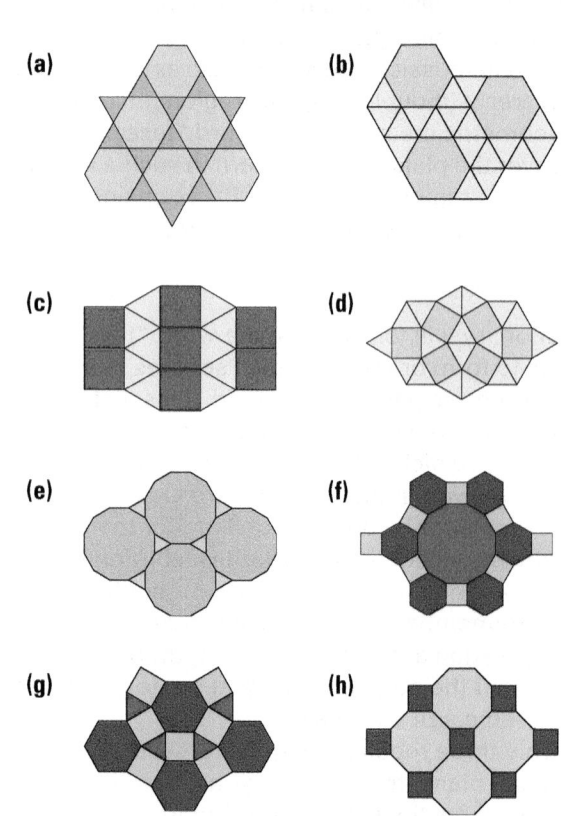

(a)   (b)

(c)   (d)

(e)   (f)

(g)   (h)

2. Why isn't this a semi-regular tessellation?

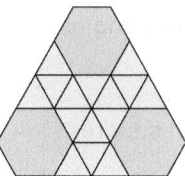

Tessellations (a) through (h) are courtesy of www.coolmath.com.

Table 4 Summary of Transformations

	Reflection	Translation	Rotation	Glide Reflection	Size Transformation
Example					
Preserve collinearity?	Yes	Yes	Yes	Yes	Yes
Preserve distance?	Yes	Yes	Yes	Yes	No
Identity transformation?	None	Magnitude 0	Magnitude 360°	None	Magnitude 1
Inverse transformation?	None	Same magnitude; opposite direction	Same center; magnitude $360° - x°$	None	Same center; magnitude $\frac{1}{k}$
Composition of n reflections?	$n = 1$	$n = 2$, parallel	$n = 2$, nonparallel	$n = 3$	No
Isometry?	Yes	Yes	Yes	Yes	No
Invariant points?	Line of reflection	None	Center of rotation	None	Center of transformation

9.6   EXERCISES

Find the reflection images of the given figures about the given lines.

1.

2.

3.

4.

5.

6.

7.

8.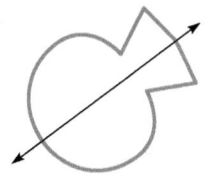

Find any lines of symmetry of the given figures.

9.

10.

11.

12.

First reflect the given figure about line m. Then reflect about line n.

13.

14.

15.

16.

17.

18.

19.

20.
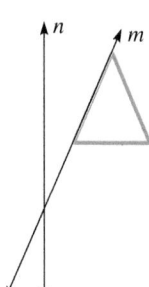

In Exercises 21–34, let T be a translation having magnitude 1.5 cm to the right in a direction parallel to the bottom edge of the page. Let r_m be a reflection about line m, and let R_P be a rotation about point P having magnitude 60° clockwise. In each of Exercises 21–32, perform the given transformations on point A of the figure below to obtain final image point A'.

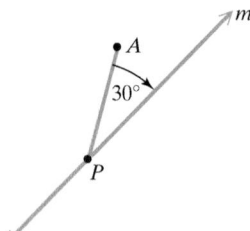

21. r_m	**22.** R_P	**23.** T
24. $r_m \cdot r_m$	**25.** $T \cdot T$	**26.** $R_P \cdot R_P$
27. $T \cdot R_P$	**28.** $T \cdot r_m$	**29.** $r_m \cdot T$
30. $R_P \cdot r_m$	**31.** $r_m \cdot R_P$	**32.** $R_P \cdot T$

33. Is $T \cdot r_m$ a glide reflection here?

34. Is $T \cdot r_m = r_m \cdot T$ true?

35. Suppose a rotation is given by $r_m \cdot r_n$, as shown in the figure below. Find the images of A, B, and C.

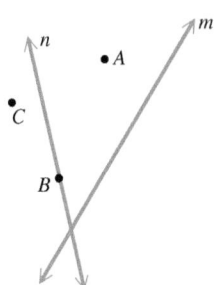

36. Does a glide reflection preserve

(a) collinearity?   **(b)** distance?

Find the point reflection images of each of the following figures with the given point Q as center.

37.

38.

39.

40.
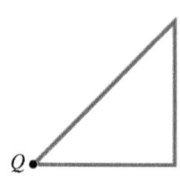

Perform the indicated size transformation.

41. magnitude 2; center M

42. magnitude $\frac{1}{2}$; center M

43. magnitude $\frac{1}{2}$; center M

44. magnitude 2; center M

45. magnitude $\frac{1}{3}$; center M

46. magnitude $\frac{1}{3}$; center M

Exercises 47–50 refer to the figure in the next column, which consists of a sequence of quadrilaterals spiraling toward a single point P. Each successive quadrilateral is obtained by a clockwise 60° rotation about P, followed by a contraction of magnitude $\frac{4}{5}$ with center P. We will call the rotation R_P and the contraction C_P.

47. A composition of ____ clockwise rotations of 60° results in an identically oriented quadrilateral.

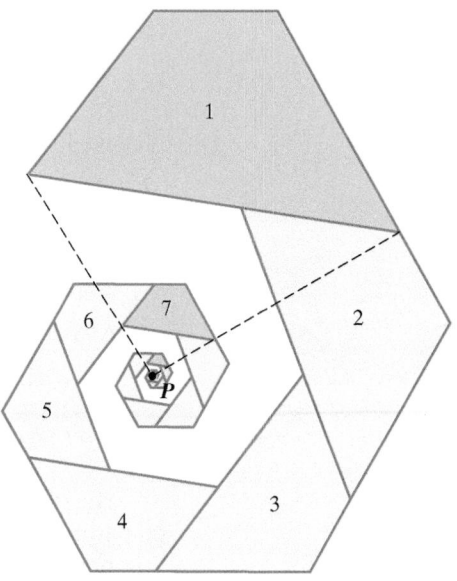

48. Quadrilateral 1 may be transformed into Quadrilateral 7 by the composition

$$C_P \cdot R_P \cdot C_P \cdot R_P \cdot C_P \cdot R_P \cdot C_P \cdot R_P \cdot C_P \cdot R_P \cdot C_P \cdot R_P.$$

Use your conclusion from **Exercise 47** to simplify this to a single contraction. Express the magnitude as a fraction.

49. Quadrilateral 1 may be transformed into Quadrilateral $6n + 1$ by repeating C_P $6n$ times. This can be expressed concisely as C_P^{6n}. Find a similar concise expression for the transformation of Quadrilateral 1 into Quadrilateral $6n + 3$.

50. What transformation will transform Quadrilateral n into Quadrilateral $n + 3$?

NON-EUCLIDEAN GEOMETRY AND TOPOLOGY

OBJECTIVES

1 Consider Euclid's postulates and axioms.
2 Understand the parallel postulate.
3 Investigate the origins of non-Euclidean geometry.
4 Project Euclidean objects onto a sphere.
5 Understand the concept of duality in projective geometry.
6 Determine the topological equivalence of figures.

Euclid's Postulates and Axioms

The *Elements* of Euclid is quite possibly the most influential mathematics book ever written. (See the margin note on **page 488.**) It begins with definitions of basic ideas such as

point, line, and plane.

Euclid then gives five postulates providing the foundation of all that follows.

Next, Euclid lists five axioms that he views as general truths and not just facts about geometry. See **Table 5** on the next page. (To some of the Greek writers, postulates were truths about a particlar field, while axioms were general truths. Today, "axiom" is used in either case.) Using only these ten statements and the basic rules of logic, Euclid was able to prove a large number of "propositions" about geometric figures.

John Playfair (1748–1819) wrote his *Elements of Geometry* in 1795. Playfair's Axiom is: Given a line *k* and a point *P* not on the line, there exists one and only one line *m* through *P* that is parallel to *k*. This is equivalent to Euclid's Postulate 5.

Table 5

Euclid's Postulates	Euclid's Axioms
1. Two points determine one and only one straight line.	**6.** Things equal to the same thing are equal to each other.
2. A straight line extends indefinitely far in either direction.	**7.** If equals are added to equals, the sums are equal.
3. A circle may be drawn with any given center and any given radius.	**8.** If equals are subtracted from equals, the remainders are equal.
4. All right angles are equal.	**9.** Figures that can be made to coincide are equal.
5. Given a line *k* and a point *P* not on the line, there exists one and only one line *m* through *P* that is parallel to *k*.	**10.** The whole is greater than any of its parts.

The statement for Postulate 5 given above is actually known as Playfair's axiom on parallel lines, which is equivalent to Euclid's fifth postulate. To understand why this postulate caused trouble for so many mathematicians for so long, we must examine the original formulation.

The Parallel Postulate (Euclid's Fifth Postulate)

In its original form, Euclid's fifth postulate states the following:

If two lines (k and m in **Figure 76***) are such that a third line, n, intersects them so that the sum of the two interior angles (A and B) on one side of line n is less than (the sum of) two right angles, then the two lines, if extended far enough, will meet on the same side of n that has the sum of the interior angles less than (the sum of) two right angles.*

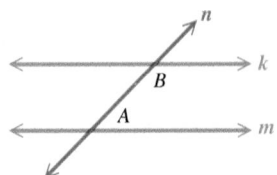

Figure 76

Euclid's parallel postulate is quite different from the other nine postulates and axioms we listed. It is long and wordy, and difficult to understand without a sketch. It was commonly believed that this was not a postulate at all but a theorem to be proved. For more than 2000 years, mathematicians tried repeatedly to prove it.

The most dedicated attempt came from an Italian Jesuit, Girolamo Saccheri (1667–1733). He attempted to prove the parallel postulate in an indirect way, by so-called "reduction to absurdity." He would assume the postulate to be false and then show that the assumption leads to a contradiction of something true (an absurdity). Such a contradiction would thus prove the statement true. Saccheri began with a quadrilateral, as in **Figure 77**. He assumed angles *A* and *B* to be right angles and sides *AD* and *BC* to be equal. His plan was as follows:

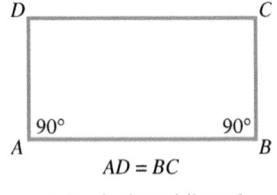

A Saccheri quadrilateral

Figure 77

1. To assume that angles *C* and *D* are obtuse angles, and to show that this leads to a contradiction.

2. To assume that angles *C* and *D* are acute angles, and to show that this also leads to a contradiction.

3. Then if *C* and *D* can be neither acute nor obtuse angles, they must be right angles.

4. If *C* and *D* are both right angles, then it can be proved that the fifth postulate is true. It thus is a theorem rather than a postulate.

Saccheri had no trouble with part 1. However, he did not actually reach a contradiction in the second part but produced some theorems so "repugnant" that he convinced himself he had vindicated Euclid. In fact, he published a book called in English *Euclid Freed of Every Flaw.* However, today we know that the fifth postulate is indeed an axiom and not a theorem. It is *consistent* with Euclid's other axioms.

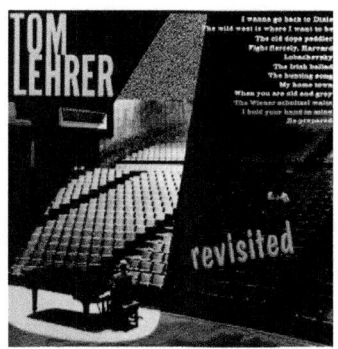

A song titled simply **Lobachevsky** appears on the CD *Tom Lehrer Revisited.* The songwriter described this song as an account of "one way to get ahead in mathematics (which happens to be the author's own academic specialty) or any other academic field." Lehrer's music is available for download. Listen to *Lobachevsky,* and see what Lehrer suggests!

The ten axioms of Euclid describe the world around us with remarkable accuracy. We now realize that the fifth postulate is necessary in Euclidean geometry to establish *flatness.* That is, the axioms of Euclid describe the geometry of *plane surfaces.* By changing the fifth postulate, we can describe the geometry of other surfaces. So, other geometric systems exist as much as Euclidean geometry exists, and they can even be demonstrated in our world. A system of geometry in which the fifth postulate is changed is a **non-Euclidean geometry.**

The Origins of Non-Euclidean Geometry

One non-Euclidean system was developed by three people working separately at about the same time. Early in the nineteenth century, Carl Friedrich Gauss worked out a consistent geometry replacing Euclid's fifth postulate. He never published his work, however, because he feared the ridicule of people who could not free themselves from habitual ways of thinking.

Nikolai Ivanovich Lobachevski (1793–1856) published a similar system in 1830 in the Russian language. At the same time, Janos Bolyai (1802–1860), a Hungarian army officer, worked out a similar system, which he published in 1832, not knowing about Lobachevski's work. Bolyai never recovered from the disappointment of not being the first and did no further work in mathematics.

Lobachevski replaced Euclid's fifth postulate with the following.

Angles C and D in the quadrilateral of Saccheri are acute angles.

Lobachevski's replacement

This postulate of Lobachevski can be rephrased as follows.

*Through a point P off a line k (***Figure 78***), at least two different lines can be drawn parallel to k.*

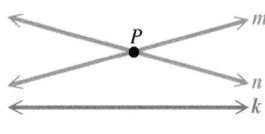

Figure 78

Compare this form of Lobachevski's postulate to the geometry of Euclid, where only one line can be drawn through *P* and parallel to *k.* At first glance, the postulate of Lobachevski does not agree with what we know about the world around us. But this is only because we think of our immediate surroundings as being flat.

Many of the theorems of Euclidean geometry are valid for the geometry of Lobachevski, but many are not. For example, in Euclidean geometry, the sum of the measures of the angles in any triangle is 180°. In Lobachevskian geometry, the sum of the measures of the angles in any triangle is *less* than 180°. Also, triangles of different sizes can never have equal angles, so similar triangles do not exist.

The geometry of Euclid can be represented on a plane. Since any portion of the earth that we are likely to see looks flat, Euclidean geometry is very useful for describing the everyday world around us. The non-Euclidean geometry of Lobachevski can be represented as a surface called a **pseudosphere.** This surface is formed by revolving a curve called a **tractrix** about the line *AB* in **Figure 79.**

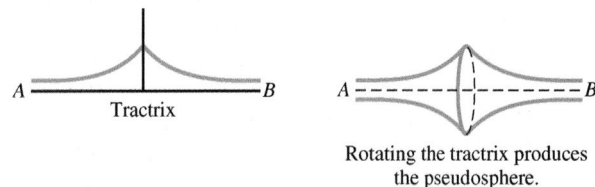

Rotating the tractrix produces the pseudosphere.

Figure 79

A second non-Euclidean system was developed by Georg Riemann (1826–1866). He pointed out the difference between a line that continues indefinitely and a line having infinite length. For example, a circle on the surface of a sphere continues indefinitely but does not have infinite length. Riemann developed the idea of geometry on a sphere and replaced Euclid's fifth postulate with the following.

Angles C and D of the Saccheri quadrilateral are obtuse angles.

Riemann's replacement

In terms of parallel lines, Riemann's postulate is stated this way.

Through a point P off a line k, no line can be drawn that is parallel to k.

Riemannian geometry is important in navigation. "Lines" in this geometry are really *great circles,* or circles whose centers are at the center of the sphere. The shortest distance between two points on a sphere lies along an arc of a great circle. Great circle routes on a globe don't look at all like the shortest distance when the globe is flattened out to form a map, but this is part of the distortion that occurs when the earth is represented as a flat surface. See **Figure 80.** The sides of a triangle drawn on a sphere would be arcs of great circles. And, in Riemannian geometry, the sum of the measures of the angles in any triangle is *more* than 180°.

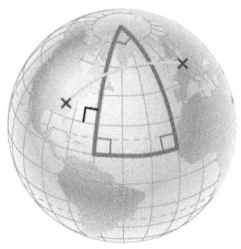

Figure 80

Projective Geometry

Beginning in the fifteenth century, artists led by Leone Battista Alberti (1404–1472), Leonardo da Vinci (1452–1519), and Albrecht Dürer (1471–1528) began to study the problems of representing three dimensions in two. What artists initiated, mathematicians developed into another non-Euclidean geometry, that of **projective geometry.**

Gerard Desargues (1591–1661), a French architect and engineer, published in 1636 and 1639 a treatise and proposals about **perspective,** thus inventing projective geometry. However, these innovations were hidden for nearly 200 years until a manuscript by Desargues was discovered in 1840, about 30 years after projective geometry had been revived by Jean-Victor Poncelet (1788–1867).

Although there are many projective geometries, an example of one that projects three-dimensional space onto a **projective sphere** is depicted in **Figure 81** on the next page. The projected image of a point *P* is the pair of points of intersection of the sphere with the line passing through *P* and the center of the sphere. These two points (labeled *P′* and *P″* in the figure) are **antipodal points** and are considered undistinguishable (that is, they are treated as a single point). The eye of the observer is thought to be at the center of the sphere, and the images of objects in space are projected onto the spherical "screen." Notice that parallel lines *m* and *n* in Euclidean space correspond to two great circles in the sphere that intersect on the "equator" of the sphere. In this configuration, the equator corresponds to infinity, which is just another great circle (line) in this geometry.

How should artists paint a realistic view of **railroad tracks vanishing into the horizon?** In reality, the tracks are always a constant distance apart, but they cannot be drawn that way except from overhead. The artist must make the tracks converge at a "vanishing point" to show how things look from the perspective of an observer.

Georg Friedrich Bernhard Riemann (1826–1866) was a German mathematician. Though he lived a short time and published few papers, his work forms a basis for much modern mathematics. He made significant contributions to the theory of functions and the study of complex numbers, as well as to geometry. Most calculus books today use the idea of a "Riemann sum" in defining the integral.

Riemann achieved a complete understanding of the non-Euclidean geometries of his day, expressing them on curved surfaces and showing how to extend them to higher dimensions.

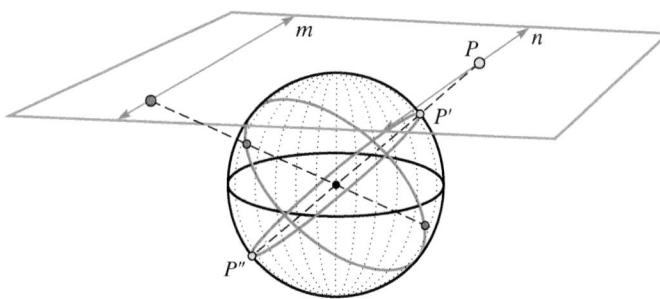

Figure 81

Figure 82 shows that intersecting lines in Euclidean space are also mapped to great circles that intersect at a single point (antipodal pair).

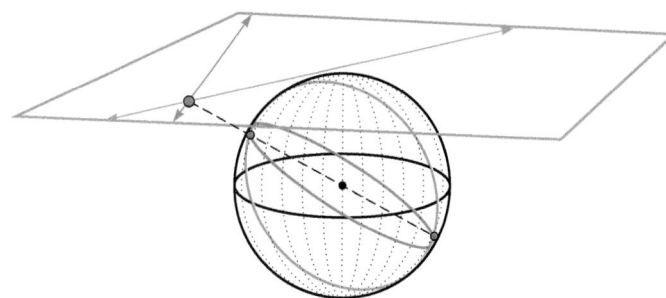

Figure 82

Projective geometries preserve points and intersections, but not distances. **Figure 82** demonstrates that a point of intersection in Euclidean space will be projected to a point of intersection in the projective plane. But **Figure 81** illustrates that distance (such as that between parallel lines) in Euclidean space does not survive the projection process.

EXAMPLE 1 Determining the Projective Image of a Plane Figure

Given a triangle in Euclidean space, draw a picture showing how the triangle would be projected onto the projective sphere.

Solution

Since antipodal points are not distinguished, we use a hemisphere for simplicity. We begin with a triangle contained in a plane above the hemisphere, and draw segments from the vertices of the triangle to the center of the sphere. We then do our best to estimate the three points where those segments intersect the sphere. Remembering that lines in the projective geometry are great circles, we connect the three points with arcs of great circles. The finished drawing is shown in **Figure 83.** ∎

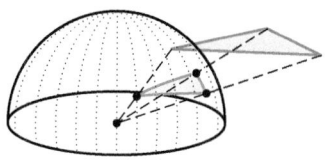

Figure 83

Consider the following statements.

Any two distinct points are contained in a unique line.

Any two distinct lines contain a unique point.

The first of these statements is true in Euclidean plane geometry, but the second is not. However, projective geometry removes the obstacle of non-intersecting parallel lines. As shown in **Figures 81 and 82,** every pair of lines (great circles) has a point of intersection. Surfaces for which both of the above statements are true are **projective planes.** Notice that these statements are identical, except that the instances of "point" and "line" are interchanged, and the containment relationship is exchanged for its inverse.

The preceding pair of statements is one example of the **duality** that is characteristic of projective geometry. Every true statement about a relationship between points and lines in the projective plane has its dual—a statement formed by interchanging "point" with "line" and replacing the relationship with its inverse.

EXAMPLE 2 Expressing a Dual

Express the dual of the following statement.

There are four distinct points, no three of which are contained in the same line.

Solution

We interchange "point" and "line" in the statement, and exchange the relationship "contained in" with its inverse, "contains." These changes give this statement.

There are four distinct lines, no three of which contain the same point. ■

Topology

The plane and space figures studied in the Euclidean system are carefully distinguished by differences in size, shape, angularity, and so on. For a given figure such properties are permanent, and, thus, we can ask sensible questions about congruence and similarity. Suppose we studied "figures" made of rubber bands, as it were: "figures" that could be stretched, bent, or otherwise distorted without tearing or scattering. **Topology** does just that.

Topological questions concern the basic structure of objects rather than size or arrangement. A typical topological question has to do with the number of holes in an object, a basic structural property that does not change during deformation. Consider these examples.

- We cannot deform a rubber ball to get a rubber band without tearing it—making a hole in it. Thus the two objects are not topologically equivalent.

- On the other hand, a doughnut and a coffee cup are topologically equivalent, because one could be stretched to form the other without changing the basic structural property.

EXAMPLE 3 Determining Topological Equivalence

Decide whether the figures in each pair are topologically equivalent.

(a) a football and a cereal box **(b)** a doughnut and an unzipped coat

Solution

(a) If we assume that a football is made of a perfectly elastic substance such as rubber or dough, it could be twisted or kneaded into the same shape as a cereal box. Thus, the two figures are topologically equivalent.

(b) A doughnut has one hole, while the coat has two (the sleeve openings). Thus, a doughnut could not be stretched and twisted into the shape of the coat without tearing another hole in it. Because of this, a doughnut and the coat are not topologically equivalent. ■

Topology and geometry software, including games for users age 10 and up, can be found at www.geometrygames.org, a site developed by Jeff Weeks. Included are Torus Games, Kali, KaleidoTile, and investigations into Curved Spaces.

In topology, figures are classified according to their **genus**—that is, the number of cuts that can be made without cutting the figures into two pieces. The genus of an object is the number of holes in it. See **Figure 84** on the next page.

Torus One of the most useful figures in topology is the torus, a doughnut-like surface. Its properties are different from those of a sphere, for example. Imagine a sphere covered with hair. You cannot comb the hairs in a completely smooth way. One fixed point remains, as you can find on your own head. In the same way, on the surface of the earth the winds are not a smooth system. There is a calm point somewhere. However, the hair on a torus could be combed smooth.

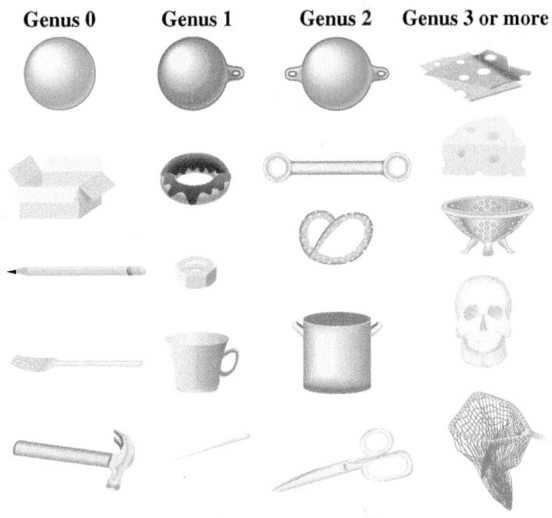

Genus of some common objects

Figure 84

FOR FURTHER THOUGHT

Two Interesting Topological Surfaces

Two examples of topological surfaces are the **Möbius strip** and the **Klein bottle**. The Möbius strip is a single-sided surface named after August Ferdinand Möbius (1790–1868), a pupil of Gauss.

To construct a Möbius strip, cut out a rectangular strip of paper, perhaps 3 cm by 25 cm. Paste together the two 3-cm ends after giving the paper a half-twist. To see how the strip now has only one side, mark an x on the strip and then mark another x on what appears to be the other "side." Begin at one of the x 's you have drawn, and trace a path along the strip. You will eventually come to the other x without crossing the edge of the strip.

A branch of chemistry called chemical topology studies the structures of chemical configurations. A recent advance in this area was the synthesis of the first molecular Möbius strip, which was formed by joining the ends of a double-stranded strip of carbon and oxygen atoms.

A mathematician confided

That a Möbius strip is one-sided.

And you'll get quite a laugh

If you cut one in half,

For it stays in one piece when divided.

Möbius strip

Klein bottle

Whereas a Möbius strip results from giving a paper *strip* a half-twist and then connecting it to itself, if we could do the same thing with a paper *tube* we would obtain a Klein bottle, named after Felix Klein (1849–1925). Klein produced important results in several areas, including non-Euclidean geometry and the early beginnings of group theory.

A mathematician named Klein

Thought the Möbius strip was divine.

Said he, "If you glue

The edges of two

You'll get a weird bottle like mine."

For Group or Individual Investigation

1. The Möbius strip has other interesting properties. With a pair of scissors, cut the strip lengthwise. Do you get two strips? Repeat the process with what you have obtained from the first cut. What happens?

2. Now construct another Möbius strip, and start cutting lengthwise about $\frac{1}{3}$ of the way from one edge. What happens?

3. What would be the advantage of a conveyor belt with the configuration of a Möbius strip?

9.7   EXERCISES

Study the chart below, and use it to respond to Exercises 1–10.

1. In which geometry is the sum of the measures of the angles of a triangle equal to 180°?

2. In which geometry is the sum of the measures of the angles of a triangle greater than 180°?

3. In which geometry is the sum of the measures of the angles of a triangle less than 180°?

4. In a quadrilateral *ABCD* in Lobachevskian geometry, the sum of the measures of the angles must be _____ 360°.
(less than/greater than)

5. In a quadrilateral *ABCD* in Riemannian geometry, the sum of the measures of the angles must be _____ 360°.
(less than/greater than)

6. Suppose *m* and *n* represent lines through *P* that are both parallel to *k*. In which geometry is this possible?

7. Suppose *m* and *n* below *must* meet at a point. In which geometry is this possible?

_____ *m*

_____ *n*

8. A globe representing the earth is a model for a surface in which geometry?

9. In which geometry is this statement possible? "Triangle *ABC* and triangle *DEF* are such that ∡*A* = ∡*D*, ∡*B* = ∡*E*, and ∡*C* = ∡*F*, and they have different perimeters."

EUCLIDEAN	NON-EUCLIDEAN	
Dates back to about 300 B.C.	**Lobachevskian (about 1830)**	**Riemannian (about 1850)**
Lines have *infinite* length.	Lines have *finite* length.	
Geometry on a plane	Geometry on a surface like a pseudosphere	Geometry on a sphere
Angles *C* and *D* of a Saccheri quadrilateral are *right* angles.	Angles *C* and *D* are *acute* angles.	Angles *C* and *D* are *obtuse* angles.
Given point *P* off line *k*, exactly *one* line can be drawn through *P* and parallel to *k*.	*More than one* line can be drawn through *P* and parallel to *k*.	*No* line can be drawn through *P* and parallel to *k*.
Typical triangle *ABC*	Typical triangle *ABC*	Typical triangle *ABC*
Two triangles with the same size angles can have different size sides (similarity as well as congruence).	Two triangles with the same size angles must have the same size sides (congruence only).	

10. Draw a figure (on a sheet of paper) as best you can showing the shape formed by the north pole *N* and two points *A* and *B* lying at the equator of a model of the earth.

In Exercises 11 and 12, project the given shape onto the hemisphere.

11.

12.

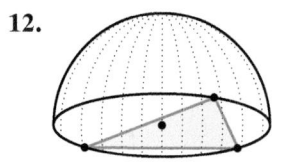

Exercises 13–18 refer to the **Fano Plane,** *shown here. It is a finite projective geometry containing seven points and seven lines.*

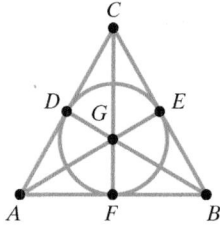

Points: *A, B, C, D, E, F,* and *G*

Lines: *ADC, AFB, AGE, BEC, BGD, CGF,* and *DEF*

(*Note: There is no requirement that a line be "straight" as in Euclidean geometry.*)

Verify that the Fano Plane satisfies each of the following statements, and state the dual in each case.

13. Any two distinct points have at least one line in common.

14. No two distinct points have more than one line in common.

15. Any two lines in a plane have at least one point of the plane in common.

16. There is at least one line on a plane.

17. Every line contains at least three points of the plane.

18. Not all of the points are contained in the same line.

Topological Equivalence *Someone once described a topologist as "a mathematician who doesn't know the difference between a doughnut and a coffee cup." This is because both are of genus 1—they are topologically equivalent! Based on this interpretation, would a topologist know the difference between each pair of objects in Exercises 19–22?*

19. a spoon and a fork

20. a mixing bowl and a colander

21. a slice of American cheese and a slice of Swiss cheese

22. a compact disc and a phonograph record

In Exercises 23–30 each figure may be topologically equivalent to none or some of the objects labeled A–E. *List all topological equivalences (by letter) for each figure.*

A.

B.

C.

D.

E.

23.

(a pair of scissors)

24.

(a needle)

25.

(a carrot)

26.

(a calculator)

27.

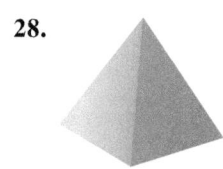

(a nut)

28.

(a pyramid)

(a pyramid)

29.

(a coin)

30.

(a skull)

Give the genus of each object.

31. a compact disc   **32.** a phonograph record

33. a sheet of loose-leaf paper made for a three-ring binder

34. a sheet of loose-leaf paper made for a two-ring binder

35. a wedding band   **36.** a postage stamp

37. Pappus, a Greek mathematician in Alexandria about A.D. 320, wrote a commentary on the geometry of the times. We will work out a theorem of his about a hexagon inscribed in two intersecting lines.

First we define an old word in a new way: a **hexagon** consists of any six lines in a plane, no three of which meet in the same point. In the figure, the vertices of several hexagons are labeled with numbers. Thus 1–2 represents a line segment joining vertices 1 and 2. Segments 1–2 and 4–5 are opposite sides of a hexagon, as are 2–3 and 5–6, and 3–4 and 6–1.

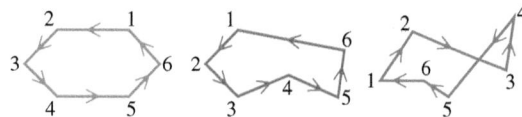

(a) Draw an angle less than 180°.

(b) Choose three points on one side of the angle. Label them 1, 5, 3 in that order, beginning with the point nearest the vertex.

(c) Choose three points on the other side of the angle. Label them 6, 2, 4 in that order, beginning with the point nearest the vertex.

(d) Draw line segments 1–6 and 3–4. Draw lines through the segments so that they extend to meet in a point. Call it *N*.

(e) Let lines through 1–2 and 4–5 meet in point *M*.

(f) Let lines through 2–3 and 5–6 meet in point *P*.

(g) Draw a straight line through points *M*, *N*, and *P*.

(h) Write in your own words a theorem generalizing your result.

38. The following theorem comes from projective geometry:

Theorem of Desargues in a Plane   In a plane, if two triangles are placed so that lines joining corresponding vertices meet in a point, then corresponding sides, when extended, will meet in three collinear points. (*Collinear* points are points lying on the same line.)

Draw a figure that illustrates Desargues' theorem.

9.8   CHAOS AND FRACTAL GEOMETRY

OBJECTIVES

1 Investigate the origins and meaning of chaos.

2 Understand the basics of fractal geometry.

Chaos

Does Chaos Rule the Cosmos?
    —One of the ten great unanswered questions of science, as found in the November 1992 issue of *Discover*

Consider the equation

$$y = kx(1 - x).$$

Choosing $k = 2$ gives the equation

$$y = 2x(1 - x),$$

which can be "iterated" by starting with an arbitrary x-value between 0 and 1, calculating the resulting y-value, substituting that y-value back in as x, calculating the resulting y-value, substituting that y-value back in as x, calculating another y-value, and so on. For example, a starting value of $x = 0.8$ produces the following sequence (which you can verify with a calculator):

$$0.8, \ 0.32, \ 0.435, \ 0.492, \ 0.500, \ 0.500, \ 0.500, \quad \text{and so on.}$$

The sequence seems to begin randomly but quickly stabilizes at the value 0.500. A different initial x-value would produce another sequence that would also "converge" to 0.500. The value 0.500 can be called an *attractor* for the sequence generated by the equation $y = 2x(1 - x)$. The values of the sequence are "attracted" toward 0.500.

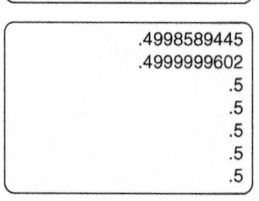

These two screens show how the TI-83 calculator can produce the sequence described. (The TI-84 plus produces a slightly different display, with the same results.)

n	$u(n)$	
0	.7	
1	.63	
2	.6993	
3	.63084	
4	.69864	

$u(n) = 3u(n-1)(1-\ldots$

n	$u(n)$	
14	.69588	
15	.63489	
16	.69542	
17	.63544	
18	.69497	
19	.63596	
20	.69454	

$u(n) = .6945436475$

These screens support the results of **Example 1.**

EXAMPLE 1 Finding Attractors

For the equation $y = kx(1 - x)$ with $k = 3$, begin with $x = 0.7$ and iterate with a calculator. What pattern emerges? How many attractors are there?

Solution

Using a TI-83/84 Plus calculator, we find that the seventeenth through twentieth iterations give this sequence of terms.

$$0.6354387337, \quad 0.6949690482, \quad 0.6359612107, \quad 0.6945436475$$

The sequence apparently converges in a manner different from the initial discussion, alternating between values near 0.636 and 0.695. Therefore, for $k = 3$, the sequence tends alternately toward *two* distinct attractors. ∎

It happens that the equation in **Example 1** exhibits the same behavior for any initial value of x between 0 and 1. You are asked to show this for several cases in the exercises.

n	$u(n)$	
0	.7	
1	.735	
2	.68171	
3	.75943	
4	.63943	

$u(n) = 3.5u(n-1)(\ldots$

n	$u(n)$	
45	.82694	
46	.50088	
47	.875	
48	.38282	
49	.82694	
50	.50088	
51	.875	

$u(n) = .8749972636$

These screens support the discussion in **Example 2.**

EXAMPLE 2 Finding Attractors

In the equation of **Example 1,** change the multiplier k to 3.5, and find the forty-fourth through fifty-first terms. What pattern emerges? How many attractors are there?

Solution

Again, using a TI-83/84 Plus calculator and rounding to three decimal places, we get

$$0.383, 0.827, 0.501, 0.875, 0.383, 0.827, 0.501, 0.875.$$

This sequence seems to stabilize around *four* alternating attractors, approximately 0.383, 0.827, 0.501, and 0.875. ∎

Notice that in our initial discussion, for $k = 2$, the sequence converged to *one* attractor. In **Example 1,** for $k = 3$, it converged to *two* attractors, and in **Example 2,** for $k = 3.5$, it converged to *four* attractors.

It turns out that as k is increased further, the number of attractors doubles over and over again, more and more often. In fact, this doubling has occurred infinitely many times before k even gets as large as 4. When we look closely at groups of these doublings, we find that they are always similar to earlier groups but on a smaller scale. This is called *self-similarity,* or *scaling,* an idea that is not new but has taken on new significance in recent years. Somewhere before k reaches 4, the resulting sequence becomes apparently totally random, with no attractors and no stability. This type of condition is one instance of what has come to be known in the scientific community as **chaos.** This name came from an early paper by the mathematician James A. Yorke, of the University of Maryland at College Park.

The equation $y = kx(1 - x)$ does not look all that complicated, but the intricate behavior exhibited by it and similar equations has occupied some of the brightest minds (not to mention computers) in various fields—ecology, biology, physics, genetics, economics, mathematics—since about 1960. Such an equation might represent, for example, the population of some animal species, where the value of k is determined by factors (such as food supply or predators that prey on the species) that affect the increase or decrease of the population. Under certain conditions there is a long-run steady-state population (a single attractor). Under other conditions the population will eventually fluctuate between two alternating levels (two attractors), or four, or eight, and so on. But after a certain value of k, the long-term population becomes totally chaotic and unpredictable.

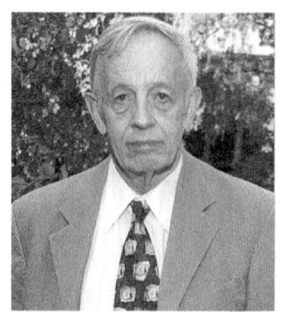

John Nash, a notable modern American mathematician (born in 1928), first came to the attention of the general public through his biography *A Beautiful Mind* (and the movie of the same name). In 1958 Nash narrowly lost out to René Thom (pictured below), topologist and inventor of catastrophe theory, for the Fields Medal. This is the mathematical equivalent of the Nobel prize.

Although his brilliant career was sadly interrupted by mental illness for a period of about thirty years, in 1994 Nash was awarded "the Central Bank of Sweden Prize in Economic Science in Memory of Alfred Nobel," generally regarded as equivalent to the Nobel prize. This award was for Nash's equilibrium theorem, published in his doctoral thesis in 1950. It turned out that Nash's work established a significant new way of analyzing rational conflict and cooperation in economics and other social sciences.

As long as k is small enough, there will be some number of attractors, and the long-term behavior of the sequence (or population) is the same regardless of the initial x-value. But once k is large enough to cause chaos, the long-term behavior of the system will change drastically when the initial x-value is changed only slightly. For example, consider the following two sequences, both generated from $y = 4x(1 - x)$.

$0.600, 0.960, 0.154, 0.520, 0.998, 0.006, 0.025, \ldots$ Starting with $x = 0.600$

$0.610, 0.952, 0.184, 0.601, 0.959, 0.157, 0.529, \ldots$ Starting with $x = 0.610$

The fact that the two sequences wander apart from one another is partly due to roundoff errors along the way. But Yorke and others have shown that even "exact" calculations of the iterates would quickly produce divergent sequences just because of the slightly different initial values. This type of "sensitive dependence on initial conditions" was discovered (accidentally) back in the 1960s by Edward Lorenz when he was looking for an effective computerized model of weather patterns. He discerned the implication that any long-range weather-predicting schemes might well be hopeless.

Patterns like those in the sequences above are more than just numerical oddities. Similar patterns apply to a great many phenomena in the physical, biological, and social sciences, many of them seemingly common natural systems that have been studied for hundreds of years. The measurement of a coastline; the description of the patterns in a branching tree, or a mountain range, or a cloud formation, or intergalactic cosmic dust; the prediction of weather patterns; the turbulent behavior of fluids of all kinds; the circulatory and neurological systems of the human body; fluctuations in populations and economic systems—these and many other phenomena remain mysteries, concealing their true nature somewhere beyond the reach of even our brightest minds and our biggest and fastest computers.

Continuous phenomena are easily dealt with. A change in one quantity produces a predictable change in another. (For example, a little more pressure on the gas pedal produces a little more speed.) Mathematical functions that represent continuous events can be graphed by unbroken lines or curves, or perhaps smooth, gradually changing surfaces. The governing equations for such phenomena are "linear," and extensive mathematical methods of solving them have been developed. On the other hand, erratic events associated with certain other equations are harder to describe or predict. The science of chaos, made possible by modern computers, continues to open up new ways to deal with such events.

One early attempt to deal with discontinuous processes in a new way, generally acknowledged as a forerunner of chaos theory, was that of the French mathematician René Thom, who, in the 1960s, applied the methods of topology. To emphasize the feature of sudden change, Thom referred to events such as a heartbeat, a buckling beam, a stock market crash, a riot, or a tornado as *catastrophes*. He proved that all catastrophic events (in our four-dimensional space-time) are combinations of seven elementary catastrophes. (In higher dimensions the number quickly approaches infinity.)

Each of the seven elementary catastrophes has a characteristic topological shape. Two examples are shown in **Figure 85**. The figure on the left is called a *cusp*. The figure on the right is an *elliptic umbilicus* (a belly button with an oval cross-section). Thom's work became known as **catastrophe theory.**

René Thom

Figure 85

Computer graphics have been indispensable in the study of chaotic processes. The plotting of large numbers of points has revealed patterns that would otherwise not have been observed. (The underlying reasons for many of these patterns, however, have still not been explained.) The images shown in **Figure 86** were created using chaotic processes.

The surface of the earth, consisting of continents, mountains, oceans, valleys, and so on, has **fractal dimension** 2.2.

Aside from providing a geometric structure for chaotic processes in nature, fractal geometry is viewed by many as a significant art form. (To appreciate why, see the 1986 publication *The Beauty of Fractals,* by H. O. Peitgen and P. H. Richter, which contains 184 figures, many in color.) Peitgen and others have also published *Fractals for the Classroom: Strategic Activities Volume One* (Springer-Verlag, 1991).

Figure 86

Fractals

If there is one structure that has provided a key for the new study of nonlinear processes, it is **fractal geometry,** developed over a period of years mainly by the IBM mathematician Benoit Mandelbrot (1924–2010). For his work in this field, and at the recommendation of the National Science Foundation, Columbia University awarded him the 1985 Bernard Medal for Meritorious Service to Science.

Lines have a single dimension. Plane figures have two dimensions, and we live in a three-dimensional spatial world. In a paper published in 1967, Mandelbrot investigated the idea of measuring the length of a coastline. He concluded that such a shape defies conventional Euclidean geometry and that, rather than having a natural number dimension, it has a "fractional dimension." A coastline is an example of a *self-similar shape*—a shape that repeats itself over and over on different scales. From a distance, the bays and inlets cannot be individually observed, but as one moves closer they become more apparent. The branching of a tree, from twig to limb to trunk, also exhibits a shape that repeats itself.

In the early twentieth century, the German mathematician H. von Koch investigated the so-called Koch snowflake. It is shown in **Figure 87.** Starting with an equilateral triangle, each side then gives rise to another smaller equilateral triangle. The process continues over and over, indefinitely, and a curve of infinite length is produced. The mathematics of Koch's era was not advanced enough to deal with such figures. However, using Mandelbrot's theory, it is shown that the Koch snowflake has dimension of about 1.26. This figure is obtained using a formula that involves logarithms. (Logarithms were introduced briefly in **Chapter 8.**)

Figure 87

The image above is a **fractal** design generated by *Fractoid,* one of several fractal-generating apps available free in the Android market. This particular application allows the user to select the generating equation and choose among several color-assigning algorithms.

The theory of fractals today finds application in many areas of science and technology. It has been used to analyze the turbulence of liquids, the branching of rivers, and price variation in economics—and even to identify certain types of cancer cells. Hollywood has used fractals in the special effects found in some blockbuster movies.

An interesting account of the science of chaos is found in the popular 1987 book *Chaos,* by James Gleick. Mandelbrot published two books on fractals. They are *Fractals: Form, Chance, and Dimension* (1975) and *The Fractal Geometry of Nature* (1982).

9.8 | EXERCISES

Exercises 1–25 are taken from an issue of Student Math Notes, *published by the National Council of Teachers of Mathematics. They were written by Dr. Tami S. Martin, Mathematics Department, Illinois State University, and the authors wish to thank N.C.T.M. and Tami Martin for permission to reproduce this activity. Because the exercises should be done in numerical order, answers to all exercises (both even- and odd-numbered) appear in the answer section of the student edition of this text.*

Most of the mathematical objects you have studied have dimensions that are whole numbers. For example, such solids as cubes and icosahedrons have dimension three. Squares, triangles, and many other planar figures are two-dimensional. Lines are one-dimensional, and points have dimension zero. Consider a square with side of length one. Gather several of these squares by cutting out or using patterning blocks.

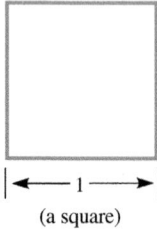

(a square)

The size of a figure is calculated by counting the number of replicas (small pieces) that make it up. Here, a replica is the original square with edges of length one.

1. What is the least number of these squares that can be put together edge to edge to form a larger square?

The original square is made up of one small square, so its size is one.

2. What is the size of the new square?

3. What is the length of each edge of the new square?

*Similar figures have the same shape but are not necessarily the same size. The **scale factor** between two similar figures can be found by calculating the ratio of corresponding edges:*

$$\frac{\text{new length}}{\text{old length}}.$$

4. What is the scale factor between the large square and the small square?

5. Find the ratio $\frac{\text{new size}}{\text{old size}}$ for the two squares.

6. Form an even larger square that is three units long on each edge. Compare this square to the small square. What is the scale factor between the two squares? What is the ratio of the new size to the old size?

7. Form an even larger square that is four units long on each edge. Compare this square to the small square. What is the scale factor between the two squares? What is the ratio of the new size to the old size?

8. Complete the table for squares.

Scale factor	2	3	4	5	6	10
Ratio of new size to old size						

9. How are the two rows in the table related?

Consider an equilateral triangle. The length of an edge of the triangle is one unit. The size of this triangle is one.

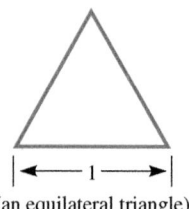

(an equilateral triangle)

10. What is the least number of equilateral triangles that can be put together edge to edge to form a similar larger triangle?

11. Complete the table for triangles.

Scale factor	2	3	4	5	6	10
Ratio of new size to old size						

12. How does the relationship between the two rows in this table compare with the one you found in the table for squares?

One way to define the dimension, d, of a figure relates the scale factor, the new size, and the old size:

$$(\text{scale factor})^d = \frac{\text{new size}}{\text{old size}}.$$

Using a scale factor of two for squares or equilateral triangles, we can see that $2^d = \frac{4}{1}$; that is, $2^d = 4$. Because $2^2 = 4$, the dimension, d, must be two. This definition of dimension confirms what we already know—that squares and equilateral triangles are two-dimensional figures.

13. Use this definition and your completed tables to confirm that the square and the equilateral triangle are two-dimensional figures for scale factors other than two.

Consider a cube, with edges of length one. Let the size of the cube be one.

14. What is the least number of these cubes that can be put together face to face to form a larger cube?

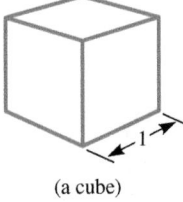

(a cube)

15. What is the scale factor between these two cubes? What is the ratio of the new size to the old size for the two cubes?

16. Complete the table for cubes.

Scale factor	2	3	4	5	6	10
Ratio of new size to old size						

17. How are the two rows in the table related?

18. Use the definition of dimension and a scale factor of two to verify that a cube is a three-dimensional object.

We have explored scale factors and sizes associated with two- and three-dimensional figures. Is it possible for mathematical objects to have fractional dimensions? Consider each figure formed by replacing the middle third of a line segment of length one by one upside-down V, each of whose two sides is equal in length to the segment removed. The first four stages in the development of this figure are shown.

Stage 0   **Stage 1**
Stage 2   **Stage 3**

Finding the scale factor for this sequence of figures is difficult, because the overall length of a representative portion of the figure remains the same while the number of pieces increases. To simplify the procedure, follow these steps.

Step 1   *Start with any stage (e.g., Stage 1).*

Step 2   *Draw the next stage (e.g., Stage 2) of the sequence and "blow it up" so that it contains an exact copy of the preceding stage (in this example, Stage 1).*

Notice that Stage 2 contains four copies, or replicas, of Stage 1 and is three times as long as Stage 1.

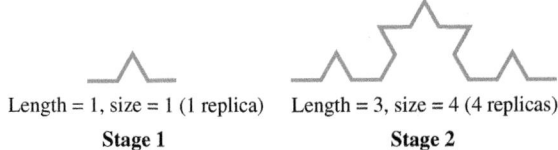

Length = 1, size = 1 (1 replica)   Length = 3, size = 4 (4 replicas)
Stage 1   **Stage 2**

19. The scale factor is equal to the ratio $\frac{\text{new length}}{\text{old length}}$ between any two consecutive stages. The scale factor between Stage 1 and Stage 2 is _____.

20. The size can be determined by counting the number of replicas of Stage 1 found in Stage 2. Old size = 1, new size = ___.

Use the definition of dimension to compute the dimension, d, of the figure formed by this process: $3^d = \frac{4}{1}$; that is, $3^d = 4$. Since $3^1 = 3$ and $3^2 = 9$, for $3^d = 4$ the dimension of the figure must be greater than one but less than two:

$$1 < d < 2.$$

21. Use your calculator to estimate d. Remember that d is the exponent that makes 3^d equal 4. For example, because d must be between 1 and 2, try $d = 1.5$. But $3^{1.5} = 5.196\ldots$, which is greater than 4; thus, d must be smaller than 1.5. Continue until you approximate d to three decimal places. (Use logarithms for maximum accuracy.)

*The original figure was a one-dimensional line segment. By iteratively adding to the line segment, an object of dimension greater than one but less than two was generated. Objects with fractional dimension are known as **fractals**. Fractals are infinitely self-similar objects formed by repeated additions to, or removals from, a figure. The object attained at the limit of the repeated procedure is the fractal.*

Next consider a two-dimensional object with sections removed iteratively. In each stage of the fractal's development, a triangle is removed from the center of each triangular region.

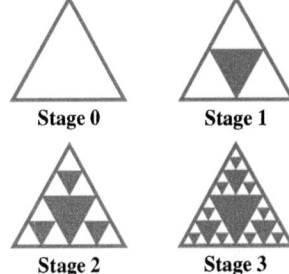

Stage 0   **Stage 1**
Stage 2   **Stage 3**

Use the process from the last example to help answer the following questions.

22. What is the scale factor of the fractal?

23. Old size = 1, new size = ___.

24. The dimension of the fractal is between what two whole number values?

25. Use the definition of dimension and your calculator to approximate the dimension of this fractal to three decimal places.

Use a calculator to determine the pattern of attractors for the equation

$$y = kx(1 - x)$$

for the given value of k and the given initial value of x.

26. $k = 3.25$, $x = 0.7$

27. $k = 3.4$, $x = 0.8$

28. $k = 3.55$, $x = 0.7$

CHAPTER 9 SUMMARY

KEY TERMS

9.1

point
line
plane
half-line
ray
line segment
parallel lines
intersecting lines
parallel planes
intersecting planes
skew lines
angle
sides
vertex
one degree
acute angle
right angle
obtuse angle
straight angle
protractor
perpendicular lines
vertical angles
complementary
supplementary
transversal
alternate interior angles
alternate exterior angles
interior angles on same
　side of transversal
corresponding angles

9.2

simple curve
closed curve
convex
polygon
regular polygon
acute triangle
right triangle
obtuse triangle
equilateral triangle
isosceles triangle
scalene triangle
trapezoid
parallelogram
rectangle
square
rhombus
interior angle
exterior angle
circle
center
radius
chord
diameter
semicircle
tangent
secant
arc
inscribed
geometric construction
compass
perpendicular bisector

9.3

congruent triangles
similar triangles
hypotenuse
legs
Pythagorean triple

9.4

perimeter
area
circumference

9.5

plane figure
rectangular parallelopiped
space figure
polyhedra
tetrahedron
hexahedron
octahedron
dodecahedron
icosahedron
pyramid
prism
volume
surface area
right circular cylinder
sphere
right circular cone

9.6

transformational geometry
reflection

reflection image
line of reflection
transformation
invariant point
collinear
line of symmetry
composition
translation
magnitude
identity translation
inverses
rotation
center of rotation
point reflection
glide reflection
isometry
size transformation
dilation
contraction

9.7

pseudosphere
tractrix
perspective
projective sphere
antipodal points
projective plane
duality
genus

9.8

chaos
catastrophe theory
fractal

NEW SYMBOLS

$\longleftrightarrow$	line	$\parallel$	parallel	$\triangle$	triangle	
$\circ\!\!\longrightarrow$	half-line	$\measuredangle$	angle	$\cong$	congruence	
$\bullet\!\!\longrightarrow$	ray	$\neg$	right angle	A'	image of A	
$\bullet\!\!-\!\!\bullet$	segment	$\frown$	arc			

TEST YOUR WORD POWER

See how well you have learned the vocabulary in this chapter.

1. **Vertical angles** are
   - **A.** angles whose measures add up to 180 degrees.
   - **B.** formed by intersecting lines and have equal measure.
   - **C.** formed by intersecting lines and do not have equal measure.
   - **D.** angles with one side pointing vertically upward.

2. A **scalene triangle** is
   - **A.** a triangle having at least two equal sides.
   - **B.** a triangle that cannot possibly be a right triangle.
   - **C.** a triangle having no two sides equal.
   - **D.** a regular polygon having three sides.

3. A **Pythagorean triple** is
   A. a special triangle with side length ratio 1:2:3.
   B. an ordered triple (a, b, c) for which $a^2 + b^2 = c^2$.
   C. a triangle with largest angle having measure three times that of the smallest angle.
   D. a triangle with base equaling triple the height.

4. A **tetrahedron** is
   A. a regular polyhedron having four sides.
   B. a pyramid with a square base.
   C. a space figure having two faces in parallel planes.
   D. a space figure with parallelogram faces.

5. An **invariant point** of a transformation is a point
   A. that is its own image under the transformation.
   B. whose image is the same distance from the line of reflection as the point itself.
   C. contained in both the image and the original figure.
   D. that cannot be changed by any transformation.

6. In topology, the **genus** of a figure is
   A. the area of its cross section.
   B. the shape of its image projected onto the unit sphere.
   C. the number of distinct surfaces it has.
   D. the number of cuts that can be made without cutting it into two pieces.

ANSWERS
1. B   2. C   3. B   4. A   5. A   6. D

QUICK REVIEW

Concepts	*Examples*

9.1 Points, Lines, Planes, and Angles

A **point** is represented by a dot. A **line** extends indefinitely in two directions, has no width, and is determined by two distinct points. A **plane** is represented by a flat surface and is determined by three points not all on the same line.

A **ray** has a starting point and extends indefinitely in one direction, and a **half-line** is a ray without a starting point. A **line segment** includes a starting point, an ending point, and all points between them.

Two lines are **parallel** if they are in the same plane but never intersect. Lines not in the same plane are **skew**.

An **angle** is made up of two rays with a common endpoint (**vertex**). The measure of an angle is given in **degrees,** where 1 degree $(1°)$ is $\frac{1}{360}$ of a full rotation.

• An angle measuring less than 90° is an **acute angle.**
• An angle measuring between 90° and 180° is an **obtuse angle.**
• An angle measuring exactly 90° is a **right angle.**
• An angle measuring 180° is a **straight angle.**
• Two angles whose measures add to 90° are **complementary angles.**
• Two angles whose measures add to 180° are **supplementary angles.**

Lines intersecting at 90° angles are **perpendicular lines.**

A line intersecting parallel lines is a **transversal.**

Intersecting lines create two pairs of **vertical angles.**

Vertical angles have equal measure.

The figure shows a line passing through points A and B, and a plane determined by points A, B, and C.

• Ray AB $(\overrightarrow{AB})$ consists of point A and all points on the line to the right of point A.
• Half-line $\overset{\circ}{A}\vec{B}$ consists only of the points to the right of point A.
• Line segment $\overline{AB}$ contains the two endpoints and all points in between.

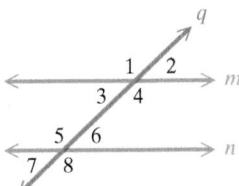

In the figure above, lines m and n are parallel. The transversal q, along with lines m and n, form eight angles.

$\angle 1$ is an **obtuse angle,** and $\angle 2$ is an **acute angle.**

$\angle 1$ and $\angle 2$ are **supplementary angles,** and together they form a **straight angle.**

$\angle 1$ and $\angle 4$ are **vertical angles.**

$\angle 1$ and $\angle 5$ are **corresponding angles** and have equal measure.

$\angle 3$ and $\angle 6$ are **alternate interior angles** and have equal measure.

$\angle 2$ and $\angle 7$ are **alternate exterior angles** and have equal measure.

$\angle 3$ and $\angle 5$ are **interior angles on the same side of the transversal** and are supplementary.

Concepts	**Examples**

9.2 Curves, Polygons, Circles, and Geometric Constructions

Simple curves can be drawn without lifting the pencil from the paper and without passing through the same point twice. A **closed curve** has the same starting and ending point, and it can be drawn without lifting the pencil from the paper.

A **polygon** is a simple closed curve made up of straight line segments; it is **regular** if all sides are equal and all angles are equal.

Triangles are three-sided polygons classified by the number of equal sides and by the measures of their angles relative to 90°.

Quadrilaterals have four sides and are classified by characteristics of their sides and angles. For example, a **rhombus** is a parallelogram (a quadrilateral having two pairs of parallel sides) with all sides having equal lengths.

The sum of the interior angles of any triangle is 180°.

Any exterior angle has measure equal to the sum of the two opposite interior angles.

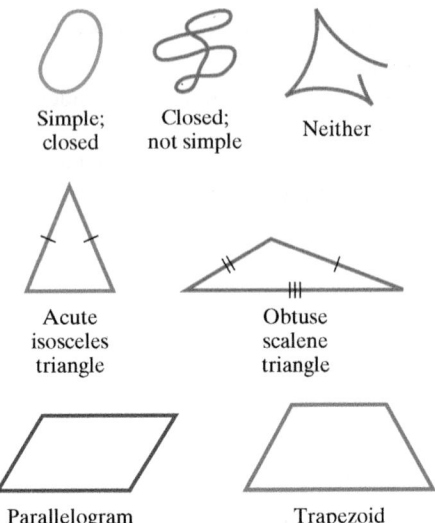

Simple; closed   Closed; not simple   Neither

Acute isosceles triangle   Obtuse scalene triangle

Parallelogram   Trapezoid

Solve for x.

$$3x + 2x - 5 = 3x + 41$$
$$5x - 5 = 3x + 41 \quad \text{Combine like terms.}$$
$$2x = 46 \quad \text{Subtract } 3x. \text{ Add 5.}$$
$$x = 23 \quad \text{Divide by 2.}$$

A **circle** is a set of points in the plane that are equidistant from a fixed point called the **center.** A **chord** is a line segment having endpoints on the circle, and the part of the circle between the endpoints of a chord, along with the endpoints themselves, form an **arc.** A chord passing through the center is a **diameter.**

An angle with its vertex on a circle and its sides passing through two (other) points on the circle is said to be **inscribed** in the circle. Any inscribed angle has a measure equal to half the intercepted arc.

A straightedge and compass can be used to complete **geometric constructions.**

The circle on the left shows the inscribed angle PQR with vertex Q on the circle, and chords PQ and QR. If chord PQ is a diameter, use a geometric construction to find the center of the circle.

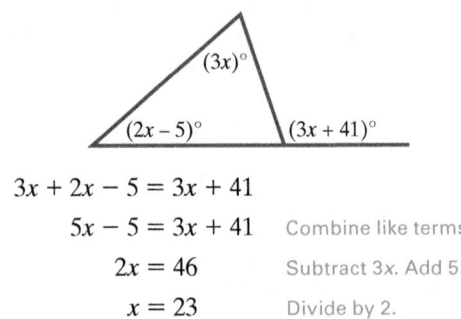

On the right, construct the perpendicular bisector of the chord QR. The center of the circle is the point where this bisector intersects the diameter PQ.

The construction reveals the point O to be the center of the circle. (*Note:* The center O could also be found by constructing the perpendicular bisector of the diameter PQ.)

Concepts	Examples

9.3 **The Geometry of Triangles: Congruence, Similarity, and the Pythagorean Theorem**

Congruent triangles have exactly the same shape and size. This means that corresponding sides have equal length and corresponding angles have equal measure.

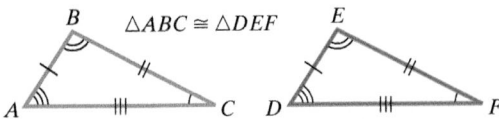

Congruence is often verified in a two-column proof.

Similar triangles have the same shape (corresponding angles are equal) but not necessarily the same size. Corresponding sides are proportional.

Properties of similar triangles can be used to solve for unknown parts of triangles, and this has many applications.

Given: $AC = BC; \sphericalangle ACD = \sphericalangle BCD$
Prove: $\triangle ADC \cong \triangle BDC$

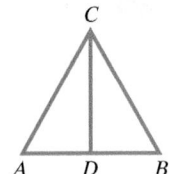

Statements	Reasons
1. $AC = BC$	1. Given
2. $\sphericalangle ACD = \sphericalangle BCD$	2. Given
3. $CD = CD$	3. Reflexive property
4. $\triangle ADC \cong \triangle BDC$	4. SAS congruence property

In the figure shown, $\overleftrightarrow{AB}$ is parallel to $\overleftrightarrow{DE}$. Verify that $\triangle ABC$ is similar to $\triangle EDC$.

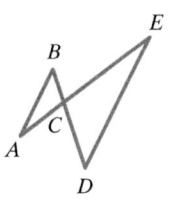

Since $\overleftrightarrow{AB}$ is parallel to $\overleftrightarrow{DE}$, $\overleftrightarrow{AE}$ is a transversal, and thus $\sphericalangle BAC = \sphericalangle DEC$ because they are alternate interior angles. Also, $\sphericalangle BCA = \sphericalangle DCE$, since they are vertical angles.

Therefore, $\triangle ABC$ is similar to $\triangle EDC$ by the Angle-Angle (AA) similarity property.

A flagpole casts a 99-ft shadow at the same time that a building 10 ft high casts an 18-ft shadow. Find the height of the flagpole.

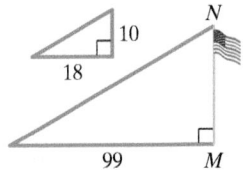

$$\frac{MN}{10} = \frac{99}{18} \quad \text{Write a proportion using similar triangles.}$$

$$MN \cdot 18 = 10 \cdot 99 \quad \text{Cross products}$$

$$MN = 55 \quad \text{Solve for } MN.$$

The flagpole is 55 ft tall.

Pythagorean Theorem
If the two legs of a right triangle have lengths a and b, and the hypotenuse has length c, then

$$a^2 + b^2 = c^2.$$

Find the length of the hypotenuse of the right triangle with the flagpole above using the Pythagorean theorem. Let c be the length of the hypotenuse.

$$99^2 + (MN)^2 = c^2 \quad a^2 + b^2 = c^2$$

$$99^2 + 55^2 = c^2 \quad \text{Let } MN = 55.$$

$$9801 + 3025 = c^2 \quad \text{Apply the exponents.}$$

$$12{,}826 = c^2 \quad \text{Add.}$$

$$c = \sqrt{12{,}826} \quad \text{Take the square root.}$$

$$c \approx 113.25 \quad \text{Approximate.}$$

The length of the hypotenuse is approximately 113.25 ft.

Concepts   *Examples*

9.4 Perimeter, Area, and Circumference

The **perimeter** of a polygon is the sum of the lengths of its sides. The **area** of a polygon is the amount of plane surface it covers.

Polygon	Perimeter	Area
Triangle 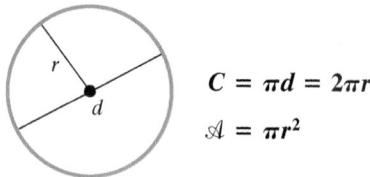	$P = a + b + c$	$\mathscr{A} = \dfrac{1}{2}bh$
Rectangle	$P = 2\ell + 2w$	$\mathscr{A} = \ell w$
Square	$P = 4s$	$\mathscr{A} = s^2$
Parallelogram		$\mathscr{A} = bh$
Trapezoid		$\mathscr{A} = \dfrac{1}{2}h(B + b)$

The distance around a circle is its **circumference.**

$$C = \pi d = 2\pi r$$
$$\mathscr{A} = \pi r^2$$

Find the perimeter of the entire figure and the area of the shaded region.

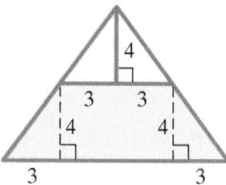

The hypotenuse of each triangle with legs of length 3 and 4 is $\sqrt{3^2 + 4^2} = \sqrt{25} = 5$.

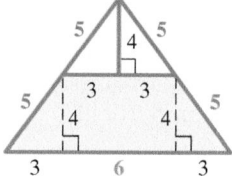

The *entire figure* is an isosceles triangle with side lengths of 12, 10, and 10.

$$P = 12 + 10 + 10 = 32$$

The shaded region is a trapezoid, with $B = 12$, $b = 6$, and $h = 4$.

$$\mathscr{A} = \frac{1}{2}h(B + b) = \frac{1}{2}(4)(12 + 6) = 36$$

Find the perimeter and area of the following figure.

The figure is made up of a rectangle and a semicircle.

$$P = (4 + 8 + 4) + \left(\frac{1}{2} \cdot \pi \cdot 8\right) = 4\pi + 16$$

$$\mathscr{A} = (8 \cdot 4) + \left(\frac{1}{2} \cdot \pi \cdot 4^2\right) = 8\pi + 32$$

Concepts   *Examples*

9.5 Volume and Surface Area

Space figures occupy three-dimensional space and have both **volume** and **surface area.** A **polyhedron** is a space figure, the faces of which are polygons. A *regular* polyhedron is one for which all faces are a copy of a single regular polygon. There are only five regular polyhedra.

The **volume** of a space figure is a measure of its capacity. The **surface area** is the total area that would be covered if the space figure were "peeled" and the peel laid flat.

Space Figure	Volume and Surface Area
Box $V = \ell w h$ $S = 2\ell w + 2\ell h + 2hw$	
Cube $V = s^3$ $S = 6s^2$	
Right Circular Cylinder $V = \pi r^2 h$ $S = 2\pi r h + 2\pi r^2$	
Sphere $V = \dfrac{4}{3}\pi r^3$ $S = 4\pi r^2$	
Right Circular Cone $V = \dfrac{1}{3}\pi r^2 h$ $S = \pi r\sqrt{r^2 + h^2} + \pi r^2$	
Pyramid $V = \dfrac{1}{3}Bh$ (B is the area of the base.)	

Regular Polyhedra

Tetrahedron   Hexahedron   Octahedron
(cube)

Dodecahedron   Icosahedron

Find the volume and surface area of the box.

$$V = \ell \cdot w \cdot h$$
$$= (8)(6)(4)$$
$$= 192\,\text{cm}^3$$

$$S = 2\ell w + 2\ell h + 2hw$$
$$= 2(8)(6) + 2(8)(4) + 2(4)(6)$$
$$= 96 + 64 + 48$$
$$= 208\text{ cm}^2$$

The grain silo consists of a half-sphere on top of a right circular cylinder. Find its volume and surface area (using $\pi \approx 3.14$).

$$V = \frac{1}{2} \cdot \frac{4}{3}\pi(4)^3 + \pi(4)^2(8)$$
$$\approx 535.89 \text{ cubic units}$$

$$S = 2\pi r h + \pi r^2 + \frac{1}{2} \cdot 4\pi r^2$$
$$= 2\pi(4)(8) + \pi(4)^2 + 2\pi(4)^2$$
$$= 64\pi + 16\pi + 32\pi$$
$$= 112\pi \text{ square units}$$
$$\approx 351.68 \text{ square units}$$

Note that in the portion of surface area for the cylinder (shown in red), the formula included πr^2 instead of $2\pi r^2$, because the top of the cylinder is not an exposed surface in this case.

Concepts   *Examples*

9.6 Transformational Geometry

One geometric figure can be transformed into another by one or more geometric **transformations.**

- A **reflection** gives the mirror image of a figure about a **line of reflection.**

- A **translation** "slides" a copy of a figure to a new location. It is equivalent to two reflections about parallel lines.

- A **rotation** revolves a figure about a point called the **center of rotation** through an angle (the **magnitude of rotation**).

- A **glide reflection** is the composition of a reflection and a translation along the line of reflection.

- A **size transformation** stretches (or shrinks) a figure away from (or toward) a point (the center).

The figure shows $\triangle ABC$ **reflected** about line m. The image $\triangle A'B'C'$ is then **translated** parallel to line m. The image of this translation, $\triangle A''B''C''$, is then **rotated** clockwise around point H through an angle of 45°, resulting in the image $\triangle A'''B'''C'''$. Finally, this triangle is **stretched** (or **dilated**) by a factor of 2 using M as the center of the size transformation, resulting in the image $\triangle JKL$.

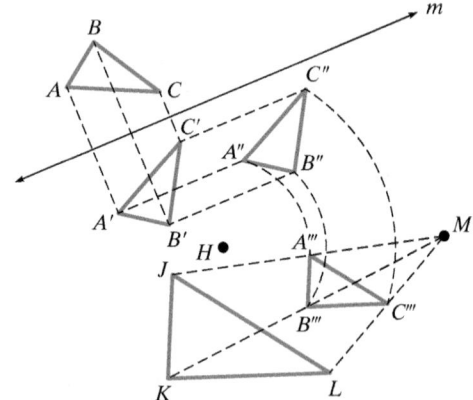

9.7 Non-Euclidean Geometry and Topology

Euclidean geometry is based on five postulates and five axioms. The fifth postulate is equivalent to "Given a line k and a point P not on the line, there exists one and only one line m through P that is parallel to k." When this postulate is changed, a **non-Eulcidean geometry** results.

Lobachevskian geometry replaces Euclid's fifth postulate with the statement "Through a point P off a line k, at least two different lines can be drawn parallel to k."

Riemannian geometry uses as its parallel postulate "Through a point P off a line k, no line can be drawn that is parallel to k."

Projective geometries exhibit **duality,** in that for each statement that holds true about points and lines in a projective plane, another true statement can be formed by interchanging "point" and "line" in the original statement.

Topology deals with properties of figures that are preserved under distortions that do not involve separating (puncturing or tearing) the figures. The topological **genus** of a figure is equal to the number of holes in the figure.

The figure shows the projection of a Euclidean triangle and line onto the sphere. The image is a Riemannian triangle with interior angles summing to more than 180°, and half of a great circle, which is a line in this projective geometry.

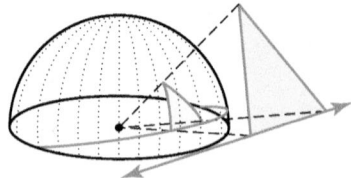

The *dual* of the statement "Every pair of distinct points determine a line" is the statement

"Every pair of distinct lines determine a point."

A sphere and a cone both have genus 0, and a torus has genus 1.

Concepts	Examples
9.8 **Chaos and Fractal Geometry** **Chaos** theory deals with systems that may become unstable with very small changes in governing parameter values. **Fractals** are infinitely self-similar objects formed by repeated additions to, or removals from, a figure. The object attained at the limit of the procedure is the fractal.	The sequence generated by the equation $$y = 2.5x(1 - x),$$ with intial value of $x = 0.5$, has one attractor at 0.6.

CHAPTER 9 — TEST

1. Consider a 42° angle. Answer each of the following.

   (a) What is the measure of its complement?

   (b) What is the measure of its supplement?

   (c) Classify it as acute, obtuse, right, or straight.

Find the measure of each marked angle.

2.

$(2x + 16)°$ $(5x + 80)°$

3.

$(7x - 25)°$ $(4x + 5)°$

4.

$(4x + 6)°$

$(10x)°$

In Exercises 5 and 6, assume that lines m and n are parallel, and find the measure of each marked angle.

5.

$(7x + 11)°$ n

$(3x - 1)°$ m

6.

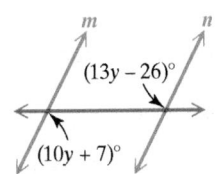

m n

$(13y - 26)°$

$(10y + 7)°$

7. Explain why a rhombus must be a quadrilateral, but a quadrilateral might not be a rhombus.

8. Which one of the statements A–D is false?

   A. A square is a rhombus.

   B. The acute angles of a right triangle are complementary.

   C. A triangle may have both a right angle and an obtuse angle.

   D. A trapezoid may have nonparallel sides of the same length.

Identify each of the following curves as simple, closed, both, *or* neither.

9.

10.

11. Find the measure of each angle in the triangle.

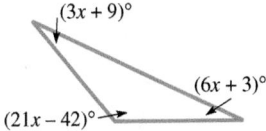

$(3x + 9)°$

$(6x + 3)°$

$(21x - 42)°$

Find the area of each of the following figures.

12.

12 cm

6 cm

13.

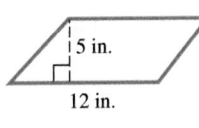

5 in.

12 in.

(a parallelogram)

14.

8 m

17 m

15.

16 m

9 m

24 m

(a trapezoid)

16. ***Area of a Shaded Figure*** What is the area (to the nearest square unit) of the colored portion of the figure? Use 3.14 as an approximation for π.

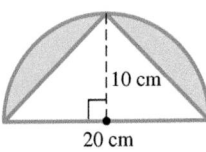

10 cm

20 cm

(a triangle within a semicircle)

17. *Circumference of a Circle* If a circle has area 144π square inches, what is its circumference?

18. *Circumference of a Dome* The Rogers Centre in Toronto, Canada, is the first stadium with a hard-shell, retractable roof. The steel dome is 630 feet in diameter. To the nearest foot, what is the circumference of this dome?

←—630 ft—→

19. Given: $\measuredangle CAB = \measuredangle DBA$; $DB = CA$
Prove: $\triangle ABD \cong \triangle BAC$

20. *Height of a Building* If an 8-ft stop sign casts a 5-ft shadow at the same time a building casts a 40-ft shadow, how tall is the building?

21. *Diagonal of a Rectangle* What is the measure of a diagonal of a rectangle that has width 20 m and length 21 m?

22. Reflect the given figure first about line n and then about line m.

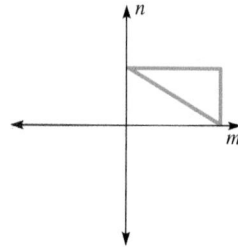

23. Find the point reflection image of the given figure with the given point as center.

Find **(a)** *the volume and* **(b)** *the surface area of each of the following space figures. When necessary, use 3.14 as an approximation for* π. *In Exercises 24 and 26, round to the nearest hundredth.*

24.

6 in.

(a sphere)

25.

8 ft

9 ft

12 ft

(a box)

26.

6 m

14 m

(a right circular cylinder)

27. List several main distinctions between Euclidean geometry and non-Euclidean geometry.

28. *Topological Equivalence* Are the following pairs of objects topologically equivalent?

(a) a page of a book and the cover of the same book

(b) a pair of glasses with the lenses removed, and the Mona Lisa

29. *Projection Image* A line segment of length 7 cm is projected onto a sphere with radius 1 cm. Will the image also have a length of 7 cm?

30. Use a calculator to determine the attractors for the sequence generated by the equation

$$y = 2.1x(1 - x),$$

with initial value of $x = 0.6$.

The ratio is $\frac{1}{2}$. **This Escher pattern** fills (tiles) the entire plane if we start with one fish, one duck, and one lizard, and then perform repeated translations in opposite directions.

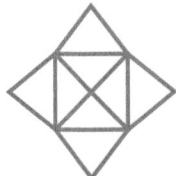

Figure 88

Networks*

Another branch of modern geometry is *graph theory*. One topic of study in graph theory is *networks*. A **network** is a diagram showing the various paths (or **arcs**) between points (called **vertices**, or **nodes**). A network can be thought of as a set of arcs and vertices. **Figure 88** shows two examples of networks.

The study of networks began formally with the so-called Königsberg Bridge problem as solved by Leonhard Euler (1707–1783). In Königsberg, Germany, the River Pregel flowed through the middle of town. There were two islands in the river. During Euler's lifetime, there were seven bridges connecting the islands and the two banks of the river.

A competition developed to see if anyone could find a route that crossed each of the seven bridges exactly once. The problem concerns what topologists today call the *traversability* of a network. No one could find a solution.

*Entire chapter on Graph Theory, of which networks is one topic.

FOR FURTHER THOUGHT

Two Interesting Topological Surfaces

Two examples of topological surfaces are the **Möbius strip** and the **Klein bottle**. The Möbius strip is a single-sided surface named after August Ferdinand Möbius (1790–1868), a pupil of Gauss.

To construct a Möbius strip, cut out a rectangular strip of paper, perhaps 3 cm by 25 cm. Paste together the two 3-cm ends after giving the paper a half-twist. To see how the strip now has only one side, mark an *x* on the strip and then mark another *x* on what appears to be the other "side." Begin at one of the *x*'s you have drawn, and trace a path along the strip. You will eventually come to the other *x* without crossing the edge of the strip.

A branch of chemistry called chemical topology studies the structures of chemical configurations. A recent advance in this area was the synthesis of the first molecular Möbius strip, which was formed by joining the ends of a double-stranded strip of carbon and oxygen atoms.

*A mathematician confided
That a Möbius strip is one-sided.
And you'll get quite a laugh
If you cut one in half,
For it stays in one piece when divided.*

Klein bottle

Whereas a Möbius strip results from giving a paper *strip* a half-twist and then connecting it to itself, if we could do the same thing with a paper *tube* we would obtain a Klein bottle, named after Felix Klein (1849–1925). Klein produced important results in several areas, including non-Euclidean geometry and the early beginnings of group theory.

From www.kleinbottle.com

*A mathematician named Klein
Thought the Möbius strip was divine.
Said he, "If you glue
The edges of two
You'll get a weird bottle like mine."*

For Group or Individual Investigation

1. The Möbius strip has other interesting properties. With a pair of scissors, cut the strip lengthwise. Do you get two strips? Repeat the process with what you have obtained from the first cut. What happens?

2. Now construct another Möbius strip, and start cutting lengthwise about $\frac{1}{3}$ of the way from one edge. What happens?

3. What would be the advantage of a conveyor belt with the configuration of a Möbius strip?

Möbius strip

Figure 89

The Königsberg Bridge problem became so famous that in 1735 it reached Euler, who was then at the court of the Russian empress Catherine the Great. In trying to solve the problem, Euler began by drawing a network representing the system of bridges, as in **Figure 89** on the next page.

Euler noticed that three routes meet at vertex *A*. Because 3 is an odd number, he called *A* an **odd vertex.** As three routes meet at *A,* it must be a starting or an ending point for any traverse of the network. Otherwise, when you got to *A* on your second trip there would be no way to get out. An **even vertex,** one where an even number of routes meet, need not be a starting or an ending point. (Why is this?)

In **Figure 89**, three paths also meet at *C* and *D*, with five paths meeting at *B*. Thus, *B, C,* and *D* are also odd vertices. An odd vertex must be a starting or an ending point of a traverse. Thus, all four vertices *A, B, C,* and *D* must be starting or ending points. Because a network can have only two starting or ending points (one of each), this network cannot be traversed. The residents of Königsberg were trying to do the impossible.

Euler's result can be summarized as follows.

RESULTS ON VERTICES AND TRAVERSABILITY

1. The number of odd vertices of any network is *even.* (That is, a network must have $2n$ odd vertices, where $n = 0, 1, 2, 3, \ldots$)

2. A network with no odd vertices or exactly two odd vertices can be traversed. In the case of exactly two, start at one odd vertex and end at the other.

3. A network with more than two odd vertices cannot be traversed.

EXAMPLE 2 Deciding Whether Networks Are Traversable

Decide whether the networks in **Figures 90** and **91** are traversable.

(a)

Figure 90

(b)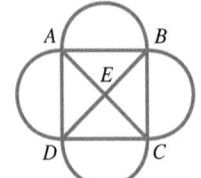

Figure 91

Solution

(a) Because there are exactly two odd vertices (*A* and *E*) in **Figure 90**, this network can be traversed. One way to traverse the network is to start at *A*, go

How should an artist paint a realistic view of railroad tracks going off to the horizon? In reality, the tracks are always at a constant distance apart, but they cannot be drawn that way except from overhead. The artist must make the tracks converge at a point. Only in this way will the scene look "real."

Beginning in the fifteenth century, artists led by Leone Battista Alberti, Leonardo da Vinci, and Albrecht Dürer began to study the problems of representing three dimensions in two. What artists initiated, mathematicians developed into a geometry different from that of Euclid—**projective geometry.**

Gerard Desargues (1591–1661), a French architect and engineer, published in 1636 and 1639 a treatise and proposals about perspective and had, thus, invented projective geometry. However, his geometric innovations were hidden for nearly 200 years. A manuscript by Desargues turned up in 1845, about 30 years after Jean-Victor Poncelet had rediscovered projective geometry.

through B to C, then back to A. (It is acceptable to go through a vertex as many times as needed.) Then go to E, to D, to C, and finally go back to E. It is traversable.

(b) In **Figure 91**, vertices A, B, C, and D are all odd because five routes meet at each of them. This network is not traversable.

▌▌EXAMPLE 3▐ Applying Traversability Concepts to a Floor Plan

Figure 92 shows the floor plan of a house. Is it possible to travel through this house, going through each door exactly once?

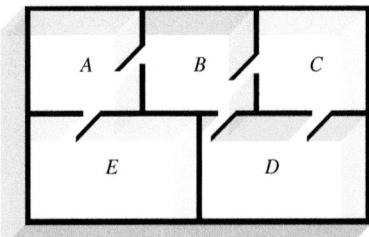

Figure 92

Solution

Rooms A, C, and D have even numbers of doors, while rooms B and E have odd numbers of doors. If we think of the rooms as the vertices of a graph, then the fact that we have exactly two odd vertices means that it is possible to travel through each door of the house exactly once. One can start in either room B or room E. **Figure 93** shows how this can be done starting in room E.

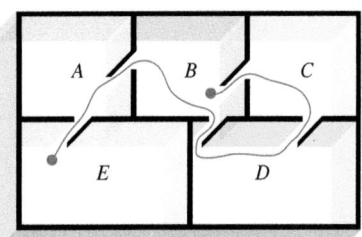

Figure 93

Counting Methods

10

When he was just a youngster, Howard became fascinated with cooking. He knew very early in life that he wanted to start his own restaurant one day. His specialty was hamburgers—people often told him that his burgers were the best they ever ate.

He got his restaurant management degree, and his small business loan soon followed. His dream had come true, and he eagerly began the process of opening Howard's Up and Down Hamburgers. Howard knew he wanted a very limited menu so that he could concentrate on ensuring the highest quality in the small number of items he offered. He decided that for his hamburger orders, he would offer his customers the following 8 choices of extras to add to the basic bun and meat patty:

a second patty, cheese, mustard, mayonnaise, lettuce, tomato, onion, pickle.

A customer could choose none, some but not others, or all of these extras.

Number of Extras	Number of Ways to Order
0	1
1	8
2	28
3	56
4	70
5	56
6	28
7	8
8	1

During construction of his restaurant, Howard needed to have a sign custom-made to let customers know that they could have their hamburger however they wanted. He recalled, from visits to Sonic and Waffle House, that he had seen large numbers indicating how many different combinations of extras their customers could select. The question became

"What number applies to my situation?"

It was easy to count the special cases:

1 way of ordering *no extras,*

8 ways of ordering only *1 extra,*

and 1 way of ordering *all 8 extras.*

Using concepts from the chapter on counting that he studied in his college mathematics class, Howard was able to determine the other numbers of ways. See the table in the margin.

He added up all the numbers (in other words, all the combinations of 8 things taken a particular number at a time), and told his sign maker to come up with a sign indicating that Howard's Up and Down burgers can be chosen in 256 different ways.

10.1 COUNTING BY SYSTEMATIC LISTING

OBJECTIVES

1 Use a systematic approach to perform a one-part counting task.

2 Use a product table to perform a two-part counting task.

3 Use a tree diagram to perform a multiple-part counting task.

4 Use systematic listing in a counting task that involves a geometric figure.

Counting

In this chapter, **counting** means finding the number of objects, of some certain type, that exist. The methods of counting presented in this section involve listing the possible results for a given task. This approach is practical only for fairly short lists. When listing possible results, it is extremely important to use a *systematic* approach, so that no possibilities are missed.

One-Part Tasks

The results for simple *one-part tasks* can often be listed easily. An example of a **one-part task** is tossing a single fair coin. The list here is *heads, tails,* with two possible results. If the task is to roll a single fair die (a cube with faces numbered 1 through 6), the different results are

1, 2, 3, 4, 5, 6,   a total of six possibilities.

EXAMPLE 1 Selecting a Club President

Consider a club N with five members:

$N = \{$Alan, Bill, Cathy, David, Evelyn$\}$,   abbreviated as $N = \{A, B, C, D, E\}$.

In how many ways can this group select a president? (All members are eligible.)

Solution

The task in this case is to select one of the five members as president. There are five possible results.

A, B, C, D, and E ∎

Product Tables for Two-Part Tasks

We now consider **two-part tasks.**

EXAMPLE 2 Building Numbers from a Set of Digits

Determine the number of two-digit numbers that can be written using only the digits 1, 2, and 3.

Solution

This task consists of two parts.

Part 1 Choose a first digit.

Part 2 Choose a second digit.

The results for a two-part task can be pictured in a **product table** such as **Table 1.** From the table we obtain our list of possible results.

$$11, 12, 13, 21, 22, 23, 31, 32, 33$$

There are nine possibilities.

Table 1

	Second Digit		
	1	**2**	**3**
First Digit **1**	11	12	13
2	21	22	23
3	31	32	33

EXAMPLE 3 Rolling a Pair of Dice

Determine the number of different possible results when two ordinary dice are rolled.

Solution

Assume the dice are easily distinguishable. Perhaps one is red and the other green. Then the task consists of two parts.

Part 1 Roll the red die.

Part 2 Roll the green die.

The product table in **Table 2** shows that there are thirty-six possible results.

Table 2   Rolling Two Fair Dice

	Green Die					
	1	**2**	**3**	**4**	**5**	**6**
Red Die **1**	(1, 1)	(1, 2)	(1, 3)	(1, 4)	(1, 5)	(1, 6)
2	(2, 1)	(2, 2)	(2, 3)	(2, 4)	(2, 5)	(2, 6)
3	(3, 1)	(3, 2)	(3, 3)	(3, 4)	(3, 5)	(3, 6)
4	(4, 1)	(4, 2)	(4, 3)	(4, 4)	(4, 5)	(4, 6)
5	(5, 1)	(5, 2)	(5, 3)	(5, 4)	(5, 5)	(5, 6)
6	(6, 1)	(6, 2)	(6, 3)	(6, 4)	(6, 5)	(6, 6)

36 possible results

You will want to refer to **Table 2** *when various dice-rolling problems occur in the remainder of this chapter and the next.*

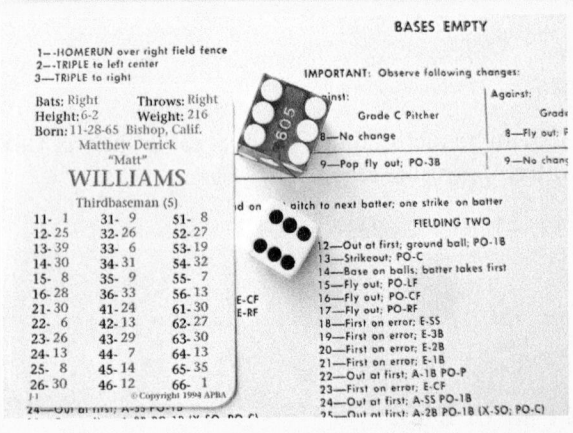

WHEN Will I Ever USE This ?

One of today's most popular sports-related pastimes is that of fantasy leagues. Members of the league draft a team and compete against other "owners," relying on the modern-day immediate availability of statistics via technology. But before the advent of fantasy leagues, a similar hobby provided hours of enjoyment for rabid sports fans (and still does for many). An author of this text spent many hours playing table-top baseball in his youth.

In 1951, a young entrepreneur named Richard Seitz transformed his love for baseball and its statistics into a successful game company that he called APBA. It was located in Lancaster, Pennsylvania, and in 2011 moved to Alpharetta, Georgia, where it still operates. His idea spawned numerous competitors over the years (such as the popular Strat-o-Matic game) that feature simulation of athletes performing according to their actual statistics. To initiate the action in a random fashion, the classic Parker Brothers game Monopoly (for example) uses the sum of a roll of two dice. But certain sums occur more than others. Therefore, to ensure that the results are equally likely, in APBA Major League Baseball, the action is begun by rolling two dice of different sizes (and colors) and reading the results in such a way that every result has an equal chance to occur. Specifically, the number that will activate play is found by reading the face of the large die followed by that of the small die. (See **Table 2** on the preceding page, which illustrates this same idea.)

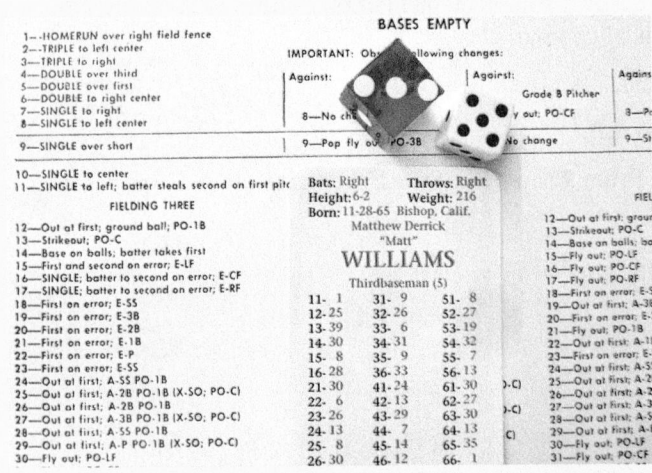

As an illustration of how this game works, see the photo of a play board and the batter card for Matt Williams, a third baseman for the San Francisco Giants in the 1990s who later went on to become manager of the Washington Nationals.

A larger red-die result of 3 followed by a small-die result of 5 is read 35. This number is located on the player card, and it corresponds to a different number, which in this case is 9. That latter number is then found on the applicable game board with a description of the play. As seen on the board, Matt gets a single over shortstop. (When their teams are at bat, APBA managers love to roll 66, because that number always leads to the best possible outcome for the batter.) In Matt's case, a roll of 66 would lead to 1, which would be a home run over the right field fence. The well-established formula devised years ago by the company for constructing batters' cards ensures that in the long run, their results in the game will accurately reflect their actual performances.

EXAMPLE 4 Electing Two Club Officers

In **Example 1,** we considered club N consisting of five members.

$$N = \{A, B, C, D, E\}$$

Find the number of ways that the club can elect both a president and a secretary. Assume that all members are eligible, but that no one can hold both offices.

Solution

Again, the required task has two parts.

Part 1 Determine the president.

Part 2 Determine the secretary.

Constructing **Table 3** gives us the possibilities (where, for example, AB denotes president A and secretary B, while BA denotes president B and secretary A).

Table 3 Electing Two Officers

		Secretary				
		A	B	C	D	E
President	A		AB	AC	AD	AE
	B	BA		BC	BD	BE
	C	CA	CB		CD	CE
	D	DA	DB	DC		DE
	E	EA	EB	EC	ED	

20 possible results

Notice that entries down the main diagonal, from upper left to lower right, are omitted from the table because the cases AA, BB, and so on would imply one person holding both offices. Altogether, there are twenty possibilities. ■

EXAMPLE 5 Selecting Committees for a Club

Find the number of ways that club N from **Example 4** can appoint a committee of two members to represent them at an association conference.

Solution

The required task again has two parts. In fact, we can refer to **Table 3** again, but this time, the order of the two letters (people) in a given pair really makes no difference. For example, BD and DB are the same committee. In **Example 4,** BD and DB were different results since the two people would be holding different offices.

In the case of committees, we can eliminate not only the main diagonal entries but also all entries below the main diagonal. The resulting list contains ten possibilities.

$$AB, \quad AC, \quad AD, \quad AE, \quad BC, \quad BD, \quad BE, \quad CD, \quad CE, \quad DE \quad ■$$

Tree Diagrams for Multiple-Part Tasks

Bone dice were unearthed in the remains of a Roman garrison, Vindolanda, near the border between England and Scotland. Life on the Roman frontier was occupied with gaming as well as fighting. Some of the Roman dice were loaded in favor of 6 and 1.

Life on the American frontier was reflected in cattle brands that were devised to keep alive the memories of hardships, feuds, and romances. A rancher named Ellis from Paradise Valley in Arizona designed his cattle brand in the shape of a pair of dice. You can guess that the pips were 6 and 1.

Problem-Solving Strategy

A task that has more than two parts is not easy to analyze with a product table. Another helpful device is the **tree diagram.**

EXAMPLE 6 Building Numbers from a Set of Digits

Find the number of three-digit numbers that can be written using only the digits 1, 2, and 3, assuming that

(a) repeated digits are allowed   **(b)** repeated digits are not allowed.

Solution

(a) The task of constructing such a number has three parts.

> ***Part 1*** Select the first digit.
>
> ***Part 2*** Select the second digit.
>
> ***Part 3*** Select the third digit.

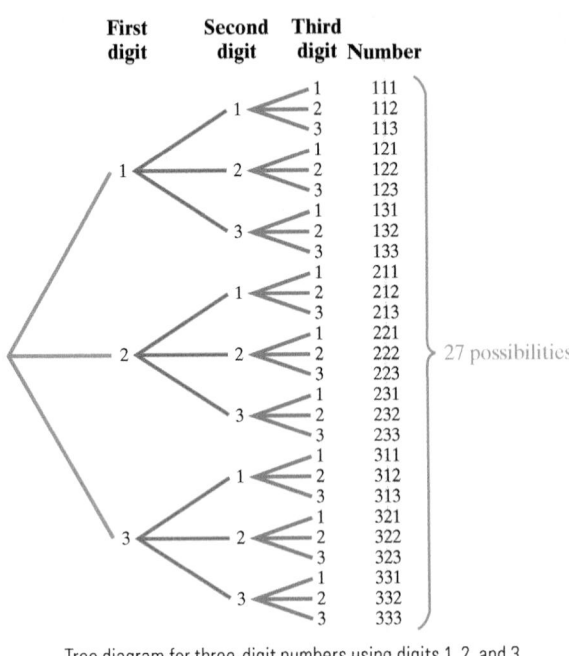

Tree diagram for three-digit numbers using digits 1, 2, and 3

Figure 1

As we move from left to right through the tree diagram in **Figure 1,** the tree branches at the first stage to all possibilities for the first digit. Then each first-stage branch again branches, or splits, at the second stage, to all possibilities for the second digit. Finally, the third-stage branching shows the third-digit possibilities. The list of twenty-seven possible results is shown in the right-hand column.

(b) For the case of nonrepeating digits, we could construct a whole new tree diagram, as in **Figure 2,** or we could simply go down the list of numbers from the first tree diagram and strike out any that contain repeated digits. In either case we obtain only six possibilities.

First digit	Second digit	Third digit	Number
1	2	3	123
	3	2	132
2	1	3	213
	3	1	231
3	1	2	312
	2	1	321

6 possibilities

Tree diagram for nonrepeating three-digit numbers using digits 1, 2, and 3

Figure 2

Notice the distinction between parts (a) and (b) of **Example 6.** There are twenty-seven possibilities when "repetitions (of digits) are allowed," but only six possibilities when "repetitions are not allowed."

Here is another way to phrase the problem of **Example 6.**

> *A three-digit number is to be determined by placing three slips of paper (marked 1, 2, and 3) into a hat and drawing out three slips in succession. Find the number of possible results if the drawing is done (a) with replacement and (b) without replacement.*

Drawing "with replacement" means drawing a slip, recording its digit, and replacing the slip into the hat so that it is again available for subsequent draws.

> *Drawing "with replacement" has the effect of "allowing repetitions," while drawing "without replacement" has the effect of "not allowing repetitions."*

The words "repetitions" and "replacement" are important in the statement of a problem. In **Example 2,** no restrictions were stated, so we assumed that *repetitions* (of digits) *were allowed,* or, equivalently, that digits were to be selected *with replacement.*

EXAMPLE 7 Selecting Switch Settings on a Printer

Pamela's computer printer allows for optional settings with a panel of four on-off switches in a row. How many different settings can she select if no two adjacent switches can both be off?

Solution

This situation is typical of user-selectable options on various devices, including computer equipment, garage door openers, and other appliances. In **Figure 3,** we denote "on" and "off" with 1 and 0, respectively. The number of possible settings is eight.

Tree diagram for printer settings

Figure 3

Notice that each time a switch is indicated as off (0), the next switch can only be on (1). This is to satisfy the restriction that no two adjacent switches can both be off. ∎

EXAMPLE 8 Seating Attendees at a Concert

Arne, Bobbette, Chuck, and Deirdre have tickets for four reserved seats in a row at a concert. In how many different ways can they seat themselves so that Arne and Bobbette will sit next to each other?

Solution

Here we have a four-part task:

Assign people to the first, second, third, and fourth seats.

Let *A*, *B*, *C*, and *D* represent the four people. The tree diagram in **Figure 4** avoids repetitions, because no person can occupy more than one seat. Also, once *A* or *B* appears in the tree, the other one *must* occur at the next stage. No splitting occurs from stage three to stage four because by that time there is only one person left unassigned. The right column in the figure shows the twelve possible seating arrangements.

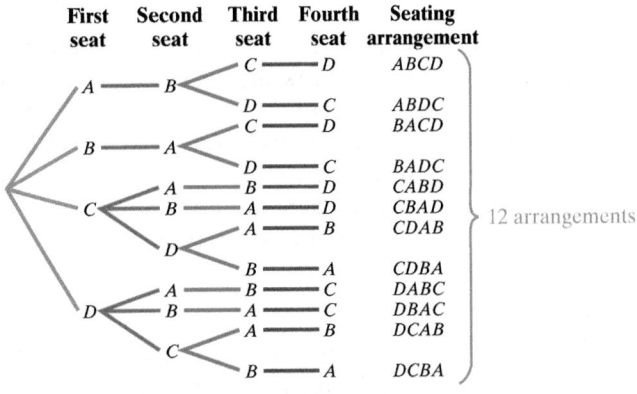

Tree diagram for concert seating

Figure 4

Although we have applied tree diagrams only to tasks with three or more parts, they can also be used for two-part or even simple, one-part tasks. Product tables, on the other hand, are practical only for two-part tasks.

Other Systematic Listing Methods

There are additional systematic ways, besides product tables and tree diagrams, to produce complete listings of possible results.

In **Example 4,** where we used a product table (**Table 3**) to list all possible president-secretary pairs for the club $N = \{A, B, C, D, E\}$, we could have systematically constructed the same list using a sort of alphabetical or left-to-right approach.

First, consider the results where A is president. Any of the remaining members ($B, C, D,$ or E) could then be secretary. That gives us the pairs $AB, AC, AD,$ and AE. Next, assume B is president. The secretary could then be $A, C, D,$ or E. We get the pairs $BA, BC, BD,$ and BE. Continuing in order, we get the complete list just as in **Example 4.**

$$AB, \quad AC, \quad AD, \quad AE, \quad BA, \quad BC, \quad BD, \quad BE, \quad CA, \quad CB,$$
$$CD, \quad CE, \quad DA, \quad DB, \quad DC, \quad DE, \quad EA, \quad EB, \quad EC, \quad ED$$

EXAMPLE 9 Counting Triangles in a Figure

How many different triangles (of any size) can be traced in **Figure 5?**

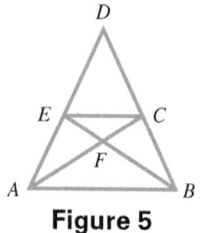

Figure 5

Solution

One systematic approach is to label points as shown, begin with A, and proceed in alphabetical order to write all three-letter combinations, and then cross out the ones that are not triangles in the figure.

$$ABC, \quad ABD, \quad ABE, \quad ABF, \quad ACD, \quad ACE, \quad \cancel{ACF}, \quad \cancel{ADE}, \quad \cancel{ADF}, \quad AEF,$$
$$\cancel{BCD}, \quad BCE, \quad BCF, \quad BDE, \quad \cancel{BDF}, \quad \cancel{BEF}, \quad CDE, \quad \cancel{CDF}, \quad CEF, \quad \cancel{DEF}$$

Finally, there are twelve different triangles in the figure. ACB and CBF (and many others) are not included in the list, because they have already been considered.

Another method might be first to identify the triangles consisting of a single region each: DEC, ECF, AEF, BCF, ABF. Then list those consisting of two regions each: AEC, BEC, ABE, ABC; and those with three regions each: ACD, BED. There are no triangles with four regions, but there is one with five: ABD. The total is again twelve. Can you think of other systematic ways of getting the same list? ▪

Notice that in the first method shown in **Example 9,** the labeled points were considered in alphabetical order. In the second method, the single-region triangles were listed by using a top-to-bottom and left-to-right order. Using a definite system helps to ensure that we get a complete list.

Counting methods can be used to find the number of moves required to solve a **Rubik's Cube.** The scrambled cube must be modified so that each face is a solid color. Rubik's royalties from sales of the cube in Western countries made him Hungary's richest man.

Although the craze over the cube of the early 1980s has waned, certain groups have remained intensely interested in not only solving the scrambled cube, but also doing so as quickly as possible. And the 30-year search for an exact number of moves (called face turns) that is guaranteed to suffice in all cases, while no smaller number will suffice, finally ended in July 2010. That number is now known to be 20.

10.1 EXERCISES

Electing Officers of a Club *Refer to* ***Examples 1 and 4,*** *involving the club*

$$N = \{Alan, Bill, Cathy, David, Evelyn\}.$$

Assuming that all members are eligible, but no one can hold more than one office, list and count the different ways the club could elect each group of officers. (Cathy and Evelyn are women, and the others are men.)

1. a president and a treasurer

2. a president and a treasurer if the president must be a female

3. a president and a treasurer if the two officers must be the same sex

4. a president, a secretary, and a treasurer, if the president and treasurer must be women

5. a president, a secretary, and a treasurer, if the president must be a man and the other two must be women

6. a president, a secretary, and a treasurer, if all three officers must be men

Appointing Committees *List and count the ways club N could appoint a committee of three members under each condition.*

7. There are no restrictions.

8. The committee must include more men than women.

Refer to **Table 2** *(the product table for rolling two dice). Of the 36 possible outcomes, determine the number for which the sum (for both dice) is the following.*

9. 2   10. 3   11. 4

12. 5   13. 6   14. 7

15. 8   16. 9   17. 10

18. 11   19. 12   20. 13

21. odd   22. even   23. prime

24. composite

25. from 5 through 10 inclusive

26. from 6 through 8 inclusive

27. between 6 and 10

28. less than 5   29. greater than 4

30. Construct a product table showing all possible two-digit numbers using digits from the set

$$\{2, 3, 5, 7\}.$$

Of the sixteen numbers in the product table for ***Exercise 30,*** *list the ones that belong to each category.*

31. numbers with repeating digits

32. even numbers

33. prime numbers

34. multiples of 3

35. Construct a tree diagram showing all possible results when three fair coins are tossed. Then list the ways of getting each result.

   (a) at least two heads

   (b) more than two heads

   (c) no more than two heads

   (d) fewer than two heads

36. Extend the tree diagram of **Exercise 35** for four fair coins. Then list the ways of getting each result.

   (a) more than three tails

   (b) fewer than three tails

   (c) at least three tails

   (d) no more than three tails

Determine the number of triangles (of any size) in each figure.

37.

38.

39.

40.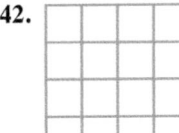

Determine the number of squares (of any size) in each figure.

41.

42.

43.   **44.**

Consider only the smallest individual cubes and assume solid stacks (no gaps). Determine the number of cubes in each stack that are not visible from the perspective shown.

45.   **46.**

47.   **48.**

49. Find the number of paths from *A* to *B* in the figure illustrated here if the directions on various segments are restricted as shown.

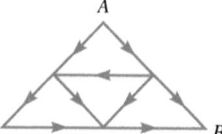

50. In the plane figure illustrated here, only movement that tends downward is allowed. Find the total number of paths from *A* to *B*.

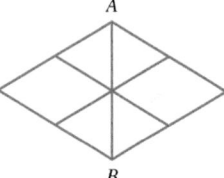

Work each problem.

51. *Rolling Unusual Dice* An unusual die has the numbers

2, 2, 3, 3, 5, and 8

on its six faces. Two of these dice are rolled, and the two numbers on the top faces are added. How many different sums are possible? (*Mathematics Teacher* calendar problem)

52. *Shaking Hands in a Group* A group of six strangers sat in a circle, and each one got acquainted only with the person to the left and the person to the right. Then all six people stood up and each one shook hands (once) with each of the others who was still a stranger. How many handshakes occurred?

53. *Number of Games in a Chess Tournament* Fifty people enter a single-elimination chess tournament. If you lose one game, you're out. Assuming no ties occur, what is the number of games required to determine the tournament champion?

54. *Sums of Digits* How many positive integers less than 100 have the sum of their digits equal to a perfect square?

55. *Sums of Digits* How many three-digit numbers have the sum of their digits equal to 22?

56. *Integers Containing the Digit 2* How many integers between 100 and 400 contain the digit 2?

57. *Filling an Order* A customer ordered fifteen Zingers. Zingers are placed in packages of four, three, or one. In how many different ways can this order be filled? (*Mathematics Teacher* calendar problem)

58. *Selecting Dinner Items* Michael and several friends are dining this evening at the Clam Shell Restaurant, where a complete dinner consists of three items.

Choice 1 soup (clam chowder or minestrone) or salad (fresh spinach or shrimp),

Choice 2 sourdough rolls or bran muffin, and

Choice 3 entree (lasagna, lobster, or roast turkey).

Michael selects his meal subject to the following restrictions. He cannot stomach more than one kind of seafood at a sitting. Also, whenever he tastes minestrone, he cannot resist having lasagna as well. Use a tree diagram to determine the number of different choices Michael has.

*Setting Options on a Computer Printer For Exercises 59–61, refer to **Example 7**. How many different settings could Pamela choose in each case?*

59. No restrictions apply to adjacent switches.

60. No two adjacent switches can be off *and* no two adjacent switches can be on.

61. There are five switches rather than four, and no two adjacent switches can be on.

Work each problem.

62. *Building Numbers from Sets of Digits* Determine the number of odd, nonrepeating three-digit numbers that can be written using only the digits 0, 1, 2, and 3.

63. *Lattice Points on a Line Segment* A line segment joins the points

$(8, 12)$ and $(53, 234)$

in the Cartesian plane. Including its endpoints, how many lattice points does this line segment contain? (A *lattice point* is a point with integer coordinates.)

64. *Lengths of Segments Joining Lattice Points* In the pattern that follows, dots are one unit apart horizontally and vertically. If a segment can join any two dots, how many segments can be drawn with each length?

(a) 1   **(b)** 2   **(c)** 3   **(d)** 4   **(e)** 5

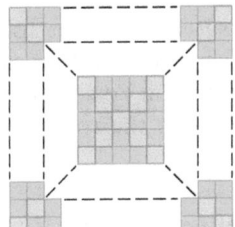

65. *Patterns in Floor Tiling* A square floor is to be tiled with square tiles as shown. There are blue tiles on the main diagonals and red tiles everywhere else. In all cases, both blue and red tiles must be used, and the two diagonals must have a common blue tile at the center of the floor.

(a) If 81 blue tiles will be used, how many red tiles will be needed?

(b) For what numbers in place of 81 would this problem still be solvable?

(c) Find an expression in k giving the number of red tiles required in general.

66. *Counting Matchsticks in a Grid* Uniform-length matchsticks are used to build a rectangular grid as shown here. If the grid is 12 matchsticks high and 25 matchsticks wide, how many matchsticks are used?

67. *Shaking Hands in a Group* Chris and his son were among four father-and-son pairs who gathered to trade baseball cards. As each person arrived, he shook hands with anyone he had not known previously. Each person ended up making a different number of new acquaintances (0–6), except Chris and his son, who each met the same number of people. How many hands did Chris shake?

68. *Sum of Primes* Determine the different number of ways the given composite number can be written as the sum of two prime numbers. (*Hint:* Consider a sum such as $2 + 3$ the same as $3 + 2$.)

(a) 30

(b) 40

(c) 95

In Exercises 69 and 70, restate the given counting problem in two ways, first **(a)** *using the word* repetition, *and then* **(b)** *using the word* replacement.

69. Example 2

70. Example 4

USING THE FUNDAMENTAL COUNTING PRINCIPLE

OBJECTIVES

1 Know the meaning of uniformity in counting, and understand the fundamental counting principle.

2 Use the fundamental counting principle to solve counting problems.

3 Determine the factorial of a whole number.

4 Use factorials to determine the number of arrangements, including distinguishable arrangements, of a given number of objects.

Uniformity and the Fundamental Counting Principle

In **Section 10.1,** we obtained complete lists of all possible results for various tasks. However, if the total number of possibilities is all we need to know, then an actual listing usually is unnecessary and often is difficult or tedious to obtain, especially when the list is long.

Figure 6 shows all possible nonrepeating three-digit numbers using only the digits 1, 2, and 3.

Figure 6

Richard Dedekind (1831–1916) studied at the University of Göttingen, where he was Gauss's last student. His work was not recognized during his lifetime, but his treatment of the infinite and of what constitutes a real number are influential even today.

While on vacation in Switzerland, Dedekind met Georg Cantor. Dedekind was interested in Cantor's work on infinite sets. Perhaps because both were working in new and unusual fields of mathematics, such as number theory, and because neither received the professional attention he deserved during his lifetime, the two struck up a lasting friendship.

The tree diagram in **Figure 6** is "uniform" in the sense that a given part of the task can be done in the same number of ways, no matter which choices were selected for previous parts. For example, there are always two choices for the second digit. (If the first digit is 1, the second can be 2 or 3. If the first is 2, the second can be 1 or 3. If the first is 3, the second can be 1 or 2.)

Example 6(a) of **Section 10.1** addressed the same basic situation:

Find the number of three-digit numbers that can be written using the digits 1, 2, and 3.

In that case repetitions were allowed. With repetitions allowed, there were many more possibilities (27 rather than 6—see **Figure 1** of **Section 10.1**). But the uniformity criterion mentioned above still applied. No matter what the first digit is, there are three choices for the second (1, 2, 3). And no matter what the first and second digits are, there are three choices for the third. This uniformity criterion can be stated in general as follows.

UNIFORMITY CRITERION FOR MULTIPLE-PART TASKS

A multiple-part task is said to satisfy the **uniformity criterion** if the number of choices for any particular part is the same *no matter which choices were selected for previous parts.*

The uniformity criterion is not always satisfied. Refer to **Example 7** and **Figure 3** of **Section 10.1**. After the first switch (two possibilities), other switches had either one or two possible settings depending on how previous switches were set. This "nonuniformity" arose, in that case, from the requirement that no two adjacent switches could both be off.

In the many cases where uniformity does hold, we can avoid having to construct a tree diagram by using the **fundamental counting principle,** stated as follows.

FUNDAMENTAL COUNTING PRINCIPLE

When a task consists of k separate parts and satisfies the uniformity criterion, if the first part can be done in n_1 ways, the second part can then be done in n_2 ways, and so on through the kth part, which can be done in n_k ways, then the total number of ways to complete the task is given by the following product.

$$n_1 \cdot n_2 \cdot n_3 \cdot \ldots \cdot n_k$$

Problem-Solving Strategy

A problem-solving strategy suggested in **Chapter 1** was "*If a formula applies, use it.*" The fundamental counting principle provides a formula that applies to a variety of problems. The strategy is to visualize the "task" at hand as being accomplished in a sequence of two or more separate parts.

A helpful technique when applying the fundamental counting principle is to write out all the separate parts of the task, with a blank for each one. Reason out how many ways each part can be done, and enter these numbers in the blanks. Finally, multiply these numbers together.

EXAMPLE 1 Counting the Two-Digit Numbers

How many two-digit numbers are there in our (base-ten) system of counting numbers? (*Hint:* 40 is a two-digit number, but 04 is not.)

Solution

Our "task" here is to select, or construct, a two-digit number. Work as follows.

Part of task	Select first digit	Select second digit
Number of ways	_____	_____

There are nine choices for the first digit (1 through 9). Since there were no stated or implied restrictions, we assume that repetition of digits is allowed. Therefore, no matter which nonzero digit is used as the first digit, all nine choices are available for the second digit. Also, unlike the first digit, the second digit may be zero, so we have ten choices for the second digit. We can now fill in the blanks and multiply.

Part of task	Select first digit		Select second digit	
Number of ways	9	$\cdot$	10	= 90

There are 90 two-digit numbers. (As a check, notice that they are the numbers from 10 through 99, a total of $99 - 10 + 1 = 90$.) ∎

EXAMPLE 2 Building Two-Digit Numbers with Restrictions

Find the number of two-digit numbers that do not contain repeated digits.

Solution

The basic task is again to select a two-digit number, and there are two parts.

Part 1 Select the first digit.   ***Part 2*** Select the second digit.

But a new restriction applies—no repetition of digits. There are nine choices for the first digit (1 through 9). Then nine choices remain for the second digit, since one nonzero digit has been used and cannot be repeated, but zero is now available. The total number is $9 \cdot 9 = 81$. ∎

EXAMPLE 3 Electing Club Officers with Restrictions

In how many ways can Club *N*, of **Examples 1** and **4** in the previous section, elect a president and a secretary if no one may hold more than one office and the secretary must be a man?

Solution

To the Student

In Club *N*,
  Alan is a man.
  Bill is a man.
  Cathy is a woman.
  David is a man.
  Evelyn is a woman.

Recall that $N = \{A, B, C, D, E\} = \{$Alan, Bill, Cathy, David, Evelyn$\}$. Considering president first, there are five choices (no restrictions). But now we have a problem with finding the number of choices for secretary. If a woman was selected president (*C* or *E*), there are three choices for secretary (*A*, *B*, and *D*). If a man was selected president, only two choices (the other two men) remain for secretary. ***In other words, the uniformity criterion is not met, and our attempt to apply the fundamental counting principle has failed.***

All is not lost, however. To find the total number of ways, we can consider secretary first. There are three choices: *A*, *B*, and *D*. Now, no matter which man was chosen secretary, both of the other men and both women are available for president, with four choices in every case. In this order, we satisfy the uniformity criterion and can use the fundamental counting principle. The total number of ways to elect a president and a secretary is $3 \cdot 4 = 12$. ∎

Problem-Solving Strategy

Example 3 suggests a useful problem-solving strategy: Whenever one or more parts of a task have special restrictions, try considering that part (or those parts) before other parts.

EXAMPLE 4 Counting Three-Digit Numbers with Restrictions

How many nonrepeating odd three-digit counting numbers are there?

Solution

The most restricted digit is the third, since it must be odd. There are five choices (1, 3, 5, 7, and 9). Next, consider the first digit. It can be any nonzero digit except the one already chosen as the third digit. There are eight choices. Finally, the second digit can be any digit (including 0) except for the two nonzero digits already used. There are eight choices.

Part of task	Select third digit		Select first digit		Select second digit	
Number of ways	5	·	8	·	8	= 320

There are 320 nonrepeating odd three-digit counting numbers. ∎

EXAMPLE 5 Counting License Plates

In some states, auto license plates have contained three letters followed by three digits. How many such licenses are possible?

Solution

The basic task is to design a license plate with three letters followed by three digits. There are six component parts to this task. There are no restrictions on letters or digits, so the fundamental counting principle gives

$$26 \cdot 26 \cdot 26 \cdot 10 \cdot 10 \cdot 10 = 26^3 \cdot 10^3 = 17{,}576{,}000 \text{ possible licenses.}$$

In practice, a few of the possible sequences of letters are considered undesirable and are not used. ∎

EXAMPLE 6 Building Numbers with Specified Digits

A four-digit number is to be constructed using only the digits 1, 2, and 3.

(a) How many such numbers are possible?

(b) How many of these numbers are odd and less than 2000?

Solution

(a) To construct such a number, we must select four digits, in succession, from the given set of three digits, where the selection is done with replacement (since repetition of digits is apparently allowed). The number of possibilities is

$$3 \cdot 3 \cdot 3 \cdot 3 = 3^4 = 81. \quad \text{Fundamental counting principle}$$

(b) The number is less than 2000 only if the first digit is 1 (just one choice) and is odd only if the fourth digit is 1 or 3 (two choices). The second and third digits are unrestricted (three choices for each). The answer is

$$1 \cdot 3 \cdot 3 \cdot 2 = 18.$$

As a check, you may want to list the eighteen possibilities. ∎

Two of the problem-solving strategies of **Chapter 1** were *"First solve a similar simpler problem"* and *"Look for a pattern."* In fact, a counting problem may sometimes prove to be essentially the same, or at least to fit the same pattern, as another problem already solved.

EXAMPLE 7 **Distributing Golf Clubs**

Vern has four antique golf clubs that he wants to give to his three sons, Mark, Chris, and Scott.

(a) How many ways can the clubs be distributed?

(b) How many choices are there if the power driver must go to Mark and the number 3 wood must go to either Chris or Scott?

Solution

(a) The task is to distribute four clubs among three sons. Consider the clubs in succession, and, for each one, ask how many sons could receive it. In effect, we must select four sons, in succession, from the list Mark, Chris, Scott, selecting with replacement. Compare this with **Example 6(a),** in which we selected four digits, in succession, from the digits 1, 2, and 3, selecting with replacement. In this case, we are selecting sons rather than digits, but the pattern is the same and the numbers are the same. Again our answer is

$$3^4 = 81.$$

(b) Just as in **Example 6(b),** one part of the task is now restricted to a single choice, and another part is restricted to two choices. As in that example, the number of possibilities is

$$1 \cdot 3 \cdot 3 \cdot 2 = 18. \qquad \blacksquare$$

EXAMPLE 8 **Seating Attendees at a Concert**

This is a repeat of **Example 8** in **Section 10.1.**

Arne, Bobbette, Chuck, and Deirdre have tickets for four reserved seats in a row at a concert. In how many different ways can they seat themselves so that Arne and Bobbette will sit next to each other?

Solution

Arne, Bobbette, Chuck, and Deirdre (A, B, C, and D) are to seat themselves in four adjacent seats (say 1, 2, 3, and 4) so that A and B are side-by-side. One approach to accomplish this task is to make three successive decisions as follows.

1. *Which pair of seats should A and B occupy?* There are *three* choices: 1 and 2, 2 and 3, 3 and 4, as illustrated in the margin.

2. *Which order should A and B take?* There are *two* choices: A left of B, or B left of A.

3. *Which order should C and D take?* There are *two* choices: C left of D, or D left of C, not necessarily right next to each other.

1	2	3	4
X	X	—	—
—	X	X	—
—	—	X	X

Seats available to *A* and *B*

The fundamental counting principle now gives the total number of choices.

$$3 \cdot 2 \cdot 2 = 12 \quad \text{Same result as in Section 10.1} \qquad \blacksquare$$

Factorials

This section began with a discussion of nonrepeating three-digit numbers using digits 1, 2, and 3. The number of possibilities was

$$3 \cdot 2 \cdot 1 = 6. \quad \text{Fundamental counting principle}$$

That product can also be thought of as the total number of distinct *arrangements* of the three digits 1, 2, and 3. Similarly, the number of distinct arrangements of four objects (say A, B, C, and D) is

$$4 \cdot 3 \cdot 2 \cdot 1 = 24. \quad \text{Fundamental counting principle}$$

Because this type of product occurs so commonly in applications, we give it a special name and symbol. For any counting number n, the product of *all* counting numbers from n down through 1 is called **n factorial**, and is denoted **$n!$**.

FACTORIAL FORMULA

For any counting number **n**, the quantity **n factorial** is defined as follows.

$$n! = n \cdot (n-1) \cdot (n-2) \cdot \ldots \cdot 2 \cdot 1$$

The first few factorial values are easily found by simple multiplication, but they rapidly become very large. The use of a calculator is advised in most cases.

Problem-Solving Strategy

Sometimes expressions involving factorials can be evaluated easily by observing that, in general, $n! = n \cdot (n-1)!$, $n! = n \cdot (n-1) \cdot (n-2)!$, and so on. For example,

$$8! = 8 \cdot 7!, \qquad 12! = 12 \cdot 11 \cdot 10 \cdot 9!, \quad \text{and so on.}$$

This pattern is especially helpful in evaluating quotients of factorials.

$$\frac{10!}{8!} = \frac{10 \cdot 9 \cdot 8!}{8!} = 10 \cdot 9 = 90$$

EXAMPLE 9 Evaluating Expressions Containing Factorials

Evaluate each expression.

(a) $3!$ **(b)** $6!$ **(c)** $(6-3)!$ **(d)** $6! - 3!$

(e) $\dfrac{6!}{3!}$ **(f)** $\left(\dfrac{6}{3}\right)!$ **(g)** $15!$ **(h)** $100!$

Solution

(a) $3! = 3 \cdot 2 \cdot 1 = 6$ **(b)** $6! = 6 \cdot 5 \cdot 4 \cdot 3 \cdot 2 \cdot 1 = 720$

(c) $(6-3)! = 3! = 6$ **(d)** $6! - 3! = 720 - 6 = 714$

(e) $\dfrac{6!}{3!} = \dfrac{6 \cdot 5 \cdot 4 \cdot 3!}{3!} = 6 \cdot 5 \cdot 4 = 120$ Note application of the Problem-Solving Strategy.

(f) $\left(\dfrac{6}{3}\right)! = 2! = 2 \cdot 1 = 2$

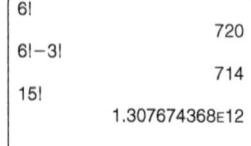

The results of **Example 9(b), (d),** and **(g)** are illustrated in this calculator screen.

(g) $15! = 1.307674368000 \times 10^{12}$ ← Done on a calculator

(h) $100! = 9.332621544 \times 10^{157}$ ← Too large for most calculators

Notice the distinction between parts (c) and (d) and between parts (e) and (f). ■

So that factorials will be defined for all whole numbers, including zero, we define 0! as follows.

DEFINITION OF ZERO FACTORIAL

$$0! = 1$$

(We will see later that this special definition makes other results easier to state.)

The definition $0! = 1$ is illustrated here.

Arrangements of Objects

When finding the total number of ways to *arrange* a given number of distinct objects, we can use a factorial. The fundamental counting principle would do, but factorials provide a shortcut.

ARRANGEMENTS OF n DISTINCT OBJECTS

The total number of different ways to arrange n distinct objects is $n!$.

EXAMPLE 10 Arranging Essays

Michelle has seven essays to include in her English 1A folder. In how many different orders can she arrange them?

Solution

The number of ways to arrange seven distinct objects is

$$7! = 5040.$$ ■

EXAMPLE 11 Arranging Preschoolers

Tricia is taking thirteen preschoolers to the park. How many ways can the children line up, in single file, to board the van?

Solution

Thirteen children can be arranged in

$$13! = 6{,}227{,}020{,}800 \text{ different ways.}$$ ■

Distinguishable Arrangements

D_1AD_2

D_2AD_1

D_1D_2A

D_2D_1A

AD_1D_2

AD_2D_1

In counting arrangements of objects that contain look-alikes, the normal factorial formula must be modified to find the number of truly different arrangements. For example, the number of distinguishable arrangements of the letters of the word DAD is not $3! = 6$ but rather $\frac{3!}{2!} = 3$. The listing in the margin shows how the six total arrangements consist of just three groups of two, where the two in a given group look alike.

ARRANGEMENTS OF n OBJECTS CONTAINING LOOK-ALIKES

The number of **distinguishable arrangements** of n objects, where one or more subsets consist of look-alikes (say n_1 are of one kind, n_2 are of another kind, ..., and n_k are of yet another kind), is given by

$$\frac{n!}{n_1! \cdot n_2! \cdot \ldots \cdot n_k!}.$$

EXAMPLE 12 Counting Distinguishable Arrangements

Determine the number of distinguishable arrangements of the letters in each word.

(a) ATTRACT   **(b)** NIGGLING

Solution

(a) For the letters of ATTRACT, the number of distinguishable arrangements is

7 letters total $\longrightarrow$
3 T's, 2 A's $\longrightarrow$ $\dfrac{7!}{3! \cdot 2!} = 420.$

(b) For the letters of NIGGLING, the number of distinguishable arrangements is

8 letters total $\longrightarrow$
2 N's, 2 I's, 3 G's $\longrightarrow$ $\dfrac{8!}{2! \cdot 2! \cdot 3!} = 1680.$ ∎

FOR FURTHER THOUGHT

Stirling's Approximation for $n!$

Although all factorial values are counting numbers, they can be approximated using **Stirling's formula,**

$$n! \approx \sqrt{2\pi n} \cdot n^n \cdot e^{-n},$$

which involves two important irrational numbers, π and e. For example, while the exact value of 5! is $5 \cdot 4 \cdot 3 \cdot 2 \cdot 1 = 120$, the corresponding approximation, using Stirling's formula, is

$$5! \approx \sqrt{2\pi \cdot 5} \cdot 5^5 \cdot e^{-5} \approx 118.019168,$$

which is off by less than 2, an error of only 1.65%.

For Group or Individual Investigation

Use a calculator to fill in the table on the right. The column values are defined as follows.

$C = n!$ (exact value, by calculator)

$S \approx n!$ (Stirling's approximation, by calculator)

$D = $ Difference $(C - S)$

$P = $ Percentage difference $\left(\dfrac{D}{C} \cdot 100\%\right)$

n	C	S	D	P
10				
15				
20				
25				
30				

Try to obtain percentage differences accurate to two decimal places. Based on your calculations, answer each of the following.

1. In general, is Stirling's approximation too low or too high?

2. Observe the values in the table as n grows larger.
   (a) Do the differences (D) get larger or smaller?
   (b) Do the percentage differences (P) get larger or smaller?
   (c) Does Stirling's formula become more accurate or less accurate as n increases?

3. An even better approximation is given by

$$n! \approx \sqrt{\left(2n + \tfrac{1}{3}\right)\pi} \cdot n^n e^{-n}.$$

Show that this formula gives a closer approximation to 5! than Stirling's formula.

Evaluate each expression without using a calculator.

1. $4!$ **2.** $6!$ **3.** $\dfrac{9!}{7!}$

4. $\dfrac{16!}{14!}$ **5.** $\dfrac{5!}{(5-2)!}$ **6.** $\dfrac{6!}{(6-3)!}$

7. $\dfrac{8!}{6!(8-6)!}$ **8.** $\dfrac{9!}{7!(9-7)!}$

9. $\dfrac{10!}{9!(10-9)!}$ **10.** $\dfrac{100!}{99!(100-99)!}$

11. $\dfrac{50!}{48! \cdot 2!}$ **12.** $\dfrac{37!}{35! \cdot 2!}$

For the given values of n and r, evaluate

(a) $\dfrac{n!}{(n-r)!}$ *and*   **(b)** $\dfrac{n!}{r!(n-r)!}$.

13. $n = 10, r = 3$ **14.** $n = 11, r = 2$

15. $n = 18, r = 2$ **16.** $n = 20, r = 3$

Use a calculator to evaluate each expression.

17. $10!$ **18.** $14!$ **19.** $\dfrac{12!}{5!}$

20. $\dfrac{14!}{8!}$ **21.** $\dfrac{16!}{(16-9)!}$ **22.** $\dfrac{13!}{(13-6)!}$

23. $\dfrac{20!}{10! \cdot 10!}$ **24.** $\dfrac{19!}{9! \cdot 10!}$

25. $\dfrac{n!}{(n-r)!}$, where $n = 17$ and $r = 8$

26. $\dfrac{n!}{(n-r)!}$, where $n = 20$ and $r = 4$

27. $\dfrac{n!}{r!(n-r)!}$, where $n = 24$ and $r = 18$

28. $\dfrac{n!}{r!(n-r)!}$, where $n = 26$ and $r = 20$

Arranging Letters *Find the number of distinguishable arrangements of the letters of each word or phrase.*

29. GOOGOL   **30.** BANANA

31. HEEBIE-JEEBIES   **32.** VICE VERSA

Settings on a Switch Panel   *A panel containing three on-off switches in a row is to be set.*

33. Assuming no restrictions on individual switches, use the fundamental counting principle to find the total number of possible panel settings.

34. Assuming no restrictions, construct a tree diagram to list all the possible panel settings of **Exercise 33.**

35. Now assume that no two adjacent switches can both be off. Explain why the fundamental counting principle does not apply.

36. Construct a tree diagram to list all possible panel settings under the restriction of **Exercise 35.**

37. **Rolling Dice**   **Table 2** in the previous section shows that there are 36 possible outcomes when two fair dice are rolled. How many outcomes would there be if three fair dice were rolled?

38. **Counting Five-Digit Numbers** How many five-digit numbers are there in our system of counting numbers?

39. **Bowling**   After the rolling of the first ball of a frame in a game of 10-pin bowling, how many different pin configurations can remain (assuming all configurations are physically possible)? (*Mathematics Teacher* calendar problem)

40. **Bowling**   Answer the question of **Exercise 39** assuming that pins 4, 7, and 8 were knocked down on the first roll.

Matching Club Members with Tasks   *Recall the club*

$$N = \{\text{Alan, Bill, Cathy, David, Evelyn}\}.$$

In how many ways could they do each of the following?

41. line up all five members for a photograph

42. schedule one member to work in the office on each of five different days, assuming members may work more than one day

43. select a male and a female to decorate for a party

44. select two members, one to open their next meeting and one to close it, given that Bill will not be present

Building Numbers with Specified Digits *In Exercises 45–48, counting numbers are to be formed using only the digits 3, 4, and 5. Determine the number of different possibilities for each type of number described.*

45. two-digit numbers

46. odd three-digit numbers

47. four-digit numbers with one pair of adjacent 4s and no other repeated digits

(*Hint:* You may want to split the task of designing such a number into three parts, such as **Part 1** position the pair of 4s, **Part 2** position the 3, and **Part 3** position the 5.)

48. five-digit numbers beginning and ending with 3 and with unlimited repetitions allowed

Selecting Dinner Items *The Gourmet de Coeur Restaurant offers*

> *five choices in the soup and salad category (two soups and three salads),*
>
> *two choices in the bread category,*

and *four choices in the entrée category.*

Find the number of dinners available in each case.

49. One item should be included from each of the three categories.

50. Only salad and entrée are to be included.

Selecting Answers on a Test *Determine the number of possible ways to mark your answer sheet (with an answer for each question) for each test.*

51. a six-question true-or-false test

52. a ten-question multiple-choice test with five answer choices for each question

Selecting a College Class Schedule *Jessica's class schedule for next semester must consist of exactly one class from each of the four categories shown in the table.*

For each situation in Exercises 53–58 in the next column, use the table to determine the number of different sets of classes Jessica can take.

Category	Choices	Number of Choices
Economics	Free Markets Controlled Markets	2
Mathematics	History of Mathematics College Algebra Finite Mathematics	3
Education	Classroom Technology Group Dynamics Language Supervision Parent/Teacher Relations	4
Sociology	Social Problems Sociology of the Middle East Aging in America Minorities in America Women in American Culture	5

53. All classes shown are available.

54. She is not eligible for Free Markets or for Group Dynamics.

55. All sections of Minorities in America and Women in American Culture already are filled.

56. She does not have the prerequisites for Controlled Markets, College Algebra, or Language Supervision.

57. Funding has been withdrawn for three of the Education courses and for two of the Sociology courses.

58. She must complete Finite Mathematics and Social Problems to fulfill her degree requirements.

59. *Selecting Clothing* Don has two pairs of shoes, four pairs of pants, and six shirts. If all items are compatible, how many different outfits can he wear?

60. *Selecting Music Equipment* A music equipment outlet stocks ten different guitars, three guitar cases, six amplifiers, and five special effects processors, with all items mutually compatible and all suitable for beginners. How many different complete setups could Lionel choose to start his musical career?

61. *Counting ZIP Codes* Tonya's ZIP code is 85726. How many ZIP codes altogether could be formed, each one using those same five digits?

62. *Listing Phone Numbers* Raj keeps the phone numbers for his seven closest friends (three men and four women) in his digital phone memory. (Refer to **Example 8.**) How many ways can he list them for the following conditions?

(a) men are listed before women

(b) men are all listed together

(c) no two men are listed next to each other?

63. *Counting Telephone Area Codes* Until 1995, the rules for three-digit area codes in the United States were as follows:

• The first digit could not be 0 or 1.
• The second digit had to be 0 or 1.
• The third digit had no such restrictions.

In 1995, the restriction on the second digit of area codes was removed. How many area codes are possible? (*Mathematics Teacher* calendar problem)

64. *Repeated Digits* Repeat **Example 4,** but this time allow repeated digits. Does the order in which digits are considered matter in this case?

Seating Arrangements at a Theater In Exercises 65–68, Arne, Bobbette, Chuck, Deirdre, Ed, and Fran have reserved six seats in a row at the theater, starting at an aisle seat. (Refer to Example 8.)

65. In how many ways can they arrange themselves? (*Hint:* Divide the task into the series of six parts shown below, performed in order.)

(a) If *A* is seated first, how many seats are available for him?

(b) Now, how many are available for *B*?

(c) Now, how many for *C*?

(d) Now, how many for *D*?

(e) Now, how many for *E*?

(f) Now, how many for *F*?

Now multiply your six answers above.

66. In how many ways can they arrange themselves so that Arne and Bobbette will be next to each other?

1	2	3	4	5	6
X	X				
	X	X			
		X	X		
			X	X	
				X	X

Seats available to *A* and *B*

(*Hint:* Answer the questions in parts (a)–(f), in order.)

(a) How many pairs of adjacent seats can *A* and *B* occupy?

(b) Now, given the two seats for *A* and *B*, in how many orders can they be seated?

(c) Now, how many seats are available for *C*?

(d) Now, how many for *D*?

(e) Now, how many for *E*?

(f) Now, how many for *F*?

Now multiply your six answers above.

67. In how many ways can they arrange themselves if the men and women are to alternate seats and a man must sit on the aisle? Arne, Chuck, and Ed are men, and the others are women. (*Hint:* First answer the following six questions in order.)

(a) How many choices are there for the person to occupy the first seat, next to the aisle? (It must be a man.)

(b) How many choices of people may occupy the second seat from the aisle? (It must be a woman.)

(c) Now, how many for the third seat? (one of the remaining men)

(d) Now, how many for the fourth seat? (a woman)

(e) Now, how many for the fifth seat? (a man)

(f) Now, how many for the sixth seat? (a woman)

Now multiply your six answers above.

68. In how many ways can they arrange themselves if the men and women are to alternate with either a man or a woman on the aisle? Arne, Chuck, and Ed are men, and the others are women. (*Hint:* First answer the following six questions in order.)

(a) How many choices of people are there for the aisle seat?

(b) Now, how many are there for the second seat? (This person must not be of the same gender as the person on the aisle.)

(c) Now, how many choices are there for the third seat?

(d) Now, how many for the fourth seat?

(e) Now, how many for the fifth seat?

(f) Now, how many for the sixth seat?

Now multiply your six answers above.

Work each problem.

69. *Six-Digit Numbers* If all the six-digit numbers formed by using the digits

1, 2, 3, 4, 5, and 6,

without repetition, are listed from least to greatest, which number will be 500th in the list? (*Mathematics Teacher* calendar problem)

70. *Palindromes* How many of the anagrams (arrangements of the letters) of

INDIANA

are palindromes, that is arrangements that read the same forward and backward? *Hint:* One such palindrome is

INADANI.

(*Mathematics Teacher* calendar problem)

71. *Divisibility* The number $2^7 \cdot 3^4 \cdot 5 \cdot 7^2 \cdot 11^3$ is divisible by many perfect squares. How many? (*Mathematics Teacher* calendar problem)

72. *Distinguishability* How many distinguishable rearrangements of the letters in the word

CONTEST

start with the two vowels? (*Mathematics Teacher* calendar problem)

10.3 USING PERMUTATIONS AND COMBINATIONS

OBJECTIVES

1 Solve counting problems involving permutations and the fundamental counting principle.

2 Solve counting problems involving combinations and the fundamental counting principle.

3 Solve counting problems that require deciding whether to use permutations or combinations.

Permutations

Again recall the club

$$N = \{\text{Alan, Bill, Cathy, David, Evelyn}\} = \{A, B, C, D, E\}$$

and consider two questions.

1. How many ways can all the club members arrange themselves in a row for a photograph?

2. How many ways can the club elect a president, a secretary, and a treasurer if no one can hold more than one office?

From **Section 10.2,** the answer to the first question above is

$$5! = 5 \cdot 4 \cdot 3 \cdot 2 \cdot 1 = 120,$$

the number of possible arrangements of 5 distinct objects. We answered questions like the second one using a tree diagram or the fundamental counting principle.

$$5 \cdot 4 \cdot 3 = 60$$

A good way to think of the second question is as follows.

> ***How many arrangements are there of five things taken three at a time?***

The factors begin with 5 and proceed downward, just as in a factorial product, but do not go all the way to 1. Here the product stops when there are three factors.

In the context of counting problems, arrangements are called **permutations.** The number of permutations of *n* distinct things taken *r* at a time is denoted $_nP_r$.*

---

*Alternative notations are $P(n, r)$ and P_r^n.

The number of objects being arranged cannot exceed the total number available, so we assume that $r \leq n$. Applying the fundamental counting principle gives

$$_nP_r = n(n-1)(n-2)\ldots[n-(r-1)].$$

The first factor is $n - 0$, the second is $n - 1$, the third is $n - 2$, and so on. The rth factor, the last one in the product, will be the one with $r - 1$ subtracted from n, as shown above. We can express permutations, in general, in terms of factorials, to obtain a formula as follows.

$$_nP_r = n(n-1)(n-2)\ldots[n-(r-1)]$$

$$= n(n-1)(n-2)\ldots(n-r+1) \qquad \text{Simplify the last factor.}$$

$$= \frac{n(n-1)(n-2)\ldots(n-r+1)(n-r)(n-r-1)\ldots2\cdot1}{(n-r)(n-r-1)\ldots2\cdot1} \qquad \begin{array}{l}\text{Multiply and divide by}\\ (n-r)(n-r-1)\ldots2\cdot1.\end{array}$$

$$_nP_r = \frac{n!}{(n-r)!} \qquad \text{Definition of factorial}$$

FACTORIAL FORMULA FOR PERMUTATIONS

The number of **permutations,** or *arrangements,* of n distinct things taken r at a time, where $r \leq n$, can be calculated as follows.

$$_nP_r = \frac{n!}{(n-r)!}$$

Although we sometimes refer to a symbol such as

$$_4P_2$$

as "a permutation," the symbol actually represents "the number of permutations of 4 distinct things taken 2 at a time."

EXAMPLE 1 Using the Factorial Formula for Permutations

Evaluate each permutation.

(a) $_4P_2$ **(b)** $_8P_5$ **(c)** $_5P_5$

Solution

(a) $_4P_2 = \dfrac{4!}{(4-2)!} = \dfrac{4!}{2!} = \dfrac{24}{2} = 12$

(b) $_8P_5 = \dfrac{8!}{(8-5)!} = \dfrac{8!}{3!} = \dfrac{40,320}{6} = 6720$

(c) $_5P_5 = \dfrac{5!}{(5-5)!} = \dfrac{5!}{0!} = \dfrac{120}{1} = 120$ ∎

```
4!/(4−2)!
                    12
8!/(8−5)!
                  6720
5!/(5−5)!
                   120
```

This screen uses factorials to support the results of **Example 1.**

Notice that $_5P_5$ is equal to 5!. The following is true for all whole numbers n.

$$_nP_n = n!$$

This is the number of arrangements of n distinct objects taken all n at a time.

Many calculators allow direct calculation of permutations.

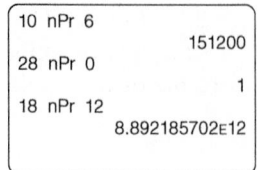

This screen uses the permutations feature to support the results of **Example 2.**

EXAMPLE 2 Calculating Permutations Directly

Evaluate each permutation.

(a) $_{10}P_6$ **(b)** $_{28}P_0$ **(c)** $_{18}P_{12}$

Solution

(a) $_{10}P_6 = 151,200$ **(b)** $_{28}P_0 = 1$ **(c)** $_{18}P_{12} = 8,892,185,702,400$

Concerning part (c), many calculators will not display this many digits, so you may obtain an answer such as 8.8921857×10^{12}. ∎

Problem-Solving Strategy

Permutations can be used any time we need to know the number of arrangements of r objects that can be selected from a collection of n objects. *The word "arrangement" implies an ordering, so we use permutations only in cases that satisfy these conditions:*

1. Repetitions are not allowed. **2. Order is important.**

Change ringing, the English way of ringing church bells, combines mathematics and music. Bells are rung first in sequence, 1, 2, 3, ... Then the sequence is permuted ("changed"). On six bells, 720 different "changes" (different permutations of tone) can be rung:
$_6P_6 = 6!$.

The church bells are swung by means of ropes attached to the wheels beside them. One ringer swings each bell, listening intently and watching the other ringers closely. If one ringer gets lost and stays lost, the rhythm of the ringing cannot be maintained; all the ringers have to stop.

A ringer can spend weeks just learning to keep a bell going and months learning to make the bell ring in exactly the right place. Errors of $\frac{1}{4}$ second mean that two bells are ringing at the same time. Even errors of $\frac{1}{10}$ second can be heard.

EXAMPLE 3 Building Numbers from a Set of Digits

How many nonrepeating three-digit numbers can be written using only the digits 3, 4, 5, 6, 7, and 8?

Solution

Repetitions are not allowed since the numbers are to be "nonrepeating." For example, 448 is not acceptable. Also, order is important. For example, 476 and 746 are *distinct* cases. So we use permutations to determine the total number. There are

$$_6P_3 = 6 \cdot 5 \cdot 4 = 120 \text{ ways.}$$ ∎

EXAMPLE 4 Designing Account Numbers

Suppose certain account numbers are to consist of two letters followed by four digits and then three more letters. Repetitions of letters or digits are not allowed *within* any of the three groups, but the last group of letters may contain one or both of those used in the first group. How many such accounts are possible?

Solution

The task of designing such a number consists of three parts.

Part 1 Determine the first set of two letters. (There are 26 letters.)

Part 2 Determine the set of four digits. (There are 10 digits.)

Part 3 Determine the final set of three letters. (There are 26 letters.)

Each part requires an arrangement without repetitions, which is a permutation.

$$\underset{\text{Part 1}}{_{26}P_2} \cdot \underset{\text{Part 2}}{_{10}P_4} \cdot \underset{\text{Part 3}}{_{26}P_3} = \underset{\text{Part 1}}{\underline{650}} \cdot \underset{\text{Part 2}}{\underline{5040}} \cdot \underset{\text{Part 3}}{\underline{15,600}} \quad \text{Fundamental counting principle}$$

$$= 51,105,600,000$$ ∎

Combinations

Permutations involve the number of arrangements of n things taken r at a time, where repetitions are not allowed. Order is important. Recall that club

$$N = \{\text{Alan, Bill, Cathy, David, Evelyn}\}$$

could elect three officers in $_5P_3 = 60$ different ways. With three-member committees, on the other hand, order is not important. The committees B, D, E and E, B, D are not different. The possible number of committees is not the number of arrangements of size 3. Rather, it is the number of *subsets* of size 3.

Recall that in the study of sets, a **set** is a collection or group of things, commonly designated using a list within braces, as we have been designating the club

$$N = \{A, B, C, D, E\}.$$

The order of listing of the members (of any set) is unimportant. For example, $\{D, B, A, E, C\}$ is the same club. A **subset** of a set is a collection of some of the members. It may be all members of the original set, or even none of them, or anywhere in between.

Such subsets are **combinations.** The number of combinations of n things taken r at a time—that is, the number of size-r subsets, given a set of size n—is written $_nC_r$.*

> **There are n things available and we are choosing r of them, so we can read $_nC_r$ as "n choose r."**

The size-3 committees (subsets) of the club (set) $N = \{A, B, C, D, E\}$ are

$$\{A, B, C\}, \quad \{A, B, D\}, \quad \{A, B, E\}, \quad \{A, C, D\}, \quad \{A, C, E\},$$
$$\{A, D, E\}, \quad \{B, C, D\}, \quad \{B, C, E\}, \quad \{B, D, E\}, \quad \{C, D, E\}.$$

There are ten subsets of size 3, so ten is the number of three-member committees possible. Repetitions are not allowed. For example, $\{E, E, B\}$ is not a valid three-member subset, just as EEB is not a valid three-member arrangement.

To see how to find the number of such subsets without listing them all, notice that each size-3 subset (combination) gives rise to six size-3 arrangements (permutations). For example, the single combination ADE yields these six permutations.

$$A, D, E \quad A, E, D \quad D, A, E \quad D, E, A \quad E, A, D \quad E, D, A$$

There must be six times as many size-3 permutations as there are size-3 combinations, or, equivalently, one-sixth as many combinations as permutations.

$$_5C_3 = \frac{_5P_3}{6} = \frac{60}{6} = 10$$

The 6 appears in the denominator because there are six different ways to arrange a set of three things and $3! = 3 \cdot 2 \cdot 1 = 6$. Generalizing, we obtain the following.

$$_nC_r = \frac{_nP_r}{r!} \qquad \text{{\small r things can be arranged in $r!$ ways.}}$$

$$= \frac{\dfrac{n!}{(n-r)!}}{r!} \qquad \text{{\small Substitute the factorial formula for $_nP_r$.}}$$

$$_nC_r = \frac{n!}{r!(n-r)!} \qquad \text{{\small Simplify algebraically.}}$$

---

*Alternative notations are $C(n, r)$, C_r^n, and $\binom{n}{r}$.

FACTORIAL FORMULA FOR COMBINATIONS

The number of **combinations,** or *subsets,* of n distinct things taken r at a time, where $r \le n$, can be calculated as follows.

$$_nC_r = \frac{_nP_r}{r!} = \frac{n!}{r!(n-r)!}$$

In **Examples 5 and 6,** we refer to $_nC_r$ as "a combination" even though it actually represents the number of combinations of n distinct things taken r at a time.

EXAMPLE 5 Using the Factorial Formula for Combinations

Evaluate each combination.

(a) $_9C_7$ **(b)** $_{24}C_{18}$

Solution

(a) $_9C_7 = \dfrac{9!}{7!(9-7)!} = \dfrac{9!}{7! \cdot 2!} = \dfrac{362,880}{5040 \cdot 2} = 36$

(b) $_{24}C_{18} = \dfrac{24!}{18!(24-18)!} = \dfrac{24!}{18! \cdot 6!} = 134,596$

```
9!/(7!*2!)
                36
24!/(18!*6!)
             134596
```

This screen uses factorials to support the results of **Example 5.**

EXAMPLE 6 Calculating Combinations Directly

Evaluate each combination.

(a) $_{14}C_6$ **(b)** $_{21}C_{15}$

Solution

(a) $_{14}C_6 = 3003$ **(b)** $_{21}C_{15} = 54,264$ Use a calculator in each case.

```
14 nCr 6
              3003
21 nCr 15
             54264
```

This screen uses the combinations feature to support the results of **Example 6.**

Problem-Solving Strategy

Combinations share an important feature with permutations in that repetitions are not allowed, and they differ from permutations in one key distinction, which is that order is *not* important with combinations. Combinations are applied only in these situations:

  1. *Repetitions are not allowed.*   **2. *Order is not important.***

EXAMPLE 7 Finding the Number of Subsets

Find the number of different subsets of size 2 in the set $\{a, b, c, d\}$. List them.

Solution

A subset of size 2 must have two distinct elements, so repetitions are not allowed. The order in which the elements of a set are listed makes no difference,

$$_4C_2 = \frac{4!}{2!(4-2)!} = \frac{4!}{2! \cdot 2!} = 6 \qquad \text{Combinations formula with } n=4 \text{ and } r=2$$

The six subsets of size 2 are $\{a, b\}, \{a, c\}, \{a, d\}, \{b, c\}, \{b, d\}, \{c, d\}$.

The set of 52 playing cards in the **standard deck** has four suits.

♠ spades   ♦ diamonds
♥ hearts   ♣ clubs

Ace is the unit card. Jacks, queens, and kings are "face cards." Each suit contains thirteen denominations: ace, 2, 3, . . . , 10, jack, queen, king. In some games, ace rates above king, instead of counting as 1.

EXAMPLE 8 Finding the Number of Possible Poker Hands

A common form of poker involves "hands" (sets) of five cards each, dealt from a standard deck consisting of 52 different cards. How many different 5-card hands are possible?

Solution

A 5-card hand must contain five distinct cards, so repetitions are not allowed. Also, the order is not important because a given hand depends only on the cards it contains, and not on the order in which they were dealt or the order in which they are displayed or played.

Order does not matter, so we use combinations and a calculator.

$$_{52}C_5 = \frac{52!}{5!(52-5)!} = \frac{52!}{5! \cdot 47!} = 2{,}598{,}960 \qquad ∎$$

EXAMPLE 9 Finding the Number of Subsets of Paintings

Keri would like to buy ten different paintings but she can afford only four of them. In how many ways can she make her selections?

Solution

The four paintings selected must be distinct. Repetitions are not allowed, and the order of the four chosen has no bearing in this case, so we use combinations.

$$_{10}C_4 = \frac{10!}{4!(10-4)!} = \frac{10!}{4! \cdot 6!} = 210 \text{ ways} \qquad ∎$$

Notice that, according to our formula for combinations,

$$_{10}C_6 = \frac{10!}{6!(10-6)!} = \frac{10!}{6! \cdot 4!} = 210,$$

which is the same as $_{10}C_4$. In fact, **Exercise 74** asks you to prove the following fact, in general, for all whole numbers n and r, with $r \leq n$.

$$_nC_r = {_nC_{n-r}}$$

Guidelines on Which Method to Use

The following table summarizes the similarities and differences between permutations and combinations and appropriate formulas for calculating their values.

Permutations	**Combinations**
Number of ways of selecting r items out of n items	
Repetitions are not allowed.	
Order is important.	Order is not important.
Arrangements of n items taken r at a time	Subsets of n items taken r at a time
$_nP_r = \dfrac{n!}{(n-r)!}$	$_nC_r = \dfrac{n!}{r!(n-r)!}$
Clue words: arrangement, schedule, order	Clue words: set, group, sample, selection

In cases where r items are to be selected from n items and repetitions are allowed, it is usually best to make direct use of the fundamental counting principle.

The exercises in this section will call for permutations and/or combinations. In the case of multiple-part tasks, the fundamental counting principle may also be required. *In all cases, decide carefully whether order is important, because that determines whether to use permutations or combinations.*

Problem-Solving Strategy

Many counting problems involve selecting some of the items from a given set of items. The particular conditions of the problem will determine which specific technique to use.

1. **If selected items can be repeated, use the fundamental counting principle.**
   Example: How many four-digit numbers are there?

   $$9 \cdot 10^3 = 9000$$

2. **If selected items cannot be repeated, and order is important, use permutations.**
   Example: How many ways can three of eight people line up at a ticket counter?

   $$_8P_3 = \frac{8!}{(8-3)!} = 336$$

3. **If selected items cannot be repeated, and order is *not* important, use combinations.**
   Example: How many ways can a committee of three be selected from a group of twelve people?

   $$_{12}C_3 = \frac{12!}{3!(12-3)!} = 220$$

EXAMPLE 10 Distributing Toys to Children

In how many ways can a mother distribute three different toys among her seven children if a child may receive anywhere from none to all three toys?

Solution

Because a given child can be a repeat recipient, repetitions are allowed here, so we use the fundamental counting principle. Each of the three toys can go to any of the seven children. The number of possible distributions is

$$7 \cdot 7 \cdot 7 = 343.$$ ∎

EXAMPLE 11 Selecting Committees

How many different three-member committees could club $N = \{$Alan, Bill, Cathy, David, Evelyn$\}$ appoint so that exactly one woman is on the committee?

Solution

Two members are women and three are men. Although the question mentioned only that the committee must include exactly one woman, to complete the committee two men must be selected as well. The task of selecting the committee members consists of two parts.

Part 1 Choose one woman. *Part 2* Choose two men.

Because order is not important for committees, use combinations for the two parts. One woman can be chosen in $_2C_1 = \frac{2!}{1!\,1!} = 2$ ways, and two men can be chosen in $_3C_2 = \frac{3!}{2!\,1!} = 3$ ways. Finally, use the fundamental counting principle to obtain $2 \cdot 3 = 6$ different committees. This small number can be checked by listing.

$$\{C, A, B\}, \quad \{C, A, D\}, \quad \{C, B, D\}, \quad \{E, A, B\}, \quad \{E, A, D\}, \quad \{E, B, D\} \quad \blacksquare$$

EXAMPLE 12 Selecting Attendees for an Event

Every member of the Alpha Beta Gamma fraternity would like to attend a special event this weekend, but only ten members will be allowed to attend. How many ways could the lucky ten be selected if there are a total of forty-eight members?

Solution

In this case, ten distinct men are required, so repetitions are not allowed, and the order of selection makes no difference. We use combinations.

$$_{48}C_{10} = \frac{48!}{10! \cdot 38!} = 6{,}540{,}715{,}896 \quad \text{Use a calculator.} \quad \blacksquare$$

EXAMPLE 13 Selecting Escorts

When the ten fraternity men of **Example 12** arrive at the event, four of them are selected to escort the four homecoming queen candidates. In how many ways can this selection be made?

Solution

Of the ten, four distinct men are required, and order is important here because different orders will pair the men with different women. Use permutations.

$$_{10}P_4 = \frac{10!}{6!} = 5040 \text{ possible selections} \quad \blacksquare$$

EXAMPLE 14 Dividing into Groups

In how many ways can the 9 members of a baseball lineup divide into groups of 4, 3, and 2 players?

Solution

Order is not important within the groups. The players within a group are interchangeable in their order of listing. Use combinations.

- First, 4 can be chosen from 9 in $_9C_4 = 126$ ways.

- Then, 3 can be chosen from the remaining 5 in $_5C_3 = 10$ ways.

- Then, 2 can be chosen from the remaining 2 in $_2C_2 = 1$ way.

The three groups also are not interchangeable. They all have different sizes. Apply the fundamental counting principle to find the number of ways.

$$_9C_4 \cdot {_5C_3} \cdot {_2C_2} = 126 \cdot 10 \cdot 1 = 1260 \quad \blacksquare$$

EXAMPLE 15 Dividing into Groups

In how many ways can the 9 players of **Example 14** divide into three groups of 3?

Solution

After the pattern of **Example 14,** the answer may *seem* to be

$$_9C_3 \cdot _6C_3 \cdot _3C_3 = 84 \cdot 20 \cdot 1 = 1680. \quad \text{INCORRECT}$$

However, this would impose an *unwanted order,* not within the groups, but *among* the groups. Ordering the three group selections was appropriate in **Example 14,** because those three groups were distinguishable. They were all different sizes. But here, all groups are size-3.

If the players are denoted $A, B, C, D, E, F, G, H,$ and $I,$ then the list

(1) *BIG, HEF, CAD*	**(2)** *BIG, CAD, HEF*	**(3)** *HEF, BIG, CAD*
(4) *HEF, CAD, BIG*	**(5)** *CAD, BIG, HEF*	**(6)** *CAD, HEF, BIG*

contains six orderings of the same three groups. Since the product 1680 calculated earlier duplicates every set of three groups in this way, we must adjust that value by dividing by $3! = 6$ to obtain the true number of *unordered* sets of three groups. The idea is the same as when we adjust the number of arrangements—orderings—of n things taken r at a time to obtain the number of unordered sets of n things taken r at a time according to the formula

$$_nC_r = \frac{_nP_r}{r!}.$$

The number of ways 9 players can divide into three groups of 3 is

$$\frac{_9C_3 \cdot _6C_3 \cdot _3C_3}{3!} = \frac{1680}{6} = 280. \quad \blacksquare$$

FOR FURTHER THOUGHT

Poker Hands

In 5-card poker, played with a standard 52-card deck, 2,598,960 different hands are possible. See **Example 8.** The desirability of the various hands depends on their relative chance of occurrence, which, in turn, depends on the number of different ways they can occur, as shown in **Table 4.** Note that an ace can generally be positioned either below 2 (as a 1) or above king (as a 14). This is important in counting straight flush hands and straight hands.

For Group or Individual Investigation

As the table on the next page shows, a full house is a relatively rare occurrence. (Only four of a kind, straight flush, and royal flush are less likely.) To verify that there are 3744 different full house hands possible, carry out the following steps.

1. Explain why there are $_4C_3$ different ways to select three aces from the deck.

2. Explain why there are $_4C_2$ different ways to select two 8s from the deck.

3. If "aces and 8s" (three aces and two 8s) is one form of a full house, show that there are

$$_{13}P_2$$

different kinds of full house altogether.

4. Multiply the expressions from Steps 1, 2, and 3. Explain why this product should give the total number of full house hands possible.

5. Find the three missing values in the right column of **Table 4.**

6. Verify the right column total shown in **Table 4.**

Table 4 Categories of Hands in 5-Card Poker

Event E	Description of Event E	Number of Outcomes Favorable to E
Royal flush	Ace, king, queen, jack, and 10, all of the same suit	4
Straight flush	5 cards of consecutive denominations, all in the same suit (excluding royal flush)	36
Four of a kind	4 cards of the same denomination, plus 1 additional card	_____
Full house	3 cards of one denomination, plus 2 cards of a second denomination	3744
Flush	Any 5 cards all of the same suit (excluding royal flush and straight flush)	_____
Straight	5 cards of consecutive denominations (not all the same suit)	10,200
Three of a kind	3 cards of one denomination, plus 2 cards of two additional denominations	54,912
Two pairs	2 cards of one denomination, plus 2 cards of a second denomination, plus 1 card of a third denomination	_____
One pair	2 cards of one denomination, plus 3 additional cards of three different denominations	1,098,240
No pair	No two cards of the same denomination (and excluding any sort of flush or straight)	1,302,540
Total		**2,598,960**

10.3 EXERCISES

Evaluate each expression.

1. $_9P_3$

2. $_{10}P_6$

3. $_{12}P_5$

4. $_{11}P_3$

5. $_{11}C_7$

6. $_{14}C_6$

7. $_{10}C_8$

8. $_{12}C_9$

Determine the number of permutations (arrangements) of each of the following.

9. 20 things taken 4 at a time

10. 15 things taken 5 at a time

11. 16 things taken 4 at a time

12. 13 things taken 7 at a time

Determine the number of combinations (subsets) of each of the following.

13. 9 things taken 4 at a time

14. 13 things taken 6 at a time

15. 12 things taken 5 at a time

16. 11 things taken 8 at a time

Use a calculator to evaluate each expression.

17. $_{22}P_9$

18. $_{23}P_{11}$

19. $_{32}C_{12}$

20. $_{31}C_{17}$

Decide whether each object is a permutation *or a* combination.

21. a telephone number

22. a Social Security number

23. a hand of cards in poker

24. a committee of politicians

25. the "combination" on a student gym locker combination lock

26. a lottery choice of six numbers where the order does not matter

27. an automobile license plate number

28. an Internet password

Exercises 29–36 can be solved using permutations even though the problem statements will not always include a form of the word "permutation," or "arrangement," or "ordering."

29. *Arranging New Home Models* Tyler, a contractor, builds homes of eight different models and presently has five lots to build on. In how many different ways can he arrange homes on these lots? Assume five different models will be built.

30. *ATM PIN Numbers* An automated teller machine (ATM) requires a four-digit personal identification number (PIN), using the digits 0–9. (The first digit may be 0.) How many such PINs have no repeated digits?

31. *Electing Officers of a Club* How many ways can a president and a vice president be determined in a club with twelve members?

32. *Counting Prize Winners* First, second, and third prizes are to be awarded to three different people. If there are ten eligible candidates, how many outcomes are possible?

33. *Counting Prize Winners* How many ways can a teacher give five different prizes to five of her 25 students?

34. *Scheduling Security Team Visits* A security team visits 12 offices each night. How many different ways can the team order its visits?

35. *Placing in a Race* How many different ways could first-, second-, and third-place finishers occur in a race with six runners competing?

36. *Sums of Digits* How many counting numbers have four distinct nonzero digits such that the sum of the four digits is

(a) 10?

(b) 11?

Exercises 37–44 can be solved using combinations even though the problem statements will not always include the word "combination" or "subset."

37. *Arranging New Home Models* Tyler (the contractor) is to build six homes on a block in a new subdivision, using two different models: standard and deluxe. (All standard model homes are the same, and all deluxe model homes are the same.)

(a) How many different choices does Tyler have in positioning the six houses if he decides to build three standard and three deluxe models?

(b) If Tyler builds two deluxes and four standards, how many different positionings can he use?

38. *Sampling Cell Phones* How many ways can a sample of five cell phones be selected from a shipment of twenty-four cell phones?

39. *Detecting Defective Cell Phones* If the shipment of **Exercise 38** contains six defective phones, how many of the size-five samples would not include any of the defective ones?

40. *Committees of U.S. Senators* How many different five-member committees could be formed from the 100 U.S. senators?

41. *Selecting Hands of Cards* Refer to the standard 52-card deck pictured in the margin near **Example 8,** and notice that the deck contains four aces, twelve face cards, thirteen hearts (all red), thirteen diamonds (all red), thirteen spades (all black), and thirteen clubs (all black). Of the 2,598,960 different five-card hands possible, decide how many would consist of the following cards.

(a) all diamonds   **(b)** all black cards

(c) all aces

42. *Selecting Lottery Entries* In a 7/39 lottery, you select seven distinct numbers from the set 1 through 39, where order makes no difference. How many different ways can you make your selection?

43. *Number of Paths from Point to Point* In a certain city, there are seven streets going north–south and four streets going east–west. How many street paths start at the southwest corner of the city, end at the northeast corner of the city, and have the shortest possible length? (*Mathematics Teacher* calendar problem)

44. *Choosing a Monogram* Sheryl Jett wants to name her new baby so that his monogram (first, middle, and last initials) will be distinct letters in alphabetical order and he will share her last name. How many different monograms could she select?

In Exercises 45–72, use permutations, combinations, the fundamental counting principle, or other counting methods, as appropriate.

45. *Identification Numbers in Research* Subject identification numbers in a certain scientific research project consist of three letters followed by three digits and then three more letters. Assume repetitions are not allowed within any of the three groups, but letters in the first group of three may occur also in the last group of three. How many distinct identification numbers are possible?

46. *Radio Station Call Letters* Radio stations in the United States have call letters that begin with K or W. Some have three call letters, such as WBZ in Boston, WLS in Chicago, and KGO in San Francisco. Assuming no repetition of letters, how many three-letter sets of call letters are possible? (Count all possibilities even though, practically, some may be inappropriate.)

47. *Radio Station Call Letters* Most stations that were licensed after 1927 have four call letters starting with K or W, such as WXYZ in Detroit and KRLD in Dallas. Assuming no repetitions, how many four-letter sets are possible? (Count all possibilities even though, practically, some may be inappropriate.)

48. *Selecting Lottery Entries* In SuperLotto Plus, a California state lottery game, you select five distinct numbers from 1 to 47, and one MEGA number from 1 to 27, hoping that your selection will match a random list selected by lottery officials.

(a) How many different sets of six numbers can you select?

(b) Paul always includes his age and his wife's age as two of the first five numbers in his SuperLotto Plus selections. How many ways can he complete his list of six numbers?

49. *Scheduling Batting Orders in Baseball* The Coyotes, a youth league baseball team, have seven pitchers, who only pitch, and twelve other players, all of whom can play any position other than pitcher. For Saturday's game, the coach has not yet determined which nine players to use or what the batting order will be, except that the pitcher will bat last. How many different batting orders may occur?

50. *Scheduling Games in a Basketball League* Each team in an eight-team basketball league is scheduled to play each other team three times. How many games will be played altogether?

51. *Arranging a Wedding Reception Line* At a wedding reception, the bride, the groom and four attendants will form a reception line. How many ways can they be arranged in each of the following cases?

(a) Any order will do.

(b) The bride and groom must be the last two in line.

(c) The groom must be last in line with the bride next to him.

52. *Ordering Performers in a Music Recital* A music class of five girls and four boys is having a recital. If each member is to perform once, how many ways can the program be arranged in each of the following cases?

(a) All girls must perform first.

(b) A girl must perform first, and a boy must perform last.

(c) Elisa (a girl) and Doug (a boy) will perform first and last, respectively.

(d) The entire program will alternate between girls and boys.

(e) The first, fifth, and ninth performers must be girls.

53. *Dividing People into Groups* In how many ways could fifteen people be divided into five groups containing, respectively, one, two, three, four, and five people?

54. *Dividing People into Groups* In how many ways could fifteen people be divided into five groups of three people?

55. Dividing People into Groups In how many ways could eight people be divided into two groups of three people and a group of two people?

56. Scheduling Daily Reading Carole begins each day by reading from one of seven inspirational books. How many ways can she arrange her reading for one week if the selection is done

(a) with replacement?

(b) without replacement?

57. Counting Card Hands How many of the possible 5-card hands from a standard 52-card deck would consist of the following cards?

(a) four clubs and one non-club

(b) two face cards and three non-face cards

(c) two red cards, two clubs, and a spade

58. Drawing Cards How many cards must be drawn (without replacement) from a standard deck of 52 to guarantee the following?

(a) Two of the cards will be of the same suit.

(b) Three of the cards will be of the same suit.

59. Flush Hands in Poker How many different 5-card poker hands would contain only cards of a single suit?

60. Screening Computer Processors A computer company will screen a shipment of 30 processors by testing a random sample of five of them. How many different samples are possible?

61. Selecting Drivers and Passengers for a Trip Natalie, her husband, her son, and four additional friends are driving in two vehicles to the seashore.

(a) If all seven people can drive, how many ways can the two drivers be selected? (Everyone wants to drive the sports car, so it is important which driver gets which car.)

(b) If the sports car must be driven by Natalie, her husband, or their son, how many ways can the drivers now be determined?

(c) If the sports car will accommodate only two people, and there are no other restrictions, how many ways can both drivers and passengers be assigned to both cars?

62. Points and Lines in a Plane If any two points determine a line, how many lines are determined by seven points in a plane, no three of which are collinear?

63. Points and Triangles in a Plane How many triangles are determined by twenty points in a plane, no three of which are collinear?

64. Counting Possibilities on a Combination Lock How many different three-number "combinations" are possible on a combination lock having 40 numbers on its dial? (*Hint:* "Combination" is a misleading name for these locks since repetitions are allowed and order makes a difference.)

65. Winning the Trifecta in Horse Racing Many race tracks offer a "trifecta" race. You win by selecting the correct first-, second-, and third-place finishers. If eight horses are entered, how many tickets must you purchase to guarantee that one of them will be a trifecta winner?

66. Winning the Daily Double in Horse Racing At a horse race, you win the "daily double" by purchasing a ticket and selecting the winners of two specific races. If there are six and eight horses running in those races, respectively, how many tickets must you buy to guarantee a win?

67. Selecting Committees Nine people are to be distributed among three committees of two, three, and four members, and a chairperson is to be selected for each committee. How many ways can this be done? (*Hint:* Break the task into the following sequence of parts.)

Part 1 Select the members of the two-person committee.

Part 2 Select the members of the three-person committee.

Part 3 Select the chair of the two-person committee.

Part 4 Select the chair of the three-person committee.

Part 5 Select the chair of the four-person committee.

68. Selecting Committee Members Repeat **Exercise 67** in the case where the three committees are to have three members each. (*Hint:* Use the same general sequence of task parts, but remember to adjust for *unwanted ordering* of the three committees.)

69. *Arranging New Home Models* (See **Exercise 37.**) Because of his good work, Tyler gets a contract to build homes on three additional blocks in the subdivision, with six homes on each block. He decides to build nine deluxe homes on these three blocks: two on the first block, three on the second, and four on the third. The remaining nine homes will be standard.

(a) Altogether on the three-block stretch, how many different choices does Tyler have for positioning the eighteen homes? (*Hint:* Consider the three blocks separately, and use the fundamental counting principle.)

(b) How many choices would he have if he built 2, 3, and 4 deluxe models on the three different blocks as before, but not necessarily on the first, second, and third blocks in that order?

70. *Sums of Digits* How many counting numbers consist of four distinct nonzero digits such that the sum of the four digits is the given number?

(a) 12

(b) 13

71. *Building Numbers from Sets of Digits* Recall that the counting numbers are

$$1, 2, 3, 4, \ldots.$$

(a) How many six-digit counting numbers use all six digits 4, 5, 6, 7, 8, and 9?

(b) Suppose all these numbers were arranged in increasing order:

$$456{,}789; \quad 456{,}798; \quad \text{and so on.}$$

Which number would be 364th in the list?

72. *Arranging Five-letter Words* The 120 permutations of AHSME are arranged in dictionary order, as if each were an ordinary five-letter word. Find the last letter of the 86th word in the list. (*Mathematics Teacher* calendar problem)

73. Verify that $_{12}C_9 = {}_{12}C_3$.

74. Use the factorial formula for combinations to prove that in general,

$$_nC_r = {}_nC_{n-r}.$$

| **10.4** | **USING PASCAL'S TRIANGLE** |

OBJECTIVES

1 Construct Pascal's triangle and recognize the relationship between its entries and values of $_nC_r$.

2 Use Pascal's triangle to solve applications involving combinations.

Pascal's Triangle

The triangular array in **Figure 7** represents what we can call "random walks" that begin at START and proceed downward according to the following rule:

At each circle (branch point), a coin is tossed. If it lands heads, we go downward to the left. If it lands tails, we go downward to the right. At each point, left and right are equally likely.

In each circle we have recorded the number of different routes that could bring us to that point. For example, the colored 3 can be reached as the result of three different coin-tossing sequences.

htt, tht, and tth   Ways to get to ③

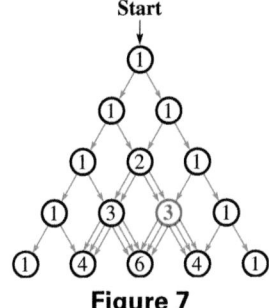

Figure 7

Another way to generate the same pattern of numbers is to begin with 1s down both diagonals and then fill in the interior entries by adding the two numbers just above a given position (to the left and right). For example, the green **28** in **Table 5** on the next page is the result of adding **7** and **21** in the row above it.

By continuing to add pairs of numbers, we extend the array indefinitely downward, always beginning and ending each row with 1s. The table shows just rows 0 through 10. This unending triangular array of numbers is called **Pascal's triangle,** because Blaise Pascal wrote a treatise about it in 1653. There is evidence, though, that it was known as early as around 1100 and may have been studied in China or India still earlier.

"Pascal's" triangle is shown in the 1303 text ***Szu-yuen Yu-chien*** (*The Precious Mirror of the Four Elements*) by the Chinese mathematician Chu Shih-chieh.

Table 5 Pascal's Triangle

Row Number											Row Sum
0					1						1
1				1		1					2
2			1		2		1				4
3		1		3		3		1			8
4	1		4		6		4		1		16
5	1	5		10		10		5		1	32
6	1	6	15		20		15		6	1	64
7	1	7	21	35		35		21	7	1	128
8	1	8	28	56	70		56	28	8	1	256
9	1	9	36	84	126	126	84	36	9	1	512
10	1	10	45	120	210	252	210	120	45	10	1	1024

At any rate, the triangle possesses many interesting properties. In counting applications, the most useful property is that, in general, entry number r in row number n is equal to $_nC_r$—the number of *combinations* of n things taken r at a time. This correspondence is shown through row 8 in **Table 6.**

Table 6 Combination Values in Pascal's Triangle

Row Number									
0					$_0C_0$				
1				$_1C_0$		$_1C_1$			
2			$_2C_0$		$_2C_1$		$_2C_2$		
3		$_3C_0$		$_3C_1$		$_3C_2$		$_3C_3$	
4	$_4C_0$		$_4C_1$		$_4C_2$		$_4C_3$		$_4C_4$
5	$_5C_0$	$_5C_1$		$_5C_2$		$_5C_3$		$_5C_4$	$_5C_5$
6	$_6C_0$	$_6C_1$	$_6C_2$		$_6C_3$		$_6C_4$	$_6C_5$	$_6C_6$
7	$_7C_0$	$_7C_1$	$_7C_2$	$_7C_3$		$_7C_4$	$_7C_5$	$_7C_6$	$_7C_7$
8	$_8C_0$	$_8C_1$	$_8C_2$	$_8C_3$	$_8C_4$	$_8C_5$	$_8C_6$	$_8C_7$	$_8C_8$

The entries in color correspond to those examined earlier in **Table 5.** Having a copy of Pascal's triangle handy gives us another option for evaluating combinations. Any time we need to know the number of combinations of n things taken r at a time, we can simply read entry number r of row number n. ***Keep in mind that the first row shown is row number 0.*** Also, the first entry of each row can be called entry number 0. This entry gives the number of subsets of size 0, which is always 1 because there is only one empty set.

Applications

EXAMPLE 1 **Applying Pascal's Triangle to Counting People**

A group of ten people includes six women and four men. If five of these people are randomly selected to fill out a questionnaire, how many different samples of five people are possible?

This **Japanese version** of the triangle dates from the eighteenth century. The "stick numerals" evolved from bamboo counting pieces used on a ruled board. Possibly Omar Khayyam, twelfth-century Persian mathematician and poet, may also have divined its patterns in pursuit of algebraic solutions. (The triangle lists the coefficients of the binomial expansion, explained in **For Further Thought** at the end of this section.)

Solution

This is simply a matter of selecting a subset of five from a set of ten, which is the number of combinations of ten things taken five at a time.

$$_{10}C_5 = 252 \quad \text{See row 10 of Pascal's triangle in } \textbf{Table 5.}$$

EXAMPLE 2 Applying Pascal's Triangle to Counting People

Among the 252 possible samples of five people in **Example 1,** how many of them would consist of exactly two women and three men?

Solution

Two women can be selected from six women in $_6C_2$ different ways, and three men can be selected from four men in $_4C_3$ different ways. These combination values can be read from Pascal's triangle. Then, since the task of obtaining two women and three men requires both individual parts, the fundamental counting principle tells us to multiply the two values.

$$_6C_2 \cdot {}_4C_3 = 15 \cdot 4 = 60 \quad \text{Rows 6 and 4 of Pascal's triangle}$$

EXAMPLE 3 Applying Pascal's Triangle to Coin Tossing

If five fair coins are tossed, in how many different ways could exactly three heads be obtained?

Solution

There are various "ways" of obtaining exactly three heads because the three heads can occur on different subsets of the coins. For example, hhtht and thhth are just two of many possibilities. When such a possibility is written down, exactly three positions are occupied by an h, the other two by a t. Each distinct way of choosing three positions from a set of five positions gives a different possibility. (Once the three positions for h are determined, each of the other two positions automatically receives a t.)

So our answer is just the number of size-three subsets of a size-five set—that is, the number of combinations of five things taken three at a time.

$$_5C_3 = 10 \quad \text{Row 5 of Pascal's triangle}$$

Notice that row 5 of Pascal's triangle also provides answers to several other questions about tossing five fair coins. They are summarized in **Table 7.**

The Pascal Identity We know that each interior entry in Pascal's triangle can be obtained by adding the two numbers just above it (to the left and right). This fact, known as the "Pascal identity," can be written as

$$_nC_r = {}_{n-1}C_{r-1} + {}_{n-1}C_r.$$

The factorial formula for combinations (along with some algebra) can be used to prove the Pascal identity.

Table 7 Tossing Five Fair Coins

Number of Heads n	Ways of Obtaining Exactly n Heads	Listing
0	$_5C_0 = 1$	ttttt
1	$_5C_1 = 5$	htttt, thttt, tthtt, tttht, tttth
2	$_5C_2 = 10$	hhttt, hthtt, httht, htttt, thhtt, ththt, thtth, tthht, tthth, ttthh
3	$_5C_3 = 10$	hhhtt, hhtht, hhtth, hthht, hthth, htthh, thhht, thhth, ththh, tthhh
4	$_5C_4 = 5$	hhhht, hhhth, hhthh, hthhh, thhhh
5	$_5C_5 = 1$	hhhhh

To analyze the tossing of a different number of fair coins, we can simply take the pertinent numbers from a different row of Pascal's triangle. Repeated coin tossing is an example of a "binomial" experiment because each toss has *two* possible outcomes:

heads and tails.

FOR FURTHER THOUGHT

The Binomial Theorem

The combination values that make up Pascal's triangle also arise in a totally different mathematical context. In algebra, "binomial" refers to a two-term expression such as

$$x + y, \quad \text{or} \quad a + 2b, \quad \text{or} \quad w^3 - 4.$$

The first few powers of the binomial $x + y$ are shown here.

$$(x + y)^0 = 1$$
$$(x + y)^1 = x + y$$
$$(x + y)^2 = x^2 + 2xy + y^2$$
$$(x + y)^3 = x^3 + 3x^2y + 3xy^2 + y^3$$
$$(x + y)^4 = x^4 + 4x^3y + 6x^2y^2 + 4xy^3 + y^4$$
$$(x + y)^5 = x^5 + 5x^4y + 10x^3y^2 + 10x^2y^3$$
$$+ 5xy^4 + y^5$$

The numerical coefficients of these expansions form the first six rows of Pascal's triangle. In our study of counting, we have called these numbers combinations, but in the study of algebra, they are called **binomial coefficients** and are usually denoted

$$\binom{n}{r} \quad \text{rather than} \quad {}_nC_r.$$

Generalizing the pattern of the powers yields the important result known as the **binomial theorem**.

Binomial Theorem

For any whole number n,

$$(x + y)^n$$

$$= \binom{n}{0} \cdot x^n + \binom{n}{1} \cdot x^{n-1}y$$

$$+ \binom{n}{2} \cdot x^{n-2}y^2 + \binom{n}{3} \cdot x^{n-3}y^3 +$$

$$\cdots + \binom{n}{n-1} \cdot xy^{n-1} + \binom{n}{n} \cdot y^n.$$

Here each binomial coefficient can be calculated by the formula

$$\binom{n}{r} = \frac{n!}{r!(n - r)!}.$$

If $n = 0$, then the first coefficient shown in the expansion is, at the same time, the last coefficient, for

$$\binom{n}{0} \cdot x^n = \binom{0}{0} \cdot x^0 = \frac{0!}{0! \cdot 0!} \cdot 1 = 1,$$

and

$$\binom{n}{n} \cdot y^n = \binom{0}{0} \cdot y^0 = \frac{0!}{0! \cdot 0!} \cdot 1 = 1.$$

EXAMPLE   Applying the Binomial Theorem

Write out the binomial expansion for $(2a + 5)^4$.

Solution

We take the initial coefficients from row 4 of Pascal's triangle and then simplify algebraically.

$$(2a + 5)^4$$

$$= \binom{4}{0} \cdot (2a)^4 + \binom{4}{1} \cdot (2a)^3 \cdot 5$$

$$+ \binom{4}{2} \cdot (2a)^2 \cdot 5^2 + \binom{4}{3} \cdot (2a) \cdot 5^3$$

$$+ \binom{4}{4} \cdot 5^4$$

> Recall that $(xy)^n = x^n \cdot y^n$.

$$= 1 \cdot 2^4 \cdot a^4 + 4 \cdot 2^3 \cdot a^3 \cdot 5 + 6 \cdot 2^2 \cdot a^2 \cdot 5^2$$

$$+ 4 \cdot 2 \cdot a \cdot 5^3 + 1 \cdot 5^4$$

$$= 16a^4 + 160a^3 + 600a^2 + 1000a + 625 \quad \blacksquare$$

For Group or Individual Investigation

Write out the binomial expansion for each of the following powers. (*Hint:* $-b$ can written $+(-b)$.)

1. $(x + y)^6$
2. $(x + y)^7$
3. $(a - b)^4$
4. $(a - b)^5$
5. $(2x + 1)^4$
6. $(3y + 2)^3$

10.4 EXERCISES

Read each combination value directly from Pascal's triangle.

1. $_4C_2$ **2.** $_5C_3$ **3.** $_6C_3$ **4.** $_7C_5$

5. $_8C_5$ **6.** $_9C_6$ **7.** $_9C_2$ **8.** $_{10}C_7$

Selecting Committees of Congressmembers   A committee of four Congressmembers will be selected from a group of seven Democrats and three Republicans. Find the number of ways of obtaining each result.

9. exactly one Democrat

10. exactly two Democrats

11. exactly three Democrats

12. exactly four Democrats

Tossing Coins   Suppose eight fair coins are tossed. Find the number of ways of obtaining each result.

13. exactly three heads

14. exactly four heads

15. exactly five heads

16. exactly six heads

Selecting Classrooms   Diana is searching for her ecology class and knows that it must be in one of nine classrooms. Since the professor does not allow people to enter after the class has begun, and there is very little time left, she decides to try just four of the rooms at random.

17. How many different selections of four rooms are possible?

18. How many of the selections of **Exercise 17** will fail to locate the class?

19. How many of the selections of **Exercise 17** will succeed in locating the class?

20. What fraction of the possible selections will lead to "success"? (Give three decimal places.)

For a set of five objects, find the number of different subsets of each size. (Use row 5 of Pascal's triangle to find the answers.)

21. 0   **22.** 1   **23.** 2

24. 3   **25.** 4   **26.** 5

27. How many subsets (of any size) are there for a set of five elements?

28. For a given row in Pascal's triangle, let n be the row number and let s be the row sum.

     (a) Write an equation relating s and n.

     (b) Explain the relationship in part (a).

29. Which rows of Pascal's triangle have a single greatest entry?

30. What is the least four-digit number in Pascal's triangle? (*Mathematics Teacher* calendar problem)

Patterns in Pascal's Triangle   Over the years, many interesting patterns have been discovered in Pascal's triangle. We explore a few of them in Exercises 31–37.

31. Refer to **Table 5**.

     (a) Choose a row whose row number is prime. Except for the 1s in this row, what is true of all the other entries?

     (b) Choose a second prime row number and see if the same pattern holds.

     (c) Use the usual method to construct row 11 in **Table 5**. Verify that the same pattern holds.

32. Name the next five numbers of the diagonal sequence in the figure. What are these numbers called? (See **Section 1.2**.)

```
              1
           1     1
        1     2     1
     1     3     3     1
  1     4     6     4     1
1     5    10    10     5     1
```

33. Complete the sequence of sums on the diagonals shown in the figure. What pattern do these sums make? What is the name of this important sequence of numbers? The presence of this sequence in the triangle apparently was not recognized by Pascal.

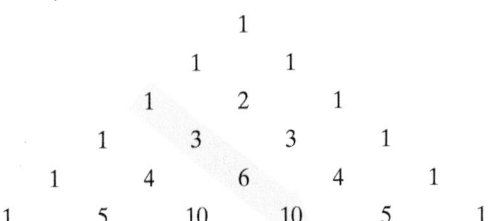

34. Construct another "triangle" by replacing every number in Pascal's triangle (rows **0** through **5**) by the remainder when it is divided by 2. What special property is shared by rows **2** and **4** of this new triangle?

35. What is the next row that would have the same property as rows **2** and **4** in **Exercise 34**?

36. (Work **Exercises 34 and 35** first.) How many even numbers are there in row **256** of Pascal's triangle?

37. The figure shows a portion of Pascal's triangle with several inverted triangular regions outlined. For any one of these regions, what can be said of the sum of the squares of the entries across its top row?

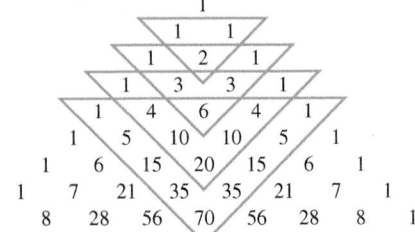

38. *Tartaglia's Rectangle* More than a century before Pascal's treatise on the triangle appeared, a work by the Italian mathematician Niccolo Tartaglia (1506–1559) came out and included the table of numbers shown here.

1	1	1	1	1	1
1	2	3	4	5	6
1	3	6	10	15	21
1	4	10	20	35	56
1	5	15	35	70	126
1	6	21	56	126	252
1	7	28	84	210	462
1	8	36	120	330	792

Explain the connection between Pascal's triangle and Tartaglia's rectangle.

Tartaglia's Rectangle The triangle that Pascal studied and published in his treatise was actually more like a truncated corner of Tartaglia's rectangle, as shown here.

1	1	1	1	1	1	1	1	1	1
1	2	3	4	5	6	7	8	9	
1	3	6	10	15	21	28	36		
1	4	10	20	35	56	84			
1	5	15	35	70	126				
1	6	21	56	126					
1	7	28	84						
1	8	36							
1	9								
1									

Each number in the truncated corner of Tartaglia's rectangle can be calculated in various ways. In each of Exercises 39–42, consider the number N to be located anywhere in the array. By checking several locations in the given array, determine how N is related to the sum of all entries in the shaded cells. Describe the relationship in words.

39.

40.

41.

42.

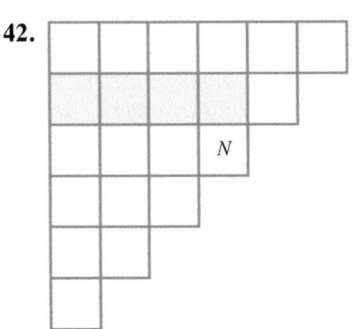

10.5 COUNTING PROBLEMS INVOLVING "NOT" AND "OR"

OBJECTIVES

1 Understand the complements principle of counting.

2 Apply the complements principle to a counting problem by considering the problem in terms of outcomes that do not occur (a "not" statement).

3 Understand the additive principle of counting.

4 Apply the additive principle to a counting problem by considering the problem in terms of the union of two outcomes (an "or" statement).

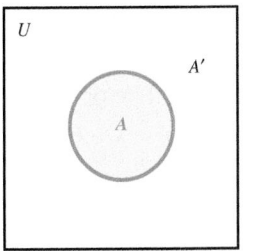

U

A'

A

The complement of a set
Figure 8

Set Theory/Logic/Arithmetic Correspondences

The counting techniques in this section, which can be thought of as *indirect techniques*, are based on some useful correspondences from **Chapters 2 and 3** among set theory, logic, and arithmetic, as shown in **Table 8.**

Table 8 Correspondences

	Set Theory	Logic	Arithmetic
Operation or Connective (Symbol)	Complement ($'$)	Not ($\sim$)	Subtraction ($-$)
Operation or Connective (Symbol)	Union ($\cup$)	Or ($\vee$)	Addition ($+$)

Problems Involving "Not"

Suppose U is the set of all possible results of some type. The "universal set U" comprises all possibilities, as discussed in **Chapter 2.** Let A be the set of all those results that satisfy a given condition. For any set S, its cardinal number is written $n(S)$, and its complement is written S'. **Figure 8** suggests that

$$n(A) + n(A') = n(U).$$

Also, $$n(A) = n(U) - n(A') \quad \text{and} \quad n(A') = n(U) - n(A).$$

We focus here on the form that expresses the following indirect counting principle based on the complement/not/subtraction correspondence from **Table 8.**

COMPLEMENTS PRINCIPLE OF COUNTING

The number of ways in which a certain condition can be satisfied is the total number of possible results minus the number of ways the condition would **not** be satisfied. Symbolically, if A is any set within the universal set U, then the following formula holds.

$$n(A) = n(U) - n(A')$$

EXAMPLE 1 Counting the Proper Subsets of a Set

A **proper subset** of a set S is a subset that is not S itself. For the set $S = \{a, b, c, d, e, f\}$, find the number of proper subsets.

Solution

A proper subset of S is any subset with fewer than all six elements. Subsets of several different sizes would satisfy this condition. Consider the one subset that is not proper, namely S itself. From set theory, we know that set S has a total of

$$2^6 = 64 \text{ subsets.}$$

Thus, from the complements principle, the number of proper subsets is

$$64 - 1 = 63.$$

In words, the number of subsets that *are* proper is the total number of subsets minus the number of subsets that are *not* proper. ∎

Proper Subsets As an illustration, the proper subsets of $\{a, b\}$ are

$$\{a\}, \quad \{b\}, \quad \text{and} \quad \varnothing.$$

Consider the tossing of three fair coins. Since each coin will land either heads (h) or tails (t), the possible results can be listed as follows.

hhh, hht, hth, thh, htt, tht, tth, ttt   Results of tossing three fair coins

Even without the listing, we could have concluded that there would be eight possibilities. There are two possible outcomes for each coin, so the fundamental counting principle gives

$$2 \cdot 2 \cdot 2 = 2^3 = 8.$$

Suppose we wanted the number of ways of obtaining *at least* one head. In this case, "at least one" means one or two or three. Rather than dealing with all three cases, we can note that "at least one" is the opposite (or complement) of "fewer than one", which is zero. Because there is only one way to get zero heads (ttt), and there are a total of eight possibilities, the complements principle gives the number of ways of getting at least one head.

$$8 - 1 = 7 \text{ ways}$$

Indirect counting methods can often be applied to problems involving "at least," or "at most," or "less than," or "more than."

EXAMPLE 2 Counting Coin-Tossing Results

If four fair coins are tossed, in how many ways can at least one tail be obtained?

Solution

By the fundamental counting principle, $2^4 = 16$ different results are possible. Exactly one of these fails to satisfy the condition of "at least one tail," and that is hhhh. So the answer from the complements principle is

$$16 - 1 = 15.$$ ∎

EXAMPLE 3 Counting Selections of Airliner Seats

Carol and three friends are boarding an airliner. There are only ten seats left, three of which are aisle seats. How many ways can the four friends arrange themselves in available seats so that at least one of them sits on the aisle?

Solution

The word "arrange" implies that order is important, so we use permutations. "At least one aisle seat" is the opposite (complement) of "no aisle seats." The total number of ways to arrange four people among ten seats is

$$_{10}P_4 = 5040.$$

The number of ways to arrange four people among seven (non-aisle) seats is

$$_7P_4 = 840.$$

Therefore, by the complements principle, the number of arrangements with at least one aisle seat is followed by subtracting.

$$\overset{_{10}P_4}{\downarrow} \qquad \overset{_7P_4}{\downarrow}$$
$$5040 - 840 = 4200$$ ∎

```
(10 nPr 4)−(7 nPr 4)
                 4200
(13 nCr 5)+(26 nCr 5)
                67067
```

Results in **Examples 3 and 4** are supported in this screen.

Nondisjoint sets
Figure 9

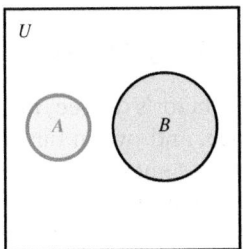

Disjoint sets
Figure 10

Problems Involving "Or"

The complements principle is one way of counting indirectly. Another technique is to count the elements of a set by breaking that set into simpler component parts. If

$$S = A \cup B,$$

the cardinal number formula from **Section 2.4** says to find the number of elements in S by adding the number in A to the number in B. We must then subtract the number in the intersection $A \cap B$ if A and B are not disjoint, as in **Figure 9**. But if A and B are disjoint, as in **Figure 10**, the subtraction is not necessary.

The following principle reflects the union/or/addition correspondence from **Table 8.**

ADDITIVE PRINCIPLE OF COUNTING

The number of ways that one **or** the other of two conditions could be satisfied is the number of ways one of them could be satisfied plus the number of ways the other could be satisfied, minus the number of ways they could both be satisfied together.

Symbolically, **if A and B are any two sets, then**

$$n(A \cup B) = n(A) + n(B) - n(A \cap B).$$

If sets A and B are disjoint, then

$$n(A \cup B) = n(A) + n(B).$$

▌EXAMPLE 4 Counting Card Hands

How many five-card poker hands consist of either all clubs or all red cards?

Solution

No hand that satisfies one of these conditions could also satisfy the other, so the two sets of possibilities (all **clubs,** all **red** cards) are disjoint. Therefore, the second formula of the additive principle applies.

$n(\text{all } \textbf{clubs} \text{ or all } \textbf{red} \text{ cards}) = n(\text{all } \textbf{clubs}) + n(\text{all } \textbf{red} \text{ cards})$ Additive counting principle

$\qquad = {}_{13}C_5 + {}_{26}C_5$ 13 clubs, 26 red cards

$\qquad = \textbf{1287} + 65{,}780$ Substitute values.

$\qquad = 67{,}067$ Add. ∎

▌EXAMPLE 5 Counting Selections from a Diplomatic Delegation

Table 9 categorizes a diplomatic delegation of 18 congressional members as to political party and gender. If one of the members is chosen randomly to be spokesperson for the group, in how many ways could that person be a Democrat (D) or a woman (W)?

Table 9

	Men (M)	Women (W)	Totals
Republican (R)	5	3	8
Democrat (D)	4	6	10
Totals	9	9	18

Solution

D and W are not disjoint because 6 delegates are both Democrats and women. The first formula of the additive principle is required.

$$n(D \text{ or } W) = n(D \cup W) \qquad \text{Union/or correspondence}$$

$$= n(D) + n(W) - n(D \cap W) \qquad \text{Additive principle}$$

$$= 10 + 9 - 6 \qquad \text{Substitute values.}$$

$$= 13 \qquad \text{Add and subtract.} \qquad \blacksquare$$

EXAMPLE 6 Counting Course Selections for a Degree Program

Chrissy needs to take twelve more specific courses for a bachelor's degree, including four in math, three in physics, three in computer science, and two in business. If five courses are randomly chosen from these twelve for next semester's program, how many of the possible selections would include at least two math courses?

Solution

Of all the information given here, what is important is that there are four math courses and eight other courses to choose from, and that five of them are being selected for next semester. If T denotes the set of selections that include at least two math courses, then we can write

$$T = A \cup B \cup C,$$

where $A =$ the set of selections with exactly two math courses

$B =$ the set of selections with exactly three math courses

$C =$ the set of selections with exactly four math courses.

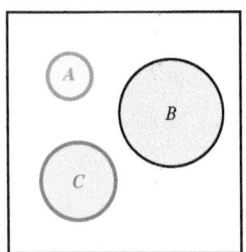

$T = A \cup B \cup C$
Figure 11

In this case, *at least two* means exactly two **or** exactly three **or** exactly four. The situation is illustrated in **Figure 11.** By previous methods, we know that

Two math courses $\longrightarrow$ $n(A) = {}_4C_2 \cdot {}_8C_3 = 6 \cdot 56 = 336$ In each case, $8 = 12 - 4$.

Three math courses $\longrightarrow$ $n(B) = {}_4C_3 \cdot {}_8C_2 = 4 \cdot 28 = 112$ In each case, the sum of the numbers

Four math courses $\longrightarrow$ $n(C) = {}_4C_4 \cdot {}_8C_1 = 1 \cdot 8 = 8.$ in red is 5.

By the additive principle,

$$n(T) = 336 + 112 + 8 = 456. \qquad \blacksquare$$

EXAMPLE 7 Counting Three-Digit Numbers with Conditions

How many three-digit counting numbers are multiples of 2 or multiples of 5?

Solution

- A multiple of 2 must end in an even digit $(0, 2, 4, 6, \text{ or } 8)$, so there are $9 \cdot 10 \cdot 5 = 450$ three-digit multiples of 2.

- A multiple of 5 must end in 0 or 5, so there are $9 \cdot 10 \cdot 2 = 180$ of those.

- A multiple of both 2 and 5 is a multiple of 10 and must end in 0. There are $9 \cdot 10 \cdot 1 = 90$ of those.

By the additive principle, there are

$$450 + 180 - 90 = 540$$

possible three-digit numbers that are multiples of 2 or multiples of 5. $\qquad \blacksquare$

EXAMPLE 8   Counting Card-Drawing Results

A single card is drawn from a standard 52-card deck.

(a) In how many ways could it be a heart or a king?

(b) In how many ways could it be a club or a face card?

Solution

(a) A single card can be both a heart and a king (the king of hearts), so use the first additive formula. There are thirteen hearts, four kings, and one card that is both a heart and a king.

$$13 + 4 - 1 = 16 \quad \text{Additive principle}$$

(b) There are 13 clubs, 12 face cards, and 3 cards that are both clubs and face cards.

$$13 + 12 - 3 = 22 \quad \text{Additive principle}$$

EXAMPLE 9   Counting Subsets of a Set with Conditions

How many subsets of a 25-element set have more than three elements?

Solution

It would be a real job to count directly all subsets of size 4, 5, 6, . . . , 25. It is much easier to count those with three or fewer elements and apply the complements principle.

- There is $_{25}C_0 = 1$ size-0 subset.
- There are $_{25}C_1 = 25$ size-1 subsets.
- There are $_{25}C_2 = 300$ size-2 subsets.
- There are $_{25}C_3 = 2300$ size-3 subsets.

Use a calculator to find that the total number of subsets of all sizes, 0 through 25, is $2^{25} = 33{,}554{,}432$. So the number with more than three elements must be

$$33{,}554{,}432 - \underbrace{(1 + 25 + 300 + 2300)}_{\text{Additive principle}} = 33{,}554{,}432 - 2626$$
$$= 33{,}551{,}806. \quad \text{Complements principle}$$

10.5   EXERCISES

How many proper subsets are there of each set?

1. $\{A, B, C, D\}$

2. $\{u, v, w, x, y, z\}$

3. $\{1, 2, 3, 4, 5, 6, 7\}$

4. $\{a, b, c, \ldots , j\}$

Tossing Coins *If you toss seven fair coins, in how many ways can you obtain each result?*

5. at least one head
("At least one" is the complement of "none.")

6. at least two heads
("At least two" is the complement of "zero or one.")

7. at least two tails

8. at least one of each (a head and a tail)

Rolling Dice *If you roll two fair dice (say red and green), in how many ways can you obtain each result? (Refer to* **Table 2** *in Section 10.1.)*

9. at least 2 on the green die

10. a sum of at least 3

11. a 4 on at least one of the dice

12. a different number on each die

Drawing Cards *If you draw a single card from a standard 52-card deck, in how many ways can you obtain each result?*

13. a card other than the ace of spades

14. a nonface card

15. a card other than a ten

16. a card other than a jack or queen

Identifying Properties of Counting Numbers *How many two-digit counting numbers meet each requirement?*

17. not a multiple of 10

18. not a multiple of 20

19. greater than 70 or a multiple of 10

20. less than 30 or a multiple of 20

21. ***Choosing Country Music Albums*** Jeanne's collection of ten country music albums includes *Sundown Heaven Town*, by Tim McGraw. She will choose three of her albums to play on a drive to Nashville. (Assume order is not important.)

  (a) How many different sets of three albums could she choose?

  (b) How many of these sets would not include *Sundown Heaven Town*?

  (c) How many of them would include *Sundown Heaven Town*?

22. ***Choosing Broadway Hits*** The ten longest Broadway runs include *The Phantom of the Opera* and *Les Misérables*. Four of the ten are chosen randomly. (Assume order is not important.)

  (a) How many ways can the four be chosen?

  (b) How many of those groups of four would include neither of the two productions mentioned?

  (c) How many of them would include at least one of the two productions mentioned?

23. ***Choosing Days of the Week*** How many different ways could three distinct days of the week be chosen so that at least one of them begins with the letter S? (Assume order of selection is not important.)

24. ***Choosing School Assignments for Completion*** Diona has nine major assignments to complete for school this week. Two of them involve writing essays. Diona decides to work on two of the nine assignments tonight. How many different choices of two would include at least one essay assignment? (Assume order is not important.)

Selecting Restaurants *Jason wants to dine at four different restaurants during a summer getaway. If three of eight available restaurants serve seafood, find the number of ways that at least one of the selected restaurants will serve seafood given the following conditions.*

25. The order of selection is important.

26. The order of selection is not important.

27. ***Seating Arrangements on an Airliner*** Refer to **Example 3.** If one of the group decided at the last minute not to fly, then how many ways could the remaining three arrange themselves among the ten available seats so that at least one of them would sit on the aisle?

28. ***Identifying Properties of Counting Numbers*** Find the number of four-digit counting numbers containing at least one zero, under each of the following conditions.

  (a) Repeated digits are allowed.

  (b) Repeated digits are not allowed.

29. ***Counting Radio Call Letters*** Radio stations in the United States have call letters that begin with either K or W. Some have a total of three letters, and others have four letters. How many different call letter combinations are possible? Count all possibilities even though, practically, some may be inappropriate. (*Mathematics Teacher* calendar problem) (*Hint:* Do *not* apply combinations.)?

30. ***Selecting Faculty Committees*** A committee of four faculty members will be selected from a department of twenty-five, which includes professors Fontana and Spradley. In how many ways could the committee include at least one of these two professors?

31. Selecting Search-and-Rescue Teams A Civil Air Patrol unit of twelve members includes four officers. In how many ways can four members be selected for a search-and-rescue mission such that at least one officer is included?

32. Choosing Team Members Three students from a class of 12 will form a math contest team that must include at least 1 boy and at least 1 girl. If 160 different teams can be formed from the 12 students, which of the following can be the difference between the number of boys and the number of girls in the class?

A. 0 **B.** 2 **C.** 4 **D.** 6 **E.** 8

(*Mathematics Teacher* calendar problem)

Drawing Cards *If a single card is drawn from a standard 52-card deck, in how many ways could it be the following? (Use the additive principle.)*

33. a club or a jack

34. a heart or a ten

35. a face card or a black card

36. an ace or a red card

Choosing Senators *The table categorizes 20 senators as to political party and gender.*

	Men (*M*)	Women (*W*)	Totals
Democrat (*D*)	8	4	12
Republican (*R*)	3	5	8
Totals	11	9	20

One member is chosen at random. In how many ways can the chosen person be as described?

37. a woman or a Republican

38. a man or a Democrat

39. a man or a Republican woman

40. a woman or a Democrat man

Counting Card Hands *Among the 2,598,960 possible 5-card poker hands from a standard 52-card deck, how many contain the following cards?*

41. at least one card that is not a heart (complement of "all hearts")

42. cards of more than one suit (complement of "all the same suit")

43. at least one face card (complement of "no face cards")

44. at least one club, but not all clubs (complement of "no clubs or all clubs")

45. Selecting Doughnuts A doughnut shop has a special on its Mix-n-Match selection, which allows customers to select three doughnuts from among the following varieties: plain, maple, frosted, chocolate, glazed, and jelly. How many different Mix-n-Match selections are possible? (*Mathematics Teacher* calendar problem)

46. Rolling Three Dice Three fair, standard six-faced dice of different colors are rolled. In how many ways can the dice be rolled such that the sum of the numbers rolled is 10? (*Mathematics Teacher* calendar problem)

The Size of Subsets of a Set *If a set has ten elements, how many of its subsets have the given numbers of elements?*

47. at most two elements

48. at least eight elements

49. more than two elements

50. from three through seven elements

51. Counting License Numbers If license numbers consist of two letters followed by three digits, how many different licenses could be created having at least one letter or digit repeated? (*Hint:* Use the complements principle of counting.)

52. Drawing Cards If two cards are drawn from a 52-card deck without replacement (that is, the first card is not replaced in the deck before the second card is drawn), in how many different ways is it possible to obtain a king on the first draw and a heart on the second? (*Hint:* Split this event into the two disjoint components "king of hearts and then another heart" and "non-heart king and then heart." Use the fundamental counting principle on each component and then apply the additive principle.)

53. Extend the additive counting principle to three overlapping sets (as in the figure) to show that

$$n(A \cup B \cup C) = n(A) + n(B) + n(C)$$
$$- n(A \cap B) - n(A \cap C)$$
$$- n(B \cap C) + n(A \cap B \cap C).$$

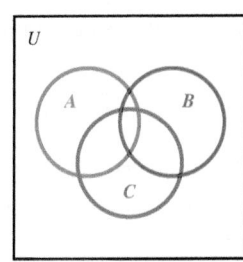

54. How many of the counting numbers 1 through 300 are *not* divisible by 2, 3, or 5? (*Hint:* Use the complements principle and the result of **Exercise 53**.)

Selecting National Monuments and Parks to Visit *Megan is planning a driving tour. Although she is interested in seeing the twelve national monuments and parks listed here, she will have to settle for seeing just three of them.*

New Mexico	Arizona	California
Gila Cliff Dwellings	Canyon de Chelly	Devils Postpile
Petroglyph	Organ Pipe Cactus	Joshua Tree
White Sands	Grand Canyon	Lava Beds
Aztec Ruins		Sequoia
		Yosemite

In how many ways could the three sites chosen include the following? (Assume that order of selection is not important.)

55. sites in only one state

56. at least one site not in California

57. sites in fewer than all three states

58. sites in exactly two of the three states

Counting Categories of Poker Hands **Table 4** *in this chapter (***For Further Thought** *in* **Section 10.3***) described the various kinds of hands in 5-card poker. Verify each statement in Exercises 59–62. (Explain all steps of your argument.)*

59. There are four ways to get a royal flush.

60. There are 36 ways to get a straight flush.

61. There are 10,200 ways to get a straight.

62. There are 54,912 ways to get three of a kind.

CHAPTER 10 SUMMARY

KEY TERMS

10.1
counting
one-part task
two-part task
product table

10.2
uniformity criterion
fundamental counting
    principle
n factorial

distinguishable
    arrangements

10.3
permutation
combination

10.4
Pascal's triangle
binomial coefficients
binomial theorem

NEW SYMBOLS

$n!$ n factorial
$_nP_r, P(n, r), P_r^n$ permutations of n things taken r at a time

$_nC_r, C(n, r), C_r^n, \binom{n}{r}$ combinations of n things taken r at a time

TEST YOUR WORD POWER

See how well you have learned the vocabulary of this chapter.

1. In counting, a **product table** can be used to analyze
  A. a one-part task.
  B. a two-part task.
  C. a problem involving distinguishable
    arrangements.
  D. a problem involving Pascal's triangle.

2. The **factorial** of a natural number n is found by
  A. multiplying all the natural numbers less than or
    equal to n.
  B. adding all the natural numbers less than or equal to n.
  C. multiplying n by $n + 1$.
  D. multiplying n by $n - 1$.

3. A **permutation** of a group of objects

    A. is a subset of those objects where order is not important.

    B. is a proper subset of those objects.

    C. is an arrangement of those objects where order is important.

    D. is exemplified by a hand of cards in poker.

4. A **combination** of a group of objects

    A. is a subset of those objects.

    B. is exactly the same as a permutation of those objects.

    C. is an arrangement of those objects where order is important.

    D. is exemplified by the process of opening a combination lock.

ANSWERS
1. B **2.** A **3.** C **4.** A

QUICK REVIEW

Concepts	*Examples*

10.1 Counting by Systematic Listing

Systematic Listing Methods

Two methods for listing the possible results of a two-part task are

(1) constructing a product table, and

(2) constructing a tree diagram.

Tree diagrams can be extended to tasks with three or more parts as well.

Construct a tree diagram showing all possible results when a die is rolled and a coin is tossed. How many possibilities are there?

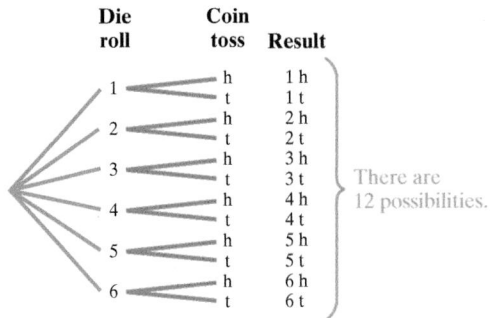

List the ways in which the die roll is even and the coin toss is heads.

$$2h, \quad 4h, \quad 6h$$

10.2 Using the Fundamental Counting Principle

Uniformity Criterion

A multiple-part task is said to satisfy the uniformity criterion if the number of choices for any particular part is the same *no matter which choices were selected for previous parts.*

If each of two adjacent switches are to be set on or off, uniformity applies if there are no restrictions. However, it does not apply if, say, they must not both be off.

Fundamental Counting Principle

When a task consists of k separate parts and satisfies the uniformity criterion, if the first part can be done in n_1 ways, the second part can then be done in n_2 ways, and so on through the kth part, which can be done in n_k ways, then the total number of ways to complete the task is given by the following product.

$$n_1 \cdot n_2 \cdot n_3 \cdot \ldots \cdot n_k$$

How many ways are there to choose a meal from 3 salads, 6 entrees, and 4 desserts?

$$3 \cdot 6 \cdot 4 = 72 \text{ ways}$$

Concepts	*Examples*

Factorial Formula

For any counting number n, the quantity **n factorial** is defined as follows.

$$n! = n \cdot (n - 1) \cdot (n - 2) \cdot \ldots \cdot 2 \cdot 1$$

By definition, $0! = 1$.

Evaluate each factorial.

$$5! = 5 \cdot 4 \cdot 3 \cdot 2 \cdot 1 = 120$$

$$3! \cdot 4 = (3 \cdot 2 \cdot 1) \cdot 4 = 24$$

$$\frac{8!}{6!} = \frac{8 \cdot 7 \cdot 6 \cdot 5 \cdot 4 \cdot 3 \cdot 2 \cdot 1}{6 \cdot 5 \cdot 4 \cdot 3 \cdot 2 \cdot 1} = 8 \cdot 7 = 56$$

Arrangements of n Distinct Objects

The total number of different ways to arrange n distinct objects is **$n!$.**

How many ways are there to arrange the letters of ROBIN?

There are 5 distinct letters, so there are

$$5! = 120 \text{ ways.}$$

Arrangements of n Objects Containing Look-Alikes

The number of distinguishable arrangements of n objects, where one or more subsets consist of look-alikes (say n_1 are of one kind, n_2 are of another kind, . . . , and n_k are of yet another kind), is given by

$$\frac{n!}{n_1! \cdot n_2! \cdot \ldots \cdot n_k!}.$$

How many distinguishable arrangements are there of the letters of MAMMOGRAM?

Of the 9 letters total, 4 are M and 2 are A. So there are

$$\frac{9!}{4! \cdot 2!} = 7560 \text{ distinguishable arrangements.}$$

10.3 Using Permutations and Combinations

Factorial Formula for Permutations

The number of permutations, or arrangements, of n distinct things taken r at a time, where $r \leq n$, can be calculated as follows.

$$_nP_r = \frac{n!}{(n - r)!}$$

How many arrangements of the letters

$$\text{W, H, I, T, E, S, U, G, A, R}$$

are there if they are taken 4 at a time?

There are 10 different letters. We use the permutations formula because order matters.

$$_{10}P_4 = \frac{10!}{(10 - 4)!} = \frac{10!}{6!} = 5040$$

Factorial Formula for Combinations

The number of combinations, or subsets, of n distinct things taken r at a time, where $r \leq n$, can be calculated as follows.

$$_nC_r = \frac{_nP_r}{r!} = \frac{n!}{r!(n - r)!}$$

How many committees of 3 politicians can be formed from a pool of 11 politicians?

We use the combinations formula because order does not matter.

$$_{11}C_3 = \frac{11!}{3! (11 - 3)!} = \frac{11!}{3! \cdot 8!} = 165$$

10.4 Using Pascal's Triangle

Pascal's Triangle

```
              1
           1     1
        1     2     1
     1     3     3     1
  1     4     6     4     1
1     5    10    10     5     1       (6 + 4 = 10)
1   6   15   20   15   6   1
```

If six fair coins are tossed, in how many different ways can exactly two heads be obtained?

The entry in green in the triangle represents

$$_6C_2.$$

There are 15 ways.

(The triangle entries can be expressed in terms of $_nC_r$. See **Table 6** in Section 10.4.)

Concepts	Examples

10.5 Counting Problems Involving "Not" and "Or"

Complements Principle of Counting
The number of ways a certain condition can be satisfied is the total number of possible results minus the number of ways the condition would **not** be satisfied. Symbolically, if A is any set within the universal set U, then

$$n(A) = n(U) - n(A').$$

If six fair coins are tossed, in how many ways can at least one head be obtained?

There are $2^6 = 64$ total ways, and only one of them (t t t t t t) does not contain a head. So there are

$$64 - 1 = 63 \text{ ways}$$

that at least one head can be obtained.

Additive Principle of Counting
The number of ways that one **or** the other of two conditions could be satisfied is the number of ways one of them could be satisfied plus the number of ways the other could be satisfied minus the number of ways they could both be satisfied together.

Symbolically, if A and B are any two sets, then

$$n(A \cup B) = n(A) + n(B) - n(A \cap B).$$

If sets A and B are disjoint, then

$$n(A \cup B) = n(A) + n(B).$$

A single card is drawn from a standard 52-card deck. In how many ways could it be black or a face card?

There are 26 black cards, 12 face cards, and 6 black face cards. So there are

$$26 + 12 - 6 = 32 \text{ ways.}$$

CHAPTER 10   TEST

Counting Three-digit Numbers   If only the digits 0, 1, 2, 3, 4, 5, and 6 may be used, find the number of possibilities in each category.

1. three-digit numbers

2. odd three-digit numbers

3. three-digit numbers without repeated digits

4. three-digit multiples of five without repeated digits

5. *Counting Triangles in a Figure*   Determine the number of triangles (of any size) in the figure shown here.

6. *Tossing Coins*   Construct a tree diagram showing all possible results when a fair coin is tossed four times, if no two consecutive tosses can both be heads.

7. *Sums of Digits*   How many nonrepeating four-digit numbers have the sum of their digits equal to 30?

8. *Arranging Children*   Yeo has invited her sister Hae and her four best friends to her birthday party. In how many ways can the six children be arranged around a rectangular table with one child at each end and two on each side if Yeo must sit at an end seat and Hae must not sit next to Yeo?

Evaluate each expression.

9. $6!$

10. $\dfrac{8!}{6!}$

11. $_{12}P_3$

12. $_8C_5$

13. *Building Words from Sets of Letters*   How many five-letter "words" without repeated letters are possible using the English alphabet? (Assume that any five letters make a "word.")

14. *Building Words from Sets of Letters*   Using the Russian alphabet (which has 32 letters), and allowing repeated letters, how many five-letter "words" are possible?

Scheduling Assignments *Eileen has seven homework assignments to complete. She wants to do two of them on Thursday and the other five on Saturday.*

15. In how many ways can she order Thursday's work?

16. Assuming she finishes Thursday's work successfully, in how many ways can she order Saturday's work?

17. *Arranging Letters* Find the number of distinguishable arrangements of the letters of the word PIPPIN.

Selecting Groups of Basketball Players *If there are ten players on a basketball team, find the number of choices the coach has in selecting each of the following.*

18. four players to carry the team equipment

19. two players for guard positions and two for forward positions

20. five starters and five subs

21. two groups of four

22. a group of three or more of the players

Choosing Switch Settings *Determine the number of possible settings for a row of five on–off switches under each condition.*

23. There are no restrictions.

24. The first and fifth switches must be on.

25. The first and fifth switches must be set the same.

26. No two adjacent switches can both be off.

27. No two adjacent switches can be set the same.

28. At least two switches must be on.

Choosing Subsets of Letters *Three distinct letters are to be chosen from the set*

$$\{A, B, C, D, E, F, G\}.$$

Determine the number of ways to obtain a subset that includes each of the following.

29. the letter B

30. both A and E

31. either A or E, but not both

32. letters to spell the word AD

33. more consonants than vowels

34. *Assigning Student Grades* A professor teaches a class of 60 students and another class of 40 students. Five percent of the students in each class are to receive a grade of A. How many different ways can the A grades be distributed?

35. *Number of Paths from Point to Point* A transit bus can travel in only two directions, north and east. From its starting point on the map shown, determine how many paths exist to reach the garage. (*Mathematics Teacher* calendar problem)

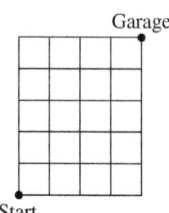

36. *Pascal's Triangle* Write down the second entry of each row of Pascal's triangle (starting with row 1). What sequence of numbers do you obtain?

Probability

The mathematics of *probability* occurs in various occupations and experiences in daily life. An important feature distinguishes probability from other topics in this text. For example, an equation such as

$$4x + 6 = 14$$

has a specific solution (in this case, 2) that we can state without reservation. Results found in probability are often theoretical—that is, we cannot say for sure what will actually happen in a certain case. We can only say what trends will occur "in the long run."

Here are a few examples.

Weather forecasts Meteorologists state the chances of rain based on data collected on days where the atmospheric conditions have been the same in the past. If the chance of rain is 90%, it's a good bet that rain will occur, but there is still a 10% chance that no rain will fall.

Insurance rates The rates that are charged on automobile or life insurance are based on data obtained from customers who fit the same basic profile. Actuarial science is devoted to analyzing data to provide information to insurance companies, which then make financial decisions based on those data.

Lotteries and casinos The *odds* favor the lottery commission and the gaming industry—games of chance are designed so that in the long run, "the house wins." Once in a while, the player wins (see **page 668**), but over a lifetime, the average gambler will likely lose.

Baseball manager History has shown that right-handed batters fare better against left-handed pitchers, and left-handed batters fare better against right-handed pitchers. Late in a close game, a manager will often make a pitching change based on this probability. This is only one instance of a manager or head coach making a decision based on the *law of averages*.

Court litigation One interesting application of probability, called the *calculus of negligence*, was mentioned in the cult movie *Fight Club*. A typical situation involves determination by a manufacturer whether to recall a product that has proved defective. The manufacturer may decide that it is financially feasible not to recall the product if

(the probability of loss in court) $\times$ (the amount of that loss)

is less than what it would cost to conduct the recall.

11.1   BASIC CONCEPTS

OBJECTIVES

1 Understand the basic terms in the language of probability.

2 Work simple problems involving theoretical and empirical probability.

3 Understand the law of large numbers (law of averages).

4 Find probabilities related to flower colors as described by Mendel in his genetics research.

5 Determine the odds in favor of an event and the odds against an event.

The Language of Probability

If you go to a supermarket and select five pounds of peaches at $2.49 per pound, you can easily predict the amount you will be charged at the checkout counter.

$$5 \cdot \$2.49 = \$12.45$$

This is an example of a **deterministic phenomenon.** It can be predicted exactly on the basis of obtainable information, namely, in this case, number of pounds and cost per pound.

On the other hand, consider the problem faced by the produce manager of the market, who must order peaches to have on hand each day without knowing exactly how many pounds customers will buy during the day. Customer demand is an example of a **random phenomenon.** It fluctuates in such a way that its value on a given day cannot be predicted exactly with obtainable information.

The study of probability is concerned with such random phenomena. Even though we cannot be certain whether a given result will occur, we often can obtain a good measure of its *likelihood*, or **probability.** This chapter discusses various ways of finding and using probabilities.

Any observation, or measurement, of a random phenomenon is an **experiment.** The possible results of the experiment are **outcomes,** and the set of all possible outcomes is the **sample space.**

Usually we are interested in some particular collection of the possible outcomes. Any such subset of the sample space is an **event.** See the Venn Diagram in **Figure 1.** Outcomes that belong to the event are "favorable outcomes," or "successes." Any time a success is observed, we say that the event has "occurred." The probability of an event, being a numerical measure of the event's likelihood, is determined in one of two ways: either *theoretically* (mathematically) or *empirically* (experimentally). We use the notation

$$P(E) \text{ to represent the probability of event } E.$$

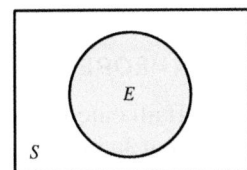

Every event *E* is a subset of the sample space *S.*

Figure 1

Examples in Probability

EXAMPLE 1 Finding Probability When Tossing a Coin

If a single coin is tossed, find the probability that it will land heads up.

Solution

There is no apparent reason for one side of a coin to land up any more often than the other (in the long run), so we assume that heads and tails are equally likely.

The experiment here is the tossing of a single fair coin, the sample space is $S = \{h, t\}$, and the event whose probability we seek is $E = \{h\}$. Since one of the two equally likely outcomes is a head, the probability of heads is the quotient of 1 and 2.

$$\text{Probability (heads)} = \frac{1}{2}, \quad \text{written} \quad P(h) = \frac{1}{2} \quad \text{or} \quad P(E) = \frac{1}{2}. \quad ■$$

EXAMPLE 2 Finding Probability When Tossing a Cup

If a Styrofoam cup is tossed, find the probability that it will land on its top.

Solution

Intuitively, it seems that such a cup will land on its side much more often than on its top or its bottom. But just how much more often is not clear. To get an idea, we performed the experiment of tossing such a cup 50 times. It landed on its side 44 times, on its top 5 times, and on its bottom just 1 time. By the frequency of "success" in this experiment, we concluded that for the cup we used,

$$P(\text{top}) \approx \frac{5}{50} = \frac{1}{10}. \quad \boxed{\text{Write in lowest terms.}} \quad ■$$

In **Example 1** involving the tossing of a fair coin, the number of possible outcomes was obviously two, both were equally likely, and one of the outcomes was a head. No actual experiment was required. The desired probability was obtained *theoretically.* Theoretical probabilities apply to dice rolling, card games, roulette, lotteries, and so on, and apparently to many phenomena in nature.

Laplace, in his famous *Analytic Theory of Probability,* published in 1812, gave a formula that applies to any such theoretical probability, as long as the sample space S is finite and all outcomes are equally likely. It is often referred to as the *classical definition of probability.*

THEORETICAL PROBABILITY FORMULA

If all outcomes in a sample space S are equally likely, and E is an event within that sample space, then the **theoretical probability** of event E is given by the following formula.

$$P(E) = \frac{\text{number of favorable outcomes}}{\text{total number of outcomes}} = \frac{n(E)}{n(S)}$$

WHEN Will I Ever USE This ?

The traditional coin flip is a tried-and-true method of making a decision when only two people (players) are involved. It is easy to see that each outcome of heads and tails has a probability of $\frac{1}{2}$. We sometimes say that "the chances are 50–50," meaning that each player has a 50% chance of winning. But suppose that we are faced with determining a winner among *three* players? *Can we use coin flipping in such a way that each player has an equal probability of winning?* The answer is yes.

The method is sometimes called "odd man wins." Each player flips a coin, and then the results are examined. If all three players show heads or all show tails, the experiment is repeated. (We are eliminating the outcomes hhh and ttt in our sample space this way.) There are 6 other possible outcomes, and each one shows 1 tail or 1 head. If a player has this "odd" result, that player is the winner. The tree diagram here shows that each player has a

$$\frac{2}{6}, \text{ or } \frac{1}{3}, \text{ probability of winning.}$$

Player A result	Player B result	Player C result	Outcome	Winner
h	h	h	h̶h̶h̶	—
h	h	t	hh(t)	C
h	t	h	h(t)h	B
h	t	t	(h)tt	A
t	h	h	(t)hh	A
t	h	t	th(t)	B
t	t	h	tt(h)	C
t	t	t	t̶t̶t̶	—

Of the 6 equally likely outcomes considered, each player wins 2 times.

On the other hand, **Example 2** involved the tossing of a cup, where the likelihoods of the various outcomes were not intuitively clear. It took an actual experiment to arrive at a probability value of $\frac{1}{10}$, and that value, based on a portion of all possible tosses of the cup, should be regarded as an approximation of the true theoretical probability. The value was found according to the *experimental,* or *empirical,* probability formula.

EMPIRICAL PROBABILITY FORMULA

If E is an event that may happen when an experiment is performed, then an **empirical probability** of event E is given by the following formula.

$$P(E) = \frac{\text{number of times event } E \text{ occurred}}{\text{number of times the experiment was performed}}$$

Usually it is clear in applications which probability formula should be used.

EXAMPLE 3 Finding the Probability of Having Daughters

Kathy wants to have exactly two daughters. Assuming that boy and girl babies are equally likely, find her probability of success for the following cases.

(a) She has a total of two children.

(b) She has a total of three children.

Solution

(a) The equal-likelihood assumption allows the use of theoretical probability. We can determine the number of favorable outcomes and the total number of possible outcomes by using a tree diagram (see **Section 10.1**) to enumerate the possibilities, as shown in **Figure 2**. From the outcome column we obtain the sample space $S = \{gg, gb, bg, bb\}$. Only one outcome, marked with an arrow, is favorable to the event of exactly two daughters: $E = \{gg\}$.

$$P(E) = \frac{n(E)}{n(S)} = \frac{1}{4} \quad \text{Theoretical probability formula}$$

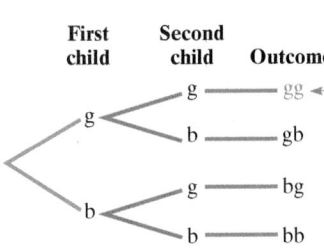

Exactly two girls among two children
Figure 2

Exactly two girls among three children
Figure 3

(b) For three children altogether, we construct another tree diagram, as shown in **Figure 3**. In this case, we see that

$$S = \{ggg, ggb, gbg, gbb, bgg, bgb, bbg, bbb\} \quad \text{and} \quad E = \{ggb, gbg, bgg\},$$

so $$P(E) = \frac{3}{8}.$$

When dealing or drawing cards, as in the next example, the dealing is generally done "without replacement." Once dealt, a card is *not* replaced in the deck. So all cards in a hand are distinct. Repetitions are *not* allowed. In many cases, such as building three-digit numbers, repetition of digits *is* allowed. For example, 255 is a legitimate three-digit number. So digit selection is done "with replacement."

▓▓▓ EXAMPLE 4 ▓ Finding Probability When Dealing Cards

Find the probability of being dealt each of the following hands in five-card poker. Use a calculator to obtain answers to eight decimal places.

(a) a full house (three of one denomination and two of another)

(b) a royal flush (the five highest cards—ace, king, queen, jack, ten—of a single suit)

Solution

(a) **Table 1** summarizes the various possible kinds of five-card hands as first seen in **Section 10.3.** Because the 2,598,960 possible individual hands all are equally likely, we can enter the appropriate numbers from the table into the theoretical probability formula.

$$P(\text{full house}) = \frac{3744}{2{,}598{,}960} = \frac{6}{4165} \approx 0.00144058$$

(b) The table shows that there are four royal flush hands, one for each suit.

$$P(\text{royal flush}) = \frac{4}{2{,}598{,}960} = \frac{1}{649{,}740} \approx 0.00000154 \qquad ■$$

Examples 3 and 4 both utilized the theoretical probability formula because we were able to enumerate all possible outcomes and all were equally likely. In **Example 3,** however, the equal likelihood of girl and boy babies was *assumed.* While male births typically occur a little more frequently, there usually are more females living at any given time, due to higher infant mortality rates among males and longer female life expectancy in general. **Example 5** shows a way of incorporating such empirical information.

Table 1

Number of Poker Hands in 5-Card Poker; Nothing Wild

Event *E*	Number of Outcomes Favorable to *E*
Royal flush	4
Straight flush	36
Four of a kind	624
Full house	3744
Flush	5108
Straight	10,200
Three of a kind	54,912
Two pairs	123,552
One pair	1,098,240
No pair	1,302,540
Total	2,598,960

▓▓▓ EXAMPLE 5 ▓ Finding the Probability of the Gender of a Resident

According to the United States Census figures, on July 1, 2012, there were an estimated 154.5 million males and 159.4 million females. If a person were selected randomly from the population in that year, what is the probability that the person would be a male? (*Source:* www.census.gov)

Solution

In this case, we calculate the empirical probability from the given experimental data.

$$P(\text{male}) = \frac{\text{number of males}}{\text{total number of persons}}$$

$$= \frac{154.5 \text{ million}}{154.5 \text{ million} + 159.4 \text{ million}}$$

$$\approx 0.492 \qquad ■$$

The Law of Large Numbers (or Law of Averages)

Recall the cup of **Example 2.** If we tossed it 50 more times, we would have 100 total tosses on which to base an empirical probability of the cup landing on its top. The new value would likely be slightly different from what we obtained before. It would still be an empirical probability, but it would be "better" in the sense that it was based on a larger set of outcomes.

If, as we increase the number of tosses, the resulting empirical probability values approach some particular number, that number can be defined as the theoretical probability of that particular cup landing on its top. We could determine this "limiting" value only as the actual number of observed tosses approached the total number of possible tosses of the cup. There are potentially an infinite number of possible tosses, so we could never actually find the theoretical probability. But we can still assume such a number exists. And as the number of actual observed tosses increases, the resulting empirical probabilities should tend ever closer to the theoretical value.

This principle is known as the **law of large numbers** or the **law of averages.**

The **law of large numbers** (or **law of averages**) also can be stated as follows.

A theoretical probability really says nothing about one, or even a few, repetitions of an experiment, but only about the proportion of successes we would expect over the long run.

LAW OF LARGE NUMBERS (LAW OF AVERAGES)

As an experiment is repeated more and more times, the proportion of outcomes favorable to any particular event will tend to come closer and closer to the theoretical probability of that event.

EXAMPLE 6 Graphing a Sequence of Proportions

A fair coin was tossed 35 times, producing the following sequence of outcomes.

tthhh, ttthh, hthtt, hhthh, ttthh, thttt, hhthh

Calculate the ratio of heads to total tosses after the first toss, the second toss, and so on through all 35 tosses, and plot these ratios on a graph.

Solution

After the first toss, we have 0 heads out of 1 toss, for a ratio of $\frac{0}{1} = 0.00$. After two tosses, we have $\frac{0}{2} = 0.00$. After three tosses, we have $\frac{1}{3} \approx 0.33$. Verify that the first six ratios are

0.00, 0.00, 0.33, 0.50, 0.60, 0.50.

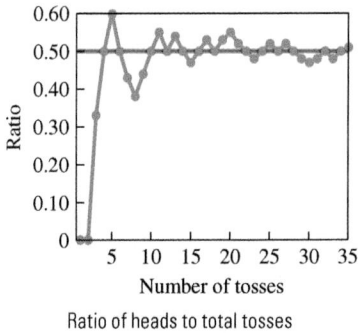

Ratio of heads to total tosses
Figure 4

The 35 ratios are plotted in **Figure 4.** The fluctuations away from 0.50 become smaller as the number of tosses increases, and the ratios appear to approach 0.50 toward the right side of the graph, in keeping with the law of large numbers.

COMPARING EMPIRICAL AND THEORETICAL PROBABILITIES

A series of repeated experiments provides an **empirical probability** for an event, which, by *inductive reasoning,* is an *estimate* of the event's *theoretical probability.* Increasing the number of repetitions increases the reliability of the estimate.

Likewise, an established **theoretical probability** for an event enables us, by *deductive reasoning,* to *predict* the proportion of times the event will occur in a series of repeated experiments. The prediction should be more accurate for larger numbers of repetitions.

Taking Your Chances

| Smoking 1.4 cigarettes |
| Spending 1 hour in a coal mine |
| Living 2 days in New York or Boston |
| Eating 40 teaspoons of peanut butter |
| Living 2 months with a cigarette smoker |
| Flying 1000 miles in a jet |
| Traveling 300 miles in a car |
| Riding 10 miles on a bicycle |

Risk is the probability that a harmful event will occur. Almost every action or substance exposes a person to some risk, and the assessment and reduction of risk account for a great deal of study and effort in our world. The list above, from *Calculated Risk*, by J. Rodricks, contains activities that increase a person's annual risk of death by one chance in a million.

Probability in Genetics

Probabilities, both empirical and theoretical, have been valuable tools in many areas of science. An important early example was the work of the Austrian monk Gregor Mendel, who used the idea of randomness to help establish the study of genetics.

In an effort to understand the mechanism of character transmittal from one generation to the next in plants, Mendel counted the number of occurrences of various characteristics. He found that the flower color in certain pea plants obeyed this scheme:

Pure red crossed with pure white produces red.

Gregor Johann Mendel (1822–1884) came from a peasant family who managed to send him to school. By 1847 he had been ordained and was teaching at the Abbey of St. Thomas. He finished his education at the University of Vienna and returned to the abbey to teach mathematics and natural science.

Mendel began to carry out experiments on plants in the abbey garden, notably pea plants, whose distinct traits (unit characters) he had puzzled over. In 1865 he published his results. His work was not appreciated at the time, even though he had laid the foundation of **classical genetics**.

Mendel theorized that red is "dominant," symbolized in this explanation with the capital letter R, while white is "recessive," symbolized with the lowercase letter r. The pure red parent carried only genes for red (R), and the pure white parent carried only genes for white (r). The offspring would receive one gene from each parent, hence one of the four combinations shown in the body of **Table 2**. Because every offspring receives one gene for red, that characteristic dominates, and each offspring exhibits the color red.

Table 2 First to Second Generation

		Second Parent	
		r	**r**
First	**R**	Rr	Rr
Parent	**R**	Rr	Rr

Table 3 Second to Third Generation

		Second Parent	
		R	**r**
First	**R**	RR	Rr
Parent	**r**	rR	rr

Now each of these second-generation offspring, though exhibiting the color red, still carries one of each gene. So when two of them are crossed, each third-generation offspring will receive one of the gene combinations shown in **Table 3**. Mendel theorized that each of the four possibilities would be equally likely, and he produced experimental counts that were close enough to support this hypothesis.

EXAMPLE 7 Finding Probabilities of Flower Colors

Referring to **Table 3**, determine the probability that a third-generation offspring will exhibit each flower color. Base the probabilities on the sample space of equally likely outcomes.

$$S = \{RR, Rr, rR, rr\}$$

(a) red   **(b)** white

Solution

(a) Since red dominates white, any combination with at least one gene for red (R) will result in red flowers. Since three of the four possibilities meet this criterion,

$$P(\text{red}) = \frac{3}{4}.$$

(b) Only the combination rr has no gene for red, so

$$P(\text{white}) = \frac{1}{4}.$$ ∎

Super Bowl Coin Tosses During the pregame coin flip of Super Bowl XLIV in 2010, the New Orleans Saints of the National Football Conference (NFC) called "heads" and won the toss. The probability of this, of course, was $\frac{1}{2}$. At the time, however, an interesting situation existed. For the twelve previous Super Bowls, the NFC representative in the Super Bowl had won the toss over the American Football Conference (AFC). The Saints continued this streak, and thus the NFC had won the toss for thirteen straight years.

Immediately following the toss, the television announcer indicated that the odds against such a run of thirteen straight wins were

"about 8100 to 1."

Where did this information come from? Someone had done the mathematics ahead of time and evaluated

$$\left(\frac{1}{2}\right)^{13} \quad \text{to obtain} \quad \frac{1}{8192}.$$

Using the concepts described in this section, the actual theoretical odds are 8191 to 1 against a run of thirteen straight wins by one conference.

Odds

Whereas probability compares the number of favorable outcomes to the total number of outcomes, **odds** compare the number of favorable outcomes to the number of unfavorable outcomes. Odds are commonly quoted, rather than probabilities, in horse racing, lotteries, and most other gambling situations. And the odds quoted normally are odds "against" rather than odds "in favor."

ODDS

If all outcomes in a sample space are equally likely, a of them are favorable to the event E, and the remaining b outcomes are unfavorable to E, then the

odds in favor of E are a to b,   and   the **odds against E** are b to a.

EXAMPLE 8 Finding the Odds of Getting an Intern Position

Theresa has been promised one of six jobs, three of which would be intern positions at the state capitol. If she has equal chances for all six jobs, find the odds *in favor* of her getting one of the intern positions.

Solution

Since three possibilities are favorable and three are not, the odds of *becoming an intern* at the capitol are 3 to 3 (or 1 to 1 in reduced terms). Odds of 1 to 1 are often termed

"even odds,"   or a   "50–50 chance." ◼

EXAMPLE 9 Finding the Odds of Winning a Raffle

Bob has purchased 12 tickets for an office raffle in which the winner will receive an iPad. If 104 tickets were sold altogether and each has an equal chance of winning, what are the odds *against* Bob's winning the iPad?

Solution

Bob has 12 chances to win and $104 - 12 = 92$ chances to lose, so the odds *against* winning are

92 to 12.

In practice, we often use the fact that each number can be divided by their greatest common factor, to express the odds in lower terms. Dividing each of 92 and 12 by 4 gives the equivalent odds of

23 to 3.   Lowest terms ◼

CONVERTING BETWEEN PROBABILITY AND ODDS

Let E be an event.

- If $P(E) = \frac{a}{b}$, then the odds in favor of E are a to $(b - a)$.

- If the odds in favor of E are a to b, then $P(E) = \frac{a}{a + b}$.

EXAMPLE 10 Converting from Probability to Odds

There is a 30% chance of rain tomorrow. Give this information in terms of odds.

Solution

$$P(\text{rain}) = 0.30 = \frac{30}{100} = \frac{3}{10}$$

Convert the decimal fraction to a quotient of integers and reduce.

By the first conversion formula, if $P(E) = \frac{a}{b}$, then the odds *in favor* of rain tomorrow are a to $(b - a)$—that is,

$$3 \text{ to } (10 - 3)$$

or

$$3 \text{ to } 7. \quad \text{Odds in favor of rain}$$

We can also say that the odds *against* rain tomorrow are

$$7 \text{ to } (10 - 7)$$

or

$$7 \text{ to } 3. \quad \text{Odds against rain}$$

EXAMPLE 11 Converting from Odds to Probability

In a certain sweepstakes, your odds of winning are 1 to 99,999. What is the probability that you will win?

Solution

Use the second conversion formula $P(E) = \frac{a}{a + b}$.

$$P(\text{win}) = \frac{1}{1 + 99,999} = \frac{1}{100,000} = 0.00001$$

11.1   EXERCISES

In Exercises 1–4, give the probability that the spinner shown would land on **(a)** *red,* **(b)** *yellow, and* **(c)** *blue.*

1.

2.

3.

4.
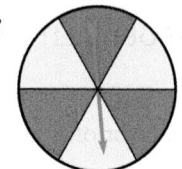

Solve each probability problem.

5. ***Using Spinners to Generate Numbers*** Suppose the spinner shown here is spun once, to determine a single-digit number, and we are interested in the event E that the resulting number is odd. Give each of the following.

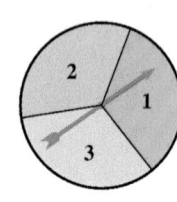

(a) the sample space

(b) the number of favorable outcomes

(c) the number of unfavorable outcomes

(d) the total number of possible outcomes

(e) the probability of an odd number

(f) the odds in favor of an odd number

6. *Lining Up Preschool Children* Kim's group of pre-school children includes nine girls and seven boys. If she randomly selects one child to be first in line, with *E* being the event that the one selected is a girl, give each of the following.

   (a) the total number of possible outcomes

   (b) the number of favorable outcomes

   (c) the number of unfavorable outcomes

   (d) the probability of event *E*

   (e) the odds in favor of event *E*

7. *Using Spinners to Generate Numbers* The spinner of **Exercise 5** is spun twice in succession to determine a two-digit number. Give each of the following.

   (a) the sample space

   (b) the probability of an odd number

   (c) the probability of a number with repeated digits

   (d) the probability of a number greater than 30

   (e) the probability of a prime number

8. *Probabilities in Coin Tossing* Two fair coins are tossed (say a dime and a quarter). Give each of the following.

   (a) the sample space

   (b) the probability of heads on the dime

   (c) the probability of heads on the quarter

   (d) the probability of getting both heads

   (e) the probability of getting the same outcome on both coins

9. *Random Selection of Fifties Music* Butch has fifty vinyl records from the fifties, including exactly one by Smiley Lewis, two by The Drifters, three by Bobby Darin, four by The Coasters, and five by Fats Domino. If he randomly selects one from his collection of fifty, find the probability it will be by each of the following.

   (a) Smiley Lewis

   (b) The Drifters

   (c) Bobby Darin

   (d) The Coasters

   (e) Fats Domino

10. *Probabilities in Coin Tossing* Three fair coins are tossed.

    (a) Write out the sample space.

    Determine the probability of each event.

    (b) no heads   (c) exactly one head

    (d) exactly two heads (e) three heads

11. *Number Sums for Rolling Two Dice* The sample space for the rolling of two fair dice appeared in **Table 2** of **Section 10.1.** Reproduce that table, but replace each of the 36 equally likely ordered pairs with its corresponding sum (for the two dice). Then find the probability of rolling each sum.

    (a) 2   (b) 3   (c) 4

    (d) 5   (e) 6   (f) 7

    (g) 8   (h) 9   (i) 10

    (j) 11   (k) 12

12. *Probabilities of Two Daughters among Four Children* In **Example 3,** what would be Kathy's probability of having exactly two daughters if she were to have four children altogether? (You may want to use a tree diagram to construct the sample space.)

Probabilities of Poker Hands In 5-card poker, find the probability of being dealt each of the following. Give each answer to eight decimal places. (Refer to **Table 1.***)*

13. a straight flush

14. two pairs

15. four of a kind

16. four queens

17. a hearts flush (*not* a royal flush or a straight flush)

18. no pair

In Exercises 19 and 20, give answers to three decimal places.

19. *Probability of Seed Germination* In a hybrid corn research project, 200 seeds were planted, and 175 of them germinated. Find the empirical probability that any particular seed of this type will germinate.

20. *Probability of Forest Land in California* According to *The World Almanac and Book of Facts,* California has 155,959 square miles of land area, 51,250 square miles of which are forested. Find the probability that a randomly selected location in California will be forested.

Selecting Class Reports Assuming that Ben, Jill, and Pam are three of the 26 members of the class, and that three of the class members will be chosen randomly to deliver their reports during the next class meeting, find the probability (to six decimal places) of each event.

21. Ben, Jill, and Pam are selected, in that order.

22. Ben, Jill, and Pam are selected, in any order.

23. *Probabilities in Olympic Curling*
In Olympic curling, the scoring area (shown here) consists of four concentric circles on the ice with radii of 6 inches, 2 feet, 4 feet, and 6 feet. If a team member lands a (43-pound) stone *randomly* within the scoring area, find the probability that it ends up centered on the given color.

(a) red   **(b)** white   **(c)** blue

24. *Probabilities in Dart Throwing* If a dart hits the square target shown here at random, what is the probability that it will hit in a colored region? (*Hint:* Compare the area of the colored regions to the total area of the target.)

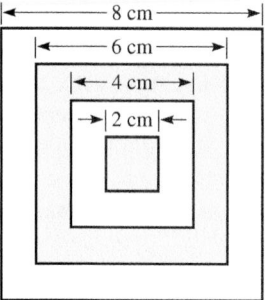

Genetics in Snapdragons *Mendel found no dominance in snapdragons (in contrast to peas) with respect to red and white flower color. When pure red and pure white parents are crossed (see* **Table 2**), *the resulting* Rr *combination (one of each gene) produces second-generation offspring with* pink *flowers. These second-generation pinks, however, still carry one red and one white gene, so when they are crossed, the third generation is still governed by* **Table 3.**

Find each probability for third-generation snapdragons.

25. $P(\text{red})$ **26.** $P(\text{pink})$ **27.** $P(\text{white})$

Genetics in Pea Plants *Mendel also investigated various characteristics besides flower color. For example, round peas are dominant over recessive wrinkled peas. First, second, and third generations can again be analyzed using* **Tables 2 and 3,** *where* R *represents round and* r *represents wrinkled.*

28. Explain why crossing pure round and pure wrinkled first-generation parents will always produce round peas in the second-generation offspring.

29. When second-generation round pea plants (each of which carries both R and r genes) are crossed, find the probability that a third-generation offspring will have the following.

(a) round peas   **(b)** wrinkled peas

Genetics of Cystic Fibrosis *Cystic fibrosis is one of the most common inherited diseases in North America (including the United States), occurring in about* 1 *of every* 2000 *Caucasian births and about* 1 *of every* 250,000 *non-Caucasian births. Even with modern treatment, victims usually die from lung damage by their early twenties.*

If we denote a cystic fibrosis gene with a c *and a disease-free gene with a* C *(since the disease is recessive), then only a* cc *person will actually have the disease. Such persons would ordinarily die before parenting children, but a child can also inherit the disease from two* Cc *parents (who themselves are healthy—that is, have no symptoms but are "carriers" of the disease). This is like a pea plant inheriting white flowers from two red-flowered parents that both carry genes for white.*

30. Find the empirical probability (to four decimal places) that cystic fibrosis will occur in a randomly selected infant birth among U.S. Caucasians.

31. Find the empirical probability (to six decimal places) that cystic fibrosis will occur in a randomly selected infant birth among U.S. non-Caucasians.

32. Among 150,000 North American Caucasian births, about how many occurrences of cystic fibrosis would you expect?

Suppose that both partners in a marriage are cystic fibrosis carriers (a rare occurrence). Construct a chart similar to **Table 3** *and determine the probability of each of the following events.*

33. Their first child will have the disease.

34. Their first child will be a carrier.

35. Their first child will neither have nor carry the disease.

Suppose a child is born to one cystic fibrosis carrier parent and one non-carrier parent. Find the probability of each of the following events.

36. The child will have cystic fibrosis.

37. The child will be a healthy cystic fibrosis carrier.

38. The child will neither have nor carry the disease.

Genetics of Sickle-Cell Anemia *Sickle-cell anemia occurs in about 1 of every 500 black baby births and about 1 of every 160,000 non-black baby births. It is ordinarily fatal in early childhood. There is a test to identify carriers. Unlike cystic fibrosis, which is recessive, sickle-cell anemia is* **codominant.** *This means that inheriting two sickle-cell genes causes the disease, while inheriting just one sickle-cell gene causes a mild (non-fatal) version (which is called* **sickle-cell trait).** *This is similar to a snapdragon plant manifesting pink flowers by inheriting one red gene and one white gene.*

In Exercises 39 and 40, find the empirical probabilities of the given events.

39. A randomly selected black baby will have sickle-cell anemia. (Give your answer to three decimal places.)

40. A randomly selected non-black baby will have sickle-cell anemia. (Give your answer to six decimal places.)

41. Among 80,000 births of black babies, about how many occurrences of sickle-cell anemia would you expect?

In Exercises 42–44, find the theoretical probability of each condition in a child both of whose parents have sickle-cell trait.

42. The child will have sickle-cell anemia.

43. The child will have sickle-cell trait.

44. The child will be healthy.

Drawing Balls from an Urn Anne Kelly randomly chooses a single ball from the urn shown here. Find the odds against each event.

45. red

46. yellow

47. blue

48. red or yellow

49. yellow or blue

50. red or blue

Random Selection of Club Officers *Five people (Alan, Bill, Cathy, David, and Evelyn) form a club:* $N = \{A, B, C, D, E\}$. *Cathy and Evelyn are women, and the others are men. If they choose a president randomly, find the odds against each of the following becoming president.*

51. Cathy

52. a woman

53. a person whose name begins with a consonant

54. a man

In Exercises 55 and 56, assume that the probability of an event E is

$$P(E) = 0.37.$$

Find each of the following.

55. the odds in favor of E

56. the odds against E

Make the requested conversions in Exercises 57 and 58.

57. If the odds in favor of event E are 12 to 19, find $P(E)$.

58. If the odds against event E are 10 to 3, find $P(E)$.

59. Women's 100-Meter Run In the history of track and field, no woman has broken the 10-second barrier in the 100-meter run.

(a) From the statement above, find the empirical probability that a woman runner will break the 10-second barrier next year.

(b) Can you find the theoretical probability for the event of part (a)?

(c) Is it possible that the event of part (a) will occur?

60. On page 27 of their book *Descartes' Dream*, Philip Davis and Reuben Hersh ask the question, "Is probability real or is it just a cover-up for ignorance?" What do you think?

The remaining exercises require careful thought to determine n(E) and n(S). (In some cases, you may want to employ counting methods from Chapter 10, such as the fundamental counting principle, permutations, or combinations.)

Probabilities of Seating Arrangements *Six people (three married couples) arrange themselves randomly in six consecutive seats in a row. In Exercises 61–64,*

(a) *determine the number of ways in which the described event can occur, and*

(b) *determine the probability of the event.*

(Hint: In each case the denominator of the probability fraction will be 6! = 720, *the total number of ways to arrange six items.)*

61. Each man will sit immediately to the left of his wife.

62. Each man will sit immediately to the left of a woman.

63. The women will be in three adjacent seats.

64. The women will be in three adjacent seats, as will the men.

Solve each problem.

65. *Altered Dice* A six-sided die has been altered so that the side that had been a single dot is now a blank face. Another die has a blank face instead of the face with four dots. What is the probability that a sum of 7 is rolled when the two dice are thrown? (*Mathematics Teacher* calendar problem)

66. *Location in a Tunnel* Mr. Davis is driving through a tunnel that is eight miles long. At this instant, what is the probability that he is at least six miles from one end of the tunnel? (*Mathematics Teacher* calendar problem)

67. *Slopes* Two lines, neither of which is vertical, are perpendicular if and only if their slopes are negative reciprocals (as are $\frac{2}{3}$ and $-\frac{3}{2}$). If two distinct numbers are chosen randomly from the set

$$\left\{-2, -\frac{4}{3}, -\frac{1}{2}, 0, \frac{1}{2}, \frac{3}{4}, 3\right\},$$

find the probability that they will be the slopes of two perpendicular lines.

68. *Drawing Cards* When drawing cards without replacement from a standard 52-card deck, find the maximum number of cards you could possibly draw and still get the following.

(a) fewer than three black cards

(b) fewer than six spades

(c) fewer than four face cards

(d) fewer than two kings

69. *Student Course Schedules* A student plans to take three courses next term. If he selects them randomly from a list of twelve courses, five of which are science courses, what is the probability that all three courses selected will be science courses?

70. *Symphony Performances* Rhonda randomly selects three symphony performances to attend this season from a schedule of ten performances, three of which feature works by Beethoven. Find the probability that she will select all of the Beethoven programs.

71. *Racing Bets* A "trifecta" is a particular horse race in which you win by picking the "win," "place," and "show" horses (the first-, second-, and third-place winners), in their proper order. If five horses of equal ability are entered in a trifecta race, and Tracy selects an entry, what is the probability that she will be a winner?

72. *Random Selection of Prime Numbers* If two distinct prime numbers are randomly selected from among the first eight prime numbers, what is the probability that their sum will be 24?

73. *Random Sums* Two integers are randomly selected from the set $\{1, 2, 3, 4, 5, 6, 7, 8, 9\}$ and are added together. Find the probability that their sum is 11 if they are selected as described.

(a) with replacement

(b) without replacement

74. *Numbers from Sets of Digits* The digits 1, 2, 3, 4, and 5 are randomly arranged to form a five-digit number. Find the probability of each event.

(a) The number is even.

(b) The first and last digits of the number both are even.

75. *Divisibility of Random Products* When a fair six-sided die is tossed on a tabletop, the bottom face cannot be seen. What is the probability that the product of the numbers on the five faces that can be seen is divisible by 6? (*Mathematics Teacher* calendar problem)

76. *Random Sums and Products* Tamika selects two different numbers at random from the set $\{8, 9, 10\}$ and adds them. Carlos takes two different numbers at random from the set $\{3, 5, 6\}$ and multiplies them. What is the probability that Tamika's result is greater than Carlos's result? (*Mathematics Teacher* calendar problem)

77. *Classroom Demographics* A high school class consists of 6 seniors, 10 juniors, 12 sophomores, and 4 freshmen. Exactly 2 of the juniors are female, and exactly 2 of the sophomores are males. If two students are randomly selected from this class, what is the probability that the pair consists of a male junior and a female sophomore? (*Mathematics Teacher* calendar problem)

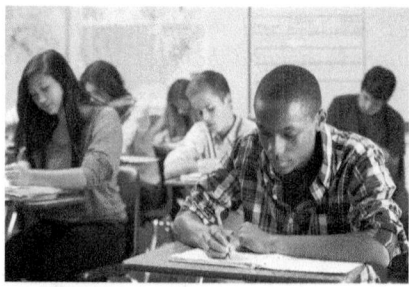

78. *Fractions from Dice Rolls* Lisa has one red die and one green die, which she rolls to make up fractions. The green die is the numerator, and the red die is the denominator. Some of the fractions have terminating decimal representations. How many different terminating decimal results can these two dice represent? What is the probability of rolling a fraction with a terminating decimal representation? (*Mathematics Teacher* calendar problem)

Palindromic Numbers *Numbers that are **palindromes** read the same forward and backward.*

30203 is a five-digit palindrome.

If a single number is chosen randomly from each set, find the probability that it will be palindromic.

79. the set of all two-digit numbers

80. the set of all three-digit numbers

Six people, call them

A, B, C, D, E, and F,

are randomly divided into three groups of two. Find the probability of each event. (Do not impose unwanted ordering among groups.)

81. *A and B are in the same group, as are C and D.*

82. *E and F are in the same group.*

11.2   EVENTS INVOLVING "NOT" AND "OR"

OBJECTIVES

1 Know that the probability of an event is a real number between 0 and 1, inclusive of both, and know the meanings of the terms *impossible event* and *certain event*.

2 Understand the correspondences among set theory, logic, and arithmetic.

3 Determine the probability of "not *E*" given the probability of *E*.

4 Determine the probability of "*A* or *B*" given the probabilities of *A*, *B*, and "*A* and *B*."

Properties of Probability

Recall that an empirical probability, based upon experimental observation, may be the best value available but still is only an approximation to the ("true") theoretical probability. For example, no human has ever been known to jump higher than 8.5 feet vertically, so the empirical probability of such an event is zero. Observing the rate at which high-jump records have been broken, we suspect that the event is, in fact, possible and may one day occur. Hence it must have some nonzero theoretical probability, even though we have no way of assessing its exact value.

Recall also that the theoretical probability formula,

$$P(E) = \frac{n(E)}{n(S)},$$

is valid only when all outcomes in the sample space *S* are equally likely. For the experiment of tossing two fair coins, we can write $S = \{hh, ht, th, tt\}$ and compute

$$P(\text{both heads}) = \frac{1}{4}. \quad \text{Correct}$$

However, if we define the sample space with non-equally likely outcomes as $S = \{\text{both heads, both tails, one of each}\}$, we are led to

$$P(\text{both heads}) = \frac{1}{3}. \quad \text{Incorrect}$$

To convince yourself that $\frac{1}{4}$ is a better value than $\frac{1}{3}$, toss two fair coins 100 times or so, to see what the empirical fraction seems to approach.

For any event *E* within a sample space *S*, we know that $0 \le n(E) \le n(S)$. Dividing all members of this inequality by $n(S)$ gives

$$\frac{0}{n(S)} \le \frac{n(E)}{n(S)} \le \frac{n(S)}{n(S)}, \quad \text{or} \quad 0 \le P(E) \le 1.$$

In words, the probability of any event is a number from 0 through 1, inclusive.

If event *E* is *impossible* (cannot happen), then $n(E)$ must be 0 (*E* is the empty set), so

$$P(E) = 0. \quad \text{E is impossible.}$$

If event *E* is *certain* (cannot help but happen), then $n(E) = n(S)$, so

$$P(E) = \frac{n(E)}{n(S)} = \frac{n(S)}{n(S)} = 1. \quad \text{E is certain.}$$

More on the Birth of Probability
The modern mathematical theory of probability came mainly from the Russian scholars **P. L. Chebyshev** (1821–1922), **A. A. Markov** (1856–1922), and **Andrei Nikolaevich Kolmogorov** (1903–1987). The Dutch mathematician and scientist **Christiaan Huygens** (1629–1695) wrote a formal treatise on probability. It appeared in 1657 and was based on the Pascal–Fermat correspondence. One of the first to apply probability to matters other than gambling was the French mathematician **Pierre Simon de Laplace** (1749–1827), who is usually credited with being the "father" of probability theory.

Pierre Simon de Laplace (1749–1827) began in 1773 to solve the problem of why Jupiter's orbit seems to shrink and Saturn's orbit seems to expand. Eventually Laplace worked out a complete theory of the solar system. *Celestial Mechanics* resulted from almost a lifetime of work. In five volumes, it was published between 1799 and 1825 and gained for Laplace the reputation "Newton of France."

Laplace's work on probability was actually an adjunct to his celestial mechanics. He needed to demonstrate that probability is useful in interpreting scientific data.

PROPERTIES OF PROBABILITY

Let E be an event within the sample space S. That is, E is a subset of S. Then the following properties hold.

1. $0 \leq P(E) \leq 1$ The probability of an event is a number from 0 through 1, inclusive.

2. $P(\varnothing) = 0$ The probability of an impossible event is 0.

3. $P(S) = 1$ The probability of a certain event is 1.

Probabilities are often expressed in terms of percents in the media. We will, however, give them in terms of fractions or decimals.

EXAMPLE 1 **Finding Probability When Rolling a Die**

When a single fair die is rolled, find the probability of each event.

(a) The number 2 is rolled.   **(b)** A number other than 2 is rolled.

(c) The number 7 is rolled.   **(d)** A number less than 7 is rolled.

Solution

(a) Since one of the six possibilities is a 2, $P(2) = \frac{1}{6}$.

(b) There are five such numbers, 1, 3, 4, 5, and 6, so $P(\text{a number other than } 2) = \frac{5}{6}$.

(c) None of the possible outcomes is 7. Thus, $P(7) = \frac{0}{6} = 0$.

(d) Since all six of the possible outcomes are less than 7,

$$P(\text{a number less than } 7) = \frac{6}{6} = 1.$$ ■

Refer to the box preceding **Example 1.** No probability in that example was less than 0 or greater than 1, which illustrates Property 1. The "impossible" event of part (c) had probability 0, illustrating Property 2. The "certain" event of part (d) had probability 1, illustrating Property 3.

Events Involving "Not"

Table 4 repeats the information of **Table 8** of **Section 10.5,** with a third correspondence added in row 3. The correspondences shown in **Table 4** are the basis for the probability rules. For example, the probability of an event *not* happening involves the *complement* and *subtraction,* according to row 1 of the table.

Table 4 Set Theory/Logic/Arithmetic Correspondences

	Set Theory	Logic	Arithmetic
1. Operation or Connective (Symbol)	Complement ($'$)	Not ($\sim$)	Subtraction ($-$)
2. Operation or Connective (Symbol)	Union ($\cup$)	Or ($\vee$)	Addition ($+$)
3. Operation or Connective (Symbol)	Intersection ($\cap$)	And ($\wedge$)	Multiplication ($\cdot$)

The rule for the probability of a complement follows and is illustrated in **Figure 5.**

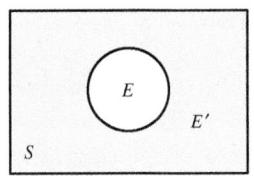

The logical connective "not" corresponds to "complement" in set theory.

$$P(not\,E) = P(S) - P(E)$$
$$= 1 - P(E)$$

Figure 5

PROBABILITY OF A COMPLEMENT (FOR THE EVENT "NOT *E*")

The probability that an event *E* will *not* occur is equal to 1 minus the probability that it *will* occur.

$$P(\text{not } E) = 1 - P(E)$$

Notice that the events of **Examples 1(a) and (b),** namely "2" and "not 2," are complements of one another, and that their probabilities add up to 1. This illustrates the above probability rule. The equation

$$P(E) + P(E') = 1$$

is a rearrangement of the formula for the probability of a complement. Another form of the equation that is also useful at times follows.

$$P(E) = 1 - P(E')$$

EXAMPLE 2 Finding the Probability of a Complement

When a single card is drawn from a standard 52-card deck, what is the probability that it will not be a king?

Solution

$$P(\text{not a king}) = 1 - P(\text{king}) = 1 - \frac{4}{52} = \frac{48}{52} = \frac{12}{13}$$

> Remember to write in lowest terms.

EXAMPLE 3 Finding the Probability of a Complement

If five fair coins are tossed, find the probability of obtaining at least two heads.

Solution

A tree diagram will show that there are $2^5 = 32$ possible outcomes for the experiment of tossing five fair coins. Most include at least two heads. In fact, only the outcomes

ttttt, htttt, thttt, tthtt, tttht, and tttth   6 of these

do *not* include at least two heads. If *E* denotes the event "at least two heads," then *E'* is the event "not at least two heads,"

$$P(E) = 1 - P(E') = 1 - \frac{6}{32} = \frac{26}{32} = \frac{13}{16}$$

Events Involving "Or"

Examples 2 and 3 showed how the probability of an event can be approached *indirectly,* by first considering the complement of the event. Another indirect approach is to break the event into simpler component events. Row 2 of **Table 4** indicates that the probability of one event *or* another should involve the *union* and *addition.*

Mary Somerville (1780–1872) is associated with Laplace because of her brilliant exposition of his *Celestial Mechanics.*

Somerville studied Euclid thoroughly and perfected her Latin so she could read Newton's *Principia.* In about 1816 she went to London and soon became part of its literary and scientific circles.

Somerville's book on Laplace's theories came out in 1831 to great acclaim. Then followed a panoramic book, *Connection of the Physical Sciences* (1834). A statement in one of its editions suggested that irregularities in the orbit of Uranus might indicate that a more remote planet, not yet seen, existed. This caught the eye of the scientists who worked out the calculations for Neptune's orbit.

EXAMPLE 4 Selecting from a Set of Numbers

If one number is selected randomly from the set $\{1, 2, 3, 4, 5, 6, 7, 8, 9, 10\}$, find the probability of each of the following events.

(a) The number is odd or a multiple of 4.

(b) The number is odd or a multiple of 3.

Solution

Define the following events.

$$S = \{1, 2, 3, 4, 5, 6, 7, 8, 9, 10\} \quad \text{Sample space}$$

$$A = \{1, 3, 5, 7, 9\} \quad \text{Odd outcomes; } P(A) = \tfrac{5}{10}$$

$$B = \{4, 8\} \quad \text{Multiples of 4; } P(B) = \tfrac{2}{10}$$

$$C = \{3, 6, 9\} \quad \text{Multiples of 3; } P(C) = \tfrac{3}{10}$$

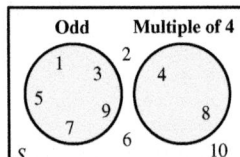

Odd | Multiple of 4

Figure 6

(a) Figure 6 shows the positioning of the 10 integers within the sample space and within the pertinent sets A and B. The composite event "A or B" corresponds to the set $A \cup B = \{1, 3, 4, 5, 7, 8, 9\}$. $A \cup B$ has **seven** elements. By the theoretical probability formula,

$$P(A \text{ or } B) = \frac{7}{10}. \quad \text{Of 10 total outcomes, seven are favorable.}$$

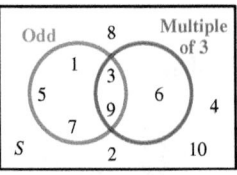

Odd | Multiple of 3

Figure 7

(b) Figure 7 shows the situation. *Of 10 total outcomes, six are favorable.*

$$P(A \text{ or } C) = \frac{6}{10} = \frac{3}{5} \qquad ■$$

Would an addition formula have worked in **Example 4?** Let's check.

Part (a): $\quad P(A \text{ or } B) = P(A) + P(B) = \dfrac{5}{10} + \dfrac{2}{10} = \dfrac{7}{10} \qquad$ Correct

Part (b): $\quad P(A \text{ or } C) = P(A) + P(C) = \dfrac{5}{10} + \dfrac{3}{10} = \dfrac{8}{10} = \dfrac{4}{5} \qquad$ Incorrect

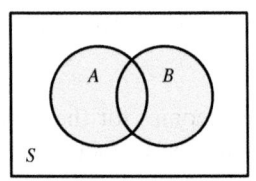

The logical connective "or" corresponds to "union" in set theory.

$P(A \text{ or } B)$
$\quad = P(A) + P(B) - P(A \text{ and } B)$

Figure 8

The trouble in part (b) is that A and C are not disjoint sets. They have outcomes in common. Just as with the additive counting principle in **Chapter 10,** an adjustment must be made here to compensate for counting the common outcomes twice.

$$P(A \text{ or } C) = P(A) + P(C) - P(A \text{ and } C)$$

$$= \frac{5}{10} + \frac{3}{10} - \frac{2}{10} = \frac{6}{10} = \frac{3}{5} \quad \text{Correct}$$

In probability theory, events that are disjoint sets are called *mutually exclusive events.*

MUTUALLY EXCLUSIVE EVENTS

Two events A and B are **mutually exclusive events** if they have no outcomes in common. Mutually exclusive events cannot occur simultaneously.

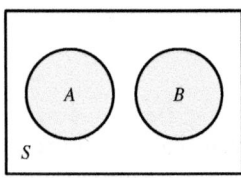

When A and B are mutually exclusive,

$P(A \text{ or } B) = P(A) + P(B).$

Figure 9

The results observed in **Example 4** are generalized as follows. The two possibilities are illustrated in **Figures 8 and 9.**

ADDITION RULE OF PROBABILITY (FOR THE EVENT "A OR B")

If A and B are any two events, then the following holds.

$$P(A \text{ or } B) = P(A) + P(B) - P(A \text{ and } B)$$

If A and B are mutually exclusive, then the following holds.

$$P(A \text{ or } B) = P(A) + P(B)$$

Actually, the first formula in the addition rule applies in all cases. The third term on the right drops out when A and B are mutually exclusive, because $P(A \text{ and } B) = 0$. Still, it is good to remember the second formula in the preceding box for the many cases where the component events are mutually exclusive. In this section, we consider only cases where the event "A and B" is simple. We deal with more involved composites involving "and" in the next section.

EXAMPLE 5   Finding the Probability of an Event Involving "Or"

If a single card is drawn from a standard 52-card deck, what is the probability that it will be a spade or a red card?

Solution

First note that "spade" and "red" cannot both occur, because there are no red spades. All spades are black. Therefore, we can use the formula for mutually exclusive events. There are 13 spades and 26 red cards in the deck.

$$P(\text{spade or red}) = P(\text{spade}) + P(\text{red}) = \frac{13}{52} + \frac{26}{52} = \frac{39}{52} = \frac{3}{4} \qquad \blacksquare$$

Two examples of "success" in Example 5

We often need to consider composites of more than two events. When each event involved is mutually exclusive of all the others, we extend the addition rule to the appropriate number of components.

EXAMPLE 6   Treating Unions of Several Components

Amy plans to spend from 1 to 6 hours on her homework. If x represents the number of hours to be spent on a given night, then the probabilities of the various values of x, rounded to the nearest hour, are as shown in **Table 5**. Find the probabilities that Amy will spend each of the following amounts of time.

(a) fewer than 3 hours

(b) more than 2 hours

(c) more than 1 but no more than 5 hours

(d) fewer than 5 hours

Solution

Because the time periods in **Table 5** are mutually exclusive of one another, we can simply add the appropriate component probabilities.

(a) $P(\text{fewer than 3}) = P(1 \text{ or } 2)$ Fewer than 3 means 1 or 2.

$\qquad\qquad\qquad\quad = P(1) + P(2)$ Addition rule

$\qquad\qquad\qquad\quad = 0.05 + 0.10$ Substitute values from **Table 5**.

$\qquad\qquad\qquad\quad = 0.15$ Add.

Table 5

x	$P(x)$
1	0.05
2	0.10
3	0.20
4	0.40
5	0.10
6	0.15

(b) $P(\text{more than } 2) = P(3 \text{ or } 4 \text{ or } 5 \text{ or } 6)$ More than 2 means 3, 4, 5, or 6.

$\qquad\qquad\qquad = P(3) + P(4) + P(5) + P(6)$ Addition rule

$\qquad\qquad\qquad = 0.20 + 0.40 + 0.10 + 0.15$ Substitute values from **Table 5**.

$\qquad\qquad\qquad = 0.85$ Add.

(c) $P(\text{more than 1 but no more than 5})$

$\qquad\qquad = P(2 \text{ or } 3 \text{ or } 4 \text{ or } 5)$ 2, 3, 4, and 5 are more than 1 and no more than 5.

$\qquad\qquad = P(2) + P(3) + P(4) + P(5)$ Addition rule

$\qquad\qquad = 0.10 + 0.20 + 0.40 + 0.10$ Substitute values from **Table 5**.

$\qquad\qquad = 0.80$ Add.

(d) Although we could take a direct approach here, as in parts (a), (b), and (c), we will combine the complement rule with the addition rule.

$\qquad P(\text{fewer than 5}) = 1 - P(\text{not fewer than 5})$ Complement rule

$\qquad\qquad\qquad\qquad = 1 - P(5 \text{ or more})$ 5 or more is equivalent to not fewer than 5.

$\qquad\qquad\qquad\qquad = 1 - P(5 \text{ or } 6)$ 5 or more means 5 or 6.

$\qquad\qquad\qquad\qquad = 1 - [P(5) + P(6)]$ Addition rule

$\qquad\qquad\qquad\qquad = 1 - (0.10 + 0.15)$ Substitute values from **Table 5**.

$\qquad\qquad\qquad\qquad = 1 - 0.25$ Add inside the parentheses first.

$\qquad\qquad\qquad\qquad = 0.75$

Table 5 in **Example 6** lists all possible time intervals so the corresponding probabilities add up to 1, a necessary condition for the way part (d) was done. The time spent on homework here is an example of a **random variable.** It is "random" because we cannot predict which of its possible values will occur.

A listing like **Table 5,** which shows all possible values of a random variable, along with the probabilities that those values will occur, is a **probability distribution** for that random variable. *All* possible values are listed, so they make up the entire sample space, and thus the listed probabilities must add up to 1 (by probability Property 3). Probability distributions will be discussed in later sections.

EXAMPLE 7 **Finding the Probability of an Event Involving "Or"**

Find the probability that a single card drawn from a standard 52-card deck will be a diamond or a face card.

Solution

One example of a card that is both a diamond and a face card

The component events "diamond" and "face card" can occur simultaneously. (The jack, queen, and king of diamonds belong to both events.) So, we must use the first formula of the addition rule. We let D denote "diamond" and F denote "face card."

$\qquad P(D \text{ or } F) = P(D) + P(F) - P(D \text{ and } F)$ Addition rule

$\qquad\qquad\qquad = \dfrac{13}{52} + \dfrac{12}{52} - \dfrac{3}{52}$ There are 13 diamonds, 12 face cards, and 3 that are both.

$\qquad\qquad\qquad = \dfrac{22}{52}$ Add and subtract.

$\qquad\qquad\qquad = \dfrac{11}{26}$ Write in lowest terms.

EXAMPLE 8 Finding the Probability of an Event Involving "Or"

Of 20 elective courses, Emily plans to enroll in one, which she will choose by throwing a dart at the schedule of courses. If 8 of the courses are recreational, 9 are interesting, and 3 are both recreational and interesting, find the probability that the course she chooses will have at least one of these two attributes.

Solution

If R denotes "recreational" and I denotes "interesting," then

$$P(R) = \frac{8}{20}, \quad P(I) = \frac{9}{20}, \quad \text{and} \quad P(R \text{ and } I) = \frac{3}{20}.$$

R and I are not mutually exclusive.

$$P(R \text{ or } I) = \frac{8}{20} + \frac{9}{20} - \frac{3}{20}$$

$$= \frac{14}{20} \qquad \text{Addition rule}$$

$$= \frac{7}{10} \qquad \text{Write in lowest terms.}$$

11.2 EXERCISES

Probabilities for Rolling a Die *For the experiment of rolling a single fair die, find the probability of each event. (Hint: Recall that 1 is neither prime nor composite.)*

1. not prime
2. not less than 2
3. even or prime
4. odd or less than 5
5. less than 3 or greater than 4
6. odd or even

Probability and Odds for Drawing a Card *For the experiment of drawing a single card from a standard 52-card deck, find* **(a)** *the probability of each event, and* **(b)** *the odds in favor of each event.*

7. king or queen
8. not an ace
9. spade or face card
10. club or heart
11. neither a heart nor a 7
12. not a heart, or a 7

Number Sums for Rolling a Pair of Dice *For the experiment of rolling an ordinary pair of dice, find the probability that the sum will be each of the following. (You may want to use a table showing the sum for each of the 36 equally likely outcomes.)*

13. even or a multiple of 3   14. 11 or 12

15. less than 3 or greater than 9
16. odd or greater than 9

Prime Results *Find the probability of getting a prime number in each case.*

17. A number is chosen randomly from the set $\{1, 2, 3, 4, \ldots, 12\}$.
18. Two dice are rolled and the sum is observed.
19. A single digit is randomly chosen from the number 578.
20. A single digit is randomly chosen from the number 1234.
21. ***Determining Whether Events Are Mutually Exclusive*** Amanda has three office assistants. If A is the event that at least two of them are men and B is the event that at least two of them are women, are A and B mutually exclusive?
22. ***Determining Whether Events Are Mutually Exclusive*** Jeanne earned her college degree several years ago. Consider the following four events.

    Her alma mater is in the East.
    Her alma mater is a private college.
    Her alma mater is in the Northwest.
    Her alma mater is in the South.

    Are these events all mutually exclusive of one another?

Probabilities of Poker Hands *If you are dealt a 5-card hand (this implies without replacement) from a standard 52-card deck, find the probability of getting each of the following. Refer to* **Table 1** *of* **Section 11.1,** *and give answers to six decimal places.*

23. a full house or a straight

24. a black flush or two pairs

25. nothing any better than two pairs

26. a flush or three of a kind

Probabilities in Golf Scoring *The table gives Josh's probabilities of scoring in various ranges on a par-70 course. In a given round, find the probability of each event in Exercises 27–31.*

x	P(x)
Below 60	0.04
60–64	0.06
65–69	0.14
70–74	0.30
75–79	0.23
80–84	0.09
85–89	0.06
90–94	0.04
95–99	0.03
100 or above	0.01

27. par or above

28. in the 80s

29. less than 90

30. not in the 70s, 80s, or 90s

31. 95 or higher

32. What are the odds of Josh's scoring below par?

33. ***Probability Distribution*** Let x denote the sum of two distinct numbers selected randomly from the set of numbers $\{1, 2, 3, 4, 5\}$. Construct the probability distribution for the random variable x.

34. ***Probability Distribution*** Anne Kelly randomly chooses a single ball from the urn shown here, and x represents the color of the ball chosen. Construct a complete probability distribution for the random variable x.

Comparing Empirical and Theoretical Probabilities for Rolling Dice *Roll a pair of dice* 50 *times, keeping track of the number of times the sum is "less than* 3 *or greater than* 9" *(that is* 2, 10, 11, *or* 12*).*

35. From your results, calculate an empirical probability for the event "less than 3 or greater than 9."

36. By how much does your answer differ from the *theoretical* probability of **Exercise 15?**

37. Explain the difference between the two formulas in the addition rule of probability, illustrating each one with an appropriate example.

38. Suppose, for a given experiment, A, B, C, and D are events, all mutually exclusive of one another, such that

$$A \cup B \cup C \cup D = S \text{ (the sample space)}.$$

By extending the addition rule of probability to this case and utilizing probability Property 3, what statement can you make?

Complemental Probability *For Exercises 39–41, let A be an event within the sample space S, and let*

$$n(A) = a \quad and \quad n(S) = s.$$

39. Use the complements principle of counting to find an expression for $n(A')$.

40. Use the theoretical probability formula to express $P(A)$ and $P(A')$.

41. Evaluate and simplify $P(A) + P(A')$.

42. What rule have you proved?

The remaining exercises require careful thought for the determination of n(E) and n(S). (In some cases, you may want to employ counting methods from Chapter 10, such as the fundamental counting principle, permutations, or combinations.)

Building Numbers from Sets of Digits *Suppose we want to form three-digit numbers using the set of digits*

$$\{0, 1, 2, 3, 4, 5\}.$$

For example, 501 *and* 224 *are such numbers, but* 035 *is not.*

43. How many such numbers are possible?

44. How many of these numbers are multiples of 10?

45. How many of these numbers are multiples of 5?

46. If one three-digit number is chosen at random from all those that can be made from the above set of digits, find the probability that the one chosen is not a multiple of 5.

47. ***Drawing Colored Marbles from Boxes*** A bag contains fifty blue and fifty green marbles. Two marbles at a time are randomly selected. If both are green, they are placed in box A; if both are blue, in box B; if one is green and the other is blue, in box C. After all marbles are drawn, what is the probability that the numbers of marbles in box A and box B are the same? (*Mathematics Teacher* calendar problem)

48. *Multiplying Numbers Generated by Spinners* An experiment consists of spinning both spinners shown here and multiplying the resulting numbers together. Find the probability that the resulting product will be even.

 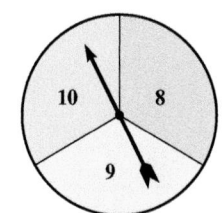

49. Luka and Janie are playing a coin toss game. If the coin lands heads up, Luka earns a point; otherwise, Janie earns a point. The first player to reach 20 points wins the game. If 19 of the first 37 tosses have been heads, what is the probability that Janie wins the game? (*Mathematics Teacher* calendar problem)

50. *Random Births on the Same Day of the Week* What is the probability that, of three people selected at random, at least two were born on the same day of the week? (*Mathematics Teacher* calendar problem)

11.3 CONDITIONAL PROBABILITY AND EVENTS INVOLVING "AND"

OBJECTIVES

1 Apply the conditional probability formula.

2 Determine whether two events are independent.

3 Apply the multiplication rule for the event "*A* and *B*."

Conditional Probability

Sometimes the probability of an event must be computed using the knowledge that some other event has happened (or is happening, or will happen — the timing is not important). This type of probability is called *conditional probability*.

CONDITIONAL PROBABILITY

The probability of event *B*, computed on the assumption that event *A* has happened, is called the **conditional probability of *B* given *A*** and is denoted

$$P(B|A).$$

EXAMPLE 1 Selecting from a Set of Numbers

From the sample space

$$S = \{1, 2, 3, 4, 5, 6, 7, 8, 9, 10\},$$

a single number is to be selected randomly. Find each probability given the events

A: The selected number is odd, and *B*: The selected number is a multiple of 3.

(a) $P(B)$ **(b)** $P(A \text{ and } B)$ **(c)** $P(B|A)$

Solution

(a) $B = \{3, 6, 9\}$, so

$$P(B) = \frac{n(B)}{n(S)} = \frac{3}{10}.$$

(b) *A* and *B* is the set $A \cap B = \{1, 3, 5, 7, 9\} \cap \{3, 6, 9\} = \{3, 9\}$.

$$P(A \text{ and } B) = \frac{n(A \cap B)}{n(S)} = \frac{2}{10} = \frac{1}{5} \qquad \text{Two elements}$$

(c) The given condition, that *A* occurs, effectively reduces the sample space from *S* to *A*, and the elements of the new sample space *A* that are also in *B* are the elements of $A \cap B$.

$$P(B|A) = \frac{n(A \cap B)}{n(A)} = \frac{2}{5} \qquad \blacksquare$$

WHEN Will I Ever USE This ?

Monty Hall

The probability is low that anyone reading this will ever be on a televised game show. But who knows? A former popular game show host, Monty Hall, has a rather famous problem named after him, and knowing the solution to the problem might help a contestant win a car instead of a goat.

Suppose that there are three doors, and you are asked to choose one of them. One of the doors hides a new car, and behind the two other doors are goats. You pick a door, say Door A. Then the host, who knows what's behind all three doors, opens another door, say Door C, and a goat appears. The host asks you whether you want to change your choice to Door B. *Is it to your advantage to do so?*

One way to look at the problem, given that the car is *not* behind Door C, is that Doors A and B are now equally likely to contain the car. Thus, switching doors will neither help nor hurt your chances of winning the car.

However, there is another way to look at the problem. When you picked Door A, the probability was $\frac{1}{3}$ that it contained the car. Being shown the goat behind Door C doesn't really give you any new information; after all, you knew that there was a goat behind at least one of the other doors. So seeing the goat behind Door C does nothing to change your assessment of the probability that Door A has the car. It remains $\frac{1}{3}$. But because Door C has been ruled out, the probability that Door B has the car is now $\frac{2}{3}$. Thus, you should switch.

Analysis of this problem depends on the psychology of the host. If we suppose that the host must *always* show you a losing door and then give you an option to switch, then you should switch. This was not specifically stated in the problem but has been pointed out by many mathematicians.

There are several Web sites that simulate the Monty Hall problem. One of them is http://stayorswitch.com/

(The authors wish to thank David Berman of the University of New Orleans for his assistance with this explanation.)

A **cosmic impact,** the collision of a meteor, comet, or asteroid with Earth could be as catastrophic as full-scale nuclear war, killing a billion or more people.

The Spaceguard Survey has discovered more than half of the estimated number of near-Earth asteroids (NEAs) 1 kilometer or more in diameter and hopes to locate 90% of them in the next decade. Although the risk of finding one on a collision course with the Earth is slight, it is anticipated that, if we did, we would be able to deflect it before impact.

The photo above shows a crater in Arizona, 4000 feet in diameter and 570 feet deep. It is thought to have been formed 20,000 to 50,000 years ago by a meteorite about 50 meters across, hitting the ground at several kilometers per second. (See http://en.wikipedia.org/wiki/Meteor_Crater.)

Example 1 illustrates some important points. First, because

$$\frac{n(A \cap B)}{n(A)} = \frac{\frac{n(A \cap B)}{n(S)}}{\frac{n(A)}{n(S)}} \quad \text{Multiply numerator and denominator by } \frac{1}{n(S)}.$$

$$= \frac{P(A \cap B)}{P(A)}, \quad \text{Theoretical probability formula}$$

the final line of the example gives the following convenient formula.

CONDITIONAL PROBABILITY FORMULA

The **conditional probability of B given A** is calculated as follows.

$$P(B|A) = \frac{P(A \cap B)}{P(A)} = \frac{P(A \text{ and } B)}{P(A)}$$

A second observation from **Example 1** is that the conditional probability of B given A was $\frac{2}{5}$, whereas the "unconditional" probability of B (with no condition given) was $\frac{3}{10}$, so the condition *did* make a difference.

▌▌▌ EXAMPLE 2   Finding Probabilities of Boys and Girls in a Family

Given a family with two children, find the probability of each event.

(a) Both are girls, given that at least one is a girl.

(b) Both are girls, given that the older child is a girl.

(Assume boys and girls are equally likely.)

Solution

We define the following events. (The older child's gender appears first.)

$$S = \{gg, gb, bg, bb\} \quad \text{Sample space } S; \ n(S) = 4$$
$$A = \{gg\} \quad \text{Both are girls. } P(A) = \frac{1}{4}$$
$$B = \{gg, gb, bg\} \quad \text{At least one is a girl. } P(B) = \frac{3}{4}$$
$$C = \{gg, gb\} \quad \text{The older one is a girl. } P(C) = \frac{2}{4}$$

Note that $A \cap B = \{gg\}$, and $A \cap C = \{gg\}$ as well. Thus

$$P(A \cap B) = P(A \cap C) = \frac{1}{4}.$$

(a) $P(A|B) = \dfrac{P(A \text{ and } B)}{P(B)} = \dfrac{\frac{1}{4}}{\frac{3}{4}} = \dfrac{1}{4} \div \dfrac{3}{4} = \dfrac{1}{4} \cdot \dfrac{4}{3} = \dfrac{1}{3}$

(b) $P(A|C) = \dfrac{P(A \text{ and } C)}{P(C)} = \dfrac{\frac{1}{4}}{\frac{2}{4}} = \dfrac{1}{4} \div \dfrac{2}{4} = \dfrac{1}{4} \cdot \dfrac{4}{2} = \dfrac{1}{2}$ ■

Independent Events

Sometimes a conditional probability is no different from the corresponding unconditional probability, in which case we call the two events *independent*.

One example of a card that is both a face card and black

INDEPENDENT EVENTS

Two events A and B are **independent events** if knowledge about the occurrence of one of them has no effect on the probability of the other one occurring. A and B are independent if

$$P(B|A) = P(B), \quad \text{or, equivalently,} \quad P(A|B) = P(A).$$

▌EXAMPLE 3 Checking Events for Independence

A single card is to be drawn from a standard 52-card deck. (The sample space S has 52 elements.) Find each of the following, given the events

    A: The selected card is a face card, and B: The selected card is black.

(a) $P(B)$ **(b)** $P(B|A)$

(c) Use the results of parts (a) and (b) to determine whether events A and B are independent.

Solution

(a) There are 26 black cards in the 52-card deck.

$$P(B) = \frac{26}{52} = \frac{1}{2} \quad \text{Theoretical probability formula}$$

(b) $P(B|A) = \dfrac{P(B \text{ and } A)}{P(A)}$ Conditional probability formula

$$= \frac{\dfrac{6}{52}}{\dfrac{12}{52}} \quad \text{Of 52 cards, 12 are face cards and 6 are black face cards.}$$

$$= \frac{6}{52} \cdot \frac{52}{12} \quad \text{To divide, multiply by the reciprocal of the divisor.}$$

$$= \frac{1}{2} \quad \text{Calculate and write in lowest terms.}$$

(c) Because $P(B|A) = P(B)$, events A and B are independent. ∎

Events Involving "And"

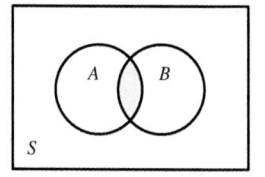

The logical connective "and" corresponds to "intersection" in set theory.

$P(A \text{ and } B) = P(A) \cdot P(B|A)$

Figure 10

If we multiply both sides of the conditional probability formula by $P(A)$, we obtain an expression for $P(A \cap B)$, which applies to events of the form "A and B." The resulting formula is related to the fundamental counting principle of **Chapter 10.** It is illustrated in **Figure 10.**

    Just as the calculation of $P(A \text{ or } B)$ is simpler when A and B are mutually exclusive, the calculation of $P(A \text{ and } B)$ is simpler when A and B are independent.

MULTIPLICATION RULE OF PROBABILITY (FOR THE EVENT "A AND B")

If A and B are *any two events,* then

$$P(A \text{ and } B) = P(A) \cdot P(B|A).$$

If A and B are *independent,* then

$$P(A \text{ and } B) = P(A) \cdot P(B).$$

The first formula in the multiplication rule actually applies in all cases, because $P(B|A) = P(B)$ when A and B are independent. The independence of the component events is clear in many cases, so it is good to remember the second formula.

Even **a rare occurrence** can sometimes cause widespread controversy. When Mattel Toys marketed a new talking Barbie doll a few years ago, some of the Barbies were programmed to say "Math class is tough." The National Council of Teachers of Mathematics (NCTM), the American Association of University Women (AAUW), and numerous consumers voiced complaints about the damage such a message could do to the self-confidence of children and to their attitudes toward school and mathematics. Mattel subsequently agreed to erase the phrase from the microchip to be used in future doll production.

Originally, each Barbie was programmed to say four different statements, randomly selected from a pool of 270 prerecorded statements. Therefore, the probability of getting a Barbie that said "Math class is tough" was only

$$\frac{1 \cdot {}_{269}C_3}{{}_{270}C_4} \approx 0.015 = 1.5\%.$$

Other messages included in the pool were "I love school, don't you?," "I'm studying to be a doctor," and "Let's study for the quiz."

EXAMPLE 4 Selecting from a Set of Books

Each year, Jacqui adds to her book collection a number of new publications that she believes will be of lasting value and interest. She has categorized each of her twenty acquisitions for 2015 as hardcover or paperback and as fiction or nonfiction. The numbers of books in the various categories are shown in **Table 6.**

Table 6 Year 2015 Books

	Fiction (*F*)	Nonfiction (*N*)	Totals
Hardcover (*H*)	3	5	8
Paperback (*P*)	8	4	12
Totals	11	9	20

Reduced sample space in part (b)

If Jacqui randomly chooses one of these 20 books, find the probability that it will be each of the following.

(a) hardcover   **(b)** fiction, given it is hardcover   **(c)** hardcover and fiction

Solution

(a) Eight of the 20 books are hardcover, so $P(H) = \frac{8}{20} = \frac{2}{5}$.

(b) The given condition that the book is hardcover reduces the sample space to eight books. Of those eight, just three are fiction, so $P(F|H) = \frac{3}{8}$.

(c) $P(H \text{ and } F) = P(H) \cdot P(F|H) = \frac{2}{5} \cdot \frac{3}{8} = \frac{3}{20}$ Multiplication rule

It is easier here if we simply notice, directly from **Table 6,** that 3 of the 20 books are "hardcover and fiction." This verifies that the general multiplication rule of probability did give us the correct answer. ∎

EXAMPLE 5 Selecting from a Set of Planets

Table 7 Mean Distance of Planets from the Sun

Mercury	58
Venus	108
Earth	150
Mars	228
Jupiter	778
Saturn	1430
Uranus	2870
Neptune	4500

Table 7 lists the eight planets of our solar system, together with their mean distances from the sun, in millions of kilometers. (Data is from *The World Almanac and Book of Facts*.) Carrie must choose two distinct planets to cover in her astronomy report. If she selects randomly, find the probability that the first one selected is closer to the sun than Mars and the second is closer to the sun than Saturn.

Solution

We define the following events.

A: The first is closer than Mars. B: The second is closer than Saturn.

Then $P(A) = \frac{3}{8}$ because three of the original eight choices are favorable to event A. If the planet selected first is closer than Mars, it is also closer than Saturn, and since that planet is no longer available, four of the remaining seven are favorable to event B. Thus $P(B|A) = \frac{4}{7}$. Now apply the multiplication rule.

$$P(A \text{ and } B) = P(A) \cdot P(B|A) = \frac{3}{8} \cdot \frac{4}{7} = \frac{3}{14} \approx 0.214 \quad \text{Multiplication rule} \quad ∎$$

In **Example 5,** the condition that A had occurred changed the probability of B, since the selection was done, in effect, without replacement. (Repetitions were not allowed.) Events A and B were not independent. On the other hand, in the next example the same events, A and B, are independent.

EXAMPLE 6 Selecting from a Set of Planets

Carrie must again select two planets, but this time one is for an oral report, the other is for a written report, and they need not be distinct. Here, the same planet may be selected for both reports. Again, find the probability that if she selects randomly, the first is closer than Mars and the second is closer than Saturn.

Solution

Defining events A and B as in **Example 5,** we have $P(A) = \frac{3}{8}$, just as before. But the selection is now done *with* replacement because repetitions *are* allowed. Event B is independent of event A, so we can use the second form of the multiplication rule.

$$P(A \text{ and } B) = P(A) \cdot P(B) = \frac{3}{8} \cdot \frac{5}{8} = \frac{15}{64} \approx 0.234 \quad \text{Answer is different than in \textbf{Example 5}.} \quad \blacksquare$$

EXAMPLE 7 Selecting from a Deck of Cards

One example of a card that is black and one example of a card that is a diamond

(No single card is both black and a diamond.)

A single card is drawn from a standard 52-card deck. Let B denote the event that the card is black, and let D denote the event that it is a diamond. Are events B and D

(a) independent? **(b)** mutually exclusive?

Solution

(a) For the unconditional probability of D, we get $P(D) = \frac{13}{52} = \frac{1}{4}$ because 13 of the 52 cards are diamonds. But for the conditional probability of D given B, we have $P(D|B) = \frac{0}{26} = 0$. None of the 26 black cards are diamonds. Since the conditional probability $P(D|B)$ is different from the unconditional probability $P(D)$, **B and D are not independent.**

(b) Mutually exclusive events are events that cannot both occur for a given performance of an experiment. Since no card in the deck is both black and a diamond, **B and D are mutually exclusive.** $\blacksquare$

EXAMPLE 8 Selecting from an Urn of Balls

Anne is still drawing balls from the same urn, as shown at the side. This time she draws three balls, without replacement. Find the probability that she gets red, yellow, and blue balls, in that order.

Solution

Using appropriate letters to denote the colors, and subscripts to indicate first, second, and third draws, the event can be symbolized "R_1 and Y_2 and B_3."

$$P(R_1 \text{ and } Y_2 \text{ and } B_3) = P(R_1) \cdot P(Y_2|R_1) \cdot P(B_3|R_1 \text{ and } Y_2)$$

$$= \frac{4}{11} \cdot \frac{5}{10} \cdot \frac{2}{9} = \frac{4}{99} \approx 0.0404 \quad \blacksquare$$

One example of five cards that are all hearts

EXAMPLE 9 Selecting from a Deck of Cards

If five cards are drawn without replacement from a standard 52-card deck, find the probability that they all are hearts.

Solution

Each time a heart is drawn, the number of available cards decreases by one and the number of hearts decreases by one.

$$P(\text{all hearts}) = \frac{13}{52} \cdot \frac{12}{51} \cdot \frac{11}{50} \cdot \frac{10}{49} \cdot \frac{9}{48} = \frac{33}{66,640} \approx 0.000495$$ ∎

We saw in **Chapter 10** that the problem of **Example 9** can also be solved by using the theoretical probability formula and combinations. The total possible number of 5-card hands, drawn without replacement, is $_{52}C_5$, and the number of those containing only hearts is $_{13}C_5$.

$$P(\text{all hearts}) = \frac{_{13}C_5}{_{52}C_5} = \frac{\dfrac{13!}{5! \cdot 8!}}{\dfrac{52!}{5! \cdot 47!}} \approx 0.000495 \quad \text{Use a calculator.}$$

EXAMPLE 10 Using Both Addition and Multiplication Rules

The local garage employs two mechanics, Ray and Tom. Your consumer club has found that Ray does twice as many jobs as Tom, Ray does a good job three out of four times, and Tom does a good job only two out of five times. If you plan to take your car in for repairs, find the probability that a good job will be done.

Solution

We define the following events.

R: work done by Ray   T: work done by Tom   G: good job done

Since Ray does twice as many jobs as Tom, the unconditional probabilities of events R and T are, respectively, $\frac{2}{3}$ and $\frac{1}{3}$. Because Ray does a good job three out of four times, the probability of a good job, given that Ray did the work, is $\frac{3}{4}$. And because Tom does well two out of five times, the probability of a good job, given that Tom did the work, is $\frac{2}{5}$. (These last two probabilities are conditional.) These four values can be summarized.

$$P(R) = \frac{2}{3}, \quad P(T) = \frac{1}{3} \quad P(G \mid R) = \frac{3}{4}, \quad \text{and} \quad P(G \mid T) = \frac{2}{5}$$

Event G can occur in two mutually exclusive ways: Ray could do the work and do a good job $(R \cap G)$, or Tom could do the work and do a good job $(T \cap G)$.

$$
\begin{aligned}
P(G) &= P(R \cap G) + P(T \cap G) && \text{Addition rule} \\
&= P(R) \cdot P(G \mid R) + P(T) \cdot P(G \mid T) && \text{Multiplication rule} \\
&= \frac{2}{3} \cdot \frac{3}{4} + \frac{1}{3} \cdot \frac{2}{5} && \text{Substitute the values.} \\
&= \frac{1}{2} + \frac{2}{15} = \frac{19}{30} \approx 0.633
\end{aligned}
$$

Multiply first, then add. ∎

The **search for extraterrestrial intelligence (SETI)** may have begun in earnest as early as 1961, when Dr. Frank Drake presented an equation for estimating the number of possible civilizations in the Milky Way galaxy whose communications we might detect. Over the years, the effort has been advanced by many scientists, including the late astronomer and exobiologist Carl Sagan, who popularized the issue in TV appearances and in his book *The Cosmic Connection: An Extraterrestrial Perspective* (Dell Paperback). "There must be other starfolk," said Sagan. In fact, some astronomers have estimated the odds against life on Earth being the only life in the universe at one hundred billion billion to one.

Other experts disagree. Freeman Dyson, a noted mathematical physicist and astronomer, says (in his book *Disturbing the Universe*) that after considering the same evidence and arguments, he believes it is just as likely as not (even odds) that there never was any other intelligent life out there.

The tree diagram in **Figure 11** shows a graphical way to organize the work of **Example 10.** Use the given information to draw the tree diagram; then find the probability of a good job by adding the probabilities from the two indicated branches of the tree.

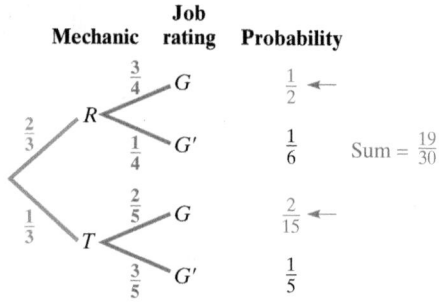

Garage mechanics experiment

Figure 11

The Birthday Problem

A classic problem (with a surprising result) involves the probability that a given group of people will include at least one pair of people with the same birthday (the same day of the year, not necessarily the same year). This problem can be analyzed using the probability of a complement formula (**Section 11.2**) and the multiplication rule of probability from this section. Suppose there are three people in the group.

P (at least one duplication of birthdays)

$= 1 - P$(no duplications)   Complement formula

$= 1 - P$(2nd is different than 1st, and 3rd is different than 1st and 2nd)

$= 1 - \dfrac{364}{365} \cdot \dfrac{363}{365}$ Multiplication rule

$\approx 1 - 0.992$

$= 0.008$

(To simplify the calculations, we have assumed 365 possible birth dates, ignoring February 29.)

By doing more calculations like the one above, we find that the smaller the group, the smaller the probability of a duplication. The larger the group, the larger the probability of a duplication. The table below shows the probability of at least one duplication for numbers of people from 2 through 52.

For Group or Individual Investigation

1. Based on the data shown in the table, what are the odds in favor of a duplication in a group of 30 people?

2. Estimate from the table the least number of people for which the probability of duplication is at least $\frac{1}{2}$.

3. How small a group is required for the probability of a duplication to be *exactly* 0?

4. How large a group is required for the probability of a duplication to be *exactly* 1?

The answers are on **page 655.**

Number of People	Probability of at Least One Duplication	Number of People	Probability of at Least One Duplication	Number of People	Probability of at Least One Duplication
2	0.003	19	0.379	36	0.832
3	0.008	20	0.411	37	0.849
4	0.016	21	0.444	38	0.864
5	0.027	22	0.476	39	0.878
6	0.040	23	0.507	40	0.891
7	0.056	24	0.538	41	0.903
8	0.074	25	0.569	42	0.914
9	0.095	26	0.598	43	0.924
10	0.117	27	0.627	44	0.933
11	0.141	28	0.654	45	0.941
12	0.167	29	0.681	46	0.948
13	0.194	30	0.706	47	0.955
14	0.223	31	0.730	48	0.961
15	0.253	32	0.753	49	0.966
16	0.284	33	0.775	50	0.970
17	0.315	34	0.795	51	0.974
18	0.347	35	0.814	52	0.978

The **search for extraterrestrial intelligence (SETI)** has been mainly accomplished in recent years through **SETI@HOME,** a very large distributed computing program. Most of the data are collected by the world's largest radio telescope, built into a 20-acre natural bowl in Aricebo, Puerto Rico (pictured above), and processed by millions of personal computers around the world.

To learn more, or for a chance to be the first to "contact" an extraterrestrial civilization, check out
www.setiathome.ssl.berkeley.edu.

EXAMPLE 11 Selecting Door Prizes

Rob is among five door prize winners at a Christmas party. The five winners are asked to choose, without looking, from a bag that, they are told, contains five tokens, four of them redeemable for candy canes and one specific token redeemable for a $100 gift certificate. Can Rob improve his chance of getting the gift certificate by drawing first among the five people?

Solution

We denote candy cane by C, gift certificate by G, and first draw, second draw, and so on by subscripts 1, 2,…. If Rob draws first, his probability of getting the gift certificate is

$$P(G_1) = \frac{1}{5}.$$

If he draws second, his probability of getting the gift certificate is

$$P(G_2) = P(C_1 \text{ and } G_2)$$
$$= P(C_1) \cdot P(G_2 | C_1)$$
$$= \frac{4}{5} \cdot \frac{1}{4} = \frac{1}{5}. \quad \text{Same result as above}$$

For the third draw,

$$P(G_3) = P(C_1 \text{ and } C_2 \text{ and } G_3)$$
$$= P(C_1) \cdot P(C_2 | C_1) \cdot P(G_3 | C_1 \text{ and } C_2)$$
$$= \frac{4}{5} \cdot \frac{3}{4} \cdot \frac{1}{3} = \frac{1}{5}. \quad \text{Same result as above}$$

The probability of getting the gift certificate is also $\frac{1}{5}$ when drawing fourth or fifth. The order in which the five winners draw does not affect Rob's chances. ∎

11.3 EXERCISES

From the sample space

$$S = \{1, 2, 3, 4, \ldots, 15\},$$

a single number is to be selected at random. Given the events

   A: *The selected number is even,*

   B: *The selected number is a multiple of 4,*

   C: *The selected number is a prime number,*

find each probability in Exercises 1–10.

1. $P(A)$ **2.** $P(B)$

3. $P(C)$ **4.** $P(A \text{ and } B)$

5. $P(A \text{ and } C)$ **6.** $P(B \text{ and } C)$

7. $P(A | B)$ **8.** $P(B | A)$

9. $P(C | A)$ **10.** $P(A | C)$

Given a family with three children, find the probability of each event.

11. All are girls.   **12.** All are boys.

13. The oldest two are boys, given that there are at least two boys.

14. The youngest is a girl, given that there are at least two girls.

15. The oldest is a boy and the youngest is a girl, given that there are at least one boy and at least one girl.

16. The youngest two are girls, given that there are at least two girls.

17. The oldest two are boys, given that the oldest is a boy.

18. The oldest is a boy, given that there is at least one boy.

19. The youngest is a boy, given that the birth order alternates between girls and boys.

20. The oldest is a girl, given that the middle child is a girl.

For each experiment, determine whether the two given events are independent.

21. *Coin Tosses* A fair coin is tossed twice. The events are "head on the first" and "head on the second."

22. *Dice Rolls* A pair of dice are rolled. The events are "even on the first" and "odd on the second."

23. *Planets' Mean Distances from the Sun* Two planets are selected, without replacement, from the list in **Table 7**. The events are "the first selected planet is closer than Jupiter" and "the second selected planet is farther than Mars."

24. *Mean Distances from the Sun* Two planets are selected, with replacement, from the list in **Table 7**. The events are "the first selected planet is closer than Earth" and "the second selected planet is farther than Uranus."

25. *Answers on a Multiple-choice Test* The answers are all guessed on a twenty-question multiple-choice test. The events are "the first answer is correct" and "the last answer is correct."

26. *Committees of U.S. Senators* A committee of five is randomly selected from the 100 U.S. senators. The events are "the first member selected is a Republican" and "the second member selected is a Republican." (Assume that there are both Republicans and non-Republicans in the Senate.)

Gender and Career Motivation of College Students One hundred college seniors attending a career fair at a university were categorized according to gender and according to primary career motivation. See the table for the results.

	Primary Career Motivation			
	Money	**Allowed to be Creative**	**Sense of Giving to Society**	**Total**
Male	19	15	14	48
Female	12	23	17	52
Total	31	38	31	100

If one of these students is to be selected at random, find the probability that the student selected will satisfy each condition in Exercises 27–32.

27. female

28. motivated primarily by creativity

29. not motivated primarily by money

30. male and motivated primarily by money

31. male, given that primary motivation is a sense of giving to society

32. motivated primarily by money or creativity, given that the student is female

Pet Selection A pet store has seven puppies, including four huskies, two terriers, and one retriever. If Rebecka and Aaron, in that order, each select one puppy at random, with replacement (they may both select the same one), find the probability of each event in Exercises 33–36.

33. Both select a husky.

34. Rebecka selects a retriever; Aaron selects a terrier.

35. Rebecka selects a terrier; Aaron selects a retriever.

36. Both select a retriever.

Pet Selection Suppose two puppies are selected as earlier, but this time without replacement (Rebecka and Aaron cannot both select the same puppy). Find the probability of each event in Exercises 37–42.

37. Both select a husky.

38. Aaron selects a terrier, given that Rebecka selects a husky.

39. Aaron selects a retriever, given that Rebecka selects a husky.

40. Rebecka selects a retriever.

41. Aaron selects a retriever, given that Rebecka selects a retriever.

42. Both select a retriever.

Card Dealing *Let two cards be dealt successively, without replacement, from a standard 52-card deck. Find the probability of each event in Exercises 43–49.*

43. spade dealt second, given a spade dealt first

44. club dealt second, given a diamond dealt first

45. two face cards   **46.** no face cards

47. The first card is a jack and the second is a face card.

48. The first card is the ace of hearts and the second is black.

49. The first card is black and the second is red.

50. **Proof of Formulas** Given events A and B within the sample space S, the following sequence of steps establishes formulas that can be used to compute conditional probabilities. Justify each statement.

(a) $P(A \text{ and } B) = P(A) \cdot P(B \mid A)$

(b) Therefore, $P(B \mid A) = \dfrac{P(A \text{ and } B)}{P(A)}$.

(c) Therefore, $P(B \mid A) = \dfrac{n(A \text{ and } B)/n(S)}{n(A)/n(S)}$.

(d) Therefore, $P(B \mid A) = \dfrac{n(A \text{ and } B)}{n(A)}$.

Conditions in Card Drawing *Use the results of **Exercise 50** to find each probability when a single card is drawn from a standard 52-card deck.*

51. $P(\text{queen} \mid \text{face card})$ **52.** $P(\text{face card} \mid \text{queen})$

53. $P(\text{red} \mid \text{diamond})$ **54.** $P(\text{diamond} \mid \text{red})$

Property of P(A and B) *Complete Exercises 55 and 56 to discover a general property of the probability of an event of the form "A and B."*

55. If one number is chosen randomly from the integers 1 through 10, the probability of getting a number that is *odd and prime*, by the multiplication rule, is

$$P(\text{odd}) \cdot P(\text{prime} \mid \text{odd}) = \frac{5}{10} \cdot \frac{3}{5} = \frac{3}{10}.$$

Compute the product $P(\text{prime}) \cdot P(\text{odd} \mid \text{prime})$, and compare to the product above.

56. What does **Exercise 55** imply, in general, about the probability of an event of the form "A and B"?

57. **Gender in Sequences of Babies** Two authors of this book each have three sons and no daughters. Assuming boy and girl babies are equally likely, what is the probability of this event?

58. **Dice Rolls** Three dice are rolled. What is the probability that the numbers shown will all be different? (*Mathematics Teacher* calendar problem)

The remaining exercises, and groups of exercises, may require concepts from earlier sections, such as the complements principle of counting and addition rules, as well as the multiplication rule of this section.

Warehouse Grocery Shopping *Therese manages a grocery warehouse that encourages volume shopping on the part of its customers. Therese has discovered that on any given weekday, 70% of the customer sales amount to* *more than $100. That is, any given sale on such a day has a probability of 0.70 of being for more than $100. (Actually, the conditional probabilities throughout the day would change slightly, depending on earlier sales, but this effect would be negligible for the first several sales of the day, so we can treat them as independent.)*

Find the probability of each event in Exercises 59–62. (Give answers to three decimal places.)

59. The first two sales on Wednesday are both for more than $100.

60. The first three sales on Wednesday are all for more than $100.

61. None of the first three sales on Wednesday is for more than $100.

62. Exactly one of the first three sales on Wednesday is for more than $100.

Pollution from the Space Shuttle Launch Site *One problem encountered by developers of the space shuttle program was air pollution in the area surrounding the launch site. A certain direction from the launch site was considered critical in terms of hydrogen chloride pollution from the exhaust cloud. It has been determined that weather conditions would cause emission cloud movement in the critical direction only 5% of the time.*

In Exercises 63–66, find the probability for each event. Assume that probabilities for a particular launch in no way depend on the probabilities for other launches. (Give answers to two decimal places.)

63. A given launch will not result in cloud movement in the critical direction.

64. No cloud movement in the critical direction will occur during any of 5 launches.

65. Any 5 launches will result in at least one cloud movement in the critical direction.

66. Any 10 launches will result in at least one cloud movement in the critical direction.

Job Interviews *Three men and three women are waiting to be interviewed for jobs. If they are all selected in random order, find the probability of each event in Exercises 67–70.*

67. All the women will be interviewed first.

68. The first interviewee will be a man, and the remaining ones will alternate gender.

69. The first three chosen will all be the same gender.

70. No man will be interviewed until at least two women have been interviewed.

Garage Door Opener *Kevin installed a certain brand of automatic garage door opener that utilizes a transmitter control with six independent switches, each one set on or off. The receiver (wired to the door) must be set with the same pattern as the transmitter. (Exercises 71–74 are based on ideas similar to those of the "birthday problem" in the* **For Further Thought** *feature in this section.)*

71. How many different ways can Kevin set the switches?

72. If one of Kevin's neighbors also has this same brand of opener, and both of them set the switches randomly, what is the probability, to four decimal places, that they will use the same settings?

73. If five neighbors with the same type of opener set their switches independently, what is the probability of at least one pair of neighbors using the same settings? (Give your answer to four decimal places.)

74. What is the minimum number of neighbors who must use this brand of opener before the probability of at least one duplication of settings is greater than $\frac{1}{2}$?

Weather Conditions on Successive Days *In November, the rain in a certain valley tends to fall in storms of several days' duration. The unconditional probability of rain on any given day of the month is 0.500. But the probability of rain on a day that follows a rainy day is 0.800, and the probability of rain on a day following a nonrainy day is 0.300. Find the probability of each event in Exercises 75–78. Give answers to three decimal places.*

75. rain on two randomly selected consecutive days in November

76. rain on three randomly selected consecutive days in November

77. rain on November 1 and 2, but not on November 3 (The October 31 weather is unknown.)

78. rain on the first four days of November, given that October 31 was clear all day

Engine Failures in a Vintage Aircraft *In a certain four-engine vintage aircraft, now quite unreliable, each engine has a 10% chance of failure on any flight, as long as it is carrying its one-fourth share of the load. But if one engine fails, then the chance of failure increases to 20% for each of the other three engines. And if a second engine fails, each of the remaining two has a 30% chance of failure.*

Assuming that no two engines ever fail simultaneously, and that the aircraft can continue flying with as few as two operating engines, find each probability for a given flight of this aircraft. (Give answers to four decimal places.)

79. no engine failures

80. exactly one engine failure (any one of four engines)

81. exactly two engine failures (any two of four engines)

82. a failed flight

Fair Decisions from Biased Coins *Many everyday decisions, like who will drive to lunch or who will pay for the coffee, are made by the toss of a (presumably fair) coin and using the criterion "heads, you will; tails, I will." This criterion is not quite fair, however, if the coin is biased (perhaps due to slightly irregular construction or wear). John von Neumann suggested a way to make perfectly fair decisions, even with a possibly biased coin. If a coin, biased so that*

$$P(h) = 0.5200 \quad \text{and} \quad P(t) = 0.4800,$$

is tossed twice, find each probability. Give answers to four decimal places.

83. $P(hh)$ **84.** $P(ht)$

85. $P(th)$ **86.** $P(tt)$

87. Having completed **Exercises 83–86,** can you suggest what von Neumann's scheme may have been?

One-and-one Free Throw Shooting in Basketball *In basketball, "one-and-one" free throw shooting (commonly called foul shooting) is done as follows: If the player makes the first shot (1 point), she is given a second shot. If she misses the first shot, she is not given a second shot (see the tree diagram).*

Christine, a basketball player, has a 70% free throw record. (She makes 70% of her free throws.) Find the probability that, on a given one-and-one free throw shooting opportunity, Christine will score each number of points.

88. no points   **89.** one point   **90.** two points

91. *Gender in Sequences of Babies*   Assuming boy and girl babies are equally likely, find the probability that it would take

   (a) at least three births to obtain two girls

   (b) at least four births to obtain two girls

   (c) at least five births to obtain two girls.

92. *Card Choices*   Cards are drawn, without replacement, from an ordinary 52-card deck.

   (a) How many must be drawn before the probability of obtaining at least one face card is greater than $\frac{1}{2}$?

   (b) How many must be drawn before the probability of obtaining at least one king is greater than $\frac{1}{2}$?

93. *A Two-Headed Coin?*   A gambler has two coins in his pocket—one fair coin and one two-headed coin. He selects a coin at random and flips it twice. If he gets two heads, what is the probability that he selected the fair coin? (*Mathematics Teacher* calendar problem)

94. *Cube Cuts*   A $4'' \times 4'' \times 4''$ cube is painted and then cut into sixty-four $1'' \times 1'' \times 1''$ cubes. A unit cube is then randomly selected and rolled. What is the probability that the top face of the rolled cube is painted? Express your answer as a common fraction. (*Mathematics Teacher* calendar problem)

95. *Anne Continues*   In **Example 8,** where Anne draws three balls without replacement, what would be her probability of getting one of each color, where the order does not matter?

96. *Card Choices*   There are three cards, one that is green on both sides, one that is red on both sides, and one that is green on one side and red on the other. One of the three cards is selected randomly and laid on the table. If it happens that the card on the table has a red side up, what is the probability that it is also red on the other side?

97. *Empirical and Theoretical Probabilities in Dice Rolling*   Roll a pair of dice until a sum of seven appears, keeping track of how many rolls it took. Repeat the process a total of 50 times, each time recording the number of rolls it took to get a sum of seven.

   (a) Use your experimental data to compute an empirical probability to two decimal places that it would take at least three rolls to get a sum of seven.

   (b) Find the theoretical probability to two decimal places that it would take at least three rolls to obtain a sum of seven.

98. Go to the Web site http://www.planetary.org/explore/space-topics/ and select the topic *Asteroids and Comets.* Write a report on the threat to humanity of cosmic impacts. Include an explanation of the acronym *NEO*.

11.4   BINOMIAL PROBABILITY

OBJECTIVES

1 Construct a simple binomial probability distribution.

2 Apply the binomial probability formula for an experiment involving Bernoulli trials.

Binomial Probability Distribution

Suppose the spinner in **Figure 12** on the next page is spun twice. We are interested in the number of times a 2 is obtained. (Assume that 1, 2, and 3 all are equally likely on a given spin.) We can think of the outcome 2 as a "success," while a 1 or a 3 would be a "failure."

When the outcomes of an experiment are divided into just two categories, success and failure, the associated probabilities are called "binomial." (The prefix *bi* means *two*.) Repeated performances of such an experiment, where the probability of success remains constant throughout all repetitions, are also known as repeated **Bernoulli trials** (after James Bernoulli). If we use an ordered pair to represent the result of each pair of spins, then the sample space for this experiment is

$$S = \{(1,1), (1,2), (1,3), (2,1), (2,2), (2,3), (3,1), (3,2), (3,3)\}.$$

The nine outcomes in *S* are all equally likely. This follows from the numbers 1, 2, and 3 being equally likely on a particular spin.

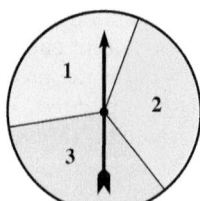

Figure 12

Table 8 Probability
Distribution for the Number
of 2s in Two Spins

x	$P(x)$
0	$\frac{4}{9}$
1	$\frac{4}{9}$
2	$\frac{1}{9}$
	Sum: $\frac{9}{9} = 1$

James Bernoulli (1654–1705) is also
known as Jacob or Jacques. He was
charmed away from theology by the
writings of Leibniz, became his pupil, and
later headed the mathematics faculty
at the University of Basel. His results in
probability are contained in the *Art of
Conjecture*, which was published in 1713,
after his death, and which also included
a reprint of the earlier Huygens paper.
Bernoulli also made many contributions to
calculus and analytic geometry.

If x denotes the number of 2s occurring on each pair of spins, then x is an
example of a *random variable*. Although we cannot predict the result of any particular pair of spins, we can find the probabilities of various events from the sample
space listing. In S, the number of 2s is 0 in four cases, 1 in four cases, and 2 in one
case, as reflected in **Table 8**. Because the table includes all possible values of x,
together with their probabilities, it is an example of a *probability distribution*. In
this case, we have a **binomial probability distribution**. The probability column in
Table 8 has a sum of 1, in agreement with probability Property 3 in **Section 11.2**.

In order to develop a general formula for binomial probabilities, we can consider another way to obtain the probability values in **Table 8**. The various spins
of the spinner are independent of one another, and on each spin the probability of
success (S) is $\frac{1}{3}$ and the probability of failure (F) is $\frac{2}{3}$. We will denote success on
the first spin by S_1, failure on the second by F_2, and so on.

$$P(x = 0) = P(F_1 \text{ and } F_2)$$
$$= P(F_1) \cdot P(F_2) \quad \text{Multiplication rule}$$
$$= \frac{2}{3} \cdot \frac{2}{3} \quad \text{Substitute values.}$$
$$= \frac{4}{9} \quad \text{Multiply.}$$

$$P(x = 1) = P[(S_1 \text{ and } F_2) \text{ or } (F_1 \text{ and } S_2)] \quad \text{2 ways to get } x = 1$$
$$= P(S_1 \text{ and } F_2) + P(F_1 \text{ and } S_2) \quad \text{Addition rule}$$
$$= P(S_1) \cdot P(F_2) + P(F_1) \cdot P(S_2) \quad \text{Multiplication rule}$$
$$= \frac{1}{3} \cdot \frac{2}{3} + \frac{2}{3} \cdot \frac{1}{3} \quad \text{Substitute values.}$$
$$= \frac{2}{9} + \frac{2}{9} \quad \text{Multiply.}$$
$$= \frac{4}{9} \quad \text{Add.}$$

$$P(x = 2) = P(S_1 \text{ and } S_2)$$
$$= P(S_1) \cdot P(S_2) \quad \text{Multiplication rule}$$
$$= \frac{1}{3} \cdot \frac{1}{3} \quad \text{Substitute values.}$$
$$= \frac{1}{9} \quad \text{Multiply.}$$

Notice the following pattern in the above calculations. There is only one way
to get $x = 0$ (namely, F_1 and F_2). And there is only one way to get $x = 2$ (namely,
S_1 and S_2). But there are two ways to get $x = 1$. One way is S_1 and F_2; the other is
F_1 and S_2. There are two ways because the one success required can occur on the
first spin or on the second spin. How many ways can exactly one success occur in
two repeated trials? This question is equivalent to

> ***How many size-one subsets are there of the set of two trials?***

The answer is $_2C_1 = 2$. The expression $_2C_1$ denotes "combinations of 2 things taken
1 at a time." Each of the two ways to get exactly one success has a probability equal
to $\frac{1}{3} \cdot \frac{2}{3}$, the probability of success times the probability of failure.

EXAMPLE 1 Constructing a Probability Distribution

Use a tree diagram to construct a probability distribution for the number of 2s in three spins of the spinner in **Figure 12.**

Solution

If the spinner is spun three times rather than two, then x, the number of successes (2s) could have values of 0, 1, 2, or 3. Then the number of ways to get exactly 1 success is $_3C_1 = 3$. They are

$$S_1 \text{ and } F_2 \text{ and } F_3, \quad F_1 \text{ and } S_2 \text{ and } F_3, \quad F_1 \text{ and } F_2 \text{ and } S_3.$$

The probability of each of these three ways is $\frac{1}{3} \cdot \frac{2}{3} \cdot \frac{2}{3} = \frac{4}{27}$.

$$P(x = 1) = 3 \cdot \frac{4}{27} = \frac{12}{27} = \frac{4}{9}$$

Figure 13 shows all possibilities for three spins, and **Table 9** gives the associated probability distribution. In the tree diagram, the number of ways of getting two successes in three trials is 3, in agreement with the fact that $_3C_2 = 3$. Also the sum of the $P(x)$ column in **Table 9** is again 1.

Table 9 Probability Distribution for the Number of 2s in Three Spins

x	$P(x)$
0	$\frac{8}{27}$
1	$\frac{12}{27}$
2	$\frac{6}{27}$
3	$\frac{1}{27}$

Sum: $\frac{27}{27} = 1$

Tree diagram for three spins

Figure 13

Problem-Solving Strategy

One of the various problem-solving strategies from **Chapter 1** was "Look for a pattern." Having constructed complete probability distributions for binomial experiments with 2 and 3 repeated trials (and probability of success $\frac{1}{3}$), we can now generalize the observed pattern to any binomial experiment, as shown next.

Binomial Probability Formula

Define the following quantities.

n = the number of repeated trials

p = the probability of success on any given trial

$q = 1 - p$ = the probability of failure on any given trial

x = the number of successes that occur

Note that p remains fixed throughout all n trials. This means that all trials are independent of one another. The random variable x representing the number of successes can have any integer value from 0 through n. In general, x successes can be assigned among n repeated trials in $_nC_x$ different ways, because this is the number of different subsets of x positions among a set of n positions. Also, regardless of which x of the trials result in successes, there will always be x successes and $n - x$ failures, so we multiply x factors of p and $n - x$ factors of q together.

BINOMIAL PROBABILITY FORMULA

When n independent repeated trials occur, where

$$p = \text{probability of success} \quad \text{and} \quad q = \text{probability of failure}$$

with p and q (where $q = 1 - p$) remaining constant throughout all n trials, the probability of exactly x successes is calculated as follows.

$$P(x) = {}_nC_x\, p^x q^{n-x} = \frac{n!}{x!(n-x)!}\, p^x q^{n-x}$$

Binomial probabilities for particular values of $n, p,$ and x can be found directly using tables, statistical software, and some handheld calculators. In the following examples, we use the formula derived above.

From the
DISTR menu

binompdf(5,.5,3)
.3125
Ans▶Frac
$\frac{5}{16}$

The TI-83/84 Plus calculator will find the probability discussed in **Example 2.**

EXAMPLE 2 Finding Probability in Coin Tossing

Find the probability of obtaining exactly three heads in five tosses of a fair coin.

Solution

Let heads be "success." Then this is a binomial experiment with

$$n = 5, \quad p = \frac{1}{2}, \quad q = \frac{1}{2}, \quad \text{and} \quad x = 3.$$

$$P(x = 3) = {}_5C_3\left(\frac{1}{2}\right)^3\left(\frac{1}{2}\right)^{5-3} = 10 \cdot \frac{1}{8} \cdot \frac{1}{4} = \frac{5}{16} \quad \text{Binomial probability formula} \quad \blacksquare$$

binompdf(6,1/6,2)
.200938786

This screen supports the answer in
Example 3.

EXAMPLE 3 Finding Probability in Dice Rolling

Find the probability of obtaining exactly two 5s in six rolls of a fair die.

Solution

Let 5 be "success." Then $n = 6$, $p = \frac{1}{6}$, $q = \frac{5}{6}$, and $x = 2$.

$$P(x = 2) = {}_6C_2\left(\frac{1}{6}\right)^2\left(\frac{5}{6}\right)^4 = 15 \cdot \frac{1}{36} \cdot \frac{625}{1296} = \frac{3125}{15{,}552} \approx 0.201 \quad \blacksquare$$

In the case of repeated independent trials, when an event involves more than one specific number of successes, we can employ the binomial probability formula along with the complement and/or addition rules.

This screen supports the answer in
Example 4.

EXAMPLE 4 Finding the Probability of Female Children

A couple plans to have 5 children. Find the probability that they will have more than 3 girls. (Assume girl and boy babies are equally likely.)

Solution

Let a girl be "success." Then $n = 5$, $p = q = \frac{1}{2}$, and $x > 3$.

$$P(x > 3) = P(x = 4 \text{ or } 5) \qquad \text{More than 3 means 4 or 5.}$$

$$= P(4) + P(5) \qquad \text{Addition rule}$$

$$= {}_5C_4\left(\frac{1}{2}\right)^4\left(\frac{1}{2}\right)^1 + {}_5C_5\left(\frac{1}{2}\right)^5\left(\frac{1}{2}\right)^0 \qquad \text{Binomial probability formula}$$

$$= 5 \cdot \frac{1}{16} \cdot \frac{1}{2} + 1 \cdot \frac{1}{32} \cdot 1 \qquad \text{Simplify.}$$

$$= \frac{5}{32} + \frac{1}{32} = \frac{6}{32} = \frac{3}{16} = 0.1875 \qquad \blacksquare$$

EXAMPLE 5 Finding the Probability of Hits in Baseball

Gary Bell, a pitcher who is also an excellent hitter, has a well-established career batting average of .300. Suppose that he bats ten times. Find the probability that he will get more than two hits in the ten at-bats.

Solution

This "experiment" involves $n = 10$ repeated Bernoulli trials, with probability of success (a hit) given by $p = 0.3$ (which implies $q = 1 - 0.3 = 0.7$). Since, in this case, "more than 2" means

"3 or 4 or 5 or 6 or 7 or 8 or 9 or 10"   (eight different possibilities),

it will be less work to apply the complement rule.

This screen supports the answer in
Example 5.

$$P(x > 2) = 1 - P(x \le 2) \qquad \text{Complement rule}$$

$$= 1 - P(x = 0 \text{ or } 1 \text{ or } 2) \qquad \text{Only three different possibilities}$$

$$= 1 - [P(0) + P(1) + P(2)] \qquad \text{Addition rule}$$

$$= 1 - [{}_{10}C_0(0.3)^0(0.7)^{10} \qquad \text{Binomial probability formula}$$
$$+ {}_{10}C_1(0.3)^1(0.7)^9 + {}_{10}C_2(0.3)^2(0.7)^8]$$

$$\approx 1 - [0.0282 + 0.1211 + 0.2335] \qquad \text{Simplify.}$$

$$= 1 - 0.3828 = 0.6172 \qquad \blacksquare$$

11.4 EXERCISES

For Exercises 1–22, give all numerical answers as common fractions reduced to lowest terms. For Exercises 23–56, give all numerical answers to three decimal places.

Coin Tossing *If three fair coins are tossed, find the probability of each number of heads.*

1. 0   **2.** 1   **3.** 2

4. 3   **5.** 1 or 2   **6.** at least 1

7. no more than 1

8. fewer than 3

9. ***Relating Pascal's Triangle to Coin Tossing*** Pascal's triangle was shown in **Table 5** of **Section 10.4.** Explain how the probabilities in **Exercises 1–4** here relate to row 3 of the "triangle." (We will refer to the topmost row of the triangle as "row number 0" and to the leftmost entry of each row as "entry number 0.")

10. Generalize the pattern in **Exercise 9** to complete the following statement. If *n* fair coins are tossed, the probability of exactly *x* heads is the fraction whose numerator is entry number _____ of row number _____ in Pascal's triangle, and whose denominator is the sum of the entries in row number _____.

Binomial Probability Applied to Tossing Coins *Use the pattern noted in* **Exercises 9 and 10** *to find the probabilities of each number of heads when seven fair coins are tossed.*

11. 0   **12.** 1   **13.** 2   **14.** 3

15. 4   **16.** 5   **17.** 6   **18.** 7

Binomial Probability Applied to Rolling Dice *A fair die is rolled three times. A 4 is considered "success," while all other outcomes are "failures." Find the probability of each number of successes.*

19. 0   **20.** 1   **21.** 2   **22.** 3

For n repeated independent trials, with constant probability of success p for all trials, find the probability of exactly x successes in each of Exercises 23–26.

23. $n = 5, \quad p = \frac{1}{3}, \quad x = 4$ **24.** $n = 10, \quad p = \frac{7}{10}, \quad x = 5$

25. $n = 20, \quad p = 0.125, \quad x = 2$

26. $n = 30, \quad p = 0.6, \quad x = 22$

For Exercises 27–30, refer to **Example 5.**

27. ***Batting Averages in Baseball*** If Gary's batting average is exactly .300 going into the series based on exactly 1200 career hits out of 4000 previous times at bat, what is the greatest his average could possibly be when he goes up to bat the tenth time of the series?

28. ***Batting Averages in Baseball*** Refer to **Exercise 27.** What is the least his average could possibly be when he goes up to bat the tenth time of the series?

29. ***Batting Averages in Baseball*** Does Gary's probability of a hit really remain constant at exactly 0.300 through all ten times at bat? Explain your reasoning.

30. Do you think the use of the binomial probability formula was justified in **Example 5,** even though *p* is not strictly constant? Explain your reasoning.

Random Selection of Answers on a Multiple-choice Test *Beth is taking a ten-question multiple-choice test for which each question has three answer choices, only one of which is correct. Beth decides on answers by rolling a fair die and marking the first answer choice if the die shows 1 or 2, the second if it shows 3 or 4, and the third if it shows 5 or 6. Find the probability of each event in Exercises 31–34.*

31. exactly four correct answers

32. exactly seven correct answers

33. fewer than three correct answers

34. at least seven correct answers

Side Effects of Prescription Drugs *It is known that a certain prescription drug produces undesirable side effects in 35% of all patients who use it. Among a random sample of eight patients using the drug, find the probability of each event in Exercises 35–38.*

35. None have undesirable side effects.

36. Exactly one has undesirable side effects.

37. Exactly two have undesirable side effects.

38. More than two have undesirable side effects.

Likelihood of Capable Students Attending College *It has been shown that 60% of the high school graduates who are capable of college work actually enroll in colleges. Find the probability that, among nine capable high school graduates in a state, each number will enroll in college.*

39. exactly 4   **40.** from 4 through 6

41. all 9   **42.** at least 3

43. ***Ball Choices*** A bag contains only white balls and black balls. Let *p* be the probability that a ball selected at random is black. Each time a ball is selected, it is placed back in the bag before the next ball is selected. Four balls are selected at random. What is the probability that two of the four balls are black and two are white? (*Mathematics Teacher* calendar problem) (*Hint*: Use the binomial probability formula to express the probability in terms of *p*.)

44. ***Ball Choices*** Evaluate the probability of **Exercise 43** in the case where the bag actually contains 15 black balls and 25 white balls.

45. ***Frost Survival among Orange Trees*** If it is known that 65% of all orange trees will survive a hard frost, then what is the probability that at least half of a group of six trees will survive such a frost?

46. ***Rate of Favorable Media Coverage of an Incumbent President*** During a presidential campaign, 64% of the political columns in a certain group of major newspapers were favorable to the incumbent president. If a sample of fifteen of these columns is selected at random, what is the probability that exactly ten of them will be favorable?

47. *Student Ownership of Personal Computers* At a large midwestern university, 90% of all students have their own personal computers. If five students at that university are selected at random, find the probability that exactly three of them have their own computers.

Taking a Random Walk Abby is parked at a mile marker on an east-west country road. She decides to toss a fair coin 10 times, each time driving 1 mile east if it lands heads up and 1 mile west if it lands tails up. The term "random walk" applies to this process, even though she drives rather than walks. It is a simplified model of Brownian motion, which is mentioned in a margin note in *Section 11.1.*

In each of Exercises 48–55, find the probability that Abby's "walk" will end as described.

48. 6 miles east of the start

49. 10 miles east of the start

50. 5 miles west of the start

51. 6 miles west of the start

52. at least 2 miles east of the start

53. 2 miles east of the start

54. exactly at the start

55. at least 2 miles from the start

11.5 EXPECTED VALUE AND SIMULATION

OBJECTIVES

1 Determine expected value of a random variable and expected net winnings in a game of chance.

2 Determine if a game of chance is a fair game.

3 Use expected value to make business and insurance decisions.

4 Use simulation in genetic processes such as flower color and birth gender.

Expected Value

We repeat the beginning of **Example 6** in **Section 11.2.**

Amy plans to spend from 1 to 6 hours on her homework. If x represents the number of hours to be spent on a given night, then the probabilities of the various values of x, rounded to the nearest hour, are as shown in **Table 10.**

If Amy's friend Tara asks her how many hours her studies will take, what would be her best guess? Six different time values are possible, with some more likely than others. One thing Amy could do is calculate a "weighted average" by multiplying each possible time value by its probability and then adding the six products.

$$1(0.05) + 2(0.10) + 3(0.20) + 4(0.40) + 5(0.10) + 6(0.15)$$
$$= 0.05 + 0.20 + 0.60 + 1.60 + 0.50 + 0.90$$
$$= 3.85$$

Thus 3.85 hours is the **expected value** (or the **mathematical expectation**) of the quantity of time to be spent.

Table 10

x	$P(x)$
1	0.05
2	0.10
3	0.20
4	0.40
5	0.10
6	0.15

EXPECTED VALUE

If a random variable x can have any of the values $x_1, x_2, x_3, \ldots, x_n$, and the corresponding probabilities of these values occurring are $P(x_1)$, $P(x_2)$, $P(x_3), \ldots, P(x_n)$, then $E(x)$, the **expected value of x,** is calculated as follows.

$$E(x) = x_1 \cdot P(x_1) + x_2 \cdot P(x_2) + x_3 \cdot P(x_3) + \cdots + x_n \cdot P(x_n)$$

EXAMPLE 1 Finding the Expected Number of Boys

Find the expected number of boys for a three-child family—that is, the expected value of the number of boys. Assume girls and boys are equally likely.

Solution

The sample space for this experiment is

$$S = \{ \text{ggg, ggb, gbg, bgg, gbb, bgb, bbg, bbb} \}.$$

The probability distribution is shown in **Table 11,** along with the products and their sum, which gives the expected value.

Table 11

Number of Boys x	Probability $P(x)$	Product $x \cdot P(x)$
0	$\frac{1}{8}$	0
1	$\frac{3}{8}$	$\frac{3}{8}$
2	$\frac{3}{8}$	$\frac{6}{8}$
3	$\frac{1}{8}$	$\frac{3}{8}$

Expected value: $E(x) = \frac{12}{8} = \frac{3}{2}$

The expected number of boys is $\frac{3}{2}$, or 1.5. This result seems reasonable. Boys and girls are equally likely, so "half" the children are expected to be boys. ∎

The expected value for the number of boys in the family could never actually occur. It is only a kind of long-run average of the various values that *could* occur. If we record the number of boys in many different three-child families, then by the law of large numbers, or law of averages, as the number of observed families increases, the observed average number of boys should approach the expected value.

Games and Gambling

EXAMPLE 2 Finding Expected Winnings

A player pays $3 to play the following game: He tosses three fair coins and receives back "payoffs" of $1 if he tosses no heads, $2 for one head, $3 for two heads, and $4 for three heads. Find the player's expected net winnings for this game.

Solution

See **Table 12.** For each possible event, "net winnings" are "gross winnings" (payoff) minus cost to play. Probabilities are derived from the sample space.

$$S = \{\text{ttt, htt, tht, tth, hht, hth, thh, hhh}\}$$

The expected net loss of 50 cents is a long-run average only. On any particular play of this game, the player would lose $2 or lose $1 or break even or win $1. Over a long series of plays, say 100, there would be some wins and some losses, but the total net result would likely be around a $100 \cdot (\$0.50) = \$50$ *loss.*

Table 12

Number of Heads	Payoff	Net Winnings x	Probability $P(x)$	Product $x \cdot P(x)$
0	$1	–$2	$\frac{1}{8}$	$-\$\frac{2}{8}$
1	2	–1	$\frac{3}{8}$	$-\frac{3}{8}$
2	3	0	$\frac{3}{8}$	0
3	4	1	$\frac{1}{8}$	$\frac{1}{8}$

Expected value: $E(x) = -\$\frac{1}{2} = -\$0.50$

∎

Eisenhower Dollar Coins

A game in which the expected net winnings are zero is called a **fair game.** The game in **Example 2** has negative expected net winnings, so it is unfair against the player. A game with positive expected net winnings is unfair in favor of the player.

▒EXAMPLE 3▒ Finding the Fair Cost to Play a Game

The $3 cost to play the game of **Example 2** makes the game unfair against the player (since the player's expected net winnings are negative). What cost would make this a fair game?

Solution

We already computed, in **Example 2,** that the $3 cost to play resulted in an expected net loss of $0.50. Therefore, we can conclude that the $3 cost was 50 cents too high. A fair cost to play the game would then be $3 − $0.50 = $2.50. ∎

The result in **Example 3** can be verified. Disregard the cost to play, and find the expected *gross* winnings by summing the products of payoff times probability.

$$E(\text{gross winnings}) = \$1 \cdot \frac{1}{8} + \$2 \cdot \frac{3}{8} + \$3 \cdot \frac{3}{8} + \$4 \cdot \frac{1}{8} = \frac{\$20}{8} = \$2.50$$

Expected gross winnings (payoff) are $2.50, so this amount is a fair cost to play.

▒EXAMPLE 4▒ Finding the Fair Cost to Play a Game

Roulette ("little wheel") was invented in France in the seventeenth or early eighteenth century. It has been a featured game of chance in the gambling casino of Monte Carlo.

The disk is divided into red and black alternating compartments numbered 1 to 36 (but not in that order). There is a compartment also for 0 (and for 00 in the United States). In roulette, the wheel is set in motion, and an ivory ball is thrown into the bowl opposite to the direction of the wheel. When the wheel stops, the ball comes to rest in one of the compartments—the number and color determine who wins.

The players bet against the banker (person in charge of the pool of money) by placing money or equivalent chips in spaces on the roulette table corresponding to the wheel's colors or numbers. Bets can be made on one number or several, on odd or even, on red or black, or on combinations. The banker pays off according to the odds against the particular bet(s). For example, the classic payoff for a winning single number is $36 for each $1 bet.

In a certain state lottery, a player chooses three digits, in a specific order. Leading digits may be 0, so numbers such as 028 and 003 are legitimate entries. The lottery operators randomly select a three-digit sequence, and any player matching that selection receives a payoff of $600. What is a fair cost to play this game?

Solution

In this case, no cost has been proposed, so we have no choice but to compute expected *gross* winnings. The probability of selecting all three digits correctly is $\frac{1}{10} \cdot \frac{1}{10} \cdot \frac{1}{10} = \frac{1}{1000}$, and the probability of not selecting all three correctly is $1 - \frac{1}{1000} = \frac{999}{1000}$. The expected gross winnings are

$$E(\text{gross winnings}) = \$600 \cdot \frac{1}{1000} + \$0 \cdot \frac{999}{1000} = \$0.60.$$

Thus the fair cost to play this game is 60 cents. (In fact, the lottery charges $1 to play, so players should expect to lose 40 cents per play *on the average.*) ∎

State lotteries must be unfair against players because they are designed to help fund benefits (such as the state's school system), as well as to cover administrative costs and certain other expenses. Among people's reasons for playing may be a willingness to support such causes, but most people undoubtedly play for the chance to "beat the odds" and be one of the few net winners.

Gaming casinos are major business enterprises, by no means designed to break even. The games they offer are always unfair in favor of the house. The bias does not need to be great, however, because even relatively small average losses per player, multiplied by large numbers of players, can result in huge profits for the house.

EXAMPLE 5 Finding Expected Winnings in Roulette

One simple type of *roulette* is played with an ivory ball and a wheel set in motion. The wheel contains thirty-eight compartments. Eighteen of the compartments are black, eighteen are red, one is labeled "zero," and one is labeled "double zero." (These last two are neither black nor red.) In this case, assume the player places $1 on either red or black. If the player picks the correct color of the compartment in which the ball finally lands, the payoff is $2. Otherwise, the payoff is zero. Find the expected net winnings.

Solution

By the expected value formula, expected net winnings are

$$E(\text{net winnings}) = (\$1)\frac{18}{38} + (-\$1)\frac{20}{38} = -\$\frac{1}{19}.$$

The expected net *loss* here is $\$\frac{1}{19}$, or about 5.3¢, per play. ∎

FOR FURTHER THOUGHT

Expected Value of Games of Chance

Slot machines are a popular game for those who want to lose their money with very little mental effort. We cannot calculate an expected value applicable to all slot machines since payoffs vary from machine to machine. But we can calculate the "typical expected value."

A player operates a classic slot machine by pulling a handle after inserting a coin or coins. (We assume one coin in this discussion.) Reels inside the machine then rotate, and come to rest in some random order. (Most *modern* machines employ an electronic equivalent rather than actual rotating reels.) Assume that three reels show the pictures listed in **Table 13.** For example, of the 20 pictures on the first reel, 2 are cherries, 5 are oranges, 5 are plums, 2 are bells, 2 are melons, 3 are bars, and 1 is the number 7.

Table 13 Pictures on Reels

Pictures	Reels		
	1	**2**	**3**
Cherries	2	5	4
Oranges	5	4	5
Plums	5	3	3
Bells	2	4	4
Melons	2	1	2
Bars	3	2	1
7s	1	1	1
Totals	**20**	**20**	**20**

This Cleveland Indians fan hit four 7s in a row on a progressive nickel slot machine at the Sands Casino in Las Vegas in 1988.

A picture of cherries on the first reel, but not on the second, leads to a payoff of 3 coins (*net* winnings: 2 coins); a picture of cherries on the first two reels, but not the third, leads to a payoff of 5 coins (*net* winnings: 4 coins). These and all other winning combinations are listed in **Table 14.**

Since, according to **Table 13,** there are 2 ways of getting cherries on the first reel, 15 ways of *not* getting cherries on the second reel, and 20 ways of getting anything on the third reel, we have a total of 2 · 15 · 20 = 600 ways of getting a net payoff of 2. Since there are 20 pictures per reel, there are a total of 20 · 20 · 20 = 8000 possible outcomes. Hence, the probability of receiving a net payoff of 2 coins is $\frac{600}{8000}$.

Table 14 takes into account all *winning* outcomes, with the necessary products for finding expectation added in the last column. However, since a *nonwinning* outcome can occur in

8000 − 988 = 7012 ways (with winnings of −1 coin),

the product (−1) · 7012/8000 must also be included. Hence, the expected value of this particular slot machine is

$$\frac{6318}{8000} + (-1) \cdot \frac{7012}{8000} \approx -0.087 \text{ coin.}$$

Table 14 Calculating Expected Loss on a Three-Reel Slot Machine

Winning Combinations	Number of Ways	Probability	Number of Coins Received	Net Winnings (in coins)	Probability Times Net Winnings
1 cherry (on first reel)	$2 \cdot 15 \cdot 20 = 600$	600/8000	3	2	1200/8000
2 cherries (on first two reels)	$2 \cdot 5 \cdot 16 = 160$	160/8000	5	4	640/8000
3 cherries	$2 \cdot 5 \cdot 4 = 40$	40/8000	10	9	360/8000
3 oranges	$5 \cdot 4 \cdot 5 = 100$	100/8000	10	9	900/8000
3 plums	$5 \cdot 3 \cdot 3 = 45$	45/8000	14	13	585/8000
3 bells	$\_ \cdot \_ \cdot \_ = \_$	__/8000	18	___	__/8000
3 melons (jackpot)	$\_ \cdot \_ \cdot \_ = \_$	__/8000	100	___	__/8000
3 bars (jackpot)	$\_ \cdot \_ \cdot \_ = \_$	__/8000	200	___	__/8000
3 7s (jackpot)	$\_ \cdot \_ \cdot \_ = \_$	__/8000	500	___	__/8000
Totals	___				6318/8000

On a machine costing one dollar per play, the expected *loss* (per play) is about

$$(0.087)(1 \text{ dollar}) = 8.7 \text{ cents}.$$

Actual slot machines vary in expected loss per dollar of play. But author Hornsby was able to beat a Las Vegas slot machine in 1988.

Table 15 comes from an article by Andrew Sterrett in *The Mathematics Teacher* (March 1967), in which he discusses rules for various games of chance and calculates their expected values. He uses expected values to find expected times it would take to lose $1000 if you played continually at the rate of $1 per play and one play per minute.

For Group or Individual Investigation

1. Explain why the entries of the "Net Winnings" column of **Table 14** are all one fewer than the corresponding entries of the "Number of Coins Received" column.

2. Find the 29 missing values in **Table 14** and verify that the final result, 6318/8000, is correct. (Refer to **Table 13** for the values in the "Number of Ways" column.)

3. In order to make your money last as long as possible in a casino, which game should you play? (Refer to **Table 15**.)

Table 15 Expected Time to Lose $1000

Game	Expected Value	Days	Hours	Minutes
Roulette (with one 0)	−$0.027	25	16	40
Roulette (with 0 and 00)	−$0.053	13	4	40
Chuck-a-luck	−$0.079	8	19	46
Keno (one number)	−$0.200	3	11	20
Numbers	−$0.300	2	7	33
Football pool (4 winners)	−$0.375	1	20	27
Football pool (10 winners)	−$0.658	1	1	19

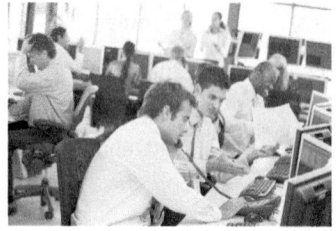

Investments

▐ EXAMPLE 6 Finding Expected Investment Profits

Nick has $5000 to invest and will commit the whole amount, for six months, to one of three technology stocks. A number of uncertainties could affect the prices of these stocks, but Nick is confident, based on his research, that one of only several possible profit scenarios will prove true of each one at the end of the six-month period. His complete analysis is shown in **Table 16**. For example, stock ABC could lose $400, gain $800, or gain $1500. Find the expected profit (or loss) for each of the three stocks, and select Nick's optimum choice based on these calculations.

Table 16

Company ABC		Company RST		Company XYZ	
Profit or Loss x	Probability $P(x)$	Profit or Loss x	Probability $P(x)$	Profit or Loss x	Probability $P(x)$
−$400	0.2	$500	0.8	$0	0.4
800	0.5	1000	0.2	700	0.3
1500	0.3			1200	0.1
				2000	0.2

Solution

Apply the expected value formula.

ABC: −$400 · (0.2) + $800 · (0.5) + $1500 · (0.3) = $770   ← Largest

RST: $500 · (0.8) + $1000 · (0.2) = $600

XYZ: $0 · (0.4) + $700 · (0.3) + $1200 · (0.1) + $2000 · (0.2) = $730

The largest expected profit is $770. Nick should invest in stock ABC. ∎

Of course, by investing in stock ABC, Nick may in fact *lose* $400 over the six months. The "expected" return of $770 is only a long-run average over many identical situations. Because this particular investment situation may never occur again, you may argue that using expected values is not the best approach for Nick to use.

An optimist would ignore most possibilities and focus on the *best* that each investment could do, while a pessimist would focus on the *worst* possibility.

▐ EXAMPLE 7 Choosing Stock Investments

Decide which stock of **Example 6** Nick would pick in each case.

(a) He is an optimist.   **(b)** He is a pessimist.

Solution

(a) Disregarding the probabilities, he would focus on the best case for each stock. Since ABC could return as much as $1500, RST as much as $1000, and XYZ as much as $2000, the optimum is $2000. He would buy stock XYZ (the best of the three *best* cases).

(b) In this situation, he would focus on the worst possible cases. Since ABC might return as little as −$400 (a $400 loss), RST as little as $500, and XYZ as little as $0, he would buy stock RST (the best of the three *worst* cases). ∎

The first **Silver Dollar Slot Machine** was fashioned in 1929 by the Fey Manufacturing Company, San Francisco, inventors of the 3-reel, automatic payout machine (1895).

Business and Insurance

EXAMPLE 8 Finding Expected Lumber Revenue

Mike, a lumber wholesaler, is considering the purchase of a (railroad) carload of varied dimensional lumber. He calculates that the probabilities of reselling the load for $10,000, for $9000, and for $8000 are 0.22, 0.33, and 0.45, respectively. In order to ensure an *expected* profit of at least $3000, how much can Mike pay for the load?

Solution

The expected revenue (or income) from resales can be found as in **Table 17.**

Table 17 Expected Lumber Revenue

Income x	Probability $P(x)$	Product $x \cdot P(x)$
$10,000	0.22	$2200
9000	0.33	2970
8000	0.45	3600

Expected revenue: $8770

In general, we have the relationship

$$\text{profit} = \text{revenue} - \text{cost}.$$

Therefore, in terms of expectations,

$$\text{expected profit} = \text{expected revenue} - \text{cost}.$$

So
$$\$3000 = \$8770 - \text{cost}$$

$$\text{cost} = \$8770 - \$3000 \quad \text{Add cost and subtract \$3000.}$$

$$\text{cost} = \$5770. \quad \text{Subtract.}$$

Mike can pay up to $5770 and still maintain an expected profit of at least $3000. ∎

EXAMPLE 9 Analyzing an Insurance Decision

Jeff, a farmer, will realize a profit of $150,000 on his wheat crop, unless there is rain before harvest, in which case he will realize only $40,000. The long-term weather forecast assigns rain a probability of 0.16. (The probability of no rain is $1 - 0.16 = 0.84$.) An insurance company offers crop insurance of $150,000 against rain for a premium of $20,000. Should he buy the insurance?

Solution

In order to make a wise decision, Jeff computes his expected profit under both options: to insure and not to insure. The complete calculations are summarized in the two "expectation" **Tables 18 and 19** on the next page.

For example, if insurance is purchased and it rains, Jeff's net profit is

$$\begin{bmatrix} \text{Insurance} \\ \text{proceeds} \end{bmatrix} + \begin{bmatrix} \text{Reduced} \\ \text{crop profit} \end{bmatrix} - \begin{bmatrix} \text{Insurance} \\ \text{premium} \end{bmatrix} \quad \text{Net profit}$$

$$\$150,000 + \$40,000 - \$20,000 = \$170,000.$$

Pilots, astronauts, race car drivers, and others train in **simulators.** Some of these devices, which may be viewed as very technical, high-cost versions of video games, imitate conditions to be encountered later in the "real world." A simulator session allows estimation of the likelihood, or probability, of different responses that the learner would display under actual conditions. Repeated sessions help the learner to develop more successful responses before actual lives and equipment are put at risk.

Table 18 Expectation When Insuring

	Net Profit x	Probability $P(x)$	Product $x \cdot P(x)$
Rain	$170,000	0.16	$27,200
No rain	130,000	0.84	109,200

Expected profit: **$136,400**

Table 19 Expectation When Not Insuring

	Net Profit x	Probability $P(x)$	Product $x \cdot P(x)$
Rain	$40,000	0.16	$6400
No rain	150,000	0.84	126,000

Expected profit: **$132,400**

By comparing expected profits ($136,400 > 132,400$), we conclude that Jeff is better off buying the insurance. ■

Simulation

An important area within probability theory is the process called **simulation.** It is possible to study a complicated, or unclear, phenomenon by *simulating*, or imitating, it with a simpler phenomenon involving the same basic probabilities. **Simulation methods** (also called **Monte Carlo methods**) require huge numbers of random digits, so computers are used to produce them. A com-

puter, however, cannot toss coins. It must use an algorithmic process, programmed into the computer, that is called a *random number generator.* It is very difficult to avoid all nonrandom patterns in the results, so the digits produced are called "pseudorandom" numbers. They must pass a battery of tests of randomness before being "approved for use."

Computer scientists and physicists have been encountering unexpected difficulties with even the most sophisticated random number generators. Therefore, these must be carefully checked along with each new simulation application proposed.

Simulating Genetic Traits

		Second Parent	
		R	**r**
First Parent	**R**	RR	Rr
	r	rR	rr

Recall from **Section 11.1** Mendel's discovery that when two Rr pea plants (red-flowered but carrying genes for both red and white flowers) are crossed, the offspring will have red flowers if an R gene is received from either parent or from both. This is because red is dominant and white is recessive. **Table 3,** reproduced here in the margin, shows that three of the four equally likely possibilities result in red-flowered offspring.

Now suppose we want to estimate the probability that three offspring in a row will have red flowers. It is much easier (and quicker) to toss coins than to cross pea plants. And the equally likely outcomes, heads and tails, can be used to simulate the transfer of the equally likely genes, R and r. If we toss two coins (say a nickel and a penny), then we can interpret the results as follows.

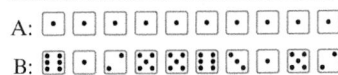

Two **possible sequences** of outcomes, when a fair die is rolled ten times in succession, are

A: 1–1–1–1–1–1–1–1–1–1 and
B: 6–1–2–5–5–6–3–1–5–2.

Which of the following options would you choose?

(a) Result A is more likely.
(b) Result B is more likely.
(c) They are equally likely.

Even though the specific sequences A and B are, in fact, equally likely (choice (c)), 67% (rounded) of the students in a class of college freshman business majors, not previously trained in probability theory, initially selected choice (b), as shown here.

Answer Choice	Pre-activity Survey	Post-activity Survey
(a)	4%	0%
(b)	67%	42%
(c)	29%	58%

Note that, even after a classroom session of hands-on simulation activities, 42% of the students persisted in their faulty reasoning.

(*Source: Mathematics Teacher*, September 2014, page 126.)

hh $\Rightarrow$ RR $\Rightarrow$ red gene from first parent and red gene from second parent
$\Rightarrow$ red flowers

ht $\Rightarrow$ Rr $\Rightarrow$ red gene from first parent and white gene from second parent
$\Rightarrow$ red flowers

th $\Rightarrow$ rR $\Rightarrow$ white gene from first parent and red gene from second parent
$\Rightarrow$ red flowers

tt $\Rightarrow$ rr $\Rightarrow$ white gene from first parent and white gene from second parent
$\Rightarrow$ white flowers

Although nothing is certain for a few tosses, the law of large numbers indicates that larger and larger numbers of tosses should become better and better indicators of general trends in the genetic process.

EXAMPLE 10 Simulating Genetic Processes

Toss two coins 50 times and use the results to approximate the probability that the crossing of Rr pea plants will produce three successive red-flowered offspring.

Solution

We actually tossed two coins 50 times and got the following sequence.

th, hh, th, tt, th, hh, ht, th, ht, th, hh, hh, tt, th, hh,
ht, ht, ht, ht, th, hh, hh, hh, tt, ht, tt, hh, ht, ht, hh, tt,
tt, tt, th, tt, tt, hh, ht, ht, ht, hh, tt, th, hh, tt, hh, ht,
tt, tt, tt

By the color interpretation described above, this gives the following sequence of flower colors in the offspring. (Only "both tails" gives white.)

red–red–red–white–red–red–red–red–red–red–red–red–white–

red–red–red–red–red–red–red–red–red–red–white–red–white–

red–red–red–red–white–white–white–red–white–white–red–red–

red–red–red–white–red–red–white–red–red–white–white–white

We now have an experimental list of 48 sets of three successive plants, the 1st, 2nd, and 3rd entries, then the 2nd, 3rd, and 4th entries, and so on. Do you see why there are 48 in all?

Now we just count up the number of these sets of three that are "red-red-red." Since there are 20 of those, our empirical probability of three successive red offspring, obtained through simulation, is $\frac{20}{48} = \frac{5}{12}$, or about 0.417. By applying the multiplication rule of probability (with all outcomes independent of one another), we find that the theoretical value is $\left(\frac{3}{4}\right)^3 = \frac{27}{64}$, or about 0.422, so our approximation obtained by simulation is very close. ∎

Simulating Other Phenomena

In human births, boys and girls are (essentially) equally likely. Therefore, an individual birth can be simulated by tossing a fair coin, letting a head correspond to a girl and a tail to a boy.

Table 20

→ 51592
77876
36500
40571
04822
→ 53033
92080
01587
36006
63698
→ 17297
22841
→ 91979
96480
74949
76896
47588
45521
02472
55184
40177
84861
86937
20931
22454
→ 73219
→ 55707
48007
→ 65191
06772
94928
→ 15709
39922
96365
14655
65587
76905
12369
54219
89329
90060
06975
05050
69774
→ 78351
11464
84086
→ 51497
12307
68009

EXAMPLE 11 **Simulating Births with Coin Tossing**

A sequence of 40 actual coin tosses produced the results below.

bbggb, gbbbg, gbgbb, bggbg, bbbbg, gbbgg, gbbgg, bgbbg

(For every head we have written g, for girl. For every tail, b, for boy.)

(a) How many pairs of two successive births are represented by the sequence?

(b) How many of those pairs consist of both boys?

(c) Find the empirical probability, based on this simulation, that two successive births both will be boys. Give your answer to three decimal places.

Solution

(a) Beginning with the 1st–2nd pair and ending with the 39th–40th pair, there are 39 pairs.

(b) Observing the above sequence, we count 11 pairs of two consecutive boys.

(c) Utilizing parts (a) and (b), we have $\frac{11}{39} \approx 0.282$. ∎

Another way to simulate births, and other phenomena, is with random numbers. The spinner in **Figure 14** can be used to obtain a table of random digits, as in **Table 20**. The 250 random digits generated have been grouped conveniently so that we can easily follow down a column or across a row to carry out a simulation.

Figure 14

EXAMPLE 12 **Simulating Births with Random Numbers**

A couple plans to have five children. Use random number simulation to estimate the probability that they will have more than three boys.

Solution

Let each sequence of five digits, as they appear in **Table 20,** represent a family with five children, and (arbitrarily) associate odd digits with boys, even digits with girls. (Recall that 0 is even.) Verify that, of the fifty families simulated, only the ten marked with arrows have more than 3 boys (4 boys or 5 boys).

$$P(\text{more than 3 boys}) = \frac{10}{50} = 0.20 \quad \text{Estimated (empirical) probability}$$ ∎

The theoretical value for the probability in **Example 12** above would be the same as that obtained in **Example 4** of **Section 11.4.** It was 0.1875. Our estimate above was fairly close. In light of the law of large numbers, a larger sampling of random digits (more than 50 simulated families) would likely yield a closer approximation.

EXAMPLE 13 **Simulating Card Drawing with Random Numbers**

Use random number simulation to estimate the probability that two cards drawn from a standard deck, with replacement, both will be of the same suit.

Solution

Use this correspondence: 0 and 1 mean clubs, 2 and 3 mean diamonds, 4 and 5 mean hearts, 6 and 7 mean spades, 8 and 9 are disregarded. Now refer to **Table 20.**

If we (arbitrarily) use the first digit of each five-digit group, omitting 8s and 9s, we obtain the sequence

$$5-7-3-4-0-5-0-3-6-1-2-7-7-4-4-0-5-4-2-2-$$
$$7-5-4-6-0-1-3-1-6-7-1-5-0-0-6-7-1-5-1-6.$$

First digits of
all groups

This 40-digit sequence of digits yields the sequence of suits shown next.

> 5 gives hearts, 7 gives spades,
> 3 gives diamonds, and so on.

hearts–spades–diamonds–hearts–clubs–hearts–clubs–diamonds–spades–

clubs–diamonds–spades–spades–hearts–hearts–clubs–hearts–hearts–

diamonds–diamonds–spades–hearts–hearts–spades–clubs–clubs–

diamonds–clubs–spades–spades–clubs–hearts–clubs–clubs–spades–

spades–clubs–hearts–clubs–spades

Verify that of the 39 successive pairs of suits (hearts–spades, spades–diamonds, diamonds–hearts, etc.), 9 of them are pairs of the same suit. This makes the estimated probability $\frac{9}{39} \approx 0.23$. (For comparison, the theoretical value is 0.25.) ■

FOR FURTHER THOUGHT

Assessing Randomness

Observe the two listings that follow, each of which simulates 200 tosses of a coin. Read from left to right across the top row, then from left to right across the second row, and so on, to the bottom row. One of the listings was obtained by actual tossing, and the other was made up by a student.

Make an educated guess about which is which, before reading the paragraph that follows the listings.

B

thhth	hthhh	thttt	ttttt	thhth
hhhtt	thtth	tthth	ttttt	hhtth
hthhh	tthth	thhtt	tttth	thhth
thhht	hthhh	tttht	thhtt	hthht
hthht	hhhth	ththh	hthtt	tthht
htttt	thhhh	thhhh	hhthh	ththh
htthh	thhtt	tthth	ttttt	hthtt
tthht	ththh	hthhh	hthth	hthth

Consider the following fact of probability. When a fair coin is tossed 200 times, there is a 97% chance that there will be a run of six consecutive heads or six consecutive tails. Now look at the listings again, and based on this *almost* certain outcome, decide whether your earlier choice is correct. The answer is in the margin above. (The authors thank Marty Triola for his input into this For Further Thought feature.)

A

thhtt	thhtt	hthhh	tthth	httth
hthht	thttt	thhth	tthht	hthhh
thhht	thttt	thhht	hthth	htthh
htthh	htthh	thttt	hhtht	thhht
thtth	hthhh	htttht	hhtth	hthth
htttth	hthhh	htttht	hhttt	thhth
htthh	hthtt	tttht	hhtth	hhtth
thhtt	thhth	hthth	thhtt	htthh

11.5 EXERCISES

1. **Coin Tosses** Five fair coins are tossed. Find the expected number of heads.

2. **Card Choices** Two cards are drawn, with replacement, from a standard 52-card deck. Find the expected number of diamonds.

Expected Winnings in a Die-rolling Game A game consists of rolling a single fair die and pays off as follows: $3 for a 6, $2 for a 5, $1 for a 4, and no payoff otherwise.

3. Find the expected winnings for this game.

4. What is a fair price to pay to play this game?

Expected Winnings in a Die-rolling Game For Exercises 5 and 6, consider a game consisting of rolling a single fair die, with payoffs as follows. If an even number of spots turns up, you receive as many dollars as there are spots up. But if an odd number of spots turns up, you must pay as many dollars as there are spots up.

5. Find the expected net winnings of this game.

6. Is this game fair, or unfair against the player, or unfair in favor of the player?

7. *Expected Winnings in a Coin-tossing Game* A certain game involves tossing 3 fair coins, and it pays 10¢ for 3 heads, 5¢ for 2 heads, and 3¢ for 1 head. Is 5¢ a fair price to pay to play this game? That is, does the 5¢ cost to play make the game fair?

8. *Expected Winnings in Roulette* In a form of roulette slightly different from that in **Example 5,** a more generous management supplies a wheel having only thirty-seven compartments, with eighteen red, eighteen black, and one zero. Find the expected net winnings if you bet $1 on red in this game.

9. *Expected Number of Absences in a Math Class* In a certain mathematics class, the probabilities have been empirically determined for various numbers of absentees on any given day. These values are shown in the table below. Find the expected number of absentees on a given day. Give the answer to two decimal places.

Number absent	0	1	2	3	4
Probability	0.18	0.26	0.29	0.23	0.04

10. *Expected Profit of an Insurance Company* An insurance company will insure a $200,000 home for its total value for an annual premium of $650. If the company spends $25 per year to service such a policy, the probability of total loss for such a home in a given year is 0.002, and you assume that either total loss or no loss will occur, what is the company's expected annual gain (or profit) on each such policy?

Profits from a College Foundation Raffle A college foundation raises funds by selling raffle tickets for a new car worth $36,000.

11. If 600 tickets are sold for $120 each, determine each of the following.

(a) The expected *net* winnings of a person buying one of the tickets

(b) The total profit for the foundation, assuming that it had to purchase the car

(c) The total profit for the foundation, assuming that the car was donated

12. For the raffle described in **Exercise 11,** if 720 tickets are sold for $120 each, determine each of the following.

(a) The expected *net* winnings of a person buying one of the tickets

(b) The total profit for the foundation, assuming that it had to purchase the car

(c) The total profit for the foundation, assuming that the car was donated

Winnings and Profits of a Raffle Five thousand raffle tickets are sold. One first prize of $1000, two second prizes of $500 each, and three third prizes of $100 each will be awarded, with all winners selected randomly.

13. If you purchased one ticket, what are your expected gross winnings?

14. If you purchased ten tickets, what are your expected gross winnings?

15. If the tickets were sold for $1 each, how much profit goes to the raffle sponsor?

16. *Expected Sales at a Theater Snack Bar* A children's theater found in a random survey that 58 customers bought one snack bar item, 49 bought two items, 31 bought three items, 4 bought four items, and 8 avoided the snack bar altogether. Use this information to find the expected number of snack bar items per customer. Round your answer to the nearest tenth.

17. *Expected Number of Children to Attend an Amusement Park* An amusement park, considering adding some new attractions, conducted a study over several typical days and found that, of 10,000 families entering the park, 1020 brought just one child (defined as younger than age twelve), 3370 brought two children, 3510 brought three children, 1340 brought four children, 510 brought five children, 80 brought six children, and 170 brought no children at all. Find the expected number of children per family attending this park. Round your answer to the nearest tenth.

18. *Expected Sums of Randomly Selected Numbers* Four cards are numbered 1 through 4. Two of these cards are chosen randomly without replacement, and the numbers on them are added. Find the expected value of this sum.

19. *Prospects for Electronics Jobs in a City* In a certain California city, projections for the next year are that there is a 20% chance that electronics jobs will increase by 200, a 50% chance that they will increase by 300, and a 30% chance that they will decrease by 800. What is the expected change in the number of electronics jobs in that city in the next year?

20. *Expected Winnings in Keno* In one version of the game *keno,* the house has a pot containing 80 balls, numbered 1 through 80. A player buys a ticket for $1 and marks on it one number from 1 to 80. The house then selects 20 of the 80 numbers at random. If the number selected by the player is among the 20 selected by the management, the player is paid $3.20. Find the expected net winnings for this game.

Contractor Decisions Based on Expected Profits   *Lori, a commercial building contractor, will commit her company to one of three projects, depending on her analysis of potential profits or losses as shown here.*

Project A		Project B		Project C	
Profit or Loss x	Probability $P(x)$	Profit or Loss x	Probability $P(x)$	Profit or Loss x	Probability $P(x)$
$60,000	0.10	$0	0.20	$40,000	0.65
180,000	0.60	210,000	0.35	340,000	0.35
250,000	0.30	290,000	0.45		

In Exercises 21–23, determine which project Lori should choose according to each approach.

21. expected values

22. the optimist viewpoint

23. the pessimist viewpoint

24. Refer to **Examples 6 and 7.** Considering the three different approaches (expected values, optimist, and pessimist), which one seems most reasonable to you, and why?

Expected Winnings in a Game Show   *A game show contestant is offered the option of receiving a computer system worth $2300 or accepting a chance to win either a luxury vacation worth $5000 or a boat worth $8000. If the second option is chosen the contestant's probabilities of winning the vacation and of winning the boat are 0.20 and 0.15, respectively.*

25. If the contestant were to turn down the computer system and go for one of the other prizes, what would be the expected winnings?

26. Purely in terms of monetary value, what is the contestant's wiser choice?

Insurance Purchase   *David, the promoter of an outdoor concert, expects a gate profit of $100,000 unless it rains, which would reduce the gate profit to $30,000. The probability of rain is 0.20. For a premium of $25,000 David can purchase insurance coverage that would pay him $100,000 in case of rain.*

Use this information for Exercises 27–30.

27. Find the expected net profit when the insurance is purchased.

28. Find the expected net profit when the insurance is not purchased.

29. Based on expected values, which is David's wiser choice in this situation?

30. If you were the promoter, would you base your decision on expected values? Explain your reasoning.

Expected Values in Book Sales   *Jessica, an educational publisher representative, presently has five accounts, and her manager is considering assigning her three additional accounts. The new accounts would bring potential volume to her business, and some of her present accounts have potential for growth as well. See the accompanying table.*

1	2	3	4	5	6
Account Number	Existing Volume	Potential Additional Volume	Probability of Getting Additional Volume	Expected Value of Additional Volume	Existing Volume plus Expected Value of Additional Volume
1	$10,000	$10,000	0.40	$4000	$14,000
2	30,000	0	—	—	30,000
3	25,000	15,000	0.20	3000	
4	35,000	0	—	—	
5	15,000	5,000	0.30		
6	0	30,000	0.10		
7	0	25,000	0.70		
8	0	45,000	0.60		

Use the preceding table to work Exercises 31–35.

31. Compute the four missing expected values in column 5.

32. Compute the six missing amounts in column 6.

33. What is Jessica's total "expected" additional volume?

34. If Jessica achieved her expected additional volume in all accounts, what would be the total volume of all her accounts?

35. If Jessica achieved her expected additional volume in all accounts, by what percentage (to the nearest tenth of a percent) would she increase her total volume?

36. *Expected Winnings in Keno* Recall that in the game keno of **Exercise 20,** the house randomly selects 20 numbers from the counting numbers 1–80. In the variation called 6-spot keno, the player pays 60¢ for his ticket and marks 6 numbers of his choice. If the 20 numbers selected by the house contain at least 3 of those chosen by the player, he gets a payoff according to this scheme.

3 of the player's numbers among the 20	$0.35
4 of the player's numbers among the 20	2.00
5 of the player's numbers among the 20	60.00
6 of the player's numbers among the 20	1250.00

Find the player's expected net winnings in this game.

[*Hint:* The four probabilities required here can be found using combinations **(Section 10.3),** the fundamental counting principle **(Section 10.2),** and the theoretical probability formula **(Section 11.1).**]

37. *Pea Plant Reproduction Simulation with Coin Tossing* Use the sequence of flower colors of **Example 10** to approximate the probability that *four* successive offspring all will have red flowers.

38. *Pea Plant Reproduction Simulation with Coin Tossing* Explain why, in **Example 10,** fifty tosses of the coins produced only 48 sets of three successive offspring.

39. *Boy and Girl Simulation with Random Numbers* Use **Table 20** to simulate fifty families with three children. Let 0–4 correspond to boys and 5–9 to girls, and use the middle three digits of the 5-digit groupings (159, 787, 650, and so on). Estimate the probability of exactly two boys in a family of three children. Compare with the theoretical probability, which is $\frac{3}{8} = 0.375$.

40. *Empirical Probability of Successive Girls* Simulate 40 births by tossing coins yourself, and obtain an empirical probability for two successive girls.

41. *Likelihoods of Girl and Boy Births* Should the probability of two successive girl births be any different from that of two successive boy births?

One-and-One Free Throw Shooting *In Exercises 88–90 of Section 11.3, Christine, who had a 70% foul-shooting record, had probabilities of scoring 0, 1, or 2 points of 0.30, 0.21, and 0.49, respectively.*

Use **Table 20** *(with digits 0–6 representing hit and 7–9 representing miss) to simulate 50 one-and-one shooting opportunities for Christine. Begin at the top left (5, 7, 3, etc., to the bottom), then move to the second column (1, 7, 6, etc.), going until 50 one-and-one opportunities are obtained. (Some "opportunities" involve one shot and one random digit, while others involve two shots and two random digits.) Keep a tally of the numbers of times 0, 1, and 2 points are scored.*

Number of Points	Tally
0	
1	
2	

From the tally, find the empirical probability (to two decimal places) of each event.

42. no points   **43.** 1 point

44. 2 points

Simulation with Coin Tossing *A coin was actually tossed 200 times, producing the following sequence of outcomes. Read from left to right across the top row, then from left to right across the second row, and so on, to the bottom row.*

```
hhtht  ththh  ttttt  tthtt  hthhh
thtth  hhhhh  htthh  hthht  hhtth
ththt  hhttt  hhhhh  tthth  ththh
thhhh  hhhht  thtth  thhth  thhtt
thhtt  thttt  hthht  thhht  htttt
htthh  htttt  tttht  tttth  ththh
hhhhh  tthht  tthht  hthtt  hhhht
hthtt  htttt  hhtth  ttthh  thtth
```

Find the empirical probability of each of the following. Round to three decimal places.

45. two consecutive heads

46. two consecutive tails

47. three consecutive tosses of the same outcome

48. six consecutive tosses of the same outcome

Path of a Random Walk Using a Die and a Coin *Exercises 49–56 of Section 11.4 illustrated a simple version of the idea of a "random walk." Atomic particles released in nuclear fission also move in a random fashion. During World War II, John von Neumann and Stanislaw Ulam used simulation with random numbers to study particle motion in nuclear reactions. Von Neumann coined the name "Monte Carlo" for the methods used.*

The figure suggests a model for random motion in two dimensions. Assume that a particle moves in a series of 1-unit "jumps," each one in a random direction, any one of 12 equally likely possibilities. One way to choose directions is to roll a fair die and toss a fair coin. The die determines one of the directions 1–6, coupled with heads on the coin. Tails on the coin reverses the direction of the die, so that the die coupled with tails gives directions 7–12. So 3h (meaning 3 with the die and heads with the coin) gives direction 3; 3t gives direction 9 (opposite to 3); and so on.

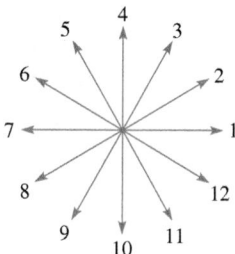

49. Simulate the motion described above with 10 rolls of a die and tosses of a coin. Draw the 10-jump path you get. Make your drawing accurate enough so you can estimate (by measuring) how far from its starting point the particle ends up.

50. Repeat the experiment of **Exercise 49** four more times. Measure distance from start to finish for each of the 5 "random trips." Add these 5 distances and divide the sum by 5, to arrive at an "expected net distance" for such a trip.

In Exercises 51 and 52, consider another two-dimensional random walk governed by the following conditions.

- *Start out from a given street corner, and travel one block north. At each intersection:*
- *Turn left with probability $\frac{1}{6}$.*
- *Go straight with probability $\frac{2}{6} \left(= \frac{1}{3} \right)$.*
- *Turn right with probability $\frac{3}{6} \left(= \frac{1}{2} \right)$.*
  (Never turn around.)

51. *A Random Walk Using a Random Number Table* Use **Table 20** to simulate this random walk. For every 1 encountered in the table, turn left and proceed for another block. For every 2 or 3, go straight and proceed for another block. For every 4, 5, or 6, turn right and proceed for another block. Disregard all other digits—that is, 0s, 7s, 8s, and 9s. (Do you see how this scheme satisfies the probabilities given above?) This time, begin at the upper right corner of the table, running down the column 2, 6, 0, and so on, to the bottom. When this column of digits is used up, stop the "walk." Describe, in terms of distance and direction, where you have ended up relative to your starting point.

52. *A Random Walk Using a Fair Die* Explain how a fair die could be used to simulate this random walk.

Buffon's Needle Problem *The following problem was posed by Georges Louis Leclerc, Comte de Buffon (1707–1788) in his* Histoire Naturelle *in 1777. A large plane area is ruled with equidistant parallel lines, the distance between two consecutive lines of the series being "a". A thin needle of length*

$$\ell < a$$

is tossed randomly onto the plane. What is the probability that the needle will intersect one of these lines?

The answer to this problem is found using integral calculus, and the probability p is shown to be $p = \frac{2\ell}{\pi a}$. Solving for π gives the formula

$$\pi = \frac{2\ell}{pa},$$

which can be used to approximate the value of π experimentally. This was first observed by Pierre Simon de Laplace, and such an experiment was carried out by Johann Wolf, a professor of astronomy at Bern, in about 1850. (Source: Burton, David M. History of Mathematics: An Introduction. *Wm. C. Brown, 1995.)*

53. On a sheet of paper, draw a series of parallel lines evenly spaced across it. Then find a thin needle, or needlelike object, with a length less than the distance between adjacent parallel lines on the paper.

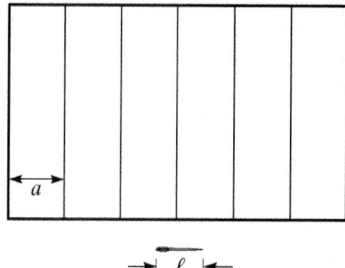

Carry out the following steps in order.

(a) Measure and record the distance between lines (a) and the length of the needle (ℓ), using the same units for both.

(b) Drop the needle onto the paper 100 times. Determine whether the needle "hits" a line or not, and keep a tally of hits and misses.

(c) Now calculate $p =$ (number of hits)/100. Is this probability value theoretical or empirical?

(d) Enter the calculated value of p and the measured values of a and ℓ into the formula to obtain an approximation for π. Round this value to four decimal places.

(e) The correct value of π, to four decimal places, is 3.1416. What value did your simulation give? How far off is it?

54. *Dynamic Simulation* See www.metablake.com/pi.swf for a dynamic illustration of the Buffon Needle Problem. (One of the authors of this text used 21,734 iterations, to get 13,805 intersections, for an empirical value of π to be 3.148569358927.)

CHAPTER 11   SUMMARY

KEY TERMS

11.1

deterministic phenomenon
random phenomenon
probability
experiment
outcome
sample space
event
theoretical probability

empirical probability
law of large numbers
   (law of averages)
odds in favor
odds against

11.2

mutually exclusive events
random variable
probability distribution

11.3

conditional probability of
  B given *A*
independent events

11.4

Bernoulli trials
binomial probability
  distribution

11.5

expected value
  (mathematical expectation)
simulation
simulation methods
  (Monte Carlo methods)
random number generator

NEW SYMBOLS

$P(E)$ probability of event E

$P(B|A)$ probability of event B, given that event A has occurred

$E(x)$ expected value of random variable x

TEST YOUR WORD POWER

See how well you have learned the vocabulary in this chapter.

1. The **sample space** of an experiment is
   A. the set of all possible events of the experiment.
   B. the set of all possible outcomes of the experiment.
   C. the number of possible events of the experiment.
   D. the number of possible outcomes of the experiment.

2. The **probability of an event** *E*
   A. must be a number greater than 1.
   B. may be a negative number.
   C. must be a number between 0 and 1, inclusive of both.
   D. cannot be 0.

3. If *E* is an event, the **probability of "not E"** must be
   A. 0.
   B. equal to 1 plus the probability of *E*.
   C. equal to 1 minus the probability of *E*.
   D. less than the probability of *E*.

4. A **probability distribution**
   A. shows all possible values of a random variable, along with the probabilities that those values will occur.
   B. is a listing of empirical values of an experiment.
   C. is a number between 0 and 1, inclusive of both.
   D. is an application of the distributive property to probability.

ANSWERS
1. B 2. C 3. C 4. A

QUICK REVIEW

Concepts	Examples
11.1 Basic Concepts **Theoretical Probability Formula** If all outcomes in a sample space S are equally likely, and E is an event within that sample space, then the **theoretical probability** of event E is given by the following formula. $$P(E) = \frac{\textbf{number of favorable outcomes}}{\textbf{total number of outcomes}} = \frac{n(E)}{n(S)}$$	The spinner shown here is spun twice. Find the probability that both spins yield the same number. The sample space S is $\{(1,1), (1,2), (1,3), (2,1), (2,2), (2,3), (3,1), (3,2)(3,3)\}$. Of these, three indicate the same number: $E = \{(1,1), (2,2), (3,3)\}$. Therefore, $$P(E) = \frac{n(E)}{n(S)} = \frac{3}{9} = \frac{1}{3}.$$

Concepts	Examples

Empirical Probability Formula

If E is an event that may happen when an experiment is performed, then an **empirical probability** of event E is given by the following formula.

$$P(E) = \frac{\text{number of times event } E \text{ occurred}}{\text{number of times the experiment was performed}}$$

A coin was actually tossed 100 times, producing the following sequence of outcomes. If E represents two consecutive tosses of heads (h), what is the empirical probability of E?

thhht	thhht	hthth	thhhh	thttt
ttttt	tthht	htthh	tttth	ttttth
hhthh	thttt	thttt	thtth	thhht
hthhh	ttthh	hhhht	ththt	hhhht

Law of Large Numbers (Law of Averages)

As an experiment is repeated more and more times, the proportion of outcomes favorable to any particular event will tend to come closer and closer to the theoretical probability of that event.

There are 99 cases of two consecutive tosses, and 24 of them show both heads, so

$$P(E) = \frac{24}{99} \approx 0.242. \quad \text{Empirical probability}$$

In the experiment above, what is the theoretical probability that two consecutive heads will occur? How does the empirical result compare?

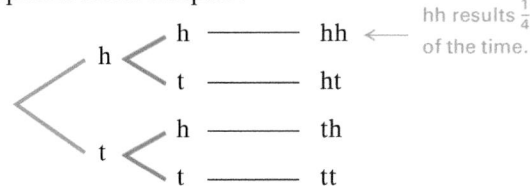

hh results $\frac{1}{4}$ of the time.

The theoretical probability is $\frac{1}{4} = 0.25$. This is very close to 0.242, the empirical value obtained above.

Odds

If all outcomes in a sample space are equally likely, a of them are favorable to the event E, and the remaining b outcomes are unfavorable to E, then

        the **odds in favor** of E are a to b,

and   the **odds against** E are b to a.

A single card is drawn from a standard deck of 52 cards.

(a) What is the probability that the card is a queen?

    There are 4 queens (and thus 48 non-queens).

$$P(\text{queen}) = \frac{4}{52} = \frac{1}{13} \quad \text{Probability of a queen}$$

Converting between Probability and Odds

Let E be an event.

- If $P(E) = \frac{a}{b}$, then the odds in favor of E are a to $(b - a)$.

- If the odds in favor of E are a to b, then $P(E) = \frac{a}{a + b}$.

(b) What are the odds in favor of drawing a queen?

    4 to 48, or 1 to 12   Odds in favor of a queen

(c) What are the odds against drawing a queen?

    48 to 4, or 12 to 1   Odds against a queen

11.2 Events Involving "Not" and "Or"

Properties of Probability

Let E be an event within the sample space S. That is, E is a subset of S. Then the following properties hold.

1. $0 \le P(E) \le 1$ (The probability of an event is a number from 0 through 1, inclusive.)

2. $P(\varnothing) = 0$ (The probability of an impossible event is 0.)

3. $P(S) = 1$ (The probability of a certain event is 1.)

If 6 fair coins are tossed, what is the probability that at most 5 will show tails?

There are $2^6 = 64$ possible outcomes. Only one of them,

        tttttt,

does not show at most 5 tails, so there are $64 - 1 = 63$ favorable outcomes.

$$P(\text{at most 5 tails}) = \frac{64 - 1}{64} = \frac{63}{64}$$

Concepts	*Examples*
Probability of a Complement (for the Event "Not E") The probability that an event E will *not* occur is equal to 1 minus the probability that it will occur. $$P(\text{not } E) = 1 - P(E)$$	If a single card is drawn from a standard 52-card deck, find the probability that it is the following. **(a)** a heart or a black card **(b)** a heart or a 6 $P(\text{heart or black}) = P(\text{heart}) + P(\text{black})$ These are mutually exclusive. $\qquad = \dfrac{13}{52} + \dfrac{26}{52}$ $\qquad = \dfrac{39}{52}$ $\qquad = \dfrac{3}{4}$
Mutually Exclusive Events Two events A and B are **mutually exclusive events** if they have no outcomes in common. Mutually exclusive events cannot occur simultaneously. **Addition Rule of Probability (for the Event "A or B")** If A and B are any two events, then the following holds. $$P(A \text{ or } B) = P(A) + P(B) - P(A \text{ and } B)$$ If A and B are mutually exclusive, then the following holds. $$P(A \text{ or } B) = P(A) + P(B)$$	$P(\text{heart or a 6}) = P(\text{heart}) + P(6) - P(6 \text{ of hearts})$ These are not mutually exclusive. $\qquad = \dfrac{13}{52} + \dfrac{4}{52} - \dfrac{1}{52}$ $\qquad = \dfrac{16}{52}$ $\qquad = \dfrac{4}{13}$
11.3 Conditional Probability and Events Involving "And" **Conditional Probability** The probability of event B, computed on the assumption that event A has happened, is the **conditional probability of B given A** and is denoted $P(B\|A)$. **Conditional Probability Formula** The **conditional probability of B given A** is calculated as $$P(B|A) = \frac{P(A \cap B)}{P(A)} = \frac{P(A \text{ and } B)}{P(A)}.$$	From the sample space $$S = \{1, 2, 3, 4, 5, 6, 7, 8, 9, 10, 11, 12\},$$ a single number is to be selected randomly. Find each probability given the events A: The selected number is even. B: The selected number is a multiple of 3. **(a)** $P(B)$ $\quad B = \{3, 6, 9, 12\}$, so $$P(B) = \frac{n(B)}{n(S)} = \frac{4}{12} = \frac{1}{3}.$$ **(b)** $P(A \text{ and } B)$ $\quad A = \{2, 4, 6, 8, 10, 12\}$, so $A \cap B = \{6, 12\}$. $$P(A \text{ and } B) = P(A \cap B) = \frac{2}{12} = \frac{1}{6}$$

Independent Events
 	
Two events A and B are **independent events** if knowledge about the occurrence of one of them has no effect on the probability of the other one occurring. A and B are independent if
 	
$$P(B|A) = P(B), \quad \text{or, equivalently,} \quad P(A|B) = P(A).$$
 	
Multiplication Rule of Probability (for the Event "A and B")
 	
If A and B are *any two events*, then
 	
$$P(A \text{ and } B) = P(A) \cdot P(B|A).$$
 	
If A and B are *independent*, then
 	
$$P(A \text{ and } B) = P(A) \cdot P(B).$$
	(c) $P(B\|A)$ Are A and B independent?
	
	In the reduced sample space of A, 2 of the 6 outcomes belong to B.
	
	$$P(B|A) = \frac{2}{6} = \frac{1}{3}$$
	
	Equivalently, $P(B\|A) = \dfrac{P(A \cap B)}{P(A)} = \dfrac{\frac{1}{6}}{\frac{1}{2}} = \dfrac{1}{6} \cdot \dfrac{2}{1} = \dfrac{1}{3}.$
	
	Because $P(B) = P(B\|A)$, A and B are independent.

Concepts	Examples

11.4 Binomial Probability

Binomial Probability Formula

When n independent repeated trials occur, where

p = probability of success and q = probability of failure

with p and q (where $q = 1 - p$) remaining constant throughout all n trials, the probability of exactly x successes is calculated as follows.

$$P(x) = {_nC_x}p^x q^{n-x} = \frac{n!}{x!(n-x)!}p^x q^{n-x}$$

A die is rolled ten times. Find the probability that exactly four of the tosses result in a 3.

The probability of rolling a 3 on one roll is $p = \frac{1}{6}$, so the probability of not rolling a 3 is

$$q = 1 - \frac{1}{6} = \frac{5}{6}.$$

Here $n = 10$ and $x = 4$.

$$P(\text{exactly four 3s}) = {_{10}C_4}\left(\frac{1}{6}\right)^4\left(\frac{5}{6}\right)^{10-4}$$

$$= 210\left(\frac{1}{1296}\right)\left(\frac{15{,}625}{46{,}656}\right)$$

$$\approx 0.054$$

11.5 Expected Value and Simulation

Expected Value

If a random variable x can have any of the values $x_1, x_2, x_3, \ldots, x_n$, and the corresponding probabilities of these values occurring are $P(x_1), P(x_2), P(x_3), \ldots, P(x_n)$, then $E(x)$, the **expected value of x**, is calculated as follows.

$$E(x) = x_1 \cdot P(x_1) + x_2 \cdot P(x_2) + x_3 \cdot P(x_3)$$
$$+ \cdots + x_n \cdot P(x_n)$$

In a certain lottery, a player chooses four digits in a specific order. The leading digit may be 0, so a number such as 0460 is legitimate. A four-digit sequence is randomly chosen, and any player matching that selection receives a payoff of $10,000. Find the expected gross winnings.

The probability of selecting the correct four digits is $\left(\frac{1}{10}\right)^4 = \frac{1}{10,000}$, and the probability of not selecting them is $1 - \left(\frac{1}{10}\right)^4 = \frac{9999}{10,000}$. The expected gross winnings are

$$E(\text{gross winnings}) = \$10{,}000 \cdot \frac{1}{10{,}000} + \$0 \cdot \frac{9999}{10{,}000}$$

$$= \$1.00. \quad \text{A fair cost to play this game}$$

CHAPTER 11 TEST

Numbers from Sets of Digits *Two numbers are randomly selected without replacement from the set*

$$\{1, 2, 3, 4, 5\}.$$

Find the probability of each event.

1. Both numbers are even.

2. Both numbers are prime.

3. The sum of the two numbers is odd.

4. The product of the two numbers is odd.

Days Off for Pizza Parlor Workers *The manager of a pizza parlor (which operates seven days a week) allows each of three employees to select one day off next week. Assuming the selection is done randomly and independently, find the probability of each event.*

5. All three select different days.

6. All three select the same day, given that all three select a day beginning with the same letter.

7. Exactly two of them select the same day.

Genetics of Cystic Fibrosis *The chart represents genetic transmission of cystic fibrosis. C denotes a normal gene, and c denotes a cystic fibrosis gene. (Normal is dominant.) Both parents in this case are Cc, which means that they inherited one of each gene. Therefore, they are both carriers but do not have the disease.*

		Second Parent	
		C	**c**
First Parent	**C**		Cc
	c		

8. Complete the chart, showing all four equally likely gene arrangements.

9. Find the probability that a child of these parents will also be a carrier without the disease.

10. What are the odds that a child of these parents actually will have cystic fibrosis?

Drawing Cards *A single card is chosen at random from a standard 52-card deck. Find the odds against its being each of the following.*

11. a heart   **12.** a red queen

13. a king or a black face card

Selecting Committees *A three-member committee is selected randomly from a group consisting of three men and two women.*

14. Let *x* denote the number of men on the committee, and complete the probability distribution table.

x	*P(x)*
0	0
1	
2	
3	

15. Find the probability that the committee members are not all men.

16. Find the expected number of men on the committee.

Rolling Dice *A pair of dice are rolled. Find the following.*

17. the probability of "doubles" (the same number on both dice)

18. the odds in favor of a sum greater than 2

19. the odds against a sum of "7 or 11"

20. the probability of a sum that is even and less than 5

Making Par in Golf *Ted has a 0.78 chance of making par on each hole of golf that he plays. Today he plans to play just three holes. Find the probability of each event. Round answers to three decimal places.*

21. He makes par on all three holes.

22. He makes par on exactly two of the three holes.

23. He makes par on at least one of the three holes.

24. He makes par on the first and third holes but not on the second.

Card Choices *Two cards are drawn, without replacement, from a standard 52-card deck. Find the probability of each event.*

25. Both cards are red.

26. Both cards are the same color.

27. The second card is a queen, given that the first card is an ace.

28. The first card is a face card and the second is black.

29. **Gender in Sequences of Babies** Assuming boy and girl babies are equally likely, find the probability that a family with three children will have exactly two boys.

30. **Simulation of Pea Plant Reproduction with Coin Tossing** Use the sequence of flower colors in **Example 10** of **Section 11.5** to approximate, to three decimal places, the probability that three successive offspring will all have white flowers.

Simulation with Coin Tossing *A coin was actually tossed 100 times, producing the following sequence of outcomes. Read from left to right across the top row, then from left to right across the second row, and so on, to the bottom row.*

tttth	ththh	htttt	hhhth	ththh
hhhth	httht	hhhht	thttt	thtth
htttth	hhhhh	hhhhh	tttht	ttttt
htthh	tttth	httth	tthhh	tthhh

Find, to three decimal places, the empirical probability of each event.

31. Two consecutive tails (tt) occur.

32. Three consecutive heads (hhh) occur.

Statistics

Suppose you're a psychological therapist who specializes in helping patients with various early-stage addictions. You have noted that under your treatment plan, 50% of your clients have been able to quit drinking (their cumulative probability of remission is 0.50) by 10 years after their dependency began. ("Remission" is defined as quitting for 1 year.)

Compare these results with the general situation, as reported in a long-term study and shown in the graph on the next page. Complete the following statements.

1. According to the long-term study, the more general cumulative probability of remission is 0.50 after about _____ years.

2. Your own results for 0.50 probability of remission are better than the average by about _____ years.

(Check your answers with those given on page 688.)

Cumulative probability of quitting vs. Years since alcohol dependency began

Data Source: G. Heyman, *Annual Review of Clinical Psychology*, March 28, 2013.

Depending on the comparison between the general results and your own results, you may want to either reconsider your treatment protocol or prepare a statistical report on your results for publication in a professional journal.

12.1 VISUAL DISPLAYS OF DATA

OBJECTIVES

1 Understand the basic concepts of data displays.

2 Work with frequency distributions.

3 Work with grouped frequency distributions.

4 Construct and interpret stem-and-leaf displays.

5 Work with bar graphs, circle graphs, and line graphs.

Basic Concepts

Governments collect and analyze an amazing quantity of "statistics." The word itself comes from the Latin *statisticus,* meaning "of the state."

In statistical work, a **population** includes *all* items of interest, and a **sample** includes *some,* but ordinarily not all, of the items in the population. See the Venn diagram in the margin.

To predict the outcome of an approaching presidential election, we may be interested in a population of many millions of voter preferences (those of all potential voters in the country). As a practical matter, however, even national polling organizations with considerable resources obtain only a relatively small sample, say 2000, of those preferences.

The study of statistics is divided into two main areas. **Descriptive statistics** has to do with collecting, organizing, summarizing, and presenting data (information). **Inferential statistics** has to do with drawing inferences or conclusions (making conjectures) about populations on the basis of information from samples.

The photos below show two random samples drawn from a large bowl of 10,000 colored beads. The 25-bead sample contains 9 green beads, from which we infer, by inductive reasoning, that the bowl (the population) must contain about

$$\frac{9}{25}, \text{ or } 36\%, \text{ that is, about 3600 green beads.}$$

Population / Sample

A population of 10,000

A random sample of 25

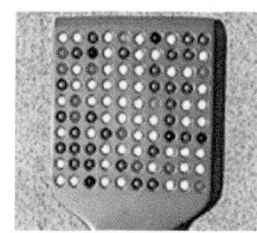
A random sample of 100

These screens give various **statistical options** on the TI-83/84 Plus.

Most scientific and graphing calculators will perform all computations we describe in this chapter, including sorting of data, once they are entered. So your purpose in studying this material should be to understand the meanings of the various computed quantities. It is recommended that the actual computations, especially for sizable collections of data, be done on a calculator or a computer with suitable statistical software.

The 100-bead sample contains 28 green beads, leading to the inference that the population must contain about

$$\frac{28}{100}, \text{ or } 28\%, \text{ that is, about 2800 green beads.}$$

This estimate, based on a larger sample, should be more accurate. In fact it is, since the bowl actually contains

$$30\%, \text{ or } 3000 \text{ green beads,}$$

and 2800 is closer to 3000 than 3600 is. (The "error" is one-third as much.)

Summarizing, if we know what a population is like, then probability theory enables us to predict what is likely to happen in a sample (deductive reasoning). If we know what a sample is like, then inferential statistics enables us to infer estimates about the population (inductive reasoning).

Information that has been collected but not yet organized or processed is called **raw data.** It is often **quantitative** (or **numerical**), but it can also be **qualitative** (or **non-numerical**), as illustrated in **Table 1.**

Table 1 Examples of Raw Data

> **Quantitative data:** The number of siblings in ten different families: 3, 1, 2, 1, 5, 4, 3, 3, 8, 2
>
> **Qualitative data:** The makes of six different automobiles: Toyota, Ford, Kia, Toyota, Chevrolet, Honda

Quantitative data are generally more useful when they are **ranked,** or arranged in numerical order. In ranked form, the first list in **Table 1** appears as follows.

$$1, 1, 2, 2, 3, 3, 3, 4, 5, 8$$

Frequency Distributions

When a data set includes many repeated items, it can be organized into a **frequency distribution,** which lists the distinct data values (x) along with their frequencies (f). The frequency designates the number of times the corresponding item occurred in the data set.

It is also helpful to show the **relative frequency** of each distinct item. This is the fraction, or percentage, of the data set represented by the item. If n denotes the total number of items, and a given item, x, occurred f times, then the relative frequency of x is

$$\frac{f}{n}.$$

Example 1 illustrates these ideas.

EXAMPLE 1 **Constructing Frequency and Relative Frequency Distributions**

The 25 members of a psychology class were polled about the number of siblings in their individual families. Construct a frequency distribution and a relative frequency distribution for their responses, which are shown here.

$$2, 3, 1, 3, 3, 5, 2, 3, 3, 1, 1, 4, 2, 4, 2, 5, 4, 3, 6, 5, 1, 6, 2, 2, 2$$

Solution

The data range from a low of 1 to a high of 6. The frequencies (obtained by inspection) and relative frequencies are shown in **Table 2** on the next page.

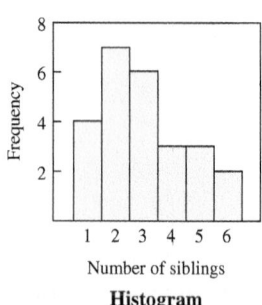

Number of siblings
Histogram
Figure 1

Number of siblings
Frequency polygon
Figure 2

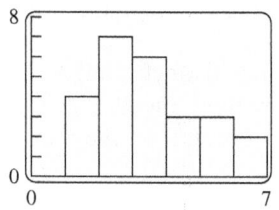

This histogram was generated with a graphing calculator using the data in **Table 2.** Compare with **Figure 1** above.

This line graph resembles the frequency polygon in **Figure 2** above. It was generated with a graphing calculator using the data in **Table 2.**

Table 2 Frequency and Relative Frequency Distributions for Numbers of Siblings

Number x	Frequency f	Relative Frequency $\frac{f}{n}$
1	4	$\frac{4}{25} = 16\%$
2	7	$\frac{7}{25} = 28\%$
3	6	$\frac{6}{25} = 24\%$
4	3	$\frac{3}{25} = 12\%$
5	3	$\frac{3}{25} = 12\%$
6	2	$\frac{2}{25} = 8\%$

Total: $n = 25$

Problem-Solving Strategy

Three of the strategies from **Chapter 1** are "Make a table or chart," "Look for a pattern," and "Draw a sketch." The techniques of this section apply all three of these to present raw data in more meaningful visual forms.

The numerical data of **Table 2** can be interpreted more easily with the aid of a **histogram.** A series of rectangles, whose lengths represent the frequencies, are placed next to one another as shown in **Figure 1.** On each axis, horizontal and vertical, a label and the numerical scale should be shown.

The information shown in the histogram in **Figure 1** can also be conveyed by a **frequency polygon,** as in **Figure 2.** Simply plot a single point at the appropriate height for each frequency, connect the points with a series of connected line segments, and complete the polygon with segments that trail down to the axis beyond 1 and 6.

The frequency polygon is an instance of the more general *line graph*, which was first introduced in **Chapter 1.**

Grouped Frequency Distributions

Data sets containing large numbers of items are often arranged into groups, or **classes.** All data items are assigned to their appropriate classes, and then a **grouped frequency distribution** can be set up and a graph displayed. Although there are no fixed rules for establishing the classes, most statisticians agree on a few general guidelines.

GUIDELINES FOR THE CLASSES OF A GROUPED FREQUENCY DISTRIBUTION

1. Make sure each data item will fit into one, and only one, class.

2. Try to make all classes the same width.

3. Make sure the classes do not overlap.

4. Use from 5 to 12 classes. Too few or too many classes can obscure the tendencies in the data.

EXAMPLE 2   **Constructing a Histogram and a Frequency Polygon**

Forty students, selected randomly in the school cafeteria one morning, were asked to estimate the number of hours they had spent studying in the past week (including both in-class and out-of-class time). Their responses are recorded here.

$$18 \quad 60 \quad 72 \quad 58 \quad 33 \quad 15 \quad 12 \quad 36 \quad 16 \quad 29$$

$$26 \quad 41 \quad 45 \quad 25 \quad 32 \quad 24 \quad 22 \quad 55 \quad 30 \quad 31$$

$$55 \quad 39 \quad 29 \quad 44 \quad 29 \quad 14 \quad 36 \quad 31 \quad 45 \quad 62$$

$$36 \quad 52 \quad 47 \quad 38 \quad 36 \quad 23 \quad 33 \quad 44 \quad 17 \quad 24$$

Tabulate a grouped frequency distribution and a grouped relative frequency distribution, and construct a histogram and a frequency polygon for the given data.

Solution

The data range from a low of 12 to a high of 72—that is, over a range of

$$72 - 12 = 60 \text{ units.}$$

The widths of the classes should be uniform (by Guideline 2), and there should be from 5 to 12 classes (by Guideline 4). Five classes would imply a class width of about $\frac{60}{5} = 12$, while twelve classes would imply a class width of about $\frac{60}{12} = 5$. A class width of 10 will be convenient. We let our classes run from 10 through 19, from 20 through 29, and so on up to 70 through 79, for a total of seven classes. All four guidelines are met.

Next go through the data set, tallying each item into the appropriate class. The tally totals produce class frequencies, which in turn produce relative frequencies, as shown in **Table 3** below. The histogram is displayed in **Figure 3**.

In **Table 3** (and **Figure 3**) the numbers 10, 20, 30, and so on are called the **lower class limits.** They are the smallest possible data values within the respective classes. The numbers 19, 29, 39, and so on are called the **upper class limits.** The common **class width** for the distribution is the difference of any two successive lower class limits (such as $30 - 20$) or of any two successive upper class limits (such as $59 - 49$). The class width for this distribution is 10, as noted earlier.

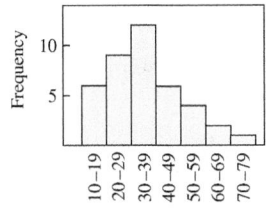

Weekly study times (in hours)
Grouped frequency histogram

Figure 3

Table 3 Grouped Frequency and Relative Frequency Distributions for Weekly Study Times

Class Limits	Tally	Frequency f	Relative Frequency $\frac{f}{n}$
10–19	ⅢⅠ	6	$\frac{6}{40} = 15.0\%$
20–29	Ⅲ ⅢⅠ	9	$\frac{9}{40} = 22.5\%$
30–39	Ⅲ Ⅲ ⅡⅠ	12	$\frac{12}{40} = 30.0\%$
40–49	ⅢⅠ	6	$\frac{6}{40} = 15.0\%$
50–59	ⅢⅠ	4	$\frac{4}{40} = 10.0\%$
60–69	ⅡⅠ	2	$\frac{2}{40} = 5.0\%$
70–79	Ⅰ	1	$\frac{1}{40} = 2.5\%$

Total: $n = 40$

14.5 24.5 34.5 44.5 54.5 64.5 74.5
Weekly study times (in hours)
Grouped frequency polygon

Figure 4

To construct a frequency polygon, notice that in a *grouped* frequency distribution, the data items in a given class are generally not all the same. We can obtain the "middle" value, or **class mark,** by adding the lower and upper class limits and dividing this sum by 2. We locate all the class marks along the horizontal axis and plot points above the class marks. The heights of the plotted points represent the class frequencies. The resulting points are connected just as for a nongrouped frequency distribution. The result is shown in **Figure 4.**

Stem-and-Leaf Displays

In **Table 3,** the tally marks give a good visual impression of how the data are distributed. In fact, the tally marks are almost like a histogram turned on its side. Nevertheless, once the tallying is done, the tally marks are usually dropped, and the grouped frequency distribution is presented as in **Table 4.**

The pictorial advantage of the tally marks is now lost. Furthermore, we cannot tell, from the grouped frequency distribution itself (or from the tally marks either, for that matter), what any of the original items were. We only know, for example, that there were six items in the class 40–49. We do not know specifically what any of them were.

One way to avoid these shortcomings is to employ a tool of exploratory data analysis, the **stem-and-leaf display,** as shown in **Example 3.**

Table 4

Grouped Frequency Distribution for Weekly Study Times

Class Limits	Frequency
10–19	6
20–29	9
30–39	12
40–49	6
50–59	4
60–69	2
70–79	1

EXAMPLE 3 **Constructing a Stem-and-Leaf Display**

Present the study times data of **Example 2** in a stem-and-leaf display.

Solution

See **Example 2** for the original raw data. We arrange the numbers in **Table 5.** The tens digits, to the left of the vertical line, are the "stems," while the corresponding ones digits are the "leaves." We have entered all items from the first row of the original data, from left to right, and then the items from the second row through the fourth row.

Table 5 Stem-and-Leaf Display for Weekly Study Times

1	8	5	2	6	4	7				
2	9	6	5	4	2	9	9	3	4	
3	3	6	2	0	1	9	6	1	6	8	6	3
4	1	5	4	5	7	4				
5	8	5	5	2						
6	0	2								
7	2									

Notice that the stem-and-leaf display of **Example 3** conveys at a glance the same pictorial impressions that a histogram would convey, without the need for constructing the drawing. It also preserves the exact data values.

Bar Graphs, Circle Graphs, and Line Graphs

A frequency distribution of non-numerical observations can be presented in the form of a **bar graph,** which is similar to a histogram except that the rectangles (bars) usually are not touching one another and sometimes are arranged horizontally rather than vertically. The bar graph of **Figure 5** shows the frequencies of occurrence of the vowels A, E, I, O, and U in this paragraph.

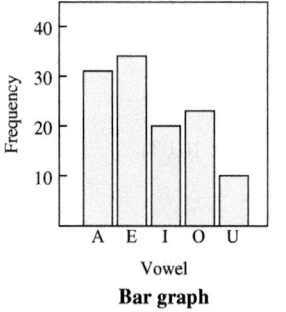

A E I O U
Vowel
Bar graph

Figure 5

EXAMPLE 4 Interpreting a Bar Graph

Refer to the bar graph in **Figure 6** to answer these questions.

(a) What was the total annual antibiotic usage?

(b) About what percentage was used in livestock production?

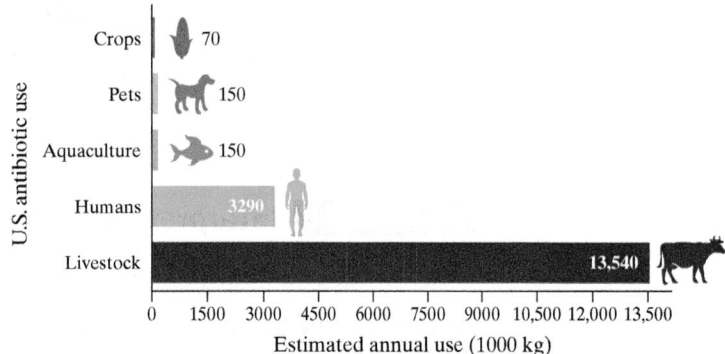

Source: A. Hollis and Z. Ahmed, *New England Journal of Medicine*, December 26, 2013.

U.S. antibiotic use (2013)

Figure 6

Solution

(a) $70,000 + 150,000 + 150,000 + 3,290,000 + 13,540,000 = 17,200,000$

The total antibiotic usage was 17,200,000 kilograms.

(b) $\dfrac{13,540,000}{17,200,000} \approx 0.787$ Livestock production was about 79% of total usage. ■

Table 6

Portfolio Allocations

Investment Category	Percent of Total
Stocks	55%
Bonds	20
Cash	15
Metals	10

A graphical alternative to the bar graph is the **circle graph,** or **pie chart,** which uses a circle to represent the total of all the categories and divides the circle into sectors, or wedges (like pieces of pie), whose sizes show the relative magnitudes of the categories. The angle around the entire circle measures 360°. For example, a category representing 20% of the whole should correspond to a sector whose central angle is 20% of 360°, that is,

$$0.20(360°) = 72°.$$

A circle graph shows, at a glance, the relative magnitudes of various categories.

EXAMPLE 5 Constructing a Circle Graph

Filipe's investment advisor recommends the portfolio allocations shown in **Table 6.** Present this information in a circle graph.

Solution

The central angles for the sectors are as follows.

Stocks: $0.55(360°) = 198°$

Bonds: $0.20(360°) = 72°$

Cash: $0.15(360°) = 54°$

Metals: $0.10(360°) = 36°$

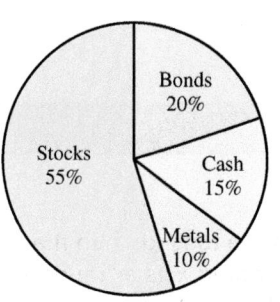

Investment allocations

Figure 7

Draw a circle and mark off the angles with a protractor. (See **Figure 7.**) ■

To demonstrate how a quantity *changes*, say with respect to time, use a **line graph.** Connect a series of line segments that rise and fall with time, according to the magnitude of the quantity being illustrated. To compare the patterns of change for two or more quantities, we can even plot multiple line graphs together in a "comparison line graph." (A line graph looks somewhat like a frequency polygon, but the quantities graphed are not necessarily frequencies.)

In December 2013, the U.S. Food and Drug Administration initiated a voluntary program phasing out antibiotics used to make livestock grow bigger (see **Figure 6** in **Example 4**) because it was thought that such usage was a cause of bacterial resistance to drugs in humans.

EXAMPLE 6 Interpreting a Comparison Line Graph

Answer the following questions by referring to **Figure 8.**

(a) What time frame is reflected in the figure?

(b) In which years was resistance to ciprofloxacin greater than resistance to ceftriaxone?

(c) Over this time span, what was the highest resistance to ceftriaxone achieved, and when did it occur?

Source: U.S. CDC.

Antibiotic resistance of Salmonella infections in humans

Figure 8

Solution

(a) 1996 through 2011

(b) 1997, 1998, and 2011

(c) About 4.5%, in 2002 and 2003

FOR FURTHER THOUGHT

Expected and Observed Frequencies

When fair coins are tossed, the results on particular tosses cannot be reliably predicted. As more and more coins are tossed, however, the proportions of heads and tails become more predictable. This is a consequence of the "law of large numbers."

For example, if five coins are tossed, then the resulting number of heads, denoted x, is a "random variable," whose possible values are

0, 1, 2, 3, 4, and 5.

If the five coins are tossed repeatedly, say 64 separate times, then the binomial probability formula can be used to get **expected frequencies** (or **theoretical frequencies**), as shown in the table below. The first two columns of the table comprise the **expected frequency distribution** for 64 tosses of five fair coins.

Number of Heads x	Expected Frequency e	Observed Frequency o
0	2	
1	10	
2	20	
3	20	
4	10	
5	2	

In an actual experiment, we could obtain **observed frequencies** (or **empirical frequencies**), which would most likely differ somewhat from the expected frequencies. But 64 repetitions of the experiment should be enough to provide fair consistency between expected and observed values.

For Group or Individual Investigation

Toss five coins a total of 64 times, keeping a record of the results.

1. Enter your experimental results in the third column of the accompanying table, producing an **observed frequency distribution.**
2. Compare the second and third column entries.
3. Construct two histograms, one from the expected frequency distribution and one from your observed frequency distribution.
4. Compare the two histograms.

12.1 EXERCISES

In Exercises 1 and 2, use the given data to do the following:

(a) *Construct frequency and relative frequency distributions, in a table similar to* **Table 2.**

(b) *Construct a histogram.*

(c) *Construct a frequency polygon.*

1. **Preparation for Summer** According to *Newsmax* (May 2010, page 76), the following are five popular "maintenance" activities performed as summer approaches.

   1. Prep the car for road trips.
   2. Clean up the house or apartment.
   3. Groom the garden.
   4. Exercise the body.
   5. Organize the wardrobe.

   The following data are the responses of 30 people who were asked, on June 1, how many of the five activities they had accomplished.

   ```
   1  1  3  1  0  3  0  0  2  1
   2  2  0  0  5  3  4  0  1  0
   4  2  0  2  0  1  0  1  2  3
   ```

2. **Favorite Numbers** The following data are the "favorite numbers" (single digits, 1 through 9) of the 28 pupils of a second grade class.

   ```
   4  7  2  7  6  3  1
   7  2  9  8  5  6  1
   4  3  8  9  5  4  5
   9  2  6  5  2  5  7
   ```

In Exercises 3–6, use the given data to do the following:

(a) *Construct grouped frequency and relative frequency distributions, in a table similar to* **Table 3.** *(Follow the suggested guidelines for class limits and class width.)*

(b) *Construct a histogram.*

(c) *Construct a frequency polygon.*

3. **Exam Scores** The scores of the 48 members of a sociology lecture class on a 50-point exam were as follows.

   ```
   40  43  44  33  41  40  33  39
   42  36  43  42  45  42  23  41
   43  40  37  47  44  48  31  46
   38  31  46  38  39  42  47  40
   47  41  48  42  45  29  32  38
   45  28  49  46  47  36  48  46
   ```

   Use six classes with a uniform class width of 5 points, and use a lower limit of 21 points for the first class.

4. **Charge Card Account Balances** The following raw data represent the monthly account balances (to the nearest dollar) for a sample of 50 brand-new charge card users.

   ```
    78  175   46  138   79  118  90  163   88  107
   126  154   85   60   42   54  62  128  114   73
    67  119  116  145  129  130  81  105   96   71
   100  145  117   60  125  130  94   88  136  112
    85  165  118   84   74   62  81  110  108   71
   ```

   Use seven classes with a uniform width of 20 dollars, where the lower limit of the first class is 40 dollars.

5. *Daily High Temperatures* The following data represent the daily high temperatures (in degrees Fahrenheit) for the month of June in a town in the Sacramento Valley of California.

79	84	88	96	102	104	99	97	92	94
85	92	100	99	101	104	97	108	106	106
90	82	74	72	83	107	98	102	97	94

Use eight classes with a uniform width of 5 degrees, where the lower limit of the first class is 70 degrees.

6. *IQ Scores of College Freshmen* The following data represent IQ scores of a group of 50 college freshmen.

113	109	118	92	130	112	114	117	122	115
127	107	108	113	124	112	111	106	116	118
121	107	118	118	110	124	115	103	100	114
104	124	116	123	104	135	121	126	116	111
96	134	98	129	102	103	107	113	117	112

Use nine classes with a uniform width of 5, where the lower limit of the first class is 91.

In each of Exercises 7–10, construct a stem-and-leaf display for the given data. In each case, treat the ones digits as the leaves. For any single-digit data, use a stem of 0.

7. *Games Won in the National Basketball Association* Approaching midseason, the teams in the National Basketball Association had won the following numbers of games.

27	20	29	11	26	11	12	7	26	18
22	19	14	13	22	9	25	11	10	15
38	10	22	23	31	8	24	15	24	15

8. *Accumulated College Units* The students in a biology class were asked how many college units they had accumulated to date. Their responses are shown below.

12	4	13	12	21	22	15	17	33	24
32	42	26	11	53	62	42	25	13	8
54	18	21	14	19	17	38	17	20	10

9. *Distances to School* The following data are the daily round-trip distances to school (in miles) for 30 randomly chosen students attending a community college in California.

16	30	10	11	18	26	34	18	8	12
21	14	5	22	4	25	9	10	6	21
12	18	9	16	44	23	4	13	36	8

10. *Yards Gained in the National Football League* The following data represent net yards gained per game by National Football League running backs who played during a given week of the season.

25	19	36	73	37	88	67	33	54	123	79
19	39	45	22	58	7	73	30	43	24	36
65	43	33	55	40	29	112	60	94	86	62
52	29	18	25	41	3	49	102	16	32	46

Federal Revenue and Spending The graph shows U.S. government receipts and outlays (both on-budget and off-budget) for 2001–2012. Refer to the graph for Exercises 11–15.

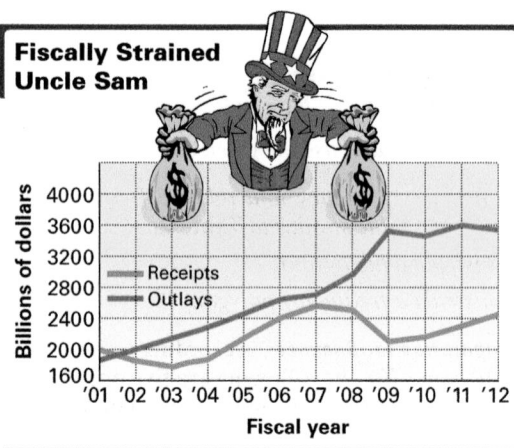

Source: Department of the Treasury, Office of Management and Budget.

11. For the period 2001–2012, list all years when receipts exceeded outlays.

12. Identify each of the following amounts, and indicate when it occurred.

  (a) the greatest one-year drop in receipts

  (b) the greatest one-year rise in outlays

13. In what years did receipts appear to climb faster than outlays?

14. About what was the greatest deficit (outlays minus receipts), and in what year did it occur?

15. Plot a point for each year and draw a line graph showing the federal surplus ($+$) or deficit ($-$) over the years 2001–2012.

Reading Bar Graphs of Economic Indicators *The bar graphs here show trends in several economic indicators over the period 2007–2012.*

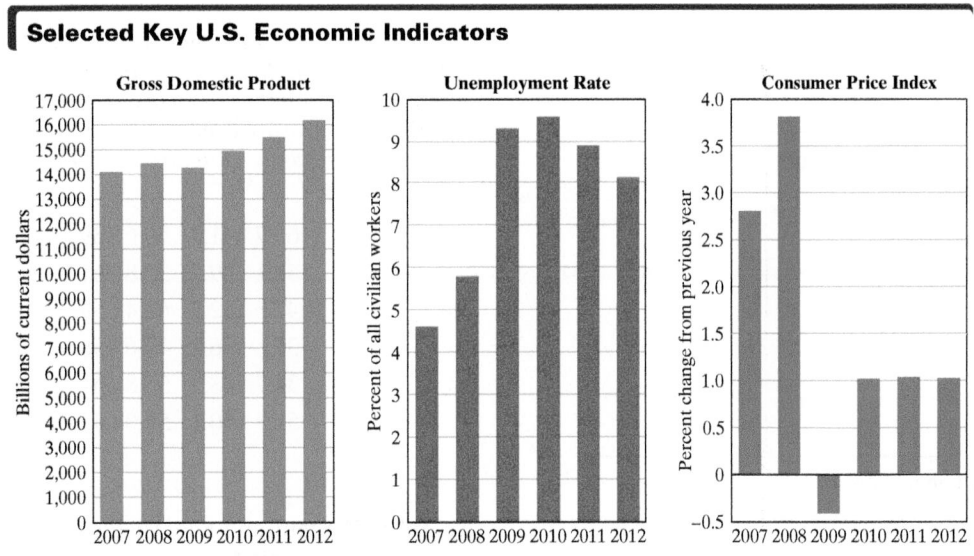

Selected Key U.S. Economic Indicators

Sources: U.S. Department of Commerce, Bureau of Economic Analysis.
U.S. Department of Labor, Bureau of Labor Statistics.

Refer to the above graphs for Exercises 16–20.

16. About what was the gross domestic product in 2012?

17. Over the six-year period, about what was the greatest change in consumer price index, and when did it occur?

18. What was the greatest year-to-year change in the unemployment rate, and when did it occur?

19. Observing these graphs, what would you say was the most unusual occurrence during the six years represented?

20. Explain why the gross domestic product would generally increase when the unemployment rate decreases.

Reading a Circle Graph of Job-Training Sources *The circle graph in the next column shows how a surveyed group of American workers were trained for their jobs. Refer to it for Exercises 21 and 22.*

21. What is the greatest single training source? To the nearest degree, what is the central angle of that category's sector?

22. What percentage of job training was provided directly from employers, either formally or informally?

23. ***Sources of U.S. Budget Receipts*** The table at the right gives the major sources of government income for 2012. Use the information to draw a circle graph.

Graph for Exercises 21 and 22

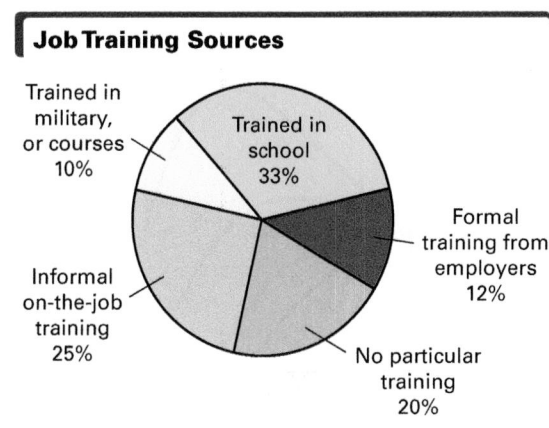

Job Training Sources

Trained in military, or courses 10%

Trained in school 33%

Formal training from employers 12%

No particular training 20%

Informal on-the-job training 25%

Table for Exercise 23

Source of Receipts	Approximate Percentage of Total
Individual income taxes	46%
Corporate income taxes	10
Social insurance and retirement receipts	35
Excise taxes	3
Other receipts	6

Source: Congressional Budget Office; *Budget of the U.S. Government,* Office of Management and Budget, Executive Office of the President.

24. *Correspondence between Education and Earnings* Data for a recent year showed that the average annual earnings of American workers corresponded to educational level as shown in the table below. Draw a bar graph that shows this information.

Educational Level	Median Weekly Earnings
Less than a high school diploma	$453
High school graduate	618
Some college, no degree	699
Associate degree	757
Bachelor's degree	1012
Master's degree	1233
Professional degree	1531
Doctoral degree	1561

Source: Bureau of Labor Statistics.

Net Worth of Retirement Savings Saura, wishing to retire at age 60, is studying the comparison line graph here, which shows (under certain assumptions) how the net worth of her retirement savings (initially $500,000 at age 60) will change as she gets older and as she withdraws living expenses from savings. Refer to the graph for Exercises 25–28.

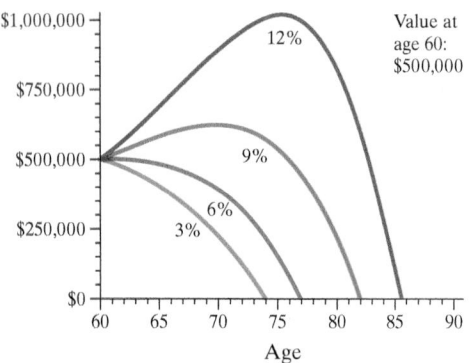

25. Assuming Saura can maintain an average annual return of 9%, how old will she be when her money runs out?

26. If she could earn an average of 12% annually, what maximum net worth would Saura achieve? At about what age would the maximum occur?

27. Suppose Saura reaches age 70 in good health, and the average annual return has proved to be 6%.

(a) About how much longer can she expect her money to last?

(b) What options might she consider in order to extend that time?

28. At age 71, about how many times more will Saura's net worth be if she averages a 12% return than if she averages a 3% return?

Sample Masses in a Geology Laboratory Stem-and-leaf displays can be modified in various ways in order to obtain a reasonable number of stems. The following data, representing the measured masses (in grams) of thirty mineral samples in a geology lab, are shown in a **double-stem** display in **Table 7**.

60.7	41.4	50.6	39.5	46.4
58.1	49.7	38.8	61.6	55.2
47.3	52.7	62.4	59.0	44.9
35.6	36.2	40.6	56.9	42.6
34.7	48.3	55.8	54.2	33.8
51.3	50.1	57.0	42.8	43.7

Table 7 Stem-and-Leaf Display for Mineral Sample Masses

(30–34)	3	4.7	3.8				
(35–39)	3	9.5	8.8	5.6	6.2		
(40–44)	4	1.4	4.9	0.6	2.6	2.8	3.7
(45–49)	4	6.4	9.7	7.3	8.3		
(50–54)	5	0.6	2.7	4.2	1.3	0.1	
(55–59)	5	8.1	5.2	9.0	6.9	5.8	7.0
(60–64)	6	0.7	1.6	2.4			

29. Describe how the stem-and-leaf display of **Table 7** was constructed.

30. Explain why **Table 7** is called a "double-stem" display.

31. In general, how many stems (total) are appropriate for a stem-and-leaf display? Explain your reasoning.

32. *Record Temperatures* According to the National Climatic Data Center, U.S. Department of Commerce, the highest temperatures (in degrees Fahrenheit) ever recorded in the 50 states (as of May 22, 2013) were as follows.

112	100	128	120	134	114	106	110	109	112
100	118	117	116	118	121	114	114	105	109
107	112	115	115	118	117	118	125	106	110
122	108	110	121	113	120	119	111	104	113
120	113	120	117	107	110	118	112	114	115

Present these data in a double-stem display.

33. *Letter Occurrence Frequencies in the English Language* The table below shows commonly accepted percentages of occurrence for the various letters in English language usage. (Code breakers have carefully analyzed these percentages as an aid in deciphering secret codes.)

For example, notice that E is the most commonly occurring letter, followed by T, A, O, N, and so on. The letters Q and Z occur least often. Referring to **Figure 5** in the text, would you say that the relative frequencies of occurrence of the vowels in the associated paragraph were typical or unusual? Explain your reasoning.

Letter	Percent	Letter	Percent
E	13	L	$3\frac{1}{2}$
T	9	C, M, U	3
A, O	8	F, P, Y	2
N	7	W, G, B	$1\frac{1}{2}$
I, R	$6\frac{1}{2}$	V	1
S, H	6	K, X, J	$\frac{1}{2}$
D	4	Q, Z	$\frac{1}{5}$

Frequencies and Probabilities of Letter Occurrence The percentages shown in **Exercise 33** are based on a very large sampling of English language text. Since they are based on experiment, they are "empirical" rather than "theoretical." By converting each percent in that table to a decimal fraction, you can produce an **empirical probability distribution.**

For example, if a single letter is randomly selected from a randomly selected passage of text, the probability that it will be an E *is* 0.13. *The probability that a randomly selected letter will be a vowel* (A, E, I, O, *or* U) *is*

$$(0.08 + 0.13 + 0.065 + 0.08 + 0.03) = 0.385.$$

34. Rewrite the distribution shown in **Exercise 33** as an empirical probability distribution. Give values to three decimal places. Note that the 26 probabilities in this distribution—one for each letter of the alphabet—should add up to 1 (except for, perhaps, a slight round-off error).

35. (a) From your distribution in **Exercise 34,** construct an empirical probability distribution just for the vowels A, E, I, O, and U. (*Hint:* Divide each vowel's probability, from **Exercise 34,** by 0.385 to obtain a distribution whose five values add up to 1.) Give values to three decimal places.

(b) Construct an appropriately labeled bar graph from your distribution in part (a).

36. Based on the occurrences of vowels in the paragraph represented by **Figure 5,** construct a probability distribution for the vowels. Give probabilities to three decimal places. The frequencies are

A–31,   E–34,   I–20,   O–23,   U–10.

37. Is the probability distribution in **Exercise 36** theoretical or empirical? Is it different from the distribution in **Exercise 35?** Which one is more accurate? Explain your reasoning.

38. *Frequencies and Probabilities of Study Times* Convert the grouped frequency distribution in **Table 3** to an empirical probability distribution, using the same classes and giving probability values to three decimal places.

39. *Probabilities of Study Times* Recall that the distribution in **Exercise 38** was based on weekly study times for a sample of 40 students. Suppose one of those students was selected randomly. Using your distribution, find the probability that the study time in the past week for the student selected would have been in each of the following ranges.

(a) 20–29 hours   (b) 50–69 hours

(c) fewer than 40 hours   (d) at least 60 hours

Favorite Sports among Recreation Students The 40 members of a recreation class were asked to name their favorite sports. The table shows the numbers who responded in various ways.

Sport	Number of Class Members
Sailing	7
Archery	4
Snowboarding	10
Bicycling	8
Rock climbing	8
Rafting	3

Use this information in Exercises 40–42.

40. If a member of this class is selected at random, what is the probability that the favorite sport of the person selected is sailing?

41. (a) Based on the data in the table, construct a probability distribution, giving probabilities to three decimal places.

(b) Do you think the distribution in part (a) is theoretical, or empirical?

(c) Explain your answer to part (b).

42. Explain the distinction between a relative frequency distribution and a probability distribution.

WHEN Will I Ever USE This ?

Imagine that you are the therapist mentioned in the chapter opener and that, again, you want to compare the results you have achieved in your own practice with the broader results. In this case, you are interested in tobacco dependency and remission. The study referred to earlier produced the following data for smokers, where

x = years since dependency began, and

y = cumulative probability of quitting (for a year).

x	y	x	y	x	y
3.3	0.08	22.9	0.39	45.8	0.63
7.9	0.17	28.0	0.45	50.9	0.69
14.0	0.26	33.2	0.52	56.1	0.78
18.2	0.32	37.9	0.57	62.6	0.84

1. To clarify the meaning of the data, plot the twelve points and sketch a smooth curve that approximately fits the points.

2. Use the graph you have prepared to complete the following statement:

   It takes about _____ years for 50% of smokers to quit the habit.

3. Compare with the graph on **page 688,** and complete the same statement for drinkers:

   It takes about _____ years before 50% of drinkers quit the habit.

   (Check your answers with those given below.)

4. Give some possible reasons for the discrepancy between the results for smokers and those for drinkers, as reflected in your answers to Questions 2 and 3 above.

12.2   MEASURES OF CENTRAL TENDENCY

OBJECTIVES

1 Find and interpret means.

2 Find and interpret medians.

3 Find and interpret modes.

4 Infer central tendency measures from stem-and-leaf displays.

5 Discern symmetry in data sets.

6 Compare measures of central tendency.

Many calculators find the **mean** (as well as other statistical measures) automatically when a set of data items are entered. To recognize these calculators, look for a key marked $\boxed{\bar{x}}$, or perhaps $\boxed{\mu}$, or look in a menu such as "LIST" for a listing of mathematical measures.

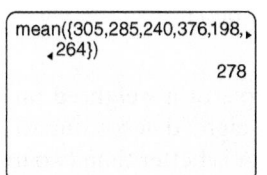

A calculator can find the mean of items in a list. This screen supports the text discussion of monthly building permits.

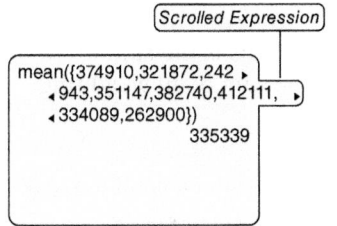

This screen supports the result in
Example 1.

A city issued the following numbers of building permits over a six-month period.

$$305, \quad 285, \quad 240, \quad 376, \quad 198, \quad 264$$

A single number that is in some sense representative of this whole set of numbers, a kind of "middle" value, would be a **measure of central tendency.**

Mean

The most common measure of central tendency is the **mean** (or **arithmetic mean**). The mean of a sample is denoted $\bar{x}$ (read "x bar"), while the mean of a complete population is denoted μ (the lowercase Greek letter *mu*). For our purposes here, data sets are considered to be samples, so we use $\bar{x}$.

    The mean of a set of data items is found by adding up all the items and then dividing the sum by the number of items. (The mean is what most people associate with the word "average.") Since adding up, or summing, a list of items is a common procedure in statistics, we use the symbol for "summation," Σ (the capital Greek letter *sigma*). Therefore, the sum of n items—say $x_1, x_2, \ldots, x_n$—can be denoted

$$\Sigma x = x_1 + x_2 + \cdots + x_n.$$

MEAN

The **mean** of n data items $x_1, x_2, \ldots, x_n$, is calculated as follows.

$$\bar{x} = \frac{\Sigma x}{n}$$

We find the central tendency of the monthly building permit figures as follows.

$$\text{Mean} = \bar{x} = \frac{\Sigma x}{n}$$

$$= \frac{305 + 285 + 240 + 376 + 198 + 264}{6} \quad \text{Add the monthly numbers.}$$
$$\text{Divide by the number of months.}$$

$$= \frac{1668}{6}, \quad \text{or} \quad 278$$

The mean value (the "average monthly permits issued") is 278.

EXAMPLE 1   Finding the Mean of a List of Sales Figures

Last year's annual sales for eight different online businesses were as follows.

$$\$374{,}910 \quad \$321{,}872 \quad \$242{,}943 \quad \$351{,}147$$
$$\$382{,}740 \quad \$412{,}111 \quad \$334{,}089 \quad \$262{,}900$$

Find the mean annual sales for the eight businesses.

Solution

$$\bar{x} = \frac{\Sigma x}{n} = \frac{2{,}682{,}712}{8} = 335{,}339 \qquad \text{Add the sales.}$$
$$\text{Divide by the number of businesses.}$$

The mean annual sales amount is \$335,339. ∎

The following table shows the units and grades earned by one student last term.

Course	Grade	Units
Mathematics	A	3
History	C	3
Chemistry	B	5
Art	B	2
PE	A	1

In one common method of defining **grade-point average,** an A grade is assigned 4 points, with 3 points for B, 2 for C, and 1 for D. Compute grade-point average as follows.

Step 1 Multiply the number of units for a course and the number assigned to each grade.

Step 2 Add these products.

Step 3 Divide by the total number of units.

Course	Grade	Grade Points	Units	(Grade Points) · (Units)
Mathematics	A	4	3	12
History	C	2	3	6
Chemistry	B	3	5	15
Art	B	3	2	6
PE	A	4	1	4
			Totals: 14	43

$$\text{Grade-point average} = \frac{43}{14} = 3.07 \ (\text{rounded})$$

The calculation of a grade-point average is an example of a **weighted mean,** because the grade points for each course grade must be weighted according to the number of units for the course. (For example, five units of A is better than two units of A.) The number of units is called the **weighting factor.**

WEIGHTED MEAN

The **weighted mean** of n numbers, $x_1, x_2, \ldots, x_n$ that are weighted by the respective factors $f_1, f_2, \ldots, f_n$ is calculated as follows.

$$\overline{w} = \frac{\Sigma(x \cdot f)}{\Sigma f}$$

In words, the weighted mean of a group of (weighted) items is the sum of all products of items times weighting factors, divided by the sum of all weighting factors.

The weighted mean formula is commonly used to find the mean for a frequency distribution. In this case, the weighting factors are the frequencies.

Salary x	Number of Employees f
$12,000	8
$16,000	11
$18,500	14
$21,000	9
$34,000	2
$50,000	1

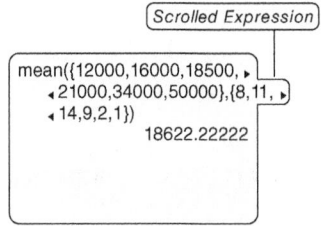

Scrolled Expression

mean({12000,16000,18500, ▸
◂21000,34000,50000},{8,11, ▸
◂14,9,2,1})
            18622.22222

In this screen supporting **Example 2**, the first list contains the salaries, and the second list contains their frequencies.

EXAMPLE 2 Finding the Mean of a Frequency Distribution of Salaries

Find the mean salary for a small company that pays annual salaries to its employees as shown in the frequency distribution in the margin.

Solution

According to the weighted mean formula, we can set up the work as follows.

Salary x	Number of Employees f	Salary · Number $x \cdot f$
$12,000	8	$96,000
$16,000	11	$176,000
$18,500	14	$259,000
$21,000	9	$189,000
$34,000	2	$68,000
$50,000	1	$50,000
Totals:	45	$838,000

$$\text{Mean salary} = \frac{\Sigma(x \cdot f)}{\Sigma f} = \frac{\$838,000}{45} = \$18,622 \quad (\text{rounded}) \qquad \blacksquare$$

For some data sets the mean can be a misleading indicator of average. Consider a small business that employs five workers at the following annual salaries.

$16,500, \quad $16,950, \quad $17,800, \quad $19,750, \quad $20,000

The employees, struggling to survive on these salaries, approach the business owner, Aiguo, with the following computation.

$$\bar{x} = \frac{\$16,500 + \$16,950 + \$17,800 + \$19,750 + \$20,000}{5}$$

$$= \frac{\$91,000}{5}, \quad \text{or} \quad \$18,200 \quad \text{Mean salary (employees)}$$

Aiguo responds with his own calculations, for *all* workers (including his own salary of $188,000).

$$\bar{x} = \frac{\$16,500 + \$16,950 + \$17,800 + \$19,750 + \$20,000 + \$188,000}{6}$$

$$= \frac{\$279,000}{6}, \quad \text{or} \quad \$46,500 \quad \text{Mean salary (including Aiguo's)}$$

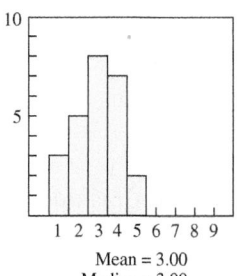

Mean = 3.00
Median = 3.00

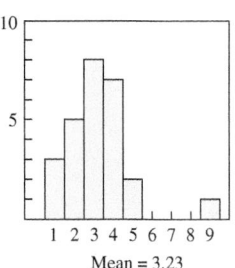

Mean = 3.23
Median = 3.00

The introduction of a single "outlier" above increased the mean by 8 percent but left the median unaffected.

Outliers should usually be considered as *possible* errors in the data.

This mean is quite different, and it looks much more respectable.

The employees, of course, would argue that when Aiguo included his own salary in the calculation, it caused the mean to be a misleading indicator of average. This was so because Aiguo's salary is not typical. It lies a good distance away from the general grouping of the items (salaries). An extreme value like this is referred to as an **outlier.** Since a single outlier can have a significant effect on the value of the mean, we say that the mean is "highly sensitive to extreme values."

Median

Another measure of central tendency, which is not so sensitive to extreme values, is the **median.** This measure divides a group of numbers into two parts, with half the numbers below the median and half above it.

MEDIAN

Find the **median** of a group of items as follows.

Step 1 Rank the items (that is, arrange them in numerical order from least to greatest).

Step 2 If the number of items is *odd,* the median is the middle item in the list.

Step 3 If the number of items is *even,* the median is the mean of the two middle items.

For Aiguo's business, all salaries (including his own), arranged in numerical order, are shown here.

$$\$16,500, \quad \$16,950, \quad \$17,800, \quad \$19,750, \quad \$20,000, \quad \$188,000$$

Thus, $\quad$ median $= \dfrac{\$17,800 + \$19,750}{2} = \dfrac{\$37,550}{2} = \$18,775.$

This figure is a representative average, based on all six salaries, that the employees would probably agree is reasonable.

EXAMPLE 3 Finding Medians of Lists of Numbers

Find the median of each list of numbers.

(a) 6, 7, 12, 13, 18, 23, 24 $\qquad$ **(b)** 17, 15, 9, 13, 21, 32, 41, 7, 12

(c) 147, 159, 132, 181, 174, 253

Solution

(a) This list is already ranked. The number of values in the list, 7, is odd, so the median is the middle value, or 13.

(b) First rank the items.

$$7, 9, 12, 13, 15, 17, 21, 32, 41$$
$$\uparrow$$
$$\text{Median}$$

The middle number can now be picked out. The median is 15.

(c) First rank the items.

$$132, 147, 159, 174, 181, 253$$

Since the list contains an even number of items, namely 6, there is no single middle item. Find the median by taking the mean of the two middle items, 159 and 174.

$$\frac{159 + 174}{2} = \frac{333}{2} = 166.5 \quad \leftarrow \quad \text{Median}$$

Scrolled Expression

median({6,7,12,13,18,23,24})
$\qquad\qquad\qquad$ 13
median({147,159,132,181,174,253})
$\qquad\qquad\qquad$ 166.5

The calculator can find the median of the entries in a list. This screen supports the results in **Examples 3(a) and (c).**

Locating the middle item (the median) of a frequency distribution is a bit more involved. First find the total number of items in the set by adding the frequencies ($n = \Sigma f$). Then the median is the item whose *position* is given by the following formula.

POSITION OF THE MEDIAN IN A FREQUENCY DISTRIBUTION

$$\text{Position of median} = \frac{n + 1}{2} = \frac{\Sigma f + 1}{2}$$

This formula gives only the position, and not the actual value, of the median.

WHEN Will I Ever USE This ?

There is considerable controversy over how important professional intervention is, in general, for addiction remission. But it seems clear that for those who *do* need help with their follow-up recovery, a complete quarterly checkup is much more effective than just a brief interview in getting them back into treatment.

The graph below reflects the results of an extensive study, *Drug and Alcohol Dependence 2012*, reported by M. L. Dennis and C. K. Scott. Conveying information graphically, and interpreting information from graphs, are important in the work of psychologists and other social scientists.

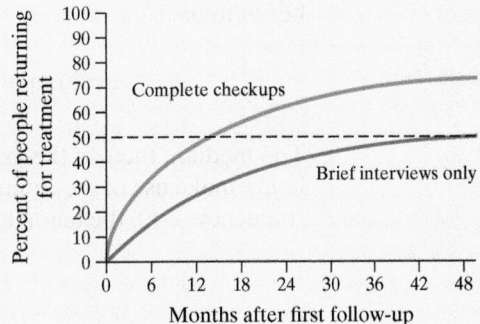

Effects of follow-up on readmission to treatment

Data Source: M. L. Dennis and C. K. Scott, *Drug and Alcohol Dependence 2012.*

The median time to readmission is the number of months by which half the people who needed help with their follow-up recovery had returned for treatment. Complete the following statements.

1. The median time for those having checkups was about _____ months.

2. The median time for those not having checkups was about _____ months.

3. For those who had complete quarterly checkups, the median time to readmission was reduced by about _____ months.

EXAMPLE 4 Finding Medians for Frequency Distributions

Find the medians for the following distributions.

(a)

Value	1	2	3	4	5	6
Frequency	1	3	2	4	8	2

(b)

Value	2	4	6	8	10
Frequency	5	8	10	6	6

Solution

(a) Arrange the work as follows. Tabulate the values and frequencies, and the **cumulative frequencies,** which tell, for each different value, how many items have that value or a lesser value.

Value	Frequency	Cumulative Frequency	
1	1	1	1 item 1 or less
2	3	4	$1 + 3 = 4$ items 2 or less
3	2	6	$4 + 2 = 6$ items 3 or less
4	4	10	$6 + 4 = 10$ items 4 or less
5	8	18	$10 + 8 = 18$ items 5 or less
6	2	20	$18 + 2 = 20$ items 6 or less

Total: 20

Adding the frequencies shows that there are

20 items total.

(The final entry in the cumulative frequency column also shows the total number of items.)

$$\text{position of median} = \frac{20 + 1}{2} = \frac{21}{2} = 10.5$$

The median, then, is the average of the tenth and eleventh items. To find these items, make use of the cumulative frequencies. Since the value 4 has a cumulative frequency of 10, the tenth item is 4 and the eleventh item is 5, making the median

$$\frac{4 + 5}{2} = \frac{9}{2} = 4.5.$$

(b)

Value	Frequency	Cumulative Frequency
2	5	5
4	8	13
6	10	23
8	6	29
10	6	35

Total: 35

There are 35 items total.

$$\text{position of median} = \frac{35 + 1}{2} = \frac{36}{2} = 18$$

From the cumulative frequency column, the fourteenth through the twenty-third items are all 6s. This means the eighteenth item is a 6, so the median is 6. ∎

median({1,2,3,4,5,6},{1,3,2, ⏴4,8,2})

4.5

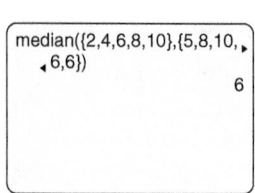

median({2,4,6,8,10},{5,8,10, ⏴6,6})

6

These two screens support the results in
Example 4.

Mode

The third important measure of central tendency is the **mode.** Suppose ten students earned the following scores on a business law examination.

$$74, 81, 39, 74, 82, 80, 100, 92, 74, 85$$

Notice that more students earned the score 74 than any other score.

MODE

The **mode** of a data set is the value that occurs most often.

EXAMPLE 5 **Finding Modes for Sets of Data**

Find the mode for each set of data.

(a) 51, 32, 49, 49, 74, 81, 92   **(b)** 482, 485, 483, 485, 487, 487, 489

(c) 10,708,   11,519,   10,972,   17,546,   13,905,   12,182

(d)

Value	19	20	22	25	26	28
Frequency	1	3	8	7	4	2

Solution

(a) 51, 32, 49, 49, 74, 81, 92
The number 49 occurs more times than any other. Therefore, 49 is the mode. *The numbers do not need to be in numerical order when you look for the mode.*

(b) 482, 485, 483, 485, 487, 487, 489
Both 485 and 487 occur twice. This list is said to have *two* modes, or to be **bimodal.**

(c) No number here occurs more than once. This list has no mode.

(d)

Value	Frequency
19	1
20	3
22	8 ← Greatest frequency
25	7
26	4
28	2

The frequency distribution shows that the most frequently occurring value (and, thus, the mode) is 22.

■

It is traditional to include the mode as a measure of *central tendency,* because many important kinds of data sets do have their most frequently occurring values "centrally" located. However, there is no reason why the mode cannot be one of the least values in the set or one of the greatest. In such a case, the mode really is not a good measure of "central tendency."

When the data items being studied are non-numerical, the mode may be the only usable measure of central tendency. For example, the bar graph of **Figure 5** in **Section 12.1** showed frequencies of occurrence of vowels in a sample paragraph. Since A, E, I, O, and U are not numbers, they cannot be added, nor can they be numerically ordered. Thus, neither their mean nor their median exists. The mode, however, does exist. As the bar graph shows, the mode is the letter E.

Sometimes a distribution is bimodal, as in **Example 5(b).** In a large distribution, this term is commonly applied even when the two modes do not have exactly the same frequency. Three or more different items sharing the highest frequency of occurrence rarely offer useful information. We say that such a distribution has *no* mode.

Central Tendency from Stem-and-Leaf Displays

As shown in **Section 12.1,** data are sometimes presented in a stem-and-leaf display in order to give a visual impression of their distribution. We can also calculate measures of central tendency from a stem-and-leaf display. The median and mode are more easily identified when the "leaves" are ranked on their "stems."

In **Table 8,** we have ranked the leaves of **Table 5** in **Section 12.1** (which showed the weekly study times from **Example 2** of that section).

Table 8 Stem-and-Leaf Display for Weekly Study Times, with Leaves Ranked

1	2	4	5	6	7	8					
2	2	3	4	4	5	6	9	9	9		
3	0	1	1	2	3	3	6	6	6	6	8	9
4	1	4	4	5	5	7					
5	2	5	5	8							
6	0	2									
7	2										

EXAMPLE 6 **Finding the Mean, Median, and Mode from a Stem-and-Leaf Display**

For the data in **Table 8,** find the following.

(a) the mean

(b) the median

(c) the mode

Solution

(a) A calculator with statistical capabilities will automatically compute the mean. Otherwise, add all items (reading from the stem-and-leaf display) and divide by $n = 40$.

$$\text{mean} = \frac{12 + 14 + 15 + \cdots + 60 + 62 + 72}{40}$$

$$= \frac{1414}{40}$$

$$= 35.35$$

(b) In this case, $n = 40$ (an even number), so the median is the average of the twentieth and twenty-first items, in order. Counting leaves, we see that these will be the fifth and sixth items on the stem 3.

$$\text{median} = \frac{33 + 33}{2} = 33$$

(c) By inspection, we see that 36 occurred four times and no other value occurred that often.

$$\text{mode} = 36$$

Symmetry in Data Sets

The most useful way to analyze a data set often depends on whether the distribution is **symmetric** or **nonsymmetric.** In a "symmetric" distribution, as we move out from the central point, the pattern of frequencies is the same (or nearly so) to the left and to the right. In a "nonsymmetric" distribution, the patterns to the left and right are significantly different.

Figure 9 shows several types of symmetric distributions, while **Figure 10** shows some nonsymmetric distributions. A nonsymmetric distribution with a tail extending out to the left, shaped like a J, is **skewed to the left.** If the tail extends out to the right, the distribution is **skewed to the right.** Notice that a bimodal distribution may be either symmetric or nonsymmetric.

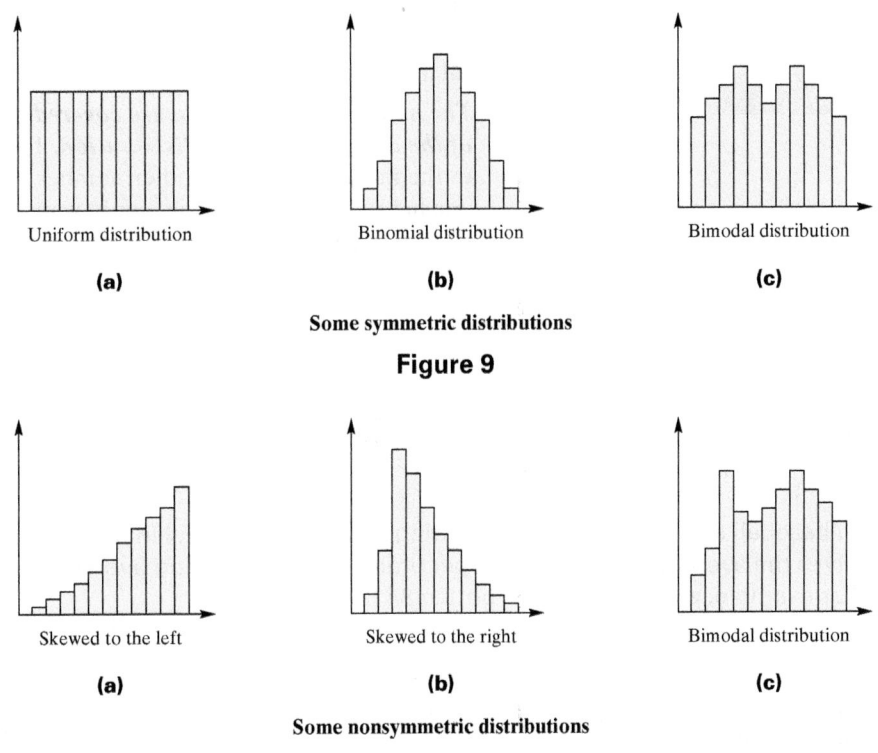

Uniform distribution
(a)

Binomial distribution
(b)

Bimodal distribution
(c)

Some symmetric distributions

Figure 9

Skewed to the left
(a)

Skewed to the right
(b)

Bimodal distribution
(c)

Some nonsymmetric distributions

Figure 10

Summary

We conclude this section with a summary of the measures presented and a brief discussion of their relative advantages and disadvantages.

SUMMARY OF THE COMMON MEASURES OF CENTRAL TENDENCY

The **mean** of a set of numbers is found by adding all the values in the set and dividing by the number of values.

The **median** is a kind of "middle" number. To find the median, first rank the values. For an *odd* number of values, the median is the middle value in the list. For an *even* number of values, the median is the mean of the two middle values.

The **mode** is the value that occurs with the greatest frequency. Some sets of numbers have two most frequently occurring values and are **bimodal.** Other sets have no mode at all (if no value occurs more often than the others or if more than two values occur most often).

Some helpful points of comparison follow.

1. For distributions of numerical data, the mean and median will always exist, while the mode may not exist. On the other hand, for non-numerical data, it may be that none of the three measures exists, or that only the mode exists.

2. Because even a single change in the data may cause the mean to change significantly, while the median and mode may not be affected at all, ***the mean is the most "sensitive" measure.***

3. In a symmetric distribution, the mean, median, and mode (if a single mode exists) will all be equal. In a nonsymmetric distribution, the mean is often unduly affected by relatively few extreme values and, therefore, may not be a good representative measure of central tendency. For example, distributions of salaries, family incomes, or home prices often include a few values that are much higher than the bulk of the items. In such cases, the median is a more useful measure.

4. ***The mode is the only measure covered here that must always be equal to one of the data items of the distribution.*** In fact, more of the data items are equal to the mode than to any other number. A fashion shop planning to stock only one hat size for next season would want to know the mode (the most common) of all hat sizes among its potential customers.

FOR FURTHER THOUGHT

Simpson's Paradox

In baseball statistics, a player's "batting average" gives the average number of hits per time at bat. For example, a player who has gotten 84 hits in 250 times at bat has a batting average of $\frac{84}{250} = .336$.

This "average" can be interpreted as the empirical probability of that player's getting a hit the next time at bat.

The following are actual comparisons of hits and at-bats for two major league players in the 2007, 2008, and 2009 seasons. The numbers illustrate a puzzling statistical occurrence known as **Simpson's paradox.** The example below, involving Mike Lowell and Jacoby Ellsbury, was provided by the alert Boston Red Sox fan Carol Merrigan.

For Group or Individual Investigation

1. Fill in the twelve blanks in the table, giving batting averages to three decimal places.

2. Which player had a better average in 2007?

3. Which player had a better average in 2008?

4. Which player had a better average in 2009?

5. Which player had a better average in 2007, 2008, and 2009 combined?

6. Did the results above surprise you? How can it be that one player's batting average leads another's for each of three years, and yet trails the other's for the combined years?

	Mike Lowell			Jacoby Ellsbury		
	Hits	**At-bats**	**Batting Average**	**Hits**	**At-bats**	**Batting Average**
2007	191	589	_____	41	116	_____
2008	115	419	_____	155	554	_____
2009	129	445	_____	188	624	_____
Combined (2007–2009)	_____	_____	_____	_____	_____	_____

12.2 EXERCISES

For each list of data, calculate **(a)** *the mean (to the nearest tenth),* **(b)** *the median, and* **(c)** *the mode or modes (if any).*

1. 6, 9, 12, 14, 21

2. 20, 27, 42, 45, 53, 62, 62, 64

3. 218, 230, 196, 224, 196, 233

4. 26, 31, 46, 31, 26, 29, 31

5. 3.1, 4.5, 6.2, 7.1, 4.5, 3.8, 6.2, 6.3

6. 14,322, 16,959, 17,337, 15,474

7. 128, 131, 136, 125, 139, 128, 125, 127

8. 8.97, 5.64, 2.31, 1.02, 4.35, 7.68

Answer each question.

9. *Gymnasts' Scores* An Olympic gymnast can earn an average score of 16.5 points for each of two vaults. Another can earn an average score of 15.5 points. The first gymnast falters, losing 2.375 points on her first vault and 1.575 points on her second vault. What average score must the second gymnast earn to win the gold? (*Mathematics Teacher* calendar problem, August 2, 2013)

10. *Quiz Grades* The average of 5 quiz grades is 10. When the lowest grade is dropped and the new average is calculated, it turns out to be 11. What was the score of the dropped grade? (*Mathematics Teacher* calendar problem, February 7, 2014)

Airline Fatalities in the United States *The table pertains to scheduled commercial carriers. Fatalities data include those on the ground except for the September 11, 2001 terrorist attacks. Use this information for Exercises 11–16.*

U.S. Airline Safety, 1999–2008

Year	Departures (in millions)	Fatal Accidents	Fatalities
1999	10.9	2	12
2000	11.1	2	89
2001	10.6	6	531
2002	10.3	0	0
2003	10.2	2	22
2004	10.8	1	13
2005	10.9	3	22
2006	10.6	2	50
2007	10.7	0	0
2008	10.6	0	0

Source: The World Almanac and Book of Facts 2010.

For each category in Exercises 11–16, find **(a)** *the mean (to the nearest tenth),* **(b)** *the median, and* **(c)** *the mode or modes (if any).*

11. departures

12. fatal accidents

13. fatalities

The year 2001 was clearly an anomaly. If the data for that year are reduced by 4 *fatal accidents and* 265 *fatalities, which of the three measures change and what are their new values for each of the following?*

14. Exercise 12   **15. Exercise 13**

16. Following 2001, in what year did airline departures start to increase again?

Leading U.S. Businesses *The table shows the top five U.S. businesses, ranked by 2012 revenue.*

Business	Revenue (in billions of dollars)	Profit (in billions of dollars)
Wal-Mart Stores	$469.2	$17.0
ExxonMobil	449.9	44.9
Chevron	233.9	26.2
Phillips 66	169.6	4.1
Berkshire Hathaway	162.5	14.8

Sources: The World Almanac and Book of Facts 2014; Fortune magazine.

Find each of the following quantities for these five businesses.

17. the mean revenue   **18.** the median profit

Measuring Elapsed Times *While doing an experiment, a physics student recorded the following sequence of elapsed times (in seconds) in a lab notebook.*

2.16, 22.2, 2.96, 2.20, 2.73, 2.28, 2.39

19. Find the mean.   **20.** Find the median.

The student from **Exercises 19 and 20,** *when reviewing the calculations later, decided that the entry* 22.2 *should have been recorded as* 2.22 *and made that change in the listing.*

21. Find the mean for the new list.

22. Find the median for the new list.

23. Which measure, the mean or the median, was affected more by correcting the error?

24. In general, which measure, mean or median, is affected less by the presence of an extreme value in the data?

Scores on Management Examinations *Thao earned the following scores on her six management exams last semester.*

$$79, \; 81, \; 44, \; 89, \; 79, \; 90$$

25. Find the mean, the median, and the mode for Thao's scores.

26. Which of the three averages probably is the best indicator of Thao's ability?

27. If Thao's instructor gives her a chance to replace her score of 44 by taking a "make-up" exam, what must she score on the make-up exam to get an overall average (mean) of 85?

For each of the following frequency distributions, find **(a)** *the mean (to the nearest tenth),* **(b)** *the median, and* **(c)** *the mode or modes (if any).*

28.

Value	Frequency
6	3
7	1
8	8
9	4

29.

Value	Frequency
615	13
540	7
605	9
579	14
586	7
600	5

30. *Average Employee Salary* A company has

15 employees with a salary of $21,500,

11 employees with a salary of $23,000,

17 employees with a salary of $25,800,

2 employees with a salary of $31,500,

4 employees with a salary of $38,900,

1 employee with a salary of $147,500.

Find the mean salary for the employees (to the nearest hundred dollars).

Grade-Point Averages *Find the grade-point average for each of the following students. Assume* A = 4, B = 3, C = 2, D = 1, *and* F = 0. *Round to the nearest hundredth.*

31.

Units	Grade
8	A
3	B
5	C

32.

Units	Grade
4	C
3	B
7	A
3	F

Federal Budget Totals *The table gives federal receipts and outlays for the years 2010–2014. (The 2013 and 2014 figures are estimates.) Use this information for Exercises 33 and 34.*

Fiscal Year	Receipts (in billions of dollars)	Outlays (in billions of dollars)
2010	$2162.7	$3457.1
2011	2303.5	3603.1
2012	2450.2	3537.1
2013	2712.0	3684.9
2014	3033.6	3777.8

Sources: The World Almanac and Book of Facts 2014; Budget of the U.S. Government, Fiscal Year 2014, Office of Management and Budget, Executive Office of the President.

Over the five-year period, find **(a)** *the mean and* **(b)** *the median for each of the following.*

33. receipts

34. outlays

World Cell Phone Use *In 2012, just the top six countries accounted for about 48% of cell phone subscriptions worldwide. Use the data in the table for Exercises 35 and 36.*

Country	Cell Phone Subscriptions (in thousands)
China	1100.0
India	864.7
United States	310.0
Indonesia	282.0
Russia	261.9
Brazil	248.3

Sources: The World Almanac and Book of Facts 2014; International Telecommunications Union.

35. Find the approximate mean number of cell phone subscriptions for these six countries in 2012.

36. The United States accounted for about 4.835% of worldwide subscriptions. About how many subscriptions were active in the world that year?

Crew, Passengers, and Hijackers on 9/11 Airliners *The table shows, for each hijacked flight on September 11, 2001, the numbers of crew members, passengers, and hijackers (not included as passengers). For each quantity in Exercises 37–39, find* **(a)** *the mean, and* **(b)** *the median.*

Flight	Crew	Passengers	Hijackers
American #11	11	76	5
United #175	9	51	5
American #77	6	53	5
United #93	7	33	4

Source: www.911research.wtc7.net

37. number of crew members per plane

38. number of passengers per plane

39. total number of persons per plane

Olympic Medal Standings *The top ten medal-winning nations in the 2014 Winter Olympics at Sochi, Russia, are shown in the table. Use the given information for Exercises 40–43.*

Medal Standings for the 2014 Winter Olympics

Place	Nation	Gold	Silver	Bronze	Total
1	Russian Federation	13	11	9	33
2	United States	9	7	12	28
3	Norway	11	5	10	26
4	Canada	10	10	5	25
5	Netherlands	8	7	9	24
6	Germany	8	6	5	19
7	Austria	4	8	5	17
8	France	4	4	7	15
9	Sweden	2	7	6	15
10	Switzerland	6	3	2	11

Source: www.nbcolympics.com

Calculate the following for all nations shown.

40. the mean number of gold medals

41. the median number of bronze medals

42. the mode, or modes, for the number of silver medals

43. each of the following for the total number of medals
  (a) mean
  (b) median
  (c) mode or modes

In Exercises 44 and 45, use the given stem-and-leaf display to identify **(a)** *the mean,* **(b)** *the median, and* **(c)** *the mode or modes (if any) for the data represented.*

44. Online Sales The display here represents prices (to the nearest dollar) charged by 23 different online sellers for a new car alternator. Give answers to the nearest dollar.

9	9
10	2 3
10	5 8 9
11	1 2 3 3
11	5 6 7 8 8
12	0 2 4
12	5 6 7 9
13	4

45. Scores on a Biology Exam The display here represents scores achieved on a 100-point biology exam by the 34 members of a class.

4	7
5	1 3 6
6	2 5 5 6 7 8 8
7	0 4 5 6 7 7 8 8 8 8 9
8	0 1 1 3 4 5 5
9	0 0 0 1 6

46. Calculating a Missing Test Score Katie's Business professor lost his computer memory, which contained her five test scores for the course. A summary of the scores (each of which was an integer from 0 to 100) indicates the following:

The mean was 88.

The median was 87.

The mode was 92.

(The data set was not bimodal.) What is the least possible number among the missing scores?

47. Explain what an "outlier" is and how it affects measures of central tendency.

48. Scores on a Math Quiz The following are scores earned by 15 college students on a 20-point math quiz.

0, 1, 3, 14, 14, 15, 16, 16, 17, 17, 18, 18, 18, 19, 20

(a) Calculate the mean, median, and mode values.

(b) Which measure in part (a) is most representative of the data?

49. *Consumer Preferences in Food Packaging* A food processing company that packages individual cups of instant soup wishes to find out the best number of cups to include in a package. A survey of 22 consumers revealed that five prefer a package of 1, five prefer a package of 2, three prefer a package of 3, six prefer a package of 4, and three prefer a package of 6.

(a) Calculate the mean, median, and mode values for preferred package size.

(b) Which measure in part (a) should the food processing company use?

(c) Explain your answer to part (b).

In Exercises 50–53, begin a list of the given numbers, in order, starting with the least one. Continue the list only until the median of the listed numbers is a multiple of 4. Stop at that point and find (a) *the number of numbers listed, and* (b) *the mean of the listed numbers (to two decimal places).*

50. counting numbers

51. prime numbers

52. Fibonacci numbers (see **page 208**)

53. triangular numbers (see **pages 13–14**)

Answer each question in Exercises 54–56.

54. Seven consecutive even whole numbers add up to 168. What is the result when their mean is subtracted from their median?

55. Bajir wants to include a fifth counting number, n, along with the numbers 2, 5, 8, and 9 so that the mean and median of the five numbers will be equal. How many choices does he have for the number n, and what are those choices?

56. If the mean, median, and mode are all equal for the set

$$\{70, 110, 80, 60, x\},$$

find the value of x.

For Exercises 57–59, refer to the grouped frequency distribution shown here.

Class Limits	Frequency f
21–25	5
26–30	3
31–35	8
36–40	12
41–45	21
46–50	38
51–55	35
56–60	20

57. Is it possible to identify, on the basis of the data shown in the table, any specific data items that occurred in this sample?

58. Is it possible to compute the actual mean for this sample?

59. Describe how you might approximate the mean for this sample. Justify your procedure.

60. *Average Employee Salaries* Refer to the salary data of **Example 2,** specifically the dollar amounts given in the salary column of the table. Explain what is wrong with simply calculating the mean salary by adding those six numbers and dividing the result by 6.

12.3 MEASURES OF DISPERSION

OBJECTIVES

1 Find the range of a data set.

2 Calculate the standard deviation of a data set.

3 Interpret measures of dispersion.

4 Calculate the coefficient of variation.

The mean is a good indicator of the central tendency of a set of data values, but it does not completely describe the data. Compare distribution A with distribution B in **Table 9** on the next page.

Both distributions have the same mean and the same median, but they are quite different. In the first, 7 is a fairly typical value, but in the second, most of the values differ considerably from 7. What is needed here is some measure of the **dispersion,** or *spread,* of the data.

Range

The **range** of a data set is a straightforward measure of dispersion.

RANGE

For any set of data, the **range** of the set is defined as follows.

Range = (greatest value in the set) − (least value in the set)

Table 9

	A	B
	5	1
	6	2
	7	7
	8	12
	9	13
Mean	7	7
Median	7	7

For a short list of data, calculation of the range is simple. For a more extensive list, it is more difficult to be sure you have accurately identified the greatest and least values.

EXAMPLE 1 Finding and Comparing Range Values

Find the ranges for distributions A and B in **Table 9,** and describe what they imply.

Solution

In distribution A, the greatest value is 9 and the least is 5.

$$\text{Range} = \text{greatest} - \text{least} = 9 - 5 = 4$$

Distribution B is handled similarly.

$$\text{Range} = 13 - 1 = 12$$

We can say that even though the two distributions have identical averages, distribution B exhibits three times more dispersion, or *spread,* than distribution A. ∎

Table 10

Quiz	Max	Molly
1	28	27
2	22	27
3	21	28
4	26	6
5	18	27
Mean	23	23
Median	22	27
Range	10	22

The range can be misleading if it is interpreted unwisely. For example, look at the points scored by Max and Molly on five different quizzes, as shown in **Table 10.** The ranges for the two students make it tempting to conclude that Max is more consistent than Molly. However, Molly is actually more consistent, with the exception of one very poor score. That score, 6, is an outlier which, if not actually recorded in error, must surely be due to some special circumstance. (Notice that the outlier does not seriously affect Molly's median score, which is more typical of her overall performance than is her mean score.)

Standard Deviation

One of the most useful measures of dispersion, the *standard deviation,* is based on *deviations from the mean* of the data values.

EXAMPLE 2 Finding Deviations from the Mean

Find the deviations from the mean for all data values in the following sample.

$$32, 41, 47, 53, 57$$

Solution

Add these values and divide by the total number of values, 5. The mean is 46. To find the deviations from the mean, subtract 46 from each data value.

Data value	32	41	47	53	57
Deviation	−14	−5	1	7	11

$$32 - 46 = -14 \qquad\qquad 57 - 46 = 11$$

To check your work, add the deviations. ***The sum of the deviations for a set of data is always 0.*** ∎

Once the data are entered, a calculator with statistical functions may actually show the range (among other things), or at least sort the data and identify the minimum and maximum items. (The associated symbols may be something like MIN Σ and MAX Σ, or min$X$ and max$X$.) Given these two values, a simple subtraction produces the range.

We cannot obtain a measure of dispersion by finding the mean of the deviations, because this number is always 0, since the positive deviations just cancel out the negative ones. To avoid this problem of positive and negative numbers canceling each other, we *square* each deviation.

The following chart shows the squares of the deviations for the data in **Example 2.**

Data value	32	41	47	53	57
Deviation	−14	−5	1	7	11
Square of deviation	196	25	1	49	121

$(-14) \cdot (-14) = 196$ $11 \cdot 11 = 121$

An average of the squared deviations could now be found by dividing their sum by the number of data values n (5 in this case), which we would do if our data values composed a population. However, since we are considering the data to be a sample, we divide by $n - 1$ instead.*

The average that results is itself a measure of dispersion, called the **variance,** but a more common measure is obtained by taking the square root of the variance. This compensates, in a way, for squaring the deviations earlier and gives a kind of average of the deviations from the mean, which is called the sample **standard deviation.** It is denoted by the letter s. (The standard deviation of a population is denoted σ, the lowercase Greek letter *sigma*.)

Continuing our calculations from the chart above, we obtain

$$s = \sqrt{\frac{196 + 25 + 1 + 49 + 121}{4}} = \sqrt{\frac{392}{4}} = \sqrt{98} \approx 9.90.$$

$n - 1$

The algorithm (process) described above for finding the sample standard deviation can be summarized as follows.

CALCULATION OF STANDARD DEVIATION

Let a sample of n numbers $x_1, x_2, \ldots, x_n$ have mean $\bar{x}$. Then the **sample standard deviation, s,** of the numbers is calculated as follows.

$$s = \sqrt{\frac{\Sigma(x - \bar{x})^2}{n - 1}}$$

The individual steps involved in this calculation follow.

Step 1 Calculate $\bar{x}$, the mean of the numbers.

Step 2 Find the deviations from the mean.

Step 3 Square each deviation.

Step 4 Sum the squared deviations.

Step 5 Divide the sum in Step 4 by $n - 1$.

Step 6 Take the square root of the quotient in Step 5.

*Although the reasons cannot be explained at this level, dividing by $n - 1$ rather than n produces a sample measure that is more accurate for purposes of inference. In most cases, the results using the two divisors are only slightly different.

The preceding description helps show why standard deviation measures the amount of spread in a data set. For actual calculation purposes, we recommend the use of a scientific calculator, or a statistical calculator, that does all the detailed steps automatically. We illustrate both methods in **Example 3.**

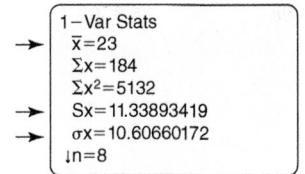

The sample in **Example 3** is stored in a list. (The last entry, 40, is not shown here.)

---

1 – Var Stats
→ $\bar{x}=23$
$\Sigma x=184$
$\Sigma x^2=5132$
→ $Sx=11.33893419$
→ $\sigma x=10.60660172$
↓$n=8$

The arrows point to the mean and the sample and population standard deviations. See **Example 3.**

EXAMPLE 3 Finding a Sample Standard Deviation

Find the standard deviation of the following sample by using **(a)** the step-by-step process, and **(b)** the statistical functions of a calculator.

$$7, 9, 18, 22, 27, 29, 32, 40$$

Solution

(a) Carry out the six steps summarized above.

Step 1   Find the mean of the values.

$$\frac{7 + 9 + 18 + 22 + 27 + 29 + 32 + 40}{8} = 23$$

Step 2   Find the deviations from the mean.

Data value	7	9	18	22	27	29	32	40
Deviation	-16	-14	-5	-1	4	6	9	17

Step 3   Square each deviation.

Squares of deviations: 256   196   25   1   16   36   81   289

Step 4   Sum the squared deviations.

$$256 + 196 + 25 + 1 + 16 + 36 + 81 + 289 = 900$$

Step 5   Divide by $n - 1 = 8 - 1 = 7$: $\frac{900}{7} \approx 128.57$

Step 6   Take the square root: $\sqrt{128.57} \approx 11.3$

(b) Enter the eight data values. (The key for entering data may look something like $\boxed{\Sigma +}$. Find out which key it is on your calculator.) Then press the key for standard deviation. It may look like one of these.

$\boxed{\text{STDEV}}$ or $\boxed{\text{SD}}$ or $\boxed{s_{n-1}}$ or $\boxed{\sigma_{n-1}}$

If your calculator also has a key that looks like σ_n, it is probably for *population* standard deviation, which involves dividing by n rather than by $n - 1$, as mentioned earlier.

The result should again be 11.3.

> If you mistakenly used the population standard deviation key, the result would be 10.6.

∎

For data given in the form of a frequency distribution, some calculators allow entry of both values and frequencies, or each value can be entered separately the number of times indicated by its frequency. Then press the standard deviation key.

The following example is included only to strengthen your understanding of frequency distributions and standard deviation, not as a practical algorithm for calculating.

Table 11

Value	Frequency
2	5
3	8
4	10
5	2

$$\text{stdDev}(\{2,3,4,5\},\{5,8,10,2\})$$
$$.9073771726$$
$$\sqrt{19.76/24}$$
$$.9073771726$$

The screen supports the result in **Example 4.**

Higher average

Lower dispersion

The more desirable basket depends on your objective.

Good average, poor consistency

Good consistency, poor average

In this case, good consistency (lesser dispersion) is more desirable than a good average (central tendency).

EXAMPLE 4 Finding the Standard Deviation of a Frequency Distribution

Find the sample standard deviation for the frequency distribution shown in **Table 11.**

Solution

Complete the calculations as shown in **Table 12** below. To find the numbers in the "Deviation" column, first find the mean, and then subtract the mean from the numbers in the "Value" column.

Table 12

Value	Frequency	Value Times Frequency	Deviation	Squared Deviation	Squared Deviation Times Frequency
2	5	10	−1.36	1.8496	9.2480
3	8	24	−0.36	0.1296	1.0368
4	10	40	0.64	0.4096	4.0960
5	2	10	1.64	2.6896	5.3792
Sums	25	84			19.76

$$\bar{x} = \frac{84}{25} = 3.36 \qquad s = \sqrt{\frac{19.76}{24}} \approx \sqrt{0.8233} \approx 0.91$$

Central tendency and dispersion (or "spread tendency") are different and independent aspects of a set of data. Which one is more critical can depend on the specific situation.

For example, suppose tomatoes sell by the basket. Each basket costs the same, and each contains one dozen tomatoes. If you want the most fruit possible per dollar spent, you would look for the basket with the highest average weight per tomato (regardless of the dispersion of the weights). On the other hand, if the tomatoes are to be served on an hors d'oeuvre tray where "presentation" is important, you would look for a basket with uniform-sized tomatoes, that is a basket with the lowest weight dispersion (regardless of the average of the weights). See the illustration at the side.

Another situation involves target shooting (also illustrated at the side). The five hits on the top target are, *on average,* very close to the bull's-eye. If the square grid is 10 by 10 units and the concentric circles have radii 2, 4, 6, and 8, then the hits shown are at

$$(-9, -7), \ (-5, 8), \ (2, -4), \ (6, 4), \ \text{and} \ (9, 2),$$

so the average position is the point

$$\left(\frac{-9 - 5 + 2 + 6 + 9}{5}, \frac{-7 + 8 - 4 + 4 + 2}{5} \right) = \left(\frac{3}{5}, \frac{3}{5} \right),$$

which is about 0.85 unit from the bull's-eye. However, the large dispersion (spread) of the hits—the lack of consistency—implies that improvement will require much effort on the part of the shooter. On the other hand, the bottom target exhibits a poorer *average.* (The hits in this case have an approximate average position at $(-3, 6)$, which is about 6.71 units from the bull's-eye.) But in this case the poor average is balanced by a small dispersion—that is, good consistency. Improvement will require only a minor adjustment of the gun sights. In general, consistent errors can be corrected more easily than more dispersed errors.

Interpreting Measures of Dispersion

A main use of dispersion measures is to compare the amounts of spread in two (or more) data sets as we did with distributions A and B at the beginning of this section. A common technique in inferential statistics is to draw comparisons between populations by analyzing samples that come from those populations.

EXAMPLE 5 Comparing Populations Based on Samples

Two companies, A and B, sell 12-ounce jars of instant coffee. Five jars of each were randomly selected from markets, and the contents were carefully weighed, with the following results.

$$A: \quad 12.02, \quad 12.08, \quad 11.99, \quad 11.96, \quad 11.99$$

$$B: \quad 12.40, \quad 12.21, \quad 12.36, \quad 12.22, \quad 12.27$$

Find **(a)** which company provides more coffee in its jars, and **(b)** which company fills its jars more consistently.

Solution

The mean and standard deviation values for both samples are shown in **Table 13**.

(a) Since $\bar{x}_B$ is greater than $\bar{x}_A$, we *infer* that Company B most likely provides more coffee (greater mean) per jar.

(b) Since s_A is less than s_B, we *infer* that Company A seems more consistent (smaller standard deviation). ∎

Table 13

Sample A	Sample B
$\bar{x}_A = 12.008$	$\bar{x}_B = 12.292$
$s_A = 0.0455$	$s_B = 0.0847$

The conclusions drawn in **Example 5** are tentative, because the samples were small. We could place more confidence in our inferences if we used larger samples, for then it would be more likely that the samples were accurate representations of their respective populations.

It is clear that a larger dispersion value means more "spread" than a smaller one. But it is difficult to say exactly what a single dispersion value says about a data set. *It is impossible* (though it would be nice) to make a general statement like: "Exactly half of the items of any distribution lie within one standard deviation of the mean of the distribution." Such a statement can be made only of specialized kinds of distributions. (See, for example, **Section 12.5** on the normal distribution.) There is, however, one useful result that does apply to all data sets, no matter what their distributions are like. This result is named for the Russian mathematician Pafnuty Lvovich Chebyshev.

Pafnuty Lvovich Chebyshev (1821–1894) was a Russian mathematician known mainly for his work on the theory of prime numbers. Chebyshev and French mathematician and statistician **Jules Bienaymé** (1796–1878) independently developed an important inequality of probability now known as the Bienaymé–Chebyshev inequality.

CHEBYSHEV'S THEOREM

For any set of numbers, regardless of how they are distributed, the fraction of them that lie within k standard deviations of their mean (where $k > 1$) is *at least*

$$1 - \frac{1}{k^2}.$$

Be sure to notice the words *at least* in the theorem statement. In certain distributions the fraction of items within k standard deviations of the mean may be more than $1 - \frac{1}{k^2}$, but in no case will it ever be less. The theorem is meaningful for any value of k greater than 1 (integer or noninteger).

EXAMPLE 6 Applying Chebyshev's Theorem

What is the minimum percentage of the items in a data set that lie within 3 standard deviations of the mean?

Solution

With $k = 3$, we calculate as follows.

$$1 - \frac{1}{3^2} = 1 - \frac{1}{9} = \frac{8}{9} \approx 0.889 = 88.9\% \quad \leftarrow \text{Minimum percentage}$$

$3^2 = 3 \cdot 3, \text{not } 3 \cdot 2$

Coefficient of Variation

Look again at the top target pictured on **page 676.** The dispersion, or spread, among the five bullet holes may not be especially impressive if the shots were fired from 100 yards, but it would be much more so at, say, 300 yards. There is another measure, the *coefficient of variation*, that takes this distinction into account. It is not strictly a measure of dispersion, as it combines central tendency and dispersion. It expresses the standard deviation as a percentage of the mean. ***Often this is a more meaningful measure than a straight measure of dispersion, especially when we are comparing distributions whose means are appreciably different.***

COEFFICIENT OF VARIATION

For any set of data, the **coefficient of variation** is calculated as follows.

$$V = \frac{s}{\bar{x}} \cdot 100\% \quad \text{for a sample} \quad \text{or} \quad V = \frac{\sigma}{\mu} \cdot 100\% \quad \text{for a population}$$

EXAMPLE 7 Comparing Samples

Compare the dispersions in the two samples A and B.

$$A: 12, \ 13, \ 16, \ 18, \ 18, \ 20 \qquad B: 125, \ 131, \ 144, \ 158, \ 168, \ 193$$

Solution

Using a calculator, we apply the first formula of the previous definition to obtain the values shown in **Table 14.** From the calculated values, we see that sample B has a much larger dispersion (standard deviation) than sample A. But sample A actually has the larger *relative* dispersion (coefficient of variation). The dispersion within sample A is larger as a percentage of that sample's mean.

Table 14

Sample A	Sample B
$\bar{x}_A = 16.167$	$\bar{x}_B = 153.167$
$s_A = 3.125$	$s_B = 25.294$
$V_A = 19.3$	$V_B = 16.5$

FOR FURTHER THOUGHT

Measuring Skewness in a Distribution

Section 12.2 included a discussion of "symmetry in data sets." Here we present a common method of measuring the amount of "skewness," or nonsymmetry, inherent in a distribution.

In a skewed distribution, the mean will be farther out toward the tail than the median, as shown in the sketch.

Skewed to the left

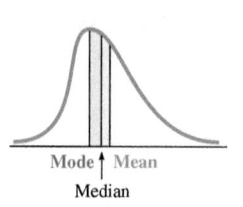

Skewed to the right

The degree of skewness can be measured by the **skewness coefficient**, which involves both central tendency and dispersion and is calculated as follows.

$$SK = \frac{3 \cdot (\text{mean} - \text{median})}{\text{standard deviation}}$$

For Group or Individual Investigation

1. Under what conditions would the skewness coefficient be each of the following?

   (a) positive   **(b)** negative

2. Explain why the mean of a skewed distribution is always farther out toward the tail than the median.

3. In a skewed distribution, how many standard deviations apart are the mean and median in each case?

   (a) $SK = \frac{1}{2}$ **(b)** $SK = 1$ **(c)** $SK = 3$

4. Suppose $SK = -6$. Complete the following statement. The mean is _____ standard
                                    (how many?)
   deviations _____ the median.
                (above/below)

12.3 EXERCISES

1. If your calculator finds both the sample standard deviation and the population standard deviation, which of the two will be a larger number for a given set of data? (*Hint:* Recall the difference in the ways the two standard deviations are calculated.)

2. If your calculator finds only one kind of standard deviation, explain how you could determine, without the calculator instructions, whether it is sample or population standard deviation.

Find **(a)** *the range, and* **(b)** *the standard deviation for each sample in Exercises 3–10. If necessary, round answers to the nearest hundredth.*

3. 2, 4, 5, 8, 9, 11, 16

4. 6, 12, 10, 8, 9, 20, 22, 16, 5

5. 34, 27, 22, 41, 30, 15, 31

6. 62, 81, 55, 63, 75, 61, 88, 72, 65

7. 74.96, 74.60, 74.58, 74.48, 74.72, 75.62, 75.03, 75.10, 74.53

8. 314.3, 310.4, 309.3, 312.1, 310.8, 313.5, 310.6, 310.5, 311.0, 314.2

9.

Value	Frequency
9	2
12	5
8	6
3	4
1	2

10.

Value	Frequency
25	6
16	8
23	5
20	6
18	12
22	2
26	5

Use Chebyshev's theorem for Exercises 11–22. Give answers as common fractions reduced to lowest terms.

Find the least possible fraction of the numbers in a data set lying within the given number of standard deviations of the mean.

11. 2

12. 4

13. $\frac{5}{2}$

14. $\frac{7}{4}$

In a certain distribution of numbers, the mean is 50 and the standard deviation is 5. At least what fraction of the numbers are between the following pairs of numbers?

15. 40 and 60

16. 35 and 65

17. 30 and 70

18. 25 and 75

In a distribution with mean 80 and standard deviation 8, find the largest fraction of the numbers that could meet the following requirements.

19. less than 64 or more than 96

20. less than 60 or more than 100

21. less than 52 or more than 108

22. less than 62 or more than 98

Travel Accommodation Costs *Gabriel and Lucia took a road trip across the country. The room costs, in dollars, for their overnight stays are listed here.*

99	105	120	165	185	178
110	245	134	134	120	260

Use this distribution of costs for Exercises 23–28.

23. Find the mean of the distribution.

24. Find the standard deviation of the distribution.

25. How many of the cost amounts are within one standard deviation of the mean?

26. How many of the cost amounts are within two standard deviations of the mean?

27. What does Chebyshev's theorem say about the number of the amounts that are within two standard deviations of the mean?

28. Explain any discrepancy between your answers for **Exercises 26 and 27.**

In Exercises 29 and 30, two samples are given. In each case, **(a)** *find both sample standard deviations,* **(b)** *find both sample coefficients of variation,* **(c)** *decide which sample has the higher dispersion, and* **(d)** *decide which sample has the higher relative dispersion.*

29. *A:* 3, 7, 4, 3, 8   *B:* 10, 8, 10, 6, 7, 3, 5

30. *A:* 68, 72, 69, 65, 71, 72, 68, 71, 67, 67
    B: 26, 35, 30, 28, 31, 36, 38, 29, 34, 33

Utilize the following sample for Exercises 31–36.

$$13, 14, 17, 19, 21, 22, 25$$

31. Compute the mean and standard deviation for the sample (each to the nearest hundredth).

32. Now add 5 to each item of the given sample, and compute the mean and standard deviation for the new sample.

33. Go back to the original sample. This time subtract 10 from each item, and compute the mean and standard deviation of the new sample.

34. Based on your answers for **Exercises 31–33,** make conjectures about what happens to the mean and standard deviation when all items of the sample have the same constant k added or subtracted.

35. Go back to the original sample again. This time multiply each item by 3, and compute the mean and standard deviation of the new sample.

36. Based on your answers for **Exercises 31 and 35,** make conjectures about what happens to the mean and standard deviation when all items of the sample are multiplied by the same constant k.

37. **Comparing Water Heater Lifetimes** Two brands of electric water heaters, both carrying 6-year warranties, were sampled and tested under controlled conditions. Five of each brand failed after the numbers of months shown here.

Brand A: 74, 65, 70, 64, 71

Brand B: 69, 70, 62, 72, 60

(a) Calculate both sample means.

(b) Calculate both sample standard deviations.

(c) Which brand apparently lasts longer?

(d) Which brand has the more consistent lifetime?

Lifetimes of Engine Control Modules *Chin manages the service department of a trucking company. Each truck in the fleet utilizes an electronic engine control module. Long-lasting modules are desirable. A preventive replacement program also avoids costly breakdowns. For this purpose it is desirable that the modules be fairly consistent in their lifetimes, so that preventive replacements can be timed efficiently.*

Chin tested a sample of 20 Brand A modules, and they lasted 48,560 highway miles on the average (mean), with a standard deviation of 2116 miles. The listing below shows how long each of another sample of 20 Brand B modules lasted. Use these data for Exercises 38–40.

44,660	51,300	45,680	48,840	47,510
61,220	49,100	48,660	47,790	47,210
48,050	49,920	47,420	45,880	50,110
52,910	47,930	45,800	46,690	49,240

38. According to the sampling, which brand of module has the longer average life (in highway miles)?

39. Which brand of module apparently has a more consistent (or uniform) length of life (in highway miles)?

40. If Brands A and B are the only modules available, which one should Chin purchase for the maintenance program? Explain your reasoning.

41. In **Section 12.2** we showed that the mean, as a measure of central tendency, is highly sensitive to extreme values. Which measure of dispersion, covered in this section, would be more sensitive to extreme values? Illustrate your answer with one or more examples.

A Cereal-Marketing Survey *A food distribution company conducted a survey to determine whether a proposed premium to be included in boxes of its cereal was appealing enough to generate new sales. Four cities were used as test markets, where the cereal was distributed with the premium, and four cities as control markets, where the cereal was distributed without the premium. The eight cities were chosen on the basis of their similarity in terms of population, per capita income, and total cereal purchase volume. The results are shown in the following table.*

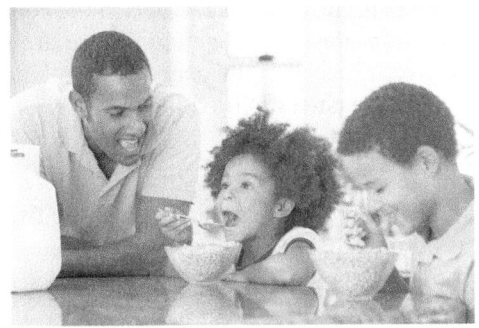

Percent Change in Average Market Share per Month

Test cities	1	+18
	2	+15
	3	+7
	4	+10
Control cities	1	+1
	2	−8
	3	−5
	4	0

42. Find the mean of the percent change in market share for the four test cities.

43. Find the mean of the percent change in market share for the four control cities.

44. Find the standard deviation of the percent change in market share for the test cities.

45. Find the standard deviation of the percent change in market share for the control cities.

46. Find the difference between the means of the test cities and the control cities. This difference represents the estimate of the percent change in sales due to the premium.

47. The two standard deviations from the test cities and the control cities were used to calculate an "error" of ±7.95 for the estimate in **Exercise 46.** With this amount of error, what are the least and greatest estimates of the increase in sales?

(On the basis of the interval estimate of **Exercise 47,** the company decided to mass produce the premium and distribute it nationally.)

*For Exercises 48–50, refer to the grouped frequency distribution shown below. (Also refer to **Exercises 57–59** in Section 12.2.)*

Class Limits	Frequency f
21–25	5
26–30	3
31–35	8
36–40	12
41–45	21
46–50	38
51–55	35
56–60	20

48. Is it possible to identify any specific data items that occurred in this sample?

49. Is it possible to compute the actual standard deviation for this sample?

50. Describe how you might approximate the standard deviation for this sample. Justify your procedure.

51. Suppose the frequency distribution of **Example 4** involved 50 or 100 (or even more) distinct data values, rather than just four. Explain why the procedure of that example would then be very inefficient.

52. A "J-shaped" distribution can be skewed either to the right or to the left. (When skewed right, it is sometimes called a "reverse J" distribution.)

(a) In a J-shaped distribution skewed to the right, which data item would be the mode, the greatest or the least item?

(b) In a J-shaped distribution skewed to the left, which data item would be the mode, the greatest or the least item?

(c) Explain why the mode is a weak measure of central tendency for a J-shaped distribution.

12.4   MEASURES OF POSITION

OBJECTIVES

1 Understand the *z*-score.

2 Compute and interpret percentiles.

3 Compute and interpret deciles and quartiles.

4 Work with box plots.

Measures of central tendency and measures of dispersion give us an effective way of characterizing an overall set of data. Central tendency indicates where, along a number scale, the overall data set is centered. Dispersion indicates how much the data set is spread out from the center point. And Chebyshev's theorem, stated in the previous section, tells us in a general sense what portions of the data set may be dispersed different amounts from the center point.

In some cases, we are interested in certain individual items within a data set, rather than in that set as a whole. So we would like to measure how an item fits into the collection, how its placement compares to those of other items in the collection, or even how it compares to another item in another collection. There are several common ways of creating such measures. Since they measure an item's position within the data set, they usually are called **measures of position.**

The *z*-Score

Each individual item in a sample can be assigned a **z-score,** which is the first measure of position that we consider. It is defined as follows.

THE *z*-SCORE

If x is a data item in a sample with mean $\bar{x}$ and standard deviation s, then the **z-score** of x is calculated as follows.

$$z = \frac{x - \bar{x}}{s}$$

Lists of **the top ten jobs of 2014** may vary somewhat, depending on which organization's ratings are consulted. The list below is based generally on (a) job prospects, (b) salaries, (c) stress levels, and (d) "work-life balance." The number in parentheses is the rating (out of a possible 10 points), and the dollar amount is the median salary for 2012. See the Web site below for detailed information.

1. Software developer (8.4) $90,060
2. Computer systems analyst (8.2) $79,680
3. Dentist (8.2) $145,240
4. Nurse practitioner (8.1) $89,960
5. Pharmacist (8.1) $116,670
6. Registered nurse (8.0) $65,470
7. Physical therapist (7.9) $79,860
8. Physician (7.8) $123,300
9. Web developer (7.8) $62,500
10. Dental hygienist (7.7) $70,210

(*Source:* www.money.usnews.com)

Because $x - \bar{x}$ gives the amount by which x differs (or deviates) from the mean $\bar{x}$, the *z*-score simply reflects the number of standard deviations by which x differs from $\bar{x}$. Notice that z will be positive if x is greater than $\bar{x}$ but negative if x is less than $\bar{x}$. Chebyshev's theorem assures us that in any distribution whatsoever, at least 89% (roughly) of the items will lie within three standard deviations of the mean. That is, at least 89% of the items will have *z*-scores between -3 and 3. In fact, many common distributions, especially symmetric ones, have considerably more than 89% of their items within three standard deviations of the mean (as we will see in the next section). Hence, a *z*-score greater than 3 or less than -3 is rare.

▓▓ EXAMPLE 1   Comparing Positions Using *z*-Scores

Two friends, Cyrus and Aisha, who take different history classes, had midterm exams on the same day. Cyrus's score was 86, and Aisha's was only 78. Based on *z*-scores, which student did relatively better, given the class data shown here?

	Cyrus	**Aisha**
Class mean	73	69
Class standard deviation	8	5

Solution

Calculate as follows.

$$\text{Cyrus: } z = \frac{86 - 73}{8} = 1.625 \qquad \text{Aisha: } z = \frac{78 - 69}{5} = 1.8$$

Because Aisha's *z*-score is higher, she was positioned relatively higher within her class than Cyrus was within his class.   ▪

Percentiles

When you take the Scholastic Aptitude Test (SAT), or any other standardized test taken by large numbers of students, your raw score usually is converted to a **percentile** score, which is defined as follows.

PERCENTILE

If approximately n percent of the items in a distribution are less than the number x, then x is the **nth percentile** of the distribution, denoted P_n.

For example, if you scored at the eighty-third percentile on the SAT, it means that you outscored approximately 83% of all those who took the test. (It does *not* mean that you got 83% of the answers correct.) Since the percentile score gives the position of an item within the data set, it is another "measure of position." The following example approximates percentiles for a fairly small collection of data.

EXAMPLE 2 Finding Percentiles

The following are the numbers of dinner customers served by a restaurant on 40 consecutive days. The numbers have been ranked least to greatest.

46	51	52	55	56	56	58	59	59	59
60	61	62	62	63	63	64	64	64	65
66	66	66	67	67	67	68	68	69	69
70	70	71	71	72	75	79	79	83	88

For this data set, find **(a)** the sixty-fifth percentile, and **(b)** the eighty-eighth percentile.

Solution

(a) The sixty-fifth percentile can be taken as the item below which 65% of the items are ranked. Since 65% of 40 is $0.65(40) = 26$, we take the twenty-seventh item, or 68, as the sixty-fifth percentile.

(b) Since 88% of 40 is $0.88(40) = 35.2$, we round *up* and take the eighty-eighth percentile to be the thirty-sixth item, or 75.   ∎

Technically, percentiles originally were conceived as a set of 99 values P_1, P_2, P_3, ..., P_{99} (not necessarily data items) along the scale that would divide the data set into 100 equal-sized parts. They were computed only for very large data sets. With smaller data sets, as in **Example 2,** dividing the data into 100 parts would necessarily leave many of those parts empty. However, the modern techniques of exploratory data analysis seek to apply the percentile concept to even small data sets. Thus, we use approximation techniques as in **Example 2.** Another option is to divide the data into a lesser number of equal-sized (or nearly equal-sized) parts, say ten parts, or just four parts, as we discuss next.

Deciles and Quartiles

Deciles are the nine values (denoted $D_1, D_2, \ldots, D_9$) along the scale that divide a data set into ten (approximately) equal-sized parts, and **quartiles** are the three values (Q_1, Q_2, and Q_3) that divide a data set into four (approximately) equal-sized parts. Since deciles and quartiles serve to position particular items within portions of a distribution, they also are "measures of position." We can evaluate deciles by finding their equivalent percentiles.

$$D_1 = P_{10}, \quad D_2 = P_{20}, \quad D_3 = P_{30}, \quad \ldots, \quad D_9 = P_{90}$$

EXAMPLE 3 Finding Deciles

Find the fourth decile for the dinner customer data of **Example 2.**

Solution

Refer to the ranked data table. The fourth decile is the fortieth percentile, and 40% of 40 is $0.40(40) = 16$. We take the fourth decile to be the seventeenth item, or 64.   ■

Although the three quartiles also can be related to corresponding percentiles, notice that the second quartile, Q_2, also is equivalent to the median, a measure of central tendency introduced in **Section 12.2.** A common convention for computing quartiles goes back to the way we computed the median.

FINDING QUARTILES

For any set of data (ranked in order from least to greatest):

The **second quartile, Q_2,** is just the median, the middle item when the number of items is odd, or the mean of the two middle items when the number of items is even.

The **first quartile, Q_1,** is the median of all items below Q_2.

The **third quartile, Q_3,** is the median of all items above Q_2.

EXAMPLE 4 Finding Quartiles

Find the three quartiles for the data of **Example 2.**

Solution

Refer to the ranked data. The two middle data items are 65 and 66.

$$Q_2 = \frac{65 + 66}{2} = 65.5$$

The least 20 items (an even number) are all below Q_2, and the two middle items in that set are 59 and 60.

$$Q_1 = \frac{59 + 60}{2} = 59.5$$

The greatest 20 items are above Q_2.

$$Q_3 = \frac{69 + 70}{2} = 69.5$$ ■

The Box Plot

A **box plot,** or **box-and-whisker plot,** involves the median (a measure of central tendency), the range (a measure of dispersion), and the first and third quartiles (measures of position), all incorporated into a simple visual display.

BOX PLOT

For a given set of data, a **box plot** (or **box-and-whisker plot**) consists of a rectangular box positioned above a numerical scale, extending from Q_1 to Q_3, with the value of Q_2 (the median) indicated within the box, and with "whiskers" (line segments) extending to the left and right from the box out to the minimum and maximum data items.

EXAMPLE 5 Constructing a Box Plot

Construct a box plot for the forty weekly study times of **Example 2** in **Section 12.1.**

Solution

To determine the quartiles and the minimum and maximum values more easily, we use the stem-and-leaf display (with leaves ranked), given in **Table 8** of **Section 12.2.**

1	2 4 5 6 7 8
2	2 3 4 4 5 6 9 9 9
3	0 1 1 2 3 3 6 6 6 6 8 9
4	1 4 4 5 5 7
5	2 5 5 8
6	0 2
7	2

The median (determined earlier in **Example 6** of **Section 12.2**) is

$$\frac{33 + 33}{2} = 33.$$

From the stem-and-leaf display,

$$Q_1 = \frac{24 + 25}{2} = 24.5 \quad \text{and} \quad Q_3 = \frac{44 + 45}{2} = 44.5.$$

The minimum and maximum items are evident from the stem-and-leaf display. They are 12 and 72. The box plot is shown in **Figure 11.**

Weekly study times (in hours)

Box plot

Figure 11

The box plot in **Figure 11** conveys the following important information:

1. central tendency (the location of the median);
2. the location of the middle half of the data (the extent of the box);
3. dispersion (the range is the extent of the whiskers); and
4. skewness (the nonsymmetry of both the box and the whiskers).

Left margin:

1–Var Stats
↑n=40
minX=12
Q_1=24.5
Med=33
Q_3=44.5
maxX=72

This screen supports the results of **Example 5.**

P:1L1
Med=33

This box plot corresponds to the results of **Example 5.** It indicates the median in the display at the bottom. The TRACE function of the TI-83/84 Plus will locate the minimum, maximum, and quartile values as well.

12.4 EXERCISES

Numbers of Restaurant Customers *Refer to the dinner customers data of **Example 2.** Approximate each of the following. Use the methods illustrated in this section.*

1. the fifteenth percentile
2. the eighty-fifth percentile
3. the second decile   4. the seventh decile

In Exercises 5–8, make use of z-scores.

5. **Relative Positions on Sociology Quizzes** In a sociology class, Neil scored 5 on a quiz for which the class mean and standard deviation were 4.6 and 2.1, respectively. Janet scored 6 on another quiz for which the class mean and standard deviation were 4.9 and 2.3, respectively. Relatively speaking, which student did better?

6. *Relative Performances in Track Events* In Saturday's track meet, Edgar, a high jumper, jumped 6 feet 3 inches. Conference high jump marks for the past season had a mean of 6 feet even and a standard deviation of 3.5 inches. Kurt, Edgar's teammate, achieved 18 feet 4 inches in the long jump. In that event the conference season average (mean) and standard deviation were 16 feet 6 inches and 1 foot 10 inches, respectively. Relative to this past season in this conference, which athlete had a better performance on Saturday?

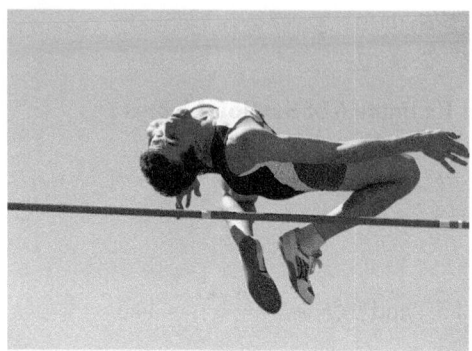

7. *Relative Lifetimes of Tires* The lifetimes of Brand A tires are distributed with mean 45,000 miles and standard deviation 4500 miles, while Brand B tires last for only 38,000 miles on the average (mean) with standard deviation 2080 miles. Nicole's Brand A tires lasted 37,000 miles, and Yvette's Brand B tires lasted 35,000 miles. Relatively speaking, within their own brands, which driver got the better wear?

8. *Relative Ratings of Fish Caught* In a certain lake, the trout average 12 inches in length with a standard deviation of 2.75 inches. The bass average 4 pounds in weight with a standard deviation of 0.9 pound. If Tobi caught an 18-inch trout and Katrina caught a 6-pound bass, then relatively speaking, which catch was the better trophy?

World's Largest Energy Producers and Consumers The table includes only countries in the top ten in 2011 for both production and consumption of energy. (Energy units are quadrillion Btu.) Population is for midyear 2013, in millions. Use this information for Exercises 9–20.

Country	Population	Production	Consumption
China	1350	97.8	109.6
United States	317	78.0	97.5
Russia	143	54.9	32.8
Canada	35	18.8	13.5
India	1221	16.0	23.6
Brazil	201	9.9	11.7

Source: The World Almanac and Book of Facts 2014.

Compute z-scores (accurate to one decimal place) for Exercises 9–12.

9. Russia's population

10. U.S. production

11. China's consumption

12. Brazil's consumption

In each of Exercises 13–16, determine which country occupied the given position.

13. the twenty-fifth percentile in population

14. the fourth decile in production

15. the third quartile in consumption

16. the ninth decile in production

17. Determine which was relatively higher: Canada in production or India in consumption.

18. Construct box plots for both production and consumption, one above the other in the same drawing.

19. What does your box plot of **Exercise 18** *for consumption* indicate about the following characteristics of the consumption data?

   (a) the central tendency

   (b) the dispersion

   (c) the location of the middle half of the data items

20. Comparing your two box plots of **Exercise 18,** what can you say about energy among the world's top producers and consumers of 2011?

21. The text stated that for *any* distribution of data, at least 89% of the items will be within three standard deviations of the mean. Why couldn't we just move some items farther out from the mean to obtain a new distribution that would violate this condition?

22. Describe the basic difference between a measure of central tendency and a measure of position.

This chapter has introduced three major characteristics, central tendency, dispersion, and position, and has developed various ways of measuring them in numerical data. In each of Exercises 23–26, a new measure is described. In each case indicate which of the three characteristics you think it would measure, and explain why.

23. Midrange $= \dfrac{\text{minimum item} + \text{maximum item}}{2}$

24. Midquartile $= \dfrac{Q_1 + Q_3}{2}$

25. Interquartile range $= Q_3 - Q_1$

26. Semi-interquartile range $= \dfrac{Q_3 - Q_1}{2}$

27. The "skewness coefficient" was defined in **For Further Thought** in the previous section, and it is calculated as follows.

$$SK = \frac{3 \cdot (\bar{x} - Q_2)}{s}$$

Is this a measure of individual data items or of the overall distribution?

28. For the energy data preceding **Exercise 9,** calculate the skewness coefficient for the following.

(a) production **(b)** consumption

29. From **Exercise 28,** how would you compare the skewness of production versus consumption?

30. In a national standardized test, Kimberly scored at the ninety-second percentile. If 67,500 individuals took the test, about how many scored higher than Kimberly?

31. Let the three quartiles (from least to greatest) for a large population of scores be denoted Q_1, Q_2, and Q_3.

(a) Is it necessarily true that
$$Q_2 - Q_1 = Q_3 - Q_2?$$

(b) Explain your answer to part (a).

In Exercises 32–35, answer yes *or* no *and explain your answer. (Consult Exercises 23–26 for definitions.)*

32. Is the midquartile necessarily the same as the median?

33. Is the midquartile necessarily the same as the midrange?

34. Is the interquartile range necessarily half the range?

35. Is the semi-interquartile range necessarily half the interquartile range?

36. *Relative Positions on a Standardized Chemistry Test* Omer and Alessandro participated in the standardization process for a new statewide chemistry test. Within the large group participating, their raw scores and corresponding *z*-scores were as shown here.

	Raw Score	z-Score
Omer	60	0.69
Alessandro	72	1.67

Find the overall mean and standard deviation of the distribution of scores (to two decimal places).

Rating Passers in the National Football League Since the National Football League began keeping official statistics in 1932, the passing effectiveness of quarterbacks has been rated by several different methods. The current system, adopted in 1973, is based on four performance components: completions, touchdowns, yards gained, and interceptions, as percentages of the number of passes attempted. The computation can be accomplished using the formula in the next column.

$$\text{Rating} = \frac{\left(250 \cdot \frac{C}{A}\right) + \left(1000 \cdot \frac{T}{A}\right) + \left(12.5 \cdot \frac{Y}{A}\right) + 6.25 - \left(1250 \cdot \frac{I}{A}\right)}{3},$$

where A = attempted passes,

C = completed passes,

T = touchdown passes,

Y = yards gained passing,

and I = interceptions.

In addition to the weighting factors (coefficients) appearing in the formula, the four category ratios are limited to non-negative values with the following maximums.

$$0.775 \text{ for } \frac{C}{A}, \quad 0.11875 \text{ for } \frac{T}{A}, \quad 12.5 \text{ for } \frac{Y}{A}, \quad 0.095 \text{ for } \frac{I}{A}$$

These limitations are intended to prevent any one component of performance from having an undue effect on the overall rating. They are not often invoked, but in special cases they can have a significant effect.

The formula rates all passers against the same performance standard and is applied, for example, after a single game, an entire season, or a career. The ratings for the ten leading passers in the league for 2013 regular season play are ranked in the following table.

Rank	NFL Passer	Rating Points
1	Nick Foles, Philadelphia	119.2
2	Peyton Manning, Denver	115.1
3	Josh McCown, Chicago	109.0
4	Philip Rivers, San Diego	105.5
5	Aaron Rodgers, Green Bay	104.9
6	Drew Brees, New Orleans	104.7
7	Russell Wilson, Seattle	101.2
8	Tony Romo, Dallas	96.7
9	Ben Roethlisberger, Pittsburgh	92.0
10	Colin Kaepernick, San Francisco	91.6

Source: www.espn.go.com

Find the measures (to one decimal place) in Exercises 37–42.

37. the three quartiles

38. the sixth decile

39. the ninety-fifth percentile

40. the midrange (See **Exercise 23.**)

41. the midquartile (see **Exercise 24.**)

42. the interquartile range (See **Exercise 25.**)

43. Construct a box plot for the rating points data.

44. Peyton Manning's brother, Eli, quarterbacking for the New York Giants, completed the 2013 season at rank 35, with a rating of 69.4. His component statistics were as follows.

$$A = 551, \ C = 317, \ T = 18, \ Y = 3818, \ I = 27$$

If Eli had managed to avoid all 27 interceptions (a tall order), without changing any of his other numbers, by what amount would his rating points have *increased?*

45. With no interceptions, would Eli have risen into the top ten rankings?

46. Given Eli Manning's 551 attempts and 27 interceptions, suppose he had completed 20 more passes, for 420 additional yards. In order to make it into the top ten, how many more of his passes would have needed to result in touchdowns?

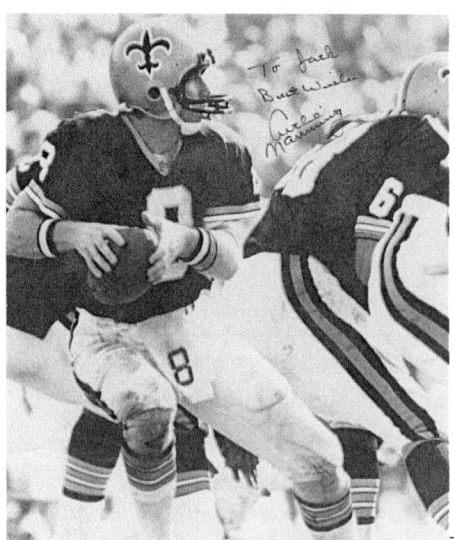

Archie Manning, father of NFL quarterbacks Peyton and Eli, signed this photo for author Hornsby's son, Jack.

47. Steve Young set a full-season rating record of 112.8 in 1994 and held that record until Peyton Manning achieved a rating of 121.1 in 2004. *His* record was broken in 2011 by Aaron Rodgers, with a rating of 122.5. If, in 2011, Rodgers had 343 completions, 45 touchdowns, and 4643 yards, in 502 attempts, how many times was he intercepted that year?

48. Use the passer rating formula to find the highest rating possible (considered a "perfect" passer rating).

*Given our method of finding quartiles, **Example 4** shows that quartiles are not necessarily data items. For each data set in Exercises 49–52, **(a)** find all three quartiles, and **(b)** state how many of them are data items.*

49. 1 2 3 4 5 6 7 8   **50.** 1 2 3 4 5 6 7 8 9

51. 1 2 3 4 5 6 7 8 9 10

52. 1 2 3 4 5 6 7 8 9 10 11

53. The pattern of **Exercises 49–52** holds in general. Complete the following statements for any data set with n distinct items (no item occurs more than once).

   (a) If $n = 4k$ for some counting number k, then _____ of the quartiles are data items.

   (b) If $n = 4k + 1$ for some counting number k, then _____ of the quartiles are data items.

   (c) If $n = 4k + 2$ for some counting number k, then _____ of the quartiles are data items.

   (d) If $n = 4k + 3$ for some counting number k, then _____ of the quartiles are data items.

54. Suppose a data set contains n distinct items (no items occur more than once). Determine how many of the three quartiles are data items in each case.

   (a) $n = 47$ **(b)** $n = 128$

   (c) $n = 101$ **(d)** $n = 166$

12.5   THE NORMAL DISTRIBUTION

OBJECTIVES

1 Understand the distinction between discrete and continuous random variables.

2 Understand the properties of a normal curve.

3 Use a table of standard normal curve areas.

4 Interpret normal curve areas in several ways.

Discrete and Continuous Random Variables

A random variable that can take on only certain fixed values is called a **discrete random variable.** For example, the number of heads in 5 tosses of a coin is discrete because its only possible values are

0, 1, 2, 3, 4, and 5.

A variable whose values are not restricted in this way is a **continuous random variable.** For example, the diameter of camellia blossoms would be a continuous variable, spread over a scale perhaps from 5 to 25 centimeters. The values would not be restricted to whole numbers, or even to tenths, or hundredths, etc. A discrete random variable takes on only a countable number of values. A continuous random variable takes on an uncountable number of values.

The normal curve was first developed by **Abraham De Moivre** (1667–1754), but his work went unnoticed for many years. It was independently redeveloped by Pierre de Laplace (1749–1827) and Carl Friedrich Gauss (1777–1855). Gauss found so many uses for this curve that it is sometimes called the *Gaussian curve*.

Most distributions discussed in this chapter were *empirical* (based on observation). The distributions covered in this section are *theoretical* (based on theoretical probabilities). A knowledge of theoretical distributions enables us to identify when actual observations are inconsistent with stated assumptions.

The theoretical probability distribution for the discrete random variable "number of heads" when 5 fair coins are tossed is shown in **Table 15. Figure 12** shows the corresponding histogram. The probability values can be found using the binomial probability formula (**Section 11.4**) or using Pascal's triangle (**Section 10.4**).

Table 15 Probability Distribution

x	P(x)
0	0.03125
1	0.15625
2	0.31250
3	0.31250
4	0.15625
5	0.03125
Sum:	1.00000

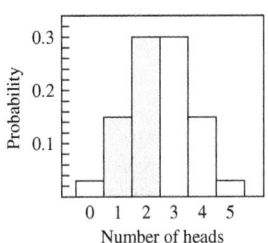

Figure 12

Since each rectangle in **Figure 12** is 1 unit wide, the *area* of the rectangle is also equal to the probability of the corresponding number of heads. The area, and thus the probability, for the event "1 head or 2 heads" is shaded in the figure. The graph consists of 6 distinct rectangles since "number of heads" is a *discrete* variable with 6 possible values. The sum of the 6 rectangular areas is exactly 1 square unit.

A probability distribution for camellia blossom diameters cannot be tabulated or graphed in quite the same way, since this variable is *continuous*. The graph would be smeared out into a "continuous" bell-shaped curve (rather than a set of rectangles) as shown in **Figure 13**. The vertical scale on the graph in this case shows what we call "probability density," the probability per unit along the horizontal axis.

Figure 13

Definition and Properties of a Normal Curve

The camellia blossom curve is highest at a diameter value of 15 cm, its center point, and drops off rapidly and equally toward a zero level in both directions. Such a symmetric, bell-shaped curve is called a **normal curve.** Any random variable whose graph has this characteristic shape is said to have a **normal distribution.**

The area under the curve along a certain interval is numerically equal to the probability that the random variable will have a value in the corresponding interval. The area of the shaded region in **Figure 13** is equal to the probability of a randomly chosen blossom having a diameter in the interval from the left extreme, say 16.4, to the right extreme, say 21.2. Normal curves are very important in the study of statistics because *a great many continuous random variables have normal distributions, and many discrete variables are distributed approximately normally.*

Each point on the horizontal scale of a normal curve lies some number of standard deviations from the mean (positive to the right, negative to the left). This number is the "standard score" for that point. It is the same as the *z*-score defined in **Section 12.4**. By relabeling the horizontal axis, as in **Figure 14,** we obtain the **standard normal curve,** which we can use to analyze *any* normal (or approximately normal) distribution. We relate the random variable value, *x*, to its *z*-score by

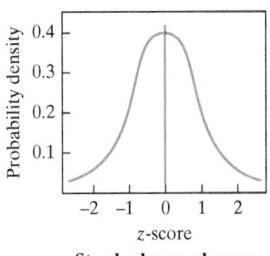

Standard normal curve

Figure 14

$$z = \frac{x - \bar{x}}{s}.$$

Close but Never Touching When a curve approaches closer and closer to a line, without ever actually meeting it (as a normal curve approaches the horizontal axis), the line is called an **asymptote,** and the curve is said to approach the line **asymptotically.**

Figure 15 shows several of infinitely many possible normal curves. Each is completely characterized by its mean and standard deviation. Only one of these, the one marked *S*, is the *standard* normal curve. That one has mean 0 and standard deviation 1.

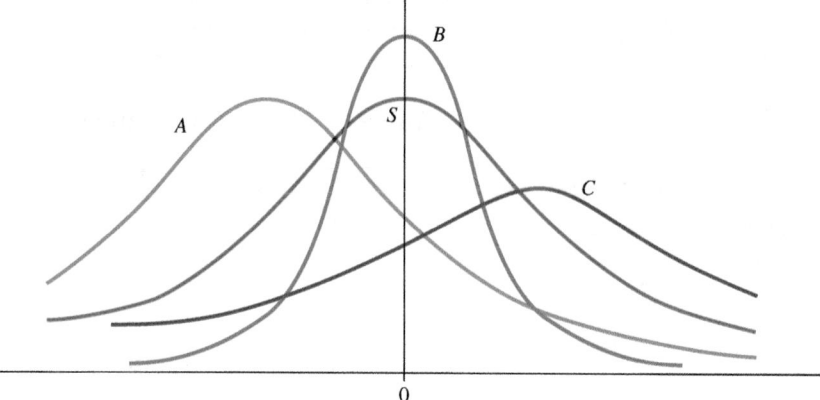

Normal curve *S* is standard, with mean = 0 and standard deviation = 1.
Normal curve *A* has mean < 0 and standard deviation = 1.
Normal curve *B* has mean = 0 and standard deviation < 1.
Normal curve *C* has mean > 0 and standard deviation > 1.

Figure 15

Mean = median = mode

↔ Standard deviation

68%
95%
99.7%

Figure 16

Several properties of normal curves are summarized below and are illustrated in **Figure 16.**

PROPERTIES OF NORMAL CURVES

The graph of a normal curve is bell-shaped and symmetric about a vertical line through its center.

The mean, median, and mode of a normal curve are all equal and occur at the center of the distribution.

Empirical Rule About 68% of all data values of a normal curve lie within 1 standard deviation of the mean (in both directions), about 95% within 2 standard deviations, and about 99.7% within 3 standard deviations.

The empirical rule indicates that a very small percentage of the items in a normal distribution will lie more than 3 standard deviations from the mean (approximately 0.3%, divided equally between the upper and lower tails of the distribution). As we move away from the center, the curve *never* actually touches the horizontal axis. No matter how far out we go, there is always a chance of an item occurring even farther out. Theoretically then, the range of a true normal distribution is infinite.

A normal distribution occurs in darts if the player, always aiming at the bull's-eye, tosses a fairly large number of times, and the aim on each toss is affected only by independent random errors.

EXAMPLE 1 Applying the Empirical Rule

Suppose that 300 chemistry students take a midterm exam and the distribution of their scores can be treated as normal. Find the number of scores falling into each of the following intervals.

(a) Within 1 standard deviation of the mean

(b) Within 2 standard deviations of the mean

Solution

(a) By the empirical rule, 68% of all scores lie within one standard deviation of the mean. There is a total of 300 scores.

$$0.68(300) = 204 \qquad \text{\small 68\% = 0.68}$$

(b) A total of 95% of all scores lie within 2 standard deviations of the mean.

$$0.95(300) = 285 \qquad \text{\small 95\% = 0.95}$$ ■

A Table of Standard Normal Curve Areas

Most questions we need to answer about normal distributions involve regions other than those within 1, 2, or 3 standard deviations of the mean. We might need the percentage of items within $1\frac{1}{2}$ or $2\frac{1}{5}$ standard deviations of the mean, or perhaps the area under the curve from 0.8 to 1.3 standard deviations above the mean.

In such cases, we need more than the empirical rule. The traditional approach is to refer to a table of area values, such as **Table 16** on the next page. Computer software designed for statistical uses generally will produce the required values on command, and some advanced calculators also have this capability. Those tools are recommended. As an option, we illustrate the use of **Table 16** here.

The table gives the fraction of all scores in a normal distribution that lie between the mean and z standard deviations from the mean. *Because of the symmetry of the normal curve, the table can be used for values above the mean or below the mean.* All of the items in the table can be thought of as corresponding to the area under the curve. The total area is arranged to be 1.000 square unit, with 0.500 square unit on each side of the mean. The table shows that at 3.30 standard deviations from the mean, essentially all of the area is accounted for. Whatever remains beyond is so small that it does not appear in the first three decimal places.

EXAMPLE 2 Applying the Normal Curve Table

Use **Table 16** to find the percent of all scores that lie between the mean and the following values.

(a) 1 standard deviation above the mean

(b) 2.45 standard deviations below the mean

Solution

(a) Here $z = 1.00$ (the number of standard deviations, written as a decimal to the nearest hundredth). Refer to **Table 16**. Find 1.00 in the z column. The table entry is 0.341, so 34.1% of all values lie between the mean and 1 standard deviation above the mean.

Another way of looking at this is to say that the area in color in **Figure 17** represents 34.1% of the total area under the normal curve.

Figure 17

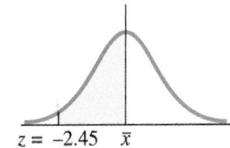
Figure 18

(b) Even though we go *below* the mean here (to the left), **Table 16** still works since the normal curve is symmetric about its mean. Find 2.45 in the z column. A total of 0.493, or 49.3%, of all values lie between the mean and 2.45 standard deviations below the mean. This region is colored in **Figure 18**. ■

The column under *A* gives the **fraction of the area under the entire curve** that is between *z* = 0 and a positive value of *z*.

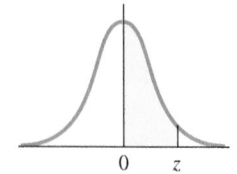

Because the curve is symmetric about the 0-value, the area between *z* = 0 and a *negative* value of *z* can be found by using the corresponding positive value of *z*.

Table 16 Areas under the Standard Normal Curve

z	A	z	A	z	A	z	A	z	A	z	A
.00	.000	.56	.212	1.12	.369	1.68	.454	2.24	.487	2.80	.497
.01	.004	.57	.216	1.13	.371	1.69	.454	2.25	.488	2.81	.498
.02	.008	.58	.219	1.14	.373	1.70	.455	2.26	.488	2.82	.498
.03	.012	.59	.222	1.15	.375	1.71	.456	2.27	.488	2.83	.498
.04	.016	.60	.226	1.16	.377	1.72	.457	2.28	.489	2.84	.498
.05	.020	.61	.229	1.17	.379	1.73	.458	2.29	.489	2.85	.498
.06	.024	.62	.232	1.18	.381	1.74	.459	2.30	.489	2.86	.498
.07	.028	.63	.236	1.19	.383	1.75	.460	2.31	.490	2.87	.498
.08	.032	.64	.239	1.20	.385	1.76	.461	2.32	.490	2.88	.498
.09	.036	.65	.242	1.21	.387	1.77	.462	2.33	.490	2.89	.498
.10	.040	.66	.245	1.22	.389	1.78	.462	2.34	.490	2.90	.498
.11	.044	.67	.249	1.23	.391	1.79	.463	2.35	.491	2.91	.498
.12	.048	.68	.252	1.24	.393	1.80	.464	2.36	.491	2.92	.498
.13	.052	.69	.255	1.25	.394	1.81	.465	2.37	.491	2.93	.498
.14	.056	.70	.258	1.26	.396	1.82	.466	2.38	.491	2.94	.498
.15	.060	.71	.261	1.27	.398	1.83	.466	2.39	.492	2.95	.498
.16	.064	.72	.264	1.28	.400	1.84	.467	2.40	.492	2.96	.498
.17	.067	.73	.267	1.29	.401	1.85	.468	2.41	.492	2.97	.499
.18	.071	.74	.270	1.30	.403	1.86	.469	2.42	.492	2.98	.499
.19	.075	.75	.273	1.31	.405	1.87	.469	2.43	.492	2.99	.499
.20	.079	.76	.276	1.32	.407	1.88	.470	2.44	.493	3.00	.499
.21	.083	.77	.279	1.33	.408	1.89	.471	2.45	.493	3.01	.499
.22	.087	.78	.282	1.34	.410	1.90	.471	2.46	.493	3.02	.499
.23	.091	.79	.285	1.35	.411	1.91	.472	2.47	.493	3.03	.499
.24	.095	.80	.288	1.36	.413	1.92	.473	2.48	.493	3.04	.499
.25	.099	.81	.291	1.37	.415	1.93	.473	2.49	.494	3.05	.499
.26	.103	.82	.294	1.38	.416	1.94	.474	2.50	.494	3.06	.499
.27	.106	.83	.297	1.39	.418	1.95	.474	2.51	.494	3.07	.499
.28	.110	.84	.300	1.40	.419	1.96	.475	2.52	.494	3.08	.499
.29	.114	.85	.302	1.41	.421	1.97	.476	2.53	.494	3.09	.499
.30	.118	.86	.305	1.42	.422	1.98	.476	2.54	.494	3.10	.499
.31	.122	.87	.308	1.43	.424	1.99	.477	2.55	.495	3.11	.499
.32	.126	.88	.311	1.44	.425	2.00	.477	2.56	.495	3.12	.499
.33	.129	.89	.313	1.45	.426	2.01	.478	2.57	.495	3.13	.499
.34	.133	.90	.316	1.46	.428	2.02	.478	2.58	.495	3.14	.499
.35	.137	.91	.319	1.47	.429	2.03	.479	2.59	.495	3.15	.499
.36	.141	.92	.321	1.48	.431	2.04	.479	2.60	.495	3.16	.499
.37	.144	.93	.324	1.49	.432	2.05	.480	2.61	.495	3.17	.499
.38	.148	.94	.326	1.50	.433	2.06	.480	2.62	.496	3.18	.499
.39	.152	.95	.329	1.51	.434	2.07	.481	2.63	.496	3.19	.499
.40	.155	.96	.331	1.52	.436	2.08	.481	2.64	.496	3.20	.499
.41	.159	.97	.334	1.53	.437	2.09	.482	2.65	.496	3.21	.499
.42	.163	.98	.336	1.54	.438	2.10	.482	2.66	.496	3.22	.499
.43	.166	.99	.339	1.55	.439	2.11	.483	2.67	.496	3.23	.499
.44	.170	1.00	.341	1.56	.441	2.12	.483	2.68	.496	3.24	.499
.45	.174	1.01	.344	1.57	.442	2.13	.483	2.69	.496	3.25	.499
.46	.177	1.02	.346	1.58	.443	2.14	.484	2.70	.497	3.26	.499
.47	.181	1.03	.348	1.59	.444	2.15	.484	2.71	.497	3.27	.499
.48	.184	1.04	.351	1.60	.445	2.16	.485	2.72	.497	3.28	.499
.49	.188	1.05	.353	1.61	.446	2.17	.485	2.73	.497	3.29	.499
.50	.191	1.06	.355	1.62	.447	2.18	.485	2.74	.497	3.30	.500
.51	.195	1.07	.358	1.63	.448	2.19	.486	2.75	.497	3.31	.500
.52	.198	1.08	.360	1.64	.449	2.20	.486	2.76	.497	3.32	.500
.53	.202	1.09	.362	1.65	.451	2.21	.486	2.77	.497	3.33	.500
.54	.205	1.10	.364	1.66	.452	2.22	.487	2.78	.497	3.34	.500
.55	.209	1.11	.367	1.67	.453	2.23	.487	2.79	.497	3.35	.500

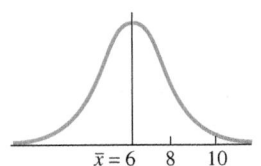

Figure 19

EXAMPLE 3 Finding Probabilities of Phone Call Durations

The time lengths of phone calls placed through a certain company are distributed normally with mean 6 minutes and standard deviation 2 minutes. If one call is randomly selected from phone company records, what is the probability that it will have lasted more than 10 minutes?

Solution

Here 10 minutes is 2 standard deviations above the mean. The probability of such a call is equal to the area of the colored region in **Figure 19**.

From **Table 16**, the area between the mean and 2 standard deviations above is 0.477 ($z = 2.00$). The total area to the right of the mean is 0.500. Find the area from $z = 2.00$ to the right by subtracting.

$$0.500 - 0.477 = 0.023$$

The probability of a call exceeding 10 minutes is 0.023, or 2.3%. ∎

EXAMPLE 4 Finding Areas under the Normal Curve

Find the total area that is shaded in each of **Figures 20** and **21**.

Solution

For **Figure 20**, find the area from 1.45 standard deviations below the mean to 2.71 standard deviations above the mean. From **Table 16**, $z = 1.45$ leads to an area of 0.426, while $z = 2.71$ leads to 0.497. The total area is the sum of these, or $0.426 + 0.497 = 0.923$.

Figure 20

Figure 21

To find the area indicated in **Figure 21**, refer to **Table 16**. From the table, $z = 0.62$ leads to an area of 0.232, and $z = 1.59$ gives 0.444. To get the area between these two values of z, subtract the areas.

$$0.444 - 0.232 = 0.212$$ ∎

Interpreting Normal Curve Areas

Examples 2–4 emphasize the *equivalence* of three quantities, as follows.

MEANING OF NORMAL CURVE AREAS

In the standard normal curve, the following three quantities are equivalent.

1. **Percentage** (of total items that lie in an interval)

2. **Probability** (of a randomly chosen item lying in an interval)

3. **Area** (under the normal curve along an interval)

Which quantity we think of depends on how a particular question is formulated. They all can be evaluated by using *A*-values from **Table 16**.

A Basic Consumer (T)issue It all started when a reporter on consumer issues for a Midwest TV station received a complaint that rolls of Brand X toilet paper manufactured by Company Y did not have the number of sheets claimed on the wrapper. Brand X is supposed to have 375 sheets, but three rolls of it were found by reporters to have 360, 361, and 363.

Shocked Company Y executives said that the **odds against** six rolls having fewer than 375 sheets each are 1 billion to 1. They counted sheets and found that several rolls of Brand X actually had 380 sheets each (machines count the sheets only in 10s). TV reporters made an independent count, and their results agreed with Company Y.

What happened the first time? Well, the reporters hadn't actually counted sheets but, rather, had measured rolls and divided the length of a roll by the length of one sheet. Small variations in length can be expected, which can add up over a roll, giving false results.

This true story perhaps points out the distinction in probability and statistics between **discrete values** and **continuous values.**

In general, when we use **Table 16,** z is the z-score of a particular data item x. When one of these values is known and the other is required, we use the formula

$$z = \frac{x - \bar{x}}{s}.$$

EXAMPLE 5 Applying the Normal Curve to Driving Distances

In one area, the distribution of monthly miles driven by motorists has mean 1200 miles and standard deviation 150 miles. Assume that the number of miles is closely approximated by a normal curve, and find the percent of all motorists driving the following distances.

(a) Between 1200 and 1600 miles per month

(b) Between 1000 and 1500 miles per month

Solution

(a) Start by finding how many standard deviations 1600 miles is above the mean. Use the formula for z.

$$z = \frac{1600 - 1200}{150} = \frac{400}{150} \approx 2.67$$

From **Table 16,** 0.496, or 49.6%, of all motorists drive between 1200 and 1600 miles per month.

(b) As shown in **Figure 22,** values of z must be found for both 1000 and 1500.

$$\text{For 1000:} \quad z = \frac{1000 - 1200}{150} = \frac{-200}{150} \approx -1.33$$

$$\text{For 1500:} \quad z = \frac{1500 - 1200}{150} = \frac{300}{150} = 2.00$$

From **Table 16,** $z = -1.33$ leads to an area of 0.408, while $z = 2.00$ gives 0.477. This means a total of

$$0.408 + 0.477 = 0.885, \quad \text{or} \quad 88.5\%,$$

of all motorists drive between 1000 and 1500 miles per month. ■

1000   1500
$\bar{x} = 1200$

Figure 22

EXAMPLE 6 Identifying a Data Value within a Normal Distribution

A particular normal distribution has mean $\bar{x} = 81.7$ and standard deviation $s = 5.21$. What data value from the distribution would correspond to $z = -1.35$?

Solution

Solve for x.

$$z = \frac{x - \bar{x}}{s} \qquad \text{z-score formula}$$

$$-1.35 = \frac{x - 81.7}{5.21} \qquad \text{Substitute the given values for z, $\bar{x}$, and s.}$$

$$-1.35(5.21) = \frac{x - 81.7}{5.21}(5.21) \qquad \text{Multiply each side by 5.21 to clear the fraction.}$$

$$-7.0335 = x - 81.7 \qquad \text{Simplify.}$$

$$74.6665 = x \qquad \text{Add 81.7.}$$

Rounding to the nearest tenth, the required data value is 74.7. ■

Figure 23

EXAMPLE 7 Finding *z*-Values for Given Areas under the Normal Curve

Assuming a normal distribution, find the *z*-value meeting each condition.

(a) 30% of the total area is to the right of *z*.

(b) 80% of the total area is to the left of *z*.

Solution

(a) Because 50% of the area lies to the right of the mean, there must be 20% between the mean and *z*. (See **Figure 23**.) In **Table 16**, $A = 0.200$ corresponds to $z = 0.52$ or 0.53, or we could average the two: $z = 0.525$.

(b) This situation is shown in **Figure 24**. The 50% to the left of the mean plus 30% additional makes up the 80%. From **Table 16**, $A = 0.300$ implies $z = 0.84$. ■

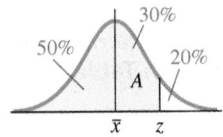

Figure 24

12.5 EXERCISES

Note: For problems requiring the calculation of z-scores or A-values, our answers are based on **Table 16**, *or the empirical rule when specified. By using a calculator or computer package, you will sometimes obtain a slightly more precise answer.*

Identify each variable quantity as discrete *or* continuous.

1. the number of heads in 30 rolled dice

2. the number of babies born in one day at a certain hospital

3. the average weight of babies born in a week

4. the heights of seedling fir trees at two years of age

5. the time as shown on a digital watch

6. the time as shown on a watch with a sweep hand

Measuring the Mass of Ore Samples *Suppose* 100 *geology students measure the mass of an ore sample. Due to human error and limitations in the reliability of the balance, not all the readings are equal. The results are found to closely approximate a normal curve, with mean 75 g and standard deviation 2 g.*

Use the symmetry of the normal curve and the empirical rule to estimate the number of students reporting readings in the following ranges.

7. more than 75 g

8. more than 73 g

9. between 71 and 79 g

10. between 69 and 77 g

Distribution of IQ Scores *On standard IQ tests, the mean is* 100, *with a standard deviation of* 15. *The results come very close to fitting a normal curve. Suppose an IQ test is given to a very large group of people. Use the empirical rule to find the percentage of people whose IQ scores fall into each category.*

11. more than 100

12. less than 85

13. between 70 and 130

14. less than 115

Find the percentage of area under a normal curve between the mean and the given number of standard deviations from the mean. (Note that positive indicates above the mean, while negative indicates below the mean.)

15. 1.60   **16.** 0.76   **17.** −1.68   **18.** −2.45

Find the percentage of the total area under a normal curve between the given values of z.

19. $z = 1.31$ and $z = 1.73$

20. $z = -1.56$ and $z = -1.02$

21. $z = -3.02$ and $z = 2.03$

22. $z = -1.42$ and $z = 0.98$

Find a value of z such that each condition is met.

23. 20% of the total area is to the right of *z*.

24. 23% of the total area is to the left of *z*.

25. 78% of the total area is to the left of *z*.

26. 63% of the total area is to the right of *z*.

Weights of Peaches *A fruit-packing company produced peaches last summer whose weights were normally distributed with mean 14 ounces and standard deviation 0.6 ounce. Among a sample of 1000 of those peaches, about how many could be expected to have weights as follows?*

27. at least 14 ounces

28. between 14 and 15.2 ounces

29. between 14.9 and 15.5 ounces

30. less than 13.4 ounces

31. more than 12 ounces

32. between 13.5 and 15.5 ounces

IQs of Employees *A large company employs workers whose IQs are distributed normally with mean 105 and standard deviation 12.5. Management uses this information to assign employees to projects that will be challenging, but not too challenging. What percentage of the employees would have IQs that satisfy the following criteria?*

33. less than 90   34. more than 125

35. between 100 and 120   36. between 80 and 100

Net Weight of Cereal Boxes *A certain dry cereal is packaged in 12-oz boxes. The machine that fills the boxes is set so that, on the average a box contains 12.4 oz. The machine-filled boxes have content weight that can be closely approximated by a normal curve. What is the probability that a randomly selected box will be underweight (net weight less than 12 oz) if the standard deviation is as follows?*

37. 0.5 oz   38. 0.4 oz   39. 0.3 oz   40. 0.2 oz

41. **Recommended Daily Vitamin Allowances** In nutrition, the recommended daily allowance of vitamins is a number set by the government to guide an individual's daily vitamin intake. Actually, vitamin needs vary drastically from person to person, but the needs are closely approximated by a normal curve. To calculate the recommended daily allowance, the government first finds the average (mean) need for vitamins among people in the population and the standard deviation. The **recommended daily allowance** is then defined as the mean plus 2.5 times the standard deviation. What fraction of the population would receive adequate amounts of vitamins under this plan?

Recommended Daily Vitamin Allowances *Find the recommended daily allowance for each vitamin if the mean need and standard deviation are as follows. (See **Exercise 41.**)*

42. mean need = 1600 units;
    standard deviation = 140 units

43. mean need = 146 units;
    standard deviation = 8 units

*Assume the following distributions are all normal, and use the areas under the normal curve given in **Table 16** to find the appropriate areas.*

44. **Assembling Cell Phones** The times taken by workers to assemble a certain kind of cell phone are normally distributed with mean 18.5 minutes and standard deviation 3.1 minutes. Find the probability that one such phone will require less than 12.8 minutes in assembly.

45. **Finding Blood Clotting Times** The mean clotting time of blood is 7.47 sec, with a standard deviation of 3.6 sec. What is the probability that an individual's blood-clotting time will be less than 7 sec or greater than 8 sec?

46. **Sizes of Fish** The average length of the fish caught in Vernal Lake is 10.6 in., with a standard deviation of 3.2 in. Find the probability that a fish caught there will be longer than 16 in.

47. **Size Grading of Eggs** To be graded extra large, an egg must weigh at least 2.2 oz. If the average weight for an egg is 1.5 oz, with a standard deviation of 0.4 oz, how many of five dozen randomly chosen eggs would you expect to be extra large?

Distribution of Student Grades *Professor Cheng teaches a marketing course. He uses the following grading system.*

Grade	Score in Class
A	Greater than $\bar{x} + 1.5s$
B	$\bar{x} + 0.5s$ to $\bar{x} + 1.5s$
C	$\bar{x} - 0.5s$ to $\bar{x} + 0.5s$
D	$\bar{x} - 1.5s$ to $\bar{x} - 0.5s$
F	Below $\bar{x} - 1.5s$

What percent of the students receive the following grades?

48. A   49. B   50. C

51. Do you think that Professor Cheng's system would be more likely to be fair in a large first-year lecture class or in a graduate seminar of five students? Why?

Normal Distribution of Student Grades   *A teacher gives a test to a large group of students. The results are closely approximated by a normal curve. The mean is 72 with a standard deviation of 5. The teacher wishes to give As to the top 8% of the students and Fs to the bottom 8%. A grade of B is given to the next 15%, with Ds given similarly. All other students get Cs. Find the bottom point cutoffs (rounded to the nearest whole number) for the following grades. (Hint: Use* **Table 16** *to find z-scores from known A-values.)*

52. A   **53.** B   **54.** C   **55.** D

56. ***Selecting Industrial Rollers***   A manufacturer makes carts with industrial swivel rollers that must support a load of at least 125 pounds. Supplier A can provide rollers supporting 130 pounds on the average, with standard deviation 2.2 pounds, and Supplier B's rollers will support 135 pounds on the average, with standard deviation 4.2 pounds.

(a) If both distributions can be assumed normal, which supplier offers the smaller percentage of unsatisfactory rollers?

(b) Give your reasoning.

A normal distribution has mean 76.8 and standard deviation 9.42. Follow the method of ***Example 6*** *and find data values corresponding to the following values of z. Round to the nearest tenth.*

57. $z = 1.44$ **58.** $z = 0.72$

59. $z = -3.87$ **60.** $z = -2.39$

61. What percentage of the items lie within 1.25 standard deviations of the mean

(a) in any distribution (using the results of Chebyshev's theorem)?

(b) in a normal distribution (by **Table 16**)?

62. Explain the difference between the answers to **Exercise 61,** parts (a) and (b).

CHAPTER 12   SUMMARY

KEY TERMS

12.1

population
sample
descriptive statistics
inferential statistics
raw data
quantitative (numerical)
   data
qualitative (non-numerical)
   data
ranked data
frequency distribution
relative frequency
   distribution
histogram
frequency polygon
classes
grouped frequency
   distribution

lower class limits
upper class limits
class width
stem-and-leaf display
bar graph
circle graph (pie chart)
line graph
expected (theoretical)
   frequencies
observed (empirical)
   frequencies

12.2

measure of central
   tendency
mean (arithmetic mean)
weighted mean
weighting factor
outlier

median
cumulative frequency
mode
bimodal
symmetry in
   data sets
skewed to the left
skewed to the right
Simpson's paradox

12.3

dispersion (spread) of
   data
range
variance
standard deviation
Chebyshev's theorem
coefficient of variation
skewness coefficient

12.4

measures of position
z-score
percentile
decile
quartile
box plot (box-and-whisker
   plot)

12.5

discrete random variable
continuous random
   variable
normal curve
normal distribution
standard normal curve
asymptote
empirical rule

TEST YOUR WORD POWER

See how well you have learned the vocabulary in this chapter.

1. Using a **sample** to gain knowledge about a **population** is part of
   A. descriptive statistics.
   B. inferential statistics.
   C. qualitative data analysis.
   D. calculus.

2. A **class mark** is the
   A. average grade of all the class members.
   B. least item in a grouped frequency distribution.
   C. middle of a class in a grouped frequency distribution.
   D. number of items in the class.

3. A common property of **bar graphs, circle graphs, line graphs,** and **stem-and-leaf displays** is that they provide
   A. a visual representation of a data set.
   B. the range value of a data set.
   C. a way of comparing two data sets.
   D. clear divisions among the various classes.

4. The measure that, when it exists, is always equal to a data item is the
   A. mean.   B. standard deviation.
   C. median.   D. mode.

5. The **median** is an example of a
   A. weighted mean.
   B. measure of central tendency.
   C. measure of dispersion.
   D. measure of position.

6. For a frequency distribution, the formula $\dfrac{\Sigma f + 1}{2}$ gives
   A. the total number of data items.
   B. one of the measures of position.
   C. the position of the mean.
   D. the position of the median.

7. **Measures of dispersion** include
   A. mean, median, and mode.
   B. range, variance, and percentile.
   C. range, variance, and standard deviation.
   D. percentiles, quartiles, and deciles.

8. The **z-score** determines
   A. how many items must lie within 1 standard deviation of the mean.
   B. how many standard deviations from the mean a data item is.
   C. the ratio of the standard deviation to the mean.
   D. the percentage of items that lie below the given item.

9. A **bimodal** distribution will never be
   A. normal.
   B. skewed.
   C. symmetric.
   D. spread out more than 3 standard deviations from its mean.

10. In any approximately normal distribution, an item with a negative *z*-score will be
   A. negative.
   B. less than the distribution range.
   C. between the first and third quartiles.
   D. less than the distribution mean.

ANSWERS
1. B   2. C   3. A   4. D   5. B
6. D   7. C   8. B   9. A   10. D

QUICK REVIEW

Concepts	Examples

12.1 Visual Displays of Data

Qualitative raw data are non-numerical.

Category	Number of Positions Available	
Surgeons	3	
GP physicians	5	Qualitative data
Nurse practitioners	7	
Registered nurses	12	
Licensed vocational nurses	8	

Quantitative raw data are numerical.

32, 41, 18, 22, 32, 41, 32, 38, 18, 28,
41, 28, 38, 28, 41, 18, 22, 32, 28, 28   Quantitative data

Concepts	*Examples*
Quantitative data can be **ranked** (arranged in numerical order).	18, 18, 18, 22, 22, 28, 28, 28, 28, 28, Quantitative 32, 32, 32, 32, 38, 38, 41, 41, 41, 41 data (ranked)

Examples

18, 18, 18, 22, 22, 28, 28, 28, 28, 28,   Quantitative data (ranked)
32, 32, 32, 32, 38, 38, 41, 41, 41, 41

A **frequency distribution** makes a data presentation more concise.

A **relative frequency distribution** shows the fraction of the total number of items represented by each value.

x	f	$\dfrac{f}{n}$	
18	3	0.15	
22	2	0.10	Frequency distribution
28	5	0.25	and relative frequency
32	4	0.20	distribution
38	2	0.10	
41	4	0.20	

Total: $n = 20$

A **grouped frequency distribution** collects multiple items into separate classes.

Class limits are the least (or greatest) items that can occur in each class.

Class marks are the center points of the classes.

A **histogram** is a graphical presentation of a grouped frequency distribution.

A **frequency polygon** is a sequence of line segments representing a frequency distribution.

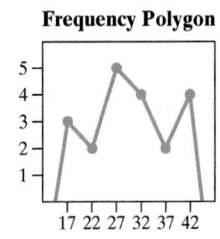

Lower class limits	15	20	25	30	35	40
Upper class limits	19	24	29	34	39	44
Class marks	17	22	27	32	37	42

A **stem-and-leaf display** shows all data items in a visual arrangement.

(15–19) 1	8 8 8	
(20–24) 2	2 2	A (double stem)
(25–29) 2	8 8 8 8 8	stem-and-leaf
(30–34) 3	2 2 2 2	display for the
(35–39) 3	8 8	above data
(40–44) 4	1 1 1 1	

Qualitative data can be effectively presented in a number of ways, including a bar graph, a circle graph, and a line graph.

Number of flu cases treated at a clinic during five days:

Mon	Tue	Wed	Thu	Fri
5	7	12	20	28

A **bar graph** is a visual depiction of a distribution, appropriate for either qualitative or quantitative data.

Concepts	Examples

A **circle graph** represents classes of data as sectors of a circle, so it conveys the relative sizes of the classes.

A **line graph** is useful especially for showing how a quantity changes over time, and it can also show comparisons of two or more quantities.

12.2 Measures of Central Tendency

The **mean**, the most common measure of central tendency, is computed using the formula

$$\bar{x} = \frac{\Sigma x}{n},$$

or, for frequency distributions,

$$\bar{x} = \frac{\Sigma(x \cdot f)}{\Sigma f}.$$

Find the mean for the distribution 2, 6, 3, 7, 4.

$$\bar{x} = \frac{\Sigma x}{n} = \frac{2 + 6 + 3 + 7 + 4}{5} = \frac{22}{5} = 4.4$$

Find the mean for the frequency distribution.

x	f	$x \cdot f$
3	2	6
4	5	20
5	3	15
Totals:	10	41

$$\bar{x} = \frac{\Sigma(x \cdot f)}{\Sigma f} = \frac{41}{10} = 4.1$$

A **weighted mean** is computed as

$$\bar{w} = \frac{\Sigma(x \cdot f)}{\Sigma f},$$

where f represents the "weighting factors." In the case of the mean of a frequency distribution, the mean is actually a weighted mean where the weighting factors are the frequencies.

Find the grade-point average. (Grade-point average is a weighted mean, where the weighting factors are the numbers of units for which each grade is assigned.)

Grade Earned	Grade Points Assigned, x	Number of Units, f	$x \cdot f$
A	4	3	12
B	3	6	18
C	2	4	8
	Totals:	13	38

$$\text{Grade-point average} = \bar{w} = \frac{\Sigma(x \cdot f)}{\Sigma f} = \frac{38}{13} \approx 2.92$$

The **median** is the "center" item of a distribution, or the mean of the two center items if there are an even number of items.

Find the median of the data set 2, 6, 3, 7, 4.

First rank the data: 2, 3, 4, 6, 7.

The median is the middle item, 4.

The **mode**, when it exists, is the item that occurs in the distribution more times than any other. A distribution having two distinct items with higher frequencies is **bimodal.**

Find the mode for the frequency distribution for which the mean (4.1) was computed above.

The mode is 4, since there were more 4s than there were of any other item.

Concepts	*Examples*

It is possible to find measures of central tendency for a distribution presented in a stem-and-leaf display.

Consider this stem-and-leaf display.

5	2 4 7 8 8
6	1 2 5 5 6
7	1 1 2 3 6 6 9
8	2 2 4 5 8 8
9	0 0 0 2 4

Counting leaves gives $n = 28$.

$$\Sigma x = 52 + 54 + 57 + 58 + 58 + 61 + \cdots + 94 = 2081$$

$$\bar{x} = \frac{\Sigma x}{n} = \frac{2081}{28} \approx 74.3 \quad \text{Mean}$$

$$\frac{73 + 76}{2} = 74.5 \quad \text{The median is the mean of the 14th and 15th items.}$$

Examining the leaves reveals that the mode is 90.

Symmetry and **skewness** are important properties of a distribution.

- If the graph of a distribution drops off about equally in both directions from the center, it is symmetric.

- If it trails off farther to the left (or right), it is "skewed" left (or right).

Symmetry and skewness are illustrated by these distributions.

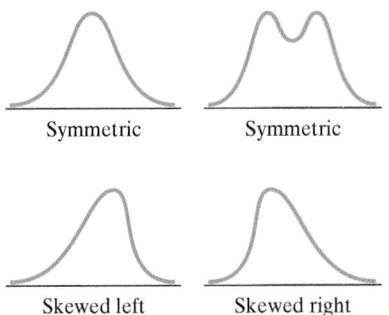

Symmetric   Symmetric

Skewed left   Skewed right

12.3 Measures of Dispersion

Range is the distance from the least item to the greatest item of the data set.

Range = (greatest value in the set) − (least value in the set)

Consider again the distribution

$$2, 6, 3, 7, 4, \quad \text{or, when ranked,} \quad 2, 3, 4, 6, 7.$$

$$\text{Range} = 7 - 2 = 5$$

Standard deviation s is a sort of "average" amount by which all items in a distribution differ from their mean.

$$s = \sqrt{\frac{\Sigma(x - \bar{x})^2}{n - 1}}$$

Since the mean is 4.4, the standard deviation is as follows.

$$s = \sqrt{\frac{(2 - 4.4)^2 + (3 - 4.4)^2 + (4 - 4.4)^2 + (6 - 4.4)^2 + (7 - 4.4)^2}{5 - 1}}$$

$$\approx 2.07$$

Chebyshev's Theorem
In any distribution, the fraction of all items that lie within k standard deviations of the mean (where $k > 1$) is *at least*

$$1 - \frac{1}{k^2}.$$

For $k = 2$, at least

$$1 - \frac{1}{2^2}, \quad \text{or} \quad 1 - \frac{1}{4} = \frac{3}{4},$$

of the items will lie within 2 standard deviations of the mean; that is, at least 3.75 items will lie between 0.26 and 8.54. In fact, in this case all 5 items lie within that range.

The **coefficient of variation** for a distribution expresses standard deviation as a percentage of the mean.

$$V = \frac{s}{\bar{x}} \cdot 100\%$$

Find the coefficient of variation for this distribution.

$$V = \frac{2.07}{4.4} \cdot 100\% \approx 47\%$$

Concepts

Examples

12.4 Measures of Position

The *z*-**score** of an item gives the number of standard deviations that item is from the mean.

$$z = \frac{x - \bar{x}}{s}$$

Earlier, we saw a stem-and-leaf display for the data set

52 54 57 58 58 61 62 65 65 66 71 71 72 73

76 76 79 82 82 84 85 88 88 90 90 90 92 94.

The mean was 74.3. The standard deviation was 12.9.

Find the *z*-score for the item 84.

$$z = \frac{84 - 74.3}{12.9} \approx 0.75$$

84 is three-fourths of a standard deviation *above* the mean.

Find the *z*-score for the item 62.

$$z = \frac{62 - 74.3}{12.9} \approx -0.95$$

62 is $\frac{95}{100}$ of a standard deviation *below* the mean.

The **percentile** corresponding to an item tells roughly the percentage of all items that are below that item. There are ninety-nine percentiles, the first through the ninety-ninth.

For the above data, find the ninety-fifth percentile. Since 95% of 28 (the number of items) is 26.6, we round up. The twenty-seventh item is 92.

For any numerical distribution, there are nine **deciles,** the first through the ninth.

Find the fourth decile (the same as the fortieth percentile).

$$40\% \text{ of } 28 \text{ is } 11.2.$$

Therefore, take the twelfth item, which is 71.

For any numerical distribution, there are three **quartiles,** the first through the third.

Find the three quartiles for the data.

The median (Q_2) was found to be

$$74.5 \quad \text{(the mean of 73 and 76)}.$$

Q_1 is the median of the lower half of the items.

$$\frac{62 + 65}{2} = 63.5$$

Q_3 is the median of the upper half of the items.

$$\frac{85 + 88}{2} = 86.5$$

A **box plot** (or **box-and-whisker plot**) for a distribution is a visual representation that shows the least value, the greatest value, and all three quartiles.

Construct a box plot for this distribution of twenty-eight items.

Concepts | *Examples*

12.5 The Normal Distribution

Many quantities are **distributed approximately "normally"**—that is, according to a characteristic bell-shaped curve. Their distributions may have any mean and any (positive) standard deviation, but we can calculate their properties by relating them to the so-called standard normal curve, which has mean 0 and standard deviation 1. The total area under the standard normal curve, from $-\infty$ to $+\infty$, is 1 square unit.

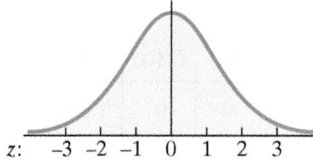

For any two items in a normal distribution, say x_1 and x_2, if we calculate their corresponding z-scores,

$$z_1 = \frac{x_1 - \bar{x}}{s} \quad \text{and} \quad z_2 = \frac{x_2 - \bar{x}}{s},$$

then **the following three quantities are equivalent.**

1. **The percentage of items in the original distribution that are between x_1 and x_2**

2. **The probability that a randomly chosen item from the original distribution will lie between x_1 and x_2**

3. **The area under the standard normal curve between z_1 and z_2**

Suppose the heights of the trainees on a large military base are normally distributed with mean 70 inches and standard deviation 5 inches.

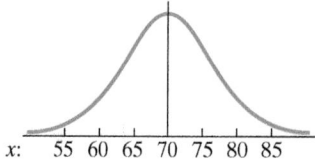

1. Find the *percentage* of trainees with heights between $x_1 = 70$ inches and $x_2 = 74$ inches.

Since x_1 is at the mean, we need only calculate

$$z_2 = \frac{x_2 - \bar{x}}{s} = \frac{74 - 70}{5} = 0.8.$$

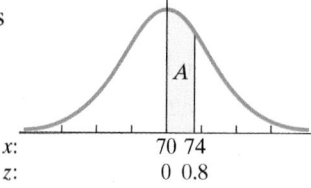

From the standard normal curve table,

$A = 0.288$, and the required percentage is 28.8%.

2. Find the *probability* that a randomly selected trainee will have a height between $x_1 = 67$ inches and $x_2 = 77$ inches.

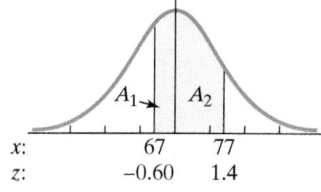

$$z_1 = \frac{67 - 70}{5} = -0.60, \quad \text{so} \quad A_1 = 0.226.$$

$$z_2 = \frac{77 - 70}{5} = 1.4, \quad \text{so} \quad A_2 = 0.419.$$

The required probability is

$$A_1 + A_2 = 0.226 + 0.419 = 0.645.$$

3. Find the *area* under the standard normal curve between the z-scores corresponding to trainee heights between 60 inches and 68 inches.

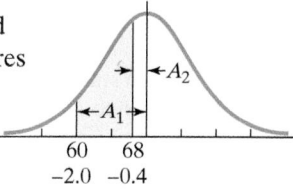

$$z_1 = \frac{60 - 70}{5} = -2.0 \quad \text{and} \quad z_2 = \frac{68 - 70}{5} = -0.4,$$

so $A_1 = 0.477$ and $A_2 = 0.155$.

The area under the curve between these two points is

$$A_1 - A_2 = 0.477 - 0.155 = 0.322.$$

CHAPTER 12	TEST

1. *Visits to Social Networking Sites* The table shows the number of persons age 2 and older in any U.S. location, in millions, who visited the listed Web sites at least once in June 2013.

Rank	Web Site	Visitors
1	Facebook	144.7
2	LinkedIn	50.6
3	Twitter	39.1
4	Tumblr	35.9
5	Pinterest	27.9

Source: comScore Media Metrix; comScore qSearch

Use this information to determine each of the following.

(a) the mean number of visitors per site

(b) the range

(c) the standard deviation

(d) the coefficient of variation

2. *Cheaters Never Learn* The table here shows the results of an educational study of university physics students, comparing exam scores with students' rates of copying others' homework. The numbers in the table approximate letter grades on a 4-point scale (4.0 is an A, 3.0 is a B, and so on). Answer the questions in terms of copy rate.

Copy Rate	Pretest	Exam 1	Exam 2	Exam 3	Final Exam
<10%	2.70	2.75	2.90	2.80	2.95
10% to 30%	2.50	2.45	2.35	2.40	2.30
30% to 50%	2.45	2.43	2.30	2.10	2.00
>50%	2.40	2.05	1.70	1.80	1.60

Source: Table created using data from research reported in Physics Review–Special Topics–Physics Education *by David J. Palazzo, Young-Jin Lee, Rasil Warnakulasooriya, and David E. Pritchard of the Massachusetts Institute of Technology (MIT) physics faculty.*

(a) Which students generally improved their exam performance over the course of the semester?

(b) Which students did better on exam 3 than on exam 2?

(c) Which students had lower scores consistently from one exam to the next throughout the semester?

(d) Do you think that copying homework is generally a *cause* of lower exam scores? Explain.

Champion Trees *The table below lists the 9 largest national champion trees, based on the formula*

$$T = G + H + 0.25C,$$

where T = *total points,*

G = *girth (circumference of trunk 4.5 feet above the ground, measured in inches)*

H = *height, measured in feet*

and C = *average crown spread, measured in feet*

Tree Type	G (in.)	H (ft)	C (ft)	T	Location
Giant sequoia	1020	274	107	1321	Sequoia National Park, CA
Coast redwood	950	321	75	1290	Jedediah Smith Redwoods State Park, CA
Coast redwood	895	307	83	1223	Jedediah Smith Redwoods State Park, CA
Coast redwood	844	349	89	1216	Redwoods National Park, CA
Coast redwood	867	299	101	1191	Prairie Creek Redwoods State Park, CA
Western red cedar	761	159	45	931	Olympic National Park, WA
Sitka spruce	668	191	96	883	Olympic National Park, WA
Coast Douglas fir	505	281	71	804	Olympic National Forest, WA
Port Orford cedar	522	242	35	773	Coos, OR

Source: The World Almanac and Book of Facts 2014.

Use this information for Exercises 3 and 4.

3. For the nine trees listed, find the following.

(a) the median height

(b) the first quartile in girth

(c) the seventh decile in total points

4. The tenth-ranking tree in the country is a common bald cypress on Cat Island, Louisiana, with $G = 647$ inches, $H = 96$ feet, and $C = 74$ feet. For this tree, answer the following questions.

(a) Find its total points.

(b) Where would it have ranked based on girth alone?

(c) How much greater would its girth need to be to exceed the seventh-ranked girth figure?

(d) Assuming a roughly circular cross section at 4.5 feet above the ground, approximate the diameter of the trunk (to the nearest foot) at that height.

College Endowment Assets   *The table shows the top six U.S. colleges for 2012 endowment assets, in billions of dollars.*

Rank	College/University	Endowment Assets
1	Harvard University	30.4
2	Yale University	19.3
3	University of Texas System	18.3
4	Stanford University	17.0
5	Princeton University	17.0
6	Massachusetts Institute of Technology	10.1

Source: World Almanac and Book of Facts 2014.

5. Construct a bar graph for these data.

6. What percentage (to one decimal place) of the total was held by Yale?

7. What was the median value?

Pediatrics Patients   *Khalida worked the 22 weekdays of last month in the pediatrics clinic and checked in the following numbers of patients.*

| 14 | 24 | 26 | 11 | 16 | 25 | 10 | 12 | 8 | 18 | 13 |
| 15 | 20 | 18 | 22 | 24 | 17 | 19 | 19 | 7 | 15 | 30 |

8. Construct grouped frequency and relative frequency distributions. Use five uniform classes of width 5 where the first class has a lower limit of 6. (Round relative frequencies to two decimal places.)

9. From your frequency distribution of **Exercise 8,** construct **(a)** a histogram and **(b)** a frequency polygon. Use appropriate scales and labels.

10. For the data above, how many uniform classes would be required if the first class had limits 7–9?

In Exercises 11–14, find the indicated measures for the following frequency distribution.

Value	8	10	12	14	16	18
Frequency	3	8	10	8	5	1

11. the mean

12. the median

13. the mode

14. the range

15. **Exam Scores in a Criminal Justice Class**   The following data are scores achieved by 30 students on a criminal justice exam. Arrange the data into a stem-and-leaf display with leaves ranked.

52	43	84	65	77	70	79	61	66	80
55	48	68	78	71	38	45	64	67	73
33	49	61	91	84	77	50	67	79	72

Use the stem-and-leaf display below for Exercises 16–21.

2	3 3 4
2	6 7 8 9 9
3	0 1 1 2 3 3 3 4
3	5 6 7 8 8 9
4	1 2 2 4
4	5 7 9
5	2 4
5	8
6	0

Compute the measures required in Exercises 16–20.

16. the median

17. the mode(s), if any

18. the range

19. the third decile

20. the eighty-fifth percentile

21. Construct a box plot for the given data, showing values for the five important quantities on the numerical scale.

22. **Test Scores in a Training Institute**   A certain training institute gives a standardized test to large numbers of applicants nationwide. The resulting scores form a normal distribution with mean 80 and standard deviation 5. Find the percent of all applicants with scores as follows. (Use the empirical rule.)

(a) between 70 and 90

(b) greater than 95 or less than 65

(c) less than 75

(d) between 85 and 90

Triple Jump Champions *All Summer Olympic championship distances in the Triple Jump from 1896 through 2012 averaged 16.38 meters, with standard deviation 1.34 meters. (As of 2015, the all-time greatest distance was 18.17 meters, achieved by Mike Conley of the United States in 1992.) Assuming the distribution of distances was approximately normal, find (to the nearest thousandth) the probability that a randomly selected distance from the distribution would fall into each of the following intervals.*

23. between 16.8 meters and 17.9 meters

24. between 14.6 meters and 16.8 meters

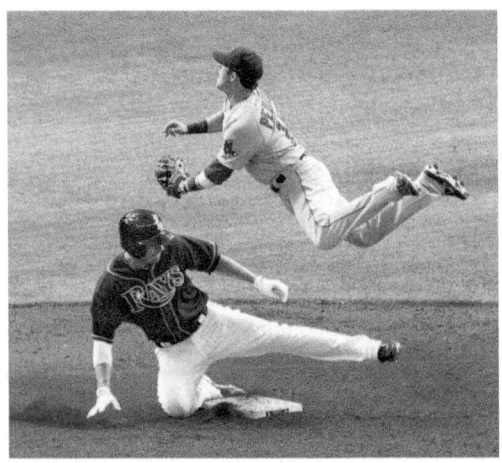

Season Statistics in Major League Baseball *The tables below show the 2013 statistics on games won for all three divisions of both major baseball leagues. In each case,*

$n =$ *number of teams in the division,*

$\bar{x} =$ *average (mean) number of games won,*

and $s =$ *standard deviation of number of games won.*

American League

East Division	Central Division	West Division
$n = 5$	$n = 5$	$n = 5$
$\bar{x} = 86.6$	$\bar{x} = 80.0$	$\bar{x} = 77.4$
$s = 8.7$	$s = 14.4$	$s = 17.8$

National League

East Division	Central Division	West Division
$n = 5$	$n = 5$	$n = 5$
$\bar{x} = 78.2$	$\bar{x} = 84.2$	$\bar{x} = 79.8$
$s = 13.1$	$s = 13.5$	$s = 7.3$

Refer to the preceding tables for Exercises 25–28.

25. Overall, who had the greatest winning average, the East teams, the Central teams, or the West teams?

26. Overall, where were the teams the least "consistent" in number of games won: East, Central, or West?

27. Find (to the nearest tenth) the average number of games won for all East Division teams.

28. The Boston Red Sox, in the American League East, and the St. Louis Cardinals, in the National League Central, each won 97 games. Use z-scores to determine which of these two teams did relatively better within its own division of 5 teams.

Remission Data for Cocaine and Marijuana Addiction *The chapter opener and the* **When Will I Ever Use This?** *feature in* **Section 12.1** *showed research results for alcohol and tobacco addiction and recovery. (A 0.5 cumulative probability of remission required about 17 years for alcoholics, and about 30 years for smokers.) This table gives data inferred from the same study for cocaine and marijuana addiction.*

Cocaine		Marijuana	
x	y	x	y
1.9	0.27	2.1	0.22
6.1	0.64	6.1	0.55
9.8	0.79	10.3	0.69
14.0	0.89	14.0	0.79
21.0	0.94	19.2	0.84

Data source: G. Heyman, *Annual Review of Clinical Psychology 2013.*

29. Plot the data points from the table, draw two smooth curves, and then estimate the 0.5 cumulative probability of remission for:

(a) cocaine.   **(b)** marijuana.

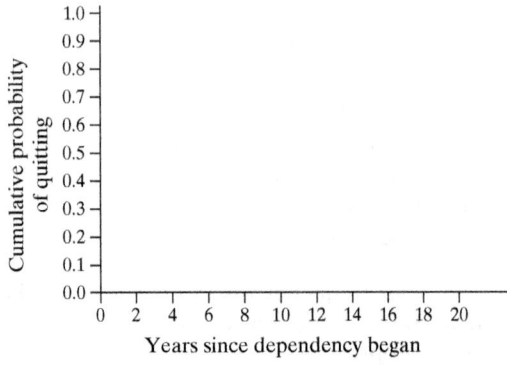

30. Make a conjecture about why remission periods are this much shorter for cocaine and marijuana than for alcohol and tobacco.

Personal Financial Management

13

Financial planners advise their clients in making decisions that will help them reach their financial goals. Many people find it beneficial to consult a professional who can offer a knowledgeable and objective perspective in this area. Financial planners can help people establish financial goals, increase their financial security, and even ask the right questions.

1. *Am I spending my income wisely?*
2. *Do I need a budget?*
3. *What are my financial priorities?*
4. *Should I buy a home, or is renting a better idea?*
5. *Am I saving enough for retirement or for my children's college education?*
6. *Am I taking advantage of available tax savings?*
7. *What are the best investment vehicles for me?*

Questions like these are within the purview of good financial planners, and many of the topics discussed in this chapter are related to them.

13.1 THE TIME VALUE OF MONEY

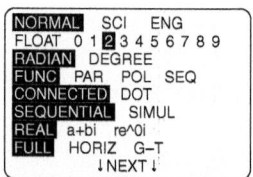

Because the calculations in this chapter involve money, answers often will be rounded to the nearest $0.01. The TI-83/84 will display answers to the nearest 0.01 with the setting shown above.

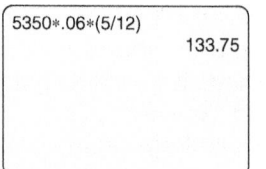

This is the computation required to solve **Example 1.**

Interest

To determine the value of money, we consider not only the amount (number of dollars) but also the particular point in time that the value is to be determined. If we borrow an amount of money today, we will repay a larger amount later. This increase in value is known as **interest.** The money *gains value over time.*

The amount of a loan or a deposit is called the **principal.** The interest is usually computed as a percent of the principal. This percent is called the **rate of interest** (or the **interest rate,** or simply the **rate**). The rate of interest is always assumed to be an annual rate unless otherwise stated.

Interest calculated only on principal is called **simple interest.** Interest calculated on principal plus any previously earned interest is called **compound interest.**

Simple Interest

Simple interest is calculated according to the following formula.

SIMPLE INTEREST

If P = principal, r = annual interest rate, and t = time (in years), then the **simple interest** I is calculated as follows.

$$I = Prt$$

EXAMPLE 1 Finding Simple Interest

Find the simple interest paid to borrow $5350 for 5 months at 6%.

Solution

$$I = Prt \qquad \text{Simple interest formula}$$

$$= \$5350(0.06)\left(\frac{5}{12}\right) \qquad \begin{array}{l}\text{5 months is } \frac{5}{12} \text{ of a year.}\\ P = \$5350,\ r = 6\% = 0.06\end{array}$$

$$= \$133.75 \qquad \text{Calculate.}$$

Future Value and Present Value

In **Example 1,** at the end of 5 months the borrower would have to repay

$$\underset{\text{Principal}}{\$5350} \ + \ \underset{\text{Interest}}{\$133.75} = \$5483.75.$$

The total amount repaid is sometimes called the **maturity value** (or simply the **value**) of the loan. We will generally refer to it as the **future value,** or **future amount,** because when a loan is being set up, repayment will be occurring in the future. We use A to denote future amount (or value). The original principal, denoted P, can also be thought of as **present value.**

Future value depends on principal (present value) and interest as follows.

$$A = P + I = P + Prt = P(1 + rt)$$

FUTURE VALUE FOR SIMPLE INTEREST

If a principal P is borrowed at simple interest for t years at an annual interest rate of r, then the **future value** of the loan, denoted A, is calculated as follows.

$$A = P(1 + rt)$$

▓▓ EXAMPLE 2 Finding Future Value for Simple Interest

James took out a simple interest loan for $210 to purchase textbooks and school supplies. If the annual interest rate is 6% and he must repay the loan after 6 months, find the future value (the maturity value) of the loan.

Solution

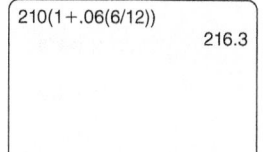

$$A = P(1 + rt) \qquad \text{Future value formula}$$

$$= \$210\left[1 + 0.06\left(\frac{6}{12}\right)\right] \qquad P = \$210,\ r = 6\% = 0.06,\ t = \frac{6}{12}$$

$$= \$216.30 \qquad \text{Calculate.}$$

This is the computation required to solve **Example 2.**

At the end of 6 months, James will need to repay $216.30. ■

Sometimes the future value is known, and we need to compute the present value. For this purpose, we solve the future value formula for P.

$$A = P(1 + rt) \qquad \text{Future value formula for simple interest}$$

$$P = \frac{A}{1 + rt} \qquad \text{Solve the formula for } P.$$

▓▓ EXAMPLE 3 Finding Present Value for Simple Interest

Suppose that James (**Example 2**) is granted a 6-month *deferral* of the $210 payment rather than a loan. That is, instead of incurring interest for 6 months, he will have to pay just the $210 at the end of that period. If he has extra money right now, and if he can earn 2% simple interest on savings, what lump sum must he deposit now so that its value will be $210 after 6 months?

Solution

```
210/(1+.02(6/12))
              207.92
```

$$P = \frac{A}{1 + rt} \qquad \text{Future value formula solved for } P$$

$$P = \frac{\$210}{1 + (0.02)\left(\frac{6}{12}\right)} = \$207.92 \qquad \text{Substitute known values and calculate.}$$

This is the computation required to solve **Example 3.**

A deposit of $207.92 now, growing at 2% simple interest, will grow to $210 over a 6-month period. ■

Compound Interest

Interest paid on principal plus interest is called *compound interest*. After a certain period, the interest earned so far is *credited* (added) to the account, and the sum (principal plus interest) then earns interest during the next period.

EXAMPLE 4 Comparing Simple and Compound Interest

Compare simple and compound interest for a $1000 deposit at 2% interest for 5 years.

Solution

$$A = P(1 + rt) \qquad \text{Future value formula}$$

$$= \$1000(1 + 0.02 \cdot 5) \qquad P = \$1000, \, r = 2\%, \, t = 5$$

$$= \$1100 \qquad \text{Calculate.}$$

After 5 years, $1000 grows to $1100 subject to 2% simple interest.

The result of compounding (annually) for 5 years is shown in **Table 1.**

Table 1 A $1000 Deposit at 2% Interest Compounded Annually

Year	Beginning Balance	Interest Earned $I = Prt$	Ending Balance
1	$1000.00	$1000.00(0.02)(1) = $20.00	$1020.00
2	$1020.00	$1020.00(0.02)(1) = $20.40	$1040.40
3	$1040.40	$1040.40(0.02)(1) = $20.81	$1061.21
4	$1061.21	$1061.21(0.02)(1) = $21.22	$1082.43
5	$1082.43	$1082.43(0.02)(1) = $21.65	$1104.08

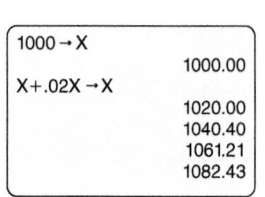

This screen supports the Ending Balance figures in **Table 1.**

Under annual compounding for 5 years, $1000 grows to $1104.08, which is $4.08 more than under simple interest. ■

Based on the compounding pattern of **Example 4,** we now develop a future value formula for compound interest. In practice, earned interest can be credited to an account at time intervals other than 1 year (usually more often). For example, it can be done semiannually, quarterly, monthly, or daily. This time interval is called the **compounding period** (or simply the **period**). Start with the following definitions:

P = original principal deposited, $\qquad r$ = annual interest rate,

n = number of periods per year, $\qquad m$ = total number of periods.

During each individual compounding period, interest is earned according to the simple interest formula, and as interest is added, the beginning principal increases from one period to the next. During the first period, the interest earned is given by

$$\text{Interest} = P(r)\left(\frac{1}{n}\right) \qquad \begin{array}{l} \text{Interest} = (\text{Principal})(\text{rate})(\text{time}), \\ \text{one period} = \frac{1}{n}\text{ year} \end{array}$$

$$= P\left(\frac{r}{n}\right). \qquad \text{Rewrite } (r)\left(\frac{1}{n}\right) \text{ as } \left(\frac{r}{n}\right).$$

At the end of the first period, the account then contains

$$\text{Ending amount} = \overset{\overset{\text{Beginning amount}}{\downarrow}}{P} + \overset{\overset{\text{Interest}}{\downarrow}}{P\left(\frac{r}{n}\right)}$$

$$= P\left(1 + \frac{r}{n}\right). \qquad \text{Factor } P \text{ from both terms.}$$

King Hammurabi tried to hold interest rates at 20% for both silver and gold, but moneylenders ignored his decrees.

Now during the second period, the interest earned is given by

$$\text{Interest} = \left[P\left(1 + \frac{r}{n}\right) \right](r)\left(\frac{1}{n}\right) \qquad \text{Interest} = [\text{Principal}](\text{rate})(\text{time})$$

$$= P\left(1 + \frac{r}{n}\right)\left(\frac{r}{n}\right),$$

so the account ends the second period containing

$$\text{Ending amount} = \overset{\text{Beginning amount}}{P\left(1 + \frac{r}{n}\right)} + \overset{\text{Interest}}{P\left(1 + \frac{r}{n}\right)\left(\frac{r}{n}\right)}$$

$$= P\left(1 + \frac{r}{n}\right)\left[1 + \frac{r}{n}\right] \qquad \text{Factor } P\left(1 + \frac{r}{n}\right) \text{ from both terms.}$$

$$= P\left(1 + \frac{r}{n}\right)^2. \qquad a \cdot a = a^2$$

Consider one more period, namely, the third. The interest earned is

$$\text{Interest} = \left[P\left(1 + \frac{r}{n}\right)^2 \right](r)\left(\frac{1}{n}\right) \qquad \text{Interest} = [\text{Principal}](\text{rate})(\text{time})$$

$$= P\left(1 + \frac{r}{n}\right)^2\left(\frac{r}{n}\right), \qquad \text{Multiply.}$$

so the account ends the third period containing

$$\text{Ending amount} = \overset{\text{Beginning amount}}{P\left(1 + \frac{r}{n}\right)^2} + \overset{\text{Interest}}{P\left(1 + \frac{r}{n}\right)^2\left(\frac{r}{n}\right)}$$

$$= P\left(1 + \frac{r}{n}\right)^2\left[1 + \frac{r}{n}\right] \qquad \text{Factor } P\left(1 + \frac{r}{n}\right)^2 \text{ from both terms.}$$

$$= P\left(1 + \frac{r}{n}\right)^3. \qquad a^2 \cdot a = a^3$$

Table 2 summarizes the preceding results.

Table 2 Compound Amount

Period Number	Beginning Amount	Interest Earned During Period	Ending Amount
1	P	$P\left(\frac{r}{n}\right)$	$P\left(1 + \frac{r}{n}\right)$
2	$P\left(1 + \frac{r}{n}\right)$	$P\left(1 + \frac{r}{n}\right)\left(\frac{r}{n}\right)$	$P\left(1 + \frac{r}{n}\right)^2$
3	$P\left(1 + \frac{r}{n}\right)^2$	$P\left(1 + \frac{r}{n}\right)^2\left(\frac{r}{n}\right)$	$P\left(1 + \frac{r}{n}\right)^3$
$\vdots$	$\vdots$	$\vdots$	$\vdots$
m	$P\left(1 + \frac{r}{n}\right)^{m-1}$	$P\left(1 + \frac{r}{n}\right)^{m-1}\left(\frac{r}{n}\right)$	$\boldsymbol{P\left(1 + \frac{r}{n}\right)^m}$

The quantity

$$\left(1 + \frac{r}{n}\right)^m$$

can be evaluated using a key such as $\boxed{y^x}$ on a scientific calculator or $\boxed{\wedge}$ on a graphing calculator.

The lower right entry of **Table 2** provides the following formulas.

FUTURE VALUE FOR COMPOUND INTEREST

If P dollars are deposited at an annual interest rate of r, compounded n times per year, and the money is left on deposit for a total of m periods (or $t = \frac{m}{n}$ years), then the **future value, A** (the final amount on deposit), is calculated as follows.

$$A = P\left(1 + \frac{r}{n}\right)^m \qquad \text{or} \qquad A = P\left(1 + \frac{r}{n}\right)^{nt}$$

TVM Calculator

Present Value	3,419	PV
Payment	0	PMT
Future Value	-3,787.38	FV
Annual Rate%	4.1	Rate
Periods	30	Period
Compounding	Monthly	▼

Mode ⦿ End ○ Beginning

Decimal Digit ⦿ two ○ three ○ four

Reset	Instruction	Email
Example	History	Save

The highlighted field in the screenshot above shows the future value calculated in **Example 5(a)**. The negative value in the Present Value field indicates a negative cash flow for the investor at the time of deposit.

Several **financial calculator apps** are available for smartphones. This one is the (free) TVM Calculator from www.fncalculator.com.

EXAMPLE 5 Finding Future Value for Compound Interest

Find the future value (final amount on deposit) and the amount of interest earned for the following deposits.

(a) $3419 at 4.1% compounded monthly for 30 months

(b) $12,450 at 3% compounded quarterly for 5 years

Solution

(a) Here $P = \$3419$, $r = 4.1\% = 0.041$, $n = 12$, and $m = 30$.

$$A = P\left(1 + \frac{r}{n}\right)^m$$

$$A = \$3419\left(1 + \frac{0.041}{12}\right)^{30} = \$3787.38$$

$$\underset{\text{Future value}}{\downarrow} \qquad \underset{\text{Present value}}{\downarrow}$$

$$\text{Interest earned} = \$3787.38 \ - \ \$3419$$

$$= \$368.38$$

(b) Here $P = \$12{,}450$, $r = 3\% = 0.03$, $n = 4$, and $t = 5$.

$$A = P\left(1 + \frac{r}{n}\right)^{nt}$$

$$A = \$12{,}450\left(1 + \frac{0.03}{4}\right)^{(4)(5)} = \$14{,}456.74$$

$$\underset{\text{Future value}}{\downarrow} \qquad \underset{\text{Present value}}{\downarrow}$$

$$\text{Interest earned} = \$14{,}456.74 \ - \ \$12{,}450$$

$$= \$2006.74 \qquad ■$$

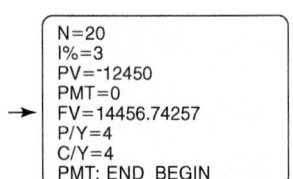

```
N=20
I%=3
PV=-12450
PMT=0
→ FV=14456.74257
P/Y=4
C/Y=4
PMT: END  BEGIN
```

The financial functions of the TI-83/84 Plus calculator allow the user to solve for a missing quantity related to the time value of money. The arrow indicates the display that supports the future value answer in **Example 5(b)**.

Compound interest problems sometimes require that we solve the formula for P to compute the present value when the future value is known.

$$A = P\left(1 + \frac{r}{n}\right)^m \qquad \text{Future value for compound interest}$$

$$P = \frac{A}{\left(1 + \frac{r}{n}\right)^m} \qquad \text{Solve the formula for } P.$$

The 1954 musical *The Pajama Game* was revived on Broadway twice, most recently in 2006 starring Harry Connick, Jr. The musical tells the story of the Sleeptite Pajama Factory workers attempting to secure a raise of $7\frac{1}{2}$ cents per hour.

The musical features a number called **"Seven and a Half Cents"** (after the novel that inspired the musical), with lyrics claiming that a small raise of $7\frac{1}{2}$ cents per hour will amount to $852.74 in 5 years, $1705.48 in 10 years, and $3411.96 in 20 years. Assuming that the figure for 5 years is correct, is the one for 10 years also correct? How about the one for 20 years? Oops! Judging by the first two figures, were the workers planning to invest their "extra" wages?

EXAMPLE 6 Finding Present Value for Compound Interest

Ashley will need $40,000 in 5 years to help pay for her college education. What lump sum, deposited today at 4% compounded quarterly, will produce the necessary amount?

Solution

This question requires that we find the present value P based on the following.

Future value:	$A = \$40{,}000$
Annual rate:	$r = 4\% = 0.04$
Periods per year:	$n = 4$
Total number of periods:	$m = (5)(4) = 20$

$$P = \frac{A}{\left(1 + \frac{r}{n}\right)^m} \qquad \text{Future value formula solved for } P$$

$$P = \frac{\$40{,}000}{\left(1 + \frac{0.04}{4}\right)^{20}} \qquad \text{Substitute known values.}$$

$$P = \$32{,}781.78 \qquad \text{Calculate.}$$

Assuming interest of 4% compounded quarterly can be maintained, $40,000 can be attained 5 years in the future by depositing $32,781.78 today.   ∎

The next example uses logarithms. See **Section 8.6** or your calculator manual.

EXAMPLE 7 Finding the Time Required to Double a Principal Deposit

In a savings account paying 3% interest, compounded daily, when will the amount in the account be twice the original principal?

Solution

The future value must equal two times the present value.

$$2P = P\left(1 + \frac{r}{n}\right)^{nt} \qquad \text{Substitute } 2P \text{ for } A \text{ in the future value formula.}$$

$$2 = \left(1 + \frac{r}{n}\right)^{nt} \qquad \text{Divide both sides by } P.$$

$$2 = \left(1 + \frac{0.03}{365}\right)^{365t} \qquad \text{Substitute values of } r \text{ and } n.$$

$$\log 2 = \log\left(1 + \frac{0.03}{365}\right)^{365t} \qquad \text{Take the logarithm of both sides.}$$

$$\log 2 = 365t \log\left(1 + \frac{0.03}{365}\right) \qquad \text{Use the power property of logarithms.}$$

$$t = \frac{\log 2}{365 \log\left(1 + \frac{0.03}{365}\right)} \qquad \text{Solve for } t.$$

$$t = 23.106 \qquad \text{Round to the nearest thousandth of a year.}$$

This equates to 23 years, 39 days (ignoring leap years).   ∎

The power of compound interest is being put to use in the town of Union City, Michigan. Eli Hooker, chairman of the local Bicentennial Committee in 1976, saw that there was not enough money to put on a proper celebration that year. So, in order to help his town prepare for the tricentennial, in 2076, he collected twenty-five dollars apiece from 42 patriotic residents and deposited the money in a local bank. Compounded at 7%, that money would grow to a million dollars by 2076.

Unfortunately, the million dollars won't be worth as much then as we might think. If the community decides to hire people to parade around in historical costumes, it might have paid them $3 per hour in 1976. The going wage in 2076, assuming 5% annual inflation for a hundred years, would be nearly $400 per hour.

Example 8 shows the importance of starting early to maximize the long-term advantage of compounding.

EXAMPLE 8 **Comparing Retirement Plans**

Compare the results at age 65 for the following two retirement plans. Both plans earn 8% annual interest throughout the account-building period.

Plan A: Angie begins saving at age 20, deposits $2000 on every birthday from age 21 to age 30 (10 deposits, or $20,000 total), and thereafter makes no additional contributions.

Plan B: Barry waits until age 30 to start saving and then makes deposits of $2000 on every birthday from age 31 to age 65 (35 deposits, or $70,000 total).

Solution

Table 3 shows how both accounts build over the years. $20,000, deposited earlier, produces $83,744 more than $70,000, deposited later.

Table 3 Retirement Plans Compared

Age	Plan A	Plan B
20	0	0
25	11,733	0
30	28,973	0
35	42,571	11,733
40	62,551	28,973
45	91,908	54,304
50	135,042	91,524
55	198,422	146,212
60	291,547	226,566
65	428,378	344,634

In **Example 8,** the *early* deposits of Plan A outperformed the *greater number* of deposits of Plan B because the interest rate was high enough to result in a Plan A balance at age 30 that Plan B could never overtake, despite additional Plan B deposits from then on. However, if the interest rate had been 6% rather than 8%, Plan B would have overtaken Plan A (at age 57) and at age 65 would have come out ahead by $20,253 (to the nearest dollar).

Effective Annual Yield

Banks, credit unions, and other financial institutions often advertise two rates: first, the actual annualized interest rate, or **nominal rate** (the "named" or "stated" rate), and second, the rate that would produce the same final amount, or future value, at the end of 1 year if the interest being paid were simple rather than compound. This is called the "effective rate," or, more commonly the **effective annual yield.** (It may be denoted **APY** for **"annual percentage yield."**) Because the interest is normally compounded multiple times per year, the effective annual yield will usually be somewhat higher than the nominal rate.

EXAMPLE 9 Finding Effective Annual Yield

What is the effective annual yield of an account paying a nominal rate of 2.50%, compounded quarterly?

Solution

From the given data, $r = 0.025$ and $n = 4$. Suppose we deposited $P = \$1$ and left it for 1 year ($m = 4$). Then the compound future value formula gives

$$A = 1 \cdot \left(1 + \frac{0.025}{4}\right)^4 \approx 1.0252.$$

The initial deposit of $1, after 1 year, has grown to $1.0252.

$$\text{Interest earned} = 1.0252 - 1 \qquad \text{Interest = future value − present value}$$

$$= 0.0252, \quad \text{or} \quad 2.52\%$$

A nominal rate of 2.50% results in an effective annual yield of 2.52%. ∎

Generalizing the procedure of **Example 9** gives the following formula.

> **EFFECTIVE ANNUAL YIELD**
>
> A nominal interest rate of r, compounded n times per year, is equivalent to the following **effective annual yield.**
>
> $$Y = \left(1 + \frac{r}{n}\right)^n - 1$$

When shopping for loans or savings opportunities, a borrower should seek the least yield available, while a depositor should look for the greatest.

EXAMPLE 10 Comparing Savings Rates

Yolanda wants to deposit $2800 into a savings account and has narrowed her choices to the three institutions represented here. Which is the best choice?

Institution	Rate on Deposits of $1000 to $5000
Friendly Credit Union	2.08% annual rate, compounded monthly
Premier Savings	2.09% annual yield
Neighborhood Bank	2.05% compounded daily

Solution

Compare the effective annual yields for the three institutions.

Friendly: $\quad Y = \left(1 + \dfrac{0.0208}{12}\right)^{12} - 1 = 0.0210 = 2.10\%$

Premier: $\quad Y = 2.09\%$

Neighborhood: $\quad Y = \left(1 + \dfrac{0.0205}{365}\right)^{365} - 1 = 0.0207 = 2.07\%$

The best of the three yields, 2.10%, is offered by Friendly Credit Union. ∎

►Eff(2.50,4)
2.523535309

Financial calculators are programmed to compute effective interest rate. Compare to the result in **Example 9.**

Table 4

Consumer Price Index
(CPI-U)*

Year	Average CPI-U	Percent Change in CPI-U
1980	82.4	13.5
1981	90.9	10.3
1982	96.5	6.2
1983	99.6	3.2
1984	103.9	4.3
1985	107.6	3.6
1986	109.6	1.9
1987	113.6	3.6
1988	118.3	4.1
1989	124.0	4.8
1990	130.7	5.4
1991	136.2	4.2
1992	140.3	3.0
1993	144.5	3.0
1994	148.2	2.6
1995	152.4	2.8
1996	156.9	3.0
1997	160.5	2.3
1998	163.0	1.6
1999	166.6	2.2
2000	172.2	3.4
2001	177.1	2.8
2002	179.9	1.6
2003	184.0	2.3
2004	188.9	2.7
2005	195.3	3.4
2006	201.6	3.2
2007	207.3	2.8
2008	215.3	3.8
2009	214.5	−0.4
2010	218.1	1.6
2011	224.9	3.2
2012	229.6	2.1
2013	233.0	1.5

Source: Bureau of Labor Statistics.
*The period 1982 to 1984: 100

Inflation

Interest reflects how money *gains value over time* when it is borrowed or lent. On the other hand, in terms of the equivalent number of goods or services that a given amount of money will buy, money normally *loses value over time.* This results in a periodic increase in the cost of living, which is called **price inflation.**

In the United States, the Bureau of Labor Statistics publishes **consumer price index (CPI)** figures, which reflect the prices of certain items purchased by large numbers of people. The items include such things as food, housing, automobiles, fuel, and clothing. Items such as yachts and expensive jewelry are not included.

Current data are published regularly at www.bls.gov/cpi. **Table 4** gives values of the primary index representing "all urban consumers" (the CPI-U). The value shown for a given year is actually the average (arithmetic mean) of the twelve monthly figures for that year. The table shows, for example, that the average CPI-U for 2007 (207.3) was 2.8% greater than the average value for 2006 (201.6).

Deflation is a *decrease* in price levels from one year to the next. A brief period of minor deflation, along with a general economic slowdown, usually is called a **recession.** (For example, in **Table 4,** note the 2009 rate of −0.4.)

Unlike account values under interest compounding, which make sudden jumps at just certain points in time (such as quarterly, monthly, or daily), price levels tend to fluctuate gradually over time. Thus, it is appropriate, for inflationary estimates, to use the formula for continuous compounding (introduced in **Section 8.6**).

FUTURE VALUE FOR CONTINUOUS COMPOUNDING

If an initial deposit of P dollars earns continuously compounded interest at an annual rate r for a period of t years, then the **future value, A,** is calculated as follows.

$$A = Pe^{rt}$$

EXAMPLE 11 Predicting Inflated Salary Levels

In 2012, the median salary for athletic trainers and exercise physiologists was $42,690 (*Source:* Bureau of Labor Statistics, U.S. Dept. of Labor). Approximately what salary would a person in this field need in 2032 to maintain purchasing power, assuming the inflation rate were to persist at each of the following levels?

(a) 3% (approximately the 2011 level)

(b) 13% (approximately the 1980 level)

Solution

(a) In this case we can use the continuous compounding future value formula with $P = \$42{,}690$, $r = 0.03$, and $t = 20$ (since 20 years pass between 2012 and 2032), along with the $\boxed{e^x}$ key on a calculator.

$$A = Pe^{rt} = \$42{,}690\, e^{(0.03)(20)} = \$77{,}786.25$$

The required salary in 2032 would be about $78,000.

(b) For this level of inflation, we have the following.

$$A = Pe^{rt} = \$42{,}690\, e^{(0.13)(20)} = \$574{,}766.98$$

The required salary in 2032 would be about $575,000. ∎

$$42690e^{0.03*20}$$
$$42690e^{0.13*20} \qquad 77786.25$$
$$574766.98$$

These are the computations required to solve the two parts of **Example 11** on the previous page.

To compare equivalent general price levels in any 2 years, we can use the proportion below. (A proportion is a statement that says that two ratios are equal. See **Section 7.3**.)

INFLATION PROPORTION

For a given consumer product or service subject to average inflation, prices in two different years are related as follows.

$$\frac{\text{Price in year A}}{\text{Price in year B}} = \frac{\text{CPI in year A}}{\text{CPI in year B}}$$

EXAMPLE 12 Comparing a Tuition Increase to Average Inflation

The average cost of tuition and fees at U.S. institutions of higher learning increased from $1626 for the 1982–83 academic year to $10,683 for the 2012–13 academic year (*Source:* National Center for Education Statistics, U.S. Dept. of Education). Compare these increases to average inflation over the same period.

Solution

Since an academic year spans the last half of one calendar year and the first half of the next, use the average of the CPI-U figures from **Table 4** over each two-year period.

1982–83 academic year: $\dfrac{96.5 + 99.6}{2} = 98.05$ Average of CPI-U figures for 1982 and 1983

2012–13 academic year: $\dfrac{229.6 + 233.0}{2} = 231.3$ Average of CPI-U figures for 2012 and 2013

Let x represent what we would expect tuition and fees to cost in 2012–13 if their cost had increased at the average rate since the 1982–83 academic year.

$$\frac{\text{Cost in 2012}-13}{\text{Cost in 1982}-83} = \frac{\text{CPI for 2012}-13}{\text{CPI for 1982}-83} \qquad \text{Inflation proportion}$$

$$\frac{x}{\$1626} = \frac{231.3}{98.05} \qquad \text{Substitute CPI values.}$$

$$x = \frac{231.3}{98.05} \cdot \$1626 \qquad \text{Solve for } x.$$

$$x \approx \$3836$$

Now compare the actual 2012–13 cost of $10,683 with the expected figure, $3836.

$$\frac{\$10,683}{\$3836} = 2.78 \qquad 2.78 = 1 + 1.78 = 100\% + 178\%$$

Over the period of interest, the cost of tuition and fees at institutions of higher learning in the United States increased at a rate approximately 178% greater than the average CPI-U rate. ∎

When working with quantities, such as inflation, where continual fluctuations and inexactness prevail, we often develop rough "rules of thumb" for obtaining quick estimates. One example is the estimation of the **years to double,** which is the number of years it takes for the general level of prices to double for a given annual rate of inflation.

Monetary inflation devalues the currency just as **price inflation** does, but it does so through a direct increase in the money supply within the economy. Examples in the United States include the issuance in 2009 and 2010 of massive government debt and massive government spending in "stimulus" programs, as well as the Federal Reserve's purchasing of government and mortgage bonds through "quantitative easing," which continues into 2014.

Debate has persisted among economists about whether actions of the government and central bank would accomplish their goals.

Would economic recovery continue, or would major deflation occur?

Most everyone agreed that the long-term result of monetary inflation would be more and more price inflation. Some deny that any real distinction exists; they maintain that because of complex interrelated economic forces, monetary inflation and price inflation are essentially the same thing.

We can derive an estimation rule as follows.

$A = Pe^{rt}$	Future value formula
$2P = Pe^{rt}$	Prices are to double.
$2 = e^{rt}$	Divide both sides by P.
$\ln 2 = rt$	Take the natural logarithm of both sides.
$t = \dfrac{\ln 2}{r}$	Solve for t.
$t = \dfrac{100 \ln 2}{100r}$	Multiply numerator and denominator by 100.

$$\text{years to double} \approx \frac{70}{\text{annual inflation rate}} \qquad \text{100 ln 2} \approx 70$$

(Because r is the inflation rate as a *decimal,* $100r$ is the inflation rate as a *percent.*) The result above usually is called the **rule of 70.** The value it produces, if not a whole number, should be rounded *up* to the next whole number of years.

(100*ln(2))/2.3
30.13683394
70/2.3
30.43478261

Because 100 ln 2 ≈ 70, the two results shown here are approximately equal. See **Example 13** and the preceding discussion.

EXAMPLE 13 **Estimating Years to Double by the Rule of 70**

Estimate the years to double for an annual inflation rate of 2.3%.

Solution

$$\text{Years to double} \approx \frac{70}{2.3} \approx 30.43 \qquad \text{Rule of 70}$$

With a sustained inflation rate of 2.3%, prices would double in about 31 years. ■

13.1 EXERCISES

In the following exercises, assume whenever appropriate that, unless otherwise known, there are 12 months per year, 30 days per month, and 365 days per year.

Find the simple interest owed for each loan.

1. $600 at 8% for 1 year

2. $5000 at 3% for 1 year

3. $920 at 7% for 9 months

4. $5400 at 5% for 4 months

5. $2675 at 5.4% for $2\frac{1}{2}$ years

6. $2620 at 4.82% for 32 months

Find the future value of each deposit if the account pays **(a)** *simple interest, and* **(b)** *interest compounded annually.*

7. $700 at 2% for 6 years

8. $4000 at 4% for 5 years

9. $2500 at 3% for 3 years

10. $3000 at 5% for 4 years

Solve each interest-related problem.

11. **Simple Interest on a Late Property Tax Payment** Andrew was late on his property tax payment to the county. He owed $7500 and paid the tax 4 months late. The county charges a penalty of 5% simple interest. Find the amount of the penalty.

12. **Simple Interest on a Loan for Equipment** Jonathan purchased new equipment for his yard maintenance business. He borrowed $2325 to pay for the equipment, and he agreed to pay off the loan in 9 months at 6% simple interest. Find the amount of interest he will owe.

13. **Simple Interest on a Small Business Loan** Tony opened a hot dog stand last April. He borrowed $6500 to pay for the stand and startup inventory, and he agreed to pay off the loan in 10 months at 7% simple interest. Find the *total amount* required to repay the loan.

14. **Simple Interest on a Tax Overpayment** Paul is owed $530 by the Internal Revenue Service for overpayment of last year's taxes. The IRS will repay the amount at 4% simple interest. Find the *total amount* Paul will receive if the interest is paid for 8 months.

Find the missing final amount (future value) and/or interest earned.

	Principal	Rate	Compounded	Time	Final Amount	Compound Interest
15.	$975	4%	quarterly	4 years	$1143.26	_____
16.	$1150	7%	semiannually	6 years	$1737.73	_____
17.	$480	6%	semiannually	9 years	_____	$337.17
18.	$2370	5%	quarterly	5 years	_____	_____
19.	$7500	$3\frac{1}{2}\%$	annually	25 years	_____	_____
20.	$3450	2.4%	semiannually	10 years	_____	_____

*For each deposit, find the future value (that is, the final amount on deposit) when compounding occurs **(a)** annually, **(b)** semiannually, and **(c)** quarterly.*

	Principal	Rate	Time
21.	$2000	4%	4 years
22.	$5000	2%	6 years
23.	$18,000	1%	3 years
24.	$10,000	3%	12 years

*Occasionally a savings account may actually pay interest compounded continuously. For each deposit, find the interest earned if interest is compounded **(a)** semiannually, **(b)** quarterly, **(c)** monthly, **(d)** daily, and **(e)** continuously.*

	Principal	Rate	Time
25.	$950	1.6%	4 years
26.	$2650	2.8%	33 months (In parts (d) and (e), assume 1003 days.)

27. Describe the effect of interest being compounded more and more often. In particular, how good is continuous compounding?

Solve each interest-related problem.

28. Finding the Amount Borrowed in a Simple Interest Loan Brandon takes out a 7% simple interest loan today that will be repaid 15 months from now with a payoff amount of $815.63. What amount is he borrowing?

29. Finding the Amount Borrowed in a Simple Interest Loan What is the maximum amount Carole can borrow today if it must be repaid in 4 months with simple interest at 8% and she knows that at that time she will be able to repay no more than $1500?

30. In the development of the future value formula for compound interest in the text, at least four specific problem-solving strategies were employed. Identify (name) as many of them as you can, and describe their use in this case.

Find the present value for each future amount.

31. $1000 (6% compounded annually for 5 years)

32. $14,000 (4% compounded quarterly for 2.5 years)

33. $9860 (8% compounded semiannually for 12 years)

34. $15,080 (5% compounded monthly for 6 years)

Finding the Present Value of a Compound Interest Retirement Account *Tanja wants to establish an account that will supplement her retirement income beginning 30 years from now. For each interest rate, find the lump sum she must deposit today so that $750,000 will be available at time of retirement.*

35. 5% compounded quarterly

36. 6% compounded quarterly

37. 5% compounded daily

38. 6% compounded daily

Finding the Effective Annual Yield in a Savings Account *Suppose a savings and loan pays a nominal rate of 2% on savings deposits. Find the effective annual yield if interest is compounded as stated in Exercises 39–45. (Give answers to the nearest thousandth of a percent.)*

39. annually

40. semiannually

41. quarterly

42. monthly

43. daily

44. 1000 times per year

45. 10,000 times per year

46. Judging from **Exercises 39–45,** what do you suppose is the effective annual yield if a nominal rate of 2% is compounded continuously? Explain your reasoning.

Comparing CD Rates and Yields *A certificate of deposit (CD) is similar to a savings account, but deposits are generally held to maturity. They usually offer higher rates than savings accounts because they "tie up" money for a period of time and often require a minimum deposit. The table shows the two best 5-year CD rates available on a certain online listing on April 18, 2014. Use this information in Exercises 47 and 48.*

5-Year CD	Rate	Yield
CiT Bank	2.274%	2.300%
GE Capital Retail Bank	2.225%	2.250%

47. If you deposit $100,000 with CiT Bank, how much will you have at the end of the 5 years?

48. How often does compounding occur in the GE Capital CD: daily, monthly, quarterly, or semiannually?

Solve each problem.

49. ***Finding Years to Double*** How long would it take to double your money in an account paying 4% compounded quarterly? (Answer in years plus days, ignoring leap years.)

50. ***Comparing Principal and Interest Amounts*** After what time period would the interest earned equal the original principal in an account paying 2% compounded daily? (Answer in years plus days, ignoring leap years.)

51. Solve the effective annual yield formula for r to obtain a general formula for nominal rate in terms of yield and the number of compounding periods per year.

52. ***Finding the Nominal Rate of a Savings Account*** Ridgeway Savings compounds interest monthly. The effective annual yield is 1.95%. What is the nominal rate?

53. ***Comparing Bank Savings Rates*** Bank A pays a nominal rate of 1.800% compounded daily on deposits. Bank B produces the same annual yield as Bank A but compounds interest only quarterly and pays no interest on funds deposited for less than an entire quarter.

(a) What nominal rate does Bank B pay (to the nearest thousandth of a percent)?

(b) Which bank should Nancy choose if she has $2000 to deposit for 10 months? How much more interest will she earn than in the other bank?

(c) Which bank should Dara choose for a deposit of $5000 for one year? How much interest will be earned?

Estimating the Years to Double by the Rule of 70 *Use the rule of 70 to estimate the years to double for each annual inflation rate.*

54. 1%   **55.** 2%

56. 8%   **57.** 9%

Estimating the Inflation Rate by the Rule of 70 *Use the rule of 70 to estimate the annual inflation rate (to the nearest tenth of a percent) that would cause the general level of prices to double in each time period.*

58. 5 years   **59.** 7 years

60. 16 years   **61.** 22 years

62. Derive a rule for estimating the "years to triple"—that is, the number of years it would take for the general levels of prices to triple for a given annual inflation rate.

Estimating Future Prices for Constant Annual Inflation *The year 2014 prices of several items are given below. Find the estimated future prices required to fill the blanks in the chart. (Give a number of significant figures consistent with the 2014 price figures provided.)*

	Item	2014 Price	2020 Price 2% Inflation	2030 Price 2% Inflation	2020 Price 10% Inflation	2030 Price 10% Inflation
63.	Fast-food meal	$6.39	___	___	___	___
64.	House	$262,000	___	___	___	___
65.	New car	$30,500	___	___	___	___
66.	Gallon of gasoline	$3.53	___	___	___	___

Estimating Future Prices for Variable Annual Inflation Assume that prices for the items below
increased at the average annual inflation rates shown in **Table 4.** Use the inflation proportion
to find the missing prices in the last column of the chart. Round to the nearest dollar.

	Item	Price	Year Purchased	Price in 2013
67.	Evening dress	$175	2000	_____
68.	Desk	$450	2002	_____
69.	Lawn tractor	$1099	1996	_____
70.	Designer puppy	$250	1998	_____

Solve each interest-related problem.

71. *Finding the Present Value of a Future Equipment Purchase*
Human gene sequencing is a major research area
of biotechnology. PE Biosystems leased 300 of its
sequencing machines to a sibling company, Celera. If
Celera was able to earn 7% compounded quarterly on
invested money, what lump sum did it need to invest in
order to purchase those machines 18 months later at a
price of $300,000 each? (*Source: Forbes,* February 21,
2000, p. 102.)

72. The CPI-U for medical care expenses was 260.8 in
2000 and 433.4 in March 2014. The overall CPI-U was
172.2 in 2000 and 236.3 in March 2014.

(a) What would we expect medical care expenses to
be in March 2014 if they had increased at the average rate of inflation since 2000?

(b) Compare actual increases in medical care expenses
to average inflation over this time period.

13.2 CONSUMER CREDIT

OBJECTIVES

1 Identify the different
types of consumer
credit.

2 Determine the interest,
payments, and cost for
installment loans.

3 Determine account
balances and finance
charges for revolving
loans.

Types of Consumer Credit

Consumer credit is the loan extended to people who borrow money to finance
the purchase of cars, furniture, appliances, jewelry, electronics, and other things.
Technically, **real estate mortgages,** loans to finance home purchases, are consumer
credit, but they usually involve much larger amounts and longer repayment periods.

In this section we discuss two common types of consumer credit. The first type,
installment loans, or **closed-end** credit, involves borrowing a set amount up front
and paying a series of equal installments (payments) until the loan is paid off. Furniture, appliances, and cars commonly are financed through closed-end credit.

With the second type of consumer credit, **revolving loans,** or **open-end** credit,
there is no fixed number of installments—the consumer continues paying until no
balance is owed. With revolving loans, additional credit often is extended before
the initial amount is paid off. Examples of open-end credit include most department store charge accounts and bank charge cards such as MasterCard and VISA.

Installment Loans

Installment loans, set up under closed-end credit, often are based on **add-on
interest.** This means that interest is calculated by the simple interest formula
$I = Prt$, and we simply "add on" this amount of interest to the principal borrowed
to arrive at the total debt (or amount to be repaid).

$$\text{Amount to be repaid} = \overset{\overset{\text{Amount}}{\text{borrowed}}}{P} + \overset{\overset{\text{Interest}}{\text{due}}}{Prt}$$

$$= P(1 + rt)$$

The total debt is then paid in equal periodic installments (usually monthly) to be
made over the t years.

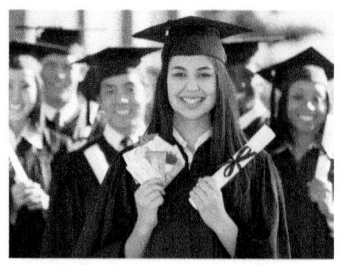

Outstanding debt among students
has become a growing concern in recent years. Though credit card balances among students have decreased since new policies were enacted in 2010, debt from student loans has continued to rise, roughly doubling from about $550 billion in 2007 to over $1 trillion in 2014.

By the end of 2012, the average balance of the nearly 40 million student loans in the United States was just under $25,000. And of the federally guaranteed loans in their payoff period, about 21% were delinquent.

A survey of graduating college seniors in 2013 showed an average of $35,200 in college-related debt. (*Sources:* www.federalreserve.gov *and* www.money.cnn.com)

EXAMPLE 1 Repaying an Installment Loan

Laura buys $5400 worth of furniture and appliances for her first apartment. She pays $1100 down and agrees to pay the balance at a 7% add-on rate for 2 years. Find

(a) the total amount to be repaid, **(b)** the monthly payment, and

(c) the total cost of the purchases, including finance charges.

Solution

(a) Amount to be financed = $5400 − $1100   *(Purchase amount − Down payment)*

$$= \$4300$$

Amount to be repaid $= P(1 + rt)$ *Future value formula*

$$= \$4300(1 + 0.07 \cdot 2)$$ *Substitute known values.*

$$= \$4902$$ *Calculate.*

(b) Monthly payment $= \dfrac{\$4902}{24}$ ← Amount to be repaid
   ← Number of payments

$$= \$204.25$$

(c) Total cost of purchases = $1100 + $4902   *(Down payment + Loan repayment)*

$$= \$6002$$

Laura will end up paying $6002, which is 11.1% more than the price tag total. ∎

Notice that the repayment amount in **Example 1,** $P(1 + rt)$, was the same as the final amount A in a savings account paying a simple interest rate r for t years. (See **Section 13.1.**) But in the case of savings, the bank keeps all of your money for the entire time period. In **Example 1,** Laura did not keep the full principal amount for the full time period. She repaid it in 24 monthly installments. The 7% add-on rate turns out to be equivalent to a much higher "true annual interest" rate.

Revolving Loans

With a typical department store account, or bank card, a **credit limit** is established initially and the consumer can make many purchases during a month (up to the credit limit). The required monthly payment can vary from a set minimum (which may depend on the account balance) up to the full balance.

For purchases made in a store, the customer may authorize the charge by signing on a paper "charge slip," or on an electronic signature pad. Authorization also can be given by telephone or Internet for mail orders and other expenditures.

At the end of each billing period (normally once a month), the customer receives an **itemized billing,** a statement listing purchases and cash advances, the total balance owed, the minimum payment required, and perhaps other account information. Any charges beyond cash advanced and cash prices of items purchased are called **finance charges.** Finance charges may include interest, an annual fee, credit insurance coverage, a time payment differential, or carrying charges.

Most revolving credit plans calculate finance charges by the **average daily balance method.** The average daily balance is the *weighted mean* (see **Section 12.2**) of the various amounts of credit utilized for different parts of the billing period, with the weighting factors being the number of days that each credit amount applied.

SEPTEMBER
30

Learning the following rhyme will help you in problems like the one found in **Example 2.**

Thirty days hath September,

April, June, and November.

All the rest have thirty-one,

Save February which has twenty-eight days clear,

And twenty-nine in each leap year.

What's *not* in your wallet? Some consumers carry high balances on their credit card(s) and fall into the habit of paying only the **minimum payment** each month. But they should read their statement carefully. The **Credit Card Act of 2009** requires that credit card issuers disclose "minimum payment" information.

For example, a VISA card charging 12.9% APR with a balance of $2994.82 has an initial minimum payment of just $60. This may sound good, but making only the minimum payment each month would result in total charges of $5689.00 over a 16-year period. Ouch!

Other features of revolving credit accounts can be at least as important as the stated interest rate. For example:

1. Is an annual fee charged? If so, how much is it?

2. Is a special "introductory" rate offered? If so, how long will it last?

3. Are there other incentives, such as rebates, credits toward certain purchases, "free" airline miles, or return of interest charges for long-time use?

EXAMPLE 2   **Using the Average Daily Balance Method**

The activity in Carmen's MasterCard account for one billing period is shown below. If the previous balance (on March 3) was $209.46, and the bank charges 1.3% per month on the average daily balance, find

(a) the average daily balance for the next billing (April 3),

(b) the finance charge to appear on the April 3 billing, and

(c) the account balance on April 3.

March 3	Billing date	
March 12	Payment	$50.00
March 17	Clothes	$28.46
March 20	Mail order	$31.22
April 1	Auto parts	$59.10

Solution

(a) First make a table that shows the beginning date of the billing period and the dates of all transactions in the billing period. Along with each of these, compute the running balance on that date.

Date	Running Balance
March 3	$209.46
March 12	$209.46 − $50 = $159.46
March 17	$159.46 + $28.46 = $187.92
March 20	$187.92 + $31.22 = $219.14
April 1	$219.14 + $59.10 = $278.24

Next, tabulate the running balance figures, along with the number of days until the balance changed. Multiply each balance amount by the number of days. The sum of these products gives the "sum of the daily balances."

Date	Running Balance	Number of Days Until Balance Changed	$\left(\begin{matrix}\text{Running}\\\text{Balance}\end{matrix}\right) \cdot \left(\begin{matrix}\text{Number}\\\text{of Days}\end{matrix}\right)$
March 3	$209.46	9	$1885.14
March 12	$159.46	5	$797.30
March 17	$187.92	3	$563.76
March 20	$219.14	12	$2629.68
April 1	$278.24	2	$556.48
		Totals: 31	$6432.36

$$\text{Average daily balance} = \frac{\text{Sum of daily balances}}{\text{Days in billing period}} = \frac{\$6432.36}{31} = \$207.50$$

Carmen will pay a finance charge based on the average daily balance of $207.50.

(b) The finance charge for the April 3 billing will be

$$1.3\% \text{ of } \$207.50 = 0.013 \cdot \$207.50 \quad {\scriptstyle 1.3\% \ = \ 1.3 \ \times \ 0.01 \ = \ 0.013}$$

$$= \$2.70.$$

(c) The account balance on the April 3 billing will be the latest running balance plus the finance charge.

$$\$278.24 + \$2.70 = \$280.94$$ ■

Credit cards and other revolving loans are relatively expensive credit. The monthly rate of 1.3% in **Example 2** is typical and is equivalent to an annual rate of 15.6%. A single card (like VISA or MasterCard), however, can be a great convenience.

The best practice is *not* to carry a balance from month to month, but to pay the entire new balance by the due date each month. Because purchases made during the month are not billed until the next billing date, and the payment due date may be 20 days or more after the billing date, items can often be charged without actually paying for them for nearly two months. To obtain this "free credit," resist the temptation to buy more than you can pay for by the next payment date.

13.2 EXERCISES

Round all monetary answers to the nearest cent unless directed otherwise. Assume that, unless otherwise known, there are 12 months per year, 30 days per month, and 365 days per year.

Financing an Appliance Purchase *Neema bought appliances costing $3795 at a store charging 6% add-on interest. She made a $1000 down payment and agreed to monthly payments over two years.*

1. Find the total amount to be financed.

2. Find the total interest to be paid.

3. Find the total amount to be repaid.

4. Find the monthly payment.

5. Find the total cost, for appliances plus interest.

Financing a New Car Purchase *Suppose you want to buy a new car that costs $18,500. You have no cash—only your old car, which is worth $2000 as a trade-in.*

6. How much do you need to finance to buy the new car?

7. The dealer says the interest rate is 4% add-on for 4 years. Find the total interest.

8. Find the total amount to be repaid.

9. Find the monthly payment.

10. Find your total cost, for the new car plus interest.

In Exercises 11–16, use the add-on method of calculating interest to find the total interest and the monthly payment.

	Amount of Loan	Length of Loan	Interest Rate
11.	$4500	3 years	4.5%
12.	$2700	2 years	4%
13.	$750	18 months	3.7%
14.	$2450	30 months	4.6%
15.	$535	16 months	5.1%
16.	$798	29 months	2.9%

Work each problem.

17. **Finding the Monthly Payment for an Add-On Interest Furniture Loan** The Giordanos buy $8500 worth of furniture for their new home. They pay $3000 down. The store charges 10% add-on interest. The Giordanos will pay off the furniture in 30 monthly payments ($2\frac{1}{2}$ years). Find the monthly payment.

18. **Finding the Monthly Payment for an Add-On Interest Auto Loan** Find the monthly payment required to pay off an auto loan of $15,780 over 3 years if the add-on interest rate is 3.9%.

19. **Finding the Monthly Payment for an Add-On Interest Home Electronics Loan** The total purchase price of a new home entertainment system is $14,240. If the down payment is $2900 and the balance is to be financed over 48 months at 6% add-on interest, what is the monthly payment?

20. **Finding the Monthly Payment for an Add-On Interest Loan** What are the monthly payments that Holly pays on a loan of $1680 for a period of 10 months if 9% add-on interest is charged?

21. **Finding the Amount Borrowed for an Add-On Interest Car Loan** Kyle has misplaced the sales contract for his car and cannot remember the amount he originally financed. He does know that the add-on interest rate was 4.9% and the loan required a total of 48 monthly payments of $314.65 each. How much did Kyle borrow (to the nearest dollar)?

22. **Finding an Add-On Interest Rate** Ella is making monthly payments of $257.49 to pay off a $3\frac{1}{2}$-year loan of $9400. What is her add-on interest rate (to the nearest tenth of a percent)?

23. **Finding the Term of an Add-On Interest Loan** How long (in years) will it take Hiroshi to pay off an $11,000 loan with monthly payments of $240.17 if the add-on interest rate is 6.2%?

24. **Finding the Number of Payments for an Add-On Interest Loan** How many monthly payments must Jawann make on a $10,000 loan if he pays $417.92 per month and the add-on interest rate is 10.15%?

Finding Finance Charges   Find the finance charge for each charge account. Assume interest is calculated on the average daily balance of the account.

	Average Daily Balance	Monthly Interest Rate
25.	$249.94	1.4%
26.	$350.75	1.5%
27.	$419.95	1.38%
28.	$450.21	1.26%
29.	$1073.40	1.425%
30.	$1320.42	1.375%

Finding Finance Charges and Account Balances Using the Average Daily Balance Method   *For each credit card account, assume one month between billing dates (with the appropriate number of days) and interest of 1.3% per month on the average daily balance. Find **(a)** the average daily balance, **(b)** the monthly finance charge, and **(c)** the account balance for the next billing.*

31. Previous balance: $728.36

May 9	Billing date	
May 17	Payment	$200.00
May 30	Dinner	$46.11
June 3	Theater tickets	$64.50

32. Previous balance: $514.79

January 27	Billing date	
February 9	Candy	$11.08
February 13	Returns	$26.54
February 20	Payment	$59.00
February 25	Repairs	$71.19

33. Previous balance: $462.42

June 11	Billing date	
June 15	Returns	$106.45
June 20	Jewelry	$115.73
June 24	Car rental	$74.19
July 3	Payment	$115.00
July 6	Flowers	$68.49

34. Previous balance: $983.25

August 17	Billing date	
August 21	Mail order	$14.92
August 23	Returns	$25.41
August 27	Beverages	$31.82
August 31	Payment	$108.00
September 9	Returns	$71.14
September 11	Concert tickets	$110.00
September 14	Cash advance	$100.00

Finding Finance Charges   In Exercises 35 and 36, assume no purchases or returns are made.

35. At the beginning of a 31-day billing period, Alicia has an unpaid balance of $720 on her credit card. Three days before the end of the billing period, she pays $600. Find her finance charge at 1.4% per month using the average daily balance method.

36. Vincent's VISA bill dated April 14 shows an unpaid balance of $1070. Five days before May 14, the end of the billing period, Vincent makes a payment of $900. Find his finance charge at 1.32% per month using the average daily balance method.

Analyzing a "90 Days Same as Cash" Offer   *One version of the "90 Days Same as Cash" promotion was offered by a "major purchase card," which established an account charging 1.3167% interest per month on the account balance. Interest charges are added to the balance each month, becoming part of the balance on which interest is computed the next month. If you pay off the original purchase charge within 3 months, all interest charges are cancelled. Otherwise, you are liable for all the interest. Suppose you purchase $2900 worth of carpeting under this plan.*

37. Find the interest charge added to the account balance at the end of

  (a) the first month,

  (b) the second month,

  (c) the third month.

38. Suppose you pay off the account 1 day late (3 months plus 1 day). What total interest amount must you pay? (Do not include interest for the one extra day.)

39. Treating the 3 months as $\frac{1}{4}$ year, find the equivalent simple interest rate for this purchase (to the nearest tenth of a percent).

Various Charges of a Bank Card Account   *Aimee's bank card account charges 1.1% per month on the average daily balance, as well as the following special fees:*

Cash advance fee:	2% *(neither less than $2 nor more than $10)*
Late payment fee:	$15
Over-the-credit-limit fee:	$5

In the month of June, Aimee's average daily balance was $1846. She was on vacation during the month and did not get her account payment in on time, which resulted in a late payment and, as a consequence, charges accumulated to a sum above her credit limit. She also used her card for six $100 cash advances while on vacation. Find the following based on account transactions in that month.

40. interest charges to the account

41. special fees charged to the account

Write out your response to each of the following.

42. Is it possible to use a bank credit card for your purchases without paying anything for credit? If so, explain how.

43. Obtain applications or descriptive brochures for several different bank card programs, compare their features (including those in fine print), and explain which deal would be best for you, and why.

44. Research and explain the difference, if any, between a "credit" card and a "debit" card.

45. Many charge card offers include the option of purchasing credit insurance coverage, whereby the insurer would make your monthly payments if you became disabled and could not work and/or would pay off the account balance if you died. Find out the details on at least one such offer, and discuss why you would or would not accept it.

46. Make a list of "special incentives" offered by bank cards you are familiar with, and briefly describe the pros and cons of each one.

47. One bank offered a card with a "low introductory rate" of 5.9%, good through the end of the year. And furthermore, you could receive back a percentage (up to 100%!) of all interest you pay, as shown in the table at the top of the next column.

Use your card for:	2 years	5 years	10 years	15 years	20 years
Get back:	10%	25%	50%	75%	100%

(As soon as you take a refund, the time clock starts over.) Because you can eventually claim all your interest payments back, is this card a good deal? Explain.

48. Recall a car-buying experience you have had, or visit a new-car dealer and interview a salesperson. Describe the procedure involved in purchasing a car on credit.

Comparing Bank Card Accounts *Ruby is considering two bank card offers that are the same in all respects except for the following:*

> *Bank A charges no annual fee and charges monthly interest of 1.18% on the unpaid balance.*

> *Bank B charges a $30 annual fee and monthly interest of 1.01% on the unpaid balance.*

From her records, Ruby has found that the unpaid balance she tends to carry from month to month is quite consistent and averages $900.

49. Estimate her total yearly cost to use the card if she chooses the card from

(a) Bank A.   **(b)** Bank B.

50. Which card is her better choice?

13.3   TRUTH IN LENDING

OBJECTIVES

1 Determine the annual percentage rate for different types of loans.

2 Calculate unearned interest.

Annual Percentage Rate (APR)

The Consumer Credit Protection Act, passed in 1968, has commonly been known as the **Truth in Lending Act.** The law addressed two major issues:

1. How can we tell the true annual interest rate a lender is charging?

2. How much of the finance charge are we entitled to save if we decide to pay off a loan sooner than originally scheduled?

Question 1 above arose because lenders were computing and describing the interest they charged in several different ways. For example, how does 1.9% per month at Sears compare to 9% per year add-on interest at a furniture store? Truth in Lending standardized the so-called true annual interest rate, or **annual percentage rate,** commonly denoted **APR.** All sellers (car dealers, stores, banks, insurance agents, credit card companies, and the like) must disclose the APR when asked, and the written contract must state the APR in all cases. This enables a borrower to more easily compare the true costs of different loans.

Theoretically, a borrower should not need to calculate APR, but it is possible to verify the value stated by the lender. Since the formulas for finding APR are quite involved, it is easiest to use a table provided by the Federal Reserve Bank. We show an abbreviated version in **Table 5** on the next page. It identifies APR values to the nearest half percent from 6.0% to 14.0%, for loans requiring *monthly* payments and extending over the most common lengths for consumer loans from 6 to 60 months.

Table 5 relates the following three quantities.

APR = true annual interest rate (shown across the top)

  n = total number of scheduled monthly payments (shown down the left side)

  h = finance charge per \$100 of amount financed (shown in the body of the table)

Table 5 Annual Percentage Rate (APR) for Monthly Payment Loans

Number of Monthly Payments (n)	Annual Percentage Rate (APR) Finance Charge per \$100 of Amount Financed (h)																
	6.0%	6.5%	7.0%	7.5%	8.0%	8.5%	9.0%	9.5%	10.0%	10.5%	11.0%	11.5%	12.0%	12.5%	13.0%	13.5%	14.0%
6	\$1.76	\$1.90	\$2.05	\$2.20	\$2.35	\$2.49	\$2.64	\$2.79	\$2.94	\$3.08	\$3.23	\$3.38	\$3.53	\$3.68	\$3.83	\$3.97	\$4.12
12	3.28	3.56	3.83	4.11	4.39	4.66	4.94	5.22	5.50	5.78	6.06	6.34	6.62	6.90	7.18	7.46	7.74
18	4.82	5.22	5.63	6.04	6.45	6.86	7.28	7.69	8.10	8.52	8.93	9.35	9.77	10.19	10.61	11.03	11.45
24	6.37	6.91	7.45	8.00	8.55	9.09	9.64	10.19	10.75	11.30	11.86	12.42	12.98	13.54	14.10	14.66	15.23
30	7.94	8.61	9.30	9.98	10.66	11.35	12.04	12.74	13.43	14.13	14.83	15.54	16.24	16.95	17.66	18.38	19.10
36	9.52	10.34	11.16	11.98	12.81	13.64	14.48	15.32	16.16	17.01	17.86	18.71	19.57	20.43	21.30	22.17	23.04
48	12.73	13.83	14.94	16.06	17.18	18.31	19.45	20.59	21.74	22.90	24.06	25.23	26.40	27.58	28.77	29.97	31.17
60	16.00	17.40	18.81	20.23	21.66	23.10	24.55	26.01	27.48	28.96	30.45	31.96	33.47	34.99	36.52	38.06	39.61

EXAMPLE 1 Finding the APR for an Add-On Loan

Recall that Laura (in **Example 1** of **Section 13.2**) paid \$1100 down on a \$5400 purchase and agreed to pay the balance at a 7% add-on rate for 2 years. Find the APR for her loan.

Solution

As shown previously, the total amount financed was

Purchase — Down
price   payment

$$\$5400 - \$1100 = \$4300.$$

The finance charge (interest) was

$$I = Prt = \$4300 \cdot 0.07 \cdot 2 = \$602.$$

Next find the finance charge per \$100 of the amount financed. To do this, divide the finance charge by the amount financed, and then multiply by \$100.

$$\left(\begin{array}{c}\text{Finance charge per} \\ \text{\$100 financed}\end{array}\right) = \frac{\text{Finance charge}}{\text{Amount financed}} \cdot \$100$$

$$= \frac{\$602}{\$4300} \cdot \$100, \quad \text{or} \quad \$14$$

This amount, \$14, represents h, the finance charge per \$100 of the amount financed. Because the loan was to be paid over 24 months, look down to the "24 monthly payments" row of **Table 5** ($n = 24$). Then look across the table for the h-value closest to \$14.00, which is \$14.10. From that point, read up the column to find the APR, 13.0% (to the nearest half percent). In this case, a 7% add-on rate is equivalent to an APR of 13.0%. ∎

TVM Calculator

Present Value	4,300	PV
Payment	-204.25	PMT
Future Value	0	FV
Annual Rate%	12.91	Rate
Periods	24	Period
Compounding	Monthly ▼	

Mode ◉ End ○ Beginning

Decimal Digit ◉ two ○ three ○ four

Reset Instruction Email

Example History Save

Financial calculator apps give another option (besides tables) for calculating APR. For **Example 1,** dividing the total amount to be repaid by the number of payments gives the monthly payment.

$$\frac{\$4300 + \$602}{24} = \$204.25$$

This amount can then be entered (as negative cash flow) into the financial calculator, and the rate calculated. We see here that the APR for Laura's loan is 12.91%.(App used: TVM Calculator)

EXAMPLE 2 Finding the APR for a Car Loan

After a down payment on her new car, Vanessa still owed $12,378. She agreed to repay the balance in 48 monthly payments of $294 each. What is the APR on her loan?

Solution

First find the finance charge.

```
N=48
▸I%=6.579891685
PV=12378
PMT=-294
FV=0
P/Y=12
C/Y=12
PMT: ▇▇ BEGIN
```

Unknown APR may be found using the TI-84's TVM Solver. Enter the number of payments (N), the present value of the loan (PV), the payment amount (PMT), the number of payments per year, and the number of compoundings per year. Then locate the cursor in the I% field and press $\boxed{\text{ALPHA}}$ $\boxed{\text{SOLVE}}$. The screen above confirms the approximate value found in **Example 2** using **Table 5.**

$$\text{Finance charge} = 48 \cdot \$294 - \$12{,}378$$

Total payments ↓   Amount financed ↓

$$= \$1734 \quad \boxed{\text{Multiply first. Then subtract.}}$$

Now find the finance charge per $100 financed as in **Example 1.**

$$\left(\begin{array}{c}\text{Finance charge per} \\ \$100 \text{ financed}\end{array}\right) = \frac{\text{Finance charge}}{\text{Amount financed}} \cdot \$100$$

$$= \frac{\$1734}{\$12{,}378} \cdot \$100, \quad \text{or} \quad \$14.01$$

Find the "48 payments" row of **Table 5,** read across to find the number closest to 14.01, which is 13.83. From there read up to find the APR, which is 6.5%. ■

Unearned Interest

Question 2 at the beginning of this section arises when a borrower decides to pay off an installment loan earlier than originally scheduled. In such a case, it turns out that the lender has not loaned as much money for as long as planned, and so he has not really "earned" the full finance charge originally disclosed.

   If a loan is paid off early, the amount by which the original finance charge is reduced is called the **unearned interest.** We will discuss two methods of calculating unearned interest, the **actuarial method** and the **rule of 78.** The Truth in Lending Act requires that the method for calculating this refund (or reduction) of finance charge (in case of an early payoff) be disclosed at the time the loan is initiated. Whichever method is used, the borrower may not, in fact, save all the unearned interest, since the lender is entitled to impose an **early payment penalty** to recover certain costs. A lender's intention to impose such a penalty in case of early payment also must be disclosed at initiation of the loan.

Rights and responsibilities apply to all credit accounts, and the consumer should read all disclosures provided by the lender. *The Fair Credit Billing Act* and *The Fair Credit Reporting Act* regulate, among other things, procedures for billing and for disputing bills, and for providing and disputing personal information on consumers.

   If you have ever applied for a charge account, a personal loan, insurance, or a job, then information about where you work and live, how you pay your bills, and whether you've been sued or arrested or have filed for bankruptcy, appears in the files of Consumer Reporting Agencies (CRAs), which sell that information to creditors, employers, insurers, and other businesses.

   For more detailed information on these and many other consumer issues, you may want to consult the Web site www.usa.gov/consumer.

UNEARNED INTEREST—ACTUARIAL METHOD

For an installment loan requiring *monthly* payments, which is paid off earlier than originally scheduled, let

R = regular monthly payment,

k = remaining number of scheduled payments (*after* current payment), and

h = finance charge per $100, corresponding to a loan with the same APR and k monthly payments.

Then the **unearned interest, u,** is calculated as follows.

$$u = kR\left(\frac{h}{\$100 + h}\right)$$

Once the unearned interest u is calculated (by any method), the amount required to pay off the loan early is easily found. It consists of the present regular payment due, plus k additional future payments, minus the unearned interest.

PAYOFF AMOUNT

An installment loan requiring regular monthly payments R can be paid off early, along with the current payment. If the original loan had k additional payments scheduled (after the current payment), and the unearned interest is u, then, disregarding any possible prepayment penalty, the **payoff amount** is calculated as follows.

$$\text{Payoff amount} = (k + 1)R - u$$

▓▓▓ EXAMPLE 3 Finding Early Payoff Amount (Actuarial Method)

Vanessa got an unexpected pay raise and wanted to pay off her car loan of **Example 2** at the end of 3 years rather than paying for 4 years as originally agreed.

(a) Find the unearned interest (the amount she will save by retiring the loan early).

(b) Find the "payoff amount" (the amount required to pay off the loan at the end of 3 years).

Solution

(a) From **Example 2,** recall that $R = \$294$ and APR $= 6.5\%$. The current payment is payment number 36, so $k = 48 - 36 = 12$. Use **Table 5,** with 12 payments and APR 6.5%, to obtain $h = \$3.56$. Then use the actuarial method formula.

$$u = 12 \cdot \$294\left(\frac{\$3.56}{\$100 + \$3.56}\right) = \$121.28$$

By this method, Vanessa will save \$121.28 in interest by retiring the loan early.

(b) The payoff amount is found by using the appropriate formula.

$$\text{Payoff amount} = (12 + 1)\$294 - \$121.28 = \$3700.72$$

The required payoff amount at the end of 3 years is \$3700.72.   ■

```
12*294(3.56/(100+3.56))
                 121.28
(12+1)*294−121.28
                3700.72
```

These are the computations required in the solution of **Example 3.**

The actuarial method, being based on the APR value, probably is the better method. However, some lenders historically used a second method, the **rule of 78.**

UNEARNED INTEREST—RULE OF 78

For a closed-end loan requiring *monthly* payments, which is paid off earlier than originally scheduled, let

   F = original finance charge,

   n = number of payments originally scheduled, and

   k = remaining number of scheduled payments (*after* current payment).

Then the **unearned interest, u,** is calculated as follows.

$$u = \frac{k(k + 1)}{n(n + 1)} \cdot F$$

EXAMPLE 4 Finding Early Payoff Amount (Rule of 78)

Again assume that the loan in **Example 2** is paid off at the time of the thirty-sixth monthly payment. This time, however, instead of the actuarial method, use the rule of 78 to find

(a) the unearned interest, and

(b) the payoff amount.

Solution

(a) From **Example 2,** the original finance charge is $F = \$1734$. Also, $n = 48$ and $k = 12$.

$$u = \frac{12(12+1)}{48(48+1)} \cdot \$1734 = \$115.01 \quad \text{Rule of 78}$$

By the rule of 78, Vanessa will save $115.01 in interest, which is $6.27 *less* than her savings by the actuarial method.

(b) Payoff amount $= (12+1)\$294 - \$115.01 = \$3706.99$

The payoff amount is $3706.99, which is $6.27 *more* than the payoff amount calculated by the actuarial method in **Example 3.** ∎

(12*(12+1))/(48(48+1))*1734
                    115.01
(12+1)*294−115.01
                   3706.99

These are the computations required in the solution of **Example 4.**

When the rule of 78 was first introduced into financial law (by the Indiana legislature in 1935), loans were ordinarily written for 1 year or less, interest rates were relatively low, and loan amounts were less than they tend to be today. For these reasons the rule of 78 was acceptably accurate then. Today, however, with very accurate tables and/or calculators readily available, the rule of 78 is used much less often than previously.

Suppose we want to compute unearned interest accurately (so we don't trust the rule of 78), but the APR value, or the number of scheduled payments, or the number of remaining payments (or at least one of the three) is not included in **Table 5.** Then what? Actually, in the actuarial method, we can evaluate h (the finance charge per $100 financed) using the same formula that was used to generate **Table 5.**

FINANCE CHARGE PER $100 FINANCED

If an installment loan requires n equal monthly payments and APR denotes the true annual interest rate for the loan (as a decimal), then h, the **finance charge per $100 financed,** is calculated as follows.

$$h = \frac{n \cdot \frac{\text{APR}}{12} \cdot \$100}{1 - \left(1 + \frac{\text{APR}}{12}\right)^{-n}} - \$100$$

EXAMPLE 5 Finding Unearned Interest and Early Payoff Amount

Mark borrowed $4000 to pay for music equipment for his band. His loan contract states an APR of 9.8% and stipulates 28 monthly payments of $160.39 each. Mark decides to pay the loan in full at the time of his nineteenth scheduled payment. Find

(a) the unearned interest, and   **(b)** the payoff amount.

(9*(.098/12)*100)/(1−(1+
.098/12)⁻⁹)−100
$$4.13$$
9*160.39*4.13/(100+4.13)
$$57.25$$

These are the computations required in the solution of **Example 5(a)**.

Solution

(a) First find h from the finance charge formula just given.

> Remember to use the remaining number of payments, $28 - 19 = 9$, as the value of n.

$$h = \frac{9\left(\frac{0.098}{12}\right)(\$100)}{1 - \left(1 + \frac{0.098}{12}\right)^{-9}} - \$100 = \$4.13$$

Next use the actuarial formula for unearned interest u.

Regular monthly payment: $R = \$160.39$

Remaining number of payments: $k = 28 - 19 = 9$

Finance charge per \$100: $h = \$4.13$

$$u = 9 \cdot \$160.39 \cdot \frac{\$4.13}{\$100 + \$4.13} = \$57.25$$

The amount of interest Mark will save is \$57.25.

(b)   Payoff amount $= (9 + 1)(\$160.39) - \$57.25 = \$1546.65.$

To pay off the loan at the time of his nineteenth scheduled payment, Mark must pay \$1546.65.   ∎

13.3   **EXERCISES**

Round all monetary answers to the nearest cent unless otherwise directed.

Finding True Annual Interest Rate   *Find the APR (true annual interest rate), to the nearest half percent, for each loan.*

	Amount Financed	Finance Charge	Number of Monthly Payments
1.	$1000	$38	12
2.	$1700	$202	24
3.	$6600	$750	30
4.	$5900	$1150	48

Finding the Monthly Payment   *Find the monthly payment for each loan.*

	Purchase Price	Down Payment	Finance Charge	Number of Monthly Payments
5.	$3500	$500	$275	24
6.	$4750	$450	$750	36
7.	$3850	$300	$800	48
8.	$9500	$1500	$1400	60

Finding True Annual Interest Rate   *Find the APR (true annual interest rate), to the nearest half percent, for each loan.*

	Purchase Price	Down Payment	Add-On Interest Rate	Number of Payments
9.	$4190	$390	3.5%	12
10.	$3250	$750	7%	36
11.	$7480	$2200	5%	18
12.	$12,800	$4500	3.5%	48

Unearned Interest by the Actuarial Method   *Each loan was paid in full before its due date.* **(a)** *Obtain the value of h from* **Table 5.** *Then* **(b)** *use the actuarial method to find the amount of unearned interest, and* **(c)** *find the payoff amount.*

	Regular Monthly Payment	APR	Remaining Number of Scheduled Payments after Payoff
13.	$346.70	11.0%	18
14.	$783.50	8.5%	12
15.	$595.80	6.5%	6
16.	$314.50	10.0%	24

Finding Finance Charge and True Annual Interest Rate For each loan, find **(a)** the finance charge, and **(b)** the APR.

17. Jesse financed a $1990 computer with 24 monthly payments of $91.50 each.

18. Margey bought a horse trailer for $6090. She paid $1240 down and paid the remainder at $175.50 per month for $2\frac{1}{2}$ years.

19. Walter still owed $2000 on his new garden tractor after the down payment. He agreed to pay monthly payments for 18 months at 4.6% add-on interest.

20. Daniel paid off a $15,000 car loan over 3 years with monthly payments of $466.59 each.

Comparing the Actuarial Method and the Rule of 78 for Unearned Interest Each loan was paid off early. Find the unearned interest by **(a)** the actuarial method, and **(b)** the rule of 78.

	Amount Financed	Regular Monthly Payments	Total Number of Payments Scheduled	Remaining Number of Scheduled Payments after Payoff
21.	$3310	$201.85	18	6
22.	$10,230	$277.00	48	12
23.	$29,850	$641.58	60	12
24.	$16,730	$539.82	36	18

Unearned Interest by the Actuarial Method Each loan was paid in full before its due date. **(a)** Obtain the value of h from the appropriate formula. Then **(b)** use the actuarial method to find the amount of unearned interest, and **(c)** find the payoff amount.

	Regular Monthly Payment	APR	Remaining Number of Scheduled Payments after Payoff
25.	$212	8.6%	4
26.	$575	5.9%	8

Comparing Loan Choices Phan needs to borrow $5000 to pay for NBA season tickets for her family. She can borrow the amount from a finance company (at 6.5% add-on interest for 3 years) or from the credit union (36 monthly payments of $164.50 each). Use this information for Exercises 27–31.

27. Find the APR (to the nearest half percent) for each loan, and decide which one is Phan's better choice.

28. Phan takes the credit union loan. At the time of her thirtieth payment she pays it off. If the credit union uses the rule of 78 for computing unearned interest, how much will she save by paying in full now?

29. What would Phan save in interest if she paid in full at the time of the thirtieth payment and the credit union used the actuarial method for computing unearned interest?

30. Under the conditions of **Exercise 29,** what amount must Phan come up with to pay off her loan?

31. Suppose the credit union uses the rule of 78 and imposes an early payoff penalty of 1% of the original finance charge per month of early payment. For example, if Phan pays the loan off 9 months early, then the penalty will be 9% of the original finance charge. Find the least value of k that would result in any savings for Phan.

32. Describe why, in **Example 1,** the APR and the add-on rate differ. Which one is more legitimate? Why?

Approximating the APR of an Add-On Rate To convert an add-on interest rate to its corresponding APR, some people recommend using the formula

$$APR = \frac{2n}{n+1} \cdot r,$$

where r is add-on rate and n is total number of payments.

33. Apply the given formula to calculate the APR (to the nearest half percent) for the loan of **Example 1** $(r = 0.07, n = 24)$.

34. Compare your APR value in **Exercise 33** to the value in **Example 1.** What do you conclude?

The Rule of 78 with Prepayment Penalty A certain retailer's credit contract designates the rule of 78 for computing unearned interest and imposes a "prepayment penalty." In case of any payoff earlier than the due date, the lender will charge an additional 10% of the original finance charge. Find the least value of k (remaining payments after payoff) that would result in any net savings in each case.

35. 24 payments originally scheduled

36. 36 payments originally scheduled

37. 48 payments originally scheduled

38. 60 payments originally scheduled

Write out your response to each exercise.

39. Why might a lender be justified in imposing a prepayment penalty?

40. Discuss reasons why a borrower might want to pay off a loan early.

41. Find out what federal agency you can contact if you have questions about compliance with the Truth in Lending Act. (Any bank, or retailer's credit department, should be able to help you with this, or you could try a Web search.)

42. Study the table below, which pertains to a 12-month loan. The column-3 entries are designed so that they are in the same ratios as the column-2 entries but will add up to 1 because their denominators are all equal to

$$1 + 2 + 3 + 4 + 5 + \ldots + 12 = \frac{12 \cdot 13}{2} = 78.$$

(This is the origin of the term "rule of 78.")

Month	Fraction of Loan Principal Used by Borrower	Fraction of Finance Charge Owed
1	12/12	12/78
2	11/12	11/78
3	10/12	10/78
4	9/12	9/78
5	8/12	8/78
6	7/12	7/78
7	6/12	6/78
8	5/12	5/78
9	4/12	4/78
10	3/12	3/78
11	2/12	2/78
12	1/12	1/78
		78/78 = 1

Suppose the loan is paid in full after eight months. Use the table to determine the unearned fraction of the total finance charge.

43. Find the fraction of unearned interest of **Exercise 42** by using the rule of 78 formula.

Understanding the Actuarial Method *The actuarial method of computing unearned interest assumes that, throughout the life of the loan, the borrower is paying interest at the rate given by APR for money actually being used by the borrower. When contemplating complete payoff along with the current payment, think of k future payments as applying to a separate loan with the same APR and of h as being the finance charge per $100 of that loan. Refer to the following formula.*

$$u = kR\left(\frac{h}{\$100 + h}\right)$$

44. Describe in words the quantity represented by

$$\frac{h}{\$100 + h}.$$

45. Describe in words the quantity represented by kR.

46. Explain why the product of the two quantities above represents unearned interest.

13.4   THE COSTS AND ADVANTAGES OF HOME OWNERSHIP

OBJECTIVES

1 Understand the characteristics of fixed-rate mortgages.

2 Understand the characteristics of adjustable-rate mortgages.

3 Be familiar with the closing costs associated with mortgages.

4 Be familiar with the recurring costs of home ownership.

Fixed-Rate Mortgages

For many decades, home ownership has been considered a centerpiece of the "American dream." For most people, a home represents the largest purchase of their lifetime, and it is certainly worth careful consideration.

A loan for a substantial amount, extending over a lengthy time interval (typically up to 30 years), for the purpose of buying a home or other property or real estate, and for which the property is pledged as security for the loan, is called a **mortgage.** (In some areas, a mortgage may also be called a **deed of trust** or a **security deed.**)

- The time until final payoff is called the **term** of the mortgage.
- The portion of the purchase price of the home that the buyer pays initially is called the **down payment.**
- The **principal amount of the mortgage** (the amount borrowed) is found by subtracting the down payment from the purchase price.

With a **fixed-rate mortgage,** the interest rate will remain constant throughout the term, and the initial principal balance, together with interest due on the loan, is repaid to the lender through regular (constant) periodic (we assume monthly) payments. This is called **amortizing** the loan. The regular monthly payment needed to amortize a loan depends on the amount financed, the term of the loan, and the interest rate, according to the formula on the next page.

Heating a house is another cost that may get you involved with banks and interest rates after you finally get a roof over your head. The roof you see above does more than keep off the rain. It holds solar panels, part of the solar heating system in the building.

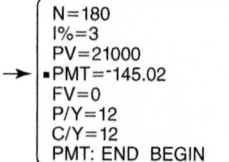

N=180
I%=3
PV=21000
→ ∎PMT=⁻145.02
FV=0
P/Y=12
C/Y=12
PMT: END BEGIN

The arrow indicates a payment of $145.02, supporting the result of **Example 1.**

REGULAR MONTHLY PAYMENT

The **regular monthly payment** required to repay a loan of P dollars, together with interest at an annual rate r, over a term of t years, is calculated as follows.

$$R = \frac{P\left(\frac{r}{12}\right)}{1 - \left(\frac{12}{12+r}\right)^{12t}}$$

EXAMPLE 1 Using a Formula to Find a Monthly Mortgage Payment

Find the monthly payment necessary to amortize a $21,000 mortgage at 3.0% annual interest for 15 years.

Solution

$$R = \frac{\$21,000\left(\frac{0.030}{12}\right)}{1 - \left(\frac{12}{12+0.030}\right)^{(12)(15)}} = \$145.02$$

With a programmable or financial calculator, you can store the monthly payment formula and minimize the work.

Another option is shown in **Table 7** on **page 776,** which gives payment values (per $1000 principal) for typical ranges of mortgage terms and interest rates. Table entries are given to five decimal places for accuracy to the nearest cent. ∎

WHEN Will I Ever USE This ?

Suppose you are a salesperson for a solar energy company. A couple who are potential customers contact you. To make your presentation more compelling, you provide cost comparisons of

"going solar" and "staying in the dark."

The customers give you permission to contact the power company and request a record of their power consumption over the last year, and they agree to meet the next day to go over the numbers.

At this meeting, you explain that the government is providing a tax incentive in the form of a tax credit equal to 30% of the cost of the system. Your company adds to the incentive by offering a 12-month "same-as-cash" loan for that 30%, and a 15-year fixed-rate mortgage at 3.0% for the other 70% of the cost. This allows the customers to have zero "out-of-pocket" expense for the purchase and installation of the system. They can use their tax refund to pay off the 30% "same-as-cash" loan before any interest charges apply.

Analysis of this couple's power consumption for the last year shows that their average monthly bill was $200 (totaling $2400 for the year), and a $30,000 solar system would initially produce enough energy to match their consumption. Energy prices are projected to increase by 5% per year. A conservative estimate of solar panel degradation is 0.5% per year, and all equipment will be under warranty for 20 years. A cost comparison can now be provided for a 20-year period using the following calculations.

Initial principal amount of 3% loan = 0.7 · $30,000 = $21,000

Monthly payment = $145.02   Example 1 calculation

First-year energy costs with solar ≈ 12 · $145 = $1740

First-year energy costs without solar = $2400 · 1.05 = $2520   5% price increase

Second-year energy costs without solar = $2400 · 1.05^2 = $2646   5% price increase

Second-year costs with solar = 0.005($2646) + $1740 ≈ $1753   0.5% degradation

Continuing these calculations results in the analysis of **Table 6.**

Cost of system:	$30,000	Interest rate:	3.0%
Same-as-cash loan:	$9,000	Term of loan (years):	15
12-yr fixed-rate mortgage:	$21,000	Monthly payment:	$145.02

Table 6   Analysis of Cost/Savings of Solar Energy

Year	Annual Cost without Solar	Energy Bills		Monthly Payments on Loan		Annual Cost with Solar
1	$2520	$0	+	$1740	=	$1740
2	2646	13	+	1740	=	1753
3	2778	28	+	1740	=	1768
4	2917	44	+	1740	=	1784
5	3063	61	+	1740	=	1801
6	3216	80	+	1740	=	1820
7	3377	101	+	1740	=	1841
8	3546	124	+	1740	=	1864
9	3723	149	+	1740	=	1889
10	3909	176	+	1740	=	1916
11	4105	205	+	1740	=	1945
12	4310	237	+	1740	=	1977
13	4526	272	+	1740	=	2012
14	4752	309	+	1740	=	2049
15	4989	349	+	1740	=	2089
16	5239	393	+	0	=	393
17	5501	440	+	0	=	440
18	5776	491	+	0	=	491
19	6065	546	+	0	=	546
20	6368	605	+	0	=	605
Totals:	**$83,326**					**$30,723**

20-Year Savings: $83,326 − $30,723 = $52,603

As you (and your customers) can see, the projected savings over the next 20 years are substantial.

Table 7 Monthly Payments to Repay Principal and Interest on a $1000 Mortgage

Annual rate (r)	Term of Mortgage (years) (t)						
	5	10	15	20	25	30	40
2.0%	$17.52776	$9.20135	$6.43509	$5.05883	$4.23854	$3.69619	$3.02826
2.5%	17.74736	9.42699	6.66789	5.29903	4.48617	3.95121	3.29778
3.0%	17.96869	9.65607	6.90582	5.54598	4.74211	4.21604	3.57984
3.5%	18.19174	9.88859	7.14883	5.79960	5.00624	4.49045	3.87391
4.0%	18.41652	10.12451	7.39688	6.05980	5.27837	4.77415	4.17938
4.5%	18.64302	10.36384	7.64993	6.32649	5.55832	5.06685	4.49563
5.0%	18.87123	10.60655	7.90794	6.59956	5.84590	5.36822	4.82197
5.5%	19.10116	10.85263	8.17083	6.87887	6.14087	5.67789	5.15770
6.0%	19.33280	11.10205	8.43857	7.16431	6.44301	5.99551	5.50214
6.5%	19.56615	11.35480	8.71107	7.45573	6.75207	6.32068	5.85457
7.0%	19.80120	11.61085	8.98828	7.75299	7.06779	6.65302	6.21431
7.5%	20.03795	11.87018	9.27012	8.05593	7.38991	6.99215	6.58071
8.0%	20.27639	12.13276	9.55652	8.36440	7.71816	7.33765	6.95312
8.5%	20.51653	12.39857	9.84740	8.67823	8.05227	7.68913	7.33094
9.0%	20.75836	12.66758	10.14267	8.99726	8.39196	8.04623	7.71361
9.5%	21.00186	12.93976	10.44225	9.32131	8.73697	8.40854	8.10062
10.0%	21.24704	13.21507	10.74605	9.65022	9.08701	8.77572	8.49146
10.5%	21.49390	13.49350	11.05399	9.98380	9.44182	9.14739	8.88570
11.0%	21.74242	13.77500	11.36597	10.32188	9.80113	9.52323	9.28294

```
N=300.00
I%=4.50
PV=160000.00
→ ▪PMT=-889.33
FV=0.00
P/Y=12.00
C/Y=12.00
PMT: END BEGIN
```

Under the conditions of **Example 2**, the monthly payment is $889.33. Compare with the table method.

![EXAMPLE 2] **Using a Table to Find a Monthly Mortgage Payment**

Find the monthly payment necessary to amortize a $160,000 loan at 4.5% for 25 years.

Solution

In **Table 7,** read down to the 4.5% row and across to the column for 25 years, to find the entry 5.55832. As this is the monthly payment amount needed to amortize a loan of $1000, and our loan is for $160,000, our required monthly payment is

$$160 \cdot \$5.55832 = \$889.33. \qquad \blacksquare$$

So that the borrower pays interest only on the money actually owed in a month, interest on real-estate loans is computed on the decreasing balance of the loan. Each equal monthly payment is first applied toward interest for the previous month. The remainder of the payment is then applied toward reduction of the principal amount owed.

Payments in the early years of a real-estate loan are mostly interest (typically 80% or more); only a small amount goes toward reducing the principal. The amount of interest decreases each month, so that larger and larger amounts of the payment will apply to the principal. During the last years of the loan, most of the monthly payment is applied toward the principal. (See **Table 9** on **page 778.**)

Longer-term mortgages have become more popular in recent years. In fact, 40-year mortgages are not uncommon today. Extending the term may help a buyer "afford" a more expensive home. For example, the monthly payments for principal and interest on a $200,000 mortgage at 4% APR would be $954.83 for a 30-yr term, but only $835.88 for a 40-yr term. In some cases, this may be advantageous, but the long-term effects of a longer term loan should be considered. Over the lives of the two loans mentioned above, the total payments would be as follows.

30-yr term: $343,739.01
40-yr term: $401,220.93
Which loan would you prefer?

Once the regular monthly payment has been determined, as in **Examples 1 and 2,** an **amortization schedule** (or **repayment schedule**) can be generated. It will show the allotment of payments for interest and principal, and the principal balance, for one or more months during the life of the loan. Tables showing these breakdowns are available from lenders or can be produced on a computer spreadsheet. The following steps demonstrate how the computations work.

Step 1 Interest for the month $= \left(\begin{array}{c} \text{Old balance} \\ \text{of principal} \end{array} \right) \left(\begin{array}{c} \text{Annual} \\ \text{interest rate} \end{array} \right) \left(\dfrac{1}{12} \text{ year} \right)$

Step 2 Payment on principal $= \left(\begin{array}{c} \text{Monthly} \\ \text{payment} \end{array} \right) - \left(\begin{array}{c} \text{Interest for} \\ \text{the month} \end{array} \right)$

Step 3 New balance of principal $= \left(\begin{array}{c} \text{Old balance} \\ \text{of principal} \end{array} \right) - \left(\begin{array}{c} \text{Payment on} \\ \text{principal} \end{array} \right)$

This sequence of steps is done for the end of each month. The new balance obtained in Step 3 becomes the Step 1 old balance for the next month.

EXAMPLE 3 Preparing an Amortization Schedule

The Petersons have a $120,000 mortgage with a term of 30 years and a 4.0% interest rate. Prepare an amortization schedule for the first 2 months of their mortgage.

Solution

First get the monthly payment. We use **Table 7.** (You could also use the formula.)

Mortgage amount in $1000s   Intersection of 4.0% row with 30-year column in **Table 7**

$$R = 120 \quad \cdot \quad \$4.77415 = \$572.90$$

Now apply Steps 1–3.

Step 1 Interest for the month $= \$120{,}000(0.04)\left(\dfrac{1}{12}\right) = \$400$

Step 2 Payment on principal $= \$572.90 - \$400 = \$172.90$

Step 3 New balance of principal $= \$120{,}000 - \$172.90 = \$119{,}827.10$

Starting with an old balance of $119,827.10, repeat the steps for the second month.

Step 1 Interest for the month $= \$119{,}827.10\,(0.04)\left(\dfrac{1}{12}\right) = \$399.42$

Step 2 Payment on principal $= \$572.90 - \$399.42 = \$173.48$

Step 3 New balance of principal $= \$119{,}827.10 - \$173.48 = \$119{,}653.62$

These calculations are summarized in **Table 8.**

The book *You Can Do the Math*, by Ron Lipsman of the University of Maryland, is a practical resource for most aspects of **personal financial management.** The associated Web site, www.math.umd.edu/~rll/cgi-bin/finance.html, provides "calculators" with which you can easily input your own values to get the results of many different financial computations.

Table 8 Amortization Schedule

Payment Number	Interest Payment	Principal Payment	Balance of Principal
			$120,000.00
1	$400.00	$172.90	$119,827.10
2	$399.42	$173.48	$119,653.62

■

Table 9 Amortization Schedules for a $120,000, 30-Year Mortgage

4.0% Interest Monthly Payment: $572.90				12.5% Interest Monthly Payment: $1280.71			
Payment Number	Interest Payment	Principal Payment	Balance of Principal	Payment Number	Interest Payment	Principal Payment	Balance of Principal
Initially →			120,000.00	Initially →			120,000.00
1	400.00	172.90	119,827.10	1	1,250.00	30.71	119.969.29
2	399.42	173.48	119,653.62	2	1,249.68	31.03	119,938.26
3	398.85	174.05	119,479.57	3	1,249.36	31.35	119,906.91
12	393.55	179.35	117,886.76	12	1,246.29	34.42	119,609.63
60	362.49	210.41	108,537.02	60	1,224.11	56.60	117,458.11
152	287.12	285.78	85,851.63	152	1,133.87	146.84	108,704.57
153	286.17	286.73	85,564.90	153	1,132.34	148.37	108,556.20
230	202.43	370.47	60,358.56	230	951.19	329.52	90,984.42
231	201.20	371.70	59,986.86	231	947.75	332.96	90,651.46
294	114.50	458.40	33,890.53	294	641.10	639.61	60,905.68
295	112.97	459.93	33,430.60	295	634.43	646.28	60,259.40
296	111.44	461.46	32,969.13	296	627.70	653.01	59,606.39
359	3.80	569.10	571.00	359	26.27	1254.44	1267.51
360	1.90	571.00	0.00	360	13.20	1267.51	0.00
Totals:	86,243.41	120,000.00		**Totals:**	341,055.35	120,000.00	

Prevailing mortgage interest rates have varied considerably over the years. **Table 9** shows portions of the amortization schedule for the Petersons' loan of **Example 3** and shows what the corresponding values would have been had their interest rate been 12.5%. (Rates that high have not been seen for many years.) Notice how much interest is involved in this home mortgage. At the (low) 4.0% rate, $86,243.41 in interest was paid, along with the $120,000 principal. At a rate of 12.5%, the interest alone would total the huge sum of $341,055.35, which is about 2.8 times the mortgage principal.

Adjustable-Rate Mortgages

The lending industry uses many variations on the basic fixed-rate mortgage. An **adjustable-rate mortgage (ARM),** also known as a **variable-rate mortgage (VRM),** generally starts out with a lower rate than similar fixed-rate loans, but the rate changes periodically, reflecting changes in prevailing rates.

Amortization Schedule			
No.	Amount	Interest	Principal	Balance
1	1,280.71	1,250.00	30.71	119,969.29
2	1,280.71	1,249.68	31.03	119,938.26
3	1,280.71	1,249.36	31.35	119,906.91

Amortizations to Go There are many free (and premium) apps for smartphones that will generate amortization tables. This screenshot is from the Loan Calculator feature of the fncalculator.com app. It agrees with the amortization of the 12.5% loan in **Table 9.**

QUANTITIES GOVERNING ADJUSTABLE-RATE MORTGAGES (ARMS)

- **Adjustment period**—Time interval between rate adjustments (typically 1, 3, or 5 years)

- **Index**—Standard fluctuating average that is the basis for the new, adjusted rate (typically the 1-, 3-, or 5-year U.S. Treasury security rate or a national or regional "cost of funds" index)

A Note on Margin When determining the margin on a loan, the lender considers the creditworthiness of the borrower. Those with lower credit scores are a higher risk to the lender, so the margin is increased to cover that risk.

Credit scores are determined in part by comparing the amount of credit a borrower has to the amount they use, as well as their record of making payments on time. The Fair Credit Reporting Act permits consumers to request a free credit report once per year from each of the three major credit-reporting agencies (Equifax, TransUnion, and Experian).

Potential homebuyers should establish good credit to qualify for lower interest rates. For sound advice on building good credit, check out http://www.fdic.gov/consumers/consumer/ccc/savvy.html

QUANTITIES GOVERNING ARMS, CONTINUED

- **Margin**—Additional amount added to the index by the lender (typically a few percentage points)

- **Discount**—Amount by which the *initial* rate may be less than the sum of the index and the margin (typically arranged between seller and lender)

- **Interest rate cap**—Limits on (interest) rate increases

- **Periodic cap**—Limit on rate increase per adjustment period (typically about 1% per 6 months or 2% per year)

- **Overall cap**—Limit on rate increases over the life of the loan (typically about 5% total)

- **Payment cap**—Limit on how much the payment can increase at each adjustment

- **Negative amortization**—An increasing loan principal (perhaps caused by a payment cap preventing the payment from covering a higher interest rate)

- **Convertibility feature**—A contractual ability to convert to a fixed-rate mortgage (usually at certain designated points in time)

- **Prepayment penalty**—Charges imposed by the lender if payments are made early

EXAMPLE 4 Comparing ARM Payments Before and After a Rate Adjustment

We pay $40,000 down on a $200,000 house and take out a 3/1 ARM (meaning that the initial rate stays fixed for the first three years and then adjusts each year after that to reflect the current index) for a 30-year term. The lender uses the 1-year Treasury index (at 0.2%) and a 2.8% margin.

(a) Find the monthly payment for the first three years.

(b) Suppose that after three years, the 1-year Treasury index has increased to 1.4%. Find the monthly payment for the fourth year.

Solution

(a)   Mortgage amount = $200,000 − $40,000 = $160,000

            ↑ Cost of house   ↑ Down payment

The interest rate for the first three years will be

ARM interest rate = Index rate + Margin = 0.2% + 2.8% = 3%.

Now from **Table 7** (using 3% over 30 years) we obtain 4.21604.

Initial monthly payment = 160 · $4.21604 = $674.57

(b) During the first three years, some of the mortgage principal has been paid, so in effect we will now have a new "mortgage amount." (Also, the term will now be three years less than the original term.) The amortization schedule for the first three years (not shown here) yields a loan balance, after the thirty-sixth monthly payment, of $149,670.66.

For the fourth year,

ARM interest rate = Index rate + Margin = 1.4% + 2.8% = 4.2%.

Because 4.2% is not included in **Table 7,** we use the regular monthly payment formula with the new mortgage balance and 27 years for the remaining term.

$$\text{Fourth-year monthly payment} = \frac{P\left(\frac{r}{12}\right)}{1 - \left(\frac{12}{12+r}\right)^{12t}} \qquad \text{Regular payment formula}$$

$$= \frac{\$149,670.66\left(\frac{0.042}{12}\right)}{1 - \left(\frac{12}{12+0.042}\right)^{(12)(27)}} \qquad \text{Substitute known values.}$$

$$= \$773.07$$

The first ARM interest rate adjustment has caused the fourth-year monthly payment to rise to $773.07, which is an increase of $98.50 over the initial monthly payment. ∎

A "seller buydown" occurs when the seller (a new-home builder, for example) pays the lender an amount in order to discount the buyer's loan. This reduces the initial rate and monthly payments, thereby giving the buyer a better chance to qualify for the loan. But it may be combined with higher initial fees or home price.

EXAMPLE 5 Discounting a Mortgage Rate

In **Example 4,** suppose that a seller buydown discounts our initial rate by 0.5%. Find the initial and fourth-year monthly payments.

Solution

The initial interest rate is discounted to 2.5% (rather than the 3% of **Example 4**), so the **Table 7** entry is 3.95121.

$$\text{Initial monthly payment} = 160(\$3.95121) = \$632.19$$

The amortization schedule shows a balance at the end of three years of $148,839.36. The discount now expires, and the index has increased to 1.4%, so for the fourth year,

$$\text{ARM interest rate} = \text{Index rate} + \text{Margin} = 1.4\% + 2.8\% = 4.2\%.$$

(This is just as in **Example 4.**) Using the monthly payment formula, with $r = 4.2\%$ and $t = 27$,

$$\text{Fourth-year monthly payment} = \frac{\$148,839.36\left(\frac{0.042}{12}\right)}{1 - \left(\frac{12}{12+0.042}\right)^{(12)(27)}} \qquad \begin{array}{l}\text{Substitute values in the}\\ \text{monthly payment formula.}\end{array}$$

$$= \$768.78.$$

The initial monthly payment of $632.19 looks better than the $674.57 of **Example 4,** but at the start of year four, monthly payments jump by $136.59. ∎

Closing Costs

Apart from principal and interest payments, buying a home involves a variety of one-time expenses called **closing costs,** or **settlement charges,** which are imposed when the loan is finalized (at "closing"). Often a buyer agrees to establish an **escrow account,** or **reserve account,** maintained by the lender for the purpose of paying property taxes and homeowner's insurance premiums. In such cases, closing costs will include an "escrow deposit" to fund the escrow account.

Because escrow deposits increase closing costs, some buyers decide to pay property taxes and insurance premiums directly. However, some lenders lower the interest rate slightly for borrowers who use an escrow account, and many homeowners prefer the simplicity of letting the lender process these payments. A buyer is entitled to a "good faith estimate" (GFE) of closing costs from the lender and, if desired, may shop for alternative providers of settlement services.

EXAMPLE 6 Computing Total Closing Costs

A buyer borrowed $130,000 at 4% interest to purchase a home. At the "closing" of the loan on June 19, the following closing costs were charged.

Loan origination fee (1% of mortgage amount)	$ __?__
Broker loan fee	1625
Lender document and underwriting fees	534
Transfer taxes (for state and local fees on mortgages)	180
Title services and lender's title insurance	401
Title insurance	457
Government recording charges	55
Escrow deposit	1032
Daily interest charges ($14.25 per day for 12 days)	__?__

Compute the total closing costs for this mortgage.

Solution

"Loan origination fees" are sometimes referred to as **points.** Each "point" amounts to 1% of the mortgage amount. By imposing points, the lender can effectively raise the interest rate without raising monthly payments (because points are normally paid at closing rather than over the life of the loan).

In this case, "one point" amounts to $1300. Because mortgage payments are typically made on the first of each month, and this loan closed on June 19, twelve days will pass before July 1. Interest on the $130,000 balance for these twelve days is

$$12 \cdot \$130,000 \cdot \frac{0.04}{365} \approx \$171.$$

Adding these amounts to those listed gives total closing costs of $5755. ∎

Recurring Costs of Home Ownership

The primary considerations for most homebuyers are the following.

1. Accumulating the down payment
2. Having sufficient cash and income to qualify for the loan
3. Making the monthly mortgage payments

Three additional expenses of homeownership, listed below, should be anticipated realistically. These are **recurring costs** (as opposed to the one-time closing costs), and they can be significant.

1. **Property taxes** are collected by a county or other local government. Depending on the location and value of the home, taxes can range up to several thousand dollars annually. Property taxes and mortgage interest are income tax deductible. Therefore, money expended for those items will decrease income taxes. This is one way in which the government has historically, through the tax code, encouraged home ownership.

Government-backed mortgages, including FHA (Federal Housing Administration) and VA (Veterans Administration) loans, carry a government guarantee to protect the lender in case the borrower fails to repay the loan. Those who obtain a conventional loan, instead, are usually required to buy private mortgage insurance (PMI), unless they are able to make a down payment of at least 20% of the purchase price of the property.

This feature can be a surprise recurring expense to first-time home purchasers. It was introduced to protect lenders but indirectly also protects the buyers, who may lose a great deal if some catastrophe makes it impossible for them to make their mortgage payments.

2. **Homeowner's insurance** usually covers losses due to fire, storm damage, and other casualties. Some types, such as earthquake, flood, or hurricane coverage, may be unavailable or very expensive, depending on location.

3. All homes require **maintenance,** but these costs can vary greatly, depending mainly on the size, construction type, age, and condition of the home.

Insurance and maintenance expenses, though necessary to protect the home investment, are not generally tax deductible.

EXAMPLE 7 Determining the Affordability of Home Ownership

Greg and Tamara Jamieson have household income that places them in a 30% combined state and local tax bracket. They can afford a net average monthly expenditure of $1700 for a home. The home of their dreams is priced at $300,000. They have saved a 20% down payment and are prequalified for a 20-year, $240,000 fixed-rate mortgage at 4.5%. Property taxes are estimated to be $3900 annually, homeowner's insurance premiums would be $600 per year, and annual maintenance costs are estimated to be $1200. Can the Jamiesons afford their dream home?

Solution

Let's "do the math."

Mortgage amount in $1000s   Value from **Table 7**

$$\text{Regular mortgage payment} = 240 \cdot \$6.32649 \approx \$1518$$

$$\text{Monthly property taxes} = \frac{\$3900 \leftarrow \text{Annual taxes}}{12 \leftarrow \text{Months per year}}$$

$$= \$325$$

$$\text{Monthly insurance and maintenance cost} = \frac{\$600 + \$1200}{12} = \$150$$

Mortgage payment   Property taxes   Insurance and maintenance

$$\text{Total monthly expense} = \$1518 + \$325 + \$150$$

$$= \mathbf{\$1993}$$

Because $1993 > $1700, it seems that the Jamiesons cannot afford this home. But wait—remember that mortgage interest and property taxes are both income tax deductible. Let's consider further.

$$\text{Monthly interest} = \$240{,}000(0.045)\left(\frac{1}{12}\right) \quad \text{Interest} = Prt$$

$$= \$900$$

Of the $1518 mortgage payment, $900 would be interest (initially).

Mortgage interest   Property tax

$$\text{Monthly deductible expenses} = \$900 + \$325 = \$1225$$

Deductible expense   Tax bracket

$$\text{Monthly income tax savings} = \$1225 \cdot 30\% \approx \$368$$

Gross cost   Tax savings

$$\text{Net monthly cost of home} = \$1993 - \$368 = \$1625$$

By considering the effect of taxes, we see that the net monthly cost of $1625 is indeed within the Jamiesons' $1700 affordability limit. ∎

Refinancing means initiating a new home mortgage and paying off the old one. In times of relatively low rates, lenders often encourage homeowners to refinance. Because setting up a new loan will involve costs, make sure you have a good reason before refinancing. Some possible reasons:

1. The new loan may be comparable to the current loan with a rate low enough to recoup the costs in a few years.
2. You may want to pay down your balance faster by switching to a shorter-term loan.
3. You may want to borrow out equity to cover other major expenses, such as education for your children.
4. Your present loan may have a large balloon feature that necessitates refinancing.
5. You may be uncomfortable with your variable (hence uncertain) ARM and want to convert to a fixed-rate loan.

Example 7 raises some reasonable questions.

1. Is it wise to buy a house close to your spending limit, in light of future uncertainties?
2. What about the fact that the interest portion of mortgage payments, and therefore the tax savings, will decrease over time?
3. Won't taxes, insurance, and maintenance costs probably increase over time, making it more difficult to keep up the payments?

Some possible responses follow.

1. The Jamiesons may have built in sufficient leeway when they decided on their limit of $1700 per month.
2. **(a)** Look again at **Table 9** to see how slowly the interest portion drops.

   (b) Most people find that their income over time increases faster than expenses for a home that carries a fixed-rate mortgage. (A variable-rate mortgage is more risky and should have its initial rate locked in for as long as possible.)

   (c) Prevailing interest rates rise and fall over time. While rising rates will not affect a fixed-rate mortgage, falling rates may offer the opportunity to reduce mortgage expenses by refinancing. (For guidelines, see the margin note on refinancing.)

3. Here again, increases in income will probably keep pace. Although most things, including personal income, tend to follow inflation, the fixed-rate mortgage ensures that mortgage amortization, a major item, will stay constant.

WHEN Will I Ever USE This ?

Suppose you are a certified financial planner (CFP) with clients who are relocating and need help in deciding whether to purchase a home or rent. Their household income puts them in a 25% combined state and federal income tax bracket. If they purchase a home, they would plan to stay in it for at least 10 years. They are interested in a $280,000 home and are prequalified for a 30-year fixed mortgage at 4.5%. There are comparable homes in the same area that rent for $1,000 per month. Home values are projected to increase by 3% per year, and rents are also projected to increase by 3% per year.

Would it be better for them to buy or rent?

To answer this question, you lay out a side-by-side comparison of the housing costs over a ten-year period. See **Table 10** on the next page.

Explanation of the Costs of Buying

Because the purchase price is $280,000 and your clients want to avoid purchasing private mortgage insurance, they will be making a down payment of $56,000 (20% of the purchase price). Closing costs—including loan origination fees, discount points, documentation fees, and prorated interest and escrow deposits—typically come to about 3% of the purchase price, or $8,400. The down payment and closing costs make up the one-time "up-front" costs.

Table 10 Comparing Buying and Renting

Buying		Renting	
Purchase Price: $280,000			
Up-front Costs of Purchasing		**Up-front Costs of Renting**	
Down payment	$56,000	Rental deposit (one month's rent)	$1,000
Closing costs (about 3% of purchase price)	$8,400		
Recurring Costs (30-yr fixed, 4.5%)		**Recurring Costs**	
Mortgage principal	$44,600	Rent (increasing 3% per year)	$137,567
Mortgage interest (incl. 25% tax deduction)	$68,698	Renter's insurance (1.32% of annual rent)	$1,816
Property Taxes (incl. 25% tax deduction)	$30,093		
Maintenance (0.5% of purchase price, rising with inflation)	$15,330		
Insurance (0.2% of home value)	$6,420		
Opportunity Costs		**Opportunity Costs**	
Down payment/closing costs	$33,244	Initial rent deposit	$516
Yearly costs	$40,455	Yearly costs	$32,083
Selling Costs		**Terminating Rental Agreement**	
Selling costs (6% of selling price)	$22,578	Return of initial deposit	−$1,000
Remaining principal	$179,400		
Proceeds from home sale	−$376,297		
Total Housing Expenditures for 10 Years	**$128,921**	**Total Housing Expenditures for 10 Years**	**$171,982**

The recurring costs of home ownership include monthly principal and interest payments, property taxes (paid from an escrow account), maintenance costs, and homeowner's insurance. The amount of $44,600 for principal paid during the first ten years on the mortgage was calculated by amortizing the mortgage and adding the principal payments for 120 months. Your clients are in a 25% income tax bracket, so only 75% of the interest payments are considered "costs." Thus amortizing interest for the first 120 months, adding up these interest payments, and multiplying by 0.75 will yield the $68,698 figure for interest.

Property taxes in the county where the house is located are 1.25% of the value of the home. Thus taxes for the first year are

$$0.0125 \cdot \$280,000 = \$3,500.$$

Because property values are expected to increase by 3% per year, the property taxes in the second year are projected to be

$$\$3,500 \cdot 1.03 = \$3,605.$$

Continuing this pattern yields the property tax amounts shown in **Table 11.** But property taxes are income tax deductible, so the actual expense for property taxes for the first ten years (considering the 25% tax bracket) is

$$(1 - 0.25) \cdot \$40,124 = 0.75 \cdot \$40,124 = \$30,093.$$

Maintenance costs are assumed to be 0.5% of the purchase price and grow at the rate of inflation, which is projected to be 2%.

$$\text{First-year maintenance costs} = 0.005 \cdot \$280,000 = \$1,400$$

$$\text{Second-year maintenance costs} = \$1,400(1.02) = \$1,428$$

Table 11

Year	Prop Tax
1	$3,500
2	3,605
3	3,713
4	3,825
5	3,939
6	4,057
7	4,179
8	4,305
9	4,434
10	4,567
Total	**$40,124**

Table 12

Year	Mainte- nance
1	$1,400
2	1,428
3	1,457
4	1,486
5	1,515
6	1,546
7	1,577
8	1,608
9	1,640
10	1,673
Total	**$15,330**

Table 13

Year	Insurance
1	$560
2	577
3	594
4	612
5	630
6	649
7	669
8	689
9	709
10	731
Total	**$6,420**

The cost increase due to inflation continues throughout the ten years, resulting in the amounts shown in **Table 12.**

Homeowner's insurance costs are assumed to be about 0.2% of the value of the home (which is projected to increase by 3% per year).

$$\text{First-year insurance costs} = 0.002 \cdot \$280,000 = \$560$$

$$\text{Second-year insurance costs} = \$560(1.03) \approx \$577$$

Table 13 shows the insurance costs projected for the ten-year period.

Opportunity cost is incurred when a choice is made to forgo an investment opportunity. For example, if your clients decide to purchase the home, they will be spending $56,000 on a down payment and $8,400 for closing costs, rather than investing it in some other investment vehicle. For the purposes of your calculations, you have assumed that monies they have that are not spent on housing will instead be invested in the stock market at a 5% annual return. It is also assumed that the capital gains from these investments will be taxed at 15% (rather than the 25% income tax rate). Thus the "after-tax" effective growth rate will be

$$(1 - 0.15)(0.05) = 0.85(0.05) = 0.0425 = 4.25\%.$$

Therefore, the net gain (opportunity cost) over ten years on the up-front costs of purchasing the home would be

$$\$64,400(1 + 0.0425)^{10} - \$64,400 \approx \$33,244.$$

To calculate the opportunity cost of the yearly expenses of home ownership, you begin with the monthly mortgage payments. The amortization of the 30-year fixed mortgage at 4.5% and beginning principal of $224,000 shows that the first month's principal payment will be $295 and the interest will be $840.

Because the interest is tax deductible, the actual "cost" of the first month's mortgage payment would be

$$\$295 + 0.75(\$840) = \$925.$$

Investing this amount over ten years would yield an "after-tax" gain of

$$\$925(1 + 0.0425)^{10} - \$925 \approx \$477.$$

Performing similar calculations for the remaining 119 months of payments, as well as for the yearly costs of property taxes, maintenance, and insurance, yields the total opportunity cost of the yearly expenses of $40,455.

If your clients were to sell the home in ten years, the value (having increased by 3% per year) would be

$$\$280,000(1.03)^{10} \approx \$376,297,$$

which amounts to the proceeds from the sale of the home. Closing costs (for realtor services, home inspection, and other necessities in selling a home) can be expected to be about 6% of the selling price.

$$\text{Closing costs} = 0.06(\$376,297) = \$22,578$$

The remaining principal on the loan after ten years can be calculated as follows.

$$\text{Original loan amount} - \text{sum of principal payments} = \text{remaining principal}$$

$$\$224,000 - \$44,600 = \$179,400$$

Explanation of the Costs of Renting

Landlords typically charge a deposit equal to one month's rent. In your clients' case, this would be $1,000. The rent is expected to increase 3% per year over the next ten years. Rental agreements are often one-year leases, so the rent payment will be fixed for 12 months before it increases. All 120 projected rent payments are added to give the $137,567 figure for the rent payments over the ten-year period.

Renter's insurance in the area where your clients would like to live typically amount to 1.32% of the annual rent, which increases by 3% per year. Projected annual premiums for the ten years total $1,816.

Opportunity costs for rental expenses are calculated in a fashion similar to those for home ownership, taking into account the 15% tax rate on capital gains.

When all the calculations are made, you are able to show your clients that the difference between rental costs and ownership costs would be approximately

Rental   Ownership
costs   costs
↓   ↓

$$\$171{,}982 - \$128{,}921 = \mathbf{\$43{,}061.}$$

Therefore, they can save, on average, about $4,306 per year by buying rather than renting.

13.4 EXERCISES

Round all monetary answers to the nearest cent unless directed otherwise.

Monthly Payment on a Fixed-Rate Mortgage *Find the monthly payment needed to amortize principal and interest for each fixed-rate mortgage. You can use either the regular monthly payment formula or* **Table 7,** *as appropriate.*

	Loan Amount	Interest Rate	Term			Loan Amount	Interest Rate	Term
1.	$100,000	8.0%	20 years		5.	$227,750	10.5%	25 years
2.	$23,000	6.0%	15 years		6.	$195,450	5.5%	10 years
3.	$135,000	5.7%	25 years		7.	$42,500	4.6%	5 years
4.	$95,000	6.9%	30 years		8.	$200,000	3.5%	10 years

Amortization of a Fixed-Rate Mortgage *Complete the first one or two months (as required) of each amortization schedule for a fixed-rate mortgage.*

9. Mortgage: $58,500
Interest rate: 10.0%
Term of loan: 30 years

Amortization Schedule

Payment Number	Total Payment	Interest Payment	Principal Payment	Balance of Principal
1	**(a)** _____	**(b)** _____	**(c)** _____	**(d)** _____

10. Mortgage: $95,000
Interest rate: 3.5%
Term of loan: 20 years

Amortization Schedule

Payment Number	Total Payment	Interest Payment	Principal Payment	Balance of Principal
1	**(a)** _____	**(b)** _____	**(c)** _____	**(d)** _____

11. Mortgage: $143,200
Interest rate: 6.5%
Term of loan: 15 years

Amortization Schedule

Payment Number	Total Payment	Interest Payment	Principal Payment	Balance of Principal
1	(a) _____	(b) _____	(c) _____	(d) _____
2	(e) _____	(f) _____	(g) _____	(h) _____

12. Mortgage: $124,750
Interest rate: 3.0%
Term of loan: 25 years

Amortization Schedule

Payment Number	Total Payment	Interest Payment	Principal Payment	Balance of Principal
1	(a) _____	(b) _____	(c) _____	(d) _____
2	(e) _____	(f) _____	(g) _____	(h) _____

13. Mortgage: $113,650
Interest rate: 8.2%
Term of loan: 10 years

Amortization Schedule

Payment Number	Total Payment	Interest Payment	Principal Payment	Balance of Principal
1	(a) _____	(b) _____	(c) _____	(d) _____
2	(e) _____	(f) _____	(g) _____	(h) _____

14. Mortgage: $150,000
Interest rate: 4.25%
Term of loan: 16 years

Amortization Schedule

Payment Number	Total Payment	Interest Payment	Principal Payment	Balance of Principal
1	(a) _____	(b) _____	(c) _____	(d) _____
2	(e) _____	(f) _____	(g) _____	(h) _____

Finding Monthly Mortgage Payments   *Find the total monthly payment, including taxes and insurance.*

	Mortgage	Interest Rate	Term of Loan	Annual Taxes	Annual Insurance
15.	$62,300	5%	20 years	$610	$220
16.	$51,800	6%	25 years	$570	$145
17.	$89,560	3.5%	10 years	$915	$409
18.	$72,890	5.5%	15 years	$1850	$545

Comparing Total Principal and Interest on a Mortgage   *Suppose $140,000 is owed on a house. The monthly payment for principal and interest at 8.5% for 30 years is*

$$140 \cdot \$7.68913 = \$1076.48.$$

19. How many monthly payments will be made over the 30-year period?

20. What is the total amount that will be paid for principal and interest?

21. The total interest charged is the total amount paid minus the amount financed. What is the total interest?

22. Which is more—the amount financed or the total interest paid? By how much?

Comparing Mortgage Options Suppose you want to purchase a $300,000 home, and you have the required $60,000 down payment in savings. Complete the table below to compare different mortgage options presented by a mortgage broker. (Source: Bankrate.com, accessed May 20, 2014)

	Principal	Interest Rate	Term (years)	Payment	Total of Payments over Life of Loan	Total Interest Paid over Life of Loan
23.	$240,000	4.250%	30			
24.	$240,000	3.875%	20			
25.	$240,000	3.250%	15			
26.	$240,000	3.000%	10			

27. Compare the monthly payments, total of payments, and total interest paid for the loans in **Exercises 23 and 25.** Which of these two loan options would you choose? Why?

28. Compare the monthly payments, total of payments, and total interest paid for the loans in **Exercises 24 and 26.** Which of these two loan options would you choose? Why?

Long-Term Effect of Interest Rates You may remember seeing home mortgage interest rates fluctuate widely in a period of not too many years. The following exercises show the effect of changing rates. Refer to **Table 9,** which compared the amortization of a $120,000, 30-year mortgage for rates of 4.0% and 12.5%. Give values of each of the following for **(a)** a 4.0% rate, and **(b)** a 12.5% rate.

29. monthly payments

30. percentage of first monthly payment that is principal

31. balance of principal after 1 year

32. the number of payments required to pay down half of the original principal

33. the first monthly payment that includes more toward principal than toward interest

34. amount of interest included in final monthly payment of mortgage

The Effect of the Term on Total Amount Paid Suppose a $60,000 mortgage is to be amortized at 7.5% interest. Find the total amount of interest that would be paid for each term.

35. 10 years

36. 20 years

37. 30 years

38. 40 years

The Effect of Adjustable Rates on the Monthly Payment For each adjustable-rate mortgage, find **(a)** the initial monthly payment, **(b)** the monthly payment for the second adjustment period, and **(c)** the change in monthly payment at the first adjustment.

	Beginning Balance	Term	Initial Index Rate	Margin	Adjustment Period	Adjusted Index Rate	Adjusted Balance	
39.	$75,000	20 years	6.5%	2.5%	1 year	8.0%	$73,595.52	*(The "adjusted balance" is the principal balance at the time of the first rate adjustment. Assume no caps apply.)*
40.	$44,500	30 years	7.2%	2.75%	3 years	6.6%	$43,669.14	

The Effect of Rate Caps on Adjustable-Rate Mortgages Millie has a 1-year ARM for $110,000 over a 20-year term. The margin is 2%, and the index rate starts out at 0.5% and increases to 3.0% at the first adjustment. The balance of principal at the end of the first year is $105,706.34. The ARM includes a periodic rate cap of 2% per adjustment period. Use this information for Exercises 41–44.

41. Find **(a)** the interest owed and **(b)** the monthly payment due for the first month of the first year.

42. Find **(a)** the interest owed and **(b)** the monthly payment due for the first month of the second year. (Remember the periodic rate cap!)

43. What is the monthly payment adjustment at the end of the first year?

44. If the index rate has dropped slightly at the end of the second year, will the third-year monthly payments necessarily drop? Why or why not?

Closing Costs of a Mortgage *For Exercises 45–48, refer to the following list of closing costs for the purchase of a $175,000 house requiring a 20% down payment, and find each requested amount.*

Title insurance premium	$400
Document recording fee	60
Loan fee (two points)	___
Appraisal fee	400
Prorated property taxes	685
Prorated fire insurance premium	295

45. mortgage amount   **46.** loan fee

47. total closing costs

48. total amount of cash required of the buyer at closing (including down payment)

Consider the scenario of **Example 7.** *Recalling that mortgage interest is income tax deductible, find (to the nearest dollar) the additional initial net monthly savings resulting from each strategy. In each case, only the designated item changes. All other features remain the same.*

49. Change the mortgage term from 20 years to 30 years.

50. Change the mortgage from fixed at 4.5% to an ARM with an initial rate of 3.5%.

For each of Exercises 51–54, find all of the following quantities for a $200,000 fixed-rate mortgage. (Give answers to the nearest dollar.)

(a) *Monthly mortgage payment (principal and interest)*

(b) *Monthly house payment (including property taxes and insurance)*

(c) *Initial monthly interest*

(d) *Income tax deductible portion of initial house payment*

(e) *Net initial monthly cost for the home (considering tax savings)*

	Term of Mortgage	Interest Rate	Annual Property Tax	Annual Insurance	Owner's Income Tax Bracket
51.	15 years	5.5%	$960	$480	20%
52.	20 years	6.0%	$840	$420	25%
53.	10 years	6.5%	$1092	$540	30%
54.	30 years	7.5%	$1260	$600	40%

*Exercises 55 and 56 refer to the **When Will I Ever Use This?** feature at the end of this section. Suppose your clients can afford to buy a $200,000 home and have the required 20% down payment in savings. Comparable rentals are available for $900 per month. Assume a combined income tax bracket of 25%, and a return on investments of 4%, with a 15% tax rate on capital gains. Compare the costs of buying and renting under the given circumstances.*

55. Your clients plan to move in five years, so they would take out a 5/1 ARM at 3.5%, and then plan to sell the home and pay off the loan before the interest rate adjusts. The table reflects an increase in home values of 3% per year, and a 2% annual increase in rents. Determine

(a) the opportunity costs that would result from the up-front costs of purchasing the home,

(b) the total costs of five years of ownership, and

(c) the difference between the costs of renting and the costs of owning over five years.

Buying		Renting	
Up-front Costs of Purchasing		**Up-front Costs of Renting**	
Down payment	$40,000	Rental deposit	$900
Closing costs	$6,000		
Recurring Costs		**Recurring Costs**	
Mortgage payments	$36,452	Rent	$56,204
Other	$17,685	Renter's insurance	$1,124
Opportunity Costs		**Opportunity Costs**	
Up-front costs	___	Initial rent deposit	$164
Yearly costs	$5,121	Yearly costs	$5,094
Selling Costs		**Terminating Agreement**	
Selling costs	$13,911	Return of deposit	−$900
Remaining principal	$143,515		
Proceeds from sale	−$231,855		
Total Costs for 5 Years	___	**Total Costs for 5 Years $62,586**	

56. Seeing the savings associated with home ownership, your clients now are considering staying in the area for 20 years. If they decided to purchase the home, they would take out a 30-year fixed mortgage at 4.5%. If home values increase by 3% per year, and rents also increase 3% per year, determine

(a) the proceeds from the sale of the same home in 20 years,

(b) the total costs of 20 years of ownership, and

(c) the difference between the costs of renting and the costs of owning over 20 years.

Buying		Renting	
Up-front Costs of Purchasing		**Up-front Costs of Renting**	
Down Payment	$40,000	Rental deposit	$900
Closing Costs	$6,000		
Recurring Costs		**Recurring Costs**	
Mortgage payments	$166,369	Rent	$290,200
Other	$87,425	Renter's insurance	$5,804
Opportunity Costs		**Opportunity Costs**	
Up-front costs	$43,778	Initial rent deposit	$857
Yearly costs	$104,715	Yearly costs	$112,388
Selling Costs		**Terminating Agreement**	
Selling costs	$21,673	Return of deposit	−$900
Remaining principal	$78,224		
Proceeds from sale	___		
Total Costs for 20 Years	___	**Total Costs for 20 Years $409,249**	

On the basis of material in this section, or your own research, give brief written responses to each problem.

57. Suppose your ARM allows conversion to a fixed-rate loan at each of the first five adjustment dates. Describe circumstances under which you would want to convert.

58. Should a home buyer always pay the smallest down payment that will be accepted? Explain.

59. Should a borrower always choose the shortest term available in order to minimize the total interest expense? Explain.

60. Under what conditions would an ARM probably be a better choice than a fixed-rate mortgage?

61. Why are fourth-year monthly payments (slightly) less in **Example 5** than in **Example 4** even though the term, 27 years, and the interest rate, 4.2%, are the same in both cases?

62. What tends to make ownership less expensive than renting, especially over many years?

63. Discuss the term "payment shock" mentioned at the end of **Example 5.**

64. Find out what is meant by each term and describe some of the features of each.

FHA-backed mortgage

VA-backed mortgage

Conventional mortgage

13.5 FINANCIAL INVESTMENTS

OBJECTIVES

1 Become familiar with stocks.

2 Become familiar with bonds.

3 Become familiar with mutual funds.

4 Evaluate investment returns.

5 Explore strategies for building a nest egg.

Stocks

In a general sense, an *investment* is a way of putting resources to work so that (one hopes) they will grow. Our main emphasis here will be on the basic mathematical aspects of a restricted class of financial investments—namely, *stocks, bonds,* and *mutual funds.*

Buying stock in a corporation makes you a part owner of the corporation. You then share in any profits the company makes, and your share of profits is called a **dividend.** If the company prospers (or if increasing numbers of investors believe it will prosper in the future), your stock will be attractive to others, so that you may, if you wish, sell your shares at a profit. The profit you make by selling for more than you paid is called a **capital gain.** A negative gain, or **capital loss,** results if you sell for less than you paid. By **return on investment,** we mean the net difference between what you receive (including your sale price and any dividends received) and what you paid (your purchase price plus any other expenses of buying and selling the stock).

EXAMPLE 1 Finding the Return on Ownership of Stock

Sarah Patterson bought 100 shares of stock in Company A on January 15, 2015, paying $30 per share. On January 15, 2016, she received a dividend of $0.50 per share, and the stock price had risen to $30.85 per share. (Ignore any costs other than the purchase price.) Find the following.

(a) Sarah's total cost for the stock

(b) The total dividend amount

(c) Sarah's capital gain if she sold the stock on January 15, 2016

(d) Sarah's total return on her one year of ownership of this stock

(e) The percentage return

Solution

(a) Cost = ($30 per share) $\cdot$ (100 shares) = $3000

She paid $3000 total.

(b) Dividend = ($0.50 per share) $\cdot$ (100 shares) = $50

The dividend amount was $50.

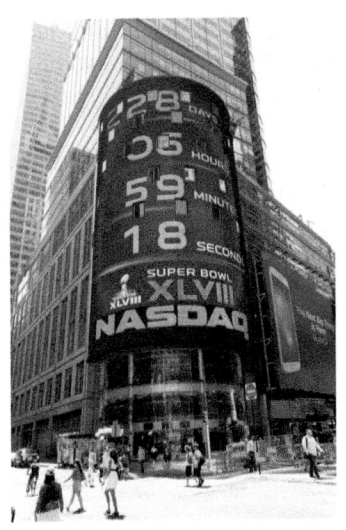

The **NASDAQ (National Association of Securities Dealers Advanced Quotations)**, unlike the NYSE and other exchanges that actually carry out trading at specific locations, is an electronic network of brokerages established in 1971 to facilitate the trading of over-the-counter (unlisted) stocks. Most of the high-tech company stocks, which grew very rapidly as a group in the 1980s and especially the 1990s (and many of which declined as rapidly in 2000–2002), are (or were) listed on the Nasdaq market.

(c)

Change in price per share → Number of shares →

$$\text{Capital gain} = (\$30.85 - \$30.00) \cdot 100 = \$0.85 \cdot 100 = \$85$$

The capital gain was $85.

(d)

Dividend → Capital gain →

$$\text{Total return} = \$50 + \$85 = \$135$$

Total return on the investment was $135.

(e) $\text{Percentage return} = \dfrac{\text{Total return}}{\text{Total cost}} \cdot 100\% = \dfrac{\$135}{\$3000} \cdot 100\% = 4.5\%$

The percentage return on the investment was 4.5%. ∎

The price of a share of stock is determined by the law of supply and demand at institutions called **stock exchanges.** In the United States, the oldest and largest exchange is the New York Stock Exchange (NYSE), established in 1792 and located on Wall Street in New York City. Members of the public buy their stock through stockbrokers, people who have access to the exchange. Stockbrokers do business in offices throughout the country. They charge a fee for buying or selling stock.

Current prices and other information about particular stocks are published daily in many newspapers and on various Web sites, where information may be updated every few minutes. **Table 14** below shows examples of trading on the NYSE, on May 22, 2014. The exchange opens at 9:30 A.M. and closes at 4:00 P.M., Eastern time.

Observe the column headings and the numbers for the first company listed, Allstate, with market symbol ALL. The first four numbers show that the first sale of Allstate shares after 9:30 A.M. was for $58.40 per share, the highest sale during the trading day was for $58.52, the lowest was for $58.26, and the last sale before 4:00 P.M. was for $58.35 per share.

Moving across to the right, the next two numbers show that the closing price for the day was $0.07 lower than that of the previous day—that is, 0.12% lower. The volume number indicates that 1,797,900 shares of Allstate stock were sold that day.

Table 14 Selected Stock Quotes (May 22, 2014)

Company	Symbol	Open	High	Low	Close	Net Change	% Change	Volume	52-Wk High	52-Wk Low	Annual Div	Dividend Yield	PE	YTD % Change
Allstate Corp	ALL	58.40	58.52	58.26	58.35	−0.07	−0.12%	1,797,900	58.69	45.60	$1.12	1.92%	10.34	6.99%
Bank of America	BAC	14.57	14.72	14.55	14.71	0.10	0.68%	51,929,398	18.03	12.13	$0.04	0.27%	17.39	−5.52%
Carmax Inc	KMX	44.26	44.92	44.22	44.53	0.19	0.43%	943,500	53.08	42.21	$0.00	0.00%	19.71	−5.30%
Caterpillar Inc	CAT	102.90	103.88	102.51	103.08	0.20	0.19%	3,112,300	108.21	80.86	$2.40	2.33%	17.00	13.51%
Chevron Corp	CVX	124.10	124.41	123.56	123.63	−0.53	−0.43%	3,262,700	127.83	109.27	$4.28	3.46%	12.09	−1.02%
Deere & Co	DE	90.00	90.50	89.60	89.99	0.01	0.01%	1,657,700	94.89	79.50	$2.04	2.27%	9.86	−1.47%
Duke Energy	DUK	70.01	70.64	70.01	70.55	0.62	0.89%	1,834,700	75.13	64.16	$3.12	4.42%	15.54	2.23%
FedEx Corp	FDX	138.84	139.69	138.34	139.33	0.28	0.20%	1,550,700	144.39	94.60	$0.60	0.43%	21.52	−3.09%
General Mills	GIS	53.50	53.80	53.31	53.74	0.26	0.49%	1,693,900	54.78	46.18	$1.64	3.05%	19.96	7.67%
Harley-Davidson	HOG	71.65	72.25	71.35	71.64	−0.45	−0.62%	1,037,600	74.13	49.15	$1.10	1.54%	20.66	3.47%
Hewlett-Packard	HPQ	32.45	33.36	31.21	31.78	−0.74	−2.28%	32,458,801	33.90	20.25	$0.58	1.83%	8.93	13.58%
Kimberly-Clark	KMB	109.91	110.37	109.71	110.13	0.11	0.10%	889,000	113.09	91.44	$3.36	3.05%	19.07	5.43%
Pearson Plc	PSO	19.21	19.37	19.09	19.28	0.07	0.36%	252,300	22.40	16.58	$0.79	4.10%	0.00	−13.93%
Walt Disney	DIS	82.19	82.79	82.04	82.35	0.16	0.19%	4,651,900	83.65	60.41	$0.86	1.04%	20.81	7.79%
Yum! Brands	YUM	74.63	75.14	74.35	74.87	0.20	0.27%	1,761,800	79.70	64.08	$1.48	1.98%	23.78	−0.98%

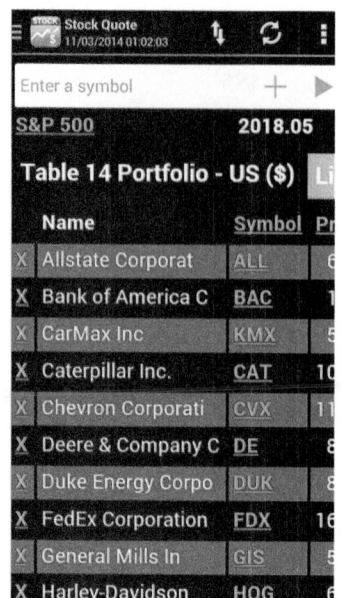

Pocket Portfolios Today, investors can use smartphones to check their portfolios, issue buy and sell orders, and view the performance history of stocks on multiple exchanges. This screenshot (using the Stock Quote app from BISHINEWS) shows part of the portfolio from **Table 14.**

The next two numbers show that, over the last year, the greatest and least prices paid for ALL were $58.69 and $45.60, respectively. The following two numbers show that Allstate's current dividend is $1.12 per share and that this represents a current yield of 1.92% (of the current stock closing price for the day).

PE is the **price-to-earnings ratio,** the current price per share divided by the earnings per share over the past 12 months. For ALL, this ratio is 10.34. Finally, the year-to-date percent change means that Allstate's price per share is now 6.99% higher than it was at the start of this calendar year.

EXAMPLE 2 Reading a Stock Table

Use the stock table (**Table 14**) to find the required amounts below.

(a) The highest price for the last 52 weeks for FedEx (FDX)

(b) The dividend for Hewlett-Packard (HPQ)

Solution

(a) Find the correct line from the stock table for FedEx.

The highest price for FedEx for the last 52 weeks was $144.39.

(b) The annual dividend value of $0.58 means that HPQ paid a dividend of $0.58 per share. ∎

EXAMPLE 3 Finding the Cost of a Stock Purchase

Find the cost for 100 shares of Deere (DE) stock, purchased at the low price for the day.

Solution

From **Table 14,** the low price for the day for Deere was $89.60 per share.

$$\underset{\underset{\text{share}}{\text{Price per}}}{\text{Total cost} = \$89.60} \cdot \underset{\underset{\text{shares}}{\text{Number of}}}{100} = \$8960.00$$

One hundred shares of this stock would cost $8960.00, plus any broker's fees. ∎

Most stock purchases and sales are done through a broker, who has representatives at the exchange to execute a buy or sell order. The broker will charge a **commission** (the broker's fee) for executing an order. Before 1974, commission rates were set by stock exchange rules and were uniform from broker to broker. Since then, however, rates are competitive and vary considerably among brokers.

Full-service brokers, who offer research, professional opinions on buying and selling individual issues, and various other services, tend to charge the highest commissions on transactions they execute. Many **discount brokers,** on the other hand, merely buy and sell stock for their clients, offering little in the way of additional services.

During the 1990s, when it often seemed that almost any reasonable choice of stock would pay off for almost any investor, a number of online companies appeared, offering much cheaper transactions than were available through conventional brokers. Subsequently, most conventional brokerage firms, as well as the major discount brokerages, introduced their own automated (online) services.

Commissions normally are a percentage of the value of a purchase or sale (called the **principal**). Some firms charge additional amounts in certain cases. For example, rates may depend on whether the order is for a **round lot** of shares (a multiple of 100) or an **odd lot** (any portions of an order for fewer than 100 shares). On the odd-lot portion, you may be charged an **odd-lot differential** (say, 10¢ per share).

Also, it is possible to place a **limit order,** where the broker is instructed to execute a buy or sell if and when a stock reaches a predesignated price. An extra fee may be added to the commission on a limit order. Many discount brokerage firms do not charge these special fees; instead, they charge different commissions depending on whether the transactions are **automated trades** or **broker-assisted trades.**

Table 15 Typical Discount Brokerage Commissions

	Automated (Online)	Automated (Phone)	Broker-Assisted
Brokerage Firm A	$8.95	$13.95	$33.95
Brokerage Firm B	$9.99	$34.99	$44.99
Brokerage Firm C	$7.95	$12.95	$32.95

Also, the Securities and Exchange Commission (SEC), a federal agency that regulates stock markets, supports its own activities by charging the exchanges, based on volume of transactions. Typically this charge is passed on to investors, through brokers, in the form of an **SEC fee** assessed on stock sales only (not on purchases). As of February 2014, this fee was $22.10 per million dollars of principal (rounded *up* to the next cent). For example, to find the fee for a sale of $1600, first divide $1600 by $1,000,000 and then multiply by $22.10.

$$\text{SEC fee} = \frac{\$1600}{\$1,000,000} \cdot \$22.10 = \$0.03536, \quad \text{which is rounded up to } \$0.04.$$

EXAMPLE 4 Finding Total Cost of Stock Purchases

Carina has a brokerage account with Brokerage Firm A, and on May 22, 2014, she executed a broker-assisted purchase of 250 shares of Harley-Davidson (HOG) stock at the average price of the day. She purchased 100 more shares online on September 12 for $73.50 per share. Find Carina's total cost for purchasing the 350 shares of HOG.

Solution

Daily high   Daily low   (**Table 14** values)

$$\text{Average price for first purchase} = \frac{\$72.25 + \$71.35}{2} \quad \text{Arithmetic mean}$$

$$= \$71.80$$

Price per share   Number of shares

$$\text{Basic cost of first purchase} = \$71.80 \quad \cdot \quad 250$$

$$= \$17,950.00$$

Because the purchase was a broker-assisted transaction, Firm A charged a commission of $33.95 (as shown in **Table 15**).

Basic cost   Commission

$$\text{Total cost of first purchase} = \$17,950.00 + \$33.95$$

$$= \$17,983.95$$

Price per share   Number of shares

$$\text{Basic cost of second purchase} = \$73.50 \quad \cdot \quad 100$$

$$= \$7350.00$$

The second purchase was automated (online), so Firm A charged a commission of $8.95.

$$\text{Total cost of second purchase} = \underset{\text{Basic cost}}{\$7350.00} + \underset{\text{Commission}}{\$8.95}$$

$$= \$7358.95$$

$$\text{Total cost for both transactions} = \$17,983.95 + \$7358.95$$

$$= \$25,342.90 \quad \longleftarrow \text{Total cost}$$

EXAMPLE 5 Finding the Return on a Stock Investment

Suppose Carina (from **Example 4**) sold all 350 shares of HOG stock using an online transaction on December 19, 2014, at a price of $74.28 per share. Find the return on the investment. (Assume that dividends were paid on September 5.)

Solution

The basic price of the stock sold is

$$(\$74.28 \text{ per share}) \cdot (350 \text{ shares}) = \$25,998.00.$$

Because Carina owned only 250 shares when dividends were paid, her dividend receipt was

$$(\$1.10 \text{ per share}) \cdot (250 \text{ shares}) = \$275.00.$$

The sale was executed online, so Firm A charged a commission of $8.95 (see **Table 15**). Find the SEC fee as described before **Example 4.**

$$\frac{\$25,998.00}{\$1,000,000} \cdot \$22.10 = \$0.574556$$

Round up to obtain an SEC fee of $0.58. Then

$$\text{Net proceeds from sale} = \underset{\text{Basic price}}{\$25,998.00} - \underset{\text{Commission}}{\$8.95} - \underset{\text{SEC fee}}{\$0.58}$$

$$= \$25,988.47.$$

Finally, the return on investment will be the sum of dividends and proceeds from the sale, less the total cost of purchasing the stock (from **Example 4**).

$$\text{Return on investment} = \$275.00 + \$25,988.47 - \$25,342.90$$

$$= \$920.57 \quad \longleftarrow \text{Final return}$$

Carina's return on the investment in HOG shares was $920.57.

Bonds

Rather than using your capital (money) to buy shares of stock in a company, you may prefer merely to *lend* money to the company, receiving an agreed-upon rate of interest for the use of your money. In this case you would buy a bond from the company rather than purchase stock. The bond (loan) is issued with a stated term (life span), after which the bond "matures" and the principal (or **face value**) is paid back to you. Over the term, the company pays you a fixed rate of interest, which depends on prevailing interest rates at the time of issue (and to some extent on the company's credit rating), rather than on the underlying value of the company.

A corporate bondholder has no stake in company profits but is (quite) certain to receive timely interest payments. If a company is unable to pay both bond interest and stock dividends, the bondholders must be paid first.

EXAMPLE 6 Finding the Return on a Bond Investment

Roy invests $10,000 in a 5-year corporate bond paying 3% annual interest, paid semiannually. Find the total return on this investment, assuming Roy holds the bond to maturity (for the entire 5 years). Ignore any broker's fees.

Solution

By the simple interest formula (see **Section 13.1**),

$$I = Prt = \$10{,}000(0.03)(5) = \$1500.$$

Notice that this amount, $1500, is the *total* return, over the 5-year period, not the annual return. Also, the fact that interest is paid twice per year (1.5% of the face value each time) has no bearing here since compounding does not occur. ■

Mutual Funds

A **mutual fund** is a pool of money collected by an investment company from many individuals and/or institutions and invested in many stocks, bonds, or money market instruments. As of 2013, in the United States alone, $15 trillion was invested in more than 7000 mutual funds. Nearly 57 million U.S. households held mutual funds, with the median mutual fund assets of these households approximately $100,000. Over a third ($6.5 trillion) of mutual fund assets were in retirement (IRA and deferred compensation plan) accounts.

The **Wall Street reform bill of 2010** put forth "the most sweeping set of changes to the financial regulatory system since the 1930s." Prompted by the failure of a number of large financial and other companies and a steep international recession beginning in 2007, the bill created a new Consumer Financial Protection Bureau within the Federal Reserve, headed by a presidentially appointed "independent" regulator, and with authority to write new rules to (theoretically) protect consumers from unfair or abusive practices in mortgages and credit cards. In fact, the bill creates vast bureaucratic control over virtually all financial areas discussed in this chapter.

A decade earlier, in 1999, congressional repeal of many earlier legal and regulatory barriers had allowed large financial conglomerates to offer one-stop shopping for services in the areas of insurance, banking, and investments.

It took over a year for the Democrat-controlled Congress to bring the 2010 bill to a vote. According to the watchdog group Public Citizen, over that period the financial industry spent nearly $600 million to hire some 1000 lobbyists to promote their interests. Debate raged about whether the bill was really to help consumers or to control business (or perhaps a combination of the two).

(*Source:* www.CNNMoney.com)

MUTUAL FUNDS VERSUS INDIVIDUAL STOCKS AND BONDS

Advantages of Mutual Funds

1. *Simplicity*
   Let someone else do the work.

2. *Diversification*
   Being part of a large pool makes it easier to own interests in many different stocks, which decreases vulnerability to large losses in one particular stock or one particular sector of the economy.

3. *Access to New Issues*
   Initial public offerings (IPOs) can sometimes be very profitable. Whereas individual investors find it difficult to get in on these, the large overall assets of a mutual fund give its managers much more access.

4. *Economies of Scale*
   Large stock purchases usually incur smaller expenses per dollar invested.

5. *Professional Management*
   Professional managers may have the expertise to pick stocks and time purchases to better achieve the stated objectives of the fund.

6. *Indexing*
   With minimal management, an index fund can maintain a portfolio that mimics a popular index (such as the S&P 500). This makes it easy for individual fund investors to achieve returns at least close to those of the index.

MUTUAL FUNDS VERSUS INDIVIDUAL STOCKS AND BONDS, CONTINUED

Disadvantages of Mutual Funds

1. *Impact of One-Time Charges and Recurring Fees*
   Sales charges, management fees, "12b-1" fees (used to pay sales representatives), and fund expenses can mount and can be difficult to identify. And paying management fees does not guarantee getting *quality* management.

2. *Hidden Cost of Brokerage*
   Recurring fees and expenses are added to give the *expense ratio* of a fund. But commissions paid by the fund for stock purchases and sales are in addition to the expense ratio. (Since 1995, funds have been required to disclose their average commission costs in their annual reports.)

3. *Some Hidden Risks of Fund Ownership*

   (a) In the event of a market crash, getting out of the fund may mean accepting securities rather than cash, and these may be difficult to redeem for a fair price.

   (b) Managers may stray from the stated strategies of the fund.

   (c) Since tax liability is passed on to fund investors and depends on purchases and sales made by fund managers, investors may be unable to avoid inheriting unwanted tax basis.

Source for advantages and disadvantages of mutual funds:
Forbes Guide to the Markets, John Wiley & Sons, Inc.

The risks and rewards associated with stocks and bonds are reflected in the mutual funds that own shares of those stocks and bonds. Historically, the rate of return over most time periods has been greater for stocks than for bonds. Accordingly, stock mutual funds have more potential for higher returns (on average) than bond mutual funds. On the other hand, there are fewer uncertainties associated with bonds, and so investors holding shares of bond mutual funds are exposed to less risk than those invested in stock funds. "Mixed asset" (or blended) mutual funds are designed to help investors balance their portfolios by dealing in both stocks and bonds, thus increasing potential earnings with stock holdings, but reducing volatility by virtue of bond holdings.

Because a mutual fund owns many different stocks, each share of the fund represents a fractional interest in each of those companies. In an "open-end" fund (by far the most common type), new shares are created and issued to buyers while the fund company absorbs the shares of sellers. Similarly, a bond mutual fund can invest in many different bonds of varying maturities, buying and selling according to market conditions. Every stock or bond held by a fund at any given time contributes to the total value of the fund. Each day, the value of a share in the fund is called the *net asset value, or* **NAV.**

An abundance of information about **mutual funds** is available on the Internet. For example, the Investment Company Institute (ICI), the national association of the American investment company industry, provides material at the site www.ici.org/.

NET ASSET VALUE OF A MUTUAL FUND

If A = Total fund assets, L = Total fund liabilities, and N = Number of shares outstanding, then the **net asset value** is calculated as follows.

$$NAV = \frac{A - L}{N}$$

EXAMPLE 7 **Finding the Number of Shares in a Mutual Fund Purchase**

Suppose, on a given day, a mutual fund has $500 million worth of stock, $500,000 in cash (not invested), and $300,000 in other assets. Total liabilities amount to $4 million, and there are 25 million shares outstanding. If Joanne invests $50,000 in this fund, how many shares will she obtain?

Solution

$$A = \$500,000,000 + \$500,000 + \$300,000$$

$$= \$500,800,000$$

$$L = \$4,000,000$$

$$N = 25,000,000$$

$$\text{NAV} = \frac{A - L}{N} \qquad \text{Formula}$$

$$= \frac{\$500,800,000 - \$4,000,000}{25,000,000} \qquad \text{Substitute values of } A, L, \text{ and } N.$$

$$= \$19.872 \qquad \text{Calculate.}$$

Because $\frac{\$50,000}{\$19.872} \approx 2516$, Joanne's $50,000 investment will purchase (to the nearest whole number) 2516 shares.   ■

Evaluating Investment Returns

Regardless of the type of investment you have or are considering (stocks, bonds, mutual funds, or others), it is important to be able to accurately evaluate and compare returns (profits or losses). Even though past performance is never a guarantee of future returns, it is crucial information. A wealth of information on stock and bond markets and mutual funds is available in many publications (for example, the *Wall Street Journal, Investor's Business Daily,* and *Barron's Weekly*) and at numerous Internet sources (for example, www.nasdaq.com).

The most important measure of performance of an investment is the **annual rate of return.** This is not *necessarily* the same as percentage return, as calculated in **Example 1,** because annual rate of return depends on the time period involved. Some commonly reported periods are daily, seven-day, monthly, month-to-date, quarterly, quarter-to-date, annual, year-to-date, 2-year, 3-year, 5-year, 10-year, 20-year, and "since inception" (since the fund or other investment vehicle was begun).

Examples 8 and 9 illustrate some of the many complications that arise when one tries to evaluate and compare different investments.

EXAMPLE 8 **Analyzing a Stock's Annual Rate of Return**

Wendell Stewart owns 50 shares of stock. His brokerage statement for the end of August showed that the stock closed that month at a price of $40 (per share), and the statement for the end of September showed a closing price of $40.12. For purposes of illustration, disregard any possible dividends, and assume that the money gained in a given month has no opportunity to earn additional returns. (Those earnings cannot be "reinvested.") Find the following.

(a) The value of these shares at the end of August

(b) Wendell's monthly return on this stock

(c) The monthly percentage return   **(d)** The annual rate of return

Solution

(a)

$$\text{Value} = \underset{\substack{\uparrow \\ \text{Price per share}}}{\$40} \cdot \underset{\substack{\uparrow \\ \text{Number of shares}}}{50} = \$2000$$

(b)

$$\text{Return} = \underset{\substack{\uparrow \\ \text{Change in price per share}}}{(\$40.12 - \$40)} \cdot \underset{\substack{\uparrow \\ \text{Number of shares}}}{50}$$

$$= \$6$$

(c)

$$\text{Percentage return} = \frac{\text{Total return}}{\text{Total value}} \cdot 100\%$$

$$= \frac{\$6}{\$2000} \cdot 100\%$$

$$= 0.3\%$$

(d) Because monthly returns do not earn more returns, we use an "arithmetic" return here. Simply add 0.3% twelve times (or multiply 0.3% by 12), to obtain 3.6%. The annual rate of return is 3.6%. ∎

EXAMPLE 9 Analyzing a Mutual Fund's Annual Rate of Return

Valerie Hoskins owns 80 shares of a mutual fund with a net asset value of $10 on October 1. Assume that the only return that the fund earns is dividends of 0.4% per month, which are automatically reinvested. Find the following.

(a) The value of Valerie's holdings in this fund on October 1

(b) The monthly return   (c) The annual rate of return

Solution

(a) Value = NAV $\cdot$ number of shares = \$10 $\cdot$ 80 = \$800

(b) Monthly return = 0.4% of \$800 = \$3.20

(c) In this case, monthly returns get reinvested. Compounding occurs. Therefore, we use a "geometric" return rather than arithmetic. To make this calculation, first find the "return relative," which is 1 plus the monthly rate of return:

$$1 + 0.4\% = 1 + 0.004 = 1.004.$$

Then multiply this return relative 12 times (raise it to the 12th power) to get an annual return relative: $1.004^{12} \approx 1.049$. Finally, subtract 1 and multiply by 100 to convert back to a percentage rate. The annual rate of return is 4.9%. ∎

A geometric return such as the one just found in **Example 9** often is called the "effective annual yield." (Notice that an arithmetic return calculation would have ignored the reinvestment compounding and would have understated the effective annual rate of return by 0.1%, because $12(0.4\%) = 4.8\%$.)

Building a Nest Egg

The most important function of investing, for most people, is to build an account for some future use, probably for retirement living. In **Example 8** of **Section 13.1,** we compared two retirement programs, Plan A and Plan B, to emphasize the importance of starting a retirement investment program early in life. The performance of investments over time is generally governed by formulas based on the summation of geometric sequences (see the margin note).

A **geometric sequence** has the property that each term is the product of the previous term and a *common ratio, r.* Thus a geometric sequence of *n* terms with first term *a* is

$$a, \ ar, \ ar^2, \ldots, ar^{n-1}.$$

The sum of these *n* terms is given by the formula

$$S = \frac{a(1 - r^n)}{1 - r}.$$

There are two major barriers to building a retirement nest egg (or whatever the goal is for accumulating wealth)—*inflation* and (*income*) *taxes*.

Table 4 (**page 756**) shows the actual historical inflation rates over 33 years (1980–2013). This reflects an average of about 3.1% per year. If we had invested for retirement over that time span, the inflation proportion (see **page 757**) indicates that we would have ended up, in 2013, paying about $\frac{233.0}{82.4} \approx 2.8$ times as much for goods and services as when we started, in 1980.

This inflationary effect, if unanticipated, could make a sizable dent in retirement living, but there is a fairly painless way to make provision for it. Periodically we can simply increase contributions by enough to keep pace with inflation.

The formula below allows us to compute the future values of an account where regular deposits are systematically adjusted for inflation. If the inflation rate is i, then the amount R is deposited at the end of year 1, $R(1 + i)$ is deposited at the end of year 2, and so on, with the deposit at the end of the year n, in general, being $R(1 + i)^{n-1}$.

FUTURE VALUE OF AN INFLATION-ADJUSTED RETIREMENT ACCOUNT

Assume annual deposits into a retirement account, adjusted for inflation. If

i = annual rate of inflation,

R = initial deposit (at the end of year 1),

r = annual rate of return on money in the account,

and n = number of years deposits are made,

then the value V of the account at the end of n years is calculated as follows.

$$V = R\left[\frac{(1 + r)^n - (1 + i)^n}{r - i}\right]$$

Putting off paying taxes for as long as possible, though often urged by financial advisors, is not always the best plan. The **Roth IRA,** available since 1998, is funded with taxed dollars, but all funds, both principal and earnings, are withdrawn later tax-free. For a young person, with many years to "grow" the investment, the prospect of avoiding taxes on that growth is attractive, especially if withdrawals will be made when the account holder is in a higher tax bracket than when contributions were made. Advantages also include less restriction on who qualifies, no forced withdrawals, and no restrictions on when withdrawals (of principal) can be made.

EXAMPLE 10 Adjusting a Retirement Account for Inflation

In **Example 8** of **Section 13.1,** Angie executed Plan A, depositing $2000 on each birthday from age 21 to age 30, then stopped depositing, and at age 65 had $428,378. Barry, with Plan B, waited until age 31 to make the first $2000 deposit, then deposited $2000 every year to age 65, and came out with only $344,634.

Compute the final account value, at age 65, for Barry's Plan B, assuming that the 35 annual deposits had been adjusted for a 3.1% annual inflation rate.

Solution

Use the "inflation-adjusted" formula given in the box. The final account value is

$$V = \$2000\left[\frac{(1 + 0.08)^{35} - (1 + 0.031)^{35}}{0.08 - 0.031}\right] \approx \$484,664.$$

Let $R = \$2000$, $r = 0.08$, $i = 0.031$, and $n = 35$.

With inflation adjustment, Plan B, by age 65, accumulates $484,664. ∎

The second barrier to building wealth—taxes—is not so easily dealt with. You will find that the more you invest and the more you earn, the higher the percentage that our progressive tax system will claim of your earnings. Probably your most effective tool in softening (though not overcoming) this effect is to take full advantage of tax-deferred accounts, such as a TSA (Tax-Sheltered Annuity, or 403(b) Plan); an IRA (Individual Retirement Account, or 401(k) plan), especially if your employer will contribute matching funds; or, if self-employed, a SEP (Simplified Employee Pension) or a SIMPLE (Savings Incentive Match Plan for Employees) plan.

With most tax-deferred retirement accounts, the accumulated money is all taxed when it is withdrawn (presumably during retirement years). To demonstrate the decided advantage of tax deferral, we will compare the two situations using the following formulas. For a fair comparison, we look at both account values *after all taxes have been paid.*

TAX-DEFERRED VERSUS TAXABLE RETIREMENT ACCOUNTS

In both cases,

R = amount withheld annually from current salary to build the retirement account,

n = number of years contributions are made,

r = annual rate of return on money in the account,

t = marginal tax rate of account holder,

V = final value of the account, **following all accumulations and payment of all taxes.**

Tax-Deferred Account

The entire amount R is contributed each year. All contributions, plus earnings, earn a return over the n years, at which time tax is paid on all money in the account. The final account value is calculated as follows.

$$V = \frac{(1 - t)R[(1 + r)^n - 1]}{r}$$

Taxable Account

Each amount R withheld from salary is taxed up front, decreasing the amount of the annual deposit to $(1 - t)R$. Furthermore, annual earnings are also taxed at the end of each year. But at the end of the accumulation period, no more tax will be due. The final account value is calculated as follows.

$$V = \frac{R[(1 + r(1 - t))^n - 1]}{r}$$

EXAMPLE 11 Comparing Tax-Deferred and Taxable Retirement Accounts

Leah Bell and Oliver Reed, both in a 20% marginal tax bracket, will each contribute $2000 annually for 20 years to retirement accounts that return 5% annually. Leah chooses a tax-deferred account, while Oliver chooses a taxable account. Compare their final account values at the end of the accumulation period, after payment of all taxes.

Solution

We have $R = \$2000$, $n = 20$, $r = 0.05$, and $t = 0.20 = 0.2$.

Leah: $V = \dfrac{(1 - 0.2)\$2000[(1 + 0.05)^{20} - 1]}{0.05} \approx \$52{,}906$ Substitute values in the "tax-deferred" formula, and calculate.

Oliver: $V = \dfrac{\$2000[(1 + 0.05(1 - 0.2))^{20} - 1]}{0.05} \approx \$47{,}645$ Substitute values in the "taxable" formula, and calculate.

$$\$52{,}906 - \$47{,}645 = \$5261$$

By deferring taxes, Leah ends up with $5261, or about 11%, more. ∎

Greater contributions, a longer accumulation period, a higher rate of return, and a higher tax bracket all will accentuate the positive effect of tax deferral.

EXAMPLE 12 Comparing Tax-Deferred and Taxable Retirement Accounts

Repeat **Example 11,** but this time let

$$R = \$5000, \quad n = 40, \quad r = 0.10, \quad \text{and} \quad t = 0.40 = 0.4.$$

Solution

Leah: $V = \dfrac{(1 - 0.4)\$5000[\,(1 + 0.10)^{40} - 1\,]}{0.10}$ Substitute values in the "tax-deferred" formula.

$\approx \$1,327,778$

Oliver: $V = \dfrac{\$5000[\,(1 + 0.10(1 - 0.4))^{40} - 1\,]}{0.10}$ Substitute values in the "taxable" formula.

$\approx \$464,286$

With these higher parameters, Leah's advantage is dramatic:

$$\$1,327,778 - \$464,286 = \$863,492, \quad \text{or about } 186\%, \text{ more.} \quad \blacksquare$$

Tax-deferred is not the same as "tax-free," which makes the result of **Example 12** less impressive than it may seem. This type of retirement income is taxed at the time it is withdrawn. People who sell tax-deferred plans stress that you will probably be in a lower tax bracket after retirement because of reduced income. But many find this is not so, especially compared to early career income, and especially if your retirement account investments have done very well, which could make your required withdrawals quite large. Besides, who can tell what general tax rates will be 30 years from now?

FOR FURTHER THOUGHT

Summary of Investments

The summary of various types of investments in **Table 16,** on the next page, is based on average cases and is intended only as a general comparison of investment opportunities. There are numerous exceptions to the characteristics shown. For example, although the table shows no selling fees for mutual funds, this is really true only for so-called no-load funds. The "loaded" funds do charge "early redemption fees" or other kinds of sales charges. This is not to say that a no-load fund is necessarily better. For example, the absence of sales fees may be offset by higher "management fees."

These various costs, as well as other important factors, will be clearly specified in a fund's prospectus and should be studied carefully before a purchase decision is made. Some expertise is advisable for mutual fund investing, just less so than with certain other options, like direct stock purchases, raw land, or collectibles.

To use the table, read across the columns to find the general characteristics of the investment.

"Liquidity" refers to the ability to get cash from the investment quickly.

For Group or Individual Investigation

List **(a)** some investment types you would recommend considering and **(b)** some you would recommend avoiding for a friend whose main investment objective is as follows.

1. Avoid losing money.
2. Avoid losing purchasing power.
3. Avoid having to learn about investments.
4. Avoid having to work on investments.
5. Be sure to realize a gain.
6. Be able to "cash in" at any time.
7. Get as high a return as possible.
8. Be able to "cash in" without paying fees.
9. Realize quick profits.
10. Realize growth over the long term.

Table 16 Summary of Investments

Investment	Protection of Principal	Protection against Inflation	Rate of Return (%)	Certainty of Return	Selling Fees	Liquidity	Long-term Growth	Requires Work from Investor	Expert Knowledge Required
Cash	excellent	none	0			excellent	no	no	no
Ordinary life insurance	good	poor	2–4	excellent	high	excellent	no	no	no
Savings bonds	excellent	poor	3–5	excellent	none	excellent	no	no	no
Bank savings	excellent	poor	2–4	excellent	none	excellent	no	no	no
Credit union	excellent	poor	3–4	excellent	none	excellent	no	no	no
Corporation bonds	good	poor	5–7	excellent	low	good	no	some	some
Tax-free municipal bonds	excellent	poor	2–5	excellent	medium	good	no	no	some
Corporation stock	good	good	3–12	good	medium	good	yes	some	some
Preferred stock	good	poor	4–8	excellent	medium	good	no	some	some
Mutual funds	good	good	3–12	good	none	good	yes	no	no
Your own home	good	good	4–10	good	medium	poor	yes	yes	no
Mortgages on the homes of others	fair	poor	5–8	fair	high	poor	no	yes	some
Raw land	fair	good	?	fair	medium	poor	yes	no	yes
Rental properties	good	good	4–8	fair	medium	poor	yes	yes	some
Stamps, coins, antiques	fair	good	0–10	fair	high	poor	yes	yes	yes
Your own business	fair	good	0–20	poor	high	poor	yes	yes	yes

13.5 EXERCISES

*Refer to the stock table (**Table 14** on **page 791**) for Exercises 1–34.*

Reading Stock Charts *Find each of the following.*

1. closing price for Deere & Co (DE)

2. 52-week high for Duke Energy (DUK)

3. percent change from the previous day for General Mills (GIS)

4. sales of the day for Kimberly-Clark (KMB)

5. high price for FedEx Corp (FDX) for the day

6. change from the previous day for Hewlett-Packard (HPQ)

7. year-to-date percentage change for Pearson Plc (PSO)

8. dividend for Chevron Corp (CVX)

9. the stock with the highest price-to-earnings ratio

10. the stock with the highest dividend yield

11. the stock with the highest volume (most shares sold) for the day

12. the stock with the lowest opening price

Finding Stock Costs *Find the basic cost (ignoring any broker fees) for each stock purchase, at the day's closing price.*

13. 300 shares of Caterpillar Inc (CAT)

14. 200 shares of Walt Disney (DIS)

15. 400 shares of General Mills (GIS)

16. 700 shares of Allstate (ALL)

Finding Stock Costs *Find the cost, at the day's closing price, for each stock purchase. Include typical discount broker commissions as described in the text, using Firm B.*

	Stock Symbol	Number of Shares	Transaction Type
17.	PSO	60	broker-assisted
18.	GIS	70	broker-assisted
19.	BAC	355	phone
20.	CAT	585	phone
21.	HOG	2500	online
22.	DUK	1500	online
23.	YUM	2400	phone
24.	DIS	20,000	broker-assisted

Finding Receipts for Stock Sales *Find the amount received by the sellers of each stock (at the day's closing prices). Deduct sales expenses as described in the text, using Firm C.*

	Stock Symbol	Number of Shares	Transaction Type
25.	ALL	400	broker-assisted
26.	KMX	600	broker-assisted
27.	CVX	500	phone
28.	DE	700	phone
29.	FDX	1350	online
30.	KMB	2740	online
31.	HPQ	1480	broker-assisted
32.	PSO	1270	online

Finding Net Results of Combined Transactions *For each combined transaction (executed at the closing price of the day), find the net amount paid out or taken in. Assume typical expenses as outlined in the text, using Firm A.*

33. Paul Barnes bought 100 shares of Walt Disney and sold 120 shares of General Mills, both broker-assisted trades.

34. Jasmine Collins bought 800 shares of Bank of America and sold 200 shares of Chevron, both online trades.

Costs and Returns of Stock Investments *For each of the following stock investments, find (a) the total purchase price, (b) the total dividend amount, (c) the capital gain or loss, (d) the total return, and (e) the percentage return. Ignore broker and SEC fees.*

	Number of Shares	Purchase Price per Share	Dividend per Share	Sale Price per Share
35.	40	$20.00	$2.00	$44.00
36.	20	$25.00	$1.00	$22.00
37.	100	$12.50	$1.08	$10.15
38.	200	$8.80	$1.12	$11.30

Total Return on Bond Investments *Find the total return earned by each bond in Exercises 39–42.*

	Face Value	Annual Interest Rate	Term to Maturity
39.	$1000	5.5%	5 years
40.	$5000	6.4%	10 years
41.	$10,000	7.11%	3 months
42.	$50,000	4.88%	6 months

Net Asset Value of a Mutual Fund *For each investment, find (a) the net asset value, and (b) the number of shares purchased.*

	Amount Invested	Total Fund Assets	Total Fund Liabilities	Total Shares Outstanding
43.	$3500	$875 million	$36 million	80 million
44.	$1800	$643 million	$102 million	50 million
45.	$25,470	$2.31 billion	$135 million	263 million
46.	$83,250	$1.48 billion	$84 million	112 million

Finding Monthly and Annual Investment Returns *For each investment, assume that there is no opportunity for reinvestment of returns. In each case find* **(a)** *the monthly return,* **(b)** *the annual return, and* **(c)** *the annual percentage return.*

	Amount Invested	Monthly Percentage Return
47.	$645	1.3%
48.	$895	0.9%
49.	$2498	2.3%
50.	$4983	1.8%

Effective Annual Rate of Return of Mutual Fund Investments *Assume that each mutual fund investment earns monthly returns that are reinvested and subsequently earn at the same rate. In each case find* **(a)** *the beginning value of the investment,* **(b)** *the first monthly return, and* **(c)** *the effective annual yield.*

	Beginning NAV	Number of Shares Purchased	Monthly Percentage Return
51.	$9.63	125	1.5%
52.	$12.40	185	2.3%
53.	$11.94	350	1.83%
54.	$18.54	548	2.22%

Inflation-Adjusted Retirement Accounts *Find the future value (to the nearest dollar) of each inflation-adjusted retirement account. Deposits are made at the end of each year.*

	Annual Inflation Rate	Initial Deposit	Annual Rate of Return	Number of Years
55.	3%	$2000	5%	25
56.	2%	$1000	6%	20
57.	1%	$5000	6.5%	40
58.	4%	$2500	7%	30

The Effect of Tax Deferral on Retirement Accounts *Find the final value, after all taxes are paid, for each account if* **(a)** *taxes are deferred, or* **(b)** *taxes are not deferred. In both cases, deposits are made at the end of each year.*

	Marginal Tax Rate	Regular Deferred Contribution	Annual Rate of Return	Number of Years
59.	15%	$1000	5%	30
60.	10%	$500	7%	15
61.	35%	$1500	6%	10
62.	28%	$3000	10%	25

Decide How Much to Put Aside *Suppose that you plan to retire in 30 years and will need $1,000,000 in your retirement account to do so. In Exercises 64 and 65, determine the required annual contribution toward retirement if your retirement account is* **(a)** *tax-deferred and* **(b)** *taxable. Assume that your marginal tax rate will remain at 25%.*

63. Suppose the annual rate of return on the money in your account is 10%.

64. Suppose the annual rate of return on the money in your account is 6%.

Solve each problem.

65. *Required Annual Contributions to Reach Retirement Goal* The formulas for finding final values of tax-deferred and taxable retirement accounts can be solved for R to find the required annual contributions necessary to reach an amount V by the time you retire.

   (a) Solve the "tax-deferred" account formula for R.

   (b) Solve the "taxable" account formula for R.

66. *Monthly Deposits Adjusted for Inflation* In an inflation-adjusted retirement account, let i denote annual inflation, let r denote annual return, and let n denote number of years, as in the text, but suppose deposits are made monthly rather than yearly with initial deposit R.

   (a) What expression represents the amount that would be deposited at the end of the second month?

   (b) Modify the future value formula for an inflation-adjusted account to accommodate the more frequent deposits.

   (c) Find (to the nearest dollar) the future value for monthly deposits of $100 (initially) for 20 years if $i = 0.03$ and $r = 0.06$.

67. *Finding an Unknown Rate* Given the compound interest formula

$$A = P\left(1 + \frac{r}{n}\right)^m,$$

do the following.

   (a) Solve the formula for r.

   (b) Find the annual rate r if $50 grows to $85.49 in 10 years with interest compounded quarterly. Give r to the nearest tenth of a percent.

68. *Comparing Continuous with Annual Compounding* It was suggested in the text that inflation is more accurately reflected by the continuous compounding formula than by periodic compounding. Compute the ratio

$$\frac{Pe^{rt}}{P(1+r)^n} = \frac{e^{rt}}{(1+r)^n}$$

to find how much (to the nearest tenth of a percent) continuous compounding exceeds annual compounding. Use a rate of 3% over a period of 30 years.

Spreading Mutual Fund Investments among Asset classes *Mutual funds (as well as other kinds of investments) normally are categorized into one of several "asset classes," according to the kinds of stocks or other securities they hold. Small capitalization funds are most aggressive, while cash is most conservative. Many investors, often with the help of an advisor, try to construct their portfolios in accordance with their stage of life. Basically, the idea is that a younger person can afford to be more aggressive (and assume more risk), while an older investor should be more conservative (assuming less risk). The investment diagrams here show typical percentage ranges that might be recommended by an investment advisor.*

In Exercises 69–72, divide the given investor's money into the five categories so as to position them right at the middle of the recommended ranges.

Asset Classes

a. Aggressive Growth (small cap)

b. Growth

c. Growth & Income

d. Income

e. Cash

69. Alyssa Smith, in her early investing years, with $20,000 to invest

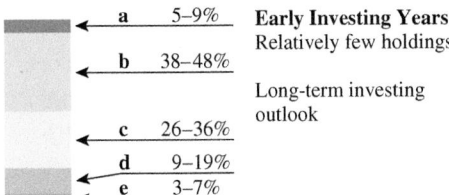

a	5–9%	**Early Investing Years**
b	38–48%	Relatively few holdings
		Long-term investing outlook
c	26–36%	
d	9–19%	
e	3–7%	

70. Justin Jones, in his good earning years, with $250,000 to invest

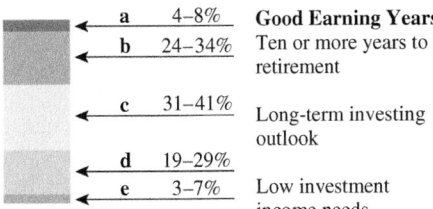

a	4–8%	**Good Earning Years**
b	24–34%	Ten or more years to retirement
c	31–41%	Long-term investing outlook
d	19–29%	
e	3–7%	Low investment income needs

71. Akira Suzuki, in his high-income/saving years, with $400,000 to invest

a	0–4%	**High-Income/**
b	23–33%	**Saving Years**
		Less than 10 years to retirement
c	31–41%	
d	24–34%	Fewer financial responsibilities
e	3–7%	

72. Eve McLean, retired, with $845,000 to invest

a	0–4%	**Retirement Years**
b	10–20%	Reduced earning power
c	39–49%	High investment income needs
d	29–39%	
e	3–7%	

The Effect of Taxes on Investment Returns *Income from municipal bonds generally is exempt from federal, and sometimes state, income tax. For an investor with a marginal combined state and federal tax rate of 35%, a taxable return of 6% would yield only 3.9% (65% of 6%). At that tax rate, a tax-exempt return of 3.9% is equivalent to a taxable return of 6%. Find the tax-exempt rate of return that is equivalent to the given taxable rate of return for each investor.*

	Investor	Marginal Combined Tax Rate	Taxable Rate of Return
73.	Joshua Sellers	25%	5%
74.	Sherry Lee	30%	7%
75.	Berna Barak	35%	8%
76.	Sean Stewart	40%	10%

Write responses to Exercises 77–84. Some research may be required.

77. Describe "dollar-cost averaging," and relate it to advantage number 1 of mutual funds as listed in the text.

78. From **Table 14** in the text, would you say that May 22, 2014, was a "good day" on Wall Street or a "bad day"?

79. Log onto www.napfa.org to research financial planners. Then report on what you would look for in a planner.

80. A great deal of research has been done in attempts to understand and predict trends in the stock market. Discuss the term *financial engineering*. In this context, what is a *rocket scientist* (or *quant*)?

81. Regarding mutual funds, discuss the difference between a *front-end load* and a *contingent deferred sales charge*.

82. What is a *growth stock?* What is an *income stock?*

83. With respect to investing in corporate America, describe the difference between being an owner and being a lender.

84. Comment on the graph shown here.

CHAPTER 13 SUMMARY

KEY TERMS

13.1

interest
principal
interest rate
simple interest
compound interest
future (maturity) value
present value
period
nominal rate
effective annual yield
price inflation
consumer price index (CPI)
deflation
recession
years to double
rule of 70

13.2

consumer credit
real estate mortgage

installment loan
closed-end credit
revolving loan
open-end credit
add-on interest
credit limit
itemized billing
finance charges
average daily balance
    method

13.3

Truth in Lending Act
annual percentage
    rate (APR)
unearned interest
actuarial method
rule of 78
early payment
    penalty
payoff amount

13.4

mortgage
term
down payment
principal amount
fixed-rate mortgage
amortizing
amortization schedule
adjustable-rate mortgage
    (ARM)
closing costs
escrow account
points
recurring costs
property taxes
homeowner's insurance
maintenance
opportunity cost

13.5

dividend

capital gain
capital loss
return on investment
stock exchanges
price-to-earnings
    ratio
commission
full-service broker
discount broker
principal
round lot
odd lot
odd-lot differential
limit order
automated trades
broker-assisted
    trades
SEC fee
face value
mutual fund
net asset value (NAV)
annual rate of return

TEST YOUR WORD POWER

See how well you have learned the vocabulary in this chapter.

1. **Compound interest** is
   A. calculated only on the original principal, and is generally more than simple interest.
   B. calculated on principal and previously earned interest.
   C. interest earned by two or more investments simultaneously.
   D. generally less than simple interest, but more easily calculated.

2. An **installment loan** is
   A. a type of open-ended credit loan with an undetermined number of payments.
   B. a loan in which additional credit may be extended before the initial amount is paid off.
   C. a type of closed-end credit that involves a predetermined number of equal payments.
   D. a loan extended specifically for the installation of appliances or furniture.

3. **Unearned interest** is
   A. the amount of income a taxpayer receives from investments as opposed to wages.

   B. the penalty paid by the borrower for being delinquent on one or more monthly payments.
   C. the amount by which the original finance charge is reduced when a loan is paid off early.
   D. the interest paid for borrowing as opposed to that received from an investment.

4. An **escrow account** (or impound account) is
   A. an account maintained by a lender and used to pay property taxes and insurance premiums.
   B. an account that is terminated when documents are signed and escrow "closes."
   C. always a requirement to obtain a mortgage.
   D. a savings account from which principal and interest payments are made.

5. A **mortgage** is
   A. an extension of unsecured credit, usually for a short period of time.
   B. a form of unsecured debt, in which wages may be garnished if payments are missed.
   C. the process of dividing principal and interest into equal periodic payments.
   D. a loan for a substantial amount, and for which property is pledged as security.

6. The **capital gain** on an investment is
  A. the overall return on the investment, including any dividends.
  B. the profit resulting from selling the investment for more than the purchase price.

C. the annual increase in the value of the investment.
D. the difference between the purchase price and the selling price.

ANSWERS
1. B **2.** C **3.** C **4.** A **5.** D **6.** B

QUICK REVIEW

Concepts   *Examples*

13.1 The Time Value of Money

Simple Interest
If principal P is borrowed for t years at an annual interest rate r, then (simple) interest is given by

$$I = Prt.$$

Future Value for Simple Interest
$$A = P(1 + rt)$$

Future Value for Compound Interest
If interest is compounded n times per year, then

$$A = P\left(1 + \frac{r}{n}\right)^{nt}.$$

If \$2000 is borrowed at 3% simple interest for 5 years, find the future value (at the end of the 5-year term).

$$A = P(1 + rt)$$
$$= \$2000[1 + 0.03(5)]$$
$$= \$2300$$

If the \$2000 is borrowed at 3% compounded monthly, find the future value (at the end of the 5-year term).

$$A = \$2000\left(1 + \frac{0.03}{12}\right)^{12(5)}$$
$$= \$2000(1.0025)^{60}$$
$$= \$2323.23$$

Thus \$300 interest was paid with the simple interest loan, while \$323.23 was paid with compound interest.

Present Value for Compound Interest
Solve the above equation for P.

$$P = \frac{A}{\left(1 + \frac{r}{n}\right)^{nt}}$$

A company anticipates needing \$20,000 to purchase new equipment in 5 years. How much would the company need to invest now at 6% annual interest, compounded daily, in order to have the necessary amount in 5 years?

$$P = \frac{\$20,000}{\left(1 + \frac{0.06}{365}\right)^{365(5)}} = \$14,816.73$$

Effective Annual Yield
The effective annual yield Y of an account paying a nominal annual rate r, compounded n times per year, is calculated as follows.

$$Y = \left(1 + \frac{r}{n}\right)^{n} - 1$$

Future Value for Continuous Compounding
$$A = Pe^{rt}$$

Find the effective annual yield of an account paying 2.000% annual interest, compounded quarterly.

$$Y = \left(1 + \frac{0.02}{4}\right)^{4} - 1 = 2.015\%$$

If \$12,500 is invested in a money market account at 2.5% compounded continuously, find the value of the account after 7 years.

$$A = \$12,500e^{0.025(7)} = \$14,890.58$$

Concepts	Examples

13.2 Consumer Credit

Common Types of Consumer Credit
Installment loans involve a set amount borrowed, to be paid off by a predetermined number of equal payments **(installments).** The total of the payments will be the loan amount plus the interest added on.

A business owner purchases $5200 worth of office equipment by making a down payment of $1000 and financing the remaining balance with an installment loan with an interest rate of 5.5% over 2 years.

Find the total cost of the purchase.

Amount financed: $P = \$5200 - \$1000 = \$4200$

Interest paid: $I = Prt$

$$= \$4200(0.055)(2)$$

$$= \$462$$

Amount to be repaid:

$$P + I = \$4200 + \$462 = \$4662$$

Monthly payment: $\dfrac{\$4662}{24} = \$194.25$

Total cost: $\$1000 \; + \; \$4662 \; = \; \$5662$

Down payment   Loan repayment

Revolving loans (such as credit card accounts) involve **open-end credit** up to a predetermined **credit limit.** Charges are made and then itemized at the end of each billing period (usually a month). **Finance charges** are generally determined by the **average daily balance** for a given billing period.

A bank charges 1.4% per month on average daily balances for credit cards it issues. A billing period opens on Sept. 3 with a balance of $327.56. Transactions on the account for the period included a payment of $100 on Sept. 13 and a purchase in the amount of $158 on Sept. 25.

Find the average daily balance, the finance charge, and the account balance for the Oct. 3 billing.

The running balance was $327.56 from Sept. 3 to Sept. 13 (for 10 days), $227.56 from Sept. 13 to Sept. 25 (for 12 days), and $385.56 from Sept. 25 to Oct. 3 (8 days).

Average daily balance for the period:

$$\frac{\$327.56(10) + \$227.56(12) + \$385.56(8)}{30} = \$303.03$$

Finance charge for Oct. 3 billing:

$$0.014(\$303.03) = \$4.24$$

The account balance for the Oct. 3 billing statement will be the sum of the last running balance and the finance charge.

$$\text{Ending balance} = \$385.56 + \$4.24$$

$$= \$389.80$$

Concepts	Examples

13.3 Truth in Lending

Lenders must (as required by the Truth in Lending Act) divulge the true cost of a loan by reporting the **annual percentage rate (APR)** to the borrower. **Table 5** on **page 767** gives the APR for a loan with a given number of monthly payments and a given finance charge (per $100 financed).

Makoto purchases a $10,200 car. He makes a $1500 down payment and agrees to pay 36 monthly payments of $270.62. The dealer claims a 7% annual interest rate.

Is this dealer being truthful in lending?

Amount financed: $10,200 − $1500 = $8700

Cost of 36 monthly payments: 36 · $270.62 = $9742.32

Total finance charge: $9742.32 − $8700 = $1042.32

Finance charge per $100 financed:

$$\frac{\$1042.32}{\$8700} \cdot \$100 = \$11.98$$

Table 5 shows that for 36 monthly payments, this finance charge per $100 financed corresponds to an APR of 7.5%. *The dealer is not being truthful in lending.*

Calculating Unearned Interest

When a borrower pays off a loan early, the lender has not "earned" the full amount of interest originally disclosed when the loan was initiated. The amount of **unearned interest u** is calculated in one of the following two ways.

Makoto straightened things out with the dealer and financed the $8700 at 7% APR, which resulted in 36 monthly payments of $268.63. But he has decided to pay the loan off 12 months early.

Which method of calculating the payoff amount would be better for Makoto?

Actuarial Method

$$u = kR\left(\frac{h}{\$100 + h}\right)$$

Here R is the regular monthly payment, k is the number of scheduled payments remaining, and h is the finance charge per $100 for a loan with the same APR and k monthly payments.

Actuarial method: We need to find h, the finance charge per $100 financed at 7% APR for 12 months. **Table 5** gives a value of $h = \$3.83$.

Unearned interest:

$$u = 12(\$268.63)\left(\frac{\$3.83}{\$100 + \$3.83}\right) = \$118.91$$

Payoff amount:

$$13 \cdot \$268.63 - \$118.91 = \$3373.28$$

Rule of 78

$$u = \frac{k(k + 1)}{n(n + 1)} \cdot F$$

Here F is the original finance charge, n is the number of payments originally scheduled, and k is the number of scheduled payments remaining.

Rule of 78: We need the corrected finance charge (using the smaller monthly payments).

$$F = 36 \cdot \$268.63 - \$8700 = \$970.68$$

Unearned interest:

$$u = \frac{12(13)}{36(37)} \cdot \$970.68 = \$113.68$$

Payoff Amount

To pay the loan off with k payments remaining (after the current payment), the borrower would need to pay the following.

$$\textbf{Payoff amount} = (k + 1)R - u$$

Payoff amount:

$$13 \cdot \$268.63 - \$113.68 = \$3378.51$$

It is to Makoto's advantage if the *actuarial method* is used, since the payoff amount would be

$$\$5.23 \text{ less.}$$

Concepts	*Examples*

Finance Charge Per $100 Financed
If a loan is structured in such a way that its APR or number of remaining payments (or both) are not found in **Table 5,** then h, the finance charge per $100 financed, may be calculated by the following formula.

$$h = \frac{n \cdot \frac{APR}{12} \cdot \$100}{1 - \left(1 + \frac{APR}{12}\right)^{-n}} - \$100$$

Here n is the number of monthly payments required to pay off the loan.

Makoto financed the $8700 at 7.8% interest and agreed to 42 monthly payments of $237.37. He decides to pay off the loan at the time of his 34th payment.
  What is the finance charge per $100 financed?

$$h = \frac{8 \cdot \frac{0.078}{12} \cdot \$100}{1 - \left(1 + \frac{0.078}{12}\right)^{-8}} - \$100 = \$2.95 \quad \text{Here } n = 42 - 34 = 8.$$

This figure can be used to calculate the unearned interest and the payoff amount by the actuarial method.

13.4 The Costs and Advantages of Home Ownership

When a buyer borrows money to make a home purchase, the lender holds the property as security for the loan. Such an arrangement is a **mortgage.** A **fixed-rate mortgage** has regular periodic payments over the life **(term)** of the loan, in the amount of

$$R = \frac{P\left(\frac{r}{12}\right)}{1 - \left(\frac{12}{12 + r}\right)^{12t}}.$$

An **amortization schedule** shows all payments for the life of the loan, broken down into allocations for principal and interest for each payment.

Find the monthly payment on an $80,000 fixed-rate loan at 4.0% over 30 years.

$$R = \frac{\$80,000\left(\frac{0.04}{12}\right)}{1 - \left(\frac{12}{12 + 0.04}\right)^{12(30)}} = \$381.93$$

Amortization schedule for this loan (in part):

Payment Number	Interest Payment	Principal Payment	Balance of Principal
			$80,000.00
1	$266.67	$115.26	$79,884.74
2	$266.28	$115.65	$79,769.09
358	$3.79	$378.14	$760.06
359	$2.53	$379.40	$380.66
360	$1.27	$380.66	$0.00

An **adjustable-rate mortgage (ARM)** has a rate based on a fluctuating **index** and a **margin** determined by the lender. The introductory rate will stay fixed for a period of time, and then it will adjust according to the current value of the index.

Molly takes out a 5/1 ARM for $120,000, with a 30-year term. The introductory rate is determined by an index at 0.7% and a margin of 2.5% (a 3.2% rate). The initial payment amount for this loan is $518.96, and the amortization schedule for the first five years shows a principal balance of $107,072.98 after the 60th payment.

Payment Number	Interest Payment	Principal Payment	Balance of Principal
			$120,000.00
1	$320.00	$198.96	$119,801.04
2	$319.47	$199.49	$119,601.55
60	$286.15	$232.81	$107,072.98

Concepts	*Examples*

When an adjustment occurs, the new payment amount is found using the above formula, replacing P with the principal balance at the end of the last adjustment period, replacing r with the new adjusted rate, and replacing t with the number of years remaining in the original term.

At the end of five years, the index has increased to 1.9%. Adding the 2.5% margin gives an adjusted rate of 4.4% for the sixth year.

Find the new amount for payments 61–72.

$$R = \frac{\$107{,}072.98\left(\frac{0.044}{12}\right)}{1 - \left(\frac{12}{12 + 0.044}\right)^{12(25)}} = \$589.09 \qquad \text{Monthly payments jump \$70.13.}$$

In addition to the **down payment** made on a mortgage, there are other one-time expenses involved in purchasing a home. These are the **closing costs.**

Mary takes out a 20-year fixed rate mortgage at 4.5% for $116,000 to purchase a $145,000 home, and uses a "direct lender" to avoid broker fees. The loan closes eight days before the end of the month. Closing costs are shown.

Loan origination fee (2%)	$?
Document fees	525
Transfer taxes	140
Title services	350
Title insurance	600
Recording fees	90
Escrow deposit	1305
Daily interest charges	?

Compute the total closing costs for this mortgage.

Loan origination fee:

$$0.02(\$116{,}000) = \$2320$$

Daily interest charges (for 8 days on the beginning balance):

$$8 \cdot \$116{,}000 \cdot \frac{0.045}{365} \approx \$114$$

Adding these amounts to those listed above gives the following.

$$\$5444 \quad \longleftarrow \text{Total closing costs}$$

Recurring Costs of Homeownership
These include

- **property taxes,**
- **homeowner's insurance,** and
- **maintenance** of the property.

Mary's combined tax bracket is 30%, and property taxes in Mary's county amount to 1.2% of property value. Her homeowner's insurance rate is 0.3% of property value, and annual maintenance costs are estimated to be 0.4% of the purchase price.

Find the recurring costs (for the first year).

$$\text{Property taxes} = 0.012(\$145{,}000)(0.7)$$

$$= \$1218$$

$$\text{Insurance} = 0.003(\$145{,}000)$$

$$= \$435$$

$$\text{Maintenance} = 0.004(\$145{,}000)$$

$$= \$580$$

Concepts	*Examples*

13.5 Financial Investments

Classes of Investments
Investing puts capital to work for the investor.

Stocks
Purchasing company stock makes the investor a part owner of the company, so the investor shares in the profits (in the form of **dividends**) and in the growth (or decline) of the company's value over time.

An investor purchased 200 shares of FedEx Corp (FDX) stock at the closing price for May 22, 2014. He kept the stock for a year (during which one dividend was paid out) and then sold at a price of $150.02 per share. Assume the brokerage firm charged $8.95 for each transaction.

Find the return on investment for the FDX shares.

Table 14 shows that the closing price of FDX stock on May 22, 2014 was $139.33.

$$\text{Basic cost:} \quad 200 \cdot \$139.33 = \$27,866.00$$

Table 14 shows the dividend to be $0.60 per share.

$$\text{Dividend for 200 shares:} \quad 200 \cdot \$0.60 = \$120.00$$

Proceeds from sale of the shares a year later:

$$200 \cdot \$150.02 = \$30,004.00$$

$$\text{SEC fee:} \quad \$30,004.00 \cdot \left(\frac{\$22.10}{\$1,000,000} \right) \approx \$0.663 \rightarrow \$0.67$$

Expenses	
Cost of purchase	$27,866.00
Purchase commission	$8.95
Sale commission	$8.95
SEC fee	$0.67
Total:	**$27,884.57**

Income	
Proceeds from sale	$30,004.00
Dividend	$120.00
Total:	**$30,124.00**

$$\underset{\substack{\text{Total} \\ \text{income}}}{\$30,124.00} - \underset{\substack{\text{Total} \\ \text{expenses}}}{\$27,884.57} = \underset{\substack{\text{Return on} \\ \text{investment}}}{\$2239.43}$$

Bonds
When an investor purchases a bond, the issuing company agrees to pay a fixed rate of interest over the term of the bond, and then to pay back the original purchase price when the bond matures (at the end of the term).

Find the return on a $2000, 2-year corporate bond paying 4% annual interest.

$$I = Prt = \$2000(0.04)(2) = \$160$$

Mutual Funds
A mutual fund is a pool of money collected by an investment company to buy stocks, bonds, and other investments.

Net Asset Value (NAV) of a Mutual Fund

$$\text{NAV} = \frac{A - L}{N}$$

Here A = total fund assets, L = total fund liabilities, and N = number of shares outstanding.

Find the net asset value of a mutual fund having $1.5 billion in assets, $280 million in liabilities, and 40 million shares outstanding.

$$\text{NAV} = \frac{\$1,500,000,000 - \$280,000,000}{40,000,000} = \$30.50$$

An investment of $10,000 would purchase

$$\frac{\$10,000}{\$30.50} \approx 328 \text{ shares.}$$

Concepts	*Examples*

Annual Rate of Return

This measure of the performance of an investment may change depending on the time period for which this rate is calculated.

Joe owns 1000 shares of a mutual fund with a net asset value of $15.00 on July 1. The fund pays a 0.2% dividend per month (reinvested in the fund), and on August 1, the NAV had increased to $15.12.

Find the annual rate of return on his investment.

Holdings July 1: $1000 \cdot \$15.00 = \$15,000.00$

Dividend for July: $0.002(\$15,000.00) = \$30.00$

New value August 1: $1000 \cdot \$15.12 = \$15,120.00$

Holdings August 1: $\$15,120.00 + \$30.00 = \$15,150.00$

Rate of return for one month:

$$\frac{\$15,150 - \$15,000}{\$15,000} \cdot 100\% = 1.0\%$$

Annual rate of return for that month:

$$(1 + 0.01)^{12} - 1 \approx 0.127 = 12.7\%$$

Future Value of an Inflation-Adjusted Retirement Account

$$V = R\left[\frac{(1 + r)^n - (1 + i)^n}{r - i}\right]$$

where

i = annual rate of inflation,

R = initial deposit (end of year 1),

r = annual rate of return on account,

n = number of years deposits are made.

The inflation rate is 3% per year, and $5000 is invested in a retirement account (with a 6% annual rate of return) at the end of year 1. Deposits are increased by 3% each year.

What will the account be worth after 20 years?

$$V = \$5000\left[\frac{(1 + 0.06)^{20} - (1 + 0.03)^{20}}{0.06 - 0.03}\right]$$

$$= \$233,504.04$$

Retirement accounts can be tax-deferred (meaning that monies invested and earnings are not taxed until they are withdrawn in retirement), or taxable. If

R = amount withheld annually from salary to build the retirement account,

n = number of years contributions are made,

r = annual rate of return on account,

t = marginal tax rate of account holder,

then the final value V of the account (including all earnings and payment of taxes) is calculated as follows.

$$V = \frac{(1 - t)R[(1 + r)^n - 1]}{r} \quad \text{Tax-deferred account}$$

$$V = \frac{R[(1 + r(1 - t))^n - 1]}{r} \quad \text{Taxable account}$$

Monique wants to contribute $10,000 annually to a retirement account and wishes to retire in 25 years. Her marginal tax rate is 30%. Assume an inflation rate of 2.5% over the next 25 years and an annual rate of return of 8% on investments.

Should Monique invest in a tax-deferred account or a taxable account?

$$V = \frac{(1 - 0.30)(\$10,000)(1.08^{25} - 1)}{0.08} \quad \text{Tax-deferred account}$$

$$= \$511,741.58 \quad \leftarrow \text{Better option}$$

$$V = \frac{\$10,000[(1 + 0.08(0.7))^{25} - 1]}{0.08} \quad \text{Taxable account}$$

$$= \$363,099.06$$

The tax-deferred account is better by
$511,741.58 - $363,099.06 = $148,642.52 or about 41%.

CHAPTER 13   TEST

Find all monetary answers to the nearest cent. Use tables and formulas from the chapter as necessary.

Finding the Future Value of a Deposit   *Find the future value of each deposit.*

1. $1000 for 5 years at 4% simple interest

2. $500 for 2 years at 6% compounded quarterly

Solve each problem.

3. **Effective Annual Yield of an Account**   Find the effective annual yield to the nearest hundredth of a percent for an account paying 2% compounded monthly.

4. **Years to Double by the Rule of 70**   Use the rule of 70 to estimate the years to double at an inflation rate of 4%.

5. **Finding the Present Value of a Deposit**   What amount deposited today in an account paying 4% compounded semiannually would grow to $100,000 in 10 years?

6. **Finding Bank Card Interest by the Average Daily Balance Method**   Jolene's MasterCard statement shows an average daily balance of $680. Find the interest due if the rate is 1.6% per month.

Analyzing a Consumer Loan   *Julio buys a koi fish pond (and fish to put in it) for his wife on their anniversary. He pays $8000 for the pond with $2000 down. The dealer charges add-on interest of 3.5% per year, and Julio agrees to pay the loan with 36 equal monthly payments. Use this information for Exercises 7–10.*

7. Find the total amount of interest he will pay.

8. Find the monthly payment.

9. Find the APR value (to the nearest half percent).

10. Find **(a)** the unearned interest and **(b)** the payoff amount if he repays the loan in full with 12 months remaining. Use the most accurate method available.

11. **True Annual Interest Rate in Consumer Financing**   Hot Tub Heaven wants to include financing terms in its advertising. If the price of a hot tub is $3000 and the finance charge with no down payment is $115 over a 12-month period (12 equal monthly payments), find the true annual interest rate (APR).

12. Explain what a mutual fund is, and discuss several of its advantages and disadvantages.

Finding the Monthly Payment on a Home Mortgage   *Find the monthly payment required for each home loan.*

13. The mortgage is for $150,000 at a fixed rate of 4.5% for 25 years. Amortize principal and interest only, disregarding taxes, insurance, and other costs.

14. The purchase price of the home is $218,000. The down payment is 20%. Interest is at 5.0% fixed for a term of 30 years. Annual taxes are $2500, and annual insurance is $750.

Solve each problem.

15. **Cost of Points in a Home Loan**   If the lender in **Exercise 14** charges two *points,* how much does that add to the cost of the loan?

16. Explain in general what *closing costs* are. Are they different from *settlement charges?*

17. **Adjusting the Rate in an Adjustable-Rate Mortgage**   To buy your home, you obtain a 1-year ARM with a 2.25% margin and a 2% periodic rate cap. The index starts at 1.85% but has increased to 4.05% by the first adjustment date. What interest rate will you pay during the second year?

18. According to **Table 14** (on **page 791**), how many shares of Pearson Plc were traded on May 22, 2014?

Finding the Return on a Stock Investment   *Barbara bought 1000 shares of stock at $12.75 per share. She received a dividend of $1.38 per share shortly after the purchase and another dividend of $1.02 per share one year later. Eighteen months after buying the stock, she sold the 1000 shares for $10.36 per share. (Disregard commissions and fees.)*

19. Find Barbara's total return on this stock.

20. Find her percentage return. Is this the *annual rate of return* on this stock transaction? Why or why not?

21. **The Final Value of a Retirement Account** $1800 is deposited at the end of each year in a tax-deferred retirement account. The account earns a 6% annual return, the account owner's marginal tax rate is 25%, and taxes are paid at the end of 30 years. Find the final value of the account.

22. What is meant by saying that a retirement account is "adjusted for inflation"?

Graph Theory

14

As a child, Ann Porter Wailes was often told that her name sounded like that of a writer. And as Ann grew up, she realized that her parents had aptly named her, because she absolutely loved writing. Even before entering college, Ann wanted to learn everything she could about England and its language. She was fortunate enough to be able to visit the United Kingdom several times before she graduated from high school. England was the land of her favorite literature, the study of British royalty fascinated her, and she visited many castles and courts with rich histories of the monarchy. John Keats became her favorite romantic poet.

Ann was enrolled in a mathematics survey course, and her interest was a bonus when she was assigned her first paper in an Introduction to English Literature class. The assignment was to analyze one of Keats's poems, and she chose his *Ode to Autumn*. The first stanza is shown on the next page, with the rhyme scheme illustrated by the letters A, B, C, D, and E.

Season of mists and mellow fruitfulness,	A
Close bosom-friend of the maturing sun;	B
Conspiring with him how to load and bless	A
With fruit the vines that round the thatch-eves run;	B
To bend with apples the moss'd cottage-trees	C
And fill all fruit with ripeness to the core;	D
To swell the gourd, and plump the hazel shells	E
With a sweet kernel; to set budding more,	D
And still more, later flowers for the bees,	C
Until they think that warm days will never cease,	C
For Summer has o'er brimm'd their clammy cells.	E

She learned in her Survey of Mathematics class that rhyme schemes can be analyzed by diagrams such as the following. This diagram is an example of a graph, the topic of this chapter.

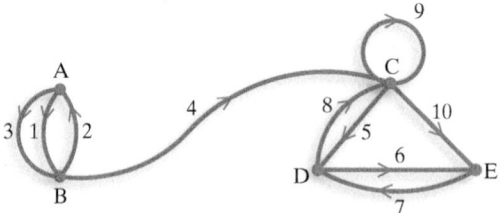

On one of Ann's visits to England, she toured Hampton Court and walked through its hedge maze, designed in 1690. In that same math class, she learned that the structure of mazes can also be analyzed by graphs. The figure on the left below is a diagram of the maze, and the one on the right offers a graphical interpretation, showing that the shortest path to the center is

$$\text{In} \to A \to B \to C \to D \to F \to G \to H \to \text{Center}.$$

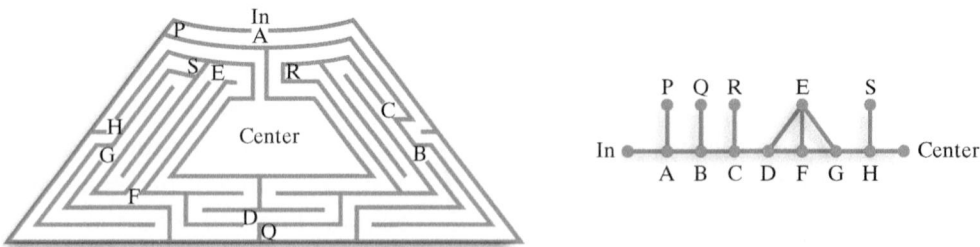

Ann soon realized that she had found her topic for a paper in yet *another* course (History of England). She had discovered mathematics in places she never dreamed it existed.

14.1   BASIC CONCEPTS

Graphs

Suppose a preschool teacher has ten children in her class:

Andy, Claire, Dave, Erin, Glen, Katy, Joe, Mike, Sam, and Tim.

The teacher wants to analyze the social interactions among these children. She observes with whom the children play during recess over a 2-week period and records her observations.

Child	Played with
Andy	no one
Claire	Dave, Erin, Glen, Katy, Sam
Dave	Claire, Erin, Glen, Katy
Erin	Claire, Dave, Katy
Glen	Claire, Dave, Sam
Katy	Claire, Dave, Erin
Joe	Mike, Tim
Mike	Joe
Sam	Claire, Glen
Tim	Joe

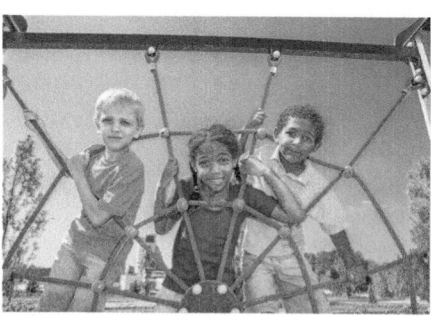

It is not easy to see patterns in the children's friendships from this list. Instead, the information may be shown in a diagram, as in **Figure 1,** where each letter is the first letter of a child's name. Such a diagram is called a *graph.** Each dot is a **vertex** (plural **vertices**) of the graph. The lines between vertices are **edges.**

> **GRAPH**
>
> A **graph** is a collection of vertices (at least one) and edges. Each edge goes from a vertex to a vertex.

In **Figure 1,** each vertex represents one of the preschool children, and the edges show the relationship "play with each other." An edge must always begin and end at a vertex. We may have a vertex with no edges joined to it, such as A in **Figure 1.**

The graph in **Figure 1** has ten vertices and twelve edges. The only vertices of the graph are the dots. There is *no* vertex where edges TJ and SG intersect, because the intersection point does not represent one of the children. The positions of the vertices and the lengths of the edges have no significance. Also, the edges do not have to be drawn as straight lines. *Only the relationship between the vertices has significance, indicated by the presence or absence of an edge between them.*

Why not draw two edges for each friendship pair? For example, why not draw one edge showing that Tim plays with Joe and another edge showing that Joe plays with Tim? Since Tim and Joe play with each other, the extra edge would yield no additional information. Graphs in which there is no more than one edge between any two vertices and in which no edge goes from a vertex to the same vertex are called **simple graphs.** See **Figure 2** on the next page.

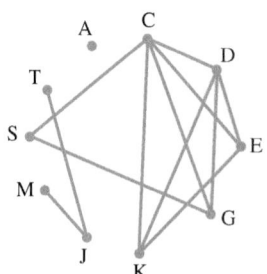

Figure 1

---

*Here *graph* will mean finite graph. A finite graph is a graph with finitely many edges and vertices.

These are simple graphs.   These are not simple graphs.

Figure 2

Why are they called graphs? The name was first used by chemist **A. Crum Brown.** He made a major breakthrough in chemistry in 1864 by inventing these now-familiar diagrams to show different molecules with the same chemical composition.

For example, both molecules illustrated above have chemical formula C_4H_{10}. Brown called his sketches **graphic formulae.** Mathematicians got involved in helping to classify all possible structures with a particular chemical composition and adopted the term "graph."

In this chapter, the word **graph** *means simple graph, unless indicated otherwise.* (The meaning of "simple" here is different from its meaning in the phrase "simple curves" used in geometry.)

From the graph in **Figure 1,** we can determine the size of a child's friendship circle by counting the number of edges coming from that child's vertex. There are five edges coming from the vertex labeled C, indicating that Claire plays with five different children. The number of edges joined to a vertex is the **degree of the vertex.** In **Figure 1,** the degree of vertex C is 5, the degree of vertex M is 1, and the degree of vertex A is 0, as no edges are joined to A. (Here, the use of *degree* has nothing to do with its use in geometry in measuring the size of an angle.)

While **Figure 1** clarifies the friendship patterns of the preschoolers, the graph can be drawn in a different, more informative way, as in **Figure 3.** The graph still has edges between the same pairs of vertices. We think of **Figure 3** as one graph, even though it has three pieces, since it represents a single situation. By drawing the graph in this way, we make the friendship patterns more apparent. Although the graph in **Figure 3** looks different from that in **Figure 1,** it shows the same relationships between the vertices. The two graphs are said to be *isomorphic.*

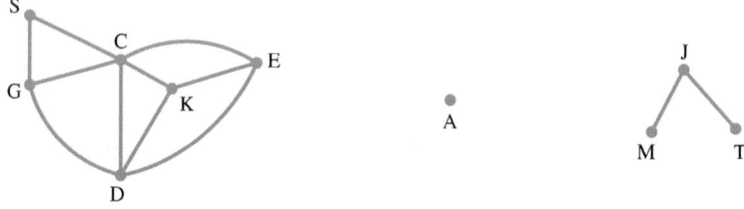

Figure 3

The word **isomorphism** comes from the Greek words *isos,* meaning "same," and *morphe,* meaning "form." Other words that come from the Greek root *isos* include the following.

isobars: lines drawn on a map connecting places with the same barometric pressure;

isosceles: a triangle with two legs (*scelos*) of equal length; and

isomers: chemical compounds with the same chemical composition but different chemical structures.

ISOMORPHIC GRAPHS

Two graphs are **isomorphic** if there is a one-to-one matching between vertices of the two graphs, with the property that whenever there is an edge between two vertices of either one of the graphs, there is an edge between the corresponding vertices of the other graph.

A useful way to think about isomorphic graphs is to imagine a graph drawn with computer software that allows you to drag vertices without detaching any of the edges from their vertices. Any graph we can obtain by simply dragging vertices in this way will be isomorphic to the original graph.

Replacing a graph with an isomorphic graph sometimes can convey more about the relationships being examined. For example, it is clear from **Figure 3** that there are no friendship links between the group consisting of Joe, Tim, and Mike, and the other children. We say that the graph is *disconnected.*

CONNECTED AND DISCONNECTED GRAPHS

A graph is **connected** if we can move from each vertex of the graph to every other vertex of the graph *along edges of the graph*. If not, the graph is **disconnected.** The connected pieces of a graph are called the **components** of the graph.

Figure 3 shows clearly that the friendship relationships among the children in the preschool class have three components. Although the graph in **Figure 1** also is disconnected and includes three components, the way in which the graph is drawn does not make this as clear.

Using the graph in **Figure 3** to analyze the relationships in her class, the teacher might make the following observations and decisions.

- Tim, Mike, and Joe do not interact with the other children.

- Andy's isolation is concerning.

- Claire seems to get along well with other children. As a result, encourage interaction between Claire and Tim, Mike, and Joe.

- Make a special attempt to encourage the children to include Andy in their games.

Showing the friendship relationships as in **Figure 3** made it much easier to analyze them.

Problem-Solving Strategy
Using different colors for different components can help determine how many components a graph has. We choose a color, begin at any vertex, and color all edges and vertices that we can get to from our starting vertex along edges of the graph. If the whole graph is not colored, we then choose a different color and an uncolored vertex, and repeat the process, continuing until the whole graph is colored.

The **World Wide Web** is sometimes studied as a very large graph. The vertices are Web pages, and the edges are links between pages. This graph is unimaginably large.

Even so, because of the way the Web is connected, one can get from any randomly chosen Web page to any other, using hyperlinks, in an average of about 19 clicks. Even if the Web becomes 10 to 100 times larger, this will still be possible in only 20 or 21 clicks. Because of this, search engines such as Google can find keywords very quickly.

(*Sources:* http://jmm.aaa.net.au/articles/15080.htm; Antonio Gulli Universit di Pisa, Informatica; Alessio Signorini, University of Iowa, Computer Science; R. Albert, H. Jeong, and A.-L. Barabsi, *Nature* 401, 130–131, 1999.)

EXAMPLE 1 **Determining Number of Components**

Is the graph in **Figure 4** connected or disconnected? How many components does the graph have?

Figure 4   **Figure 5**

Solution

Coloring the graph helps to answer the question. The original graph in **Figure 4** is disconnected. The graph with color (**Figure 5**) shows three components. ∎

James Joseph Sylvester (1814–1897) was the first mathematician to use the word *graph* for these diagrams in the context of mathematics. Sylvester spent most of his life in Britain, but he had an important influence on American mathematics from 1876 to 1884 as a professor at the newly founded Johns Hopkins University in Baltimore, Maryland. As a young man he worked as an actuary and lawyer in London, tutoring math on the side. One of his students was **Florence Nightingale.** His only published book, *The Laws of Verse*, was about poetry.

EXAMPLE 2 **Deciding Whether Graphs Are Isomorphic**

Are the two graphs in **Figure 6** isomorphic? Justify your answer.

(a)   (b)

Figure 6

Solution

These graphs are isomorphic. To show this, we label corresponding vertices with the same letters and color-code the matching edges in graphs (a) and (b) of **Figure 7.**

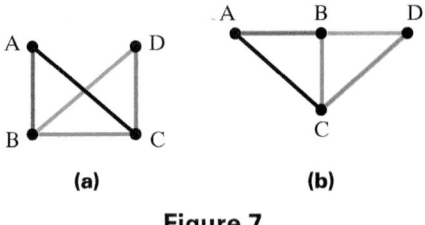

(a)   (b)

Figure 7

EXAMPLE 3 **Deciding Whether Graphs Are Isomorphic**

Are the two graphs in **Figure 8** isomorphic?

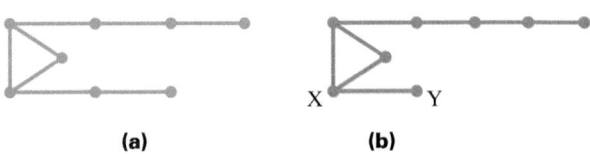

(a)   (b)

Figure 8

Solution

These graphs are not isomorphic. If we imagine graph (a) drawn with our special computer software, we can see that no matter how we drag the vertices, we can not get this graph to look exactly like graph (b). For example, graph (b) has vertex X of degree 3 joined to vertex Y of degree 1. Neither of the vertices of degree 3 in graph (a) is joined to a vertex of degree 1.

EXAMPLE 4 **Summing Degrees**

For each graph in **Figure 9,** determine the number of edges and the sum of the degrees of the vertices. Note that graph (b) is not a simple graph.

(a)   (b)

Figure 9

Solution

Start by writing the degree of each vertex next to the vertex, as in **Figure 10**.

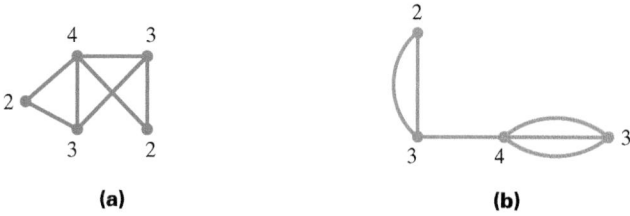

Figure 10

For graph (a):   For graph (b):
Number of edges = 7   Number of edges = 6
Sum of degrees of vertices   Sum of degrees of vertices
$= 2 + 3 + 2 + 3 + 4 = 14$ $= 2 + 3 + 4 + 3 = 12$

For each graph in **Example 4,** the sum of the degrees of the vertices is twice the number of edges. This is true for all graphs. Check that it is true for graphs in previous examples.

> **SUM-OF-THE-DEGREES THEOREM**
>
> In any graph, the sum of the degrees of the vertices equals twice the number of edges.

To understand why this theorem is true, we think of any graph and imagine cutting each edge at its midpoint (without adding any vertices to the graph, however). Now we have precisely twice as many half edges as we had edges in our original graph. For each vertex, we count the number of half edges joined to the vertex. This is, of course, the degree of the vertex. We add these answers to determine the sum of the degrees of the vertices. We know that the number of half edges is twice the number of edges in our original graph. So, the sum of the degrees of the vertices in the graph is twice the number of edges in the graph.

EXAMPLE 5 **Using the Sum-of-the-Degrees Theorem**

A graph has precisely six vertices, each of degree 3. How many edges does this graph have?

Solution

The sum of the degrees of the vertices of the graph is

$$3 + 3 + 3 + 3 + 3 + 3 = 18.$$

By the theorem above, this number is twice the number of edges, so the number of edges in the graph is

$$\frac{18}{2}, \text{ or } 9.$$

Massive graphs are of great current interest in graph theory. One example is the **World Wide Web**, with Web sites as vertices, and edges indicating a link from one page to another. Social networks such as **Facebook** are another example. These networks become enormously large if one creates links from each individual to all individuals with whom that person has contact.

If we consider "people with whom an individual has contact over the past two weeks," a massive graph can describe the spread of a highly infectious disease. Massive graphs often have giant components, and just one link can cause two of them to become an even more huge component. Several years ago, the spread of SARS (sudden acute respiratory syndrome) occurred when a few individual travelers from China caused additional networks of infection in Toronto. More recently, a similar issue has arisen with the Ebola virus. In this case, West Africa was the center of infection.

The 2011 movie *Contagion* provides a fictional—but actually possible—example of the spread of a deadly disease, initiated by a single cough.

EXAMPLE 6 Planning a Tour

Suppose we decide to explore the upper Midwest next summer. We plan to travel by Greyhound bus and would like to visit Grand Forks, Fargo, Bemidji, St. Cloud, Duluth, Minneapolis, Escanaba, and Green Bay. A check of the Greyhound Web site shows direct bus links between destinations as indicated.

City	Direct bus links with
Grand Forks	Bemidji, Fargo
Fargo	Grand Forks, St. Cloud, Minneapolis
Bemidji	Grand Forks, St. Cloud
St. Cloud	Bemidji, Fargo, Minneapolis
Duluth	Escanaba, Minneapolis
Minneapolis	Fargo, St. Cloud, Duluth, Green Bay
Escanaba	Duluth, Green Bay
Green Bay	Escanaba, Minneapolis

Draw a graph with vertices representing the destinations, and with edges representing the relation "there is a direct bus link." Is this a connected graph? Explain.

Solution

Begin with eight vertices representing the eight destinations, as in **Figure 11.** Use the bus link information to fill in the edges of the graph.

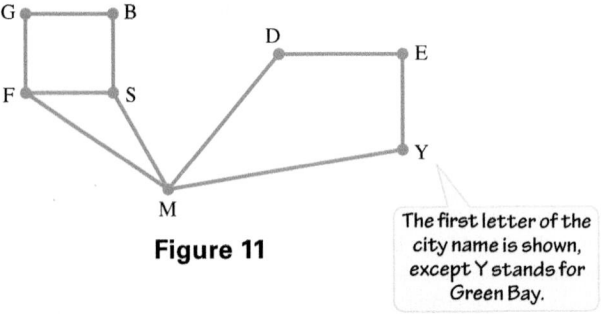

Figure 11

The first letter of the city name is shown, except Y stands for Green Bay.

Figure 11 is a connected graph. It shows that we can travel by bus from any of our chosen destinations to any other. ∎

Walks, Paths, and Circuits

Example 6 suggests several important ideas. For example, what trips could we take among the eight destinations, using only direct bus links? If we do not mind riding the same bus route more than once, we could take the following route.

$$M \to S \to F \to S \to B$$

Note that we used the "St. Cloud to Fargo" link twice. We could not take the $M \to D \to S$ route, however, since there is no direct bus link from Duluth to St. Cloud. Each possible route on the graph is called a *walk*.

Maps of subway systems in large cities usually do not faithfully represent the positions of stations or the distances between them. They are essentially graphs with vertices representing stations, and edges showing subway links.

WALK

A **walk** in a graph is a sequence of vertices, each linked to the next vertex by a specified edge of the graph.

We can think of a walk as a route that we can trace with a pencil without lifting the pencil from the graph.

$M \rightarrow S \rightarrow F \rightarrow S \rightarrow B$ and $F \rightarrow M \rightarrow D \rightarrow E$ Walks in **Figure 11**

$M \rightarrow D \rightarrow S$ Not a walk (There is no edge between D and S in **Figure 11**.)

Suppose that the travel time for our trip is restricted, and we do not want to use any bus link more than once. A *path* is a special kind of walk.

PATH

A **path** in a graph is a walk that uses no edge more than once.*

$M \rightarrow S \rightarrow F \rightarrow M,$ $F \rightarrow M \rightarrow D \rightarrow E,$ $M \rightarrow S \rightarrow F \rightarrow M \rightarrow D$ Paths

On the graph in **Figure 11,** trace these paths with a finger. Note that a path may use a *vertex* more than once.

$B \rightarrow S \rightarrow F \rightarrow M \rightarrow S \rightarrow B$ Not a path (It uses edge BS more than once.)

$M \rightarrow D \rightarrow S$ Not a path (It is not even a walk.)

Perhaps we want to begin and end our tour in the same city (and still not use any bus route more than once). A path such as this is known as a *circuit*. Two circuits that we could take are shown here.

$M \rightarrow S \rightarrow F \rightarrow M,$ $M \rightarrow S \rightarrow F \rightarrow M \rightarrow D \rightarrow E \rightarrow Y \rightarrow M$ Circuits

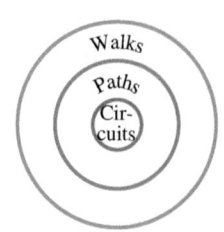

This diagram shows a **Venn diagram** relationship among walks, paths, and circuits.

CIRCUIT

A **circuit** in a graph is a path that begins and ends at the same vertex.

Notice that a circuit is a kind of path and, therefore, is also a kind of walk.

EXAMPLE 7 Classifying Walks

Using the graph in **Figure 12,** classify each sequence as a walk, a path, or a circuit.

(a) $E \rightarrow C \rightarrow D \rightarrow E$ **(b)** $A \rightarrow C \rightarrow D \rightarrow E \rightarrow B \rightarrow A$

(c) $B \rightarrow D \rightarrow E \rightarrow B \rightarrow C$ **(d)** $A \rightarrow B \rightarrow C \rightarrow D \rightarrow B \rightarrow A$

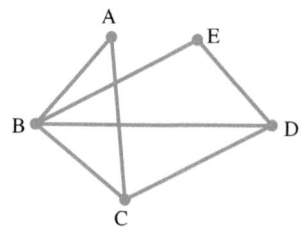

Figure 12

Solution

Walk	Path	Circuit
(a) No (no edge E to C)	No	No
(b) Yes	Yes	Yes
(c) Yes	Yes	No
(d) Yes	No (edge AB is used twice)	No

If a sequence of vertices is not a walk, it cannot possibly be either a walk or a circuit.

If a sequence of vertices is not a path, it cannot possibly be a circuit, since a circuit is defined as a special kind of path.

---

*Some texts call such a walk a *trail* and use the term *path* for a walk that visits no vertex more than once.

Mazes have always fascinated people. Mazes are found on coins from ancient Knossos (Greece), in the sand drawings at Nazca in Peru, on Roman pavements, on the floors of Renaissance cathedrals in Europe, as the popular cornfield mazes accompanying Halloween pumpkin patches, and as hedge mazes in gardens. Graphs can be used to clarify the structure of mazes.

When planning our tour in **Example 6,** it would be useful to know the length of time the bus rides take. We write the time for each bus ride on the graph, as shown in **Figure 13.**

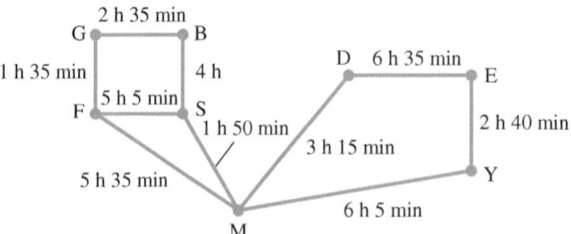

Figure 13

A graph with numbers on the edges, as in **Figure 13,** is a **weighted graph.** The numbers on the edges are **weights.**

Problem-Solving Strategy

Drawing a sketch is a useful problem-solving strategy. **Example 8** illustrates how drawing a sketch can simplify a problem that at first seems complicated.

EXAMPLE 8 **Analyzing a Round-Robin Tournament**

In a round-robin tournament, every contestant plays every other contestant. The winner is the contestant who wins the most games. Suppose six tennis players compete in a round-robin tournament. How many matches will be played?

Solution

Draw a graph with six vertices to represent the six players. Then, as in **Figure 14,** draw an edge for each match between a pair of contestants.

Figure 14

We can count the edges to find out how many matches must be played. Or we can reason as follows: There are 6 vertices each of degree 5, so the sum of the degrees of the vertices in this graph is $6 \cdot 5$, or 30. We know that the sum of the degrees is twice the number of edges. Therefore, there are 15 edges in this graph and, thus, 15 matches in the tournament.

Another way of solving this problem is to use combinations from **Chapter 10.** We must find $_6C_2$, the number of combinations of 6 things taken 2 at a time.

$$_6C_2 = \frac{6!}{2!(6-2)!} = \frac{6!}{2! \cdot 4!} = 15$$ ∎

Complete Graphs and Subgraphs

The graph for **Example 8** in **Figure 14** is an example of a *complete graph*.

> **COMPLETE GRAPH**
>
> A **complete graph** is a graph in which there is exactly one edge going from each vertex to each other vertex in the graph.

▓▓EXAMPLE 9▓▓ Deciding Whether a Graph Is Complete

Decide whether each of the graphs in **Figure 15** is complete. If a graph is not complete, explain why it is not.

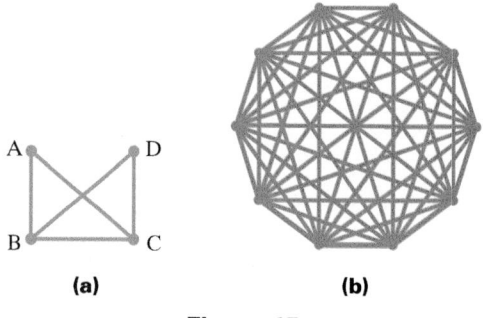

(a)　　　(b)

Figure 15

Solution

Graph (a) is not complete. There is no edge from vertex A to vertex D. Graph (b) is complete. (Check that there is an edge from each of the ten vertices to each of the other nine vertices in the graph.) ∎

A good source for **real-life examples of graphs** is

Networks, Crowds and Markets,

by David Easley and Jon Kleinberg. It is available in book form from Cambridge University Press or as a pdf at

http://www.cs.cornell.edu/home/kleinber/networks-book/

Many of the real-life graphs shown are from scholarly research. Section 2.2 deals with graphs describing romantic relationships at a large American high school during an 18-month period. It turns out that many students who believe they are in monogamous relationships are in fact connected to much larger networks via their partner. This has obvious relevance to the transmission of sexual diseases. Section 3.4 includes examples related to Facebook. Search engines such as Google use measures like page rank to order the results of a search. Section 14.3 of the book gives a fairly simple account of page rank.

▓▓EXAMPLE 10▓▓ Finding a Complete Graph

Find a complete graph with four vertices in the preschoolers' friendship pattern depicted in **Figure 3,** repeated here.

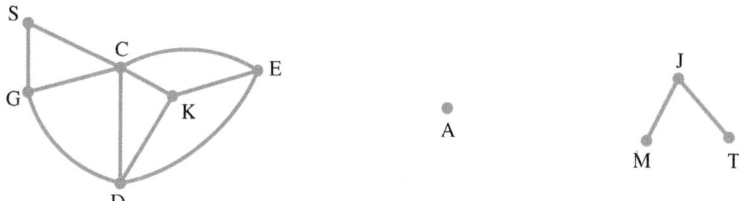

Figure 3 (repeated)

Solution

Figure 16 shows a portion of the friendship graph from **Figure 3.**

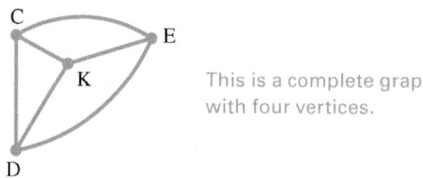

This is a complete graph with four vertices.

Figure 16 ∎

Figure 16 includes some complete graphs with three vertices. In general, a graph consisting of some of the vertices of the original graph and some of the original edges between those vertices is called a **subgraph.** Vertices or edges not included in the original graph cannot be in the subgraph.

A subgraph may include anywhere from one to all of the vertices of the original graph and anywhere from none to all of the edges of the original graph. Notice that a subgraph is a graph, and recall that in a graph, every edge goes from a vertex to a vertex. Therefore, no edge can be included in a subgraph without the vertices at both of its ends also being included.

- The subgraph shown in **Figure 16** is a complete graph, but a subgraph does not have to be complete. For example, the graphs in **Figures 17(a) and (b)** are both subgraphs of the graph in **Figure 3**.

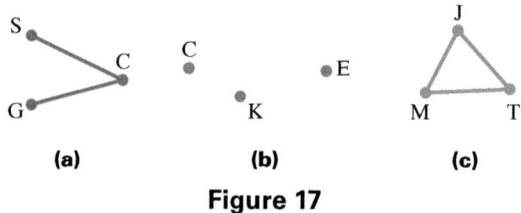

(a)   (b)   (c)

Figure 17

- The graph in **Figure 17(b)** is a subgraph even though it has no edges. (However, we could not form a subgraph by taking edges without vertices. In a graph, every edge goes from a vertex to a vertex.)

- The graph in **Figure 17(c)** is *not* a subgraph of the graph in **Figure 3,** since there was no edge between M and T in the original graph.

Graph Coloring

Tabatha schedules nurse trainees for the hospital departments listed on the left below. Trainee groups must be scheduled at different times if there are trainees working in both departments. The column on the right shows, for each department, which of the other departments have trainees in common with it. For example, the first row shows that each of the departments Radiology, Surgery, Obstetrics, and Pediatrics has one trainee, or more, also working in the ER.

Department	Other departments in which trainees in this department also work
Emergency (ER)	Radiology, Surgery, Obstetrics, Pediatrics
Obstetrics	Radiology, Surgery, Oncology, ER
Surgery	Pediatrics, Oncology, Geriatrics, ER, Obstetrics
Oncology	Pediatrics, Radiology, Geriatrics, Obstetrics, Surgery
Pediatrics	Radiology, ER, Surgery, Oncology
Radiology	Geriatrics, ER, Obstetrics, Oncology, Pediatrics
Geriatrics	Surgery, Oncology, Radiology

Tabatha's task is to figure out the least number of time slots needed for the seven trainee groups and to decide which (if any) can be scheduled at the same time. We can draw a graph, with a vertex for each department, and with an edge between two vertices *if there are trainees working in both departments.* See **Figure 18** on the next page.

The Mathematics of Time Scheduling

Time is money.

This short sentence says a lot when it comes to productivity in the workplace. A branch of graph theory called **mathematical theory of scheduling** investigates how tasks can be arranged for a project to maximize efficiency. The terms *processors, tasks, processing time, precedence relations, project, critical time, finishing time, schedule, scheduling algorithms, priority list,* and *optimal schedule* are used in the theory of scheduling.

Tasks are represented by vertices, and precedence relations are represented by directed arrows from one vertex to another (similar to edges in a graph). The resulting diagram is called a directed graph (or digraph).

The Web site

http://www.ctl.ua.edu/math103/ scheduling/schedmnu.htm#Digraphs

gives a concise explanation of this branch of graph theory and uses the question

"How long does it take to build a house?"

to illustrate some of the problems associated with time scheduling.

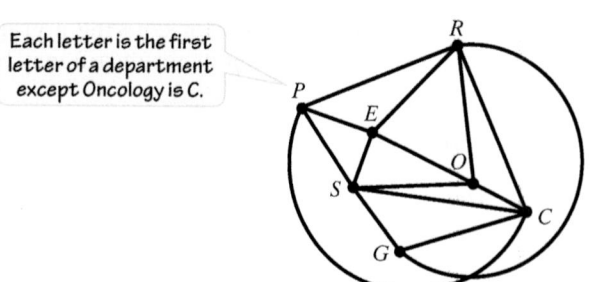

Figure 18

If there is an edge between two vertices, then the corresponding departments have trainees in common, and the trainee groups must *not* be scheduled at the same time. To show this, we use a different color for each time slot for trainee groups. We will color the vertices with the different colors to show when the trainee groups could be scheduled.

To make sure that trainee groups are scheduled at different times if the departments have trainees in common, we must make sure that any two vertices joined by an edge have different colors. To ensure the least number of time slots, we use as few colors as possible. In **Figure 19,** we show one possible coloring of the vertices using three colors. We cannot color the graph as required with fewer than three colors.

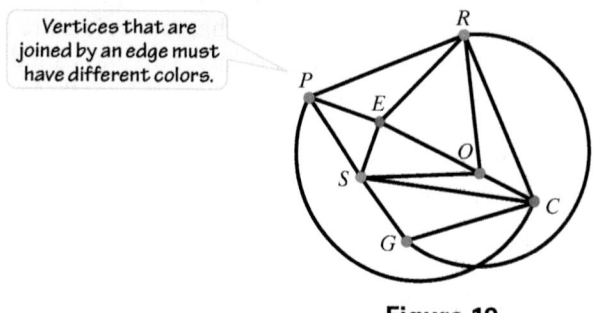

Figure 19

Tabatha can schedule the required trainee groups in no fewer than three time slots. She can schedule Radiology and Surgery at one time, Pediatrics, Obstetrics, and Geriatrics at a second time, and Oncology and ER at a third time.

The result we achieved is called a *coloring** for the graph.

COLORING AND CHROMATIC NUMBER

A **coloring** for a graph is an assignment of a color to each vertex in such a way that vertices joined by an edge have different colors. The **chromatic number** of a graph is the least number of colors needed to achieve a coloring.

Using this terminology, Tabatha had to determine the chromatic number for the graph in **Figure 18.** The chromatic number was 3, which equaled the least number of time slots needed for the trainee groups.

The idea of using vertex coloring to solve this particular problem was straightforward. However, determining the chromatic number for a graph with many vertices or producing a coloring using the least possible number of colors can be difficult. No one has yet found an efficient method for finding the exact chromatic number for arbitrarily large graphs. (The term *efficient algorithm* has a specific, technical meaning for computer scientists. See **Section 14.3.**)

---

*This method is sometimes called a *vertex* coloring for the graph.

Networks are at the forefront of research in biology. Biologists have made enormous strides in understanding the structure of molecules in living organisms. It is now important to understand how these molecules interact with each other. This can be viewed as a network, or graph.

For example, current research aims to identify how proteins in cells interact with other proteins. Insights into such networks may help explain the growth of cancerous tumors. This may lead to better treatments for cancer. It was discovered that as graphs, these biological networks are surprisingly similar to the graphs representing the World Wide Web.

The following method for coloring a graph may not give a coloring with the least number of colors, but its result still may be helpful.

COLORING A GRAPH

Step 1 Choose a vertex with greatest degree, and color it. Use the same color to color as many vertices as you can without coloring two vertices the same color if they are joined by an edge.

Step 2 Choose a new color, and repeat what you did in Step 1 for vertices not already colored.

Step 3 Repeat Step 1 until all vertices are colored.

Graph coloring is used to solve many practical problems. It is useful in management science for solving scheduling problems, such as the "trainee groups" example. Graph coloring is also related to allocating transmission frequencies to TV and radio stations and cell phone companies.

The coloring of graphs has an interesting history involving maps. Maps need to be colored so that territories with common boundaries have different colors. How many colors are needed? For map makers, four colors have always sufficed. In about 1850, mathematicians started pondering this. For over a hundred years, they were able neither to prove that four colors are always enough nor to find a map that needed more than four colors. This was called the **four-color problem.**

In 1976 two mathematicians, Kenneth Appel and Wolfgang Haken, provided a proof that four colors are always enough. This proof created a controversy in mathematics, because it relied on computer calculations so lengthy (fifty 24-hour days of computer time) that no person could check the entire proof.

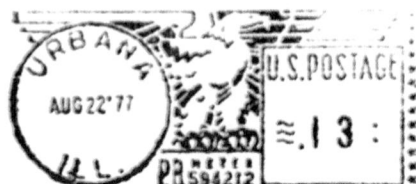

The postmark shown above was used by the Urbana, Illinois, post office to commemorate the proof of the four-color theorem. (Appel and Haken were colleagues at the University of Illinois at Urbana-Champaign when they completed their proof.)

Bacon Numbers

The popular game *The Six Degrees of Kevin Bacon* was developed by three Albright College friends a number of years ago. The object of the game is to connect actor Kevin Bacon to another actor or actress using a sequence of movies, with six or fewer titles in the sequence. Thanks to the International Movie Data Base (www.imdb.com), this goal can be reached almost instantaneously. The minimum number of links necessary is called the **Bacon number** for the other performer. For example, Hayley Mills has a Bacon number of 2, because she can be connected to Kevin Bacon in 2 steps as follows:

- Hayley Mills was in *That Darn Cat!* (1965) with Roddy McDowall.

- Roddy McDowall was in *The Big Picture* (1989) with Kevin Bacon.

The process used in *The Six Degrees of Kevin Bacon* can be applied to other situations (Web pages, for example).

EXAMPLE 11 Determining a Bacon Number

Use the Web site

oracleofbacon.org

to determine the Bacon number for Mary Kaye Hebert, a lifelong friend of one of the authors of this text. She had a small speaking role in *Easy Rider* (1969). Use the default option of theatrical movies only.

Solution

According to the site, Mary Kaye Hebert has a Bacon number of 2.

- Mary Kaye Hebert was in *Easy Rider* (1969) with Jack Nicholson.
- Jack Nicholson was in *A Few Good Men* (1992) with Kevin Bacon.

It takes only 2 titles to connect Mary Kaye and Kevin. Her Bacon number is 2. ∎

14.1 EXERCISES

Vertices and Edges *In Exercises 1–6, determine how many vertices and how many edges each graph has.*

1.

2.

3.

4.

5.

6.

Sum of Degrees *For each graph indicated, find the degree of each vertex in the graph. Then add the degrees to get the sum of the degrees of the vertices of the graph. What relationship do you notice between the sum of degrees and the number of edges?*

7. Exercise 1   **8. Exercise 2**

9. Exercise 3   **10. Exercise 4**

Isomorphic or Not Isomorphic? *In Exercises 11–16, determine whether the two graphs are isomorphic. If so, label corresponding vertices of the two graphs with the same letters and color-code corresponding edges, as in **Example 2**. (Note that there is more than one correct answer for many of these exercises.)*

11.

(a)   (b)

12.

(a)   (b)

13.

(a)   (b)

14.

(a)   (b)

15.

(a)   (b)

16.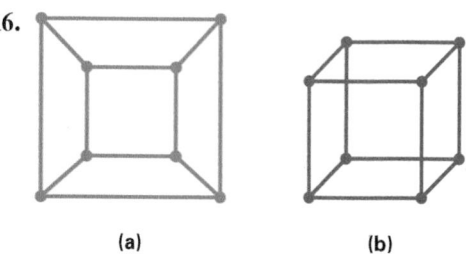

(a)   (b)

Connected or Disconnected? *In Exercises 17–22, determine whether the graph is connected or disconnected. Then determine how many components the graph has.*

17.

18.

19.

20.

21.   **22.**

Number of Edges *In Exercises 23–26, use the theorem that relates the sum of degrees to the number of edges to determine the number of edges in the graph (without drawing).*

23. A graph with 5 vertices, each of degree 4

24. A graph with 7 vertices, each of degree 4

25. A graph with 5 vertices, three of degree 1, one of degree 2, and one of degree 3

26. A graph with 8 vertices, two of degree 1, three of degree 2, one of degree 3, one of degree 5, and one of degree 6

Walks, Paths, Circuits *In Exercises 27–29, refer to the following graph.*

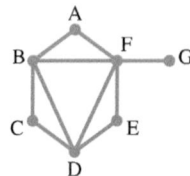

27. Which are walks in the graph? If not, why not?

  (a) A → B → C

  (b) B → A → D

  (c) E → F → A → E

  (d) B → D → F → B → D

  (e) D → E

  (f) C → B → C → B

28. Which are paths in the graph? If not, why not?

  (a) B → D → E → F

  (b) D → F → B → D

  (c) B → D → F → B → D

  (d) D → E → F → G → F → D

  (e) B → C → D → B → A

  (f) A → B → E → F → A

29. Which are circuits in the graph? If not, why not?

  (a) A → B → C → D → E → F

  (b) A → B → D → E → F → A

  (c) C → F → E → D → C

  (d) G → F → D → E → F

  (e) F → D → F → E → D → F

Walks and Paths *In Exercises 30 and 31, refer to the following graph.*

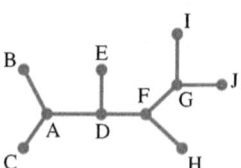

30. Which are walks in the graph? If not, why not?

  (a) F → G → J → H → F

  (b) D → F

  (c) B → A → D → F → H

  (d) B → A → D → E → D → F → H

  (e) I → G → J

  (f) I → G → J → I

31. Which are paths in the graph? If not, why not?

  (a) A → B → C

  (b) J → G → I → G → F

  (c) D → E → I → G → F

  (d) C → A

  (e) C → A → D → E

  (f) C → A → D → E → D → A → B

Walks, Paths, Circuits *In Exercises 32–37, refer to the following graph. In each case, determine whether the sequence of vertices is **(i)** a walk, **(ii)** a path, **(iii)** a circuit in the graph.*

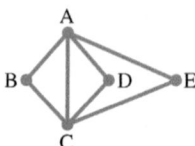

32. A → B → C → D → E

33. A → B → C

34. A → B → C → D → A

35. A → B → A → C → D → A

36. A → B → C → A → D → C → E → A

37. C → A → B → C → D → A → E

Complete or Not Complete? *In Exercises 38–43, determine whether the graph is a complete graph. If not, explain why it is not complete.*

38.

39.

40.

41.

42.

43.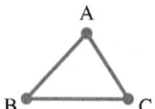

Solve each problem.

44. *Chess Competition* Students from two schools compete in chess. Each school has a team of four students. Each student must play one game against each student on the opposing team. Draw a graph with vertices representing the students, and edges representing the chess games. How many games must be played in the competition?

45. *Chess Competition* A chess master plays seven simultaneous games with seven other players. Draw a graph with vertices representing the players, and edges representing the chess games. How many games are being played?

46. *Dancing Partners* At a party there were four males and five females. During the party each male danced with each female (and no female pair or male pair danced together). Draw a graph with vertices representing the people at the party, and edges of the graph showing the relationship

"danced with."

How many edges are there in the graph?

47. *Number of Handshakes* There are six members on a hockey team (including the goalie). At the end of a hockey game, each member of the team shakes hands with each member of the opposing team. How many handshakes occur?

48. *Number of Handshakes* There are seven people at a business meeting. One of these shakes hands with four people, four shake hands with two people, and two shake hands with three people. How many handshakes occur? (*Hint:* Use the theorem that the sum of the degrees of the vertices in a graph is twice the number of edges.)

49. *Spread of a Rumor* A lawyer is preparing his argument in a libel case. He has evidence that a libelous rumor about his client was discussed in various telephone conversations among eight people. Two of the people involved had four telephone conversations in which the rumor was discussed, one person had three, four had two, and one had one such telephone conversation. How many telephone conversations were there in which the rumor was discussed among the eight people?

50. *Vertices and Edges of a Cube* Draw a graph with vertices representing the vertices (the corners) of a cube, and edges representing the edges of the cube. In your graph, find a circuit that visits four different vertices. What figure does your circuit form on the actual cube?

51. *Vertices and Edges of a Tetrahedron* Draw a graph with vertices representing the vertices (or corners) of a tetrahedron, and edges representing the edges of the tetrahedron. In the graph, identify a circuit that visits three different vertices. What figure does the circuit form on the actual tetrahedron?

52. **Students in the Same Class** Mary, Erin, Sue, Jane, Katy, and Brenda are friends at college. Mary, Erin, Sue, and Jane are in the same math class. Sue, Jane, and Katy take the same English composition class.

    (a) Draw a graph with vertices representing the six students, and edges representing the relation "take a common class."

    (b) Is the graph connected or disconnected? How many components does the graph have?

    (c) In the graph, identify a subgraph that is a complete graph with four vertices.

    (d) In the graph, identify three different subgraphs that are complete graphs with three vertices. (There are several correct answers.)

53. Here is another theorem about graphs: **In any graph, the number of vertices with odd degree must be even.** Explain why this theorem is true. (*Hint:* Use the theorem about the relationship between the number of edges and the sum of degrees.)

54. Draw two nonisomorphic (simple) graphs with 6 vertices, with each vertex having degree 3.

55. Explain why the two graphs drawn in **Exercise 54** are not isomorphic.

56. **Analyzing a Cube with a Graph** Draw a graph whose vertices represent the *faces* of a cube and in which an edge between two vertices shows that the corresponding faces of the actual cube share a common boundary. What is the degree of each vertex in the graph? What does the degree of any vertex in the graph reveal about the actual cube?

Coloring and Chromatic Numbers In Exercises 57–62, color the graph using as few colors as possible. Determine the chromatic number of the graph. (*Hint: The chromatic number is fixed, but there may be more than one correct coloring.*)

57.

58.

59.

60.

61.

62.

63. Color each graph using as few colors as possible. Use this to determine the chromatic number of the graph. (Graphs like these are called **cycles.**)

    (a)   (b)

    (c)   (d)

    (e) Use the results from parts (a)–(d) to make a prediction about the chromatic number of a cycle. (*Hint:* Consider two cases.)

64. Sketch a complete graph with the specified number of vertices, color the graph with as few colors as possible, and use this to determine the chromatic number of the graph.

    (a) 3 vertices

    (b) 4 vertices

    (c) 5 vertices

    (d) Write a general principle by completing this statement: A complete graph with *n* vertices has chromatic number ___.

    (e) Why is the statement in part (d) true?

    (f) Generalize further by completing this statement: If a graph has a *subgraph* that is a complete graph with *n* vertices, then the chromatic number of the graph must be at least ___.

Coloring and Chromatic Numbers In Exercises 65–68, color the vertices using as few colors as possible. Then state the chromatic number of the graph. (*Hint: It might help to first identify the largest subgraph that is a complete graph.*)

65.   66.

67.   68.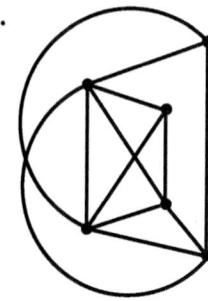

69. **Scheduling Meeting Times** Campus Life must schedule weekly meeting times for the six organizations listed below so that organizations with members in common meet at different times.

Use graph coloring to determine the least number of different meeting times needed, and which organizations should meet at the same time.

Organization	Members also belong to
Choir	Caribbean Club, Dance Club, Theater, Service Club
Caribbean Club	Dance Club, Service Club, Choir
Service Club	Forensics, Choir, Theater, Caribbean Club
Forensics	Dance Club, Service Club
Theater	Choir, Service Club
Dance Club	Choir, Caribbean Club, Forensics

70. **Assigning Frequencies to Transmitters** Interference can occur between radio stations. To avoid this, transmitters that are less than 60 miles apart must be assigned different broadcast frequencies. The transmitters for 7 radio stations are labeled A through G. The information below shows, for each transmitter, which of the others are within 60 miles.

Use graph coloring to determine the least number of different broadcast frequencies that must be assigned to the 7 transmitters. Include a plan for which transmitters could broadcast on the same frequency to use this least number of frequencies.

Transmitters	Transmitter within 60 miles of this
A	B, E, F
B	A, C, E, F, G
C	B, D, G
D	C, F, G
E	A, B, F
F	A, B, D, E, G
G	B, C, D, F

71. **Inviting Colleagues to a Gathering** Several of Tiffany's colleagues do not get along with each other, as summarized below. Tiffany plans to organize several gatherings, so that colleagues who do not get along are not there at the same time.

Use graph coloring to determine the least number of gatherings needed, and which colleagues should be invited each time.

- Joe does not get along with Brad and Phil.
- Caitlin does not get along with Lindsay and Brad.
- Lindsay does not get along with Phil.
- Mary does not get along with Lindsay.
- Eva gets along with everyone.

Graph Coloring In Exercises 72–74, each graph shows the vertices and edges of the figure specified. Color the vertices of each graph in such a way that vertices with an edge between them have different colors. Use graph coloring to find a way to do this, and specify the least number of colors needed.

72. Cube

73. Octahedron

74. Dodecahedron

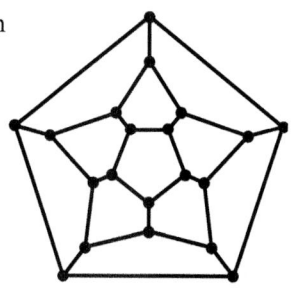

Graph Coloring In Exercises 75 and 76, draw a vertex for each region shown in the map. Draw an edge between two vertices if the two regions have a common boundary. Then find a coloring for the graph, using as few colors as possible.

75.

76.

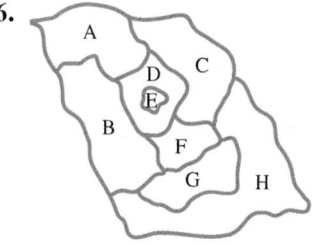

77. **Map Coloring** Use graph coloring to determine the least number of colors that can be used to color the map so that areas with common boundaries have different colors.

Upstate New York

78. *Map Coloring* Use graph coloring to determine the least number of colors that can be used to color the map so that countries with common boundaries have different colors.

Countries of Southern Africa

Map Drawing *In Exercises 79–81, draw a map with the specified number of countries that can be colored using the stated number of colors, and no fewer. (Countries may not consist of disconnected pieces.) If it is not possible to draw such a map, explain why not.*

79. 6 countries, 3 colors

80. 6 countries, 4 colors

81. 6 countries, 5 colors

82. Write a paper on the four-color problem. Include a discussion of the proof by Appel and Haken.

The Six Degrees of Kevin Bacon *Use the Web site*

oracleofbacon.org

to determine the Bacon number for each actor or actress in Exercises 83–92. Use the default option of theatrical movies only, and use the first performer listed in the event of duplicate names.

83. Cameron Diaz

84. Drew Barrymore

85. Mae West

86. John Wayne

87. Theda Bara

88. Jackie Robinson (baseball player)

89. Erich Bergen

90. Joe Mantegna

91. Brad Pitt

92. Jack Nicholson

Poetry Analysis *Graphs may be used to clarify the rhyme schemes in poetry. Vertices represent words at the end of a line, edges are drawn, and a path is used to indicate the rhyme scheme. See the chapter opener, where the first stanza of* Ode to Autumn *by John Keats has its rhyme scheme analyzed using a graph. In Exercises 93–96, use a graph to analyze the rhyme scheme.*

93. Lines from *She Walks in Beauty,* by Lord Byron

She walks in beauty, like the night	A
Of cloudless climes and starry skies;	B
And all that's best of dark and bright	A
Meet in her aspect and her eyes;	B
Thus mellowed to that tender light	A
Which heaven to gaudy day denies.	B

94. Lines from *Annabel Lee,* by Edgar Allan Poe

It was many and many a year ago,	A
In a kingdom by the sea,	B
That a maiden there lived whom you may know	A
By the name of Annabel Lee;	B
And this maiden she lived with no other thought	C
Than to love and be loved by me.	B

95. Sonnet 3 of William Shakespeare

Look in thy glass, and tell the face thou viewest	A
Now is the time that face should form another;	B
Whose fresh repair if now thou not renewest,	A
Thou dost beguile the world, unless some mother,	B
For where is she so fair whose unear'd womb	C
Disdains the tillage of thy husbandry?	D
Or who is he so fond will be the tomb	C
Of his self-love, to stop posterity?	D
Thou art thy mother's glass, and she in thee	D
Calls back the lovely April of her prime:	E
So thou through windows of thine age shall see	D
Despite of wrinkles this thy golden time.	E
But if thou live, remember'd not to be,	D
Die single, and thine image dies with thee.	D

96. Lines from *Sailing to Byzantium,* by William Butler Yeats

An aged man is but a paltry thing,	A
A tattered coat upon a stick, unless	B
Soul clap its hands and sing, and louder sing	A
For every tatter in its mortal dress,	B
Nor is there singing school but studying	A
Monuments of its own magnificence;	B
And therefore I have sailed the seas and come	C
To the holy city of Byzantium.	C

14.2 | EULER CIRCUITS AND ROUTE PLANNING

OBJECTIVES

1 State the Königsberg bridge problem and explain its historical relevance to graph theory.

2 State and apply Euler's theorem for Euler circuits.

3 Identify a cut edge of a graph.

4 Apply Fleury's algorithm to find an Euler circuit.

5 Minimize deadheading on a street grid by converting it to a graph with an Euler circuit.

Königsberg Bridge Problem

In the early 1700s, the city of Königsberg was the capital of East Prussia. (Königsberg is now called Kaliningrad and is in Russia.) The river Pregel ran through the city in two branches with an island between the branches, as shown in **Figure 20.**

Figure 20

There were seven bridges joining various parts of the city as shown in **Figure 21.**

Figure 21

According to Leonhard Euler (pronounced "oiler"), the following problem (the **Königsberg bridge problem**) was well known in his time (around 1730).

> *Is it possible for a citizen of Königsberg to take a stroll through the city, crossing each bridge exactly once, and beginning and ending at the same place?*

Try to find such a route on the map in **Figure 21.** (Do not cross the river anywhere except at the bridges shown on the map.)

We can simplify the problem by drawing the map as a graph. See **Figure 22.** The graph focuses on the relations between the vertices. This is the relation "there is a bridge."

Leonhard Euler (1707–1783) was a devoted father and grandfather. He had thirteen children and frequently worked on mathematics with children playing around him. He lost the sight in his right eye at age 31, a couple of years after writing the Königsberg bridge paper. He became completely blind at age 58 but produced more than half his mathematical work after that. Euler wrote nearly a thousand books and papers.

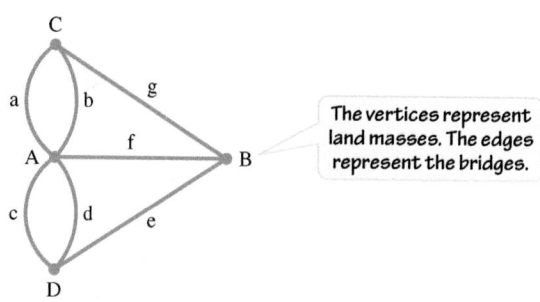

The vertices represent land masses. The edges represent the bridges.

Figure 22

A university was founded in Königsberg in 1544. It was established as a Lutheran center of learning. Its most famous professor was the philosopher **Immanual Kant,** who was born in Königsberg in 1724. The university was completely destroyed during World War II.

In the graph in **Figure 22,** we have *two* edges between vertices A and C and *two* edges between vertices A and D. Thus, this graph is not a simple graph. We have labeled the edges with lowercase letters. Now try to find a route as required in the problem.

Euler Circuits

The Königsberg bridge problem requires more than a path and more than a circuit. (Recall that a path is a walk that uses no edge more than once, and a circuit is a path that begins and ends at the same vertex.) The problem requires a circuit that uses *every* edge, *exactly* once. This is called an *Euler circuit.*

> **EULER PATH AND EULER CIRCUIT**
>
> An **Euler path** in a graph is a path that uses every edge of the graph exactly once. An **Euler circuit** in a graph is a circuit that uses every edge of the graph exactly once.

EXAMPLE 1 **Recognizing Euler Circuits**

Consider the graph in **Figure 23.**

(a) Is $A \rightarrow B \rightarrow C \rightarrow D \rightarrow E \rightarrow F \rightarrow A$ an Euler circuit for this graph? Justify your answer.

(b) Does the graph have an Euler circuit?

Solution

(a) $A \rightarrow B \rightarrow C \rightarrow D \rightarrow E \rightarrow F \rightarrow A$ is a circuit, but not an Euler circuit, because it does not use every edge of the graph. For example, the edge BD is not used in this circuit.

(b) In the graph in **Figure 23,** the circuit

$$A \rightarrow B \rightarrow C \rightarrow D \rightarrow E \rightarrow F \rightarrow D \rightarrow B \rightarrow F \rightarrow A$$

is an Euler circuit. Trace this path on the graph to check that it does use every edge of the graph exactly once. ∎

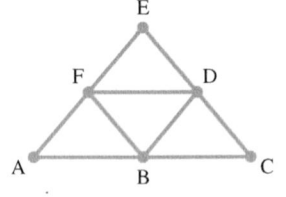

Figure 23

Returning to the Königsberg bridge problem, it seemed that no route of the type required could be found. Why was this so? Euler published a paper in 1736 that explained why it is impossible to find a walk of the required kind, and he provided a simple way of deciding whether a given graph has an Euler circuit. Euler did not use the terms *graph* and *circuit,* but his paper was, in fact, the first paper on graph theory. In modern terms, Euler proved the first part of the theorem below. Part 2 was not proved until 1873.

> **EULER'S THEOREM**
>
> Suppose we have a connected graph.
>
> **1.** If the graph has an Euler circuit, then each vertex of the graph has even degree.
>
> **2.** If each vertex of the graph has even degree, then the graph has an Euler circuit.

The following is from Euler's paper on the **Königsberg bridge problem:** "I was told that while some denied the possibility of doing this and others were in doubt, no one maintained that it was actually possible. On the basis of the above, I formulated the following very general problem for myself:

Given any configuration of the river and the branches into which it may divide, as well as any number of bridges, to determine whether or not it is possible to cross each bridge exactly once."

(*Source:* Newman, James R. (ed.), "The Königsberg Bridges," *Scientific American,* July 1953, in *Readings from Scientific American: Mathematics in the Modern World,* 1968.)

What does Euler's theorem predict about the connected graph in **Figure 23?** The degrees of the vertices are as follows.

$$A: 2 \quad B: 4 \quad C: 2 \quad D: 4 \quad E: 2 \quad F: 4$$

Each vertex has even degree, so it follows from part 2 of the theorem that the graph has an Euler circuit. (We already knew this, since we found an Euler circuit for this graph in **Example 1.**)

What does Euler's theorem suggest about the Königsberg bridge problem? Note that the degree of vertex C in **Figure 22** is 3, which is an odd number, and the graph is connected. So, by part 1 of the theorem, the graph cannot have an Euler circuit. (In fact, the graph has many vertices with odd degree, but the presence of *any* vertex of odd degree indicates that the graph does not have an Euler circuit.)

Why is Euler's theorem true? Consider the first part of the theorem:

If a connected graph has an Euler circuit, then each vertex has even degree.

Suppose we have a connected graph with an Euler circuit in the graph. Suppose the circuit begins and ends at a vertex A. Imagine traveling along the Euler circuit, from A all the way back to A, putting an arrow on each edge in our direction of travel. (Of course, we travel along each edge exactly once.)

Now consider any vertex B in the graph. It has edges joined to it, each with an arrow. Some of the arrows point toward B, some point away from B. The number of arrows pointing toward B is the same as the number of arrows pointing away from B, for every time we visit B, we come in on one unused edge and leave via a different unused edge. In other words, we can pair off the edges joined to B, with each pair having one arrow pointing toward B and one arrow pointing away from B. Thus, the total number of edges joined to B must be an even number, and therefore, the degree of B is even. A similar argument shows that our starting vertex, A, also has even degree.

The second part of Euler's theorem states the following:

If each vertex of a connected graph has even degree,
then the graph has an Euler circuit.

To show that this is true, we will provide a recipe (Fleury's algorithm) for finding an Euler circuit in any such graph. First, however, we consider more examples of how Euler's theorem can be applied.

EXAMPLE 2 **Using Euler's Theorem**

Decide which of the graphs in **Figure 24** has an Euler circuit. Justify your answers.

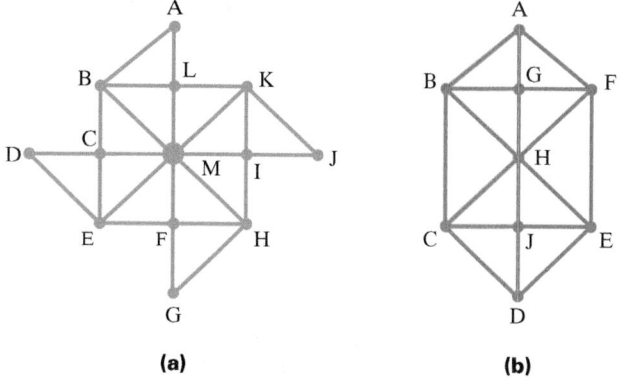

(a)   (b)

Figure 24

By 1875 a new bridge had been built in Königsberg, joining the land areas we labeled C and D in **Figure 21.** It was now possible for a citizen of Königsberg to take a walk that used each bridge exactly once, provided that he or she started at A and ended at B, or vice versa.

Solution

(a) The graph in **Figure 24(a)** is connected. If we write the degree next to each vertex on the graph, as in **Figure 25,** we see that each vertex has even degree. Since the graph is connected, and each vertex has even degree, it follows from Euler's theorem that the graph has an Euler circuit.

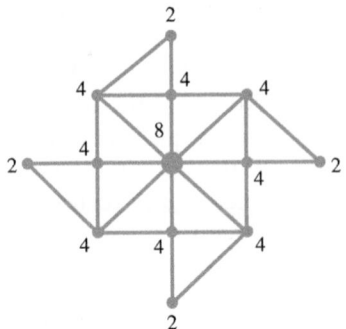

Figure 25

(b) In **Figure 24(b),** check the degrees of the vertices. Note that vertex A has degree 3, an odd degree. We need look no further. It follows from Euler's theorem that this connected graph does not have an Euler circuit. (All the other vertices in this graph except for D have even degree. However, if just one vertex has odd degree, then the graph does not have an Euler circuit.) ∎

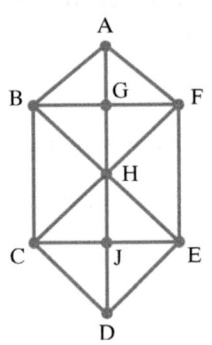

Figure 24(b) (repeated)

Problem-Solving Strategy

When solving a challenging problem, it is useful to ask whether the problem is related to another problem that you already know how to solve. **Example 3** illustrates this strategy.

EXAMPLE 3 **Tracing Patterns**

Beginning and ending at the same place, is it possible to trace the pattern shown in **Figure 26** below without lifting the pencil off the page and without tracing over any part of the pattern (except isolated points) more than once?

Solution

The pattern in **Figure 26** is not a graph. (It has no vertices.) But what we are being asked to do is very much like being asked to find an Euler circuit. So we imagine that there are vertices at points where lines or curves of the pattern meet, obtaining the graph in **Figure 27**.

Figure 26

Figure 27

Now we can use Euler's theorem to decide whether we can trace the pattern. Vertex A has odd degree. Thus, by Euler's theorem, this graph does not have an Euler circuit. It follows that we cannot trace the original pattern in the manner required. ∎

The word **algorithm** comes from the name of the Persian mathematician, **Abu Ja'far Muhammad ibn Musa Al-Khowârizmî,** who lived from about A.D. 780 to A.D. 850. One of the books he wrote was on the Hindu-Arabic system of numerals (the system we use today) and calculations using them. The Latin translation of this book was called *Algoritmi de numero Indorum,* meaning "Al-Khowârizmî on the Hindu Art of Reckoning."

The tracing problem in **Example 3** illustrates a practical problem that occurs when designing robotic arms to trace patterns. Automated machines that engrave identification tags for pets require such a mechanical arm.

Fleury's Algorithm

Fleury's algorithm can be used to find an Euler circuit in any connected graph in which each vertex has even degree. An algorithm is like a recipe—follow the steps and we achieve what we need. Before introducing Fleury's algorithm, we need a definition.

CUT EDGE

A **cut edge** in a graph is an edge whose removal disconnects a component of the graph.

We call such an edge a cut edge, since removing the edge *cuts* a connected piece of a graph into two pieces.*

EXAMPLE 4 Identifying Cut Edges

Identify the cut edges in the graph in **Figure 28.**

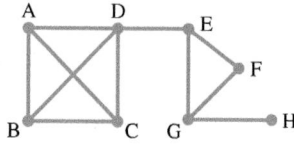

Figure 28

Solution

This graph has only one component, so we must look for edges whose removal would disconnect the graph.

DE is a cut edge. If we removed this edge, we would disconnect the graph into two components, obtaining the graph of **Figure 29(a).** HG is also a cut edge. Its removal would disconnect the graph as shown in **Figure 29(b).**

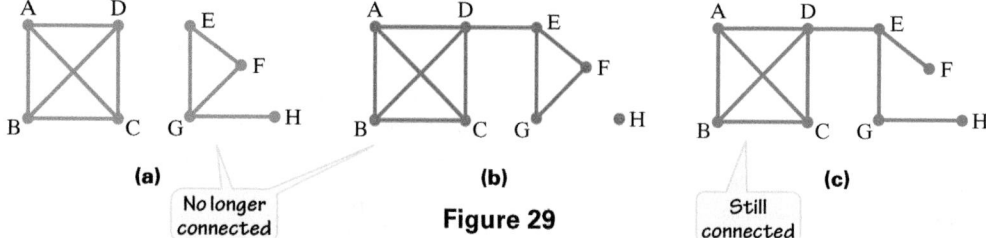

Figure 29

None of the other edges is a cut edge. We could remove any *one* of the other edges and still have a connected graph (that is, we would still have a path from each vertex of the graph to each other vertex). For example, if we remove edge GF, we end up with a graph that still is connected, as shown in **Figure 29(c).** ∎

Fleury's algorithm is used for finding an Euler circuit in a connected graph in which each vertex has even degree.

*Some mathematicians use "bridge" instead of "cut edge" to describe such an edge.

FLEURY'S ALGORITHM

Step 1 Start at any vertex. Go along any edge from this vertex to another vertex. *Remove this edge from the graph.*

Step 2 You are now on a vertex of the revised graph. Choose any edge from this vertex, subject to only one condition: Do not use a cut edge (*of the revised graph*) unless you have no other option. Go along your chosen edge. *Remove this edge from the graph.*

Step 3 Repeat Step 2 until you have used all the edges and returned to the vertex at which you started.

▋EXAMPLE 5 Using Fleury's Algorithm

Find an Euler circuit for the graph in **Figure 30.**

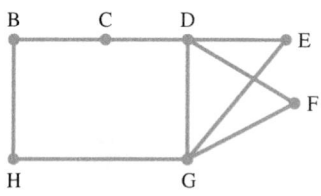

Figure 30

Solution

First we must check that this graph does indeed have an Euler circuit. A check shows that the graph is connected and that each vertex has even degree.

We can start at any vertex. We choose C. We could go from C to B or from C to D. We go to D, removing the edge CD. (We show it scratched out, but we must think of this edge as gone.) Our path begins: C → D. The revised graph is shown in **Figure 31.**

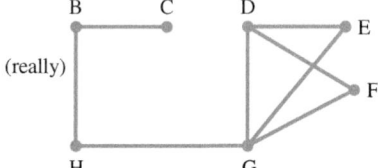

Figure 31

None of the edges DE, DF, and DG is a cut edge for our current graph, so we can choose to go along any one of these. We go from D to G, removing edge DG. So far, our path is C → D → G. (Keep a record of this path.) See **Figure 32.**

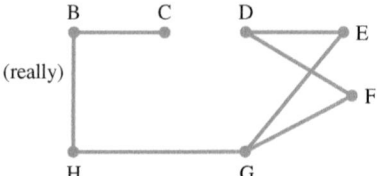

Figure 32

The remaining edges at G are GE, GF, and GH. Note, however, that GH is a cut edge for our revised graph, and we have other options. Thus, according to Fleury's algorithm, *we must not use GH at this stage.* (If we used GH now, we would never be able to get back to use the edges GF, GE, and so on.) We go from G to F.

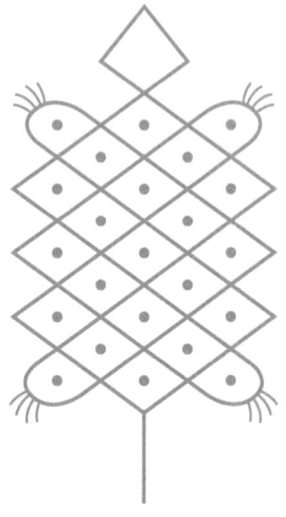

The **Tshokwe people of northeastern Angola** have a tradition involving continuous patterns in sand. The tracings are called *sona,* and they have ritual significance. They are used as mnemonics for stories about the gods and ancestors. Elders trace the drawings while telling the stories. The example shown here is called *skin of a leopard.*

(*Source:* Gerdes, Paul. *Geometry from Africa–Mathematical and Educational Explorations.* Mathematical Association of America, 1999, p. 171.)

Our path is C → D → G → F, and we show our revised graph in **Figure 33.**

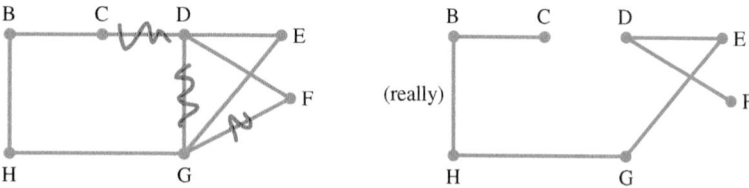

Figure 33

Now we have only one edge from F, namely, FD. This is a cut edge of the revised graph, but *since we have no other option,* we may use this edge. Our path is C → D → G → F → D, and our revised graph is shown in **Figure 34.**

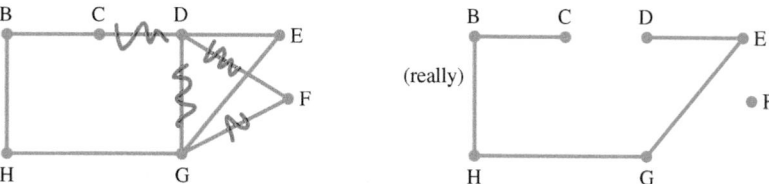

Figure 34

We have only one edge left at D, namely DE. It is a cut edge of the remaining graph, but since we have no other option, we may use it.

It is now clear how to complete the Euler circuit. (Be sure to return to the starting vertex.) The complete Euler circuit is as follows.

$$C \rightarrow D \rightarrow G \rightarrow F \rightarrow D \rightarrow E \rightarrow G \rightarrow H \rightarrow B \rightarrow C.$$ ∎

If we start with a connected graph with all vertices having even degree, then Fleury's algorithm will always produce an Euler circuit for the graph. ***Note that a graph that has an Euler circuit always has more than one Euler circuit.***

Even for a large graph, a computer can successfully apply Fleury's algorithm. This is not the case for all algorithms. (See **For Further Thought** on The Speed of Algorithms in **Section 14.3.**)

Route Planning

When planning routes for mail delivery, street sweeping, or snow plowing, the roads in the region to be covered usually do not have an Euler circuit. Unavoidably, certain stretches of road must be traveled more than once. This is referred to as **deadheading.** Planners then try to find a route on which the driver will spend as little time as possible deadheading.

In **Example 6,** for simplicity we use street grids for which the distances from corner to corner in any direction are the same.

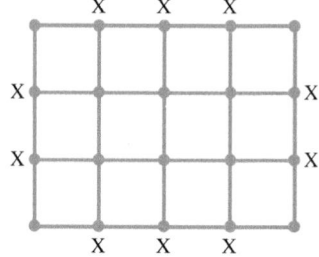

Figure 35

▌▌▌▌EXAMPLE 6 Finding an Euler Circuit on a Street Grid

The street grid in **Figure 35** has every vertex of odd degree marked with an X. Insert edges coinciding with existing roads to change it to a graph with an Euler circuit.

Solution

A certain amount of trial and error is needed to find the least number of edges that must be inserted to ensure that the street grid graph has an Euler circuit.

If we insert edges as shown in **Figure 36(a),** we obtain a graph having an Euler circuit. (Check that all vertices now have even degree.) This solution introduces 11 additional edges, which turns out to be more deadheading than is necessary.

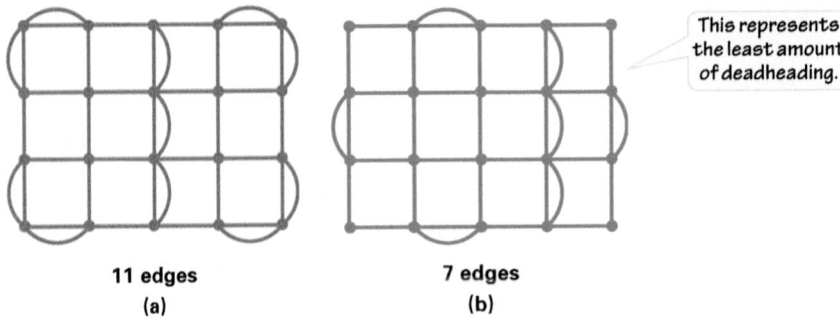

This represents the least amount of deadheading.

11 edges
(a)

7 edges
(b)

Figure 36

If we insert edges as shown in **Figure 36(b),** with just 7 additional edges we obtain a graph with an Euler circuit. This is, in fact, the least number of edges that must be inserted (keeping to the street grid) to change the original street grid graph into a graph that has an Euler circuit. (There are different ways to insert the seven edges.) ∎

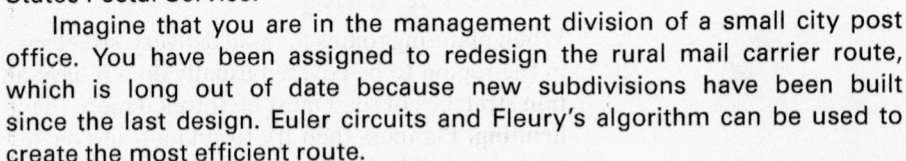

WHEN Will I Ever USE This ?

In the midst of the technology revolution, there is no replacement for the old-fashioned method of product delivery:

Load the product onto a vehicle, drive to the destination, and physically drop off the product there.

This is the job of courier services such as UPS, FedEx, and the United States Postal Service.

Imagine that you are in the management division of a small city post office. You have been assigned to redesign the rural mail carrier route, which is long out of date because new subdivisions have been built since the last design. Euler circuits and Fleury's algorithm can be used to create the most efficient route.

The figure shows a map of your rural district. In rural areas, mailboxes are placed along the same side of a road, so the mail delivery vehicle needs to travel along the road in one direction only. Suppose the roads off the main road in the figure show a mail delivery region.

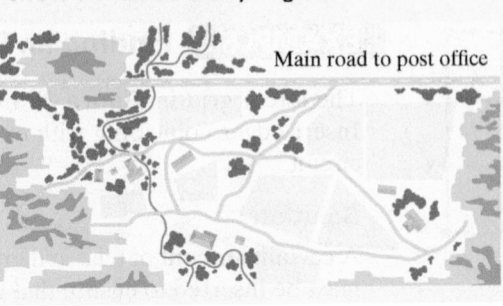

Main road to post office

As seen in Chapter 9, there are only five **regular polyhedra**: the cube, the tetrahedron, the octahedron, the dodecahedron, and the icosahedron. There is only one which has the property that you can trace your finger along each edge exactly once, beginning and ending at the same vertex. It is the octahedron, because it is the only one with an even number of edges meeting each vertex.

It would be ideal if, in your new route, you could find an Euler circuit covering the entire route. If such a circuit existed, it would minimize the distance traveled for the delivery. A glance at the map (thinking of road intersections as vertices) reveals that there is no Euler circuit for this route.

As the next best thing, the delivery vehicle should retrace its path as little as possible. For simplicity, you assume that the time to travel any of the stretches of road when not delivering mail is roughly the same. In following the figure, you added dotted edges to indicate stretches of road to be covered twice. For this delivery route, it is easy to see that you effectively inserted as few edges as possible to obtain a graph that has an Euler circuit.

Main road to post office

Now you can use Fleury's algorithm to find an Euler circuit on the graph in the new figure, and this will give the most efficient route for mail delivery.

14.2 EXERCISES

Euler Circuits *In Exercises 1–3, a graph is shown and some sequences of vertices are specified. Determine which of these sequences show Euler circuits. If not, explain why not.*

1.

A   D

B   C

(a) $A \rightarrow B \rightarrow C \rightarrow D \rightarrow A \rightarrow B \rightarrow C \rightarrow D \rightarrow A$

(b) $C \rightarrow B \rightarrow A \rightarrow D \rightarrow C$

(c) $A \rightarrow C \rightarrow D \rightarrow B \rightarrow A$

(d) $A \rightarrow B \rightarrow C \rightarrow D$

2.

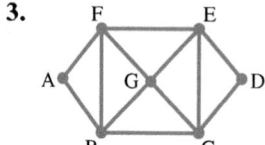

(a) $A \rightarrow B \rightarrow C \rightarrow D \rightarrow E \rightarrow F \rightarrow A$

(b) $F \rightarrow B \rightarrow D \rightarrow B$

(c) $A \rightarrow B \rightarrow C \rightarrow D \rightarrow E \rightarrow F \rightarrow B \rightarrow D \rightarrow F \rightarrow A$

(d) $A \rightarrow B \rightarrow F \rightarrow D \rightarrow B \rightarrow C \rightarrow D \rightarrow E \rightarrow F \rightarrow A$

3.

F   E

A   G   D

B   C

(a) $A \rightarrow B \rightarrow C \rightarrow D \rightarrow E \rightarrow F \rightarrow A$

(b) $A \rightarrow B \rightarrow C \rightarrow D \rightarrow E \rightarrow G \rightarrow C \rightarrow E \rightarrow$
$F \rightarrow G \rightarrow B \rightarrow F \rightarrow A$

(c) $A \rightarrow B \rightarrow C \rightarrow D \rightarrow E \rightarrow C \rightarrow G \rightarrow E \rightarrow$
$F \rightarrow G \rightarrow E \rightarrow F \rightarrow A$

(d) $A \rightarrow B \rightarrow G \rightarrow E \rightarrow D \rightarrow C \rightarrow G \rightarrow F \rightarrow$
$B \rightarrow C \rightarrow E \rightarrow F \rightarrow A$

Euler's Theorem *In Exercises 4–8, use Euler's theorem to decide whether the graph has an Euler circuit. (Do not actually find an Euler circuit.) Justify each answer briefly.*

4.

5.

6.

7.

8.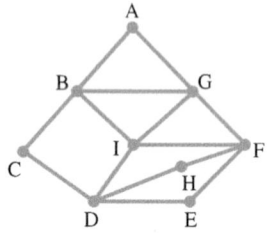

Euler's Theorem *In Exercises 9 and 10, use Euler's theorem to determine whether it is possible to begin and end at the same place, trace the pattern without lifting your pencil, and trace over no line in the pattern more than once.*

9.   **10.**

Euler's Theorem *In Exercises 11–14, use Euler's theorem to determine whether the graph has an Euler circuit, justifying each answer. Then determine whether the graph has a circuit that visits each vertex exactly once, except that it returns to its starting vertex. If so, write down the circuit. (There may be more than one correct answer.)*

11.

12.

13.

14.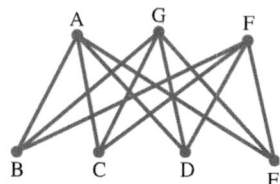

Floor Tilings *In Exercises 15–18, different floor tilings are shown. The material applied between tiles is called grout. For which of these floor tilings could the grout be applied beginning and ending at the same place, without going over any joint twice, and without lifting the tool? Justify each answer.*

15.

16.

17.

18.

Cut Edges *In Exercises 19–22, identify all cut edges in the graph. If there are none, say so.*

19.

20.

21.   **22.**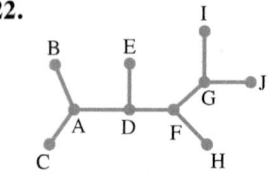

Fleury's Algorithm   *In Exercises 23–25, a graph is shown for which a student has been asked to find an Euler circuit starting at* A. *The student's revisions of the graph after the first few steps of Fleury's algorithm are shown, and in each case the student is now at* B. *For each graph, determine all edges that Fleury's algorithm permits the student to use for the next step.*

23.

24.   **25.**

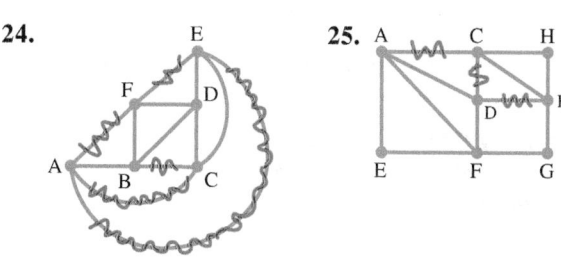

Fleury's Algorithm   *In Exercises 26–28, use Fleury's algorithm to find an Euler circuit for the graph, beginning and ending at* A. *(There are many different correct answers.)*

26.

27.

28.

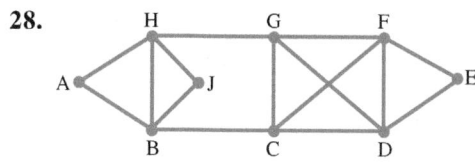

Euler's Theorem and Fleury's Algorithm   *In Exercises 29–31 in the next column, use Euler's theorem to determine whether the graph has an Euler circuit. If not, explain why not. If the graph does have an Euler circuit, use Fleury's algorithm to find an Euler circuit for the graph. (There are many different correct answers.)*

29.

30.

31.

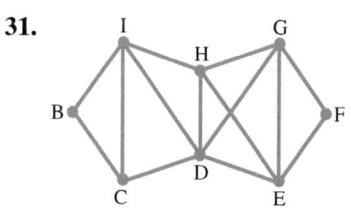

32. *Garden Design*   The graph below shows the layout of the paths in a botanical garden. The edges represent the paths. Has the garden been designed in such a way that it is possible for a visitor to find a route that begins and ends at the entrance to the garden (represented by the vertex A) and that goes along each path exactly once? If so, use Fleury's algorithm to find such a route.

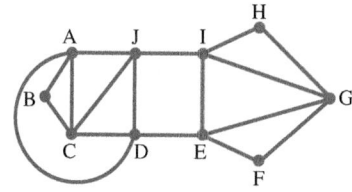

33. *Parking Pattern*   The map shows the roads on which parking is permitted at a national monument. This is a pay-and-display facility. A security guard has the task of periodically checking that all parked vehicles have a valid parking ticket displayed. He is based at the central complex, labeled A. Is there a route that he can take to walk along each of the roads exactly once, beginning and ending at A? If so, use Fleury's algorithm to find such a route.

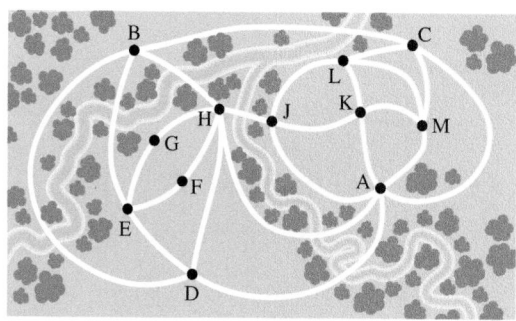

Floor Plans In Exercises 34–36, the floor plan of a building is shown. For which of these is it possible to start outside, walk through each door exactly once, and end up back outside? Justify each answer. (Hint: Think of the rooms and "outside" as the vertices of a graph, and think of the doors as the edges of the graph.)

34.

35.

36.

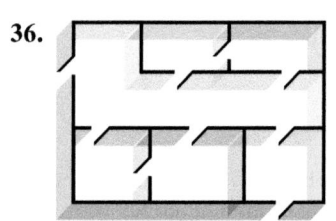

Exercises 37–44 are based on the following theorem:

1. *If a graph has an Euler path that begins and ends at different vertices, then these two vertices are the only vertices with odd degree. (All the rest have even degree.)*

2. *If exactly two vertices in a connected graph have odd degree, then the graph has an Euler path beginning at one of these vertices and ending at the other.*

In Exercises 37–40, determine whether the graph has an Euler path that begins and ends at different vertices. Justify your answer. If the graph has such a path, say at which vertices the path must begin and end.

37.

38.

39.

40.

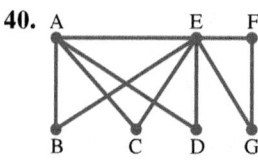

Floor Plans In Exercises 41–43, refer to the floor plan indicated, and determine whether it is possible to start in one of the rooms of the building, walk through each door exactly once, and end up in a different room from the one you started in. Justify each answer.

41. Refer to the floor plan shown in **Exercise 34.**

42. Refer to the floor plan shown in **Exercise 35.**

43. Refer to the floor plan shown in **Exercise 36.**

New York City Bridges The accompanying schematic map shows a portion of the New York City area, including tunnels and bridges.

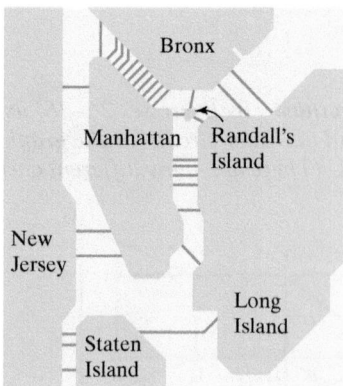

44. Is it possible to take a drive around the New York City area using each tunnel and bridge exactly once, beginning and ending in the same place?

45. Is it possible to take a drive around the New York City area using each tunnel and bridge exactly once, beginning and ending in different places? If so, where must the drive begin and end?

Circuits with Maximum Edges In Exercises 46–48, the graph does not have an Euler circuit. For each graph find a circuit that uses as many edges as possible. (There is more than one correct answer in each case.) How many edges did you use in the circuit?

46.

47.

48.

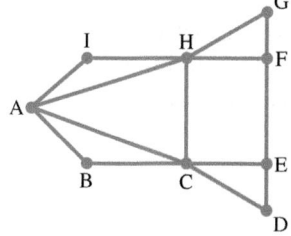

49. *Route Planning* In the graph shown here, we have inserted just six edges in the original street grid from **Example 6.** Why is this not a better solution than the one in **Figure 36(b)**?

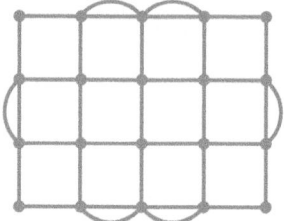

Route Planning For each street grid in Exercise 50–52, insert edges to obtain a street grid that has an Euler circuit. Try to insert as few edges as possible.

50.

51.

52.

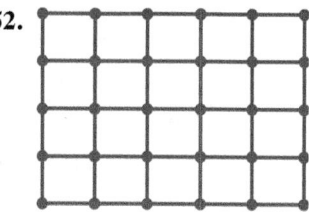

14.3 HAMILTON CIRCUITS AND ALGORITHMS

OBJECTIVES

1 Define and identify a Hamilton circuit in a graph.

2 Determine the number of Hamilton circuits in a complete graph with *n* vertices.

3 Know the meanings of the terms *weighted graph* and *minimum Hamilton circuit.*

4 Apply the brute force algorithm for a complete, weighted graph.

5 Know the meanings of the terms *efficient algorithm* and *approximate algorithm.*

6 Apply the nearest neighbor algorithm.

Hamilton Circuits

In this section we examine *Hamilton circuits* in graphs. The story of Hamilton circuits is a story of very large numbers and of unsolved problems in both mathematics and computer science. We start with a game, called the **Icosian game,** invented by Irish mathematician William Hamilton in the mid-nineteenth century. It uses a wooden board marked with the graph shown in **Figure 37.**

The Icosian Game

Figure 37

The game includes 20 pegs numbered 1 through 20. (The word *Icosian* comes from the Greek word for 20.) At each vertex of the graph there is a hole for a peg.

The simplest version of the game is as follows:

> *Put the pegs into the holes in order, following along the edges of the graph, in such a way that peg 20 ends up in a hole that is joined by an edge to the hole of peg 1.*

Try this now, numbering the vertices in the graph in **Figure 37,** starting at vertex 1.

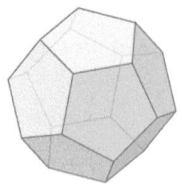

Dodecahedron

Hamilton sold the **Icosian game** idea to a games dealer for 25 British pounds. It went on the market in 1859, but it was not a huge success. A later version of the game, *A Voyage Around the World,* consisted of a regular dodecahedron with pegs at each of the 20 vertices. The vertices had names such as Brussels, Delhi, and Zanzibar. The aim was to travel to all vertices along the edges of the dodecahedron, visiting each vertex exactly once. We can show the vertices and edges of a dodecahedron precisely as in **Figure 37.**

The Icosian game asks that we find a circuit in the graph, but the circuit need not be an Euler circuit. The circuit must visit each *vertex* exactly once, except for returning to the starting vertex to complete the circuit. (The circuit may or may not travel all edges of the graph.) Circuits such as this are called *Hamilton circuits.*

HAMILTON CIRCUIT

A **Hamilton circuit** in a graph is a circuit that visits each vertex exactly once (returning to the starting vertex to complete the circuit).

EXAMPLE 1 Identifying Hamilton Circuits

Which of the following are Hamilton circuits for the graph in **Figure 38?** Justify your answers briefly.

(a) $A \rightarrow B \rightarrow E \rightarrow D \rightarrow C \rightarrow F \rightarrow A$

(b) $A \rightarrow B \rightarrow C \rightarrow D \rightarrow E \rightarrow F \rightarrow C \rightarrow$
$E \rightarrow B \rightarrow F \rightarrow A$

(c) $B \rightarrow C \rightarrow D \rightarrow E \rightarrow F \rightarrow B$

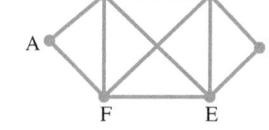

Figure 38

Solution

(a) $A \rightarrow B \rightarrow E \rightarrow D \rightarrow C \rightarrow F \rightarrow A$ is a Hamilton circuit for the graph. It visits each vertex of the graph exactly once and then returns to the starting vertex. (Trace this circuit on the graph to check it.)

(b) $A \rightarrow B \rightarrow C \rightarrow D \rightarrow E \rightarrow F \rightarrow C \rightarrow E \rightarrow B \rightarrow F \rightarrow A$ is not a Hamilton circuit, since it visits vertex B (and vertices C, E, and F) more than once. (This is, however, an Euler circuit for the graph.)

(c) $B \rightarrow C \rightarrow D \rightarrow E \rightarrow F \rightarrow B$ is not a Hamilton circuit since it does not visit all vertices in the graph. ∎

Some graphs, such as the graph in **Figure 39,** do not have a Hamilton circuit. There is no way to visit all the vertices and return to the starting vertex without visiting vertex I more times than allowed.

It can be difficult to determine whether a particular graph has a Hamilton circuit, since there is no theorem that gives necessary and sufficient conditions for a Hamilton circuit to exist. This remains an unsolved problem in Hamilton circuits.

Fortunately, in many real-world applications of Hamilton circuits we are dealing with complete graphs, and any complete graph with three or more vertices does have a Hamilton circuit. For example,

$$A \rightarrow B \rightarrow C \rightarrow D \rightarrow E \rightarrow F \rightarrow A$$

is a Hamilton circuit for the complete graph shown in **Figure 40.** We could form a Hamilton circuit for any complete graph with three or more vertices in a similar way.

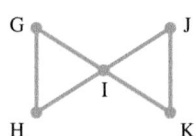

Figure 39

HAMILTON CIRCUITS FOR COMPLETE GRAPHS

Any complete graph with three or more vertices has a Hamilton circuit.

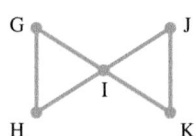

Figure 40

The graph in **Figure 40** has many Hamilton circuits. Try finding some that are different from the one given above.

The Tutte graph, shown here, has no Hamilton circuit. This graph has a history connected to the four-color problem for map coloring (**Section 14.1**). In 1880 Peter Tate provided a "proof" for the four-color theorem. It was based on the assumption that every connected graph with all vertices of degree 3, and which can be drawn with edges crossing nowhere except at vertices, has a Hamilton circuit. But in 1946, Tutte produced the graph shown here, showing that Tate's basic assumption was wrong, and his proof was, therefore, invalid.

How many Hamilton circuits does a complete graph have? Before we count, we need an agreement about when two sequences of vertices will be considered to be *different* Hamilton circuits. For example, the Hamilton circuits

$$B \rightarrow C \rightarrow D \rightarrow E \rightarrow F \rightarrow A \rightarrow B \quad \text{and} \quad A \rightarrow B \rightarrow C \rightarrow D \rightarrow E \rightarrow F \rightarrow A$$

visit the vertices in essentially the same order in the graph in **Figure 40,** although the sequences start with different vertices. If we mark the circuit on the graph, we can describe it starting at any vertex. For our purposes, it is convenient to consider the two sequences above as representing the same Hamilton circuit.

WHEN HAMILTON CIRCUITS ARE THE SAME

Hamilton circuits that differ *only* in their starting points will be considered to be the same circuit.

Problem-Solving Strategy

Tree diagrams are often useful for counting.

We begin by counting the number of Hamilton circuits in a complete graph with four vertices. See **Figure 41.** We can use the same starting point for all the circuits we count. We choose A as the starting point. From A we can go to any of the three remaining vertices (B, C, or D). No matter which vertex we choose, we then have two unvisited vertices for our next choice. Then there is only one way to complete the Hamilton circuit. We illustrate this counting procedure in **Figure 42,** where the tree diagram shows that we have $3 \cdot 2 \cdot 1$ Hamilton circuits in the graph. We write this as 3! (read "3 factorial"). See **Chapter 10.**

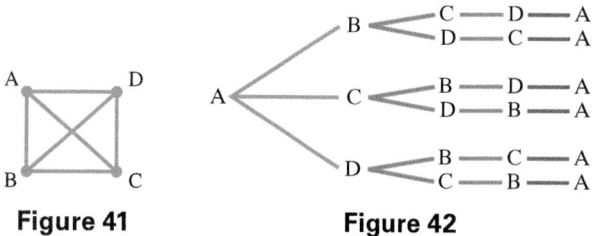

Figure 41   **Figure 42**

Returning to **Figure 40,** we can count the number of Hamilton circuits in the complete graph with 6 vertices. Start at vertex A. From A we can proceed to any of the five remaining vertices. No matter which we choose, we then have four choices for the next vertex along the circuit, three choices for the next, and two for the next. This means that we have

$$5 \cdot 4 \cdot 3 \cdot 2 \cdot 1 = 5! \quad \text{different Hamilton circuits in all.}$$

We would find that a complete graph with 10 vertices has 9! Hamilton circuits. The number of Hamilton circuits in a complete graph can be obtained by calculating the factorial of the number that is one less than the number of vertices.

NUMBER OF HAMILTON CIRCUITS IN A COMPLETE GRAPH

A complete graph with *n* vertices has the following number of Hamilton circuits.

$$(n - 1)!$$

Traveling Salesman Problems and Archaeology Archaeologists often excavate sites in which there is no clear evidence to show which deposits were made earlier, and which later. Some archaeologists have used minimum Hamilton circuits to solve the problem. For example, if a site consists of a number of burials, they consider a complete graph with vertices representing the various burials, and weights on the edges corresponding roughly to how dissimilar the burials are. A minimum Hamilton circuit in this graph gives the best guess for the order in which the deposits were made.

Dr. Edward C. Harris, in his *Principles of Archaeological Stratigraphy*, provided a system known today as **Harris matrices** (which are actually graphs) to assist archaeologists in determining how stratification occurred at a dig site.

(*Source:* http://enwikipedia.org/wiki/Harris_matrix)

As the number of vertices in a complete graph increases, the number of Hamilton circuits for that graph increases very quickly. Previously we considered how quickly exponential functions increase. Factorials increase quickly as well. For example,

$$25! = 15{,}511{,}210{,}043{,}330{,}985{,}984{,}000{,}000,$$

or approximately 1.6×10^{25} —more than a trillion trillion.

Minimum Hamilton Circuits

Consider that on a typical day, a UPS van might have to make deliveries to 100 different locations. For simplicity, assume that none are priority deliveries, so they can be made in any order. UPS wants to minimize the time to make these deliveries. Think of the 100 locations and the UPS distribution center as the vertices of a complete graph with 101 vertices.

In principle, the van can go from any of these locations directly to any other, shown by having an edge between each pair of vertices. Suppose we estimate the travel time between each pair of locations (of course, this would depend on distance and traffic conditions along the route). These estimates provide weights on the edges of the graph. The objective is to visit each location exactly once, to begin and end at the same place, and to take as little time as possible.

In graph theory terms, we need a Hamilton circuit for the graph with the *least possible total weight*. The **total weight** of a circuit is the sum of the weights on the edges in the circuit. We call such a circuit a *minimum Hamilton circuit* for the graph.

MINIMUM HAMILTON CIRCUIT

In a weighted graph, a **minimum Hamilton circuit** is a Hamilton circuit with the least possible total weight.

A problem whose solution requires us to find a minimum Hamilton circuit for a complete, weighted graph is often called a **traveling salesman problem** (or TSP). Think of the vertices of the complete graph as the cities that a salesperson must visit, and think of the weights on the edges as the cost of traveling directly between the cities. To minimize costs, the salesperson needs a minimum Hamilton circuit for the graph.

Traveling salesman problems are relevant to efficient routing of telephone calls and Internet connections. As another example, to manufacture integrated circuit silicon chips, many lines have to be etched on a silicon wafer. Minimizing production time involves deciding the order in which to etch the lines: a traveling salesman problem. Likewise, to manufacture circuit boards for integrated circuits, laser-drilled holes must be made for connections. Again, the order for drilling the holes is a critical factor in production time.

Brute Force Algorithm

Suppose we are given a complete, weighted graph. How can we find a minimum Hamilton circuit for the graph? One way is to systematically list all the Hamilton circuits in the graph, find the total weight of each, and choose a circuit with least total weight. (In fact, it is sufficient to add up the weights on the edges for just half of the Hamilton circuits, since the total weight of a circuit is the same as the total weight of the circuit that uses the same edges in reverse order.)

The method just described is sometimes called the **brute force algorithm** since we find the solution by checking *all* the Hamilton circuits.

> **BRUTE FORCE ALGORITHM**
>
> **Step 1** Choose a starting point.
>
> **Step 2** List all the Hamilton circuits with that starting point.
>
> **Step 3** Find the total weight of each circuit.
>
> **Step 4** Choose a Hamilton circuit with the least total weight.

EXAMPLE 2 Using the Brute Force Algorithm

Find a minimum Hamilton circuit for the complete, weighted graph shown in **Figure 43.**

Solution

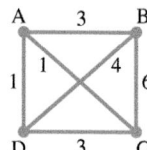

Figure 43

Choose a starting point. For this example, we choose A. Now list all the Hamilton circuits starting at A. Because this is a complete graph with 4 vertices, there are

$$3! = 3 \cdot 2 \cdot 1 = 6 \text{ circuits.}$$

Thus, we must find 6 Hamilton circuits.

We need a systematic way of writing down all the Hamilton circuits. The "counting tree" of **Figure 42** on **page 849** provides a guide. We start by finding all the Hamilton circuits that begin A → B, then include those that begin A → C, and finally include those that begin A → D, as shown below. Once all the Hamilton circuits are listed, pair those that visit the vertices in precisely opposite orders. (Circuits in these pairs have the same total weight. This will save some adding.) Finally, determine the sum of the weights in each circuit.

Circuit	Total weight of the circuit
1. A → B → C → D → A	3 + 6 + 3 + 1 = 13
2. A → B → D → C → A	3 + 4 + 3 + 1 = **11** Minimum
3. A → C → B → D → A	1 + 6 + 4 + 1 = 12
4. A → C → D → B → A (opposite of 2)	11
5. A → D → B → C → A (opposite of 3)	12
6. A → D → C → B → A (opposite of 1)	13

We can now see that A → B → D → C → A is a minimum Hamilton circuit for the graph. The weight of this circuit is 11. ∎

William Rowan Hamilton (1805–1865) spent most of his life in Dublin, Ireland. He was good friends with the poet William Wordsworth, whom he met while touring England and Scotland. Hamilton tried writing poetry, but Wordsworth tactfully suggested that his talents lay in mathematics rather than verse. Catherine Disney was the first great love of his life, but under pressure from her parents, she married another man, much wealthier than Hamilton. Hamilton never seemed to quite get over this.

In principle, the brute force algorithm provides a way to find a minimum Hamilton circuit in any complete, weighted graph. In practice, it takes far too long, even for a complete, weighted graph with only 7 vertices. There are 6!, or 720, Hamilton circuits in such a graph, and we would have to calculate the total weight for half of these. That means we would have to do 360 separate calculations, in addition to listing the Hamilton circuits.

Most real-world problems involve a great deal more than 7 vertices. Manufacturing a large integrated circuit can involve a graph with almost one million vertices. Likewise, telecommunications companies routinely deal with graphs with millions of vertices. As the number of vertices in the graph increases, the task of finding a minimum Hamilton circuit using the brute force algorithm soon becomes too time-consuming for even our fastest computers. For example, if one of today's supercomputers had started using the brute force algorithm on a 100-vertex traveling salesman problem when the universe was created, it would not yet be done.

The P = NP Problem The traveling salesman problem can be solved using brute force as long as the number of cities is relatively small. A computer program is required to solve problems involving more cities. One such program is the *Concorde TPS Solver,* or Concorde. Developed by a team of researchers led by William J. Cook, Concorde broke the world record for finding an optimal tour through the most locations. The problem, which involved 85,900 cities, was developed at Bell Labs in the late 1980s and took 15 years for Concorde to solve.

Probably the most important unsolved problem in computer science is either to find an efficient algorithm for the traveling salesman problem or to explain why no one could create such an algorithm. In mathematical circles, this is known as the **P = NP problem.** It was once mentioned in an episode of *The Simpsons.*

Cook has written a book on the traveling salesman problem in lay terms. It is titled *In Pursuit of the Traveling Salesman.* His Web site (see the source note below) contains links to the following related articles.

- $500 prize for best tour through 115,475 U.S. cities
- Short piece on Yogi Berra and the TSP
- Thriller movie centered around a solution of the TSP
- 49,512-city tour of Colbert Nation via the *iPhone App*
- $1000 Prize for a 100,000-city challenge problem
- Plot an optimal TSP tour with a Google interface
- Solution of an 85,900-city TSP
- Optimal route for a 99-county campaign tour

(*Sources:* www.math.uwaterloo.ca/tsp; http://jhered.oxfordjournals.org)

In contrast, Fleury's algorithm for finding an Euler circuit in a graph does not take too long for our computers, even for rather large graphs. Algorithms that do not take too much computer time are called **efficient algorithms.** Computer scientists have so far been unable to find an efficient algorithm for the traveling salesman problem, and they suspect that it is simply impossible to create such an algorithm.

For the traveling salesman problem, there are some algorithms that do not take too much computer time and that give *reasonably good* solutions *most of the time.* Such algorithms are called **approximate algorithms,** because they give an approximate solution to the problem. The underlying idea is that from each vertex, we proceed to a "nearest" available vertex.

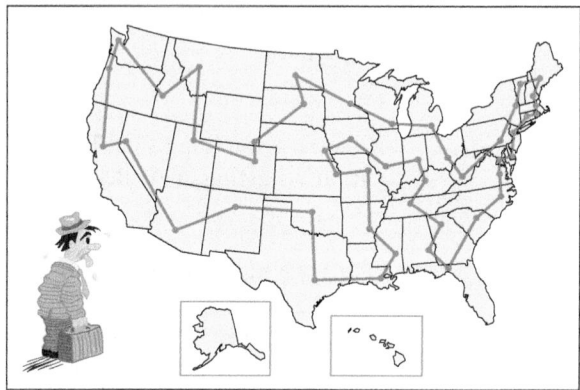

Figure 44

Nearest Neighbor Algorithm

One approximate algorithm for problems such as the traveling salesman problem is the **nearest neighbor algorithm.**

NEAREST NEIGHBOR ALGORITHM

Step 1 Choose a starting point for the circuit. Call this vertex A.

Step 2 Check all the edges joined to A, and choose one that has the least weight. Proceed along this edge to the next vertex.

Step 3 At each vertex you reach, check the edges from there *to vertices not yet visited.* Choose one with the least weight. Proceed along this edge to the next vertex.

Step 4 Repeat Step 3 until you have visited all the vertices.

Step 5 Return to the starting vertex.

EXAMPLE 3 **Using the Nearest Neighbor Algorithm**

A courier is based at the head office (A) and must deliver documents to four other offices (B, C, D, and E). The estimated time of travel (in minutes) between each of these offices is shown on the graph in **Figure 45** on the next page. The courier wants to visit the locations in an order that takes the least time. Use the nearest neighbor algorithm to find an approximate solution to this problem. Calculate the total time required to cover the chosen route.

In 1985, researcher **Shen Lin** came up with the route shown in **Figure 44** for a salesman who wants to visit all capital cities in the forty-eight contiguous states, starting and ending at the same capital and traveling the shortest possible total distance. He could not prove that his 10,628-mile route was the shortest possible, but he offered $100 to anyone who could find a shorter one.

Figure 45

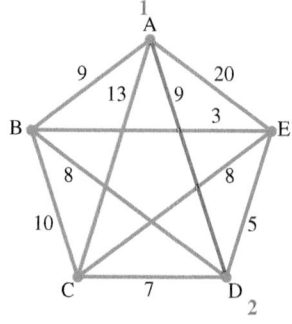

Figure 46

Solution

Step 1   Choose a starting point. Let's start at A.

Step 2   Choose an edge with least weight joined to A. Both AB and AD have weight 9, which is less than the weights of the other two edges joined to A. We choose AD* and keep a record of the circuit as we form it.

$$A \xrightarrow{9} D$$

To help ensure that we do not visit a vertex twice, we number the vertices as we visit them and color the edges used, as in **Figure 46.**

Continue to number the vertices as we work through the rest of the solution.

Step 3   Now check edges joined to D, excluding DA (since we have already been to A). DC has weight 7, DB has weight 8, and DE has weight 5. DE has the least weight, so proceed along DE to E. Our circuit begins this way.

$$A \xrightarrow{9} D \xrightarrow{5} E$$

Step 4   Now repeat the process at E. Check all edges from E that go to a vertex not yet visited. EC has weight 8 and EB has weight 3. Proceed along EB to B.

$$A \xrightarrow{9} D \xrightarrow{5} E \xrightarrow{3} B$$

Step 5   We have one vertex not yet visited, C. We go next to C and now have visited all the vertices. We return to our starting point, A. Our Hamilton circuit is

$$A \xrightarrow{9} D \xrightarrow{5} E \xrightarrow{3} B \xrightarrow{10} C \xrightarrow{13} A.$$

Its total weight is $9 + 5 + 3 + 10 + 13 = 40$.

Our advice to the courier would thus be to visit the offices in the order shown in this circuit. This route will take about 40 minutes. ■

The circuit we found in **Example 3** is not the minimum Hamilton circuit for the graph in **Figure 45.** (We shall investigate this.) However, the point of an approximate algorithm is that a computer can implement it without taking too much time, and most of the time it will give a reasonably good solution to the problem.

If we had a computer performing the nearest neighbor algorithm for us, we could make a small adjustment that would give better results without taking too much longer. We could repeat the nearest neighbor algorithm for all possible starting points, and then choose from these the Hamilton circuit with the least weight. If we do this for the example above, we obtain the results in **Table 1** on the next page.

Large Numbers 70! is the first factorial greater than 10^{100}. Most calculators will calculate numbers up to only about 10^{99}, so if you try calculating 70! you probably will get an error message. (Try it.) 10^{100} is called one googol, a name invented by a nine-year-old child who was asked to make up a name for a very, very large number.

These numbers are unimaginably large. Consider:

$$25! \approx 2 \times 10^{25}$$
$$50! \approx 3 \times 10^{64}$$
$$100! \approx 9 \times 10^{157}$$

Comparison:

Approximate number of *meters* from Saturn to the sun: 10^{12}

Estimate of the number of *inches* to the farthest object in the universe: 10^{27}

Approximate number of molecules we would have if we filled a sphere the size of Earth with water: 10^{49}

*If using a computer to do this, we would instruct the computer to make a random choice between AB and AD.

Table 1

Starting Vertex	Circuit Using Nearest Neighbor	Total Weight
A	A → D → E → B → C → A	9 + 5 + 3 + 10 + 13 = 40
B	B → E → D → C → A → B	3 + 5 + 7 + 13 + 9 = 37
C	C → D → E → B → A → C	7 + 5 + 3 + 9 + 13 = 37
D	D → E → B → A → C → D	5 + 3 + 9 + 13 + 7 = 37
E	E → B → D → C → A → E	3 + 8 + 7 + 13 + 20 = 51

We would recommend that the courier use a circuit with total weight 37—for example,

$$D \to E \to B \to A \to C \to D.$$

This does not force him to start his journey at D. If he followed the route

$$A \to C \to D \to E \to B \to A,$$

he would be using the same edges as in $D \to E \to B \to A \to C \to D$, and his traveling time still would be 37 minutes.

Can we now be sure that we have found the minimum Hamilton circuit for the graph in **Figure 45**? No. This is still an *approximate* solution. If we check the total weights of all possible Hamilton circuits in the graph, we find the Hamilton circuit

$$A \xrightarrow{9} B \xrightarrow{3} E \xrightarrow{8} C \xrightarrow{7} D \xrightarrow{9} A$$

with total weight just 36 minutes. The nearest neighbor algorithm simply will not find this minimum Hamilton circuit for the graph. However, all we expect of an approximate algorithm is that it give a reasonably good solution for the problem in a reasonable amount of time.

One method for generating solutions for the traveling salesman problem uses ant colony simulation. It models by creating paths observed in actual ant behavior to find the shortest paths between the ant nest and food sources. See **Figure 47**. (*Source:* wikipedia.org/wiki/Traveling_salesman_problem)

Figure 47

FOR FURTHER THOUGHT

The Speed of Algorithms

How do computer scientists classify the speed of algorithms? First, they write the number of steps a computer using the algorithm takes to solve a problem as a function of the "size" of the problem. We can think of the size of the problem as the number of vertices in a graph.

Let's suppose that our graph has n vertices. For some algorithms the number of steps is a **polynomial function of n**—for example, $n^4 + 2n$. For other algorithms, the number of steps is an **exponential function of n**—for example, 2^n. (See **Chapters 7 and 8** for more on polynomial and exponential functions.) As n increases, the number of steps increases much faster for exponential functions than for polynomial functions. Functions that involve factorials increase even faster.

In the table below we show approximate values for functions of the three types for different values of n. (We use scientific notation to make it easier to compare the sizes of the numbers.)

n	n^4	2^n	$n!$
5	6.3×10^2	3.2×10	1.2×10^2
10	1.0×10^4	1.0×10^3	3.6×10^6
15	5.1×10^4	3.3×10^4	1.3×10^{12}
20	1.6×10^5	1.0×10^6	2.4×10^{18}
25	3.9×10^5	3.4×10^7	1.6×10^{25}
30	8.1×10^5	1.1×10^9	2.7×10^{32}
40	2.6×10^6	1.1×10^{12}	8.2×10^{47}
50	6.3×10^6	1.1×10^{15}	3.0×10^{64}

In the first line of the table (where $n = 5$), n^4 gives the largest value. But as n gets larger, 2^n grows much faster than n^4, while $n!$ grows extremely fast. For example, if we double the size of n from 15 to 30, n^4 becomes a little more than 10 times as large, 2^n becomes about 3×10^4 (or 30,000) times as large, while $n!$ becomes approximately 2×10^{20} times as large. 10^{20} is more than a billion billion.

Algorithms whose time functions grow no faster than a polynomial function are called **polynomial time algorithms.** These are *efficient* algorithms—they do not take too much computer time.

Algorithms whose time functions grow faster than any polynomial function are called **exponential time algorithms.** These are *not* efficient algorithms. They are by nature too time-consuming for our computers. Our silicon chip computers are getting faster each year, but even this increase in speed hardly puts a dent in the time required for a computer to implement an exponential time algorithm for a very large graph.

Because the brute force algorithm for the traveling salesman problem has a time function involving $n!$, which grows faster than an exponential function of n, this algorithm is an exponential time algorithm.

For Group or Individual Investigation

Use the table to help answer these questions:

1. By approximately what factor does n^4 grow if we double n from 10 to 20?

2. By approximately what factor does 2^n grow if we double n from 10 to 20?

3. By approximately what factor does $n!$ grow if we double n from 10 to 20?

4. Repeat Exercises 1–3 if we double n from 25 to 50.

5. Suppose it would take 2^{30} years using computers at their present speeds to solve a certain problem. (2^{30} is a little over one billion.) If we assume that computers double in speed each year, how long would we have to wait before we could solve the problem in 1 year?

14.3 EXERCISES

Hamilton Circuits In Exercises 1 and 2, a graph is shown, and some paths in the graph are specified. Determine which paths are Hamilton circuits for the graph. If not, say why not.

1.

   (a) $A \rightarrow E \rightarrow C \rightarrow D \rightarrow E \rightarrow B \rightarrow A$

   (b) $A \rightarrow E \rightarrow C \rightarrow D \rightarrow B \rightarrow A$

   (c) $D \rightarrow B \rightarrow E \rightarrow A \rightarrow B$

   (d) $E \rightarrow D \rightarrow C \rightarrow B \rightarrow E$

2.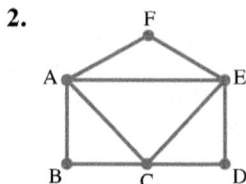

   (a) $A \rightarrow B \rightarrow C \rightarrow D \rightarrow E \rightarrow C \rightarrow A \rightarrow E \rightarrow F \rightarrow A$

   (b) $A \rightarrow C \rightarrow D \rightarrow E \rightarrow F \rightarrow A$

   (c) $F \rightarrow A \rightarrow C \rightarrow E \rightarrow F$

   (d) $C \rightarrow D \rightarrow E \rightarrow F \rightarrow A \rightarrow B$

Euler and Hamilton Circuits In Exercises 3 and 4, determine whether each sequence of vertices is a circuit, whether it is an Euler circuit, and whether it is a Hamilton circuit. Justify your answers.

3.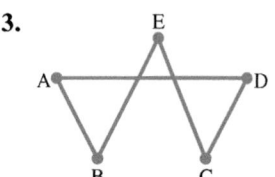

   (a) $A \rightarrow B \rightarrow C \rightarrow D \rightarrow E \rightarrow A$

   (b) $B \rightarrow E \rightarrow C \rightarrow D \rightarrow A \rightarrow B$

   (c) $E \rightarrow B \rightarrow A \rightarrow D \rightarrow A \rightarrow D \rightarrow C \rightarrow E$

4.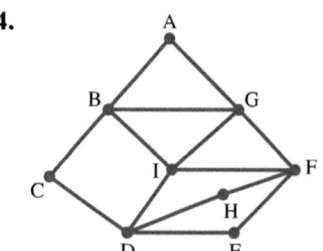

   (a) $A \rightarrow B \rightarrow C \rightarrow D \rightarrow E \rightarrow F \rightarrow G \rightarrow A$

   (b) $B \rightarrow I \rightarrow G \rightarrow F \rightarrow E \rightarrow D \rightarrow H \rightarrow F \rightarrow I \rightarrow D \rightarrow C \rightarrow B \rightarrow G \rightarrow A \rightarrow B$

   (c) $A \rightarrow B \rightarrow C \rightarrow D \rightarrow E \rightarrow F \rightarrow G \rightarrow H \rightarrow I \rightarrow A$

Hamilton Circuits *In Exercises 5–10, determine whether the graph has a Hamilton circuit. If so, find one. (There may be many different correct answers.)*

5.

6.

7.

8.

9.

10.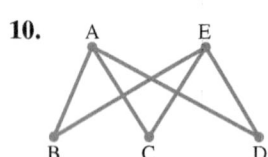

Hamilton and Euler Circuits *Work each problem.*

11. Draw a graph that has a Hamilton circuit but no Euler circuit. Specify the Hamilton circuit, and explain why the graph has no Euler circuit. (There are many different correct answers.)

12. Draw a graph that has an Euler circuit but no Hamilton circuit. Specify an Euler circuit in your graph. (There are many different correct answers.)

13. Draw a graph that has both an Euler circuit and a Hamilton circuit. Specify these circuits. (There are many different correct answers.)

14. Decide whether each statement is true or false. If the statement is false, give an example to show that it is false.

(a) A Hamilton circuit for a graph must visit each vertex in the graph.

(b) An Euler circuit for a graph must visit each vertex in the graph.

(c) A Hamilton circuit for a graph must use each edge in the graph.

(d) An Euler circuit for a graph must use each edge in the graph.

(e) A circuit cannot be both a Hamilton circuit and an Euler circuit.

(f) An Euler circuit must visit no vertex more than once, except the vertex where the circuit begins and ends.

Hamilton and Euler Circuits *In Exercises 15–20, determine whether an Euler circuit, a Hamilton circuit, or neither would solve the problem.*

15. Bandstands at a Festival The vertices of a graph represent bandstands at a festival, and the edges represent paths between the bandstands. A visitor wants to visit each bandstand exactly once, returning to her starting point when she is finished.

16. Relay Team Running Order The vertices of a complete graph represent the members of a five-person relay team. The team manager wants a circuit that will show the order in which the team members will run. (He will decide later who will start.)

17. Paths in a Botanical Garden The vertices of a graph represent places where paths in a botanical garden cross, and the edges represent the paths. A visitor wants to walk along each path in the garden exactly once, returning to his starting point when finished.

18. Western Europe The vertices of a graph represent the countries on the continent (Western Europe), and the edges represent border crossings between the countries. A traveler wants to travel over each border crossing exactly once, returning to the first country visited for his flight home to the United States.

19. Africa Vertices represent countries in sub-Saharan Africa, with an edge between two vertices if those countries have a common border. A traveler wants to visit each country exactly once, returning to the first country visited for her flight home to the United States.

20. X-Rays In using X-rays to analyze the structure of crystals, an X-ray diffractometer measures the intensity of reflected radiation from the crystal in thousands of different positions. Consider the complete graph with vertices representing the positions where measurements must be taken. The researcher must decide the order in which to take these readings, with the diffractometer returning to its starting point when finished.

Factorials *In Exercises 21–24, use a calculator, if necessary, to find the value.*

21. 4!

22. 6!

23. 9!

24. 14!

Hamilton Circuits *In Exercises 25–28, determine how many Hamilton circuits there are in a complete graph with this number of vertices. (Leave answers in factorial notation.)*

25. 10 vertices

26. 15 vertices

27. 18 vertices

28. 60 vertices

29. List all Hamilton circuits in the graph that start at P.

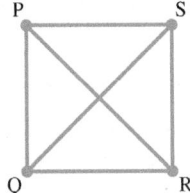

Hamilton Circuits *In Exercises 30–36, refer to the following graph. List all Hamilton circuits in the graph that start with the indicated vertices.*

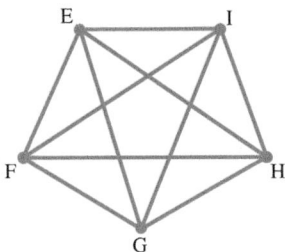

30. Starting E → F → G

31. Starting E → H → I

32. Starting E → I → H

33. Starting E → F

34. Starting E → I

35. Starting E → G

36. Starting at E

37. **Hamilton Circuits** List all Hamilton circuits in the graph that start at A.

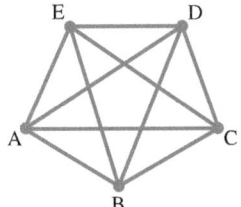

Brute Force Algorithm *In Exercises 38–41, use the brute force algorithm to find a minimum Hamilton circuit for the graph. In each case determine the total weight of the minimum Hamilton circuit.*

38.

39.

40.

41.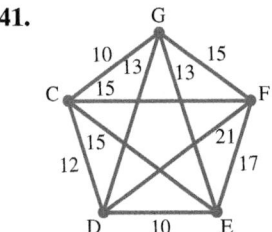

Nearest Neighbor Algorithm *In Exercises 42–44, use the nearest neighbor algorithm starting at each of the indicated vertices to determine an approximate solution to the problem of finding a minimum Hamilton circuit for the graph. In each case, find the total weight of the circuit found.*

42.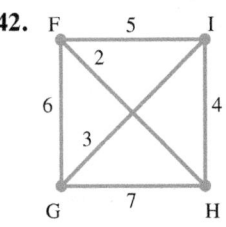

    (a) Starting at F

    (b) Starting at G

    (c) Starting at H

    (d) Starting at I

43.

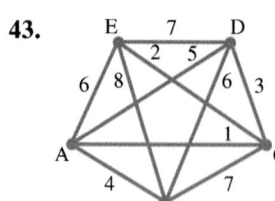

(a) Starting at A

(b) Starting at C

(c) Starting at D

(d) Starting at E

44.

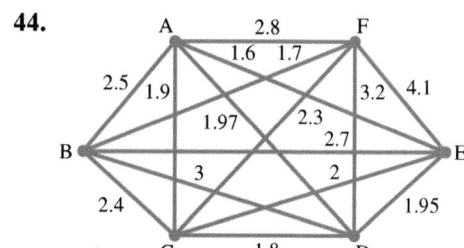

(a) Starting at A

(b) Starting at B

(c) Starting at C

(d) Starting at D

(e) Starting at E

(f) Starting at F

45. *Nearest Neighbor Algorithm* Refer to the accompanying graph. Complete parts (a)–(c) in order.

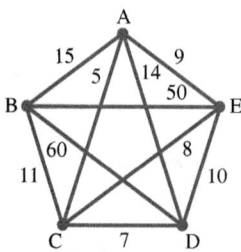

(a) Use the nearest neighbor algorithm starting at each of the vertices in turn to determine an approximate solution to the problem of finding a minimum Hamilton circuit for the graph. In each case, find the total weight of the circuit.

(b) Which of the circuits found in part (a) gives the best solution to the problem of finding a minimum Hamilton circuit for the graph?

(c) Just by looking carefully at the graph, find a Hamilton circuit in the graph that has lower total weight than any of the circuits found in part (a).

46. *Complete Bipartite Graph* A graph is called a complete bipartite graph if the vertices can be separated into two groups in such a way that there are no edges between vertices in the same group, and there is an edge between each vertex in the first group and each vertex in the second group. An example is shown below.

The notation we use for these graphs is $K_{m,n}$, where m and n are the numbers of vertices in the two groups. For example, the graph shown in this exercise is $K_{4,3}$ (or $K_{3,4}$). Complete parts (a)–(d) in order.

(a) Draw $K_{2,2}$, $K_{2,3}$, $K_{2,4}$, $K_{3,3}$, and $K_{4,4}$.

(b) For each of the graphs you have drawn in part (a), find a Hamilton circuit or say that the graph has no Hamilton circuit.

(c) Make a conjecture: What must be true about m and n for $K_{m,n}$ to have a Hamilton circuit?

(d) What must be true about m and n for $K_{m,n}$ to have an Euler circuit? Justify your answer.

Hamilton Circuits In Exercises 47–50, find all Hamilton circuits in the graph that start at A. (Hint: Use counting trees.)

47.

48.

49.

50.

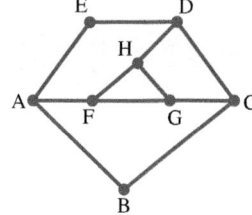

51. *Traveling Salesman Problem* The diagram represents seven cities, A through G, along with the distances in miles between many of the pairs.

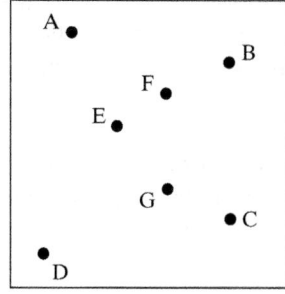

AB = 51   AF = 36   BF = 22   CG = 22   EF = 22
AD = 71   BC = 50   BG = 45   DE = 45   EG = 28
AE = 32   BE = 45   CD = 61   DG = 45   FG = 30

Determine what you believe to be the shortest possible distance that can be traveled so that the starting point and ending point are the same, and all cities have been visited.

The Icosian Game *The graph below shows the Icosian game (described in the text) with the vertices labeled. In Exercises 52–54, find a Hamilton circuit for the graph in the specified version of the game. (We suggest that you write numbers on the graph in the order in which you visit the vertices. There are different correct answers for these exercises.)*

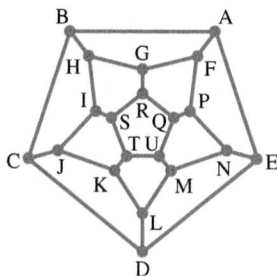

52. The circuit begins at A.

53. The circuit begins A → F.

54. The circuit begins A → B → H.

55. *Dirac's Theorem* Paul A. M. Dirac proved the following theorem in 1952.

Suppose G is a (simple) graph with n vertices, n ≥ 3. If the degree of each vertex is greater than or equal to $\frac{n}{2}$, then the graph has a Hamilton circuit.

Refer to graphs (1)–(5) and answer parts (a)–(e) in order.

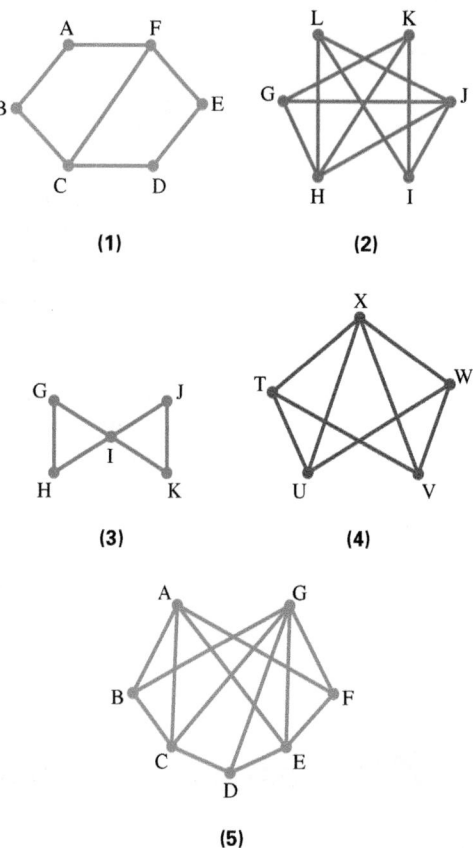

(a) Which graphs satisfy the condition that the degree of each vertex is greater than or equal to $\frac{n}{2}$?

(b) For which of the graphs can we conclude from Dirac's theorem that the graph has a Hamilton circuit?

(c) If a graph does *not* satisfy the condition that the degree of each vertex is greater than or equal to $\frac{n}{2}$, can we be sure that the graph does *not* have a Hamilton circuit? Justify your answer. (*Hint*: Study the accompanying graphs.)

(d) Is Dirac's theorem still true if n < 3? Justify your answer.

(e) Use Dirac's theorem to write a convincing argument that any complete graph with 3 or more vertices has a Hamilton circuit.

WHEN Will I Ever USE This ?

Do you hate waiting in lines?

TouringPlans.com is a Web site that helps its subscribers minimize their wait times for attractions at Walt Disney World and other popular theme parks. The site offers personalized, step-by-step itineraries that list the most efficient way to tour the parks.

Len Testa is the founder of TouringPlans.com, as well as the co-author of the *Unofficial Guide to Walt Disney World*. While on a vacation to Walt Disney World during the summer before he started graduate school, he waited in line almost two hours for the Great Movie Ride at the Disney-MGM Studios. Testa decided to make minimizing wait times the subject of his master's thesis in computer programming.

Using a variant of the traveling salesman problem that accounts for time dependency, Testa developed a computer program that would find the most efficient order in which to visit attractions in a theme park. The program uses a genetic algorithm that accounts for distance between attractions, duration of the attractions themselves, scheduled breaks, and average wait times. For a small fee, subscribers can create their own customized touring plans for each theme park by choosing which attractions they wish to visit and optimizing the plan for a given day. TouringPlans.com claims that it can save its users up to four hours in line per day at Walt Disney World, Disneyland, and Universal Studios Florida.

Source: Interview with Len Testa on episode 42 of the Betamouse Podcast, accessed from http://blog.touringplans.com

14.4 TREES AND MINIMUM SPANNING TREES

OBJECTIVES

1 Determine whether a graph is a *tree*.

2 Understand the unique path property of trees.

3 Know the meanings of the terms *spanning tree* and *minimum spanning tree*.

4 Apply Kruskal's algorithm to find a minimum spanning tree.

5 Understand the relationship between the number of vertices and the number of edges in a tree.

Connected Graphs and Trees

Peggy wants to install an underground irrigation system in her garden. The system must connect the faucet (F) to outlets at various points, specifically the rose bed (R), perennial bed (P), daffodil bed (D), annuals bed (A), berry patch (B), vegetable patch (V), cut flower bed (C), and shade bed (S). These are the vertices of the graph in **Figure 48.**

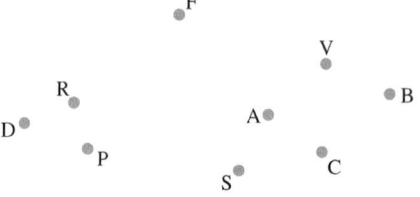

Figure 48

The irrigation system will have pipes connecting these points. For the irrigation system to work well, there should be as few pipes as possible connecting all the outlets.

In graph theory, the botanical words go beyond trees. A **forest** is a graph with all components trees, as shown here. Later in this section you will find the words **root** and **leaf** applied to graphs. The terms **pruning** and **separating** arise in applications of trees to the computer analysis of images.

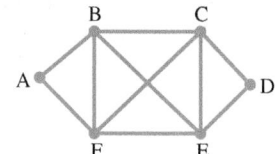

Figure 49

Think about this problem in terms of a graph with edges representing pipes. Peggy wants water to flow from the faucet (F) to each of the outlets. This means that we need to create a *connected* graph that includes all the vertices in **Figure 48.**

CONNECTED GRAPH (ALTERNATIVE DEFINITION)

A **connected graph** is one in which there is *at least one path* between each pair of vertices.

To see that this definition agrees with our definition in **Section 14.1,** observe that if we select any pair of vertices in the connected graph in **Figure 49** (for example, A and C), then there is at least one path between them. (In fact, there are many paths between A and C.) Two examples are

$$A \to B \to E \to C \quad \text{and} \quad A \to F \to C.$$

Peggy needs a *connected* graph. Also, she must use as few pipes as possible to connect all the outlets to the system. This means that the graph *must not contain any circuits.* If the graph had a circuit, we could remove one of the pipes in the circuit and still have a connected system of pipes.

Figure 50 shows one possible solution to Peggy's problem.

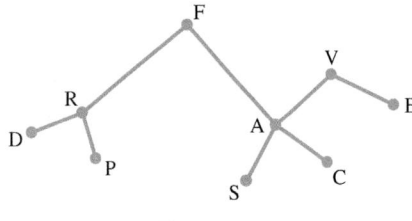

Figure 50

There is a name for graphs that are connected and contain no circuits.

TREE

A graph is a **tree** if the graph is *connected* and contains *no circuits.*

All five of the graphs shown in **Figure 51** are trees.

All are trees.

Figure 51

In contrast, none of the graphs shown in **Figure 52** is a tree. The graph in **Figure 52(a)** is not a tree, because it is not connected. Those in **Figures 52(b) and (c)** are not trees, because each contains at least one circuit.

Benzene

It seems mathematician **Arthur Cayley** invented the term "tree" in graph theory in about 1857 in connection with problems related to counting all trees of certain types. Later he realized the relevance of his work to nineteenth-century organic chemistry and, in the 1870s, published a note on this. Of course, not all molecules have treelike structures. Friedrich Kekulé's realization that the structure of benzene is *not* a tree is considered one of the most brilliant breakthroughs in organic chemistry.

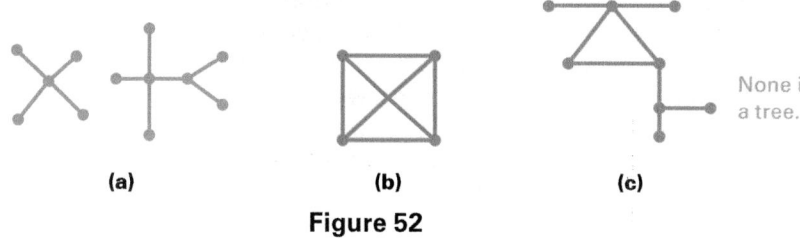

None is a tree.

(a)   (b)   (c)

Figure 52

Just how fast are the fastest computers? Computer speeds are sometimes measured in **flops** (floating point operations per second). A speed of one gigaflop means that the computer can perform about one billion (10^9) calculations per second.

UNIQUE PATH PROPERTY OF TREES

In a tree, there is always **exactly one path** from each vertex in the graph to any other vertex in the graph.

For example, consider the vertices S and B in the tree in **Figure 50.** There is exactly one path from vertex S to vertex B, namely $S \rightarrow A \rightarrow V \rightarrow B$.

This property follows from the definition of a tree. Because a tree is connected, there is always at least one path between each pair of vertices. And if the graph is a tree, there cannot be two different paths between a pair of vertices. If there were, these together would contain a circuit.

It is the unique path property of trees that makes them so important in real-world applications. This also is the reason why trees are not a very useful model for telephone networks. Each edge of a tree is a cut edge, so failure along one link would disrupt the service. Telephone companies rely on networks with many circuits to provide alternative routes for calls.

Figure 53

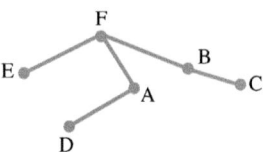

Figure 54

▌EXAMPLE 1 Renovating an Irrigation System

Joe has an old underground irrigation system in his garden, with connections at the faucet (F), outlets A through E in the garden, and existing underground pipes as shown in the graph in **Figure 53.** He wants to renovate this system, keeping only some of the pipes. Water must still be able to flow to each of the original outlets, and the graph of the irrigation system must be a tree. Design an irrigation system that meets Joe's objectives.

Solution

In graph theory terms, we need a *subgraph* of the graph in **Figure 53.** Because water still must be able to flow to each of the original outlets, we need a connected subgraph that *includes all the vertices of the original graph.* Finally, this subgraph must be a *tree.* Thus, we must remove edges (but no vertices) from the graph, without disconnecting the graph, to obtain a subgraph that is a tree. One way to achieve this is shown in **Figure 54.** ∎

FOR FURTHER THOUGHT

Binary Coding

The unique path property of a tree can be used to make a code. We illustrate with a **binary code,** that is, one that uses 0s and 1s. (Recall from **Chapter 4** that when we represent numbers in binary form, we use only the symbols 0 and 1.)

To set up the code we use a special kind of tree like that shown in the figure at right. This tree is a **directed graph** (there are arrows on the edges). The vertex at the top (with no arrows pointing toward it) is called the **root** of the directed tree. The vertices with no arrows pointing away from them are called **leaves** of the directed tree. We label each leaf with a letter we want to encode. The diagram shown encodes only 8 letters, but we could easily draw a bigger tree with more leaves to represent more letters.

We now write a 0 on each branch that goes left and a 1 on each branch that goes right.

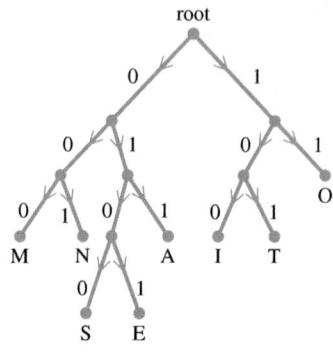

To show how the encoding works, we write the word MAT using the code. Follow the unique path from the root of the tree down to the appropriate leaf, noting in order the labels on the edges.

M is written **000**.

A is written **011**.

T is written **101**.

So MAT is written **000011101**.

We can easily translate this code using our tree. Let us see how we could decode 000011101. Referring to the tree, there is only one path from the root to a leaf that can give rise to those first three 0s, and that is the path leading to M. So we can begin to separate the code word into letters: 000–011101. Again following down from the root, the path 011 leads us unambiguously to A. So we have 000–011–101. The path 101 leads unambiguously to T.

The reason why we can translate the string of 0s and 1s back to letters without ambiguity is that no letter has a code the same as the first part of the code for a different letter.

For Group or Individual Investigation

1. Use the binary encoding tree to write the binary code for each of the following words:

ANT, SEAT

2. Use the encoding tree to find the word represented by each of the following codes:

0001111001, 0100011101

3. Decode the following messages (commas are inserted to show separation of words).

(a) 0110011010100, 100001, 1010101001101

(b) 0101011101, 0001000011010100, 100001, 101100001

(c) 011, 0000101011001, 1010101011000

(d) 00001010101101, 0000101, 011101, 1010101011

The answers are on **page 864**.

Spanning Trees

A subgraph of the type shown in **Figure 54** from **Example 1** is called a *spanning tree* for the graph. This kind of subgraph "spans" the graph in the sense that it connects all the vertices of the original graph into a subgraph.

Arthur Cayley (1821–1895) was a close friend of James Sylvester. They worked together as lawyers at the courts of Lincolns Inn in London and discussed mathematics with each other during work hours. Cayley considered his work as a lawyer simply a way to support himself so that he could do mathematics. In the fourteen years he worked as a lawyer, he published 250 mathematical papers. At age 42, he took a huge paycut to become a mathematics professor at Cambridge University.

> **SPANNING TREE**
>
> A **spanning tree** for a graph is a subgraph that includes every vertex of the original graph and is a tree.

We can find a spanning tree for any connected graph (think about that), and if the original graph has at least one circuit, it will have several different spanning trees.

EXAMPLE 2 Finding Spanning Trees

Consider the graph shown in **Figure 55**. Find two different spanning trees for the graph.

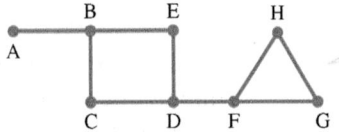

To obtain a tree, we must break the two circuits by removing a single edge from each.

Figure 55

Solution

There are several choices for which edges to remove. We could remove edges CD and FH, leaving the subgraph in **Figure 56(a).** Alternatively, we could remove edges ED and FG, leaving the subgraph in **Figure 56(b).** There are other correct solutions.

Figure 56

If two spanning trees use different edges from the original graph, we consider them to be different spanning trees even when they are isomorphic graphs. The subgraphs shown in **Figure 56** are *different* spanning trees, even though they happen to be isomorphic graphs. To decide whether they are isomorphic, change the labels in graph (a) as follows: Interchange C and E, and interchange G and H. By dragging vertices without detaching edges, we can obtain graphs that look alike.

Minimum Spanning Trees

Suppose there are six villages in a rural district. At present all the roads in the district are gravel roads. There is not enough funding to pave all the roads, but there is a pressing need to have good paved roads so that emergency vehicles can travel easily between the villages. The vertices in the graph in **Figure 57** represent the villages in the district, and the edges represent the existing gravel roads. Estimated costs for paving the different roads are shown, in millions of dollars. (These estimates take into account distances, as well as features of the terrain.)

The district council wants to pave just enough roads so that emergency vehicles will be able to travel from any village to any other along paved roads, though possibly by a roundabout route. The council would like to achieve this at the *lowest possible cost.*

The problem calls for exactly one path from each vertex in the graph to any other, so it requires a spanning tree. This spanning tree should have minimum total weight. The total weight of a spanning tree is the sum of the weights of the edges in the tree.

Figure 57

> **MINIMUM SPANNING TREE**
>
> A spanning tree that has minimum total weight is called a **minimum spanning tree** for the graph.

Computer analysis of images is a field of active research, particularly in medicine. (Computer analysis of images consists of having a computer detect relevant features of an image.) Some of this research uses minimum spanning trees. They have been used to identify protein fibers in photographs of cells. The computer detects some points lying on the fibers and then determines a minimum spanning tree to deduce the overall structure of the fiber. Some studies have used minimum spanning trees to analyze cancerous tissue.

Kruskal's Algorithm

Fortunately for the district planners, there is a good algorithm for finding a minimum spanning tree for any connected, weighted graph. It is called **Kruskal's algorithm.** The algorithm is an efficient algorithm, because it does not take too much computer time for even very large graphs.

Minimum Spanning Trees in Astronomy The structure of the universe may hold clues about its formation. The image shows the large-scale structure of the Milky Way against a background of many other galaxies. Galaxies are not uniformly distributed throughout the universe. Instead they seem to be arranged in clusters, which are grouped together into superclusters, which themselves seem to be arranged in vast chains called filaments. Some astronomers are using spanning trees to help map the filamentary structure of the universe.

KRUSKAL'S ALGORITHM FOR FINDING A MINIMUM SPANNING TREE FOR ANY CONNECTED, WEIGHTED GRAPH

Choose edges for the spanning tree as follows.

Step 1 First edge: Choose any edge with minimum weight.

Step 2 Next edge: Choose any edge with minimum weight from *those not yet selected.* (At this stage, the subgraph may look disconnected.)

Step 3 Continue to choose edges of minimum weight from those not yet selected, except *do not select any edge that creates a circuit* in the subgraph.

Step 4 Repeat Step 3 until the subgraph connects all vertices of the original graph.

Because Kruskal's algorithm gives a subgraph that is connected, includes all vertices of the original graph, and has no circuits, it certainly provides a spanning tree for the graph. Also, the algorithm always will give us a *minimum* spanning tree for the graph. The explanation for this fact is beyond the scope of this text. (Algorithms such as Kruskal's often are called *greedy* algorithms.)

EXAMPLE 3 Applying Kruskal's Algorithm

Use Kruskal's algorithm to find a minimum spanning tree for the graph in **Figure 57.**

Solution

Note that the graph is connected, so Kruskal's algorithm applies. Choose an edge with minimum weight. ED has the least weight of all the edges, so it is selected first. We color the edge a different color to show that it has been selected. See **Figure 58.**

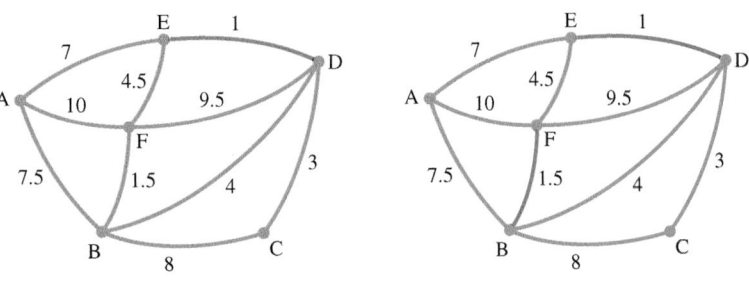

Figure 58   Figure 59

Of the remaining edges, BF has the least weight, so it is the second edge chosen, as shown in **Figure 59.** Note that it does not matter that at this stage the subgraph is not connected.

Continuing, we choose CD and then BD, as shown in **Figure 60** on the next page. Of the edges remaining, EF has the least weight. However, EF *would create a circuit* in the subgraph. We ignore EF and note that, of the edges remaining, AE has the least weight. Thus, AE is included in the spanning tree, as shown in **Figure 61** on the next page.

We now have a subgraph of the original that connects all vertices of the original graph into a tree. This subgraph is the required minimum spanning tree for the original graph. Its total weight is

$$1 + 1.5 + 3 + 4 + 7 = 16.5.$$

Thus, the district council can achieve its objective at a cost of 16.5 million dollars, by paving only the roads represented by edges in the minimum spanning tree.

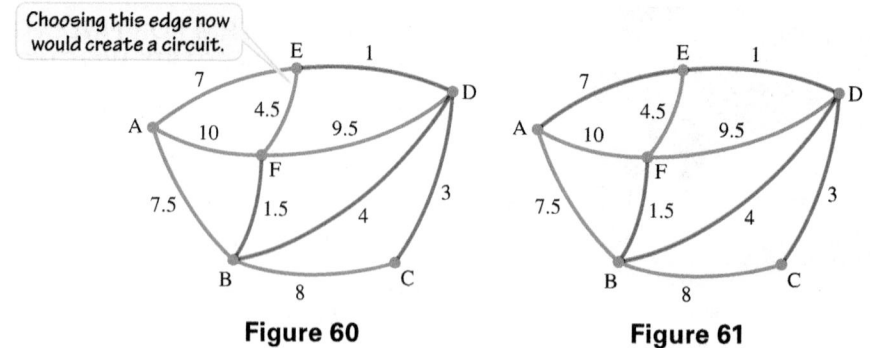

Figure 60   **Figure 61**

Number of Vertices and Edges

There is an interesting relationship between the number of vertices and the number of edges in a tree (sometimes called the **vertex/edge relationship**).

> ### NUMBER OF VERTICES AND EDGES IN A TREE
>
> If a graph is a tree, then the number of edges in the graph is one less than the number of vertices.
>
> **A tree with n vertices has $n - 1$ edges.**

Weather data are complex, involving numerous readings of temperature, pressure, and wind velocity over huge areas. Some current research uses minimum spanning trees to help computers interpret these data. For example, minimum spanning trees are used to identify developing cold fronts.

Consider the graphs shown in **Figure 62**. Information about these graphs is shown in **Table 2**. The three graphs in (a), (b), and (c) are not trees, and there is no uniform relation between the number of edges and the number of vertices for these graphs. In general, graphs may have more or fewer vertices than edges or an equal number of both. In contrast, the three graphs in (d), (e), and (f) are trees. The number of edges is indeed one less than the number of vertices for these trees.

Figure 62

Table 2

Graph	Tree?	Number of Vertices	Number of Edges	
(a)	No	12	10	
(b)	No	7	7	
(c)	No	6	9	
(d)	Yes	7	6	$6 = 7 - 1$
(e)	Yes	6	5	$5 = 6 - 1$
(f)	Yes	5	4	$4 = 5 - 1$

If we consider only connected graphs, then the converse of the theorem on the previous page is also true.

> ***For a connected graph, if the number of edges is one less than the number of vertices, then the graph is a tree.***

▉ EXAMPLE 4   Using the Vertex/Edge Relationship

A chemist has synthesized a new chemical compound. She knows from her analyses that a molecule of the compound contains 54 atoms and that the molecule has a tree-like structure. How many chemical bonds are there in the molecule?

Solution

Think of the atoms in the molecule as the vertices of a tree, and think of the bonds as edges of the tree. This tree has 54 vertices. Since the number of edges in a tree is one less than the number of vertices, the molecule must have 53 bonds.   ▉

> **Problem-Solving Strategy**
>
> Trial and error is a good problem-solving strategy. Choose an arbitrary proposed solution to the problem, and check whether it works. If it does not work, we may gain insight into what to try next.

▉ EXAMPLE 5   Finding a Graph with Specified Properties

Suppose a graph is a tree and has 15 vertices. What is the greatest number of vertices of degree 5 that this graph could have? Draw such a tree.

Solution

Because the graph is a tree with 15 vertices, it must have 14 edges. Recall that the sum of the degrees of the vertices of a graph is twice the number of edges. Therefore, the sum of the degrees of the vertices in the tree must be $2 \cdot 14$, which is 28.

   Now we use trial and error. We want the greatest possible number of vertices of degree 5. Four vertices of degree 5 would contribute 20 to the total degree sum. This would leave $28 - 20 = 8$ as the degree sum of the remaining 11 vertices, but this would mean that some of those vertices would have no edges joined to them. The graph would not be connected and would not be a tree.

   If we try 3 vertices of degree 5, this would contribute 15 to the total degree sum. It would leave $28 - 15 = 13$ as the degree sum for the remaining 12 vertices. We can draw a graph with these specifications, as in **Figure 63**. Thus, the greatest possible number of vertices of degree 5 in a tree with 15 vertices is 3.   ▉

Figure 63

14.4   EXERCISES

Tree Identification   *In Exercises 1–7, determine whether the graph is a tree. If not, explain why it is not.*

1.

2.

3.

4.

5.

6. a complete graph with 6 vertices

7. a connected graph with all vertices of even degree

Tree Identification *In Exercises 8–10, add edges (no vertices) to the graph to change the graph into a tree or explain why this is not possible. (Note: There may be more than one correct answer.)*

8.

9.

10.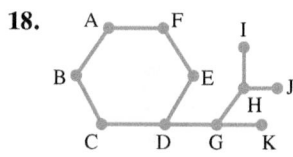

Tree or Not a Tree? *In Exercises 11–13, determine whether the graph described must be a tree.*

11. ***Spread of a Rumor*** A sociologist is investigating the spread of a rumor. He finds that 18 people know of the rumor. One of these people must have started the rumor, and each must have heard the rumor for the first time from one of the others. He draws a graph with vertices representing the 18 people and edges showing from whom each person first heard the rumor.

12. ***Internet Search Engine*** You are using the Google search engine to search the Web for information on a topic for a paper. You start at the Google page and follow links you find, sometimes going back to a site you've already visited. To keep a record of the sites you visit, you show each site as a vertex of a graph. You draw an edge each time you connect for the *first* time to a *new* site.

13. ***Tracking Ebola*** A patient has contracted Ebola. An employee of the Centers for Disease Control is trying to quarantine all people who have had contact, over the past week, either with the patient or with someone already included in the contact network. The employee draws a graph with vertices representing the patient and all people who have had contact as described. The edges of the graph represent the relation "the two people have had contact."

Trees and Cut Edges *In Exercises 14–17, determine whether the statement is* true *or* false. *If the statement is false, draw an example to show that it is false.*

14. Every graph with no circuits is a tree.

15. Every connected graph in which each edge is a cut edge is a tree.

16. Every graph in which there is a path between each pair of vertices is a tree.

17. Every graph in which each edge is a cut edge is a tree.

Spanning Trees *In Exercises 18–20, find three different spanning trees for each graph. (There are many different correct answers.)*

18.

19.

20.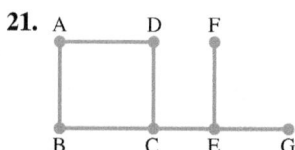

Spanning Trees *In Exercises 21–23, find all spanning trees for the graph.*

21.

22.

23.

Spanning Trees *In Exercises 24–26, determine how many spanning trees the graph has.*

24.

25.

26.

27. What is a general principle about the number of spanning trees in graphs such as those in **Exercises 24–26?**

28. Spanning Trees Complete the parts of this exercise in order.

(a) Find all the spanning trees of each of the following graphs.

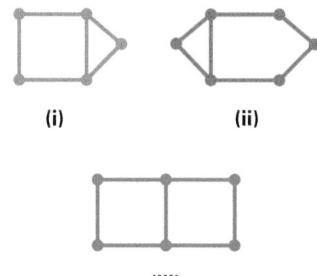

(i) (ii)

(iii)

(b) For each of the following graphs, determine how many spanning trees the graph has.

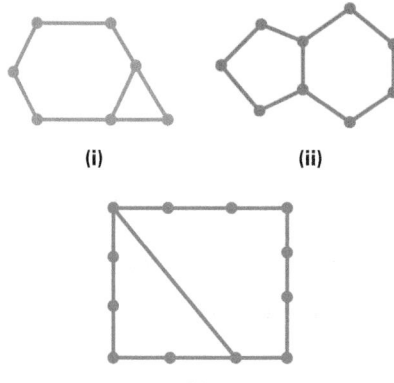

(i) (ii)

(iii)

(c) What is a general principle about the number of spanning trees in graphs of the kind shown in (a) and (b)?

Minimum Spanning Trees *In Exercises 29–32, use Kruskal's algorithm to find a minimum spanning tree for the graph. Find the total weight of this minimum spanning tree.*

29.

30.

31.

32.

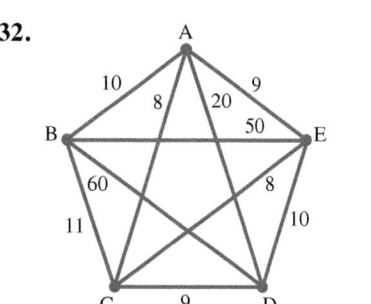

33. School Building Layout A school consists of 6 separate buildings, represented by the vertices in the graph.

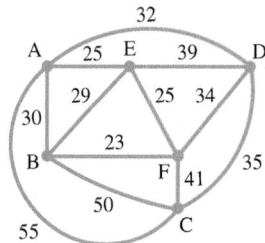

There are paths between some of the buildings as shown. The graph also shows the length in feet of each path. School administrators want to cover some of these paths with roofs so that students will be able to walk between buildings without getting wet when it rains. To minimize cost, they must select paths to be covered such that the total length to be covered is as small as possible.

Use Kruskal's algorithm to determine which paths to cover. Also determine the total length of pathways to be covered.

34. Town Water Distribution A town council is planning to provide town water to an area that previously relied on private wells. Water will be fed into the area at the point represented by the vertex labeled A in the graph on the next page. Water must be piped to each of five main distribution points, represented by the vertices labeled B through F in the graph. Town engineers have estimated the cost of laying the pipes to carry the water between each pair of points in millions of dollars, as indicated in the graph. They must now select which pipes should be laid, so that there is exactly one route for the water to be pumped from A to any one of the five distribution points (possibly via another distribution point), and they want to achieve this at minimum cost.

Use Kruskal's algorithm to decide which pipes should be laid. Find the total cost of laying the pipes.

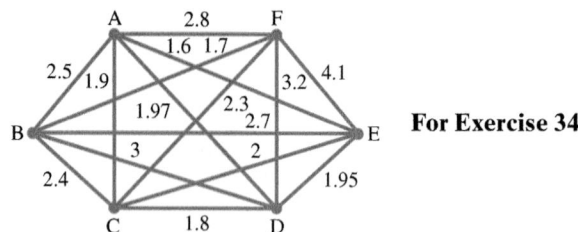

For Exercise 34

Trees, Edges, and Vertices *Work Exercises 35–42.*

35. How many edges are there in a tree with 34 vertices?

36. How many vertices are there in a tree with 40 edges?

37. How many edges are there in a spanning tree for a complete graph with 63 vertices?

38. A connected graph has 27 vertices and 43 edges. How many edges must be removed to form a spanning tree for the graph?

39. We have said that we can always find at least one spanning tree for a connected graph—and usually more than one. Could it happen that different spanning trees for the same graph have different numbers of edges? Justify your answer.

40. Suppose we have a tree with 9 vertices.

(a) Determine the number of edges in the graph.

(b) Determine the sum of the degrees of the vertices in the graph.

(c) Determine the least possible number of vertices of degree 1 in this graph.

(d) Determine the greatest possible number of vertices of degree 1 in this graph.

(e) Answer parts (a) through (d) for a tree with n vertices.

41. Suppose we have a tree with 10 vertices.

(a) Determine the number of edges in the graph.

(b) Determine the sum of the degrees of the vertices in the graph.

(c) Determine the least possible number of vertices of degree 4 in this graph.

(d) Determine the greatest possible number of vertices of degree 4 in this graph.

(e) Draw a graph to illustrate your answer in part (d).

42. Suppose we have a tree with 17 vertices.

(a) Determine the number of edges in the graph.

(b) Determine the sum of the degrees of the vertices in the graph.

(c) Determine the greatest possible number of vertices of degree 5 in this graph.

(d) Draw a graph to illustrate your answer in part (c).

43. *Computer Network Layout* A business has 23 employees, each with his or her own desk computer, all working in the same office. The managers want to network the computers. They need to install cables between individual computers so that every computer is linked into the network. Because of the way the office is laid out, it is not convenient to simply connect all the computers in one long line. Determine the least number of cables the managers need to install to achieve their objective.

44. *Design of a Garden* Maria has 12 vegetable and flower beds in her garden and wants to build flagstone paths between the beds so that she can get from each bed along flagstone paths to every other bed. She also wants a path linking her front door to one of the beds. Determine the minimum number of flagstone paths she must build to achieve this.

Tree or Not a Tree? *Exercises 45–47 refer to the following situation: We start with a tree and then draw in extra edges and vertices. For each, say whether it is possible to draw in the number of edges and vertices specified to end up with a connected graph. If it is possible, determine whether the resulting graph must be a tree, may be a tree, or cannot possibly be a tree. Justify each answer briefly.*

45. Draw in the same number of vertices as edges.

46. Draw in more vertices than edges.

47. Draw in more edges than vertices.

48. Starting with a tree, is it possible to draw in the same number of vertices as edges and end up with a disconnected graph? If so, give an example. If not, justify briefly.

Cayley's Theorem *Exercises 49–51 require the following theorem, which was proved by Cayley in 1889: **A complete graph with n vertices has n^{n-2} spanning trees.***

49. How many spanning trees are there for a complete graph with 3 vertices? Draw a complete graph with 3 vertices, and find all the spanning trees.

50. How many spanning trees are there for a complete graph with 4 vertices? Draw a complete graph with 4 vertices, and find all the spanning trees.

51. How many spanning trees are there for a complete graph with 5 vertices?

Isomorphism *Work Exercises 52–55.*

52. Find all nonisomorphic trees with 4 vertices. How many are there?

53. Find all nonisomorphic trees with 5 vertices. How many are there?

54. Find all nonisomorphic trees with 6 vertices. How many are there?

55. Find all nonisomorphic trees with 7 vertices. How many are there?

56. *Vertex/Edge Relationship* In this exercise, we explore why the number of edges in a tree is one less than the number of vertices. Because the statement is clearly true for a tree with only one vertex, we will consider a tree *with more than one vertex.* Answer parts (a)–(h) in order.

(a) How many components does the tree have?

(b) Why must the tree have at least one edge?

(c) Remove one edge from the tree. How many components does the resulting graph have?

(d) You have not created any new circuits by removing the edge, so each of the components of the resulting graph is a tree. If the remaining graph still has edges, choose any edge and remove it. (You have now removed 2 edges from the original tree.) Altogether, how many components remain?

(e) Repeat the procedure described in (d). If you remove 3 edges from the original tree, how many components remain? If you remove 4 edges from your original tree, how many components remain?

(f) Repeat the procedure in (d) until you have removed all the edges from the tree. If you have to remove n edges to achieve this, determine an expression involving n for the number of components remaining.

(g) What *are* the components that remain when you have removed all the edges from the tree?

(h) What can you conclude about the number of vertices in a tree with n edges?

CHAPTER 14 SUMMARY

KEY TERMS

14.1
vertex
edge
simple graph
degree of a vertex
isomorphic graphs
connected graph
disconnected graph
components of a graph
walk
path
circuit

weighted graph
weights
complete graph
subgraph
coloring
chromatic number
four-color problem
Bacon number

14.2
Königsberg bridge problem
Euler path

Euler circuit
cut edge
Fleury's algorithm
deadheading

14.3
Icosian game
Hamilton circuit
total weight
minimum Hamilton circuit
traveling salesman problem
brute force algorithm

efficient algorithms
approximate algorithms
nearest neighbor algorithm

14.4
connected graph
tree
spanning tree
minimum spanning tree
Kruskal's algorithm
vertex/edge relationship

NEW SYMBOLS

$n!$ n factorial

$A \rightarrow B$ a walk from vertex A to vertex B

TEST YOUR WORD POWER

See how well you have learned the vocabulary in this chapter.

1. Two graphs are **isomorphic** if
   A. they have the same number of edges.
   B. they have the same number of vertices.
   C. there is a one-to-one matching between vertices, with the property that whenever there is an edge between two vertices of either one of the graphs, there is an edge between the corresponding vertices of the other graph.
   D. each graph has the same chromatic number.

2. A **circuit** in a graph is
   A. a path that begins and ends with the same vertex.
   B. a path that begins and ends with different vertices.
   C. a path whose edges are assigned weights.
   D. a path that is not a walk.

3. An **Euler circuit** in a graph
   A. is a path that uses every edge of the graph exactly once.
   B. is a circuit that uses every edge of the graph exactly once.
   C. is a circuit that is composed of cut edges.
   D. has at least one vertex of odd degree.

4. A **Hamilton circuit** in a graph
   A. is a circuit that uses every edge exactly once (returning to the starting edge to complete the circuit).
   B. is a circuit that visits each vertex exactly once (returning to the starting vertex to complete the circuit).
   C. cannot exist if there are an odd number of vertices.
   D. cannot exist if there are an even number of vertices.

5. A graph is a **tree** if
   A. it is disconnected and contains no circuits.
   B. it has more than one Euler circuit.
   C. it has more than one Hamilton circuit.
   D. it is connected and contains no circuits.

ANSWERS
1. C **2.** A **3.** B **4.** B **5.** D

QUICK REVIEW

Concepts	Examples

14.1 Basic Concepts

Graph
A **graph** is a collection of vertices (at least one) and edges. Each edge goes from a vertex to a vertex.

These two graphs are isomorphic.

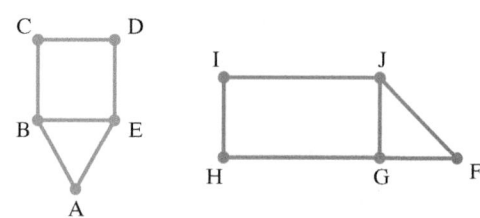

Isomorphic Graphs
Two graphs are **isomorphic** if there is a one-to-one matching between vertices of the two graphs, with the property that whenever there is an edge between two vertices of either one of the graphs, there is an edge between the corresponding vertices of the other graph.

Connected and Disconnected Graphs
A graph is **connected** if we can move from each vertex of the graph to every other vertex of the graph *along edges of the graph.* If not, the graph is **disconnected.**

The connected pieces of a graph are the **components** of the graph.

The graph on the left is disconnected, as illustrated by the colors shown on the right.

Sum-of-the-Degrees Theorem
In any graph, the sum of the degrees of the vertices equals twice the number of edges.

Consider each graph.

Number of edges = 7
Sum of degrees of vertices = 14

Number of edges = 6
Sum of degrees of vertices = 12

Walks, Paths, and Circuits
A **walk** in a graph is a sequence of vertices, each linked to the next vertex by a specified edge of the graph.

A **path** is a walk that uses no edge more than once.

A **circuit** is a path that begins and ends at the same vertex.

Complete Graph
A **complete graph** is a graph in which there is exactly one edge going from each vertex to each other vertex.

Consider the graph at the right.
$E \rightarrow C \rightarrow D \rightarrow E$ is not a walk (and thus is neither a path nor a circuit).

$B \rightarrow D \rightarrow E \rightarrow B \rightarrow C$ is a walk and a path, but not a circuit.

$A \rightarrow C \rightarrow D \rightarrow E \rightarrow B \rightarrow A$ is all three: walk, path, and circuit.

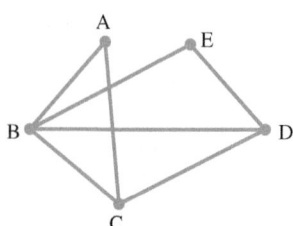

Concepts	*Examples*
Coloring and Chromatic Number A **coloring** for a graph is an assignment of a color to each vertex in such a way that vertices joined by an edge have different colors. The **chromatic number** of a graph is the least number of colors needed to achieve a coloring. **Coloring a Graph** *Step 1* Choose a vertex with greatest degree, and color it. Use the same color to color as many vertices as you can without coloring two vertices the same color if they are joined by an edge. *Step 2* Choose a new color, and repeat what you did in Step 1 for vertices not already colored. *Step 3* Repeat Step 1 until all vertices are colored.	This graph has chromatic number 3. 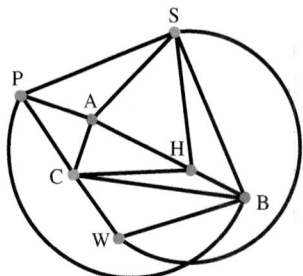

14.2 Euler Circuits and Route Planning

Euler Path and Euler Circuit An **Euler path** in a graph is a path that uses every edge of the graph exactly once. An **Euler circuit** in a graph is a circuit that uses every edge of the graph exactly once. **Euler's Theorem** Suppose we have a connected graph. **1.** If the graph has an Euler circuit, then each vertex of the graph has even degree. **2.** If each vertex of the graph has even degree, then the graph has an Euler circuit.	This graph has an Euler circuit, because all vertices have even degree. 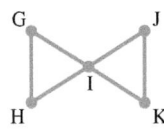 This graph has no Euler circuit, because some vertices have odd degree. 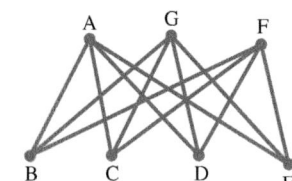
Cut Edge A **cut edge** in a graph is an edge whose removal disconnects a component of the graph.	DE and HG are cut edges in this graph. 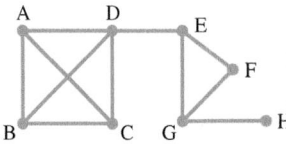
Fleury's Algorithm *Step 1* Start at any vertex. Go along any edge from this vertex to another vertex. *Remove this edge from the graph.* *Step 2* You are now on a vertex of the revised graph. Choose any edge from this vertex, subject to only one condition: Do not use a cut edge (*of the revised graph*) unless you have no other option. Go along your chosen edge. *Remove this edge from the graph.* *Step 3* Repeat Step 2 until you have used all the edges and returned to the vertex at which you started.	Fleury's algorithm can be used to show that $$A \to C \to B \to F \to E \to D \to C \to F \to D \to A$$ is one of many Euler circuits for this graph. 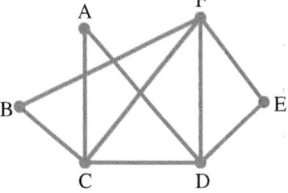

Concepts	*Examples*

14.3 Hamilton Circuits and Algorithms

Hamilton Circuit

A **Hamilton circuit** in a graph is a circuit that visits each vertex exactly once (returning to the starting vertex to complete the circuit). Any complete graph with three or more vertices has a Hamilton circuit. In this text, Hamilton circuits that differ *only* in their starting points are considered to be the same circuit.

Consider the following graph.

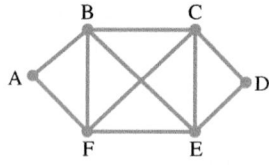

$$A \to B \to E \to D \to C \to F \to A$$

is a Hamilton circuit.

$$A \to B \to C \to D \to E \to F \to C \to E \to B \to F \to A$$

and

$$B \to C \to D \to E \to F \to B$$

are not Hamilton circuits.

Number of Hamilton Circuits in a Complete Graph

A complete graph with n vertices has the following number of Hamilton circuits.

$$(n - 1)!$$

Consider the following graph.

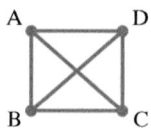

This complete graph has 4 vertices, and thus has

$$(4 - 1)! = 3! = 3 \cdot 2 \cdot 1 = 6 \text{ Hamilton circuits.}$$

Minimum Hamilton Circuit

In a weighted graph, a **minimum Hamilton circuit** is a Hamilton circuit with the least possible total weight.

Nearest Neighbor Algorithm

Step 1 Choose a starting point for the circuit. Call this vertex A.

Step 2 Check all the edges joined to A, and choose one that has the least weight. Proceed along this edge to the next vertex.

Step 3 At each vertex you reach, check the edges from there *to vertices not yet visited*. Choose one with the least weight. Proceed along this edge to the next vertex.

Step 4 Repeat Step 3 until you have visited all the vertices.

Step 5 Return to the starting vertex.

Consider the following graph.

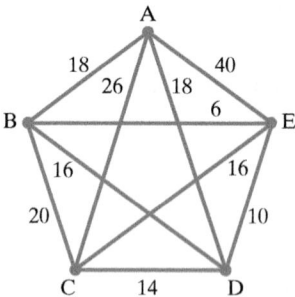

The nearest neighbor algorithm shows that an approximate minimum Hamilton circuit is

$$A \to D \to E \to B \to C \to A$$

and has weight 80.

Concepts	*Examples*

14.4 Trees and Minimum Spanning Trees

Connected Graph (Alternative Definition)
A **connected graph** is one in which there is *at least one path* between each pair of vertices.

Tree
A graph is a **tree** if the graph is *connected* and contains *no circuits*.

These are trees.

These are not trees.

Unique Path Property of Trees
In a tree, there is always **exactly one path** from each vertex in the graph to any other vertex in the graph.

If we choose any two vertices in the following graph, there is only one path from one to the other. See the red path as an illustration.

Spanning Tree and Minimum Spanning Tree
A **spanning tree** for a graph is a subgraph that includes every vertex of the original graph and is a tree.

A spanning tree that has minimum total weight is a **minimum spanning tree** for the graph.

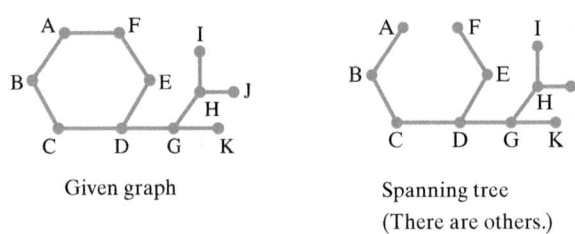

Given graph

Spanning tree
(There are others.)

Kruskal's Algorithm for Finding a Minimum Spanning Tree for Any Connected, Weighted Graph
Choose edges for the spanning tree as follows.

Step 1 First edge: Choose any edge with minimum weight.

Step 2 Next edge: Choose any edge with minimum weight from *those not yet selected*. (At this stage, the subgraph may look disconnected.)

Step 3 Continue to choose edges of minimum weight from those not yet selected, except *do not select any edge that creates a circuit* in the subgraph.

Step 4 Repeat Step 3 until the subgraph connects all vertices of the original graph.

Consider the following graph.

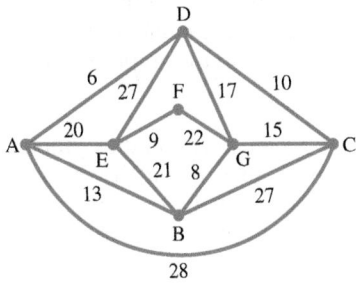

Kruskal's algorithm shows that this graph has the minimum spanning tree below, with total weight 66.

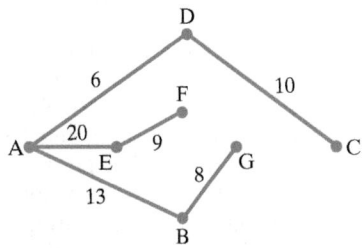

Number of Vertices and Edges in a Tree
If a graph is a tree, then the number of edges in the graph is one less than the number of vertices.

A tree with *n* vertices has *n* − 1 edges.

In the tree above, there are 7 vertices and

$$7 - 1 = 6 \text{ edges.}$$

CHAPTER 14 | TEST

Basic Concepts In Exercises 1–5, refer to the following graph.

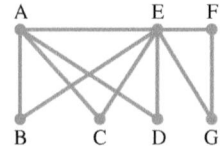

1. Determine how many vertices the graph has.

2. Determine the sum of the degrees of the vertices.

3. Determine how many edges the graph has.

4. Which of the following are paths in the graph? If not, why not?
   (a) $B \rightarrow A \rightarrow C \rightarrow E \rightarrow B \rightarrow A$
   (b) $A \rightarrow B \rightarrow E \rightarrow A$
   (c) $A \rightarrow C \rightarrow D \rightarrow E$

5. Which of the following are circuits in the graph? If not, why not?
   (a) $A \rightarrow B \rightarrow E \rightarrow D \rightarrow A$
   (b) $A \rightarrow B \rightarrow C \rightarrow D \rightarrow E \rightarrow F \rightarrow G \rightarrow A$
   (c) $A \rightarrow B \rightarrow E \rightarrow F \rightarrow G \rightarrow E \rightarrow D \rightarrow A \rightarrow E \rightarrow C \rightarrow A$

6. *Components* Draw a graph that has 2 components.

7. *Sum of Degrees* A graph has 10 vertices, 3 of degree 4, and the rest of degree 2. Use the theorem that relates the sum of degrees to the number of edges to determine the number of edges in the graph (without drawing the graph).

8. *Isomorphism* Determine whether graphs (a) and (b) are isomorphic. If they are, justify this by labeling corresponding vertices of the two graphs with the same letters and color-coding the corresponding edges.

   (a)   **(b)**

9. *Planning for Dinner* Julia is planning to invite some friends for dinner. She plans to invite John, Adam, Bill, Tina, Nicole, and Rita. John, Nicole, and Tina all know each other. Adam knows John and Tina. Bill also knows Tina, and he knows Rita. Draw a graph with vertices representing the six friends whom Julia plans to invite to dinner and edges representing the relationship "know each other." Is your graph connected or disconnected? Which of the guests knows the greatest number of other guests?

10. *Chess Competition* There are 8 contestants in a chess competition. Each contestant plays one chess game against every other contestant. The winner is the contestant who wins the most games. How many chess games will be played in the competition?

11. *Complete or Not Complete?* Is the accompanying graph a complete graph? Justify your answer.

Coloring and Chromatic Number Color each graph using as few colors as possible. Use the result to determine the chromatic number of the graph.

12.   13.

14. *Scheduling Exams* A teacher at a high school must schedule exams for the senior class. Subjects in which there are exams are listed on the left. Several students must take more than one of the exams, as shown on the right. Exams in subjects with students in common must not be scheduled at the same time. Use graph coloring to determine the least number of exam times needed and to identify exams that can be given at the same times.

Exam	Students taking this must also take
History	English, Mathematics, Biology, Geography, Psychology
English	Mathematics, Psychology, History
Mathematics	Chemistry, Biology, History, English
Chemistry	Biology, Mathematics
Biology	Mathematics, Chemistry, History
Psychology	English, History, Geography
Geography	Psychology, History

15. *Euler Circuits* Refer to the graph for **Exercises 1–5.** Which of the following are Euler circuits for the graph? If not, why not?
    (a) $A \rightarrow B \rightarrow E \rightarrow D \rightarrow A$
    (b) $A \rightarrow B \rightarrow C \rightarrow D \rightarrow E \rightarrow F \rightarrow G \rightarrow A$
    (c) $A \rightarrow B \rightarrow E \rightarrow F \rightarrow G \rightarrow E \rightarrow D \rightarrow A \rightarrow E \rightarrow C \rightarrow A$

Euler's Theorem *In Exercises 16 and 17, use Euler's theorem to decide whether the graph has an Euler circuit. (Do not actually find an Euler circuit.) Justify your answer briefly.*

16.

17.

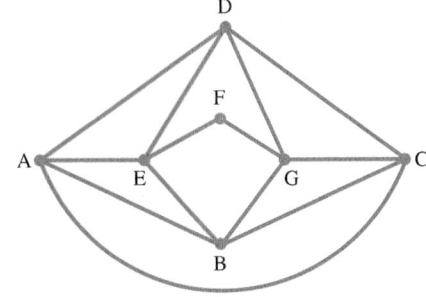

18. Floor Plan The floor plan of a building is shown. Is it possible to start outside, walk through each door exactly once, and end up back outside? Justify your answer.

19. Fleury's Algorithm Use Fleury's algorithm to find an Euler circuit for the accompanying graph, beginning

F → B.

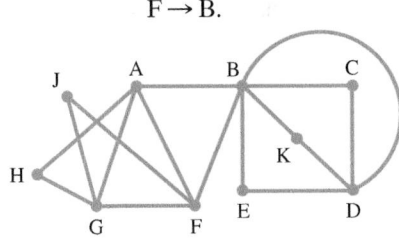

20. Hamilton Circuits Refer to the graph for **Exercises 1–5.** Which of the following are Hamilton circuits for the graph? If not, why not?

(a) A → B → E → D → A

(b) A → B → C → D → E → F → G → A

(c) A → B → E → F → G → E → D → A → E → C → A

21. Hamilton Circuits List all Hamilton circuits in the graph that start F → G. How many are there?

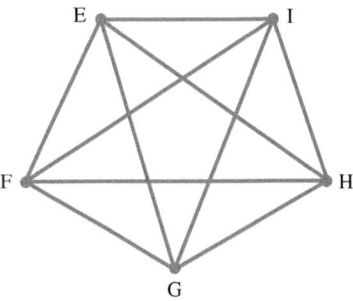

22. Brute Force Algorithm Use the brute force algorithm to find a minimum Hamilton circuit for the accompanying graph. Determine the total weight of the minimum Hamilton circuit.

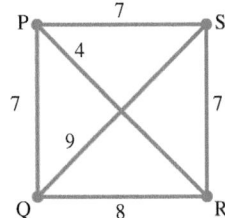

23. Nearest Neighbor Algorithm Use the nearest neighbor algorithm starting at A to find an approximate solution to the problem of finding a minimum Hamilton circuit for the graph below. Find the total weight of this circuit.

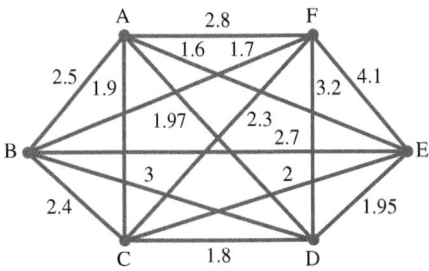

24. Hamilton Circuits How many Hamilton circuits are there in a complete graph with 25 vertices? (Leave your answer as a factorial.)

25. Rock Band Tour Plan The agent for a rock band based in Milwaukee is planning a tour for the band. He plans for the band to visit Minneapolis, Santa Barbara, Orlando, Phoenix, and St. Louis. Since the band members want to minimize the time they are away from home, they do not want to go to any of these cities more than once on the tour. Consider the complete graph with vertices representing the 6 cities mentioned. Does the problem of planning the tour require an Euler circuit, a Hamilton circuit, or neither for its solution?

26. Nonisomorphic Trees Draw three nonisomorphic trees with 7 vertices.

Trees *In Exercises 27–29, decide whether the statement is true or false.*

27. Every tree has a Hamilton circuit.

28. In a tree, each edge is a cut edge.

29. Every tree is connected.

30. Find all the different spanning trees for the following graph.

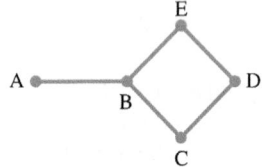

31. *Kruskal's Algorithm* Use Kruskal's algorithm to find a minimum spanning tree for the following graph.

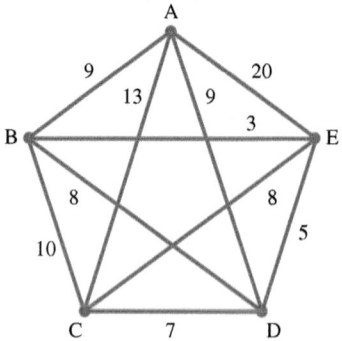

32. *Edges and Vertices* Determine the number of edges in a tree with 50 vertices.

APPENDIX: THE METRIC SYSTEM

Joseph Louis Lagrange (1736–1813) was born in Turin, Italy, and became a professor at age 19. In 1776 he came to Berlin at the request of Frederick the Great to take the position Euler left. A decade later Lagrange settled permanently in Paris. Napoleon was among many who admired and honored him.

Lagrange's greatest work was in the theory and application of **calculus.** He carried forward Euler's work of putting calculus on firm algebraic ground in his theory of functions. His *Analytic Mechanics* (1788) applied calculus to the motion of objects.

Lagrange's contributions to algebra had great influence on Galois and, hence, the theory of groups. He also wrote on number theory, proving that every integer is the sum of at most four squares.

The metric system was developed by a committee of the French Academy just after the French Revolution of 1789. The president of the committee was the mathematician Joseph Louis Lagrange. The advantages of the metric system can be seen when compared to our English system. In the English system, one inch is one-twelfth of a foot, while one foot is one-third of a yard. One mile is equivalent to 5280 feet, or 1760 yards. Obviously, there is no consistency in subdivisions.

In the metric system, prefixes are used to indicate multiplications or divisions by powers of ten. For example, the basic unit of length in the metric system is the *meter* (which is a little longer than one yard). To indicate one thousand meters, attach the prefix **"kilo-"** to get **kilo**meter. To indicate one one-hundredth of a meter, use the prefix **"centi-"** to obtain **centi**meter. A complete list of the prefixes of the metric system is shown in **Table 1**, with the most commonly used prefixes appearing in bold type.

Table 1 Metric Prefixes

Prefix	Multiple	Prefix	Multiple
exa	1,000,000,000,000,000,000	deci	0.1
peta	1,000,000,000,000,000	**centi**	0.01
tera	1,000,000,000,000	**milli**	0.001
giga	1,000,000,000	micro	0.000001
mega	1,000,000	nano	0.000000001
kilo	1000	pico	0.000000000001
hecto	100	femto	0.000000000000001
deka	10	atto	0.000000000000000001

Length and Area

Lagrange urged the committee devising the metric system to find some natural measure for length from which weight and volume measures could be derived. It was decided that one **meter (m)** would be the basic unit of length, with a meter being defined as one ten-millionth of the distance from the equator to the North Pole.

To obtain measures longer than one meter, Greek prefixes were added. For measures smaller than a meter, Latin prefixes were used. A meter is a little longer than a yard (about 39.37 inches). A **centimeter (cm)** is one one-hundredth of a meter and is about $\frac{2}{5}$ of an inch. See **Figure 1**.

Because the metric system is based on decimals and powers of ten, conversions within the system involve multiplying and dividing by powers of ten. For example, to convert 2.5 m to centimeters, multiply 2.5 by 100 (since 100 cm = 1m) to obtain 250 cm. On the other hand, to convert 18.6 cm to meters, divide by 100 to obtain 0.186 m. Other conversions are made in the same manner, using the meanings of the prefixes. Why is 42 m equal to 42,000 millimeters (mm)?

Long distances usually are measured in kilometers. A **kilometer (km)** is 1000 meters. (According to a popular dictionary, the word *kilometer* may be pronounced with the accent on either the first or the second syllable. Scientists usually stress the second syllable.) A kilometer is equal to about 0.6 mile. **Figure 2** shows the ratio of 1 kilometer to 1 mile.

1 cm

1 inch

Figure 1

A Comparison of Distances

Length in Meters	Approximate Related Distances
10^{19}	Distance to the North Star
10^{12}	Distance of Saturn from the sun
10^{11}	Distance of Venus from the sun
10^{9}	Diameter of the sun
10^{8}	Diameter of Jupiter
10^{7}	Diameter of Earth; distance from Washington, D.C. to Tokyo
10^{6}	Distance from Chicago to Wichita, Kansas
10^{5}	Average distance across Lake Michigan
10^{4}	Average width of the Grand Canyon
10^{3}	Length of the Golden Gate Bridge
10^{2}	Length of a football field
10^{1}	Average height of a two-story house
10^{0}	Width of a door
10^{-1}	Width of your hand
10^{-2}	Diameter of a piece of chalk
10^{-3}	Thickness of a dime
10^{-4}	Thickness of a piece of paper
10^{-5}	Diameter of a red blood cell
10^{-7}	Thickness of a soap bubble
10^{-8}	Average distance between molecules of air in a room
10^{-9}	Diameter of a molecule of oil
10^{-14}	Diameter of an atomic nucleus
10^{-15}	Diameter of a proton

According to Paul G. Hewitt, in *Conceptual Physics*, 7th edition (HarperCollins):

The distance from the equator to the North Pole was thought at the time to be close to 10,000 kilometers. One ten-millionth of this, the meter, was carefully determined and marked off by means of scratches on a bar of platinum-iridium alloy. This bar is kept at the International Bureau of Weights and Measures in France. The standard meter in France has since been calibrated in terms of the wavelength of light—it is 1,650,763.73 times the wavelength of orange light emitted by the atoms of the gas krypton-86. The meter is now defined as being the length of the path traveled by light in a vacuum during a time interval of 1/299,792,458 of a second.

Conversions from meters to kilometers, and vice versa, are made by multiplying or dividing by 1000 as necessary. For example, 37 kilometers equals 37,000 meters, while 583 meters equals 0.583 km.

The area of a figure can be measured in square metric units. **Figure 3** shows a square that is 1 cm on each side. Thus, it is a **square centimeter (cm^2).** One square meter (m^2) is the area of a square with sides one meter long. How many cm^2 are in one m^2?

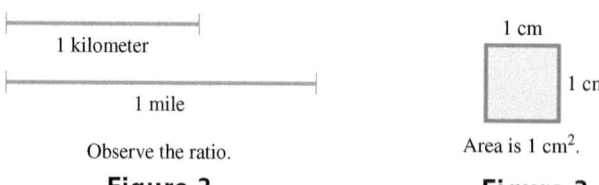

1 kilometer

1 mile

Observe the ratio.

Figure 2

1 cm

1 cm

Area is 1 cm^2.

Figure 3

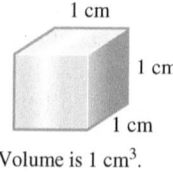

In September 1999, the **Mars Climate Orbiter** was lost due to "a failure to use metric units in the coding of a ground software file. . . ." According to Edward Weiler, associate administrator for NASA's Office of Space Science, the metric conversion error that led to the loss "should have been caught five ways to Sunday," but it wasn't. (*Source:* "NASA's Mars Losses Spark Anger and Opportunity" by Leonard David, Washington Contributing Editor to www.space.com.)

Volume, Mass, and Weight

The volume of a three-dimensional figure is measured in cubic units. If, for example, the dimensions are given in centimeters, the volume may be determined by the appropriate formula from geometry, and it will be in **cubic centimeters (cm^3).** See **Figure 4** for a sketch of a box whose volume is one cm^3?

1 cm

1 cm

1 cm

Volume is 1 cm^3.

Figure 4

The original scale of **Anders Celsius** had the freezing point of water at 100° and the boiling point at 0°, but biologist Carl von Linne inverted the scale, giving us the familiar Celsius scale of today.

In the metric system, one **liter (L)** is the quantity assigned to the volume of a box that is 10 cm on a side. (See **Figure 5**.) A liter is a little more than a quart as seen in **Figure 6**. Notice the advantage of this definition over the equivalent one in the English system—using a ruler marked in centimeters, a volume of 1 liter (symbolized 1 L) can be constructed. On the other hand, given a ruler marked in inches, it would be difficult to construct a volume of 1 quart.

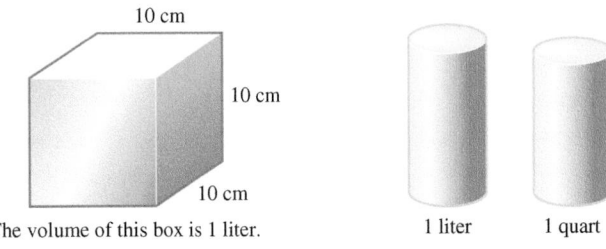

The volume of this box is 1 liter.

Figure 5

1 liter   1 quart

Figure 6

The prefixes mentioned earlier are used throughout the metric system, so one **milliliter (ml)** is one one-thousandth of a liter, one **centiliter (cl)** is one one-hundredth of a liter, one **kiloliter (kl)** is 1000 liters, and so on. Milliliters are used extensively in science and medicine. Many beverages now are sold by milliliters and by liters. For example, 750 ml is a common size for wine bottles, and many soft drinks now are sold in 1- and 2-liter bottles.

Because of the way a liter is defined as the volume of a box 10 cm on a side,

$$1\,L = 10\,cm \times 10\,cm \times 10\,cm = 1000\,cm^3 \quad \text{or} \quad \frac{1}{1000}\,L = 1\,cm^3.$$

Since $\frac{1}{1000}\,L = 1\,ml$, we have the following relationship.

1 ml = 1 cm3

For example, the volume of a box which is 8 cm by 6 cm by 5 cm may be given as 240 cm^3 or as 240 ml.

The box in **Figure 4** is 1 cm by 1 cm by 1 cm. The volume of this box is

$$1\,cm^3, \quad \text{or} \quad 1\,ml.$$

This photo shows that 13 feet, 6 inches is equal to 4.1 meters. Use this information and a proportion to show that one yard is equal to 0.91 meter.

By definition, the mass of the water that fills such a box is **1 gram (g).** A nickel five-cent piece has a mass close to 5 grams, or 5 g. The volume of water used to define a gram is very small, so a gram is a very small mass. For everyday use, a **kilogram (kg),** or one thousand grams, is more practical. A kilogram weighs about 2.2 pounds. A common abbreviation for kilogram is the word **kilo.**

Extremely small masses can be measured with **milligrams (mg)** and **centigrams (cg).** These measures are so small that they, like centiliters and milliliters, are used mainly in science and medicine.

Temperature

In the metric system temperature is measured in **degrees Celsius.** On the Celsius temperature scale, water freezes at 0° and boils at 100°. These two numbers are easier to remember than the corresponding numbers on the Fahrenheit scale, 32° and 212°. The thermometer in **Figure 7** shows some typical temperatures in both Fahrenheit and Celsius.

°Fahrenheit   °Celsius

Figure 7

The formulas given below can be used to convert between Celsius and Fahrenheit temperatures.

CELSIUS-FAHRENHEIT CONVERSION FORMULAS

To convert a reading from Fahrenheit to Celsius, use $C = \frac{5}{9}(F - 32).$

To convert from Celsius to Fahrenheit, use $F = \frac{9}{5}C + 32.$

Metric Conversions

Due to legislation enacted by Congress, the metric system is used in the United States, and an ultimate goal is for the two systems to be in use, side-by-side, with public acceptance of both systems. Industries that export a great many goods are using the metric system, since this is compatible with most of the countries with which they trade.

Some scientific calculators are programmed to do conversions between the English and metric systems. Approximate conversions can be made with the aid of **Tables 2 and 3** on the next page.

Table 2 Metric to English

To Convert from	To	Multiply by
meters	yards	1.0936
meters	feet	3.2808
meters	inches	39.37
kilometers	miles	0.6214
grams	pounds	0.0022
kilograms	pounds	2.20
liters	quarts	1.0567
liters	gallons	0.2642

Table 3 English to Metric

To Convert from	To	Multiply by
yards	meters	0.9144
feet	meters	0.3048
inches	meters	0.0254
miles	kilometers	1.609
pounds	grams	454
pounds	kilograms	0.454
quarts	liters	0.9464
gallons	liters	3.785

APPENDIX EXERCISES

Perform each conversion by multiplying or dividing by the appropriate power of 10.

1. 8 m to millimeters

2. 14.76 m to centimeters

3. 8500 cm to meters

4. 250 mm to meters

5. 68.9 cm to millimeters

6. 3.25 cm to millimeters

7. 59.8 mm to centimeters

8. 3.542 mm to centimeters

9. 5.3 km to meters

10. 9.24 km to meters

11. 27,500 m to kilometers

12. 14,592 m to kilometers

Use a metric ruler to perform each measurement, first in centimeters, then in millimeters.

13. ├─────────────┤

14. ├──────────────┤

15. ├──────────────────┤

16. Based on your measurement of the line segment in **Exercise 13,** one inch is about how many centimeters? How many millimeters?

Perform each conversion by multiplying or dividing by the appropriate power of 10.

17. 6 L to centiliters

18. 4.1 L to milliliters

19. 8.7 L to milliliters

20. 12.5 L to centiliters

21. 925 cl to liters

22. 412 ml to liters

23. 8974 ml to liters

24. 5639 cl to liters

25. 8000 g to kilograms

26. 25,000 g to kilograms

27. 5.2 kg to grams

28. 12.42 kg to grams

29. 4.2 g to milligrams

30. 3.89 g to centigrams

31. 598 mg to grams

32. 7634 cg to grams

Use the formulas given in the text to perform each conversion. Round to the nearest degree.

33. 86°F to Celsius

34. 536°F to Celsius

35. −114°F to Celsius

36. −40°F to Celsius

37. 10°C to Fahrenheit

38. 25°C to Fahrenheit

39. −40°C to Fahrenheit

40. −15°C to Fahrenheit

Solve each problem. Refer to geometry formulas as necessary.

41. **Weight of Nickels**   One nickel weighs 5 g. How many nickels are in 1 kg of nickels?

42. **Salt in Sea Water**   Sea water contains about 3.5 g salt per 1000 ml of water. How many grams of salt would be in one liter of sea water?

43. **Weight of Helium**   Helium weighs about 0.0002 g per milliliter. How much would one liter of helium weigh?

44. **Sugar Solution**   About 1500 g sugar can be dissolved in a liter of warm water. How much sugar could be dissolved in one milliliter of warm water?

45. **Cost of Metal**   Northside Foundry needed seven metal strips, each 67 cm long. Find the total cost of the strips, if they sell for $8.74 per meter.

46. **Cost of Lace**   Uptown Dressmakers bought fifteen pieces of lace, each 384 mm long. The lace sold for $54.20 per meter. Find the cost of the fifteen pieces.

47. **Cost of Marble**   Imported marble for desktops costs $174.20 per square meter. Find the cost of a piece of marble 128 cm by 174 cm.

48. *Cost of Paper* A special photographic paper sells for $63.79 per square meter. Find the cost to buy 80 pieces of the paper, each 9 cm by 14 cm.

49. *Volume of a Box* An importer received some special coffee beans in a box measuring 82 cm by 1.1 m by 1.2 m. Give the volume of the box, both in cubic centimeters and cubic meters.

50. *Volume of a Crate* A fabric center receives bolts of woolen cloth in crates measuring 1.5 m by 74 cm by 97 cm. Find the volume of a crate, both in cubic centimeters and cubic meters.

51. *Medicine Bottles* A medicine is sold in small bottles holding 800 ml each. How many of these bottles can be filled from a vat holding 160 L of the medicine?

52. *Bottles of Soda Pop* How many 2-liter bottles of soda pop would be needed for a wedding reception if 80 people are expected, and each drinks 400 ml of soda?

Perform each conversion. Use a calculator and/or the table in the text as necessary.

53. 982 yd to meters

54. 12.2 km to miles

55. 125 mi to kilometers

56. 1000 mi to kilometers

57. 1816 g to pounds

58. 1.42 lb to grams

59. 47.2 lb to grams

60. 7.68 kg to pounds

61. 28.6 L to quarts

62. 59.4 L to quarts

63. 28.2 gal to liters

64. 16 qt to liters

Metric measures are very common in medicine. Since we convert among metric measures by moving the decimal point, errors in locating the decimal point in medical doses are not unknown. Decide whether each dose of medicine seems reasonable *or* unreasonable.

65. Take 2 kg of aspirin three times a day.

66. Take 4 L of liquid Mylanta every evening just before bedtime.

67. Take 25 ml of cough syrup daily.

68. Soak your feet in 6 L of hot water.

69. Inject $\frac{1}{2}$ L of insulin every morning.

70. Apply 40 g of salve to a cut on your finger.

Select the most reasonable choice for each of the following.

71. length of an adult cow
   A. 1 m   **B.** 3 m   **C.** 5 m

72. length of a Lexus
   A. 1 m   **B.** 3 m   **C.** 5 m

73. distance from Seattle to Miami
   A. 500 km   **B.** 5000 km   **C.** 50,000 km

74. length across an average nose
   A. 3 cm   **B.** 30 cm   **C.** 300 cm

75. distance across a page of a book
   A. 1.93 mm   **B.** 19.3 mm   **C.** 193 mm

76. weight of a book
   A. 1 kg   **B.** 10 kg   **C.** 1000 kg

77. weight of a large automobile
   A. 1300 kg   **B.** 130 kg   **C.** 13 kg

78. volume of a 12-ounce bottle of beverage
   A. 35 ml   **B.** 355 ml   **C.** 3550 ml

79. height of a person
   A. 180 cm   **B.** 1800 cm   **C.** 18 cm

80. diameter of the earth
   A. 130 km   **B.** 1300 km   **C.** 13,000 km

81. length of a long freight train
   A. 8 m   **B.** 80 m   **C.** 800 m

82. volume of a grapefruit
   A. 1 L   **B.** 4 L   **C.** 8 L

83. the length of a pair of Levi jeans
   A. 70 cm   **B.** 700 cm   **C.** 7 cm

84. a person's weight
   A. 700 kg   **B.** 7 kg   **C.** 70 kg

85. diagonal measure of a small TV monitor
   A. 5 cm   **B.** 50 cm   **C.** 500 cm

86. width of a standard bedroom door
   A. 1 m   **B.** 3 m   **C.** 5 m

87. thickness of a marking pen
   A. 0.9 mm   **B.** 9 mm   **C.** 90 mm

88. length around the rim of a coffee mug

    A. 300 mm   **B.** 30 mm   **C.** 3000 mm

89. the temperature at the surface of a frozen lake

    A. 0°C   **B.** 10°C   **C.** 32°C

90. the temperature in the middle of Death Valley on a July afternoon

    A. 25°C   **B.** 40°C   **C.** 65°C

91. surface temperature of desert sand on a hot summer day

    A. 30°C   **B.** 60°C   **C.** 90°C

92. temperature of boiling water

    A. 100°C   **B.** 120°C   **C.** 150°C

93. air temperature on a day when you need a sweater

    A. 30°C   **B.** 20°C   **C.** 10°C

94. air temperature on a day when you go swimming

    A. 30°C   **B.** 15°C   **C.** 10°C

95. temperature when baking a cake

    A. 120°C   **B.** 170°C   **C.** 300°C

96. temperature of bath water

    A. 35°C   **B.** 50°C   **C.** 65°C

ANSWERS TO SELECTED EXERCISES

CHAPTER 1 THE ART OF PROBLEM SOLVING

1.1 Exercises (pages 6–8)

1. inductive **3.** deductive **5.** deductive **7.** inductive
9. deductive **11.** deductive **13.** inductive
15. inductive **17.** Answers will vary. **19.** 21 **21.** 3072
23. 63 **25.** $\frac{11}{12}$ **27.** 216 **29.** 52 **31.** 5
33. One such list is 10, 20, 30, 40, 50, ...
35. $(98{,}765 \times 9) + 3 = 888{,}888$
37. $3367 \times 15 = 50{,}505$
39. $33{,}334 \times 33{,}334 = 1{,}111{,}155{,}556$
41. $3 + 6 + 9 + 12 + 15 = \frac{15(6)}{2}$
43. $5(6) + 5(36) + 5(216) + 5(1296) + 5(7776)$
$= 6(7776 - 1)$
45. $\frac{1}{2} + \frac{1}{4} + \frac{1}{8} + \frac{1}{16} + \frac{1}{32} = 1 - \frac{1}{32}$ **47.** 20,100 **49.** 320,400
51. 15,400 **53.** 2550 **55.** 1 (These are the numbers of
chimes a clock rings, starting with 12 o'clock, if it rings the
number of hours on the hour, and 1 chime on the half-hour.)
57. (a) Answers will vary. **(b)** The middle digit is
always 9, and the sum of the first and third digits is always
9 (considering 0 as the first digit if the difference has only
two digits). **(c)** Answers will vary.
59. 142,857; 285,714; 428,571; 571,428; 714,285; 857,142.
Each result consists of the same six digits, but in a different
order. $142{,}857 \times 7 = 999{,}999$

1.2 Exercises (pages 15–19)

1. arithmetic; 56 **3.** geometric; 1215 **5.** neither
7. geometric; 8 **9.** neither **11.** arithmetic; 22
13. 79 **15.** 450 **17.** 4032 **19.** 32,758 **21.** 57; 99
23. $(4321 \times 9) - 1 = 38{,}888$ **25.** $999{,}999 \times 4 = 3{,}999{,}996$
27. $21^2 - 15^2 = 6^3$ **29.** $5^2 - 4^2 = 5 + 4$
31. $1 + 5 + 9 + 13 = 4 \times 7$ **33.** 45,150 **35.** 228,150
37. 2601 **39.** 250,000 **41.** $S = n(n + 1)$
43. Answers will vary. **45.** *row 1:* 28, 36; *row 2:* 36,
49, 64; *row 3:* 35, 51, 70, 92; *row 4:* 28, 45, 66, 91, 120;
row 5: 18, 34, 55, 81, 112, 148; *row 6:* 8, 21, 40, 65, 96,
133, 176
47. $8(1) + 1 = 9 = 3^2$; $8(3) + 1 = 25 = 5^2$;
$8(6) + 1 = 49 = 7^2$; $8(10) + 1 = 81 = 9^2$
49. The pattern is 1, 0, 1, 0, 1, 0, ...

51.

53. 256 **55.** 117 **57.** 235 **59.** $N_n = \frac{n(7n - 5)}{2}$
61. a square number **63.** a perfect cube **65.** 42
67. 419 **69.** $\frac{101}{2}$ **71.** 2048 **73.** $\frac{1}{2048}$ **75.** $\frac{5}{2048}$ **77.** 495
79. To find any entry within the body of the triangle, add
the two entries immediately to the left and to the right in the
row above it. For example, in the sixth row, $10 = 4 + 6$.
The next three rows of Pascal's triangle are as follows.

$$\begin{array}{ccccccccccccc}
 & & & 1 & & 6 & & 15 & & 20 & & 15 & & 6 & & 1 \\
 & & 1 & & 7 & & 21 & & 35 & & 35 & & 21 & & 7 & & 1 \\
 & 1 & & 8 & & 28 & & 56 & & 70 & & 56 & & 28 & & 8 & & 1
\end{array}$$

81. The sums along the diagonals are 1, 1, 2, 3, 5, 8. These
are the first six terms of the Fibonacci sequence.

1.3 Exercises (pages 25–30)

1. 50 **3.** [figure] **5.** IN **7.** 41 **9.** 15

11. 32 **13.** 0 (The product of the first and last digits is
the two-digit number between them.) **15.** 11
17. infinitely many (Any line through the center of the
square will do this.) **19.** 48.5 in. **21.** 42 **23.** 6
25. If you multiply the two digits in the numbers in the
first row, you will get the second row of numbers. The
second row of numbers is a pattern of two numbers
(8 and 24) repeating. **27.** 59 **29.** A **31.** You should
choose a sock from the box labeled *red and green socks*.
Because it is mislabeled, it contains only red socks or only
green socks, determined by the sock you choose. If the
sock is green, relabel this box *green socks*. Since the other
two boxes were mislabeled, switch the remaining label to
the other box and place the label that says *red and green
socks* on the unlabeled box. No other choice guarantees
a correct relabeling because you can remove only one
sock. **33.** D

35. One example of a solution follows.

37. Here is one solution.   **39.** D   **41.** $\frac{1}{3}$

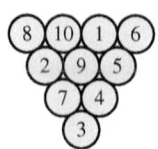

43. 90   **45.** 55 mph   **47.** 07   **49.** 437   **51.** 3
53. 21 stamps (5 five-cent stamps and 16 eight-cent stamps)   **55.** 3 socks   **57.** 6   **59.** the nineteenth day   **61.** 1967   **63.** Eve has $5, and Adam has $7.

65.
$$\begin{array}{r} 4\ 0\ 2 \\ \times\quad 3\ 9 \\ \hline 1\ 5,\ 6\ 7\ 8 \end{array}$$

67.

6	12	7	9
1	15	4	14
11	5	10	8
16	2	13	3

69. 25 pitches (The visiting team's pitcher retires 24 consecutive batters through the first eight innings, using only one pitch per batter. His team does not score either. Going into the bottom of the ninth tied 0–0, the first batter for the home team hits his first pitch for a home run. The pitcher threw 25 pitches and loses the game by a score of 1–0.)   **71.** Q   **73.** Here is one solution.

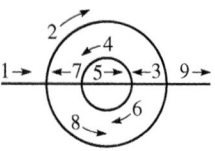

75. 6 ways   **77.** 86 cm   **79.** Dan (36) is married to Jessica (29); James (30) is married to Cathy (31).
81. 6

	X	X
X		X
X	X	

One of the possibilities

1.4 Exercises (pages 39–41)
1. 43.8   **3.** 2.3589   **5.** 7.48   **7.** 7.1289   **9.** 6340.338097
11. 1   **13.** 1.061858759   **15.** 2.221441469
17. 3.141592653   **19.** 0.7782717162   **21.** yes
23. positive   **25.** 1   **27.** the same as   **29.** 0
31. negative   **33.** Answers will vary.

35. Answers will vary.   **37.** 63   **39.** 14   **41.** B   **43.** A
45. D   **47.** 6%   **49.** about 4.5 million
51. 2007, 2008, 2009, 2010   **53.** 2004: about 171 billion lb; 2010: about 193 billion lb   **55.** 2009 to 2010; about 1.5 million   **57.** The number of cars imported each year was decreasing.

Chapter 1 Test (pages 45–46)
1. inductive   **2.** deductive   **3.** 31
4. 65,359,477,124,183 × 68 = 4,444,444,444,444,444
5. 351   **6.** 31,375   **7.** 65; 65 = 1 + 7 + 13 + 19 + 25
8. 1, 8, 21, 40, 65, 96, 133, 176; The pattern is 1, 0, 1, 0, 1, 0, 1, 0, ...   **9.** The first two terms are both 1. Each term after the second is found by adding the two previous terms. The next term is 34.   **10.** $\frac{1}{4}$ **11.** 9   **12.** 35
13. Answers will vary. One possible solution is
1 + 2 + 3 − 4 + 5 + 6 + 78 + 9 + 0 = 100.
14. 108 in., or 9 ft   **15.** 3   **16.** The sum of the digits is always 9.   **17.** 9.907572861 (Answers may vary due to the model of calculator used.)   **18.** 34.328125   **19.** B
20. (a) between 2003 and 2004, 2004 and 2005, and 2005 and 2006   **(b)** The unemployment rate was increasing.
(c) 2008: 5.8%; 2009: 9.3%; increase: 3.5%

CHAPTER 2 THE BASIC CONCEPTS OF SET THEORY

2.1 Exercises (pages 52–54)
1. F   **3.** E   **5.** B   **7.** H   **9.** $\{1, 2, 3, 4, 5, 6\}$
11. $\{0, 1, 2, 3, 4\}$ **13.** $\{6, 7, 8, 9, 10, 11, 12, 13, 14\}$
15. $\{2, 4, 8, 16, 32, 64, 128, 256\}$ **17.** $\{0, 2, 4, 6, 8, 10\}$
19. $\{220, 240, 260, \ldots\}$ **21.** $\{$Lake Erie, Lake Huron, Lake Michigan, Lake Ontario, Lake Superior$\}$
23. $\left\{1, \frac{1}{2}, \frac{1}{3}, \frac{1}{4}, \frac{1}{5}, \ldots\right\}$ **25.** $\{(0, 5), (3, 4), (4, 3), (5, 0)\}$
In Exercises 27 and 29, there are other ways to describe the sets.   **27.** $\{x \mid x$ is a rational number$\}$ **29.** $\{x \mid x$ is an odd natural number less than 76$\}$ **31.** the set of single-digit integers   **33.** the set of states of the United States
35. finite   **37.** infinite   **39.** infinite   **41.** infinite   **43.** 8
45. 500   **47.** 26   **49.** 39   **51.** 28   **53.** Answers will vary.
55. well defined   **57.** not well defined   **59.** $\notin$ **61.** $\in$
63. $\in$ **65.** false   **67.** false   **69.** true   **71.** true
73. false   **75.** true   **77.** true   **79.** true
81. false   **83.** true   **85.** Answers will vary.
87. $\{2\}$ and $\{3, 4\}$ (Other examples are possible.)
89. $\{a, b\}$ and $\{a, c\}$ (Other examples are possible.)

91. (a) {Bernice, Heather, Marcy}, {Bernice, Heather, Natalie}, {Bernice, Susan, Marcy}, {Bernice, Susan, Natalie}, {Heather, Susan, Marcy}, {Heather, Susan, Natalie}
(b) {Bernice, Marcy, Natalie}, {Heather, Marcy, Natalie}, {Susan, Marcy, Natalie}   **(c)** {Bernice, Heather, Susan}

2.2 Exercises *(pages 58–60)*

1. D   **3.** B   **5.** ⊄   **7.** ⊆   **9.** ⊆   **11.** ⊄   **13.** both
15. ⊆   **17.** both   **19.** neither   **21.** true   **23.** false
25. true   **27.** false   **29.** true   **31.** false   **33.** true
35. false   **37. (a)** 64   **(b)** 63   **39. (a)** 32   **(b)** 31   **41.** ∅
43. {5, 7, 9, 10}   **45.** {Higher cost, Lower cost, Educational, More time to see the sights in California, Less time to see the sights in California, Cannot visit friends along the way, Can visit friends along the way}
47. {Higher cost, More time to see the sights in California, Cannot visit friends along the way}
49. ∅   **51.** {A, B, C, D, E} (All are present.)
53. {A, B, C}, {A, B, D}, {A, B, E}, {A, C, D}, {A, C, E}, {A, D, E}, {B, C, D}, {B, C, E}, {B, D, E}, {C, D, E}   **55.** {A}, {B}, {C}, {D}, {E}   **57.** 32
59. $2^{25} - 1 = 33,554,431$ **61. (a)** 15   **(b)** 16; It is now possible to select *no* bills.
63. (a) s **(b)** s **(c)** $2s$ **(d)** Adding one more element will always double the number of subsets, so the expression 2^n is true in general.

2.3 Exercises *(pages 69–71)*

1. B   **3.** A   **5.** E   **7.** {a, c}   **9.** {a, b, c, d, e, f}
11. {b, d, f}   **13.** {d, f}   **15.** {a, b, c, e, g}   **17.** {e, g}
19. {a}   **21.** {e, g}   **23.** {d, f}
In Exercises 25–28, there may be other acceptable descriptions.   **25.** the set of all elements that either are in A, or are not in B and not in C **27.** the set of all elements that are in C but not in B, or are in A **29.** {e, h, c, l, b}
31. {e, h, c, l, b}   **33.** the set of all tax returns filed in 2014 without itemized deductions   **35.** the set of all tax returns with itemized deductions or showing business income, but not selected for audit   **37.** always true   **39.** not always true
41. (a) {1, 3, 5, 2}   **(b)** {1, 2, 3, 5}   **(c)** For any sets X and Y, $X \cup Y = Y \cup X$.   **43. (a)** {1, 3, 5, 2, 4}
(b) {1, 3, 5, 2, 4}   **(c)** For any sets X, Y, and Z, $X \cup (Y \cup Z) = (X \cup Y) \cup Z$.   **45.** true   **47.** true
49. $A \times B = \{(d, p), (d, i), (d, g), (o, p), (o, i), (o, g), (g, p), (g, i), (g, g)\}; B \times A = \{(p, d), (p, o), (p, g), (i, d), (i, o), (i, g), (g, d), (g, o), (g, g)\}$
51. $n(A \times B) = 210; n(B \times A) = 210$ **53.** 6

55.

57.
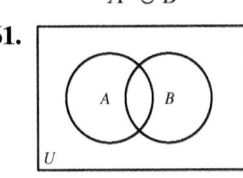
$A' \cup B$

59.
$B \cap A'$

61.
$B' \cap B = \varnothing$

63.
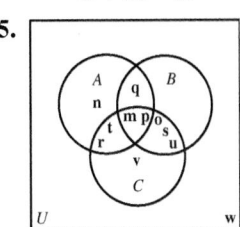
$B' \cup (A' \cap B')$

65.

67.
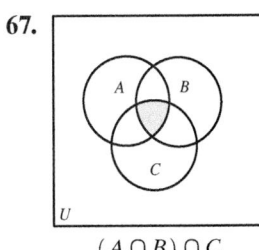
$(A \cap B) \cap C$

69.
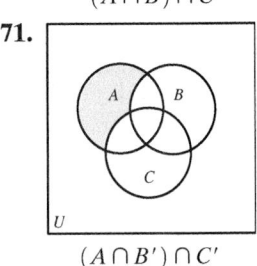
$(A' \cap B') \cap C$

71.
$(A \cap B') \cap C'$

73. $A' \cap B'$, or $(A \cup B)'$
75. $(A \cup B) \cap (A \cap B)'$, or $(A \cup B) - (A \cap B)$, or $(A - B) \cup (B - A)$
77. $(A \cap B) \cup (A \cap C)$, or $A \cap (B \cup C)$

79. $A \cap B = \varnothing$ **81.** This statement is true for any set A.
83. $B \subseteq A$ **85.** always true   **87.** not always true
89. Answers will vary.

2.4 Exercises *(pages 75–78)*

1. (a) 5   **(b)** 7   **(c)** 0   **(d)** 2   **(e)** 8   **3. (a)** 1   **(b)** 3
(c) 4   **(d)** 0   **(e)** 2   **(f)** 8   **(g)** 2   **(h)** 6   **5.** 21
7. 7   **9.** 35

11.

13.

15.

17.
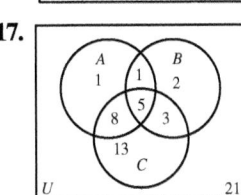

19. (a) 2 **(b)** 4 **21. (a)** 25 **(b)** 30 **(c)** 2 **(d)** 10
(e) 19 **(f)** 57 **23. (a)** 8 **(b)** 26 **(c)** 60 **25. (a)** 500
(b) 91 **27. (a)** 31 **(b)** 24 **(c)** 11 **(d)** 45 **29. (a)** 1
(b) 1, 2, 3, 4, 5, 6, 7, 8, 9, 10, 11, 12, 13, 14, 15 **(c)** 1, 2, 3, 4,
5, 9, 11 **(d)** 5, 8, 13 **31. (a)** 9 **(b)** 9 **(c)** 20 **(d)** 20
(e) 27 **(f)** 15 **33.** Answers will vary.

Chapter 2 Test *(page 82)*

1. {a, b, c, d, e} **2.** {a, b, d} **3.** {c, f, g, h} **4.** {a, c}
5. false **6.** true **7.** true **8.** true **9.** false **10.** false
11. true **12.** true **13.** 16 **14.** 15
Answers may vary in Exercises 15–18. **15.** the set of odd
integers between –4 and 10 **16.** the set of days of the week
17. {$x \mid x$ is a negative integer} **18.** {$x \mid x$ is a multiple of 8
between 20 and 90} **19.** $\subseteq$ **20.** neither

21.

$X \cup Y'$

22.

$X' \cap Y'$

23.
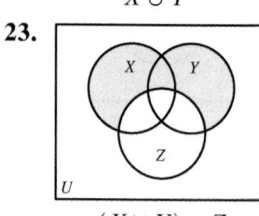
$(X \cup Y) - Z$

24.
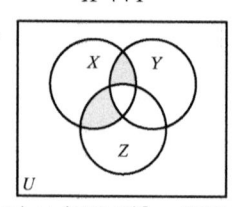
$[(X \cap Y) \cup (X \cap Z)] - (Y \cap Z)$

25. Answers will vary. **26.** {Electric razor}
27. {Adding machine, Baking powder, Pendulum clock,
Thermometer} **28.** {Telegraph, Zipper} **29. (a)** 22
(b) 12 **(c)** 28 **30. (a)** 16 **(b)** 32 **(c)** 33 **(d)** 45
(e) 14 **(f)** 26

Extension Exercises *(pages 87–88)*

1. B; 1 **3.** A; $\aleph_0$ **5.** F; 0
7. (Other correspondences are possible.)

$$\{I, \quad II, \quad III\}$$
$$\updownarrow \quad \updownarrow \quad \updownarrow$$
$$\{x, \quad y, \quad z\}$$

9. (Other correspondences are possible.)

$$\{a, \quad d, \quad i, \quad t, \quad o, \quad n\}$$
$$\updownarrow \quad \updownarrow \quad \updownarrow \quad \updownarrow \quad \updownarrow \quad \updownarrow$$
$$\{a, \quad n, \quad s, \quad w, \quad e, \quad r\}$$

11. 11 **13.** 0 **15.** $\aleph_0$ **17.** $\aleph_0$ **19.** $\aleph_0$ **21.** 12
23. $\aleph_0$ **25.** both **27.** equivalent **29.** equivalent

31. $\{2, \quad 4, \quad 6, \quad 8, \quad \ldots, \quad 2n, \quad \ldots\}$
$\quad\;\; \updownarrow \quad \updownarrow \quad \updownarrow \quad \updownarrow \qquad\quad \updownarrow$
$\{1, \quad 2, \quad 3, \quad 4, \quad \ldots, \quad n, \quad \ldots\}$

33. $\{1{,}000{,}000, \quad 2{,}000{,}000, \quad 3{,}000{,}000, \quad \ldots, \quad 1{,}000{,}000n, \quad \ldots\}$
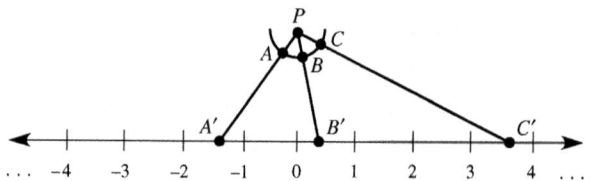
$\{ \quad 1, \qquad\qquad 2, \qquad\qquad 3, \qquad \ldots, \qquad n, \qquad \ldots\}$

35. $\{2, \quad 4, \quad 8, \quad 16, \quad 32, \quad \ldots, \quad 2^n, \quad \ldots\}$
$\quad\; \updownarrow \quad \updownarrow \quad \updownarrow \quad \updownarrow \quad \updownarrow \qquad\quad \updownarrow$
$\{1, \quad 2, \quad 3, \quad 4, \quad 5, \quad \ldots, \quad n, \quad \ldots\}$

37. This statement is not always true. For example, let
A = the set of counting numbers, B = the set of real numbers.
39. This statement is not always true. For example, A
could be the set of all subsets of the set of reals. Then $n(A)$
would be an infinite number *greater* than c.
41. (a) Rays emanating from point P will establish a
geometric pairing of the points on the semicircle with the
points on the line.

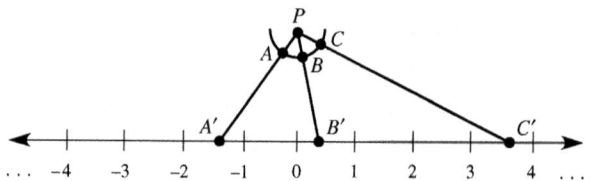

(b) The set of real numbers is infinite, having been placed
in a one-to-one correspondence with a proper subset of
itself.

43. $\{3, \quad 6, \quad 9, \quad 12, \quad \ldots, \quad 3n, \quad \ldots\}$
$\quad\; \updownarrow \quad \updownarrow \quad \updownarrow \quad \updownarrow \qquad\quad \updownarrow$
$\{6, \quad 9, \quad 12, \quad 15, \quad \ldots, \quad 3n + 3, \quad \ldots\}$

45.
$$\left\{\frac{3}{4}, \quad \frac{3}{8}, \quad \frac{3}{12}, \quad \frac{3}{16}, \quad \ldots, \quad \frac{3}{4n}, \quad \ldots\right\}$$
$$\updownarrow \quad \updownarrow \quad \updownarrow \quad \updownarrow \qquad\quad \updownarrow$$
$$\left\{\frac{3}{8}, \quad \frac{3}{12}, \quad \frac{3}{16}, \quad \frac{3}{20}, \quad \ldots, \quad \frac{3}{4n + 4}, \quad \ldots\right\}$$

47.
$$\left\{\frac{1}{9}, \quad \frac{1}{18}, \quad \frac{1}{27}, \quad \ldots, \quad \frac{1}{9n}, \quad \ldots\right\}$$
$$\updownarrow \quad \updownarrow \quad \updownarrow \qquad\quad \updownarrow$$
$$\left\{\frac{1}{18}, \quad \frac{1}{27}, \quad \frac{1}{36}, \quad \ldots, \quad \frac{1}{9n + 9}, \quad \ldots\right\}$$

49. Answers will vary. **51.** Answers will vary.

CHAPTER 3 INTRODUCTION TO LOGIC

3.1 Exercises *(pages 94–96)*

1. statement **3.** not a statement **5.** statement
7. statement **9.** statement **11.** not a statement
13. statement **15.** compound **17.** not compound
19. not compound **21.** compound **23.** Her aunt's name
is not Hermione. **25.** No book is longer than this book.
27. At least one computer repairman can play blackjack.
29. Someone does not love somebody sometime.
31. The trash does not need to be collected. **33.** $x \leq 12$

35. $x < 5$ **37.** Answers will vary.   **39.** She does not have green eyes.   **41.** She has green eyes and he is 60 years old. **43.** She does not have green eyes or he is 60 years old. **45.** She does not have green eyes or he is not 60 years old. **47.** It is not the case that she does not have green eyes and he is 60 years old.   **49.** $p \wedge \sim q$ **51.** $\sim p \vee q$ **53.** $\sim (p \vee q)$ or, equivalently, $\sim p \wedge \sim q$ **55.** Answers will vary.   **57.** C   **59.** A, B   **61.** A, C **63.** B   **65.** true   **67.** false   **69.** true   **71.** true **73.** false   **75.** Answers will vary.   **77.** Every person here has made mistakes before.   **79.** $(\forall c)(\sim f)$

3.2 Exercises (pages 106–107)

1. false   **3.** true   **5.** true   **7.** They must both be false. **9.** T   **11.** T   **13.** F   **15.** T   **17.** T   **19.** T   **21.** It is a disjunction, because it means "6 > 2 or 6 = 2."   **23.** T **25.** F   **27.** T   **29.** T   **31.** F   **33.** F   **35.** T   **37.** T **39.** T   **41.** 4   **43.** 16   **45.** 128   **47.** six   **49.** FFTF **51.** FTTT   **53.** TTTT   **55.** TFFF   **57.** FFFFTFFF **59.** FTFTTTTT   **61.** TTTTTTTTTTTFTTT **63.** You can't pay me now and you can't pay me later. **65.** It is not summer or there is snow.   **67.** I did not say yes or she did not say no.   **69.** $6 - 1 \neq 5$ or $9 + 13 = 7$ **71.** Neither Prancer nor Vixen will lead Santa's reindeer sleigh next Christmas.   **73.** T   **75.** F

77.

p	q	$p \vee q$
T	T	F
T	F	T
F	T	T
F	F	F

79. F   **81.** T

83. The lady is behind Door 2. *Reasoning:* Suppose that the sign on Door 1 is true. Then the sign on Door 2 would also be true, but this is impossible. So the sign on Door 2 must be true, and the sign on Door 1 must be false. Because the sign on Door 1 says the lady is in Room 1, and this is false, the lady must be behind Door 2.   **85.** The negation of a conjunction is equivalent to the disjunction of the negations.

3.3 Exercises (pages 115–117)

1. If you just believe, then you can do it.   **3.** If it is an even integer divisible by 5, then it is divisible by 10.   **5.** If it is a grizzly bear, then it does not live in California.   **7.** If they are surfers, then they can't stay away from the beach. **9.** true   **11.** true   **13.** false   **15.** true   **17.** Answers will vary.   **19.** F   **21.** T   **23.** T   **25.** If they do not collect classics, then he fixes cars.   **27.** If she sings for a living, then they collect classics and he fixes cars.   **29.** If he does

not fix cars, then they do not collect classics or she sings for a living.   **31.** $b \rightarrow p$ **33.** $p \wedge (s \rightarrow \sim b)$ **35.** $p \rightarrow s$ **37.** T   **39.** T   **41.** F   **43.** T   **45.** T   **47.** Answers will vary.   **49.** TTTF   **51.** TTFT   **53.** TTTT; tautology **55.** TTTTTTFT   **57.** TTTFTTTTTTTTTTT   **59.** one **61.** That is an authentic Coach bag and I am not surprised. **63.** The bullfighter doesn't get going and doesn't get gored. **65.** You want to be happy for the rest of your life and you make a pretty woman your wife.   **67.** You do not give your plants tender, loving care or they flourish.   **69.** She does or he will.   **71.** The person is not a resident of Pensacola or is a resident of Florida.   **73.** equivalent   **75.** equivalent **77.** equivalent   **79.** equivalent   **81.** $(p \wedge q) \vee (p \wedge \sim q)$; The statement simplifies to p.   **83.** $p \vee (\sim q \wedge r)$ **85.** $\sim p \vee (p \vee q)$; The statement simplifies to T. **87.** The statement simplifies to $p \wedge q$.

89. The statement simplifies to F.

91. The statement simplifies to $(r \wedge \sim p) \wedge q$.

93. The statement simplifies to $p \vee q$.

95. \$525.60   **97.** The circuit is equivalent to $\sim (A \wedge A) \vee B \equiv \sim A \vee B \equiv A \rightarrow B$.

3.4 Exercises (pages 122–123)

1. (a) If you were an hour, then beauty would be a minute. **(b)** If beauty were not a minute, then you would not be an hour.   **(c)** If you were not an hour, then beauty would not be a minute.

3. (a) If you don't fix it, then it ain't broke. **(b)** If it's broke, then fix it.   **(c)** If you fix it, then it's broke.   **5. (a)** If it is dangerous to your health, then you walk in front of a moving car.   **(b)** If you do not walk in front of a moving car, then it is not dangerous to your health.   **(c)** If it is not dangerous to your health, then you do not walk in front of a moving car.   **7. (a)** If they flock together, then they are birds of a feather.   **(b)** If they are not birds of a feather, then they do not flock together. **(c)** If they do not flock together, then they are not birds of a feather.   **9. (a)** If he comes, then you built it.   **(b)** If you don't build it, then he won't come.   **(c)** If he doesn't come, then you didn't build it.

11. (a) $\sim q \rightarrow p$ **(b)** $\sim p \rightarrow q$ **(c)** $q \rightarrow \sim p$ **13. (a)** $\sim q \rightarrow \sim p$ **(b)** $p \rightarrow q$ **(c)** $q \rightarrow p$

15. (a) $(q \lor r) \to p$ **(b)** $\sim p \to (\sim q \land \sim r)$
(c) $(\sim q \land \sim r) \to \sim p$ **17.** Answers will vary.
19. If the Kings go to the playoffs, then pigs will fly.
21. If it has legs of 3 and 4, then it has a hypotenuse of 5.
23. If a number is a whole number, then it is a rational number.
25. If I do logic puzzles, then I am driven crazy.
27. If the graffiti are to be covered, then two coats of paint must be used. **29.** If employment improves, then the economy recovers. **31.** If a number is a whole number, then it is an integer. **33.** If their pitching improves, then the Phillies will win the pennant. **35.** If the figure is a rectangle, then it is a parallelogram with perpendicular adjacent sides. **37.** If a triangle has two perpendicular sides, then it is a right triangle. **39.** If a three-digit number whose units digit is 5 is squared, then the square will end in 25. **41.** D **43.** Answers will vary. **45.** true **47.** false **49.** false **51.** contrary **53.** contrary **55.** consistent **57. (1)** $p \to (p \to q)$ **(2)** $(p \to q) \to p$

3.5 Exercises *(pages 127–128)*
1. valid **3.** invalid **5.** valid **7.** invalid **9.** invalid
11. invalid **13.** yes
15. All people with blue eyes have blond hair.
    Erin does not have blond hair.
    Erin does not have blue eyes.
17. invalid **19.** valid **21.** invalid **23.** valid **25.** invalid
27. invalid **29.** valid

3.6 Exercises *(pages 136–138)*
1. valid by reasoning by transitivity **3.** valid by modus ponens **5.** fallacy by fallacy of the converse **7.** valid by modus tollens **9.** fallacy by fallacy of the inverse
11. valid by disjunctive syllogism **13.** invalid **15.** valid
17. invalid **19.** valid **21.** valid **23.** invalid
25. invalid
27. Every time something squeaks, I use WD-40.
    Every time I use WD-40, I go to the hardware store.
    Every time something squeaks, I go to the hardware store.

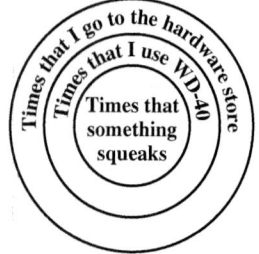

29. valid **31.** invalid **33.** invalid **35.** valid **37.** valid
39. (a) When the cable company keeps you on hold, your dad gets punched over a can of soup. **(b)** The cable company doesn't keep you on hold. **41.** If it is my poultry, then it is a duck. **43.** If it is a guinea pig, then it is hopelessly ignorant of music. **45.** If it is a teachable kitten, then it does not have green eyes. **47.** If I can read it, then I have not filed it. **49. (a)** $p \to \sim s$ **(b)** $r \to s$ **(c)** $q \to p$
49. (d) None of my poultry are officers. **51. (a)** $r \to \sim s$
(b) $u \to t$ **(c)** $\sim r \to p$ **(d)** $\sim u \to \sim q$ **(e)** $t \to s$
(f) All pawnbrokers are honest. **53. (a)** $r \to w$
(b) $\sim u \to \sim t$ **(c)** $v \to \sim s$ **(d)** $x \to r$ **(e)** $\sim q \to t$
(f) $y \to p$ **(g)** $w \to s$ **(h)** $\sim x \to \sim q$ **(i)** $p \to \sim u$
(j) I can't read any of Brown's letters.

Chapter 3 Test *(pages 143–144)*
1. $6 - 3 \neq 3$ **2.** Some men are not created equal.
3. No members of the class went on the field trip.
4. I fall in love and it will not be forever. **5.** She did not apply or she got a student loan. **6.** $\sim p \to q$
7. $p \to q$ **8.** $\sim q \leftrightarrow \sim p$ **9.** You won't love me and I will love you. **10.** It is not the case that you will love me or I will not love you. (Equivalently: You won't love me and I will love you.) **11.** T **12.** T **13.** T **14.** F
15. Answers will vary. **16. (a)** The antecedent must be true and the consequent must be false. **(b)** Both component statements must be true. **(c)** Both component statements must be false. **(d)** Both component statements must have the same truth value. **17.** TFFF **18.** TTTT (tautology)
19. false **20.** true
Wording may vary in the answers for Exercises 21–25.
21. If the number is an integer, then it is a rational number.
22. If a polygon is a rhombus, then it is a quadrilateral.
23. If a number is divisible by 4, then it is divisible by 2.
24. If she digs dinosaur bones, then she is a paleontologist.
25. (a) If the graph helps me understand it, then a picture paints a thousand words. **(b)** If a picture doesn't paint a thousand words, then the graph won't help me understand it. **(c)** If the graph doesn't help me understand it, then a picture doesn't paint a thousand words. **26. (a)** $(q \land r) \to \sim p$ **(b)** $p \to (\sim q \lor \sim r)$
(c) $(\sim q \lor \sim r) \to p$ **27.** valid **28. (a)** A **(b)** F **(c)** C
(d) D **29.** valid **30.** invalid

CHAPTER 4 NUMERATION SYSTEMS

4.1 Exercises *(pages 154–156)*

1. 12,034   **3.** 7,610,729   **5.** ⋔⋔ 𝕊 𝕊 𝕊 𝟡 ∩ ∩ ∩ |||||

7. 𝕏𝕏𝕏𝕏 ⌢ ⌢ ⌢ ⋔⋔⋔ 𝕊 𝕊 𝕊
𝕏𝕏𝕏𝕏 ⌢ ⌢ ⌢ ⋔⋔ 𝕊 𝕊 𝕊

9. ⋔⋔⋔ 𝕊 𝕊 𝕊 𝕊 𝟡 𝟡 𝟡
⋔⋔ 𝕊 𝕊 𝕊 𝕊 𝕊

11. ⋔⋔⋔⋔ 𝕊 𝕊 𝟡 𝟡 𝟡
⋔⋔⋔ 𝕊 𝕊 𝟡 𝟡 𝟡
    13. ⋔⋔⋔ 𝕊 𝕊 𝟡 𝟡 𝟡 𝟡
⋔⋔⋔ 𝕊 𝕊 𝟡 𝟡 𝟡

15. 173   **17.** 14,000,000   **19.** MMDCCCLXI

21. $\overline{\text{XXV}}$DCXIX   **23.** 935   **25.** 2007

27. 𝒽 百 六 十 五   **29.** ⺂ 千 零 十 二   **31.** 千 三 百 六 十 八 to 千 六 百 十 四   **33.** 六 百 十 八 to 𝒽 百 零 七

35. 206   **37.** 53,601   **39.** 113   **41.** 7598   **43.** 2021

45. 903   **47.** 1504   **49.** 8128   **51.** 622,500 shekels

53. Answers will vary.   **55.** Answers will vary.   **57.** 99,999

59. 3124   **61.** $10^d - 1$ **63.** $7^d - 1$ **65.** 9999

4.2 Exercises *(pages 160–161)*

1. Mayan; 12   **3.** Babylonian; 32   **5.** Greek; 234

7. Mayan; 242   **9.** Babylonian; 1282   **11.** Babylonian; 2601   **13.** Mayan; 2640   **15.** Mayan; 59,954

17. Babylonian; 80,474   **19.** Greek; 15,149

21. ⟨⟨▼   **23.** ▼▼⟨⟨⟨▼ ▼▼⟨⟨ ▼▼   **25.** ⟨⟨▼▼▼⟨▼▼ ▼▼⟨⟨ ▼▼   **27.** ▼⟨⟨⟨▼▼▼⟨⟨ ▼

29. ⟨⟨▼▼▼⟨⟨ ▼▼▼⟨⟨   **31.** ⟨ ⟨⟨▼▼▼ ▼▼   **33.** 𝍠   **35.** 𝍡

37. 𝍢   **39.** 𝍣   **41.** 𝍤   **43.** λθ   **45.** ϟβ   **47.** υιβ

49. ͵βψξθ   **51.** M̅ͅ͵δψκϛ   **53.** χπα   **55.** ωπη

4.3 Exercises *(pages 167–168)*

1. $(7 \cdot 10^1) + (3 \cdot 10^0)$

3. $(8 \cdot 10^3) + (3 \cdot 10^2) + (3 \cdot 10^1) + (5 \cdot 10^0)$

5. $(3 \cdot 10^3) + (6 \cdot 10^2) + (2 \cdot 10^1) + (4 \cdot 10^0)$

7. $(1 \cdot 10^7) + (4 \cdot 10^6) + (2 \cdot 10^5) + (0 \cdot 10^4) + (6 \cdot 10^3) + (0 \cdot 10^2) + (4 \cdot 10^1) + (0 \cdot 10^0)$

9. 75   **11.** 4380   **13.** 70,401,009   **15.** 79   **17.** 53   **19.** 109

21. 733   **23.** 6   **25.** 206   **27.** 242   **29.** 49,801   **31.** 256

33. 63,259   **35.**   **37.**

39. 1885   **41.** 38,325   **43.** 3,035,154   **45.** 496

47. 217,204   **49.** 460   **51.** 32,798   **53.** Answers will vary.

4.4 Exercises *(pages 178–180)*

1. 1, 2, 3, 4, 5, 6, 10, 11, 12, 13, 14, 15, 16, 20, 21, 22, 23, 24, 25, 26   **3.** 1, 2, 3, 4, 5, 6, 7, 8, 10, 11, 12, 13, 14, 15, 16, 17, 18, 20, 21, 22   **5.** 13_{five}; 20_{five} **7.** $\text{B6E}_{\text{sixteen}}$; $\text{B70}_{\text{sixteen}}$ **9.** 3

11. 11   **13.** least: $1000_{\text{three}} = 27$; greatest: $2222_{\text{three}} = 80$

15. 956   **17.** 881   **19.** 28,854   **21.** 139   **23.** 5601

25. 93_{sixteen} **27.** 2131101_{five} **29.** 1001001010_{two}

31. 102112101_{three} **33.** 111134_{six} **35.** 32_{seven}

37. 1031321_{four} **39.** 11110111_{two} **41.** 467_{eight}

43. 11011100_{two} **45.** $2D_{\text{sixteen}}$ **47.** 37_{eight} **49.** 1427

51. 1000011_{two} **53.** 1101011_{two} **55.** HELP

57. $100111011001011110111_{\text{two}}$ **59.** Answers will vary; 11000000.10101000.00000011.00011110   **61.** 192.172.3.64

63. Answers will vary.   **65. (a)** The binary ones digit is 1. **(b)** The binary twos digit is 1.   **(c)** The binary fours digit is 1.   **(d)** The binary eights digit is 1.   **(e)** The binary sixteens digit is 1.   **67.** 6   **69.** yes   **71.** yes   **73.** yes

75. yes   **77.** Answers will vary.   **79.** no   **81.** yes

83. Append a 0 on the right.   **85.** Answers will vary.

87. Answers will vary.   **89.** 20120011_{three} **91.** 25657_{nine}

93. 808080   **95.** FF69B4

Chapter 4 Test *(page 184)*

1. Egyptian; 1534   **2.** Roman; 10,474   **3.** Chinese; 385

4. Babylonian; 155,540   **5.** Mayan; 50,511   **6.** Greek; 53,524   **7.** 1035   **8.** 23,862   **9.** 13,227   **10.** 73   **11.** 37

12. 48,879   **13.** 110001_{two} **14.** 43210_{five} **15.** 256_{eight}

16. $\text{E8D}_{\text{sixteen}}$ **17.** 1105   **18.** $101110101101_{\text{two}}$

19. There is less repetition of symbols.   **20.** Place values are understood by position.   **21.** There are fewer symbols to learn.   **22.** There are fewer digits in the numerals.   **23.** Answers will vary.

24. $7_{\text{nine}} = 21_{\text{three}}$, $6_{\text{nine}} = 20_{\text{three}}$, and $5_{\text{nine}} = 12_{\text{three}}$. So $765_{\text{nine}} = 212012_{\text{three}}$.

4.5 Exercises *(Pages 195–199)*

1. 5   **3.** 6   **5.** row 2: 0, 6, 10;   row 3: 9, 0, 9;   row 4: 0, 4, 0, 8, 0;   row 5: 1, 9, 2, 7;   row 6: 6, 0, 0;   row 7: 4, 11, 6, 8,

3, 5;   row 8: 8, 4, 0, 0;   row 9: 6, 3, 9, 3, 9, 6, 3;
row 10: 6, 4, 0, 10, 8, 6, 4;   row 11: 10, 9, 8, 7, 6, 5, 4, 3, 2
7. yes **9.** row 1: 0;   row 2: 0;   row 3: 0, 1, 2
row 4: 0, 1, 2 **11.** yes **13.** yes (0 is its own inverse, 1 and
4 are inverses of each other, and 2 and 3 are inverses of
each other.) **15.** yes **17.** yes (1 is the identity element.)
19. 3 **21.** 4 **23.** Answers will vary. **25.** 0700
27. 0000 **29.** false **31.** true **33.** 3 **35.** 3
37. 1 **39.** 10 **41.** Answers will vary. **43.** 5 **45.** 4
47. row 1: 0;   row 2: 2, 3, 4, 5, 6, 0, 1;   row 3: 3, 4, 5, 6, 0,
1, 2;   row 4: 4, 5, 6, 0, 1, 2, 3;   row 5: 5, 6, 0, 1, 2, 3, 4;
row 6: 6, 0, 1, 2, 3, 4, 5 **49.** row 2: 1 **51.** row 2: 1, 3, 7;
row 3: 3, 0;   row 4: 3, 2, 1;   row 5: 6, 7, 4;   row 7: 3, 1, 6, 4;
row 8: 6, 5, 2 **53.** {3, 10, 17, 24, 31, 38, . . . }
55. {1, 2, 3, 4, 5, 6, . . . } **57.** 100,000 **59. (a)** 365
(b) Friday **61.** 62 **63.** Chicago: July 23 and 29;
New Orleans: July 5 and August 16; San Francisco:
August 9 **65.** Sunday **67.** Wednesday **69.** June
71. June **73.** yes **75.** 6 **77.** 2

4.6 Exercises *(Pages 202–204)*
1. all properties; 1 is the identity element; 1 is its own inverse,
as is 2. **3.** closure, commutative, associative, and identity properties; 1 is the identity element; 2, 4, and 6 have no
inverses. **5.** all properties except the inverse; 1 is the identity
element; 5 has no inverse. **7.** all properties; F is the identity
element; A and B are inverses; F is its own inverse. **9.** all
properties; t is the identity element; s and r are inverses; t and
u are their own inverses. **11.** a **13.** a **15.** row b: d;   row
c: d, b;   row d: b, c **17.** associative, commutative, identity
(U), closure **19.** Answers may vary.
One possibility is shown.

	a	b	c	d
a	a	b	c	d
b	b	a	d	c
c	c	d	a	b
d	d	c	b	a

21. no **23. (a)** true **(b)** true **(c)** true **(d)** true
25. $a + b + c = 1$ or $a = 0$ **27. (a)** $a = 0$ **(b)** $a = 0$
29. Each side simplifies to e. **31.** Each side simplifies to
d. **33.**

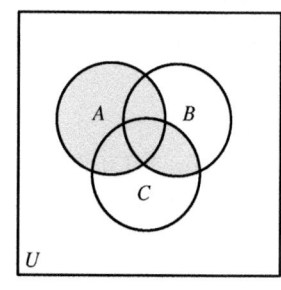

$A \cup (B \cap C) = (A \cup B) \cap (A \cup C)$

35. Both final columns read TTTTTFFF, when set up in
the manner described in Chapter 3.

4.7 Exercises *(Pages 210–211)*
1. No operation is specified. **3.** yes **5.** no; closure,
inverse **7.** yes **9.** no; inverse **11.** no; associative, identity,
inverse **13.** no; inverse **15.** yes **17.** no; closure, identity,
inverse **19.** Answers will vary. **21.** S **23.** N **25.** Each
side is equal to M. **27.** Each side is equal to
Q. **29.** N **31.** R **33.** T **35.** no **37.** yes **39.** Answers
will vary. **41.** Answers will vary. **43.** row B: D;   row
C: D, B;   row D: C, B **45. (a)** yes **(b)** Answers will
vary. **47. (a)** no **(b)** Answers will vary.

Chapter 4 Test *(Pages 213)*
1. ancient Egyptian; 2426 **2.** 7561
3. $(6 \cdot 10^4) + (0 \cdot 10^3) + (9 \cdot 10^2) + (2 \cdot 10^1) + (3 \cdot 10^0)$
4. 1998 **5.** 22,184 **6.** 12,827 **7.** 89 **8.** 50 **9.** 57,007
10. 110001_{two} **11.** 43210_{five} **12.** 256_{eight} **13.** {2, 7, 12, 17,
22, 27, . . . } **14. (a)** 5 **(b)** 4 **(c)** 9 **(d)** 8
15. (a) 3 **(b)** 1 **16.** 48 **17.** There is less repetition of
symbols. **18.** There are fewer symbols to learn. **19.** There
are fewer digits in the numerals. **20.** 0 **21.** $\frac{1}{3}$
22. commutative **23.** row 3: 1, 7;   row 5: 7, 3;   row 7: 5, 1
24. (a) yes **(b)** 1 **25. (a)** yes **(b)** Answers will vary.
26. (a) yes **(b)** Answers will vary. **27. (a)** no
(b) Answers will vary. **28. (a)** yes **(b)** Answers will
vary.

CHAPTER 5 NUMBER THEORY

5.1 Exercises *(pages 220–222)*
1. true **3.** true **5.** false **7.** true **9.** 1, 2, 3, 4, 6, 12
11. 1, 2, 4, 7, 14, 28 **13. (a)** no **(b)** yes **(c)** no
(d) no **(e)** no **(f)** no **(g)** no **(h)** no **(i)** no
15. (a) yes **(b)** yes **(c)** yes **(d)** yes **(e)** yes
(f) yes **(g)** yes **(h)** yes **(i)** yes
17. (a) Answers will vary. **(b)** 13 **(c)** square root;
square root; square root **(d)** prime **19.** 179 and 193,
181 and 197, 191 and 197, 193 and 199 **21.** 2, 3; no
23. It must be 0.
25.

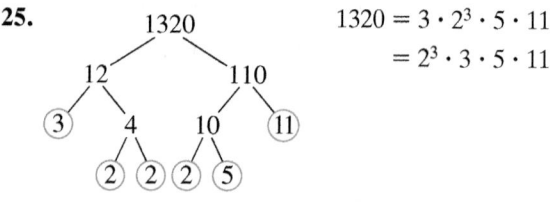

$1320 = 3 \cdot 2^3 \cdot 5 \cdot 11$
$= 2^3 \cdot 3 \cdot 5 \cdot 11$

27. $2 \cdot 3^2 \cdot 7$ **29.** $7 \cdot 13^2$ **31.** yes   **33.** no   **35.** no
37. yes   **39.** The number must be divisible by both 3 and
5. That is, the sum of the digits must be divisible by 3, and
the last digit must be 5 or 0.   **41.** 0, 2, 4, 6, 8   **43.** 0, 4, 8
45. 0, 6   **47.** 8   **49.** 27   **51.** leap year   **53.** not a leap year
55. Answers will vary.   **57.** Answers will vary.
59. 1981 and 1987   **61.** 2041

5.2 Exercises *(pages 228–229)*

1. true   **3.** false   **5.** true
7. $37 = 1^2 + 6^2; 41 = 4^2 + 5^2; 53 = 2^2 + 7^2$
9. Answers will vary.   **11. (a)** 1681; composite $(41 \cdot 41)$
(b) 1763; composite $(41 \cdot 43)$ **(c)** 1847; prime
13. (a) 1681; composite $(41 \cdot 41)$ **(b)** 1763; composite
$(41 \cdot 43)$ **(c)** 1847; prime   **15. (a)** 65,537   **(b)** 251
17. Answers will vary.   **19.** Answers will vary.
21. composite; $30,031 = 59 \cdot 509$ **23.** 63   **25.** $2^p - 1$
27. 3 and 31   **29.** Answers will vary.

5.3 Exercises *(pages 234–236)*

1. true   **3.** true   **5.** true   **7.** false   **9.** false   **11.** The sum
of the proper divisors is 496: $1 + 2 + 4 + 8 + 16 + 31 +$
$62 + 124 + 248 = 496.$ **13.** 8191 is prime; 33,550,336
15. $1 + \frac{1}{2} + \frac{1}{4} + \frac{1}{7} + \frac{1}{14} + \frac{1}{28} = 2$ **17.** deficient
19. abundant   **21.** 12, 18, 20, 24   **23.** $1 + 3 + 5 + 7 +$
$9 + 15 + 21 + 27 + 35 + 45 + 63 + 105 + 135 + 189$
$315 = 975$, and $975 > 945$, so 945 is abundant.
25. $1 + 2 + 4 + 8 + 16 + 32 + 37 + 74 + 148 + 296 +$
$592 = 1210$ and $1 + 2 + 5 + 10 + 11 + 22 + 55 +$
$110 + 121 + 242 + 605 = 1184$ **27.** $5 + 7$ **29.** $11 + 29$
31. (a) Let $a = 5$ and $b = 3$; $11 = 5 + 2 \cdot 3$
(b) $17 = 3 + 2 \cdot 7 = 7 + 2 \cdot 5 = 11 + 2 \cdot 3 = 13 + 2 \cdot 2$
33. 59 and 61   **35. (a)** $3^4 - 1 = 80$ is divisible by 5.
(b) $2^6 - 1 = 63$ is divisible by 7.   **37.** $5^2 + 2 = 27 = 3^3$
39. Answers will vary.   **41.** False; For the first six, the
sequence is 6, 8, 6, 8, 6, 6.   **43.** one; not happy
45. both; happy   **47.** Answers will vary.   **49.** B   **51.** 7; yes
53. 15; no   **55.** 24; 23; 25; yes; no   **57.** Answers will vary.
59. B   **61.** $18 = 1 + 2 + 6 + 9 = 3 + 6 + 9$
63. $1 + 2 + 5 + 7 + 10 + 14 + 35 = 74 > 70$
65. 1,000,000,000,000,066,600,000,000,000,001   **67.** 13

5.4 Exercises *(pages 244–245)*

1. true   **3.** false   **5.** false   **7.** true   **9.** false   **11.** 28
13. 11   **15.** 17   **17.** 10   **19.** 30   **21.** 6   **23.** 6   **25.** 18
27. 45   **29.** 240   **31.** 405   **33.** 300   **35.** 108   **37.** 693
39. 2160   **41.** 180   **43.** 180   **45.** 9450   **47.** Answers

will vary.   **49. (a)** $p^a q^a r^b$ **(b)** $p^b q^b r^c$ **51.** 15   **53.** 12
55. p and q are relatively prime.   **57.** Answers will vary.
59. 144th   **61.** 48 (5 stacks of 48 pennies, 6 stacks of
48 nickels)   **63.** $600; 25 books

5.5 Exercises *(pages 250–252)*

1. 987   **3.** o, o, e, o, o, e, o, o, e, o, o, e   **5.** $\frac{1 + \sqrt{5}}{2}$
7. $1 + 1 + 2 + 3 + 5 = 13 - 1$; Each expression is equal
to 12.   **9.** $1 + 2 + 5 + 13 + 34 = 55$; Each expression is
equal to 55.   **11.** $13^2 - 5^2 = 144$; Each expression is equal
to 144.   **13.** $1 - 2 + 5 - 13 + 34 = 5^2$; Each expression is
equal to 25.   **15.** (There are other ways to do this.)
(a) $39 = 34 + 5$ **(b)** $59 = 55 + 3 + 1$ **(c)** $99 = 89 + 8 + 2$
17. (a) The greatest common factor of 10 and 4 is 2, and
the greatest common factor of $F_{10} = 55$ and $F_4 = 3$ is $F_2 = 1$.
(b) The greatest common factor of 12 and 6 is 6, and the
greatest common factor of $F_{12} = 144$ and $F_6 = 8$ is $F_6 = 8$.
(c) The greatest common factor of 14 and 6 is 2, and the
greatest common factor of $F_{14} = 377$ and $F_6 = 8$ is $F_2 = 1$.
19. (a) $8^2 - 3 \cdot 21 = 1$ **(b)** $2 \cdot 34 - 8^2 = 4$
(c) $8^2 - 1 \cdot 55 = 9$ **(d)** The difference will be 25,
because we are obtaining the squares of the terms of the
Fibonacci sequence. $13^2 - 1 \cdot 144 = 25 = 5^2$.
21. 123   **23.** Each sum is 2 less than a Lucas number.
25. (a) $8 \cdot 18 = 144$; Each expression is equal to 144.
(b) $8 + 21 = 29$; Each expression is equal to 29.
(c) $8 + 18 = 2 \cdot 13$; Each expression is equal to 26.
(d) $18 + 47 = 5 \cdot 13$; Each expression is equal to 65.
27. 3, 4, 5   **29.** 105, 208, 233
31. The sums are 1, 1, 2, 3, 5, 8, 13. They are terms of the
Fibonacci sequence.
33. $\frac{1 + \sqrt{5}}{2} \approx 1.618033989$ and $\frac{1 - \sqrt{5}}{2} \approx -0.618033989$.
After the decimal point, the digits are the same.
35. 987

Chapter 5 Test *(page 256)*

1. true   **2.** false   **3.** true   **4.** true   **5.** false   **6.** true
7. (a) yes   **(b)** yes   **(c)** yes   **(d)** no   **(e)** yes   **(f)** yes
(g) no   **(h)** no   **(i)** yes   **8. (a)** composite   **(b)** prime
(c) neither   **9.** $2 \cdot 3^3 \cdot 5 \cdot 11$ **10.** Answers will vary.
11. (a) abundant   **(b)** deficient   **(c)** perfect   **12.** B
13. 71 and 73   **14.** 9   **15.** 2002   **16.** Monday
17. 28,657   **18.** $55 - (5 + 8 + 13 + 21) = 8$; Each expression is equal to 8.   **19.** B   **20.** 60   **21.** The process will
yield 11 for any term chosen.   **22.** A

CHAPTER 6 THE REAL NUMBERS AND THEIR REPRESENTATIONS

6.1 Exercises *(pages 266–268)*

1. 5   **3.** 0   **5.** $\sqrt{14}$ (There are others.)   **7.** true
9. true   **11. (a)** 3, 7   **(b)** 0, 3, 7   **(c)** $-9, 0, 3, 7$
(d) $-9, -1\frac{1}{4}, -\frac{3}{5}, 0, 3, 5.9, 7$ **(e)** $-\sqrt{7}, \sqrt{5}$
(f) All are real numbers.   **13.** 2,259,000
15. -3424 **17.** 46.77   **19.** 5436   **21.** $-220°$
23. Pacific Ocean, Indian Ocean, Caribbean Sea, South
China Sea, Gulf of California   **25.** true
27. ◆+◆+◆+++++◆◆➤   **29.** +◆+◆◆+ ◆+◆+◆+➤
      $-6\ -4\ -2\ \ 0\ \ 2\ \ 4$ $-4\ -2\ \ 0\ \ 2\ \ 4$
31. (a) A   **(b)** A   **(c)** B   **(d)** B   **33. (a)** 2   **(b)** 2
35. (a) -6 **(b)** 6   **37. (a)** -3 **(b)** 3   **39. (a)** 0
(b) 0   **41.** -12 **43.** -8 **45.** 3   **47.** $|-3|$, or 3
49. $-|6|$, or -6 **51.** $|5-3|$, or 2   **53.** true
55. true   **57.** true   **59.** false   **61.** true   **63.** false
65. (a) Las Vegas; The population increased by 45.4%.
(b) Detroit; The population decreased by 3.6%.
67. Appliances (because $|-4.5| > |-0.4|$)

6.2 Exercises *(pages 277–281)*

1. positive; $18 + 6 = 24$ **3.** greater; $-14 + 9 = -5$
5. the number with the greater absolute value is
subtracted from the one with the lesser absolute value;
$5 - 12 = -7$ **7.** additive inverses; $4 + (-4) = 0$
9. negative; $-5(15) = -75$ **11.** -20 **13.** -4
15. -11 **17.** 9   **19.** 20   **21.** 24   **23.** -1296 **25.** 6
27. -6 **29.** 0   **31.** -6 **33.** 27   **35.** undefined   **37.** -1
39. -4 **41.** 7   **43.** 13   **45.** A, B, C   **47.** commutative
property of addition   **49.** inverse property of addition
51. identity property of multiplication   **53.** identity property
of addition   **55.** associative property of multiplication
57. closure property of multiplication   **59.** associative
property of addition   **61.** distributive property
63. identity   **65. (a)** messing up your room
(b) spending money   **(c)** decreasing the volume on your
MP3 player   **67.** -81 **69.** 81   **71.** -81 **73.** -81
75. (a) -11; The returns decreased 11 percent.
(b) -13; The returns decreased 13 percent.   **(c)** 13; The
returns increased 13 percent.   **(d)** -1; The returns decreased 1 percent.   **77.** 50,395 ft   **79.** 1345 ft
81. 136 ft   **83.** -10 **85.** $+10$ **87.** $+5$ degrees
89. -2 degrees   **91.** 0 degrees (no change)
93. $+5$ degrees   **95.** 43; 34; 29; 36; 38; 36; 37; 41
97. 27 feet   **99.** 469 B.C.   **101.** $5540
103. $-69°$F   **105.** $120°$F

6.3 Exercises *(pages 292–295)*

1. rational number   **3.** 1   **5.** 459; 221; 5967
7. $\frac{7}{12}; \frac{4}{3}$ **9.** 6 or 4 (Either answer is acceptable.)
11. A, C, D   **13.** C   **15.** $\frac{1}{3}$ **17.** $-\frac{3}{7}$ **Answers will vary**
in Exercises 19 and 21.   **19.** $\frac{6}{16}, \frac{9}{24}, \frac{12}{32}$ **21.** $-\frac{10}{14}, -\frac{15}{21}, -\frac{20}{28}$
23. (a) $\frac{1}{3}$ **(b)** $\frac{1}{4}$ **(c)** $\frac{2}{5}$ **(d)** $\frac{1}{3}$ **25.** the dots in the intersection of the triangle and the rectangle as a part of the
dots in the entire figure   **27. (a)** Christine   **(b)** Leah
(c) Leah   **(d)** Anne   **(e)** Otis and Carol; $\frac{1}{2}$ **29.** $\frac{1}{2}$
31. $\frac{43}{48}$ **33.** $-\frac{5}{24}$ **35.** $\frac{23}{56}$ **37.** $\frac{27}{20}$ **39.** $\frac{5}{12}$ **41.** $\frac{1}{9}$ **43.** $\frac{3}{2}$
45. $\frac{3}{2}$ **47.** $\frac{13}{3}$ **49.** $\frac{29}{10}$ **51.** $6\frac{3}{4}$ **53.** $6\frac{1}{8}$ **55.** $-17\frac{7}{8}$
57. $1\frac{5}{16}$ **59.** $37\frac{7}{8}$ **61.** $7\frac{3}{8}$ **63.** $4\frac{1}{8}$ **65.** $\frac{9}{16}$ inch
67. $30\frac{1}{4}$ in.   **69. (a)** $1\frac{1}{8}$ in.   **(b)** $1\frac{7}{8}$ in.   **71.** $11\frac{55}{64}$ in.
73. 8 cakes (There will be some sugar left over.)
75. $16\frac{5}{8}$ yd   **77.** $6757   **79.** $\frac{5}{8}$ **81.** $\frac{19}{30}$ **83.** $-\frac{3}{4}$
85. repeating   **87.** terminating   **89.** terminating
91. 0.75   **93.** 0.1875   **95.** $0.\overline{27}$ **97.** $0.\overline{285714}$ **99.** $\frac{2}{5}$
101. $\frac{17}{20}$ **103.** $\frac{467}{500}$ **105.** $\frac{67}{99}$ **107.** $\frac{7}{165}$ **109.** $\frac{1}{90}$
111. (a) $0.\overline{3}$, or 0.333 . . .   **(b)** $0.\overline{6}$, or 0.666 . . .
(c) $0.\overline{9}$, or 0.999 . . .   **(d)** $1 = 0.\overline{9}$

6.4 Exercises *(pages 303–306)*

1. rational   **3.** irrational   **5.** rational   **7.** rational
9. irrational   **11.** rational   **13.** irrational   **15. (a)** $0.\overline{8}$
(b) irrational; rational   **The number of digits shown**
will vary among calculator models in Exercises 17–23
and 45–53.   **17.** 6.244997998   **19.** 3.885871846
21. 29.73213749   **23.** 1.060660172   **25.** 6   **27.** 2.4 m²
29. 5.4 ft   **31.** 2.5 sec   **33.** 1.7 amps   **35.** 71 mph
37. 54 mph   **39.** 392,000 mi²   **41.** The area and the perimeter are both numerically equal to 36.   **43.** $5\sqrt{2}$;
7.071067812   **45.** $5\sqrt{3}$; 8.660254038   **47.** $12\sqrt{2}$;
16.97056275   **49.** $\frac{5\sqrt{6}}{6}$; 2.041241452   **51.** $\frac{\sqrt{7}}{2}$; 1.322875656
53. $\frac{\sqrt{21}}{3}$; 1.527525232   **55.** $3\sqrt{17}$ **57.** $4\sqrt{7}$ **59.** $10\sqrt{2}$
61. $3\sqrt{3}$ **63.**

65. The result is 3.1415929, which agrees with the first
seven digits in the decimal for π.   **67.** 3   **69.** 4
71. The computer will forever be occupied by this task "to
the exclusion of all else" and thus will no longer be able to
interfere.   **73.** ϕ is positive, while its conjugate is negative.

The units digit of ϕ is 1, and the units digit of its conjugate is 0. The decimal digits agree.   **75.** If a 9 were under the radical, the number would equal the "nice" integer value 3. $\sqrt{3}$ is irrational, and its decimal is not so nice.

77. It is just a coincidence that 1828 appears back-to-back early in the decimal. There is no repetition indefinitely, which would be indicative of a rational number.

79. 4   **81.** 7   **83.** 6   **85.** 1   **87.** 4   **89.** 8   **The number of decimal digits shown will vary among calculator models in Exercises 91–97.**   **91.** 3.50339806

93. 5.828476683   **95.** 10.06565066   **97.** 5.578019845

6.5 Exercises *(pages 314–320)*

1. true   **3.** true   **5.** true   **7.** false   **9.** 11.315

11. −4.215   **13.** 0.8224   **15.** 47.5   **17.** 31.6   **19.** $30.13

21. (a) $466.02   **(b)** $190.68   **23.** $1229.09

25. (a) 50,000   **(b)** 55,000   **(c)** 54,800   **(d)** 54,790

27. (a) 0.89245   **(b)** 0.8925   **(c)** 0.892   **(d)** 0.89

(e) 0.9   **(f)** 1   **29. (a)** E   **(b)** D   **(c)** B   **(d)** F   **(e)** C

(f) A   **31. (a)** $33\frac{1}{3}$%   **(b)** 25%   **(c)** 40%   **(d)** $33\frac{1}{3}$%

33. 42%   **35.** 36.5%   **37.** 0.8%   **39.** 210%   **41.** 0.96

43. 0.0546   **45.** 0.003   **47.** 4.00   **49.** 0.005   **51.** 0.035

53. 20%   **55.** 1%   **57.** $37\frac{1}{2}$%   **59.** 150%   **61.** Answers will vary.   **63.** 124.8   **65.** 2.94   **67.** 150%   **69.** 600

71. 1.4%   **73.** 8%   **75.** 9.4%   **77.** 9.8%   **79.** 892%

81. about 140%   **83.** 21.2%   **85.** $895 million   **87.** A

89. C   **91.** No, the price is $96.00.   **93.** 0.79 m^2

95. 0.44 m^2 **97.** 116 mg   **99.** 129 mg

101. (a) $14.7 - 40 \cdot 0.13$ **(b)** 9.5   **(c)** 8.075; walking (5 mph)   **103. (a)** 0.031   **(b)** 0.035   **105.** 297

107. (a) .599   **(b)** .564   **(c)** .525   **(d)** .457   **109.** $4.50

111. $0.75   **113.** $12.00   **115.** $36.00   **117.** three (and you would have 0.01¢ left over)   **119.** $0.06, or 6¢

121. 1000   **123.** 25,000%

Chapter 6 Test *(pages 326–328)*

1. (a) 12   **(b)** 0, 12   **(c)** −4, 0, 12   **(d)** $-4, -\frac{3}{2}, -0.5,$ 0, 4.1, 12   **(e)** $-\sqrt{5}, \sqrt{3}$ **(f)** $-4, -\sqrt{5}, -\frac{3}{2}, -0.5,$ 0, $\sqrt{3}$, 4.1, 12   **2. (a)** C   **(b)** B   **(c)** D   **(d)** A

3. (a) false   **(b)** true   **(c)** true   **(d)** false   **4.** 4

5. 10   **6.** 3   **7.** −43   **8.** 214°F   **9.** 5296 ft   **10. (a)** E

(b) A   **(c)** B   **(d)** D   **(e)** F   **(f)** C   **11. (a)** Ben and Jason   **(b)** Ed and Charlie   **(c)** Ben   **(d)** Jack and Chuck; $\frac{2}{5}$ **(e)** Jason   **12.** $\frac{11}{16}$ **13.** $\frac{57}{160}$ **14.** $-\frac{2}{5}$ **15.** $\frac{4}{9}$

16. (a) $\frac{3}{50}$ **(b)** $\frac{41}{50}$ **(c)** $4\frac{4}{5}$ million   **17. (a)** 0.45   **(b)** $0.41\overline{6}$

18. (a) $\frac{18}{25}$ **(b)** $\frac{58}{99}$ **19. (a)** irrational   **(b)** rational

(c) rational   **(d)** rational   **(e)** irrational   **(f)** irrational

20. (a) 12.247448714   **(b)** $5\sqrt{6}$ **21. (a)** 4.913538149

(b) $\frac{13\sqrt{7}}{7}$ **22. (a)** −45.254834   **(b)** $-32\sqrt{2}$

23. 0.08, or 8%   **24. (a)** 13.81   **(b)** −0.315   **(c)** 38.7

(d) −24.3   **25. (a)** 350   **(b)** 346.04   **(c)** 346.045

26. $54.00   **27. (a)** $26\frac{2}{3}$%   **(b)** $66\frac{2}{3}$%   **28.** D

29. 1656; 1008; 16%; 6%   **30.** 75 mg

CHAPTER 7 THE BASIC CONCEPTS OF ALGEBRA

7.1 Exercises *(pages 337–338)*

1. $\{-1\}$ **3.** $\{3\}$ **5.** $\{-7\}$ **7.** $\{0\}$ **9.** $\left\{-\frac{5}{3}\right\}$

11. $\left\{-\frac{1}{2}\right\}$ **13.** $\{2\}$ **15.** $\{-2\}$ **17.** $\{7\}$ **19.** $\{2\}$

21. $\{4\}$ **23.** $\{0\}$ **25.** $\{-2\}$ **27.** $\{2000\}$ **29.** $\{25\}$

31. $\{40\}$ **33.** contradiction; $\varnothing$ **35.** conditional; $\{-8\}$

37. conditional; $\{0\}$ **39.** identity; {all real numbers}

41. $A = \frac{150p}{w}$ **43.** $\ell = \frac{v \cdot \text{ACH}}{60}$ **45.** $t = 2\ell - 2a - 2b$

47. $\ell = \frac{r_1 x - r_2 x}{r_2}$, or $\ell = \frac{r_1 x}{r_2} - x$ **49.** $r = \frac{\ell + h^2}{2h}$

51. $t = \frac{d}{r}$ **53.** $b = \frac{\mathcal{A}}{h}$ **55.** $a = P - b - c$ **57.** $b = \frac{2\mathcal{A}}{h}$

59. $h = \frac{S - 2\pi r^2}{2\pi r}$, or $h = \frac{S}{2\pi r} - r$ **61.** $h = \frac{3V}{\pi r^2}$

63. 59   **65.** −4   **67.** 5   **69.** −25   **71.** about 40 L of air per second   **73.** minimum: 17.78%; maximum: 86.68%

7.2 Exercises *(pages 347–350)*

1. expression   **3.** equation   **5.** expression

7. $x - 12$ **9.** $(x - 6)(x + 4)$ **11.** $\frac{25}{x}$ $(x \neq 0)$ **13.** 3

15. 6   **17.** −3   **19.** Madonna: $228 million; Bruce Springsteen: $199 million   **21.** wins: 66; losses: 16

23. Democrats: 52; Republicans: 46   **25.** shortest piece: 15 inches; middle piece: 20 inches; longest piece: 24 inches

27. gold: 38; silver: 27; bronze: 23   **29.** 70 milliliters

31. $250   **33.** $24.85   **35.** 4 liters   **37.** 5 liters

39. 1 gallon   **41.** $4000 at 3%; $8000 at 4%

43. $10,000 at 4.5%; $19,000 at 3%   **45.** 17 pennies, 17 dimes, 10 quarters   **47.** 305 students, 105 nonstudents

49. 54 seats on Row 1; 51 seats on Row 2   **51.** 328 miles

53. No. The distance is $55\left(\frac{1}{2}\right) = 27.5$ miles.

55. 18 miles   **57.** $1\frac{3}{4}$ hours   **59.** 11:00 A.M.   **61.** 8 hours

63. 2.668 hours   **65.** 1.715 hours   **67.** 9.14 meters per second   **69.** 10.35 meters per second

7.3 Exercises *(pages 359–362)*

1. $\frac{5}{8}$ **3.** $\frac{1}{4}$ **5.** $\frac{2}{1}$ **7.** $\frac{3}{1}$ **9.** 10-lb size; $0.429

11. 32-oz size; $0.093   **13.** 128-oz size; $0.051

15. 36-oz size; $0.049   **17.** $\{35\}$ **19.** $\{-1\}$

21. $\left\{-\frac{27}{4}\right\}$ **23.** 2 tablets **25.** 0.8 milliliter

27. 910 milligrams **29.** 7.5 milliliters **31.** 12 milligrams

33. $44.55 **35.** 12,500 fish **37.** $25\frac{2}{3}$ inches

39. 2.0 inches **41.** $2\frac{5}{8}$ cups **43.** 20 pounds

45. about 302 pounds **47.** $428.82

49. 100 pounds per square inch **51.** 144 feet

53. 448.1 pounds **55.** 24 **57.** 42 **59.** 6.2 pounds

61. $239 **63.** $280 **65.** about 267 square miles

7.4 Exercises (pages 370–372)

1. D **3.** B **5.** F

7. $[7, \infty)$ **9.** $[5, \infty)$

11. $(7, \infty)$ **13.** $(-4, \infty)$

15. $(-\infty, -40]$ **17.** $(-\infty, 4]$

19. $\left(-\infty, -\frac{15}{2}\right)$ **21.** $\left[\frac{1}{2}, \infty\right)$

23. $(3, \infty)$ **25.** $(-\infty, 4)$

27. $\left(-\infty, \frac{23}{6}\right]$ **29.** $(1, 11)$

31. $[-14, 10]$ **33.** $[-5, 6]$

35. $\left[-\frac{14}{3}, 2\right]$ **37.** $\left[-\frac{1}{2}, \frac{35}{5}\right]$

39. $\left(-\frac{1}{3}, \frac{1}{9}\right]$ **41.** after 40 miles

43. 2 miles

45. 80 or greater

47. 90 or greater **49.** 71 or greater

51. $-0.15 \le x - 18 \le 0.15$; between and inclusive of 17.85 and 18.15 ounces **53.** $-0.75 \le x - 52.5 \le 0.75$; between and inclusive of 51.75 and 53.25 milliliters

55. (a) 140 to 184 pounds **(b)** Answers will vary.

57. 26 DVDs

7.5 Exercises (pages 380–382)

1. 10^3 **3.** 10^6 **5.** 10^9 **7.** 625 **9.** -32 **11.** -8

13. -81 **15.** $\frac{1}{8}$ **17.** $\frac{1}{49}$ **19.** $-\frac{1}{49}$ **21.** $\frac{16}{5}$ **23.** 125

25. $\frac{25}{16}$ **27.** $\frac{9}{20}$ **29.** 1 **31.** 1 **33.** 0 **35.** 10^{16} **37.** $\frac{1}{10}$

39. $\frac{1}{5}$ **41.** 10^2 **43.** 10^3 **45.** 10^1, or 10 **47.** 5^2 **49.** 10^{11}

51. $\frac{1}{10^6}$ **53.** $\frac{4}{10^{14}}$ **55.** 2.3×10^2 **57.** 8.1×10^9

59. 1.4×10^{12} **61.** 2×10^{-2} **63.** 5.623×10^{-1}

65. 4.4×10^{-6} **67.** 6500 **69.** 28,000,000

71. 15,000,000,000 **73.** 0.42 **75.** 0.0152

77. 0.00000833 **79.** 6×10^5 **81.** 2×10^5 **83.** 2×10^5

85. (a) 3.174×10^8 **(b)** 1×10^{12} (or 10^{12}) **(c)** $3151

87. $40,045 **89.** approximately 9.5×10^{-7} parsec

91. 300 seconds **93.** approximately 5.87×10^{12} miles

95. (a) 5.16×10^2 people per square mile

(b) 998 square miles **97.** When Kirk said "one to the fourth power," he indicated that the sound would *not* be changed at all, because $1^4 = 1$.

7.6 Exercises (page 388)

1. $x^2 - x + 3$ **3.** $9x^2 - 4x + 4$ **5.** $6x^4 - 2x^3 - 7x^2 - 4x$

7. $-2x^2 - 13x + 11$ **9.** $x^2 - 5x - 24$ **11.** $28x^2 + x - 2$

13. $12x^5 - 20x^3 + 4x^2$ **15.** $4x^2 - 9$

17. $x^2 + 14x + 49$ **19.** $25x^2 - 30x + 9$

21. $10x^4 + 34x^3 + 7x^2 - 13x + 6$ **23.** $12(x + 3)$

25. $2x(4x^2 - 2x + 3)$ **27.** $2x^2(4x^2 + 3x - 6)$

29. $(x - 5)(x + 3)$ **31.** $(x + 7)(x - 5)$

33. $6(x - 10)(x + 2)$ **35.** $3x(x + 1)(x + 3)$

37. $(3x - 2)(2x + 3)$ **39.** $(5x + 3)(x - 2)$

41. $(7x + 2)(3x - 1)$ **43.** $2x^2(4x - 1)(3x + 2)$

45. $(x - 4)^2$ **47.** $(x + 7)^2$ **49.** $(3x - 2)^2$

51. $2(4x - 3)^2$ **53.** $(2x + 7)^2$ **55.** $(x + 6)(x - 6)$

57. $(10 + x)(10 - x)$ **59.** $(3x + 4)(3x - 4)$

61. $(5x^2 + 3)(5x^2 - 3)$ **63.** $(x^2 + 25)(x + 5)(x - 5)$

65. $13x(x^2 + 3x + 4)$ **67.** $(6x - 7)(2x + 5)$

69. $(2x + 7)^2$ **71.** $(x^4 + 9)(x^2 + 3)(x^2 - 3)$

73. $-1(x + 7)(x - 3)$ **75.** $-1(3x + 4)(x - 1)$

77. $-1(x + 2)(2x + 1)$

7.7 Exercises (pages 393–395)

1. $\{-3, 9\}$ **3.** $\left\{\frac{7}{2}, -\frac{1}{5}\right\}$ **5.** $\{-7, 0\}$ **7.** $\{-3, 4\}$

9. $\{-7, -2\}$ **11.** $\left\{-\frac{5}{2}, 1\right\}$ **13.** $\left\{-\frac{1}{2}, \frac{1}{6}\right\}$ **15.** $\{-2, 4\}$

17. $\{\pm 8\}$ **19.** $\left\{\pm 2\sqrt{6}\right\}$ **21.** $\varnothing$ **23.** $\{1, 7\}$

25. $\left\{4 \pm \sqrt{3}\right\}$ **27.** $\left\{\frac{5 \pm \sqrt{13}}{2}\right\}$ **29.** $\left\{\frac{-3 \pm \sqrt{37}}{2}\right\}$

31. $\left\{\frac{1 \pm \sqrt{3}}{2}\right\}$ **33.** $\left\{\frac{1 \pm \sqrt{5}}{2}\right\}$ **35.** $\left\{\frac{-1 \pm \sqrt{2}}{2}\right\}$

37. $\left\{\frac{1 \pm \sqrt{29}}{2}\right\}$ **39.** $\varnothing$ **41.** eastbound ship: 80 miles; southbound ship: 150 miles **43.** 120 feet **45.** 412.3 feet

47. 8, 15, 17 **49.** 5 centimeters, 12 centimeters, 13 centimeters **51. (a)** 1 second and 8 seconds **(b)** 9 seconds after it is projected **53.** 0.7 second and 4.0 seconds **55.** 1 foot **57.** length: 26 meters; width: 16 meters

Chapter 7 Test *(pages 401–402)*

1. {2} **2.** {4} **3.** identity; {all real numbers}
4. $v = \dfrac{S + 16t^2}{t}$, or $v = \dfrac{S}{t} + 16t$ **5.** Hawaii: 4021 square miles; Maui: 728 square miles; Kauai: 551 square miles
6. 5 liters **7.** 2.2 hours **8.** 16 slices for $4.38
9. 3 tablets **10.** 2300 miles **11.** 200 amps
12. $(-\infty, 4]$ **13.** $(-2, 6]$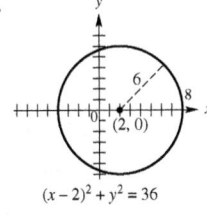
14. 82 or greater **15.** $\dfrac{16}{9}$ **16.** -64 **17.** $\dfrac{64}{27}$ **18.** 0
19. 1 **20.** 10^1, or 10 **21. (a)** 693,000,000
(b) 0.000000125 **22.** 3×10^{-4} **23.** about 15,300 seconds
24. $4x^2 + 6x + 10$ **25.** $15x^2 - 14x - 8$ **26.** $16x^4 - 9$
27. $x^2 + 12x + 36$ **28.** $(x + 7)(x - 4)$
29. $(2x + 9)(x + 5)$ **30.** $(5x + 7)(5x - 7)$
31. $(x - 9)^2$ **32.** $2x(x - 5)(x - 4)$ **33.** $\left\{-\dfrac{3}{2}, \dfrac{1}{3}\right\}$
34. $\left\{\pm \sqrt{13}\right\}$ **35.** $\left\{\dfrac{1 \pm \sqrt{29}}{2}\right\}$ **36.** 0.87 second

CHAPTER 8 GRAPHS, FUNCTIONS, AND SYSTEMS OF EQUATIONS AND INEQUALITIES

8.1 Exercises *(pages 411–413)*

1. x **3.** $(0, 0)$ **5. (a)** I **(b)** III
(c) II **(d)** IV **(e)** none
7.–15.

17. (a) $\sqrt{34}$ **(b)** $\left(\dfrac{1}{2}, \dfrac{5}{2}\right)$
19. (a) $\sqrt{61}$ **(b)** $\left(\dfrac{1}{2}, 1\right)$
21. (a) $\sqrt{146}$ **(b)** $\left(-\dfrac{1}{2}, \dfrac{3}{2}\right)$
23. (a) $\sqrt{40} = 2\sqrt{10}$
(b) $(-1, 4)$

25. B **27.** D **29.** $x^2 + y^2 = 36$
31. $(x + 1)^2 + (y - 3)^2 = 16$ **33.** $x^2 + (y - 4)^2 = 3$
35. $(-2, -3); 2$ **37.** $(-5, 7); 9$ **39.** $(2, 4); 4$

41.

$x^2 + y^2 = 36$

43.
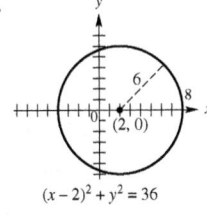
$(x - 2)^2 + y^2 = 36$

45.
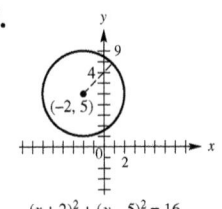
$(x + 2)^2 + (y - 5)^2 = 16$

47.
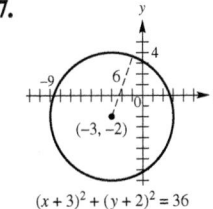
$(x + 3)^2 + (y + 2)^2 = 36$

49. (a) 25.35%; **(b)** This is very close to the actual figure.
51. $20,665 **53.** Answers will vary.
55. The epicenter is $(-2, -2)$.

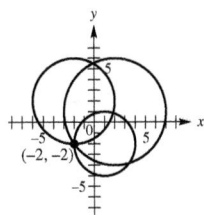

8.2 Exercises *(pages 420–423)*

1. $(0, -4), (4, 0), (2, -2),$ **3.** $(0, 5), \left(\dfrac{5}{2}, 0\right), (1, 3),$
$(3, -1)$ $(2, 1)$

$x - y = 4$

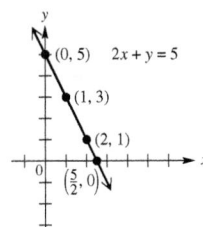
$2x + y = 5$

5. $(0, 4), (5, 0), \left(3, \dfrac{8}{5}\right),$ **7.** $(0, 4), \left(\dfrac{8}{3}, 0\right), (2, 1),$
$\left(\dfrac{5}{2}, 2\right)$ $(4, -2)$

$4x + 5y = 20$

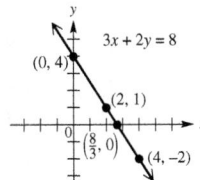
$3x + 2y = 8$

9. $(4, 0); \quad (0, 6)$ **11.** $(2, 0); \quad \left(0, \dfrac{5}{3}\right)$

$3x + 2y = 12$

$5x + 6y = 10$

13. $\left(\dfrac{5}{2}, 0\right); \quad (0, -5)$ **15.** $(2, 0); \quad \left(0, -\dfrac{2}{3}\right)$

$2x - y = 5$

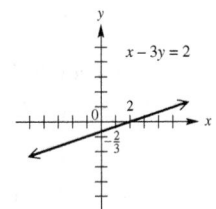
$x - 3y = 2$

17. $(0,0)$; $(0,0)$

19. $(0,0)$; $(0,0)$

21. $(2,0)$; none

23. none; $(0,4)$

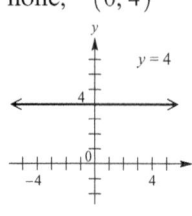

25. C **27.** A **29.** D **31.** B **33.** $\frac{3}{10}$ **35. (a)** $\frac{3}{2}$
(b) $-\frac{7}{4}$ **37.** 8 **39.** $-\frac{5}{6}$ **41.** 0 **43.** undefined

45.

47.

49.

51.

53.

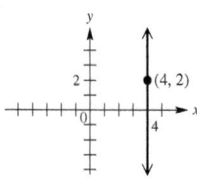

55. parallel **57.** perpendicular
59. neither parallel nor
perpendicular **61.** $\frac{7}{10}$
63. $-\$4000$ per year; The value
of the machine is decreasing by
an average of \$4000 per year
during those years.

65. (a) 0.42 **(b)** positive; increased **(c)** 0.42%
67. (a) 14.2 **(b)** The number of subscribers increased
by an average of 14.2 million per year from 2007 through
2012. **69.** -1859 thousand; The number of digital cameras sold decreased by an average of 1859 thousand per year
from 2010 through 2013. **71.** \$0.08; The price of a gallon
of gasoline increased by an average of \$0.08 per year from
1980 through 2012.

8.3 Exercises *(pages 427–429)*

1. D **3.** B **5.** A **7.** C **9.** H **11.** B **13.** $y = 3x - 3$
15. $y = -x + 3$ **17.** $y = -\frac{3}{4}x + \frac{5}{2}$ **19.** $y = -2x + 18$
21. $y = \frac{1}{2}x + \frac{13}{2}$ **23.** $y = 4x - 12$ **25.** $y = 5$ **27.** $x = 9$

29. $x = 0.5$ **31.** $y = 8$ **33.** $y = 2x - 2$
35. $y = -\frac{1}{2}x + 4$ **37.** $y = 5$ **39.** $x = 7$ **41.** $y = -3$
43. $y = 5x + 15$ **45.** $y = -\frac{2}{3}x + \frac{4}{5}$ **47.** $y = \frac{2}{5}x + 5$
49. (a) $y = -x + 12$ **(b)** -1 **(c)** $(0, 12)$
51. (a) $y = -\frac{5}{2}x + 10$ **(b)** $-\frac{5}{2}$ **(c)** $(0, 10)$
53. (a) $y = \frac{2}{3}x - \frac{10}{3}$ **(b)** $\frac{2}{3}$ **(c)** $\left(0, -\frac{10}{3}\right)$
55. $y = 3x - 19$ **57.** $y = \frac{1}{2}x - 1$ **59.** $y = -\frac{1}{2}x + 9$
61. $y = 7$ **63.** $C = \frac{5}{9}F - \frac{160}{9}$ **65.** -40 degrees

8.4 Exercises *(pages 435–437)*
1. set of ordered pairs **3.** range; dependent **5.** linear;
line **7.** 5 **9.** 2 **11.** -1 **13.** -13 **15.** 3 **17.** 0

19.

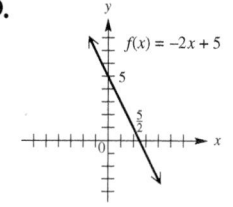

domain and range:
$(-\infty, \infty)$

21.

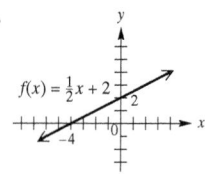

domain and range:
$(-\infty, \infty)$

23.

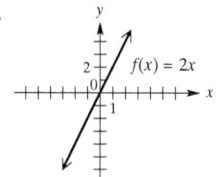

domain and range:
$(-\infty, \infty)$

25.

domain: $(-\infty, \infty)$;
range: $\{5\}$

27. 4 **29.** 16 **31. (a)** $C(x) = 0.02x + 200$
(b) $R(x) = 0.04x$ **(c)** 10,000
(d)

For $x < 10{,}000$, a loss
For $x > 10{,}000$, a profit

33. (a) $C(x) = 3.00x + 2300$ **(b)** $R(x) = 5.50x$ **(c)** 920
(d)

For $x < 920$, a loss
For $x > 920$, a profit

35. (a) $f(x) = 422.6x + 5492$ **(b)** \$8450
37. (a) $f(x) = 0.996x + 34.3$ **(b)** 79.1%
39. (a) $f(x) = 76.9x$ **(b)** 30,760 kilometers per second

41. (a) $0; $2.50; $5.00; $7.50

(b) 2.50x **(c)**

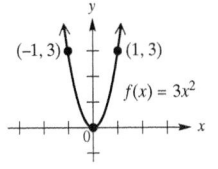

43. (a) $160

(b) 70 mph **(c)** 66 mph

(d) for speeds more than 80 mph

8.5 Exercises *(pages 445–446)*

1. F **3.** C **5.** E **7.** $(0, 0)$ **9.** $(0, 4)$ **11.** $(1, 0)$

13. $(-3, -4)$ **15.** downward; narrower

17. upward; wider

19.

21.

23.

25.

27.

29.

31.

33.

35.

37.

39.

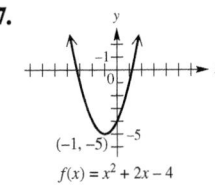

41. 25 meters; 625 square meters **43.** 16 feet; 2 seconds **45.** 4.1 seconds; 81.6 meters

47. $f(45) = 161.5$; This means that when the speed is 45 mph, the stopping distance is 161.5 feet.

8.6 Exercises *(pages 455–457)*

1. rises; falls **3.** does not **5.** rises; falls **7.** does not

9. 2.56425419972 **11.** 1.25056505582

13. 7.41309466897 **15.** 0.0000210965628481

17.

19.

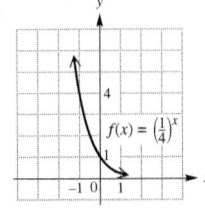

21. 20.0855369232 **23.** 0.018315638889 **25.** $2 = \log_4 16$

27. $-3 = \log_{2/3}\left(\frac{27}{8}\right)$ **29.** $2^5 = 32$ **31.** $3^1 = 3$

33. 1.38629436112 **35.** -1.0498221245

37.

39.

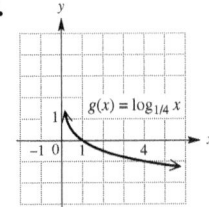

41. (a) $22,510.18 **(b)** $22,529.85 **43. (a)** $31,870.48

(b) $31,870.67 **45.** Plan A is better by $121.81.

47. (a) 7% compounded quarterly **(b)** $800.32

49. 27.73 years **51.** 13.52 years **53. (a)** 7.374 billion

(b) 27.1 years after 2010, or about 2037

55. about 9000 years **57. (a)** 440 grams **(b)** 387 grams

(c) 264 grams **(d)** 21.66 years **59.** 1611.97 years

61. 4 hours **63. (a)** 0.6°C **(b)** 0.3°C **65. (a)** 1.4°C

(b) 0.5°C

8.7 Exercises *(pages 461–463)*

1. 3; -6 **3.** D; The ordered-pair solution must be in quadrant IV. **5.** yes **7.** no **9.** B **11.** A

13. $\{(2, 2)\}$ **15.** $\{(3, -1)\}$ **17.** $\{(2, -3)\}$

19. $\left\{\left(\frac{3}{2}, -\frac{3}{2}\right)\right\}$ **21.** $\left\{\left(\frac{6-2y}{7}, y\right)\right\}$

23. $\varnothing$ **25.** $\{(2, -4)\}$

27. $\{(1, 2)\}$ **29.** $\left\{\left(\frac{22}{9}, \frac{22}{3}\right)\right\}$

31. $\{(2, 3)\}$ **33.** $\{(5, 4)\}$

35. $\left\{\left(-5, -\frac{10}{3}\right)\right\}$ **37.** $\{(2, 6)\}$ **39.** hiking

41. $(8.7, 35.9)$ **43.** $80x - 7y = -420$ **45.** $\{(4.375, 110)\}$

8.8 Exercises *(pages 468–470)*

1. wins: 97; losses: 65 **3.** length: 94 feet; width: 50 feet

5. dark clay: $5 per kilogram; light clay: $4 per kilogram

7. square: 12 cm; triangle: 8 cm **9.** cappuccino: $3.19; cafe mocha: $3.59 **11.** Madonna: $140; Springsteen: $92

13. New York: $622; Washington, D.C: $564
15. Wal-Mart: $422 billion; ExxonMobil: $355 billion
17. NHL: $313.68; NBA: $287.85
19. (a) 12 ounces **(b)** 30 ounces **(c)** 48 ounces
(d) 60 ounces **21.** $4.29x **23.** 15% solution: $26\frac{2}{3}$ liters;
33% solution: $13\frac{1}{3}$ liters **25.** 3 liters **27.** 50% juice:
150 liters; 30% juice: 50 liters **29.** $1.20 candy:
100 pounds; $2.40 candy; 60 pounds **31.** 4%: $10,000;
3%: $5000 **33. (a)** $(10 - x)$ mph **(b)** $(10 + x)$ mph
35. train: 60 mph; plane: 160 mph **37.** boat: 21 mph;
current: 3 mph

8.9 Exercises *(pages 475–476)*
1. C **3.** B

5.

7.

9.

11.

13.

15.

17.

19.

21.

23. maximum of 65 at $(5, 10)$; minimum of 8 at $(1, 1)$
25. $\left(\frac{6}{5}, \frac{6}{5}\right); \frac{42}{5}$ **27.** $\left(\frac{17}{3}, 5\right); \frac{49}{3}$

29. Ship 20 to A and 80 to B, for a minimum cost of $1040.
31. Take 3 red pills and 2 blue pills, for a minimum cost of
$0.70 per day. **33.** Make 3 batches of cakes and 6 batches
of cookies, for a maximum profit of $210. **35.** Ship 0
medical kits and 4000 containers of water.

Chapter 8 Test *(pages 485–486)*
1. $\sqrt{41}$ **2.** $(x + 1)^2 + (y - 2)^2 = 9$

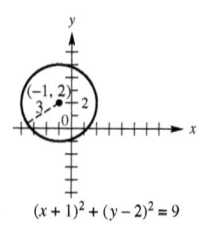

$(x + 1)^2 + (y - 2)^2 = 9$

3. $151.0 billion; This amount is $5.9 billion less than the
actual figure.

4. x-intercept: $\left(\frac{8}{3}, 0\right)$;
y-intercept: $(0, -4)$

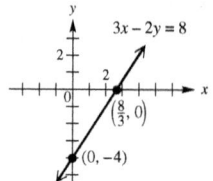

5. $\frac{2}{7}$ **6. (a)** $y = -\frac{2}{5}x + \frac{13}{5}$ **(b)** $y = -\frac{1}{2}x - \frac{3}{2}$
(c) $y = -\frac{1}{2}x + 2$ **7.** B **8. (a)** $y = 0.238x + 63.3$
(b) 80.0 years **9.** 17.5 million; The number of subscribers
increased by an average of 17.5 million per year.
10. (a) $y = 0.05x + 0.50$ **(b)** $(1, 0.55), (5, 0.75), (10, 1.00)$
11. $y = \frac{2}{3}x + 1$ **12. (a)** –5 **(b)** 2 **13.** 500 units; $30,000
14. axis: $x = -3$; vertex: $(-3, 4)$

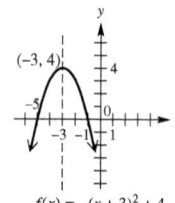

$f(x) = -(x + 3)^2 + 4$

15. 80 feet by 160 feet; 12,800 square feet
16. (a) 2116.31264888
(b) 0.157237166314 **(c)** 3.15955035878
17. (a) $12,740.13 **(b)** $12,742.04
18. (a) 1.62 grams **(b)** 1.18 grams
(c) 0.69 gram **(d)** 2.00 grams
19. $\{(4, -2)\}$ **20.** $\varnothing$

21. Red Sox: $53.38; Yankees: $51.83 **22.** $6-per-lb nuts:
30 lb; $3-per-lb candy: 70 lb

23.

24. Raise 4 pigs and 12 geese,
for a maximum profit of $1120.

CHAPTER 9 GEOMETRY

9.1 Exercises *(pages 494–495)*
(The art here is not to scale with the exercise art.)

1. 90 **3.** equal **5.** true **7.** false **9.** true
11. false **13.** true **15.** false

17. (a) $\overleftrightarrow{AB}$ (b)

19. (a) $\overrightarrow{CB}$ (b)

21. (a) $\overleftrightarrow{BC}$ (b)

23. (a) $\overrightarrow{BA}$ (b)

25. F **27.** D **29.** B **31.** E

There may be other correct forms of the answers in Exercises 33–39. **33.** $\overleftrightarrow{MO}$ **35.** $\overrightarrow{NO}$ **37.** $\varnothing$
39. $\overrightarrow{OP}$ **41.** 62° **43.** 1° **45.** $(90 - x)°$
47. 48° **49.** 154° **51.** $(180 - y)°$ **53.** 40°
55. 52° **57.** $\angle CBD$ and $\angle ABE$; $\angle CBE$ and $\angle DBA$
59. (a) 52° (b) 128° **61.** 107° and 73° **63.** 75° and 75°
65. 139° and 139° **67.** 35° and 55° **69.** 49° and 49°
71. 48° and 132° **73.** (a) 3 (b) 6 (c) 7 (d) 7; exterior
75. (a) 180 (b) 180 (c) 180; 180 (d) 0 (e) 0 (f) 3

9.2 Exercises *(pages 501–503)*

1. chord **3.** equilateral (or equiangular) **5.** false
7. false **9.** true **11.** Answers will vary. **13.** both
15. closed **17.** closed **19.** neither **21.** convex
23. convex **25.** not convex **27.** right, scalene
29. acute, equilateral **31.** right, scalene **33.** right, isosceles **35.** obtuse, scalene **37.** An isosceles right triangle is a triangle having a 90° angle and two perpendicular sides of equal length.
39. $A = 50°$; $B = 70°$; $C = 60°$ **41.** $A = B = C = 60°$
43. $A = B = 55°$; $C = 70°$ **45.** 155° **47.** 360°
49. (a) O (b) $\overrightarrow{OA}$, $\overrightarrow{OC}$, $\overrightarrow{OB}$, $\overrightarrow{OD}$ (c) $\overleftrightarrow{AC}$, $\overleftrightarrow{BD}$
(d) $\overleftrightarrow{AC}$, $\overleftrightarrow{BD}$, $\overleftrightarrow{BC}$, $\overleftrightarrow{AB}$ (e) $\overleftrightarrow{BC}$, $\overleftrightarrow{AB}$ (f) $\overleftrightarrow{AE}$
51. With the radius of the compass greater than one-half the length PQ, place the point of the compass at P and swing arcs above and below line r. Then, with the same radius and the point of the compass at Q, swing two more arcs above and below line r. Locate the two points of intersection of the arcs above and below, and call them A and B. With a straightedge, join A and B. AB is the perpendicular bisector of PQ.
53. With the radius of the compass greater than the distance from P to r, place the point of the compass at P and swing an arc intersecting line r in two points. Call these points A and B. Swing arcs of equal radius to the left of line r, with the point of the compass at A and at B, intersecting at point Q. With a straightedge, join P and Q. PQ is the perpendicular from P to line r.
55. With any radius, place the point of the compass at P and swing arcs to the left and right, intersecting line r in two points. Call these points A and B. With an arc of

sufficient length, place the point of the compass first at A and then at B, and swing arcs either both above or both below line r, intersecting at point Q. With a straightedge, join P and Q. PQ is perpendicular to line r at P.
57. With any radius, place the point of the compass at A and swing an arc intersecting the sides of angle A at two points. Call the point of intersection on the horizontal side B and call the other point of intersection C. Draw a horizontal working line, and locate any point A' on this line. With the same radius used earlier, place the point of the compass at A' and swing an arc intersecting the working line at B'. Return to angle A, and set the radius of the compass equal to BC. On the working line, place the point of the compass at B' and swing an arc intersecting the first arc at C'. Now draw line $A'C'$. Angle A' is equal to angle A.
59. Answers will vary.

9.3 Exercises *(pages 510–514)*

1.

STATEMENTS	REASONS
1. $AC = BD$	**1.** Given
2. $AD = BC$	**2.** Given
3. $AB = AB$	**3.** Reflexive property
4. $\triangle ABD \cong \triangle BAC$	**4.** SSS congruence property

3.

STATEMENTS	REASONS
1. $\angle BAC = \angle DAC$	**1.** Given
2. $\angle BCA = \angle DCA$	**2.** Given
3. $AC = AC$	**3.** Reflexive property
4. $\triangle ABC \cong \triangle ADC$	**4.** ASA congruence property

5.

STATEMENTS	REASONS
1. $\overleftrightarrow{DB}$ is perpendicular to $\overleftrightarrow{AC}$.	**1.** Given
2. $AB = BC$	**2.** Given
3. $\angle ABD = \angle CBD$	**3.** Both are right angles by definition of perpendicularity.
4. $DB = DB$	**4.** Reflexive property
5. $\triangle ABD \cong \triangle CBD$	**5.** SAS congruence property

7. 110° **9.** 67°, 67° **11.** Answers will vary.
13. $\angle H$ and $\angle F$; $\angle K$ and $\angle E$; $\angle HGK$ and $\angle FGE$; $\overleftrightarrow{HK}$ and $\overleftrightarrow{FE}$; $\overleftrightarrow{GK}$ and $\overleftrightarrow{GE}$; $\overleftrightarrow{HG}$ and $\overleftrightarrow{FG}$
15. $\angle A$ and $\angle P$; $\angle C$ and $\angle R$; $\angle B$ and $\angle Q$; $\overleftrightarrow{AC}$ and $\overleftrightarrow{PR}$; $\overleftrightarrow{CB}$ and $\overleftrightarrow{RQ}$; $\overleftrightarrow{AB}$ and $\overleftrightarrow{PQ}$
17. $\angle P = 76°$; $\angle M = 48°$; $\angle A = \angle N = 56°$

19. $\angle T = 20°$; $\angle V = 64°$; $\angle R = \angle U = 96°$

21. $\angle T = 74°$; $\angle Y = 28°$; $\angle Z = \angle W = 78°$

23. $a = 12$; $b = 9$ **25.** $x = 6$ **27.** $a = 6$; $b = \frac{15}{2}$

29. $x = 165$ **31.** $c = 111\frac{1}{9}$ **33.** $r = \frac{108}{7}$ **35.** 60 m

37. 250 m, 350 m **39.** 112.5 ft **41.** 10 **43.** $c = 17$

45. $a = 13$ **47.** $c = 50$ m **49.** $a = 20$ in.

51. The sum of the squares of the two shorter sides of a right triangle is equal to the square of the longest side.

53. $(3, 4, 5)$ **55.** $(7, 24, 25)$ **57.** Answers will vary.

59. $(3, 4, 5)$ **61.** $(7, 24, 25)$ **63.** Answers will vary.

65. $(4, 3, 5)$ **67.** $(8, 15, 17)$ **69.** Answers will vary.

71. 24 m **73.** 18 ft **75.** 4.55 ft **77.** 19 ft, 3 in.

79. 28 ft, 10 in. **81.** (a) b (b) k (c) cj (d) ck

(e) $j + k$; $j + k$; $a^2 + b^2 = c^2$ **83.** 9 **85.** 16 **87.** 55°

89. 360° **91.** Answers will vary. **93.** Answers will vary.

9.4 Exercises *(pages 522–526)*

1. 24 **3.** 10 **5.** perimeter **7.** 48 cm² **9.** 10 cm²

11. 8 in.² **13.** 418 mm² **15.** 8 cm² **17.** 3.14 cm²

19. 1017 m² **21.** 4 m **23.** 300 ft, 400 ft, 500 ft

25. 50 ft **27.** 23,800.10 ft² **29.** 14,600 mi²

31. 12 in., 12π in., 36π in.² **33.** 5 ft, 10π ft, 25π ft²

35. 6 cm, 12 cm, 36π cm² **37.** 10 in., 20 in., 20π in.

39. $\frac{20}{\pi}$ yd, $\frac{40}{\pi}$ yd, 40 yd **41.** 14.5 **43.** 7 **45.** 5.7

47. 6 **49.** 5 **51.** 1.5 **53.** (a) 20 cm² (b) 80 cm²

(c) 180 cm² (d) 320 cm² (e) 4 (f) 3; 9 (g) 4; 16

(h) n^2 **55.** n^2 **57.** $800 **59.** 80 **61.** 76.26

63. 132 ft² **65.** 5376 cm² **67.** 145.34 m²

69. 16-in. pizza **71.** 16-in. pizza **73.** $\frac{1}{2}(a + b)(a + b)$

75. $\frac{1}{2}(a + b)(a + b) = \frac{1}{2}ab + \frac{1}{2}ab + \frac{1}{2}c^2$

77. 26 in. **79.** 625 ft² **81.** 6 cm² **83.** $\frac{(4 - \pi)r^2}{4}$

85. $24 + 4\sqrt{6}$ **87.** 5 in.

9.5 Exercises *(pages 531–534)*

1. true **3.** true **5.** false **7.** (a) $22\frac{1}{2}$ m³ (b) $49\frac{1}{4}$ m²

9. (a) 267,946.67 ft³ (b) 20,096 ft² **11.** (a) 549.5 cm³

(b) 376.8 cm² **13.** (a) 65.94 m³ (b) 100.00 m²

15. 168 in.³ **17.** 1969.10 cm³ **19.** 427.29 cm³

21. 508.68 cm³ **23.** 1,694,000 m³ **25.** 0.52 m³

27. 288π in.³, 144π in.² **29.** 2 cm, 16π cm²

31. 1 m, $\frac{4}{3}\pi$ m³ **33.** volume **35.** 270 ft³

37. $\sqrt[3]{2}x$ **39.** $8100 **41.** $37,500 **43.** 65.7%

45. 2.5 **47.** 6 **49.** 210 in.³ **51.** 300 mi **53.** 2 to 1

55. 288 **57.** Answers will vary. **59.** 4, 4, 6, 2

61. 8, 6, 12, 2 **63.** 20, 12, 30, 2

9.6 Exercises *(pages 543–545)*

(The answers are given in blue for this section.)

1.   **3.**

5. 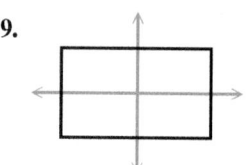   **7.** The figure is its own reflection image.

9.   **11.**

13.   **15.**

17.   **19.**

21.   **23.**

25.

27.

29.

31.

33. no

35.

37.

39.

41.

43.

45.

47. 6   **49.** $R_P^2 \cdot C_P^{6n+2}$

9.7 Exercises *(pages 552–554)*

1. Euclidean   **3.** Lobachevskian   **5.** greater than

7. Riemannian   **9.** Euclidean

11.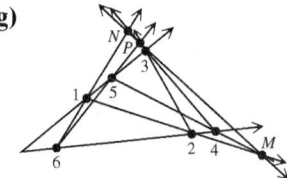

13. Yes; any two distinct lines have at least one point in common.   **15.** Yes; any two points in a plane have at least one line of the plane in common.   **17.** Yes; every point is contained by at least three lines of the plane.

19. no   **21.** yes   **23.** C   **25.** A, E   **27.** B, D

29. A, E   **31.** 1   **33.** 3   **35.** 1

37. (a)–(g)

37. (h) Suppose that a hexagon is inscribed in an angle. Let each pair of opposite sides be extended so as to intersect. Then the three points of intersection thus obtained will lie in a straight line.

9.8 Exercises *(pages 558–559)*

1. 4   **2.** 4   **3.** 2   **4.** $\frac{2}{1} = 2$ **5.** $\frac{4}{1} = 4$ **6.** $\frac{3}{1} = 3; \frac{9}{1} = 9$

7. $\frac{4}{1} = 4; \frac{16}{1} = 16$ **8.** 4, 9, 16, 25, 36, 100

9. Each ratio in the bottom row is the square of the scale factor in the top row.   **10.** 4   **11.** 4, 9, 16, 25, 36, 100

12. Each ratio in the bottom row is again the square of the scale factor in the top row.   **13.** Answers will vary. Some examples are: $3^d = 9$, thus $d = 2$; $5^d = 25$, thus $d = 2$; $4^d = 16$, thus $d = 2$.   **14.** 8   **15.** $\frac{2}{1} = 2; \frac{8}{1} = 8$

16. 8, 27, 64, 125, 216, 1000   **17.** Each ratio in the bottom row is the cube of the scale factor in the top row.

18. Since $2^3 = 8$, the value of d in $2^d = 8$ must be 3.

19. $\frac{3}{1} = 3$ **20.** 4   **21.** 1.262, or $\frac{\ln 4}{\ln 3}$ **22.** $\frac{2}{1} = 2$ **23.** 3

24. It is between 1 and 2.   **25.** 1.585, or $\frac{\ln 3}{\ln 2}$

27. 0.842, 0.452, 0.842, 0.452, ... The two attractors are approximately 0.842 and 0.452.

Chapter 9 Test *(pages 567–568)*

1. (a) 48°   **(b)** 138°   **(c)** acute   **2.** 40°, 140°

3. 45°, 45°   **4.** 30°, 60°   **5.** 130°, 50°   **6.** 117°, 117°

7. Answers will vary.   **8.** C   **9.** both   **10.** neither

11. 30°, 45°, 105°   **12.** 72 cm²   **13.** 60 in.²   **14.** 68 m²

15. 180 m²   **16.** 57 cm²   **17.** 24π in.   **18.** 1978 ft

19.

STATEMENTS	REASONS
1. $\angle CAB = \angle DBA$	1. Given
2. $DB = CA$	2. Given
3. $AB = AB$	3. Reflexive property
4. $\triangle ABD \cong \triangle BAC$	4. SAS congruence property

20. 64 ft   **21.** 29 m   **22.**

23.

24. (a) 904.32 in.³   **(b)** 452.16 in.²

25. (a) 864 ft³   **(b)** 552 ft²

26. (a) 1582.56 m³   **(b)** 753.60 m²

27. Answers will vary.   **28. (a)** yes

(b) no   **29.** no   **30.** The only attractor is approximately 0.524.

CHAPTER 10 COUNTING METHODS

10.1 Exercises *(pages 581–583)*

1. $AB, AC, AD, AE, BA, BC, BD, BE, CA, CB, CD,$ $CE, DA, DB, DC, DE, EA, EB, EC, ED$; 20 ways
3. $AB, AD, BA, BD, CE, DA, DB, EC$; 8 ways
5. $ACE, AEC, BCE, BEC, DCE, DEC$; 6 ways
7. $ABC, ABD, ABE, ACD, ACE, ADE, BCD, BCE,$
BDE, CDE; 10 ways **9.** 1 **11.** 3 **13.** 5 **15.** 5
17. 3 **19.** 1 **21.** 18 **23.** 15 **25.** 27 **27.** 15 **29.** 30
31. 22, 33, 55, 77 **33.** 23, 37, 53, 73
35.

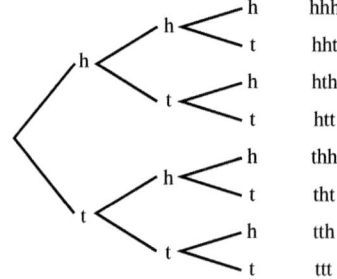

First coin	Second coin	Third coin	Result

(a) hhh, hht, hth, thh (b) hhh (c) hht, hth, htt, thh,
tht, tth, ttt (d) htt, tht, tth, ttt
37. 16 **39.** 36 **41.** 17 **43.** 72 **45.** 12 **47.** 10 **49.** 6
51. 9 **53.** 49 **55.** 21 **57.** 15 **59.** 16 **61.** 13 **63.** 4
65. (a) 1600 (b) $4k + 1$ for all positive integers k
(c) $4k^2$ **67.** 3

Wording may vary in the answers for Exercise 69.
69. (a) Determine the number of two-digit numbers that
can be formed using only the digits 1, 2, and 3 if repetition
of digits is allowed.
(b) Determine the number of two-digit numbers that can
be formed using only the digits 1, 2, and 3 if the selection
is done with replacement.

10.2 Exercises *(pages 591–594)*

1. 24 **3.** 72 **5.** 20 **7.** 28 **9.** 10 **11.** 1225
13. (a) 720 (b) 120 **15.** (a) 306 (b) 153
17. 3,628,800 **19.** 3,991,680 **21.** 4,151,347,200
23. 184,756 **25.** 980,179,200 **27.** 134,596 **29.** 60
31. 2,162,160 **33.** $2^3 = 8$ **35.** Answers will vary.
37. $6^3 = 216$ **39.** $2^{10} = 1024$ **41.** $5! = 120$
43. $3 \cdot 2 = 6$ **45.** $3 \cdot 3 = 9$ **47.** $3 \cdot 2 \cdot 1 = 6$
49. $5 \cdot 2 \cdot 4 = 40$ **51.** $2^6 = 64$ **53.** $2 \cdot 3 \cdot 4 \cdot 5 = 120$
55. $2 \cdot 3 \cdot 4 \cdot 3 = 72$ **57.** $2 \cdot 3 \cdot 1 \cdot 3 = 18$
59. $2 \cdot 4 \cdot 6 = 48$ **61.** $5! = 120$ **63.** 800 **65.** (a) 6
(b) 5 (c) 4 (d) 3 (e) 2 (f) 1; 720 **67.** (a) 3 (b) 3
(c) 2 (d) 2 (e) 1 (f) 1; 36 **69.** 516,243 **71.** 48

10.3 Exercises *(pages 603–607)*

1. 504 **3.** 95,040 **5.** 330 **7.** 45 **9.** 116,280
11. 43,680 **13.** 126 **15.** 792 **17.** $1.805037696 \times 10^{11}$
19. 225,792,840 **21.** permutation **23.** combination
25. permutation **27.** permutation **29.** $_8P_5 = 6720$
31. $_{12}P_2 = 132$ **33.** $_{25}P_5 = 6,375,600$ **35.** $_6P_3 = 120$
37. (a) $_6C_3 = 20$ (b) $_6C_2 = 15$ **39.** $_{18}C_5 = 8568$
41. (a) $_{13}C_5 = 1287$ (b) $_{26}C_5 = 65,780$
(c) 0 (impossible) **43.** $_9C_3 = 84$
45. $_{26}P_3 \cdot {}_{10}P_3 \cdot {}_{26}P_3 = 175,219,200,000$
47. $2 \cdot {}_{25}P_3 = 27,600$ **49.** $7 \cdot {}_{12}P_8 = 139,708,800$
51. (a) $6! = 720$ (b) $2 \cdot 4! = 48$ (c) $4! = 24$
53. $_{15}C_1 \cdot {}_{14}C_2 \cdot {}_{12}C_3 \cdot {}_9C_4 \cdot {}_5C_5 = 37,837,800$
55. $\frac{_8C_3 \cdot {}_5C_3 \cdot {}_2C_2}{2!} = 280$ **57.** (a) $_{13}C_4 \cdot 39 = 27,885$
(b) $_{12}C_2 \cdot {}_{40}C_3 = 652,080$ (c) $_{26}C_2 \cdot {}_{13}C_2 \cdot 13 = 329,550$
59. $4 \cdot {}_{13}C_5 = 5148$ **61.** (a) $_7P_2 = 42$ (b) $3 \cdot 6 = 18$
(c) $_7P_2 \cdot 5 = 210$ **63.** $_{20}C_3 = 1140$ **65.** $_8P_3 = 336$
67. $_9C_2 \cdot {}_7C_3 \cdot {}_4C_4 \cdot 2 \cdot 3 \cdot 4 = 30,240$
69. (a) $_6C_2 \cdot {}_6C_3 \cdot {}_6C_4 = 4500$
(b) $3! \cdot {}_6C_2 \cdot {}_6C_3 \cdot {}_6C_4 = 27,000$
71. (a) $6! = 720$ (b) 745,896
73. Each equals 220.

10.4 Exercises *(pages 611–612)*

1. 6 **3.** 20 **5.** 56 **7.** 36 **9.** $_7C_1 \cdot {}_3C_3 = 7$
11. $_7C_3 \cdot {}_3C_1 = 105$ **13.** $_8C_3 = 56$ **15.** $_8C_5 = 56$
17. $_9C_4 = 126$ **19.** $1 \cdot {}_8C_3 = 56$ **21.** 1 **23.** 10 **25.** 5
27. 32 **29.** the even-numbered rows
31. (a) All are multiples of the row number.
(b) The same pattern holds. (c) The same pattern
holds. Each entry is a multiple of 11. **33.** . . . 8, 13, 21,
34, . . . ; A number in this sequence is the sum of the two
preceding terms. This is the Fibonacci sequence.
35. row 8 **37.** The sum of the squares of the entries
across the top row equals the entry at the bottom vertex.

Wording may vary in the answers for Exercises 39 and 41.
39. sum $= N$; Any entry in the array equals the sum of
the column of entries from its immediate left upward to
the top of the array. **41.** sum $= N - 1$; Any entry in the
array equals 1 more than the sum of all entries whose
cells make up the largest rectangle entirely to the left and
above that entry.

10.5 Exercises *(pages 617–620)*

1. $2^4 - 1 = 15$ **3.** $2^7 - 1 = 127$ **5.** $2^7 - 1 = 127$
7. 120 **9.** $36 - 6 = 30$ **11.** $6 + 6 - 1 = 11$ **13.** 51
15. 48 **17.** $90 - 9 = 81$ **19.** $29 + 9 - 2 = 36$

21. (a) $_{10}C_3 = 120$ **(b)** $_9C_3 = 84$ **(c)** $120 - 84 = 36$
23. $_7C_3 - _5C_3 = 25$ **25.** $_8P_4 - _5P_4 = 1560$
27. $_{10}P_3 - _7P_3 = 510$ **29.** $2 \cdot 26^2 + 2 \cdot 26^3 = 36{,}504$
31. $_{12}C_4 - _8C_4 = 425$ **33.** $13 + 4 - 1 = 16$
35. $12 + 26 - 6 = 32$ **37.** $9 + 8 - 5 = 12$
39. $11 + 5 = 16$ **41.** $2{,}598{,}960 - _{13}C_5 = 2{,}597{,}673$
43. $2{,}598{,}960 - _{40}C_5 = 1{,}940{,}952$ **45.** 56
47. $_{10}C_0 + _{10}C_1 + _{10}C_2 = 56$ **49.** $2^{10} - 56 = 968$
51. $26^2 \cdot 10^3 - _{26}P_2 \cdot _{10}P_3 = 208{,}000$
53. Answers will vary. **55.** $_4C_3 + _3C_3 + _5C_3 = 15$
57. $_{12}C_3 - _4C_1 \cdot _3C_1 \cdot _5C_1 = 160$ **59.** Answers will vary.
61. Answers will vary.

Chapter 10 Test (pages 623–624)
1. $6 \cdot 7 \cdot 7 = 294$ **2.** $6 \cdot 7 \cdot 3 = 126$ **3.** $6 \cdot 6 \cdot 5 = 180$
4. $6 \cdot 5 \cdot 1 = 30$ end in 0; $5 \cdot 5 \cdot 1 = 25$ end in 5;
$30 + 25 = 55$ **5.** 13
6.

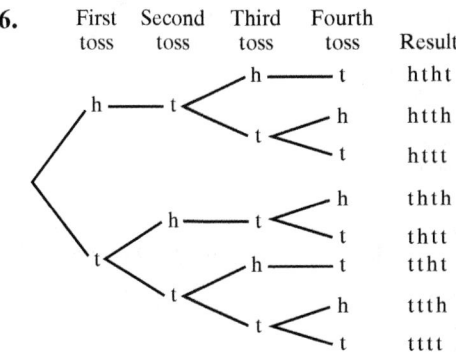

	First toss	Second toss	Third toss	Fourth toss	Result

7. $4! = 24$ **8.** $2 \cdot 3 \cdot 4! = 144$ **9.** 720 **10.** 56
11. 1320 **12.** 56 **13.** $_{26}P_5 = 7{,}893{,}600$
14. $32^5 = 33{,}554{,}432$ **15.** $_7P_2 = 42$ **16.** $5! = 120$
17. $\frac{6!}{2! \cdot 3!} = 60$ **18.** $_{10}C_4 = 210$ **19.** $_{10}C_2 \cdot _8C_2 = 1260$
20. $_{10}C_5 \cdot _5C_5 = 252$ **21.** $\frac{_{10}C_4 \cdot _6C_4}{2!} = 1575$
22. $2^{10} - (_{10}C_0 + _{10}C_1 + _{10}C_2) = 968$ **23.** $2^5 = 32$
24. $2^3 = 8$ **25.** $2 \cdot 2^3 = 16$ **26.** 13 **27.** 2
28. $32 - (1 + 5) = 26$ **29.** $1 \cdot _6C_2 = 15$
30. $1 \cdot 1 \cdot _5C_1 = 5$ **31.** $2 \cdot _5C_2 = 20$ **32.** $1 \cdot _5C_1 = 5$
33. $_5C_3 + _5C_2 \cdot _2C_1 = 30$ **34.** $_{60}C_3 \cdot _{40}C_2 = 26{,}691{,}600$
35. $_9C_4 = 126$ **36.** the counting numbers

CHAPTER 11 PROBABILITY

11.1 Exercises *(pages 634–639)*

1. (a) $\frac{1}{3}$ **(b)** $\frac{1}{3}$ **(c)** $\frac{1}{3}$ **3. (a)** $\frac{1}{2}$ **(b)** $\frac{1}{3}$ **(c)** $\frac{1}{6}$
5. (a) $\{1, 2, 3\}$ **(b)** 2 **(c)** 1 **(d)** 3 **(e)** $\frac{2}{3}$ **(f)** 2 to 1
7. (a) $\{11, 12, 13, 21, 22, 23, 31, 32, 33\}$ **(b)** $\frac{2}{3}$ **(c)** $\frac{1}{3}$
(d) $\frac{1}{3}$ **(e)** $\frac{4}{9}$ **9. (a)** $\frac{1}{50}$ **(b)** $\frac{2}{50} = \frac{1}{25}$ **(c)** $\frac{3}{50}$ **(d)** $\frac{4}{50} = \frac{2}{25}$

9. (e) $\frac{5}{50} = \frac{1}{10}$ **11. (a)** $\frac{1}{36}$ **(b)** $\frac{2}{36} = \frac{1}{18}$ **(c)** $\frac{3}{36} = \frac{1}{12}$
(d) $\frac{4}{36} = \frac{1}{9}$ **(e)** $\frac{5}{36}$ **(f)** $\frac{6}{36} = \frac{1}{6}$ **(g)** $\frac{5}{36}$ **(h)** $\frac{4}{36} = \frac{1}{9}$
(i) $\frac{3}{36} = \frac{1}{12}$ **(j)** $\frac{2}{36} = \frac{1}{18}$ **(k)** $\frac{1}{36}$ **13.** $\frac{36}{2{,}598{,}960} \approx 0.00001385$
15. $\frac{624}{2{,}598{,}960} \approx 0.00024010$ **17.** $\frac{1}{4} \cdot \frac{5108}{2{,}598{,}960} \approx 0.00049135$
19. $\frac{175}{200} = 0.875$ **21.** $\frac{1}{_{26}P_3} \approx 0.000064$ **23. (a)** $\frac{5}{9}$
(b) $\frac{49}{144}$ **(c)** $\frac{5}{48}$ **25.** $\frac{1}{4}$ **27.** $\frac{1}{4}$ **29. (a)** $\frac{3}{4}$ **(b)** $\frac{1}{4}$
31. $\frac{1}{250{,}000} = 0.000004$ **33.** $\frac{1}{4}$ **35.** $\frac{1}{4}$ **37.** $\frac{2}{4} = \frac{1}{2}$
39. $\frac{1}{500} = 0.002$ **41.** 160 **43.** $\frac{2}{4} = \frac{1}{2}$ **45.** 7 to 4
47. 9 to 2 **49.** 4 to 7 **51.** 4 to 1 **53.** 2 to 3
55. 37 to 63 **57.** $\frac{12}{31}$ **59. (a)** 0 **(b)** no **(c)** yes
61. (a) $3 \cdot 1 \cdot 2 \cdot 1 \cdot 1 \cdot 1 = 6$ **(b)** $\frac{6}{720} = \frac{1}{120} \approx 0.0083$
63. (a) $4 \cdot 3! \cdot 3! = 144$ **(b)** $\frac{144}{720} = \frac{1}{5} = 0.2$ **65.** $\frac{1}{9}$
67. $\frac{2}{_7C_2} = \frac{2}{21} \approx 0.095$ **69.** $\frac{_5C_3}{_{12}C_3} = \frac{10}{220} \approx 0.045$
71. $\frac{1}{_5P_3} = \frac{1}{60} \approx 0.017$ **73. (a)** $\frac{8}{9^2} = \frac{8}{81} \approx 0.099$
(b) $\frac{4}{_9C_2} = \frac{1}{9} \approx 0.111$ **75.** 1 **77.** $\frac{5}{31}$ **79.** $\frac{9}{9 \cdot 10} = \frac{1}{10}$ **81.** $\frac{1}{15}$

11.2 Exercises *(pages 645–647)*

1. $\frac{1}{2}$ **3.** $\frac{5}{6}$ **5.** $\frac{2}{3}$ **7. (a)** $\frac{2}{13}$ **(b)** 2 to 11 **9. (a)** $\frac{11}{26}$
(b) 11 to 15 **11. (a)** $\frac{9}{13}$ **(b)** 9 to 4 **13.** $\frac{2}{3}$ **15.** $\frac{7}{36}$
17. $\frac{5}{12}$ **19.** $\frac{2}{3}$ **21.** yes **23.** 0.005365 **25.** 0.971285
27. 0.76 **29.** 0.92 **31.** 0.04

33.

x	$P(x)$
3	0.1
4	0.1
5	0.2
6	0.2
7	0.2
8	0.1
9	0.1

35. Answers will vary.
37. Answers will vary.
39. $n(A') = s - a$
41. $P(A) + P(A') = 1$
43. 180 **45.** 60
47. 1 **49.** $\frac{1}{4}$

11.3 Exercises *(pages 655–659)*

1. $\frac{7}{15}$ **3.** $\frac{2}{5}$ **5.** $\frac{1}{15}$ **7.** 1 **9.** $\frac{1}{7}$ **11.** $\frac{1}{8}$ **13.** $\frac{2}{4} = \frac{1}{2}$
15. $\frac{2}{6} = \frac{1}{3}$ **17.** $\frac{2}{4} = \frac{1}{2}$ **19.** $\frac{1}{2}$ **21.** independent
23. not independent **25.** independent **27.** $\frac{52}{100} = \frac{13}{25}$
29. $\frac{69}{100}$ **31.** $\frac{14}{31}$ **33.** $\frac{4}{7} \cdot \frac{4}{7} = \frac{16}{49}$ **35.** $\frac{2}{7} \cdot \frac{1}{7} = \frac{2}{49}$ **37.** $\frac{4}{7} \cdot \frac{3}{6} = \frac{2}{7}$
39. $\frac{1}{6}$ **41.** 0 **43.** $\frac{12}{51} = \frac{4}{17}$ **45.** $\frac{12}{52} \cdot \frac{11}{51} = \frac{11}{221}$ **47.** $\frac{4}{52} \cdot \frac{11}{51} = \frac{11}{663}$
49. $\frac{26}{52} \cdot \frac{26}{51} = \frac{13}{51}$ **51.** $\frac{1}{3}$ **53.** 1 **55.** $\frac{3}{10}$ (the same)
57. $\frac{1}{2} \cdot \frac{1}{2} \cdot \frac{1}{2} \cdot \frac{1}{2} \cdot \frac{1}{2} \cdot \frac{1}{2} = \frac{1}{64}$ **59.** 0.490 **61.** 0.027

63. 0.95 **65.** 0.23 **67.** $\frac{1}{20}$ **69.** $\frac{1}{10}$ **71.** $2^6 = 64$

73. 0.1479 **75.** 0.400 **77.** 0.080 **79.** $(0.90)^4 = 0.6561$

81. $_4C_2 \cdot (0.10) \cdot (0.20) \cdot (0.70)^2 = 0.0588$ **83.** 0.2704

85. 0.2496 **87.** Answers will vary. **89.** 0.21 **91.** (a) $\frac{3}{4}$

(b) $\frac{1}{2}$ **(c)** $\frac{5}{16}$ **93.** $\frac{1}{5}$ **95.** $\frac{8}{33}$ **97.** (a) Answers will

vary. **(b)** $\frac{25}{36} \approx 0.69$

11.4 Exercises *(pages 663–665)*

1. $\frac{1}{8}$ **3.** $\frac{3}{8}$ **5.** $\frac{3}{4}$ **7.** $\frac{1}{2}$ **9.** Answers will vary. **11.** $\frac{1}{128}$

13. $\frac{21}{128}$ **15.** $\frac{35}{128}$ **17.** $\frac{7}{128}$ **19.** $\frac{125}{216}$ **21.** $\frac{5}{72}$ **23.** 0.041

25. 0.268 **27.** .302 **29.** Answers will vary. **31.** 0.228

33. 0.299 **35.** 0.032 **37.** 0.259 **39.** 0.167 **41.** 0.010

43. $6p^2(1-p)^2$ **45.** 0.883 **47.** 0.073 **49.** $\frac{1}{1024} \approx 0.001$

51. $\frac{45}{1024} \approx 0.044$ **53.** $\frac{210}{1024} = \frac{105}{512} \approx 0.205$ **55.** $\frac{772}{1024} \approx 0.754$

11.5 Exercises *(pages 675–679)*

1. $\frac{5}{2}$ **3.** \$1 **5.** \$0.50 **7.** no $\left(\text{expected net winnings:} -\frac{3}{4}¢\right)$

9. 1.69 **11.** (a) –\$60 (b) \$36,000 (c) \$72,000

13. \$0.46 **15.** \$2700 **17.** 2.7 **19.** a decrease of 50

21. Project B **23.** Project A **25.** \$2200 **27.** \$81,000

29. Do not purchase the insurance (because

\$86,000 > \$81,000). **31.** \$1500; \$3000; \$17,500; \$27,000

33. \$56,000 **35.** 48.7% **37.** $\frac{15}{47} \approx 0.319$ **39.** $\frac{18}{50} = 0.36$;

This is quite close to 0.375, the theoretical value. **41.** no

43. $\frac{6}{50} = 0.12$ **45.** $\frac{48}{199} \approx 0.241$ **47.** $\frac{48}{198} \approx 0.242$

49. Answers will vary. **51.** The walk ends 12 blocks

north of the starting point. **53.** (a) Answers will vary.

(c) The value of p will vary; empirical (d) Answers will

vary. (e) Answers will vary.

Chapter 11 Test *(pages 683–684)*

1. $\frac{_2C_2}{_5C_2} = \frac{1}{10}$ **2.** $\frac{_3C_2}{_5C_2} = \frac{3}{10}$ **3.** $\frac{6}{10} = \frac{3}{5}$ **4.** $\frac{3}{10}$

5. $\frac{7}{7} \cdot \frac{6}{7} \cdot \frac{5}{7} = \frac{30}{49}$ **6.** $\frac{7}{19}$ **7.** $1 - \left(\frac{30}{49} + \frac{1}{49}\right) = \frac{18}{49}$

8. row 1: CC; row 2: cC, cc **9.** $\frac{1}{2}$ **10.** 1 to 3 **11.** 3 to 1

12. 25 to 1 **13.** 11 to 2 **14.** $\frac{3}{10}; \frac{6}{10}; \frac{1}{10}$ **15.** $\frac{9}{10}$

16. $\frac{18}{10} = \frac{9}{5}$ **17.** $\frac{6}{36} = \frac{1}{6}$ **18.** 35 to 1 **19.** 7 to 2 **20.** $\frac{4}{36} = \frac{1}{9}$

21. $(0.78)^3 \approx 0.475$ **22.** $_3C_2 \cdot (0.78)^2 \cdot (0.22) \approx 0.402$

23. $1 - (0.22)^3 \approx 0.989$

24. $(0.78) \cdot (0.22) \cdot (0.78) \approx 0.134$

25. $\frac{25}{102}$ **26.** $\frac{25}{51}$ **27.** $\frac{4}{51}$ **28.** $\frac{3}{26}$ **29.** $\frac{3}{8}$ **30.** $\frac{1}{24} \approx 0.042$

31. $\frac{29}{99} \approx 0.293$ **32.** $\frac{18}{98} \approx 0.184$

CHAPTER 12 STATISTICS

12.1 Exercises *(pages 693–697)*

1. (a)

x	f	$\frac{f}{n}$
0	10	$\frac{10}{30} \approx 33\%$
1	7	$\frac{7}{30} \approx 23\%$
2	6	$\frac{6}{30} = 20\%$
3	4	$\frac{4}{30} \approx 13\%$
4	2	$\frac{2}{30} \approx 7\%$
5	1	$\frac{1}{30} \approx 3\%$

(b)

(c)

3. (a)

Class Limits	Tally	Frequency f	Relative Frequency $\frac{f}{n}$
21–25		1	$\frac{1}{48} \approx 2.1\%$
26–30		2	$\frac{2}{48} \approx 4.2\%$
31–35		5	$\frac{5}{48} \approx 10.4\%$
36–40		12	$\frac{12}{48} = 25.0\%$
41–45		16	$\frac{16}{48} \approx 33.3\%$
46–50		12	$\frac{12}{48} = 25.0\%$

Total: $n = 48$

(b)

(c)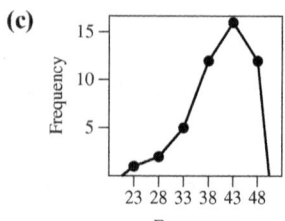

5. (a)

Class Limits	Tally	Frequency f	Relative Frequency $\frac{f}{n}$
70–74	||	2	$\frac{2}{30} \approx 6.7\%$
75–79	|	1	$\frac{1}{30} \approx 3.3\%$
80–84	|||	3	$\frac{3}{30} = 10.0\%$
85–89	||	2	$\frac{2}{30} \approx 6.7\%$
90–94	⦀⦀	5	$\frac{5}{30} \approx 16.7\%$
95–99	⦀⦀ ||	7	$\frac{7}{30} \approx 23.3\%$
100–104	⦀⦀ |	6	$\frac{6}{30} = 20.0\%$
105–109	||||	4	$\frac{4}{30} \approx 13.3\%$

Total: $n = 30$

(b)   **(c)**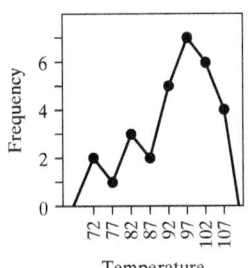

7.

```
0 | 7 9 8
1 | 1 1 2 8 9 4 3 1 0 5 0 5 5
2 | 7 0 9 6 6 2 2 5 2 3 4 4
3 | 8 1
```

9.

```
0 | 8 5 4 9 6 9 4 8
1 | 6 0 1 8 8 2 4 0 2 8 6 3
2 | 6 1 2 5 1 3
3 | 0 4 6
4 | 4
```

11. 2001   **13.** 2005, 2006, 2007, 2010, and 2012

15.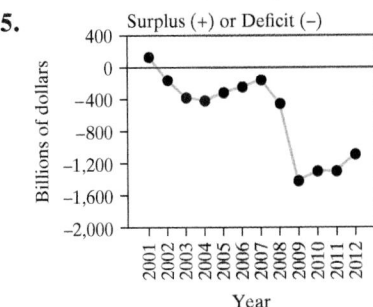

17. 3.8% in 2008   **19.** Answers will vary.

21. school; 120°

23.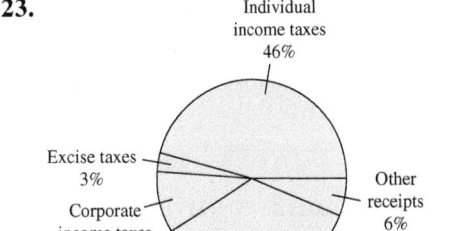

25. about 82 years   **27. (a)** about 7 years
(b) Answers will vary.   **29.** Answers will vary.
31. Answers will vary.   **33.** Answers will vary.

35. (a)

Letter	Probability
A	0.208
E	0.338
I	0.169
O	0.208
U	0.078

(b) [bar graph: Probability vs. Vowel — A, E, I, O, U]

37. Answers will vary.   **39. (a)** 0.225   **(b)** 0.150
(c) 0.675   **(d)** 0.075

41. (a)

Sport	Probability
Sailing	0.175
Archery	0.100
Snowboarding	0.250
Bicycling	0.200
Rock climbing	0.200
Rafting	0.075

(b) empirical   **(c)** Answers will vary.

12.2 Exercises *(pages 709–712)*

1. (a) 12.4   **(b)** 12   **(c)** none   **3. (a)** 216.2   **(b)** 221
(c) 196   **5. (a)** 5.2   **(b)** 5.35   **(c)** 4.5 and 6.2
7. (a) 129.9   **(b)** 128   **(c)** 125 and 128   **9.** more than
14.525   **11. (a)** 10.7 million   **(b)** 10.65 million
(c) 10.6 million   **13. (a)** 73.9   **(b)** 17.5   **(c)** 0
15. mean $= 47.4$; median and mode remain the same
17. $297.0 billion   **19.** 5.27 seconds   **21.** 2.42 seconds
23. the mean   **25.** mean $= 77$; median $= 80$; mode $= 79$
27. 92   **29. (a)** 589.6   **(b)** 586   **(c)** 579   **31.** 3.19
33. (a) $2,532.4 billion   **(b)** $2,450.2 billion
35. about 511,200   **37. (a)** 8.25   **(b)** 8   **39. (a)** 66.25
(b) 64.5   **41.** 6.5   **43. (a)** 21.3   **(b)** 21.5   **(c)** 15
45. (a) 74.8   **(b)** 77.5   **(c)** 78   **47.** Answers will vary.

49. (a) mean $= 3$; median $= 3$; mode $= 4$
(b) mode **(c)** Answers will vary. **51. (a)** 4 **(b)** 4.25
53. (a) 6 **(b)** 9.33 **55.** three choices: 1, 6, 16 **57.** no
59. Answers will vary.

12.3 Exercises *(pages 719–721)*
1. the sample standard deviation **3. (a)** 14 **(b)** 4.74
5. (a) 26 **(b)** 8.38 **7. (a)** 1.14 **(b)** 0.37 **9. (a)** 11
(b) 3.89 **11.** $\frac{3}{4}$ **13.** $\frac{21}{25}$ **15.** $\frac{3}{4}$ **17.** $\frac{15}{16}$ **19.** $\frac{1}{4}$ **21.** $\frac{4}{49}$
23. \$154.58 **25.** nine **27.** There are at least nine.
29. (a) $s_A = 2.35$; $s_B = 2.58$ **(b)** $V_A = 46.9\%$; $V_B = 36.9\%$
(c) sample B ($s_B = 2.58 > 2.35$) **(d)** sample A
($V_A = 46.9\% > 36.9\%$) **31.** 18.71; 4.35
33. 8.71; 4.35 **35.** 56.14; 13.04
37. (a) $\bar{x}_A = 68.8$; $\bar{x}_B = 66.6$ **(b)** $s_A = 4.21$; $s_B = 5.27$
(c) brand A ($\bar{x}_A > \bar{x}_B$) **(d)** brand A ($s_A < s_B$)
39. Brand A ($s_B = 3539 > 2116$) **41.** Answers will
vary. **43.** -3.0 **45.** 4.2 **47.** 7.55 and 23.45 **49.** no
51. Answers will vary.

12.4 Exercises *(pages 725–728)*
1. 58 **3.** 59 **5.** Janet (since $z = 0.48 > 0.19$)
7. Yvette (since $z = -1.44 > -1.78$) **9.** -0.7 **11.** 1.4
13. Russia **15.** United States **17.** India in consumption
(India's consumption z-score was -0.6, Canada's production z-score was -0.7, and $-0.6 > -0.7$.)
19. (a) The median is 28.2 quadrillion Btu.
(b) The range is $109.6 - 11.7 = 97.9$ quadrillion Btu.
(c) The middle half of the items extend from 13.5 to 97.5
quadrillion Btu. **21.** Answers will vary. **23.** Answers
will vary. **25.** Answers will vary. **27.** the overall distribution **29.** Both are skewed to the right, consumption
nearly twice as much as production. **31. (a)** no
(b) Answers will vary. **33.** no; Answers will vary.
35. yes; Answers will vary. **37.** $Q_1 = 96.7$, $Q_2 = 104.8$,
$Q_3 = 109.0$ **39.** $P_{95} = 119.2$ **41.** 102.9
43.

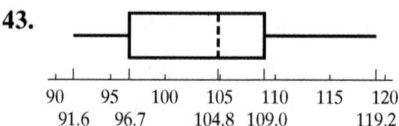

45. No; $69.4 + 20.4 = 89.8$, still less than 91.6 **47.** 6
49. (a) 2.5, 4.5, 6.5 **(b)** none **51. (a)** 3, 5.5, 8
(b) two **53. (a)** none **(b)** one **(c)** two **(d)** three

12.5 Exercises *(pages 735–737)*
1. discrete **3.** continuous **5.** discrete **7.** 50 **9.** 95
11. 50% **13.** 95% **15.** 44.5% **17.** 45.4% **19.** 5.3%
21. 97.8% **23.** 0.84 **25.** 0.77 **27.** 500 **29.** 61
31. 1000 **33.** 11.5% **35.** 54.0% **37.** 0.212 **39.** 0.092

41. 0.994, or 99.4% **43.** 166 units **45.** 0.888
47. about 2 eggs **49.** 24.2% **51.** Answers will vary.
53. 76 **55.** 65 **57.** 90.4 **59.** 40.3
61. (a) at least 36% **(b)** 78.8%

Chapter 12 Test *(pages 744–746)*
1. (a) 59.6 million **(b)** 116.8 million **(c)** 48.2 million
(d) 80.9% **2. (a)** those who copied less than 10%
(b) those with copy rates from 10% to 30% or greater
than 50% **(c)** those with a copy rate from 30% to 50%
(d) Answers will vary. **3. (a)** 281 feet **(b)** 595 inches
(c) 1223 **4. (a)** 762 **(b)** 8th **(c)** 22 inches **(d)** 17 feet
5.

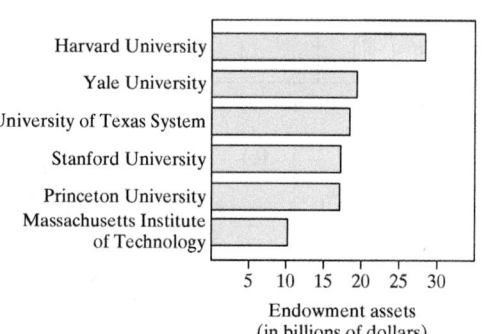

Top Six U.S. College Endowment Funds

6. 17.2% **7.** \$17.65 billion
8.

Class Limits	Frequency f	Relative Frequency $\frac{f}{n}$
6–10	3	$\frac{3}{22} \approx 0.14$
11–15	6	$\frac{6}{22} \approx 0.27$
16–20	7	$\frac{7}{22} \approx 0.32$
21–25	4	$\frac{4}{22} \approx 0.18$
26–30	2	$\frac{2}{22} \approx 0.09$

9. (a)

(b)

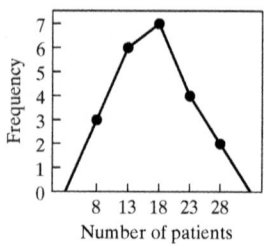

10. 8 **11.** 12.4 **12.** 12 **13.** 12 **14.** 10
15.

```
3 | 3 8
4 | 3 5 8 9
5 | 0 2 5
6 | 1 1 4 5 6 7 7 8
7 | 0 1 2 3 7 7 8 9 9
8 | 0 4 4
9 | 1
```

Answers to Selected Exercises

16. 35   **17.** 33   **18.** 37   **19.** 31   **20.** 49

21.

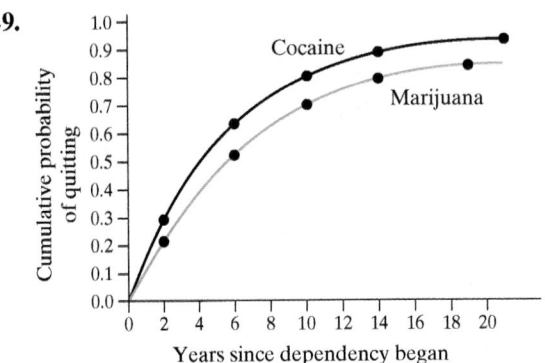

22. (a) about 95%   **(b)** about 0.3%   **(c)** about 16%
(d) about 13.5%   **23.** 0.249   **24.** 0.530
25. East   **26.** Central   **27.** 82.4
28. Red Sox (since $z = 1.20 > 0.95$)

29.

(a) about 4 years   **(b)** about 6 years

30. Answers will vary.

CHAPTER 13 PERSONAL FINANCIAL MANAGEMENT

13.1 Exercises (pages 758–761)

1. $48   **3.** $48.30   **5.** $361.13   **7. (a)** $784   **(b)** $788.31
9. (a) $2725   **(b)** $2731.82   **11.** $125   **13.** $6879.17
15. $168.26   **17.** $817.17   **19.** $17,724.34; $10,224.34
21. (a) $2339.72   **(b)** $2343.32   **(c)** $2345.16
23. (a) $18,545.42   **(b)** $18,546.80   **(c)** $18,547.49
25. (a) $62.53   **(b)** $62.66   **(c)** $62.74   **(d)** $62.79
(e) $62.79   **27.** Answers will vary.   **29.** $1461.04
31. $747.26   **33.** $3846.60   **35.** $168,910.81
37. $167,364.81   **39.** 2.000%   **41.** 2.015%
43. 2.020%   **45.** 2.020%   **47.** $112,041.31
49. 17 years, 152 days   **51.** $r = n\left[(Y + 1)^{1/n} - 1\right]$
53. (a) 1.804%   **(b)** Bank A; $2.63   **(c)** no difference;
$90.81   **55.** 35 years   **57.** 8 years   **59.** 10.0%   **61.** 3.2%
63. $7.20; $8.80; $11.60; $31.60   **65.** $34,400; $42,000;
$55,600; $151,000   **67.** $237   **69.** $1632
71. $81,102,828.75

13.2 Exercises (pages 764–766)

1. $2795   **3.** $3130.40   **5.** $4130.40   **7.** $2640
9. $398.75   **11.** $607.50; $141.88   **13.** $41.63; $43.98
15. $36.38; $35.71   **17.** $229.17   **19.** $292.95
21. $12,628   **23.** 5 years   **25.** $3.50   **27.** $5.80

29. $15.30   **31. (a)** $607.33   **(b)** $7.90   **(c)** $646.87
33. (a) $473.96   **(b)** $6.16   **(c)** $505.54   **35.** $9.27
37. (a) $38.18   **(b)** $38.69   **(c)** $39.20   **39.** 16.0%
41. $32.00   **43.–47.** Answers will vary.   **49. (a)** $127.44
(b) $139.08

13.3 Exercises (pages 771–773)

1. 7.0%   **3.** 8.5%   **5.** $136.46   **7.** $90.63   **9.** 6.5%
11. 9.5%   **13. (a)** $8.93   **(b)** $511.60   **(c)** $6075.70
15. (a) $1.90   **(b)** $66.65   **(c)** $4103.95   **17. (a)** $206
(b) 9.5%   **19. (a)** $138   **(b)** 8.5%   **21. (a)** $41.29
(b) $39.70   **23. (a)** $420.68   **(b)** $368.47
25. (a) $1.80   **(b)** $14.99   **(c)** $1045.01
27. finance company APR: 12.0%; credit union APR:
11.5%; choose credit union   **29.** $32.27   **31.** 13
33. 13.5%   **35.** 8   **37.** 15   **39.–41.** Answers will vary.
43. $\frac{5}{39}$ **45.** Answers will vary.

13.4 Exercises (pages 786–790)

1. $836.44   **3.** $845.22   **5.** $2150.37   **7.** $794.26
9. (a) $513.38   **(b)** $487.50   **(c)** $25.88   **(d)** $58,474.12
11. (a) $1247.43   **(b)** $775.67   **(c)** $471.76
(d) $142,728.24   **(e)** $1247.43   **(f)** $773.11   **(g)** $474.32
(h) $142,253.92   **13. (a)** $1390.93   **(b)** $776.61
(c) $614.32   **(d)** $113,035.68   **(e)** $1390.93
(f) $772.41   **(g)** $618.52   **(h)** $112,417.16   **15.** $480.31
17. $995.95   **19.** 360   **21.** $247,532.80   **23.** $1180.66;
$425,037.60; $185,037.60   **25.** $1686.41; $303,553.80;
$63,553.80   **27.** Answers will vary.   **29. (a)** $572.90
(b) $1280.71   **31. (a)** $117,886.76   **(b)** $119,609.63
33. (a) payment 153   **(b)** payment 295   **35.** $25,465.20
37. $91,030.80   **39. (a)** $674.79   **(b)** $746.36
(c) an increase of $71.57   **41. (a)** $229.17   **(b)** $582.89
43. $107.66   **45.** $140,000   **47.** $4640   **49.** $302
51. (a) $1634   **(b)** $1754   **(c)** $917   **(d)** $997   **(e)** $1555
53. (a) $2271   **(b)** $2407   **(c)** $1083   **(d)** $1174
(e) $2055   **55. (a)** $8370   **(b)** $39,199   **(c)** $23,387
57.–63. Answers will vary.

13.5 Exercises (pages 802–805)

1. $89.99   **3.** 0.49% higher   **5.** $139.69   **7.** 13.93% lower
9. YUM   **11.** BAC   **13.** $30,924.00   **15.** $21,496.00
17. $1201.79   **19.** $5257.04   **21.** $179,109.99
23. $179,722.99   **25.** $23,306.53   **27.** $61,800.68
29. $188,083.39   **31.** $47,000.41   **33.** $1854.25 net paid out
35. (a) $800   **(b)** $80   **(c)** $960   **(d)** $1040   **(e)** 130%
37. (a) $1250   **(b)** $108   **(c)** −$235   **(d)** −$127
(e) −10.16%   **39.** $275.00   **41.** $177.75
43. (a) $10.49   **(b)** 334   **45. (a)** $8.27   **(b)** 3080

47. (a) $8.39 **(b)** $100.68 **(c)** 15.6% **49. (a)** $57.45
(b) $689.40 **(c)** 27.6% **51. (a)** $1203.75 **(b)** $18.06
(c) 19.56% **53. (a)** $4179 **(b)** $76.48 **(c)** 24.31%
55. $129,258 **57.** $993,383 **59. (a)** $56,473.02
(b) $49,712.70 **61. (a)** $12,851.28 **(b)** $11,651.81
63. (a) $8105.66 **(b)** $12,894.98
65. (a) $R = \dfrac{rV}{(1-t)[(1+r)^n - 1]}$ **(b)** $R = \dfrac{rV}{(1 + r(1-t))^n - 1}$
67. (a) $r = n\left[\left(\dfrac{A}{P}\right)^{1/m} - 1\right]$ **(b)** 5.4%

Aggressive Growth	Growth	Growth & Income	Income	Cash
69. $1400	$8600	$6200	$2800	$1000
71. $8000	$112,000	$144,000	$116,000	$20,000

73. 3.75% **75.** 5.2% **77.–83.** Answers will vary.

Chapter 13 Test *(page 814)*
1. $1200 **2.** $563.25 **3.** 2.02% **4.** 18 years
5. $67,297.13 **6.** $10.88 **7.** $630 **8.** $184.17
9. $6.5% **10. (a)** $75.97 **(b)** $2318.24 **11.** 7.0%
12. Answers will vary. **13.** $833.75 **14.** $1207.05
15. $3488 **16.** Answers will vary. **17.** 6.1%
18. 252,300 **19.** $10.00 **20.** 0.078%; no; The
percentage return was not for a 1-year period.
21. $106,728.55 **22.** Answers will vary.

CHAPTER 14 GRAPH THEORY

14.1 Exercises *(pages 829–834)*
1. 7 vertices, 7 edges **3.** 10 vertices, 9 edges
5. 6 vertices, 9 edges **7.** Two have degree 3. Three have
degree 2. Two have degree 1. Sum of degrees is 14. This is
twice the number of edges. **9.** Six have degree 1. Four
have degree 3. Sum of degrees is 18. This is twice the number of edges. **11.** not isomorphic
13. isomorphic; Corresponding edges should be the same
color. AB should match AB, etc.

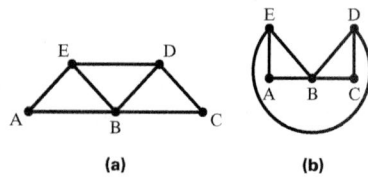

(a)   (b)

15. not isomorphic **17.** connected, 1 component
19. disconnected, 3 components **21.** disconnected,
2 components **23.** 10 **25.** 4 **27. (a)** yes **(b)** No,
because there is no edge from A to D. **(c)** No, because
there is no edge from A to E. **(d)** yes **(e)** yes **(f)** yes

29. (a) No, because it does not return to the starting vertex.
(b) yes **(c)** No, because there is no edge from C to F.
(d) No, because it does not return to starting vertex.
(e) No, because the edge from F to D is used more than
once. **31. (a)** No, because there is no edge from B to C.
(b) No, because the edge from I to G is used more than
once. **(c)** No, because there is no edge from E to I.
(d) yes **(e)** yes **(f)** No, because the edge from A to D
is used more than once. **33.** It is a walk and a path, not a
circuit. **35.** It is a walk, not a path, not a circuit.
37. It is a walk and a path, not a circuit.
39. No. For example, there is no edge from A to C.
41. No. For example, there is no edge from A to F.
43. yes

45. 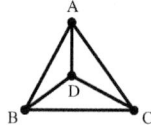   7 games **47.** 36 handshakes

49. 10 telephone conversations
51. A → B → D → A corresponds to
tracing around the edges of a single
face. (The circuit is a triangle.)
53. Answers will vary. **55.** Answers will vary.

57.   **59.**

61.

63. (a) **(b)** **(c)**

(d)   **(e)** A cycle with an odd number of vertices
has chromatic number 3. A cycle
with an even number of vertices has
chromatic number 2.

65. **67.**

69. 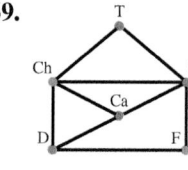   Three times: Choir and Forensics,
Service Club and Dance Club, and
Theater and Caribbean Club.
(There are other possible
groupings.)

71. 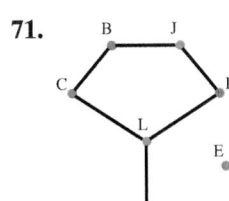 Three gatherings: Brad and Phil and Mary, Joe and Lindsay, and Caitlin and Eva. (There are other possible groupings.)

73.   **75.**

77.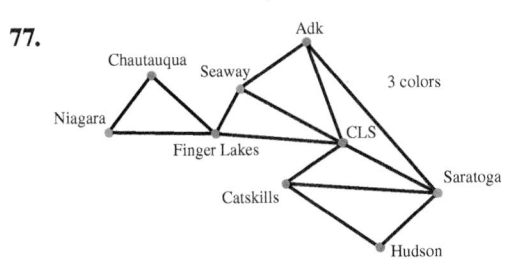

In Exercise 79, there are many different ways to draw the map.

79.

81. By the four-color theorem, this is not possible.

83. 2   **85.** 2   **87.** 3   **89.** 2   **91.** 1

93.

95.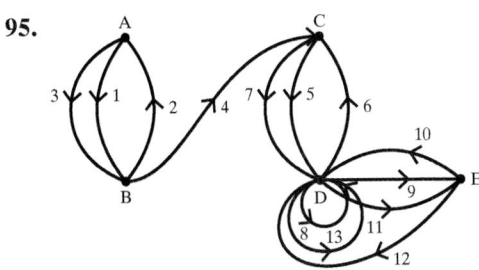

14.2 Exercises *(pages 843–847)*

1. **(a)** No, it is not a path.   **(b)** yes   **(c)** No, it is not a walk.   **(d)** No, it is not a circuit.   **3.** **(a)** No, some edges are not used (e.g., B → F).   **(b)** yes   **(c)** No, it is not a path.   **(d)** yes   **5.** Yes, all vertices have even degree.

7. No, some vertices (e.g., G) have odd degree.

9. yes   **11.** It has an Euler circuit. All vertices have even degree. No circuit visits each vertex exactly once.

13. It has an Euler circuit. All vertices have even degree. A → B → H → C → G → D → F → E → A visits each vertex exactly once.

15. No, some vertices have odd degree.   **17.** Yes, all vertices have even degree.   **19.** none   **21.** FG

23. B → E or B → D   **25.** B → C or B → H

27. A → C → B → F → E → D → C → F → D → A

29. The graph has an Euler circuit.
A → G → H → J → I → L → J → K → I →
H → F → G → E → F → D → E → C → D →
B → C → A → E → B → A

31. The graph does not have an Euler circuit. Some vertices (e.g., C) have odd degree.   **33.** There is such a route: A → D → B → C → A → H → D → E → B →
H → G → E → F → H → J → L → C → M → A → K →
M → L → K → J → A   **35.** It is not possible. Some vertices (e.g., room at upper left) have odd degree.

37. No. There are more than two vertices with odd degree.   **39.** yes; B and G   **41.** It is possible. Exactly two of the rooms have odd numbers of doors.   **43.** It is not possible. All rooms have even numbers of doors.

45. yes; Manhattan and Randall's Island.

There are other correct answers in Exercise 47.

47. A → B → C → D → E → C → F → B → E → F → A; There are 10 edges in any such circuit.

49. In the graph shown, not all vertices have even degree. For example, the vertex marked X is of degree 5. So this graph still does not have an Euler circuit.

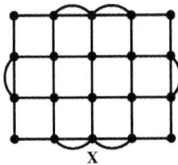

51. (There are other ways of inserting the additional edges.)

8 edges added

14.3 Exercises *(pages 855–859)*

1. **(a)** No, because it visits E twice.   **(b)** yes
(c) No, because it does not visit C.   **(d)** No, because it does not visit A.   **3.** **(a)** None, because there is no edge from B to C.   **(b)** all three   **(c)** none; Edge AD is used twice.   **5.** A → B → D → E → F → C → A

7. G→H→J→I→G **9.** X→T→U→W→V→X
11. Hamilton circuit: A→B→C→D→A. The graph has no Euler circuit, because at least one of the vertices has odd degree. (In fact, all have odd degree.)

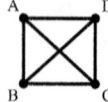

13. A→B→C→D→E→F→A is both a Hamilton and an Euler circuit.

15. Hamilton circuit **17.** Euler circuit **19.** Hamilton circuit **21.** 24 **23.** 362,880 **25.** 9! **27.** 17!

29. P→Q→R→S→P P→Q→S→R→P
P→R→Q→S→P P→R→S→Q→P
P→S→Q→R→P P→S→R→Q→P

31. E→H→I→F→G→E E→H→I→G→F→E

33. E→F→G→H→I→E E→F→G→I→H→E
E→F→H→G→I→E E→F→H→I→G→E
E→F→I→G→H→E E→F→I→H→G→E

35. E→G→F→H→I→E E→G→F→I→H→E
E→G→H→F→I→E E→G→H→I→F→E
E→G→I→F→H→E E→G→I→H→F→E

37. A→B→C→D→E→A
A→B→C→E→D→A
A→B→D→C→E→A
A→B→D→E→C→A
A→B→E→C→D→A
A→B→E→D→C→A
A→C→B→D→E→A
A→C→B→E→D→A
A→C→D→B→E→A
A→C→D→E→B→A
A→C→E→B→D→A
A→C→E→D→B→A
A→D→B→C→E→A
A→D→B→E→C→A
A→D→C→B→E→A
A→D→C→E→B→A
A→D→E→B→C→A
A→D→E→C→B→A
A→E→B→C→D→A
A→E→B→D→C→A
A→E→C→B→D→A
A→E→C→D→B→A
A→E→D→B→C→A
A→E→D→C→B→A

39. Minimum Hamilton circuit is P→Q→R→S→P; Weight is 2200. **41.** Minimum Hamilton circuit is C→D→E→F→G→C; Weight is 64.
43. (a) A→C→E→D→B→A; Total weight is 20.
(b) C→A→B→D→E→C; Total weight is 20.
(c) D→C→A→B→E→D; Total weight is 23.
(d) E→C→A→B→D→E; Total weight is 20.
45. (a) A→C→D→E→B→A; Total weight is 87.
B→C→A→E→D→B; Total weight is 95.
C→A→E→D→B→C; Total weight is 95.
D→C→A→E→B→D; Total weight is 131.
E→C→A→D→B→E; Total weight is 137.
(b) A→C→D→E→B→A with total weight 87
(c) For example, A→B→C→D→E→A has total weight 52.
47. A→B→C→D→E→F→A
A→B→C→F→E→D→A
A→B→E→D→C→F→A
A→B→E→F→C→D→A
A→D→E→F→C→B→A
A→D→E→B→C→F→A
A→D→C→B→E→F→A
A→D→C→F→E→B→A
A→F→E→B→C→D→A
A→F→E→D→C→B→A
A→F→C→D→E→B→A
A→F→C→B→E→D→A

49. A→B→C→D→E→F→A
A→B→C→E→D→F→A
A→B→C→E→F→D→A
A→B→C→F→E→D→A
A→D→E→F→C→B→A
A→D→F→E→C→B→A
A→F→D→E→C→B→A
A→F→E→D→C→B→A

51. 252 miles

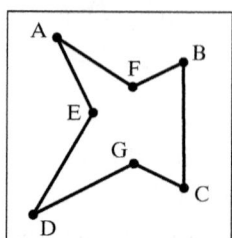

53. A→F→G→R→S→T→U→Q→P→N→M→L→K→J→I→H→B→C→D→E→A

55. (a) graphs (2) and (4) **(b)** graphs (2) and (4)
(c) No. Graph (1) provides a counterexample.
(d) No. If $n < 3$, the graph will have no circuits at all.
(e) The degree of each vertex in a complete graph with n vertices is $(n - 1)$. If $n \geq 3$, then $(n - 1) > \frac{n}{2}$. So we can conclude from Dirac's theorem that the graph has a Hamilton circuit.

14.4 Exercises *(pages 867–871)*
1. tree **3.** No, because it is not connected. **5.** tree
7. No, because it has a circuit. **9.** It is not possible, because the graph has a circuit. **11.** tree
13. not necessarily a tree **15.** true
17. false

19.

21.

23.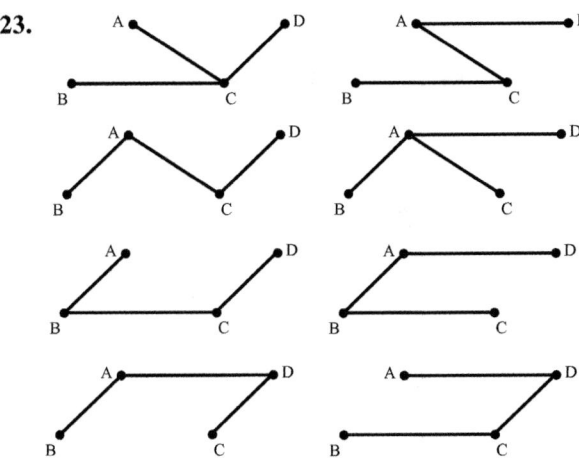

25. 20 **27.** If a connected graph has circuits, none of which have common edges, then the number of spanning trees for the graph is the product of the numbers of edges in all the circuits.

29. Total weight is 51.

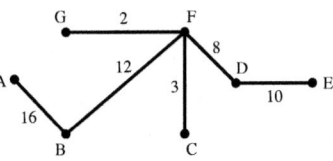

31. Total weight is 66.

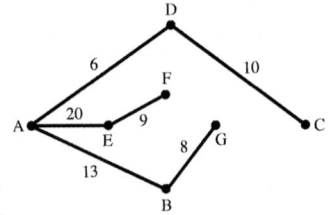

33. Total length to be covered is 140 ft.

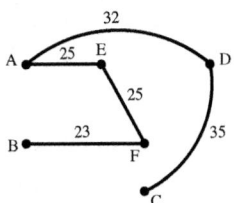

35. 33 **37.** 62 **39.** Different spanning trees must have the same number of edges. The number of vertices in the tree is the number of vertices in the original graph, and the number of edges has to be one less than this.
41. (a) 9 **(b)** 18 **(c)** 0 **(d)** 2
(e)

43. 22 cables **45.** This is possible. The graph must be a tree because it has one fewer edge(s) than vertices.
47. This is possible. The graph cannot be a tree, because it would have at least as many edges as vertices.
49. 3: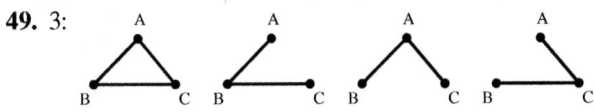
51. 125
53. 3 nonisomorphic trees:

55. 11 nonisomorphic trees:

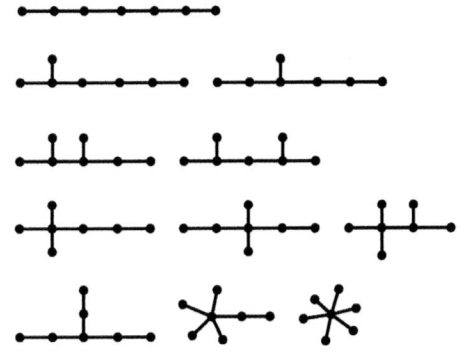

Chapter 14 Test *(pages 876–878)*

1. 7 **2.** 20 **3.** 10 **4.** (a) No, because edge AB is used twice. **(b)** yes **(c)** No, because there is no edge from C to D. **5.** (a) yes **(b)** No, because (for example) there is no edge from B to C. **(c)** yes

6. For example: **7.** 13 edges

8. The graphs are isomorphic. Corresponding edges should be the same color. AB should match AB, etc.

9. 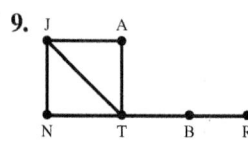 The graph is connected. Tina knows the greatest number of other guests.

10. 28 games **11.** Yes, because there is an edge from each vertex to each of the remaining 6 vertices.

12. **13.**

Chromatic number: 3

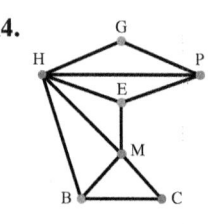

Chromatic number: 5

14. The chromatic number is 3, so three separate exam times are needed. Exams could be at the same times as follows: Geography, Biology, and English; History and Chemistry; Mathematics and Psychology.

15. (a) No, because it does not use all the edges. **(b)** No, because it is not a circuit (for example, there is no edge from B to C). **(c)** yes **16.** No, because some vertices have odd degree. **17.** Yes, because all vertices have even degree. **18.** No, because two of the rooms have odd numbers of doors.

19. $F \to B \to E \to D \to B \to C \to D \to K \to B \to A \to$ $H \to G \to F \to A \to G \to J \to F$

20. (a) No, because it does not visit all vertices. **(b)** No, because it is not a circuit (for example, there is no edge from B to C). **(c)** No, because it visits some vertices twice before returning to the starting vertex.

21. $F \to G \to H \to I \to E \to F$ $F \to G \to H \to E \to I \to F$
   $F \to G \to I \to H \to E \to F$ $F \to G \to I \to E \to H \to F$
   $F \to G \to E \to H \to I \to F$ $F \to G \to E \to I \to H \to F$
There are 6 such Hamilton circuits.

22. $P \to Q \to S \to R \to P$; Total weight is 27.

23. $A \to E \to D \to C \to F \to B \to A$; Total weight is 11.85. **24.** 24! **25.** Hamilton circuit

26. Any three of these:

27. false **28.** true **29.** true

30. There are 4 spanning trees.

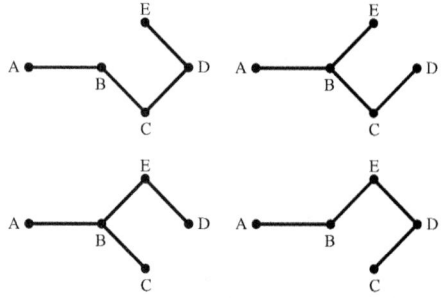

31. Weight is 24. **32.** 49

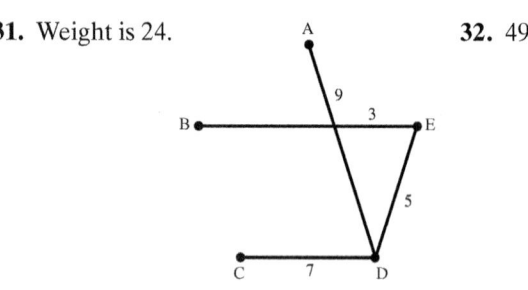

CREDITS

Text Credits

CHAPTER 1: **25–30** Exercises 1–47, 49, 53, 77, 80, 82: From the monthly calendar of *Mathematics Teacher*. Copyright © by National Council of Teachers of Mathematics. Used by permission of National Council of Teachers of Mathematics. **34** Margin note: Excerpt from *Innumeracy: Mathematical Illiteracy and Its Consequences* by John Allen Paulos. Published by Macmillan & Company, © 1988.

CHAPTER 3: **107** Exercise 83: Problem from *The Lady or the Tiger and Other Logic Puzzles* by Raymond M. Smullyan. Copyright © 2009 by Dover Publications. Used by permission of Dover Publications. **136** Exercise 6: Quote by Paul Erdos; Exercise 9: Quote by Winston Churchill; Exercise 10: Quote by George Bernard Shaw. **137** Exercise 39: Excerpt from DirecTV commercial. Used by permission of DirecTV, LLC.

CHAPTER 4: **154** Margin note: Excerpt from *Ethnomathematics: A Multicultural View of Mathematical Ideas* by Marcia Ascher. Published by Brooks/Cole Publishing Company. **166** Margin note: "Napier's Abacus." Used by permission of Google Inc. and Bonaventura Novellino. **188** Tom Wurt/Stock Boston **206** Courtesy, Professor Noether **210** St. Andrew's University

CHAPTER 6: **257** Chapter opener text: Excerpt from "Old Math or Common Core Math: Which Troubles You More?" by Jarvis DeBerry, as published in *The Times-Picayune* and NOLA .com. Used by permission of Jarvis DeBerry. **298** Example 2: Excerpt from *Mathematics for the Trades: A Guided Approach* by Robert A. Carman, Emeritus, and Hal M. Saunders. Published by Pearson Education, © 2014. **305** Exercise 63: "Move One Matchstick to Make the Equation Approximately True" from *The Joy of Pi*. Used by permission of 63p.com. **307** Margin note: Excerpt from "Computation, Calculators, and Common Sense" from National Council of Teachers of Mathematics. Copyright © 2005 by National Council of Teachers of Mathematics. Used by permission of National Council of Teachers of Mathematics. **309** Margin note: Excerpt from *Historical Topics for the Mathematics Classroom, Thirty-First Yearbook* by National Council of Teachers of Mathematics. Published by National Council of Teachers of Mathematics, © 1969.

CHAPTER 7: **338** Exercises 41–50: Formulas from *Math Skills for Allied Health Careers* by Daniel L. Timmons and Catherine W. Johnson, published by Pearson Education, © 2008, and *Mathematics for the Trades: A Guided Approach* by Robert A. Carman, Emeritus, and Hal M. Saunders, published by Pearson Education, © 2014.

CHAPTER 8: **437** Exercise 44: Problem from "A Sourcebook of Applications of School Mathematics" by National Council of Teachers of Mathematics and Mathematical Association of America. Copyright © 1980 by National Council of Teachers of Mathematics. Used by permission of National Council of Teachers of Mathematics.

CHAPTER 9: **503** Exercises 47–48: From the monthly calendar of *Mathematics Teacher* by John Grant McLoughlin. Copyright © 2002 by National Council of Teachers of Mathematics. Used by permission of National Council of Teachers of Mathematics. **514** Exercises 83–90: From the monthly calendar of *Mathematics Teacher* by John Grant McLoughlin. Copyright © 2002 by National Council of Teachers of Mathematics. Used by permission of National Council of Teachers of Mathematics. **521** Margin note: Malaysia Airlines, Flight 370 map from Google Inc. Used by permission of Google Inc. **523** Exercise 29 (map): Search area map from Google Inc. Used by permission of Google Inc. **527** Screenshot (Dice App): From Teazel.com. Used with permission of Teazel.com and Google Inc. **541–542** For Further Thought: Excerpt from the article "What is a Tesselation?" from The Math Forum @ Drexel. Used by permission of The Math Forum @ Drexel. **547** Margin note: Excerpt from *LP Songs* by Tom Lehrer. Used by permission of Tom Lehrer. **554** "Does Chaos Rule the Cosmos?" from *Discover Magazine*. Published by Kalmbach Publishing Company, © 1992. **557** Screenshot (Fractoid): Android Apps of Dave Byrne. Used by permission of Dave Byrne and Google Inc. **558–559** Exercises 1–25: From *Student Math Notes*. Used by permission of National Council of Teachers of Mathematics.

CHAPTER 10: **591** Exercise 39: From the monthly calendar of *Mathematics Teacher* by John Grant McLoughlin. Copyright © 2002 by National Council of Teachers of Mathematics. Used by permission of National Council of Teachers of Mathematics. **593** Exercises 63 and 69: From the monthly calendar of *Mathematics Teacher* by John Grant McLoughlin. Copyright © 2002 by National Council of Teachers of Mathematics. Used by permission of National Council of Teachers of Mathematics. **594** Exercises 70–72: From the monthly calendar of *Mathematics Teacher* by John Grant McLoughlin. Copyright © 2002 by National Council of Teachers of Mathematics. Used by permission of National Council of Teachers of Mathematics. **604** Exercise 43: From the monthly calendar of *Mathematics Teacher* by John Grant McLoughlin. Copyright © 2002 by National Council of Teachers of Mathematics. Used by permission of National Council of Teachers of Mathematics. **607** Exercise 72: From the monthly calendar of *Mathematics Teacher* by John Grant McLoughlin. Copyright © 2002 by National Council of Teachers of Mathematics. Used by permission of National Council of Teachers of Mathematics. **611** Exercise 30: From the monthly calendar of *Mathematics Teacher* by John Grant McLoughlin. Copyright © 2002 by National Council of Teachers of Mathematics. Used by permission of National Council of Teachers of Mathematics. **618** Exercise 29: From the monthly calendar of *Mathematics Teacher* by John Grant McLoughlin. Copyright © 2002 by National Council of Teachers of Mathematics. Used by permission of National Council of Teachers of Mathematics. **619** Exercises 32, 45, and 46: From the monthly calendar of *Mathematics Teacher* by John Grant McLoughlin. Copyright © 2002 by National Council of Teachers of Mathematics. Used by permission of National Council of Teachers of Mathematics. **624** Exercise 35: From the monthly calendar of *Mathematics Teacher* by John Grant McLoughlin. Copyright © 2002 by National Council of Teachers of Mathematics. Used by permission of National Council of Teachers of Mathematics.

INDEX OF APPLICATIONS

Dimensions of a lot, 523
Dimensions of a rectangular region,
    395, 464, 468, 486, 513, 515–516
Dimensions of a square, 468
Dimensions of a triangle, 468
Drawing a circle, 413
Equilateral triangles, 25
Frustum of a pyramid, 534–535
Geometry puzzle, 30
Height of a sail, 520
Heron triangles, 304
Lengths of chords of a circle, 526
Matching triangles and squares, 27
Maximum area, 443–445
Pennant side lengths, 523
Perfect triangles, 304
Perimeter of a rectangular region,
    515–516
Perimeter of a square, 534
Perimeter of a triangle, 30, 526
Points, lines, and triangles in a plane,
    606
Radius of a circle, 523, 526
Radius of a circular region, 523
Radius of an aluminum can, 303
Ratio of areas, 533
Ratio of side lengths, 534
Ratios of volumes, 530, 533
Rectangles in a figure, 28
Side length of a cube, 533
Side lengths of a triangle, 394, 512, 514
Total area, 525
Unfolding and folding a box, 27
Vertices and edges of a cube, 831
Vertices and edges of a tetrahedron, 831
Volume of a box, 531, 533
Volume of a pyramid, 531–532
Volume of a right circular cylinder,
    529, 532
Volume of a sphere, 530, 532
Volumes of common objects, 532

GOVERNMENT

Aid to earthquake victims, 474–476
Appointing committees, 577, 581,
    600–601, 606, 611, 619, 684
Army housing, 78
Breaking codes, 25, 178
Campaign promises, 60–61
Committees of U.S. senators, 604, 656
Cryptography, 227
Cybercrime, 227–228
Diplomatic delegation, 615–616
Election, 127, 577, 581, 585, 594, 604
Federal budget totals, 710
Government spending, 694
National debt, 381
National health care expenditure, 380
Postage stamps, 29, 319
Rate of favorable media coverage of
    an incumbent president, 664

TANF program, 413
Town water distribution, 869
U.S. House of Representatives, 348
U.S. presidents, 52
U.S. Food and Drug Administration,
    692
U.S. post offices, 437
U.S. Senate, 348, 619

LABOR

Committees, 600–601, 606
Days off, 256, 683
Employees, 74
Flight attendant schedules, 196
Garage employing mechanics, 653–654
Hiring nurses, 54
Inflated salary levels, 756–757
Intern position, 633
Night off for security guards, 245
Occupational rates of change,
    265–266, 268
Ordering job interviews, 658
Poverty level income cut-offs, 413
Prospects for electronics jobs in a city,
    676
RN and LPN job outlook, 47–48
Salaries, 701, 710, 712
Score on management exams, 710
Security team visits, 604
Sources of job training, 695
Top ten jobs, 722
Training in simulators, 673
Unemployment rate, 46, 695

MEDICAL

Adverse effects of alcohol and
    tobacco, 69
Alcohol mixture in first aid spray, 348
Antibiotic usage, 691–692
Blood alcohol concentration, 318
Body mass index, 359, 362, 372
Body surface area, 303, 313, 317
Calories, 54, 362
Child's dose of a drug, 314, 318, 328
Cystic fibrosis, 636, 684
Drug dosage calculations, 360, 402
Finding blood clotting times, 736
Flu vaccination, 134–135
Hospital patient symptoms, 77
Living with AIDS, 463
Metabolic units, 318
Nurse trainee groups, 826–827
Pediatric patients, 745
Reading X-rays, 856
Recommended daily vitamin
    allowances, 736
Search and rescue teams, 619
Sickle-cell anemia, 637
Side effects of prescription drugs, 664
Target heart rate, 372
Time intervals for drugs, 454, 457

Tracking infectious disease, 868
Treating addictions, 685–686, 698, 703,
    746
Vitamin pill costs, 476

NUMBERS

Abundant number, 235–236
Alphametic, 28
Amicable (or friendly) numbers, 231,
    236
Building a fraction, 45
Building numbers from sets of digits,
    575, 578, 582, 586, 592, 593, 596,
    607, 638, 646, 683
Coins and fractions, 285
Counting, 583, 591, 616
Deficient number, 235
Difference triangle, 28
Digit puzzle, 28
Envelopes with money, 26
Expected sums of randomly selected
    numbers, 676
Fibonacci sequence, 246–248, 250, 302
Final digit of a power of seven, 28
Forming perfect square sums, 28
Fractional parts, 292–293
Golden ratio, 248–249
Integers containing the digit 2, 582
Irrational numbers, 305
Lattice points on a line segment,
    582–583
Magic square, 30 (also in online
    section)
Number in a sequence, 27
Number of inches in a mile, 382
Number pattern, 27
Numbers generated by spinners,
    634–635, 661
Number trick, 251
Palindromes, 28, 594, 639
Pascal's triangle, 19, 624
Percent of, 310–311, 316, 320
Perfect number, 29, 230, 235
Perfect square, 28
Prime numbers, 638
Pseudoperfect, 236
Random sums, 638, 676
Sudoku, 25
Sum of hidden dots on dice, 27
Sums of digits, 582, 604, 607, 623
Sums of primes, 583
Twin primes, 232, 235–236
Units digit of a product, sum, or
    power, 28–29, 45
Unknown numbers, 27, 347

PHYSICS

Elapsed time in a physics experiment,
    709
Expansion and contraction of gases, 437
Falling body, 357, 361

INDEX

Additional Appendices

Taken from: *Mathematical Ideas,* Eighth Edition by Charles D. Miller, Vern E. Heeren, and E. John Hornsby, Jr.

Mathematical Ideas, Sixth Edition by Charles D. Miller, Vern E. Heeren, and E. John Hornsby, Jr.

14

Taken from: *Mathematical Ideas*, Eighth Edition by Charles D. Miller, Vern E. Heeren, and E. John Hornsby, Jr.

Matrices and Their Applications

Although cryptography has been used by the military for centuries, only recently has the public found a need for it. Because of the large amount of electronic communication today, businesses, banks, and private individuals use cryptography to keep information secret. The process of disguising plain text into a cipher is called encryption. When a message is received, the cipher must be decoded into the original plain text using decryption.

Codes that encrypt a letter of the alphabet in the same way each time are usually easy to break. Suppose a simple code changes letters into numbers using the following technique: A = 01, B = 02, C = 03, . . . , Z = 26. After a few messages a person may be able to decipher the code because letters in the English language do not occur with equal likelihood. The most frequently used letter in the alphabet is E, which occurs approximately 13% of the time, whereas the least frequent is Z, which occurs only .1% of the time. One can quickly determine which number is associated with E and which one is associated with Z. According to one sample, the percentage *P* of occurrence for the most frequent letters in English text are as shown in the table.

Letter	P	Letter	P	Letter	P
E	13.0%	T	9.3%	N	7.8%
R	7.7%	O	7.4%	I	7.4%
A	7.3%	S	6.3%	D	4.4%

Matrices can be used to create sophisticated encryption methods that code blocks of letters rather than a single letter at one time. As a result, the letter E would be coded differently in the words THE and EAT. To decipher the message, the inverse of the matrix is required.

Sources: Schneier, B., *Applied Cryptography: Protocols, Algorithms, and Source Code in C,* John Wiley & Sons, Inc., 1994.

Sinkov, A., *Elementary Cryptanalysis: A Mathematical Approach,* Random House, 1968.

805

This chapter is concerned with the mathematical object called a *matrix,* which can be defined as follows.

Matrix

A **matrix** is a rectangular array of numbers. (The plural of *matrix* is *matrices.*) The numbers in the array are called the **entries,** or *elements,* of the matrix. Each horizontal line of entries is called a **row,** while each vertical line of entries is called a **column.**

Sometimes a matrix is simply a table, a convenient way of summarizing numerical data. Other times, it may reveal numerical patterns or show special relationships between two quantities. Examples already seen elsewhere in this book include magic squares, number base tables, addition and multiplication tables, probability and frequency distributions, compound interest tables, amortization schedules, and stock market listings. As you will see in this chapter, when a rectangular array is thought of as a matrix, particular symbols, notation, and manipulation techniques are utilized.

As an example, suppose you run the snack bar at the campus cinema and want to keep track of the revenue from your various snacks. For the Friday night showings of *Casablanca* with Humphrey Bogart, you list the dollar amounts as in Table 1.

TABLE 1   Friday Night Snack Bar Revenues

	Candy	Popcorn	Soft drinks
7 P.M. show	$0	$12	$10
9 P.M. show	$5	$8	$9

Following common mathematical practice, you can convey the information of this table in a matrix, enclosing the entries in brackets and denoting the matrix with an appropriate capital letter (in this case F, for Friday) as follows.

$$F = \begin{array}{c} \text{7 P.M. show} \\ \text{9 P.M. show} \end{array} \begin{bmatrix} 0 & 12 & 10 \\ 5 & 8 & 9 \end{bmatrix}$$

For example, the specific entry in row 1, column 3, namely 10, indicates that the soft drink revenue at the 7 P.M. show was $10.

Our main interest in this chapter will be to develop some algebraic operations on matrices, which make them useful in practical applications. We will see matrix F again in Section 1, where matrices will be added, subtracted, and multiplied by numbers. Section 2 involves multiplying matrices by other matrices. In Sections 3 and 4, we will discover how matrices can be used to solve systems of linear equations. Solving such systems was an important motivation for the English mathematicians who, in the 1850s, originated the development of matrix theory. These men were Arthur Cayley (1821–1895) and James Sylvester (1814–1897). (Linear systems were solved by the *elimination method* in an earlier chapter.) Section 5 of the chapter will introduce some basic ideas from *game theory,* a practical modern branch of mathematics.

Throughout the chapter we will discover various properties of matrices as a mathematical system. Some of these will probably be what you would expect, while others may surprise you.

14.1 Basic Operations on Matrices

Recall from the definition above that a matrix is a rectangular array of numbers. The number of rows and columns in a matrix determines its *size,* or its **order.** For example, we say that matrix F above is a 2 × 3 (read "2 by 3") matrix, or that it has order 2 × 3. (Notice that, when specifying the order of a matrix, we give the number of rows first and then the number of columns.)

If a matrix has the same number of rows as columns, it is called a **square matrix.** A matrix with only one row is called a **row matrix.** A matrix with only one column is called a **column matrix.** A matrix in which all entries are zero is called a **zero matrix.**

The figures above show how matrices A and B of Example 1 appear on a graphing calculator screen.

EXAMPLE 1 Give the order of each of the following matrices, and identify any that are square matrices, row matrices, column matrices, or zero matrices.

$$A = \begin{bmatrix} 7 & -5 \\ -3 & 1 \end{bmatrix} \quad B = \begin{bmatrix} 12 \\ 8 \\ 20 \end{bmatrix} \quad C = \begin{bmatrix} 1 & 4 \\ 9 & 5 \\ 6 & 2 \end{bmatrix} \quad D = \begin{bmatrix} -5 & 0 & 0 \\ 2 & 3 & 1 \\ 9 & 4 & 0 \end{bmatrix}$$

$$E = \begin{bmatrix} 10 & 50 & 30 \end{bmatrix} \quad F = \begin{bmatrix} 0 & 0 & 0 \\ 0 & 0 & 0 \end{bmatrix} \quad G = \begin{bmatrix} 6 \end{bmatrix}$$

The orders of the seven given matrices are as follows.

Matrix	A	B	C	D	E	F	G
Order	2 × 2	3 × 1	3 × 2	3 × 3	1 × 3	2 × 3	1 × 1

A, D, and G are square matrices. E and G are row matrices. B and G are column matrices. F is a zero matrix.

Notice that matrix G (in Example 1) is both a row matrix and a column matrix. Notice also that, even though G has only a single entry, G is a matrix and not a number. Pure numbers are commonly distinguished from matrices by referring to the numbers as *scalars.* For example, 6 is a scalar, whereas $[6]$ is a matrix. This distinction is sometimes important, so the brackets must always be included around the entries of a matrix.

Equal Matrices

Two matrices are said to be **equal** if they have the same order and if all corresponding entries are equal.

The fact that matrices A and B are not equal is illustrated by the 0 returned by the calculator in the bottom screen. Had they been equal, a 1 would have been returned.

The result of Example 3 is supported in these two screens.

This screen, indicating a dimension (or order) mismatch, was the result of attempting to add matrices A and B as defined in Example 4.

EXAMPLE 2 In each case, determine whether matrices A and B are equal.

(a) $A = \begin{bmatrix} 4 & 3 \\ 2 & 6 \end{bmatrix}$ $\qquad B = \begin{bmatrix} 4 & 2 \\ 3 & 6 \end{bmatrix}$

Even though A and B have the same order (2×2) and include the same numbers as entries, not all *corresponding* entries are equal. For example, the row 2, column 1 entry of matrix A is 2, while the corresponding entry of matrix B is 3. Matrices A and B are not equal.

(b) $A = \begin{bmatrix} 1 & 2 & 3 \\ 6 & 5 & 1 \end{bmatrix}$ $\qquad B = \begin{bmatrix} 1 & 2 \\ 6 & 5 \end{bmatrix}$

Matrix A has order 2×3, while B has order 2×2. Since they do not have the same order, matrices A and B are not equal.

(c) $A = \begin{bmatrix} 12 & -2 & 4 \end{bmatrix}$ $\qquad B = \begin{bmatrix} 12 & -2 & 4 \end{bmatrix}$

A and B have the same order (1×3) and all corresponding entries are equal, so matrices A and B are equal. ◆

In the remainder of this section, we introduce three operations on matrices: addition, subtraction, and scalar multiplication. In each case the result is another matrix. Addition (and subtraction) can only be done when the two matrices to be added (or subtracted) have the same order. If a matrix operation can be done, we say the result is **computable.** However, if any condition (such as different orders) makes the operation impossible, we say the result is **not computable.**

Addition of Matrices

The **sum** of two matrices of the same order is found by *adding* corresponding entries. If two matrices have different orders, their sum is not computable.

EXAMPLE 3 Let $A = \begin{bmatrix} 2 & -1 & 3 & 2 \\ 1 & 0 & 4 & 2 \end{bmatrix}$ and $B = \begin{bmatrix} 5 & 6 & -2 & 5 \\ 3 & -1 & 4 & 7 \end{bmatrix}$. Find $A + B$.

Add the corresponding entries.

$$A + B = \begin{bmatrix} 2 & -1 & 3 & 2 \\ 1 & 0 & 4 & 2 \end{bmatrix} + \begin{bmatrix} 5 & 6 & -2 & 5 \\ 3 & -1 & 4 & 7 \end{bmatrix}$$
$$= \begin{bmatrix} 2+5 & -1+6 & 3+(-2) & 2+5 \\ 1+3 & 0+(-1) & 4+4 & 2+7 \end{bmatrix}$$
$$= \begin{bmatrix} 7 & 5 & 1 & 7 \\ 4 & -1 & 8 & 9 \end{bmatrix} \quad ◆$$

EXAMPLE 4 Let $A = \begin{bmatrix} 2 & 1 \\ 3 & 4 \end{bmatrix}$ and let $B = \begin{bmatrix} 4 & -1 & 0 \\ 2 & 5 & 0 \end{bmatrix}$. Find $A + B$.

Since A is 2×2 and B is 2×3, the matrices have different orders. Their sum is not computable. ◆

EXAMPLE 5 Matrix F from the chapter introduction showed snack bar revenues for the Friday night movie showings. The corresponding Saturday night revenues are shown here.

$$S = \begin{array}{c} \text{7 P.M. show} \\ \text{9 P.M. show} \end{array} \begin{bmatrix} 4 & 15 & 11 \\ 4 & 10 & 10 \end{bmatrix}$$

(columns labeled) Candy · Popcorn · Drinks

Derive a matrix that shows the various revenues for the weekend (Friday and Saturday combined).

The sum of matrices F and S will show the required quantities, since it adds corresponding entries in all six matrix positions.

$$W = F + S$$

$$= \begin{bmatrix} 0 & 12 & 10 \\ 5 & 8 & 9 \end{bmatrix} + \begin{bmatrix} 4 & 15 & 11 \\ 4 & 10 & 10 \end{bmatrix}$$

$$= \begin{bmatrix} 0+4 & 12+15 & 10+11 \\ 5+4 & 8+10 & 9+10 \end{bmatrix}$$

$$= \begin{array}{c} \text{7 P.M. show} \\ \text{9 P.M. show} \end{array} \begin{bmatrix} 4 & 27 & 21 \\ 9 & 18 & 19 \end{bmatrix}$$

(columns labeled) Candy · Popcorn · Drinks

Specifically, total weekend popcorn revenues from the 9 P.M. show was $18. (Other similar amounts can also be read from matrix W.)

Subtraction of Matrices

The **difference** of two matrices of the same order is found by *subtracting* corresponding entries. If two matrices have different orders, their difference is not computable.

EXAMPLE 6 Find the indicated difference.

$$\begin{bmatrix} 4 & -3 \\ -1 & 5 \end{bmatrix} - \begin{bmatrix} -2 & 4 \\ 1 & 5 \end{bmatrix} = \begin{bmatrix} 4-(-2) & -3-4 \\ -1-1 & 5-5 \end{bmatrix}$$

$$= \begin{bmatrix} 6 & -7 \\ -2 & 0 \end{bmatrix}$$

EXAMPLE 7 Refer to the revenue matrices of Example 5. Find a matrix that shows, for each of the six revenue categories, how much more (or less) was taken in on Saturday night than on Friday night. Call this matrix E (for *Excess* revenue).

[A]
[[4 -3]
 [-1 5]]
[B]
[[-2 4]
 [1 5]]

[A]-[B]
[[6 -7]
 [-2 0]]

The result of Example 6 is supported in these two screens.

Compute the following difference.

$$E = S - F$$

$$= \begin{bmatrix} 4 & 15 & 11 \\ 4 & 10 & 10 \end{bmatrix} - \begin{bmatrix} 0 & 12 & 10 \\ 5 & 8 & 9 \end{bmatrix}$$

$$= \begin{bmatrix} 4 - 0 & 15 - 12 & 11 - 10 \\ 4 - 5 & 10 - 8 & 10 - 9 \end{bmatrix}$$

$$= \begin{array}{c} \text{7 P.M. show} \\ \text{9 P.M. show} \end{array} \begin{bmatrix} \overset{\text{Candy}}{\underset{\downarrow}{}} & \overset{\text{Popcorn}}{\underset{\downarrow}{}} & \overset{\text{Drinks}}{\underset{\downarrow}{}} \\ 4 & 3 & 1 \\ -1 & 2 & 1 \end{bmatrix}$$

This result shows, for example, that candy sales at the 9 P.M. show were $1 *less* on Saturday than on Friday. (Revenues in all other categories were *greater* on Saturday.)

As mentioned earlier, a real number is called a *scalar* in distinction to a matrix. Multiplication of a matrix by a scalar is defined as follows.

Scalar Multiplication of Matrices

The **product of a scalar and a matrix** is found by *multiplying each entry* of the matrix by the scalar.

This screen supports the result of Example 8.

EXAMPLE 8 Let $A = \begin{bmatrix} 3 & -2 \\ -4 & 6 \end{bmatrix}$ and let b represent the scalar -2, or $b = -2$. Find bA, that is, $-2A$.

Multiply each element of A by -2.

$$-2A = -2 \begin{bmatrix} 3 & -2 \\ -4 & 6 \end{bmatrix} = \begin{bmatrix} -2(3) & -2(-2) \\ -2(-4) & -2(6) \end{bmatrix} = \begin{bmatrix} -6 & 4 \\ 8 & -12 \end{bmatrix}$$

EXAMPLE 9 Refer to Example 5. Suppose the weekend revenues, shown in matrix W, are to be equally divided by two campus clubs sponsoring the sales. Find a matrix showing the amounts each club should get from each of the six revenue categories.

Since there are two clubs, the required amounts will be shown by the following product.

$$\frac{1}{2}W = \frac{1}{2} \begin{bmatrix} 4 & 27 & 21 \\ 9 & 18 & 19 \end{bmatrix} = \begin{array}{c} \text{7 P.M. show} \\ \text{9 P.M. show} \end{array} \begin{bmatrix} \overset{\text{Candy}}{\underset{\downarrow}{}} & \overset{\text{Popcorn}}{\underset{\downarrow}{}} & \overset{\text{Drinks}}{\underset{\downarrow}{}} \\ 2 & 13.5 & 10.5 \\ 4.5 & 9 & 9.5 \end{bmatrix}$$

For example, each club gets $13.50 from the popcorn sales at the 7 P.M. shows.

One of our objectives throughout this chapter will be to observe what we can about the way matrices behave as mathematical entities. We want to notice some properties possessed by matrices and by the operations that apply to them. For example, is addition of matrices commutative? Is it associative? What about subtraction of matrices? What about multiplication?

Problem Solving

Notice that addition, subtraction, and (scalar) multiplication *of matrices* have been defined in this section in terms of addition, subtraction, and multiplication *of real numbers*. Therefore, we should expect to be able to deduce certain properties of these operations on matrices by considering what we already know about the corresponding operations on real numbers. This idea of extending our previous knowledge to new or different situations is a key concept in mathematics (as well as other areas). As you study the following example, try to observe specific problem-solving techniques at work.

EXAMPLE 10   Consider the set of all matrices of the same order. Is addition of matrices, on this set, a *commutative* operation?

The question here pertains to all matrices of "the same order." Let us start by narrowing our attention to a particular order, say 2×3. And let us consider two particular 2×3 matrices, say

$$A = \begin{bmatrix} 1 & 3 & 5 \\ 2 & 4 & 6 \end{bmatrix} \quad \text{and} \quad B = \begin{bmatrix} 2 & 4 & 6 \\ 8 & 10 & 12 \end{bmatrix}.$$

Check to see whether $A + B = B + A$:

$$A + B = \begin{bmatrix} 1 + 2 & 3 + 4 & 5 + 6 \\ 2 + 8 & 4 + 10 & 6 + 12 \end{bmatrix} = \begin{bmatrix} 3 & 7 & 11 \\ 10 & 14 & 18 \end{bmatrix}$$

and

$$B + A = \begin{bmatrix} 2 + 1 & 4 + 3 & 6 + 5 \\ 8 + 2 & 10 + 4 & 12 + 6 \end{bmatrix} = \begin{bmatrix} 3 & 7 & 11 \\ 10 & 14 & 18 \end{bmatrix}.$$

By inspection, these two results are, indeed, equal. On the basis of this result, you may be led to conclude (inductively) that the answer to the original question is "yes." But we really have not verified the result except for the particular matrices A and B. Let us extend our attention to *all* 2×3 matrices by considering matrices

$$C = \begin{bmatrix} a & c & e \\ b & d & f \end{bmatrix} \quad \text{and} \quad D = \begin{bmatrix} g & i & k \\ h & j & l \end{bmatrix}$$

for *any* real numbers $a, b, c, \ldots, l$. Now

$$C + D = \begin{bmatrix} a + g & c + i & e + k \\ b + h & d + j & f + l \end{bmatrix}$$

and

$$D + C = \begin{bmatrix} g + a & i + c & k + e \\ h + b & j + d & l + f \end{bmatrix}.$$

We can now use our previous knowledge that addition is, in fact, commutative on the set of real numbers to conclude that $a + g = g + a, c + i = i + c$, etc., and that therefore $C + D = D + C$. This conclusion is based on *deductive* reasoning, which is totally reliable (unlike inductive reasoning).

The desired result has still only been established for 2×3 matrices (by considering C and D). Our final step is to observe that our deduction with C and D would still be valid for two equal order matrices of *any* order. (Why is this so?) Therefore, addition of matrices, on *any* set of equal order matrices, is indeed commutative. ◢

14.1 EXERCISES

Perform the indicated matrix operations. If a required result is not computable, state why not.

1. $\begin{bmatrix} 3 & 2 \\ 5 & 1 \end{bmatrix} + \begin{bmatrix} 8 & -1 \\ 4 & 3 \end{bmatrix}$

2. $\begin{bmatrix} -6 & 9 \\ 2 & 4 \end{bmatrix} + \begin{bmatrix} -2 & 5 \\ -1 & 3 \end{bmatrix}$

3. $\begin{bmatrix} 2 & 8 & -1 \\ 4 & 0 & 3 \end{bmatrix} - \begin{bmatrix} -1 & 5 & 2 \\ 0 & 4 & 3 \end{bmatrix}$

4. $\begin{bmatrix} -1 & 2 & 4 \\ -2 & 3 & 0 \end{bmatrix} - \begin{bmatrix} 2 & -1 & 4 \\ -5 & 6 & 9 \end{bmatrix}$

5. $\begin{bmatrix} -2 & 3 & 1 \\ 4 & 0 & -2 \\ 5 & -1 & 6 \end{bmatrix} + \begin{bmatrix} -1 & 1 & 1 \\ 4 & 2 & 3 \\ -1 & 4 & 7 \end{bmatrix}$

6. $\begin{bmatrix} 3 & 4 & -1 \\ 7 & -8 & 2 \\ 9 & -1 & 3 \end{bmatrix} - \begin{bmatrix} -4 & 2 & -1 \\ 3 & -1 & 8 \\ 4 & 9 & 0 \end{bmatrix}$

7. $\begin{bmatrix} -4 & 3 & 2 \\ -8 & 0 & 1 \\ 4 & 2 & 1 \end{bmatrix} - \begin{bmatrix} 3 & -4 \\ 2 & -3 \\ 8 & 9 \end{bmatrix}$

8. $\begin{bmatrix} -1 & 6 & 2 \\ 3 & 4 & 7 \\ 9 & 8 & 2 \end{bmatrix} + \begin{bmatrix} -4 & 9 & 2 & 0 \\ -3 & 1 & 4 & 0 \\ 8 & 9 & 7 & 0 \end{bmatrix}$

9. $\begin{bmatrix} 3 \\ 4 \\ 2 \end{bmatrix} + \begin{bmatrix} -1 \\ 9 \\ 8 \end{bmatrix} - \begin{bmatrix} 2 \\ 1 \\ 3 \end{bmatrix}$

10. $\begin{bmatrix} 7 \\ 8 \\ 9 \end{bmatrix} + \begin{bmatrix} 1 \\ 9 \\ 3 \end{bmatrix} - \begin{bmatrix} -4 \\ 3 \\ 8 \end{bmatrix}$

11. $\begin{bmatrix} -2 & 4 \\ 0 & 9 \end{bmatrix} + \begin{bmatrix} -8 & 1 \\ 3 & 6 \end{bmatrix} - \begin{bmatrix} 4 & 7 \\ -2 & 5 \end{bmatrix}$

12. $\begin{bmatrix} -3 & 2 \\ 4 & 8 \end{bmatrix} + \begin{bmatrix} -9 & -1 \\ 6 & 3 \end{bmatrix} + \begin{bmatrix} -2 & 5 \\ 0 & 8 \end{bmatrix}$

Let $A = \begin{bmatrix} -4 & 0 \\ 3 & -4 \end{bmatrix}$ *and let* $B = \begin{bmatrix} 2 & -1 \\ -4 & 0 \end{bmatrix}$. *Compute the following.*

13. $A + B$

14. $A - B$

15. $2A$

16. $3B$

17. $-4B$

18. $-5A$

19. $2A + 3B$

20. $-7A + 4B$

21. $(-1)A + A$

A dietician prepares a diet specifying the allowable amounts of four main food groups: group I, meats; group II, fruits and vegetables; group III, breads and starches; and group IV, milk products. Amounts are given in appropriate units (1 ounce for meat, 1/2 cup for fruits and vegetables, 1 slice for bread, and 8 ounces for milk).

22. The numbers of units for breakfast for the four food groups respectively are 2, 1, 2, and 1; for lunch, 3, 2, 2, and 1; and for dinner, 4, 3, 2, and 1. Write a 3×4 matrix to display this information.

23. The amounts of fat, carbohydrates, and protein in the food groups respectively are as follows:

    Fat: 5, 0, 0, 10   Carbohydrates: 0, 10, 15, 12   Protein: 7, 1, 2, 8.

    Display this information in a 4×3 matrix.

24. Assume there are 8 calories per unit of fat, 4 calories per unit of carbohydrate, and 5 calories per unit of protein. Show these data in a 3×1 matrix.

Don and Connie run a business (D&C Creations) in California building and selling gold rush era tables and chairs. They maintain factories in Sloughhouse (F1) and Nevada City (F2) and ship their products to warehouses in Sacramento (W1), San Francisco (W2), and Reno (W3). The table here shows shipping costs per item from each factory to each warehouse.

Route	Cost Per Item
F1 to W1	$12
F1 to W2	20
F1 to W3	25
F2 to W1	16
F2 to W2	25
F2 to W3	30

25. Construct a 2×3 matrix, C, showing the data for shipping cost per item.

26. On April 1, the freight company that $D\&C$ utilizes adjusted per item shipping costs as shown here. Construct a 2×3 matrix, A, showing the shipping cost adjustments.

Route	Adjustment
F1 to W1	$3
F1 to W2	−2
F1 to W3	2
F2 to W1	4
F2 to W2	2
F2 to W3	−2

27. Show an appropriate matrix operation whose result gives $D\&C$'s shipping costs per item after April 1.

28. Each month, Don and Connie send to each of their warehouses 10 model-A tables, 12 model-B tables, 5 model-C tables, 15 model-A chairs, 20 model-B chairs, and 8 model-C chairs. Exhibit this information in a 2×3 matrix (with tables represented in the top row).

29. The matrix here shows stock on hand at the $D\&C$ Reno warehouse as of September 1.

$$R = \begin{matrix} & A & B & C \\ \text{Tables} \\ \text{Chairs} \end{matrix} \begin{bmatrix} 45 & 35 & 20 \\ 65 & 40 & 35 \end{bmatrix}$$

    If no stock is sent out of the warehouse during September, how much stock will be on hand October 1? Use the result of Exercise 28 and matrix methods.

30. In Exercise 29, how many model-B chairs were on hand October 1 at the Reno warehouse?

31. In Exercise 29, how many model-C tables were on hand October 1 at the Reno warehouse?

32. The number of each model held on September 1 at the Sacramento and San Francisco warehouses of *D&C* are:

$$S = \begin{bmatrix} 22 & 25 & 38 \\ 31 & 34 & 35 \end{bmatrix} \quad \text{and} \quad F = \begin{bmatrix} 30 & 32 & 28 \\ 43 & 47 & 30 \end{bmatrix}.$$

Find the total inventory in all three warehouses on September 1.

33. Suppose the Sacramento warehouse of *D&C* shipped the following numbers of items during September:

$$K = \begin{bmatrix} 5 & 10 & 8 \\ 11 & 14 & 15 \end{bmatrix}.$$

Find the stock on hand October 1, taking into account the numbers of items received and shipped during the month.

Matrix K shows the weights of four men and four women at the beginning of a diet designed to produce weight loss. Matrix M shows the weights after the diet.

$$K = \begin{matrix} \text{Men} \\ \text{Women} \end{matrix} \begin{bmatrix} 160 & 158 & 172 & 193 \\ 132 & 143 & 119 & 157 \end{bmatrix} \qquad M = \begin{matrix} \text{Men} \\ \text{Women} \end{matrix} \begin{bmatrix} 154 & 148 & 163 & 178 \\ 132 & 154 & 112 & 136 \end{bmatrix}$$

34. Show a matrix operation whose result gives the weight losses of all eight people on the diet.

35. In Exercise 34, how much weight did the third man lose?

36. In Exercise 34, what result did the second woman experience?

Find all real values of the variables that will make each of the following equalities true. In case the given equality is impossible, state why.

37. $\begin{bmatrix} x & y & z \\ 2 & 5 & 1 \end{bmatrix} = \begin{bmatrix} 7 & 2 \\ 4 & 5 \\ 2 & 1 \end{bmatrix}$

38. $\begin{bmatrix} 3 & 4 \\ z & x \end{bmatrix} = \begin{bmatrix} 3z & 4x \end{bmatrix}$

39. $\begin{bmatrix} 5 & y \\ z & 2 \end{bmatrix} = \begin{bmatrix} 5 & z \\ y & 2 \end{bmatrix}$

40. $\begin{bmatrix} x & y & z \end{bmatrix} = \begin{bmatrix} 2x & 3y & 4z \end{bmatrix}$

41. $\begin{bmatrix} 6 & y \\ k & m \end{bmatrix} = \begin{bmatrix} 6 & 3 \\ 8 & 1 \end{bmatrix}$

42. $\begin{bmatrix} 5 & 7 \\ 1 & 8 \end{bmatrix} = \begin{bmatrix} a & b \\ 1 & c \end{bmatrix}$

43. $\begin{bmatrix} x+2 & 5 & 9 \\ 1 & 3 & y \end{bmatrix} = \begin{bmatrix} 2x+1 & z-3 & 9 \\ 1 & 3 & 8 \end{bmatrix}$

44. $\begin{bmatrix} 2 & m+5 & a \\ 1 & n-3 & -1 \end{bmatrix} = \begin{bmatrix} 2 & 2m+6 & 2a \\ 1 & 4n-12 & -1 \end{bmatrix}$

45. $\begin{bmatrix} -2 & 6 \\ x & 2 \end{bmatrix} + \begin{bmatrix} x & y \\ 3 & 5 \end{bmatrix} = \begin{bmatrix} 8 & 2 \\ 7 & 7 \end{bmatrix}$

46. $\begin{bmatrix} 5 & m & 3 \\ 2 & y & 5 \end{bmatrix} - \begin{bmatrix} 3 & 4 & a \\ 1 & 6 & a \end{bmatrix} = \begin{bmatrix} 2 & 5 & 2 \\ 1 & 4 & 1 \end{bmatrix}$

The dates in the calendar display for February 1998 form a 4 × 7 matrix, as shown here.

February 1998

Sun	Mon	Tue	Wed	Thu	Fri	Sat
1	2	3	4	5	6	7
8	9	10	11	12	13	14
15	16	17	18	19	20	21
22	23	24	25	26	27	28

47. Will the month of March on a calendar ever form a matrix? Why or why not?

48. What is the next year following 1998 in which February will again form a matrix? (*Hint:* You *may* want to consider "leap years" or "perpetual calendars." You can look up these concepts in this text or elsewhere.)

Example 10 in this section established the commutative property for addition of matrices. Use similar reasoning in Exercises 49–56 to determine whether each statement is true *or* false *for matrices A, B, and C of the same order and for scalars a and b.*

49. $A - B = B - A$

50. $A + (B + C) = (A + B) + C$ (associative property for addition)

51. $A + B$ is a matrix. (closure property)

52. If 0 is a matrix of the same order as A, containing only zero entries, then $0 + A = A$ and $A + 0 = A$. (identity property for addition)

53. If $-A = (-1)A$, then $A + (-A) = 0$ and $-A + A = 0$. (inverse property for addition)

54. $A - B = A + (-B)$, where $-B = (-1)B$.

55. $a(B + C) = aB + aC$

56. $(a + b)C = aC + bC$

57. Does the set of all 2×2 matrices and the operation of addition form a *mathematical system?* Explain why or why not. (*Hint:* Look up the definition of "mathematical system.")

58. Does the system of Exercise 57 form a *group?* Explain why or why not. (*Hint:* Look up the definition of a mathematical "group.")

  Multiplication of Matrices

D&C Creations is a business that manufactures and sells unfinished tables and chairs. (See Exercises 25–33 of Section 1.) Table 2 shows the units of materials required for each table, while Table 3 shows the per unit cost of materials.

TABLE 2 Materials Required for a Table

		Materials	
		Wood	**Hardware**
Furniture	**Table**	8	5

TABLE 3 Cost of Materials

		Cost Per Unit
Materials	**Wood**	$2
	Hardware	$3

From the tabulated data we see that each table manufactured requires 8 units of wood and 5 units of hardware, and wood costs $2 per unit while hardware costs $3 per unit.

The cost of materials for each table will then be

$$8 \cdot (\$2) + 5 \cdot (\$3) = \$16 + \$15 = \$31.$$

(Make sure you understand this calculation.) To see how matrix notation can be of use here, first exhibit the material requirements for a table in the **row** matrix M:

$$M = \text{Table} \begin{array}{cc} \text{Wood} & \text{Hardware} \\ [\ 8 & 5\ ] \end{array}$$

Matrix M relates the furniture item (table—on the left) to its materials (wood and hardware—at the top). Also exhibit the data on cost per unit (for materials) in the **column** matrix C:

$$C = \begin{array}{c} \text{Wood} \\ \text{Hardware} \end{array} \begin{array}{c} \text{Cost per unit} \\ \left[\begin{array}{c} 2 \\ 3 \end{array} \right] \end{array}$$

Matrix C relates materials (on the left) to cost (at the top).

Now define *row-column multiplication* as follows.

___

Row-Column Multiplication

If a row matrix and a column matrix have equal numbers of entries, then their **row-column product** is the *scalar* obtained by multiplying all of their corresponding entries (first with first, second with second, and so on) and adding the resulting products. Always position the row matrix first (on the left) and the column matrix second (on the right). If the row matrix and column matrix have different numbers of entries, their row-column product is not computable.

___

We can now see that the cost of materials for each table ($31 as calculated above) is the row-column product of M and C.

$$MC = \text{Table} \begin{array}{cc} \text{Wood} & \text{Hardware} \\ [\ 8 & 5\ ] \end{array} \cdot \begin{array}{c} \text{Wood} \\ \text{Hardware} \end{array} \begin{array}{c} \text{Cost per unit} \\ \left[\begin{array}{c} 2 \\ 3 \end{array} \right] \end{array}$$

$$= 8 \cdot 2 + 5 \cdot 3$$
$$= 31.$$

Notice that matrix M relates furniture (table) to materials and matrix C relates materials to cost, so the product MC relates furniture (table) to cost. These relationships are illustrated in Figure 1.

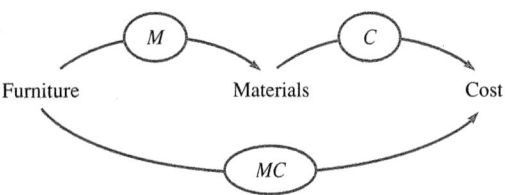

■ FIGURE 1
Quantities Related by Matrices *M* and *C* and their Row-Column Product *MC*

The row-column multiplication of *M* and *C* is reiterated below, without the labels, and with arrows emphasizing which entries are multiplied together.

$$MC = \begin{bmatrix} 8 & 5 \end{bmatrix} \cdot \begin{bmatrix} 2 \\ 3 \end{bmatrix} = 8 \cdot 2 + 5 \cdot 3 = 31$$

Recall that, for a row-column product to be computable, the following conditions are required.

1. The first (left) matrix must be a row matrix, and the second (right) matrix must be a column matrix.
2. The two matrices must have the same number of entries.

Row-column multiplication is important because it is the basis for defining matrix multiplication in general. To show the usefulness of general matrix multiplication, we continue our illustration with *D&C* Creations.

It is found that each *chair* made by *D&C* requires 6 units of wood and 4 units of hardware. Representing this information in the row matrix $N = \begin{bmatrix} 6 & 4 \end{bmatrix}$, we can now discover the material cost of a chair by computing another row-column product.

$$NC = \begin{bmatrix} 6 & 4 \end{bmatrix} \cdot \begin{bmatrix} 2 \\ 3 \end{bmatrix} = 6 \cdot 2 + 4 \cdot 3 = 24$$

Note that *N* relates a chair to its materials, and *C* relates those materials to their costs. Thus *NC* relates a chair to its cost ($24).

Now observe that the known relationships between furniture and materials (for *both tables and chairs*) can be combined into a single matrix, say *R*, which shows materials needed for both types of furniture.

$$R = \begin{matrix} \text{Table} \\ \text{Chair} \end{matrix} \begin{bmatrix} \overset{\text{Wood}}{8} & \overset{\text{Hardware}}{5} \\ 6 & 4 \end{bmatrix}$$

We can now exhibit both row-column products *MC* and *NC* within a single matrix product, *RC*, as follows.

$$RC = \begin{matrix} \text{Table} \\ \text{Chair} \end{matrix} \begin{bmatrix} \overset{\text{Wood}}{8} & \overset{\text{Hardware}}{5} \\ 6 & 4 \end{bmatrix} \cdot \begin{matrix} \text{Wood} \\ \text{Hardware} \end{matrix} \begin{bmatrix} \overset{\text{Cost per unit}}{2} \\ 3 \end{bmatrix}$$

The computation of this matrix product involves two row-column products: row 1 of R times the column of C, and row 2 of R times the column of C. The actual calculation appears as follows.

$$RC = \begin{array}{c} \\ \text{Table} \\ \text{Chair} \end{array} \begin{array}{c} \text{Cost} \\ \begin{bmatrix} 8 \cdot 2 + 5 \cdot 3 \\ 6 \cdot 2 + 4 \cdot 3 \end{bmatrix} \end{array}$$

$$= \begin{array}{c} \\ \text{Table} \\ \text{Chair} \end{array} \begin{array}{c} \text{Cost} \\ \begin{bmatrix} 31 \\ 24 \end{bmatrix} \end{array}$$

This result shows that the materials (wood and hardware) cost \$31 for each table and \$24 for each chair.

Without labels, the above matrix product appears as follows.

$$RC = \begin{bmatrix} 8 & 5 \\ 6 & 4 \end{bmatrix} \cdot \begin{bmatrix} 2 \\ 3 \end{bmatrix} = \begin{bmatrix} 31 \\ 24 \end{bmatrix}$$

In this product, the 31 (a scalar) in row 1, column 1 is simply the row-column product of row 1 from R with column 1 from C. The 24 in row 2, column 1 is the row-column product of row 2 from R with column 1 from C. These row-column products are computable only because the rows of R have the same number of entries as the column of C. In other words, R has as many columns as C has rows (2 in both cases).

In general, the following diagram shows when the matrix product AB is computable and what the order of the product will be.

In summary, the product of two matrices can be defined as follows.

Multiplication of Two Matrices

If A is an $m \times n$ matrix and B is an $n \times p$ matrix, then the **product of the two matrices,** AB, is an $m \times p$ matrix where each particular entry, say the entry in row i, column j, is the row-column product of row i in matrix A with column j in matrix B. (If the number of columns in A is different from the number of rows in B, the product AB is not computable.)

EXAMPLE 1 Find each matrix product AB if it exists.

(a) $A = \begin{bmatrix} 2 & -1 & 3 & 1 \\ 0 & 1 & 0 & 2 \end{bmatrix} \qquad B = \begin{bmatrix} -1 & 2 & 3 \\ 0 & 0 & -1 \\ 1 & 2 & 0 \\ 0 & -1 & 0 \end{bmatrix}$

These screens illustrate how the product AB in Example 1(a) is found with a graphing calculator. Attempting to find BA would lead to an error message, however.

By the definition above, since A is of order 2×4 and B is of order 4×3, the product exists and will be of order 2×3.

$$AB = \begin{bmatrix} \square & \square & \square \\ \square & \square & \square \end{bmatrix}$$

Each entry of AB is the appropriate row-column product. For example, the row 1, column 2 entry is found as shown in Figure 2.

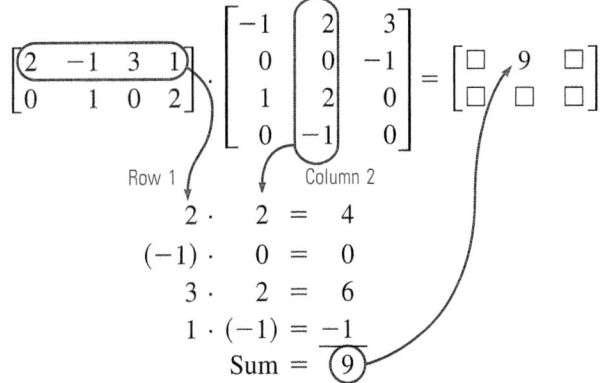

$$
\begin{array}{rcl}
2 \cdot & 2 & = 4 \\
(-1) \cdot & 0 & = 0 \\
3 \cdot & 2 & = 6 \\
1 \cdot & (-1) & = -1 \\
\text{Sum} & = & \boxed{9}
\end{array}
$$

■ **FIGURE 2**
Finding the Row 1, Column 2 Entry of a Matrix Product

Compute the other five entries similarly to find that

$$AB = \begin{bmatrix} 1 & 9 & 7 \\ 0 & -2 & -1 \end{bmatrix}.$$

(b) $A = \begin{bmatrix} -2 & 1 \\ 3 & 4 \end{bmatrix}$ $B = \begin{bmatrix} -1 & 2 \\ 0 & 1 \\ 4 & 0 \end{bmatrix}$

Since A is of order 2×2 and B is of order 3×2 (that is, the number of columns of A is different from the number of rows of B), the product AB is not computable. ◢

The following example establishes an important fact about matrix multiplication.

EXAMPLE 2 Decide in each case whether or not $AB = BA$.

(a) $A = \begin{bmatrix} 6 & -2 \\ 1 & 4 \\ 0 & 3 \end{bmatrix}$ $B = \begin{bmatrix} 2 & -1 & 0 & 4 \\ 1 & 3 & 2 & -2 \end{bmatrix}$

In this case, AB is computable but BA is not. (Why not?) Therefore AB and BA cannot be equal. (There is no need to compute AB.)

The results of Example 2(b) are illustrated on these screens.

The results of Example 2(c) are illustrated on these screens.

(b) $A = \begin{bmatrix} 4 & 2 \\ 6 & 2 \end{bmatrix} \qquad B = \begin{bmatrix} 5 & 1 \\ 3 & 4 \end{bmatrix}$

Here, AB and BA are both computable.

$$AB = \begin{bmatrix} 4 & 2 \\ 6 & 2 \end{bmatrix} \cdot \begin{bmatrix} 5 & 1 \\ 3 & 4 \end{bmatrix} = \begin{bmatrix} 26 & 12 \\ 36 & 14 \end{bmatrix}$$

$$BA = \begin{bmatrix} 5 & 1 \\ 3 & 4 \end{bmatrix} \cdot \begin{bmatrix} 4 & 2 \\ 6 & 2 \end{bmatrix} = \begin{bmatrix} 26 & 12 \\ 36 & 14 \end{bmatrix}$$

In this case, AB and BA are equal.

(c) $A = \begin{bmatrix} -2 & 3 \\ 2 & -1 \end{bmatrix} \qquad B = \begin{bmatrix} -1 & -3 \\ -2 & 2 \end{bmatrix}$

Again, AB and BA are both computable.

$$AB = \begin{bmatrix} -2 & 3 \\ 2 & -1 \end{bmatrix} \cdot \begin{bmatrix} -1 & -3 \\ -2 & 2 \end{bmatrix} = \begin{bmatrix} -4 & 12 \\ 0 & -8 \end{bmatrix}$$

$$BA = \begin{bmatrix} -1 & -3 \\ -2 & 2 \end{bmatrix} \cdot \begin{bmatrix} -2 & 3 \\ 2 & -1 \end{bmatrix} = \begin{bmatrix} -4 & 0 \\ 8 & -8 \end{bmatrix}$$

In this case, AB and BA are *not* equal! ◈

Suppose we had asked the following question: Given two matrices A and B such that AB and BA are both computable, are AB and BA *sometimes* equal, *always* equal, or *never* equal? In light of parts (b) and (c) of Example 2, AB and BA are *sometimes* equal. Generally, the condition "sometimes" is established by exhibiting one case where the statement is true and another case where it is false. The conditions "always" and "never" take more than examples for their proofs. (See Example 5.)

Part (c) of Example 2 shows that AB and BA are not always equal. Therefore *matrix multiplication is not commutative.* This fact delayed the acceptance of matrix theory during its early development since mathematicians tended to doubt the usefulness of a non-commutative multiplication operation. The significance of this result is emphasized in the following statement.

Matrix Multiplication Is *Not* Commutative

Given two matrices A and B, even when the products AB and BA are both computable, AB does not always equal BA. (In fact, AB and BA are equal only in rare cases.)

EXAMPLE 3   Recall that $D\&C$ Creations makes unfinished tables and chairs. The matrices

$$R = \begin{array}{c} \\ \text{Table} \\ \text{Chair} \end{array} \begin{array}{cc} \text{Wood} & \text{Hardware} \\ \begin{bmatrix} 8 & 5 \\ 6 & 4 \end{bmatrix} \end{array} \qquad \text{and} \qquad C = \begin{array}{c} \\ \text{Wood} \\ \text{Hardware} \end{array} \begin{array}{c} \text{Cost per unit} \\ \begin{bmatrix} 2 \\ 3 \end{bmatrix} \end{array}$$

relate furniture to materials and materials to cost, respectively.

Don and Connie have observed that most potential customers prefer to buy furniture that is already finished, so they have begun to finish their tables and chairs. They find that each table requires 3 units of paint, each chair requires 2 units of paint, and paint costs $1 per unit.

(a) Expand the original matrices R and C to reflect this new information.

The expanded matrices are as follows.

$$R = \begin{array}{c} \text{Table} \\ \text{Chair} \end{array} \begin{bmatrix} 8 & 5 & 3 \\ 6 & 4 & 2 \end{bmatrix} \quad \text{and} \quad C = \begin{array}{c} \text{Wood} \\ \text{Hardware} \\ \text{Paint} \end{array} \begin{bmatrix} 2 \\ 3 \\ 1 \end{bmatrix}$$

(with column headings Hardware: Wood, Paint for R and Cost per unit for C)

Notice that, in their new versions, R still relates furniture (on the left) to materials (at the top) and C still relates materials (at the left) to cost (at the top).

(b) Compute the new product RC, if possible, and explain its meaning.

The new product RC is still computable. A 2×3 matrix times a 3×1 matrix will produce a 2×1 matrix.

$$RC = \begin{array}{c} \text{Table} \\ \text{Chair} \end{array} \begin{bmatrix} 8 & 5 & 3 \\ 6 & 4 & 2 \end{bmatrix} \cdot \begin{array}{c} \text{Wood} \\ \text{Hardware} \\ \text{Paint} \end{array} \begin{bmatrix} 2 \\ 3 \\ 1 \end{bmatrix} = \begin{array}{c} \text{Table} \\ \text{Chair} \end{array} \begin{bmatrix} 34 \\ 26 \end{bmatrix}$$

The result shows that (including paint) the materials will now cost $34 for each table and $26 for each chair.

EXAMPLE 4 Let $M = \begin{bmatrix} -8 & 6 \\ 2 & 1 \end{bmatrix}$ and $I = \begin{bmatrix} 1 & 0 \\ 0 & 1 \end{bmatrix}$. Find MI and IM.

Use the definition of matrix multiplication to find MI.

$$MI = \begin{bmatrix} -8 & 6 \\ 2 & 1 \end{bmatrix} \cdot \begin{bmatrix} 1 & 0 \\ 0 & 1 \end{bmatrix}$$
$$= \begin{bmatrix} -8 \cdot 1 + 6 \cdot 0 & -8 \cdot 0 + 6 \cdot 1 \\ 2 \cdot 1 + 1 \cdot 0 & 2 \cdot 0 + 1 \cdot 1 \end{bmatrix} = \begin{bmatrix} -8 & 6 \\ 2 & 1 \end{bmatrix} = M$$

Here $MI = M$. Multiplying in the same way will show that $IM = M$.

Matrix I of Example 4 preserves the identity of matrix M for multiplication and is called the **identity matrix.**

Identity matrices of any square order can be found. For example, the 3×3 identity matrix is displayed here.

$$\begin{bmatrix} 1 & 0 & 0 \\ 0 & 1 & 0 \\ 0 & 0 & 1 \end{bmatrix} \quad \text{3 × 3 identity matrix}$$

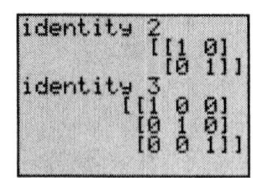

The identity matrices of orders 2 and 3 are shown in this screen.

Notice the similarity between I, the identity for matrix multiplication, and 1, the identity for multiplication of real numbers. Just as $a \cdot 1 = a$ and $1 \cdot a = a$ for every real number a, it is also true that $MI = M$ and $IM = M$ for any square matrix M and identity matrix I of the same order.

EXAMPLE 5 Prove that the equalities $MI = M$ and $IM = M$ are both *always* true for 2×2 matrices M.

Let $M = \begin{bmatrix} a & c \\ b & d \end{bmatrix}$ for any real numbers a, b, c, and d. Then

$$MI = \begin{bmatrix} a & c \\ b & d \end{bmatrix} \cdot \begin{bmatrix} 1 & 0 \\ 0 & 1 \end{bmatrix} = \begin{bmatrix} a \cdot 1 + c \cdot 0 & a \cdot 0 + c \cdot 1 \\ b \cdot 1 + d \cdot 0 & b \cdot 0 + d \cdot 1 \end{bmatrix} = \begin{bmatrix} a & c \\ b & d \end{bmatrix} = M$$

and

$$IM = \begin{bmatrix} 1 & 0 \\ 0 & 1 \end{bmatrix} \cdot \begin{bmatrix} a & c \\ b & d \end{bmatrix} = \begin{bmatrix} 1 \cdot a + 0 \cdot b & 1 \cdot c + 0 \cdot d \\ 0 \cdot a + 1 \cdot b & 0 \cdot c + 1 \cdot d \end{bmatrix} = \begin{bmatrix} a & c \\ b & d \end{bmatrix} = M.$$

We complete this section with an application of matrices to communication networks. The ideas apply to a great variety of situations, including computer networks, telephone systems, genetic evolution, spread of rumors or diseases, and many other kinds of communication among countries, individuals, businesses, or other social and economic groups.

Suppose four computers in a small office are connected as shown in Figure 3. Computer A is connected directly to computers B and C, C is connected to A, B, and D, and so on. All direct connections can be shown in the **communication matrix** M, where an entry of 1 indicates a direct connection while a 0 indicates no direct connection. (The main diagonal of the matrix, from upper left to lower right, contains all 0s since a computer is not considered to be directly connected to itself.)

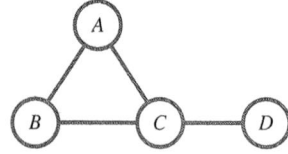

■ FIGURE 3
A Small Computer Network

$$M = \begin{array}{c} \\ A \\ B \\ C \\ D \end{array} \begin{array}{c} \begin{array}{cccc} A & B & C & D \end{array} \\ \begin{bmatrix} 0 & 1 & 1 & 0 \\ 1 & 0 & 1 & 0 \\ 1 & 1 & 0 & 1 \\ 0 & 0 & 1 & 0 \end{bmatrix} \end{array}$$

Define the column matrix K (of all 1s) as follows.

$$K = \begin{bmatrix} 1 \\ 1 \\ 1 \\ 1 \end{bmatrix}$$

Then compute the product MK.

$$MK = \begin{bmatrix} 0 & 1 & 1 & 0 \\ 1 & 0 & 1 & 0 \\ 1 & 1 & 0 & 1 \\ 0 & 0 & 1 & 0 \end{bmatrix} \cdot \begin{bmatrix} 1 \\ 1 \\ 1 \\ 1 \end{bmatrix} = \begin{bmatrix} 2 \\ 2 \\ 3 \\ 1 \end{bmatrix}$$

Verify, by comparing Figure 3, that MK gives, for each computer in the network, the number of other computers with which it has a direct connection.

Notice that A and D are not directly connected. To communicate with D, A must go through one or more intermediaries. For example, A could send data to D through the single intermediary C or by way of the two intermediaries B and C.

The following example utilizes the matrix M^2. (Exponents on matrices work just as on real numbers.)

EXAMPLE 6 For matrix M above, find M^2 and explain its meaning.

$$M^2 = MM = \begin{bmatrix} 0 & 1 & 1 & 0 \\ 1 & 0 & 1 & 0 \\ 1 & 1 & 0 & 1 \\ 0 & 0 & 1 & 0 \end{bmatrix} \cdot \begin{bmatrix} 0 & 1 & 1 & 0 \\ 1 & 0 & 1 & 0 \\ 1 & 1 & 0 & 1 \\ 0 & 0 & 1 & 0 \end{bmatrix} = \begin{bmatrix} 2 & 1 & 1 & 1 \\ 1 & 2 & 1 & 1 \\ 1 & 1 & 3 & 0 \\ 1 & 1 & 0 & 1 \end{bmatrix}$$

Each entry in M^2 indicates the number of different ways one computer can send data to another through a single intermediary. For example, the 1 in row 3, column 2 shows that C can get to B through a single intermediary in just 1 way. (Figure 3 shows that the one way is through A.)

Practical applications of matrices often involve orders much greater than what we have illustrated here, and can require tremendous amounts of calculation. (A 30×20 matrix times a 20×40 matrix requires 24,000 individual products of entries, plus 1,200 sums of 20 terms each. And the original entries may involve several decimal places.)

Fortunately, modern computers, and even handheld calculators, can do matrix operations directly.

EXAMPLE 7 Compute the following matrix product.

$$\begin{bmatrix} 2.8 & 8.1 & 7.7 \\ 3.6 & 4.6 & 6.4 \\ 4.7 & 8.2 & 5.5 \\ 1.9 & 9.3 & 8.9 \\ 7.3 & 4.6 & 7.8 \\ 3.5 & 2.5 & 4.2 \end{bmatrix} \cdot \begin{bmatrix} 3.2 & 8.2 & 6.4 & 8.6 & 2.9 \\ 2.7 & 3.7 & 6.1 & 4.8 & 8.6 \\ 9.3 & 3.4 & 1.8 & 2.5 & 4.7 \end{bmatrix}$$

The 90 required products (2.8 times 3.2, and so on) could be done individually, but with a calculator we just enter the two matrices A and B and then enter matrix A times matrix B. (Most of the work is in keying in the entries.) The resulting product is

$$\begin{bmatrix} 102.44 & 79.11 & 81.19 & 82.21 & 113.97 \\ 83.46 & 68.30 & 62.62 & 69.04 & 80.08 \\ 88.33 & 87.58 & 90.00 & 93.53 & 110.00 \\ 113.96 & 80.25 & 84.91 & 83.23 & 127.32 \\ 108.32 & 103.40 & 88.82 & 104.36 & 97.39 \\ 57.01 & 52.23 & 45.21 & 52.60 & 51.39 \end{bmatrix} \cdot$$

The computation in Example 7 is easily accomplished with a graphing calculator having matrix capability. Notice that the second and third screens are incomplete. The user must scroll to the right in order to read the hidden entries (indicated by the ellipsis . . .).

The ability to accomplish all the tedious calculations on a machine helps make matrix theory of practical use. For example, if *D&C* Creations expanded to a product line of, say, 30 items utilizing 20 materials (rather than 2 or 3 of each), the matrices *R* and *C* (relating products to materials and materials to cost) would become quite large, but the relationship between products and material costs would still be exhibited in the single matrix product *RC*.

14.2 EXERCISES

Compute each of the following products, if possible. If a product is not computable, state why not.

1. $\begin{bmatrix} -3 & 2 \\ 4 & 1 \end{bmatrix} \cdot \begin{bmatrix} -2 & 0 \\ 1 & 3 \end{bmatrix}$

2. $\begin{bmatrix} -5 & 2 \\ 1 & 4 \end{bmatrix} \cdot \begin{bmatrix} -1 & 4 \\ 3 & 0 \end{bmatrix}$

3. $\begin{bmatrix} 0 & -2 \\ 5 & 1 \end{bmatrix} \cdot \begin{bmatrix} -3 & 6 \\ 1 & 4 \end{bmatrix}$

4. $\begin{bmatrix} -3 & 5 \\ 1 & 0 \end{bmatrix} \cdot \begin{bmatrix} 8 & -2 \\ 1 & 7 \end{bmatrix}$

5. $\begin{bmatrix} 1 & 3 \\ 4 & 1 \end{bmatrix} \cdot \begin{bmatrix} 2 & 1 & 0 \\ 5 & 2 & 3 \end{bmatrix}$

6. $\begin{bmatrix} -5 & 6 \\ 3 & 4 \end{bmatrix} \cdot \begin{bmatrix} -3 & 5 & 0 \\ 0 & 1 & 5 \end{bmatrix}$

7. $\begin{bmatrix} 3 & 2 \\ 5 & 1 \\ 0 & 4 \end{bmatrix} \cdot \begin{bmatrix} 2 & -1 \\ 1 & 3 \end{bmatrix}$

8. $\begin{bmatrix} -1 & 0 \\ 4 & 1 \\ 2 & 0 \end{bmatrix} \cdot \begin{bmatrix} -5 & 0 \\ 4 & 2 \end{bmatrix}$

9. $\begin{bmatrix} -5 & 1 \\ 6 & 2 \end{bmatrix} \cdot \begin{bmatrix} -3 & 2 \\ 4 & 1 \\ 5 & 8 \end{bmatrix}$

10. $\begin{bmatrix} -7 & 3 \\ 9 & 2 \end{bmatrix} \cdot \begin{bmatrix} 4 & -1 \\ 2 & -5 \\ 3 & 6 \end{bmatrix}$

11. $\begin{bmatrix} -5 & 1 & 3 \\ 2 & 0 & 4 \\ 3 & 0 & 2 \end{bmatrix} \cdot \begin{bmatrix} -2 & 0 & 0 \\ 4 & 1 & 0 \\ 0 & 1 & 0 \end{bmatrix}$

12. $\begin{bmatrix} -3 & 4 & 0 \\ 2 & -1 & 5 \\ 0 & 4 & 1 \end{bmatrix} \cdot \begin{bmatrix} 0 & 4 & 0 \\ 2 & 0 & 3 \\ 0 & 5 & 1 \end{bmatrix}$

13. Harry's Donuts, a small neighborhood bakery, sells four main items: sweet rolls, bread, cakes, and pies. Matrix *A* below shows the number of units of the main ingredients needed for these items.

		Eggs	Flour	Sugar	Shortening	Milk
	Sweet rolls	1	4	1/4	1/4	1
$A =$	Bread	0	3	0	1/4	0
	Cakes	4	3	2	1	1
	Pies	0	1	0	1/3	0

The cost, in cents per egg or per cup, of each ingredient when purchased in large lots or in small lots is given by matrix *B*.

PURCHASE OPTION

		Large lot	Small lot
	Eggs	5	5
	Flour	8	10
$B =$	Sugar	10	12
	Shortening	12	15
	Milk	5	6

Use matrix multiplication to find a matrix representing the comparative costs per item for the two purchase options (buying in large lots or in small lots).

Suppose a day's orders at Harry's (see Exercise 13) consist of 20 dozen sweet rolls, 200 loaves of bread, 50 cakes, and 60 pies.

14. Write this day's orders as a 1 × 4 matrix *D*, and use matrix multiplication to write as a matrix the amount of each ingredient needed to fill the day's orders.

15. Use matrix multiplication to find a matrix representing the costs to fill the day's orders under the two purchase options.

Refer to the expanded matrices of Example 3, part (a). Assume that Don and Connie have now expanded their product line to include desks, each requiring 10 units of wood, 7 units of hardware, and 4 units of paint.

16. Set up a matrix R relating furniture to materials for the complete line of *D&C* Creations.

17. Set up and compute an appropriate matrix product that will relate furniture to cost of materials.

18. Don and Connie have found that the *labor* required for assembling and finishing is four hours per table, two hours per chair, and five hours per desk, and that their labor cost is $9 per hour. Write a column matrix relating furniture to labor cost.

19. Combine your answers from Exercises 17 and 18 to obtain a 3×2 matrix relating furniture (table, chair, desk) to cost of resources (materials, labor).

20. Write a column matrix relating furniture to selling price. Assume the selling price of each furniture item must cover its own material and labor costs, plus $10 in overhead expenses, plus a profit ($20 per table, $10 per chair, and $25 per desk).

In Ohio, high school football teams are ranked by the Harbin Football Team Rating System. A team is granted one level 1 point for each team it defeats, and is also granted one level 2 point for each time that a team it defeats beats another team. Teams A, B, C, and D all played one another. The results are shown in matrix H, where an entry of 1 indicates a win. For example, A beat C only, B beat both A and D, and so on.

$$H = \begin{array}{c} \\ A \\ B \\ C \\ D \end{array} \begin{array}{c} \begin{array}{cccc} A & B & C & D \end{array} \\ \begin{bmatrix} 0 & 0 & 1 & 0 \\ 1 & 0 & 0 & 1 \\ 0 & 1 & 0 & 1 \\ 1 & 0 & 0 & 0 \end{bmatrix} \end{array}$$

21. Complete the table below for these four teams.

Team	Level 1 Points	Level 2 Points	Total Points
A	____	____	____
B	____	____	____
C	____	____	____
D	____	____	____

22. Let K be a 4×1 matrix with every entry a 1.
    (a) Compute the product HK.
    (b) What does HK represent?

23. (a) Compute H^2K.
    (b) What does H^2K represent?

24. (a) Compute $HK + H^2K$.
    (b) What does $HK + H^2K$ represent?

25. Is it true that $(H + H^2)K = HK + H^2K$? If so, verify it by direct computation.

26. Is it true that $(I + H)HK = HK + H^2K$? If so, verify it by direct computation. (In this case, I is the 4×4 identity matrix.)

Consider the matrices $A = \begin{bmatrix} 1 & 2 \\ 3 & 2 \end{bmatrix}$, $B = \begin{bmatrix} -1 & -3 \\ 2 & 2 \end{bmatrix}$, $C = \begin{bmatrix} 1 & 2 \\ -1 & -3 \end{bmatrix}$, *and* $I = \begin{bmatrix} 1 & 0 \\ 0 & 1 \end{bmatrix}$.

The following statements illustrate (but do not prove) several algebraic properties of the system of 2×2 matrices. In each case, verify the given statement by direct computation.

27. AB is computable and is of order 2×2. (closure property)

28. $AI = IA = A$. (identity property)

29. $(AB)C = A(BC)$. (associative property)

30. $(A + B)C = AC + BC$. (the right distributive property for addition)

31. $(A - B)C = AC - BC$. (the right distributive property for subtraction)

32. Explain why the verifications in Exercises 27–31 do not actually prove the corresponding properties for the system of 2×2 matrices.

In Exercises 33–36, determine whether $AB = BA$.

33. $A = \begin{bmatrix} 8 & 6 \\ 3 & 5 \end{bmatrix}$ $B = \begin{bmatrix} 10 & 14 \\ 7 & 3 \end{bmatrix}$

34. $A = \begin{bmatrix} -5/3 & -2/3 \\ -2 & -1 \end{bmatrix}$ $B = \begin{bmatrix} -3 & 2 \\ 6 & -5 \end{bmatrix}$

35. $A = \begin{bmatrix} 2 & 7 \\ -3 & 4 \end{bmatrix}$ $B = \begin{bmatrix} 6 & -4 \\ 1 & 2 \end{bmatrix}$

36. $A = \begin{bmatrix} 1 & 0 \\ 1 & 1 \end{bmatrix}$ $B = \begin{bmatrix} 1 & 1 \\ 0 & 1 \end{bmatrix}$

37. Find an original example of 2×2 matrices A and B such that $AB = BA$.

38. Let $M = \begin{bmatrix} 1 & 1 \\ 1 & 1 \end{bmatrix}$.
    (a) Compute M^2.
    (b) Compute M^3.
    (c) Compute M^4.
    (d) Without actually computing it, what is M^{10}?

39. (a) Prove that $SI = S$ for every 3×3 matrix S.

(b) Does part (a) establish that $I = \begin{bmatrix} 1 & 0 & 0 \\ 0 & 1 & 0 \\ 0 & 0 & 1 \end{bmatrix}$ is the identity for multiplication of 3×3 matrices? Explain why or why not.

40. In Example 6, how do you interpret the entry 3 in row 3, column 3 of the matrix M^2?

41. Refer to Example 6. Compute the matrix M^3 and interpret the meaning of its entries.

Assume that a fifth computer is introduced into the network referred to in Example 6. It is connected as shown here.

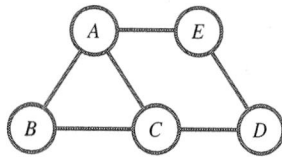

42. Write the communication matrix M for this new network.

43. Compute M^2.

44. According to M^2, how many ways can computer E send data to C through a single intermediary?

45. Without computing M^3, how many channels of communication would it show from B to E? What are those channels?

46. How many channels of communication from B to E would be shown in the matrix M^4?

The real numbers $2/5$ and $5/2$ are "multiplicative inverses" of each other because $(2/5) \cdot (5/2) = 1$, which is the identity for multiplication of real numbers. Similarly, two matrices A and B are multiplicative inverses of each other if $AB = I$ and $BA = I$, where I is the identity (of the same order in both cases) for multiplication of matrices. (In Section 4, we will address matrix inverses in more detail.)

47. In verifying that A and B are inverses, is it really necessary to compute both AB and BA? Why or why not?

48. What can you say about the orders of A and B if they are to be multiplicative inverses of each other?

Use the definition of matrix inverses (preceding Exercise 47) to determine whether each of the following pairs are inverses of each other.

49. $\begin{bmatrix} 1 & 0 \\ 0 & -1 \end{bmatrix}$ and $\begin{bmatrix} 1 & 0 \\ 0 & -1 \end{bmatrix}$

50. $\begin{bmatrix} 0 & 1 \\ 1 & 0 \end{bmatrix}$ and $\begin{bmatrix} 0 & 1 \\ 1 & 0 \end{bmatrix}$

51. $\begin{bmatrix} 2 & 1 \\ 4 & 3 \end{bmatrix}$ and $\begin{bmatrix} 3/2 & -1/2 \\ -2 & 1 \end{bmatrix}$

52. $\begin{bmatrix} -3 & 2 \\ 6 & -5 \end{bmatrix}$ and $\begin{bmatrix} -5/3 & -2/3 \\ -2 & -1 \end{bmatrix}$

53. $\begin{bmatrix} 3 & 1 & 4 \\ 1 & 0 & 1 \end{bmatrix}$ and $\begin{bmatrix} -1 & 1 \\ 0 & 1 \\ 1 & -1 \end{bmatrix}$

54. $\begin{bmatrix} -2 & 1/3 & 1 \\ 1/4 & 3 & 2 \end{bmatrix}$ and $\begin{bmatrix} 1 & 3 \\ 1/2 & 3/2 \end{bmatrix}$

55. $\begin{bmatrix} 5 & 6 \\ -10 & -13 \end{bmatrix}$ and $\begin{bmatrix} 13/5 & 6/5 \\ -2 & 1 \end{bmatrix}$

56. $\begin{bmatrix} 1 & 1 \\ 1 & -1 \end{bmatrix}$ and $\begin{bmatrix} 1/2 & 1/2 \\ 1/2 & 1/2 \end{bmatrix}$

57. $\begin{bmatrix} 1 & 3 & 3 \\ 1 & 4 & 3 \\ 1 & 3 & 4 \end{bmatrix}$ and $\begin{bmatrix} 7 & -3 & -3 \\ -1 & 1 & 0 \\ -1 & 0 & 1 \end{bmatrix}$

58. $\begin{bmatrix} -1 & 0 & 2 \\ 3 & 1 & 0 \\ 0 & 2 & -3 \end{bmatrix}$ and $\begin{bmatrix} -1/5 & 4/15 & -2/15 \\ 3/5 & 1/5 & 2/5 \\ 2/5 & 2/15 & -1/15 \end{bmatrix}$

59. Explain in your own words what a *row-column product* is, and how it is related to multiplication of matrices in general.

60. Explain why, in Example 7, the matrix product involves 90 products of entries.

Use a calculator to compute the following matrix products.

61. $\begin{bmatrix} 23.8 & 10.6 & 12.8 & 21.9 \\ 15.8 & 24.5 & 11.6 & 14.8 \\ 13.8 & 10.6 & 13.3 & 14.7 \\ 16.4 & 12.8 & 11.1 & 15.9 \\ 21.3 & 12.3 & 13.2 & 32.1 \end{bmatrix} \cdot \begin{bmatrix} 8.23 & 7.45 & 8.25 & 6.27 & 9.91 & 7.29 \\ 2.29 & 6.52 & 3.35 & 5.94 & 6.37 & 6.73 \\ 2.58 & 9.88 & 1.28 & 7.53 & 1.23 & 3.28 \\ 8.45 & 5.27 & 6.37 & 4.38 & 4.39 & 3.46 \end{bmatrix}$

62.

$$\begin{bmatrix} 4.56 & 9.87 & 2.91 \\ 6.37 & 2.81 & 6.81 \\ 5.28 & 4.79 & 4.21 \\ 5.28 & 6.97 & 1.38 \\ 3.84 & 5.28 & 3.91 \\ 4.68 & 2.38 & 1.54 \\ 4.44 & 5.55 & 6.66 \\ 9.63 & 8.52 & 7.41 \end{bmatrix} \cdot \begin{bmatrix} 8.23 & 4.19 & 2.28 & 9.28 & 8.27 \\ 1.32 & 6.58 & 7.17 & 8.23 & 9.82 \\ 3.37 & 8.26 & 1.49 & 6.54 & 9.87 \end{bmatrix}$$

14.3 Matrix Row Operations and Systems of Equations

Linear systems of equations were solved in an earlier chapter by the elimination method. That method can be streamlined into a systematic procedure based on matrices. Matrix methods are particularly suitable for computer solutions of large systems of equations having many unknowns.

To begin, consider a system of three equations and three unknowns such as

$$a_1 x + b_1 y + c_1 z = d_1$$
$$a_2 x + b_2 y + c_2 z = d_2$$
$$a_3 x + b_3 y + c_3 z = d_3.$$

This system can be written in an abbreviated form as the following 3×4 matrix.

$$\begin{bmatrix} a_1 & b_1 & c_1 & d_1 \\ a_2 & b_2 & c_2 & d_2 \\ a_3 & b_3 & c_3 & d_3 \end{bmatrix}$$

(Recall that each number in a matrix is called an *element,* or *entry.*) The last column of this matrix consists of the constants from the right in the original system of equations. By using a vertical line to set that column apart from the others (which consist of the coefficients of the variables), we obtain the following **augmented matrix.** (The square coefficient matrix is "augmented" with the column of constants.)

$$\left[\begin{array}{ccc|c} a_1 & b_1 & c_1 & d_1 \\ a_2 & b_2 & c_2 & d_2 \\ a_3 & b_3 & c_3 & d_3 \end{array}\right]$$

Each row of this augmented matrix represents one of the equations in the original system. By making a series of legitimate transformations in the matrix, we can eventually obtain a matrix that will produce an equivalent simpler system, one whose solution will be apparent. (Two systems of equations are *equivalent* if they have identical solutions.)

The trick is to use only matrix transformations such that the system corresponding to each successive matrix is equivalent to the previous system. The allowed transformations are the same as those used in the elimination method. In matrix language, they are called **matrix row operations.** They are listed here.

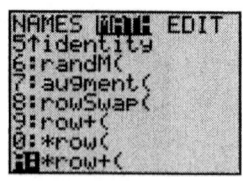

Options 8, 9, 0, and A in this menu allow the user to perform the matrix row operations described in the text.

Matrix Row Operations

For any nonzero real number k and any augmented matrix of a system of linear equations, the following **matrix row operations** will produce the matrix of an equivalent system:

1. **interchanging any two rows of a matrix,**
2. **multiplying the elements of any row of a matrix by the same nonzero number k, and**
3. **adding a common multiple of the elements of one row to the corresponding elements of another row.**

Our objective is to use row operations to transform the augmented matrix above into the form

$$\begin{bmatrix} 1 & 0 & 0 & | & a \\ 0 & 1 & 0 & | & b \\ 0 & 0 & 1 & | & c \end{bmatrix}$$

since the corresponding system will then be

$$\begin{cases} 1 \cdot x + 0 \cdot y + 0 \cdot z = a \\ 0 \cdot x + 1 \cdot y + 0 \cdot z = b \\ 0 \cdot x + 0 \cdot y + 1 \cdot z = c \end{cases} \quad \text{or} \quad \begin{cases} x = a \\ y = b. \\ z = c \end{cases}$$

The solution set is then $\{(a, b, c)\}$.

In effect, we use row operations to produce the elements of the identity

$$\begin{matrix} 1 & 0 & 0 \\ 0 & 1 & 0 \\ 0 & 0 & 1 \end{matrix}$$

to the left of the vertical line, and then read the solution (the variable values) from the right side of the vertical line. Any number of variables may occur in the system to be solved. For example, if we were solving a system of two equations with two unknowns, we would want to obtain a matrix of the form

$$\begin{bmatrix} 1 & 0 & | & a \\ 0 & 1 & | & b \end{bmatrix}.$$

This procedure is called the **Gauss-Jordan method.** It is illustrated in the following examples.

EXAMPLE 1 Solve the linear system

$$3x - 4y = 1$$
$$5x + 2y = 19.$$

The equations should all be in the same form, with the variable terms in the same order on the left, and the constant term on the right. Begin by writing the augmented matrix.

$$\begin{bmatrix} 3 & -4 & | & 1 \\ 5 & 2 & | & 19 \end{bmatrix}$$

The goal is to transform this augmented matrix into the form

$$\begin{bmatrix} 1 & 0 & | & k \\ 0 & 1 & | & j \end{bmatrix}$$

for real numbers k and j. Once the augmented matrix is in this form, the matrix can be rewritten as a linear system to get

$$x = k$$
$$y = j.$$

The necessary transformations are performed as follows. It is best to work in columns beginning in each column with the element that is to become a 1. In the augmented matrix

$$\begin{bmatrix} 3 & -4 & | & 1 \\ 5 & 2 & | & 19 \end{bmatrix}$$

there is a 3 in the first row, first column position. Use row operation 2, multiplying each entry in the first row by $1/3$ to get a 1 in this position. (This step is abbreviated as $(1/3)$R1.)

$$\begin{bmatrix} 1 & -4/3 & | & 1/3 \\ 5 & 2 & | & 19 \end{bmatrix} \quad \tfrac{1}{3}\text{R1}$$

Get a 0 in the second row, first column by multiplying each element of the first row by -5 and adding the result to the corresponding element in the second row, using row operation 3.

$$\begin{bmatrix} 1 & -4/3 & | & 1/3 \\ 0 & 26/3 & | & 52/3 \end{bmatrix} \quad -5\text{R1} + \text{R2}$$

Get a 1 in the second row, second column by multiplying each element of the second row by $3/26$, using row operation 2.

$$\begin{bmatrix} 1 & -4/3 & | & 1/3 \\ 0 & 1 & | & 2 \end{bmatrix} \quad \tfrac{3}{26}\text{R2}$$

Finally, get a 0 in the first row, second column by multiplying each element of the second row by $4/3$ and adding the result to the corresponding element in the first row, using row operation 3.

$$\begin{bmatrix} 1 & 0 & | & 3 \\ 0 & 1 & | & 2 \end{bmatrix} \quad \tfrac{4}{3}\text{R2} + \text{R1}$$

This last matrix corresponds to the system

$$x = 3$$
$$y = 2,$$

which has the solution set $\{(3, 2)\}$. This solution could have been read directly from the third column of the final matrix. ◢

The **determinant** of the 2×2 matrix $\begin{bmatrix} a & c \\ b & d \end{bmatrix}$ is symbolized with vertical "fences" rather than brackets:

$$\begin{vmatrix} a & c \\ b & d \end{vmatrix}.$$

This determinant stands for a real number: by definition, the product of the two numbers on the diagonal from NW to SE minus the product of the two numbers on the diagonal from SW to NE. (See Exercises 33–36 in the next section.) For example,

$$\begin{vmatrix} 4 & 1 \\ 6 & -2 \end{vmatrix} = 4(-2) - 6(1) = -14.$$

In 1750, Gabriel Cramer (1704–1752) published the theory of determinants. It provided a way of solving linear systems which predated more general matrix methods by a century. Cramer's rule is still used today. The system

$$3x + y = 5$$
$$2x - y = 10$$

is solved by first forming three determinants as follows.

$D = \begin{vmatrix} 3 & 1 \\ 2 & -1 \end{vmatrix}$ (the determinant of the coefficient matrix)

$D_x = \begin{vmatrix} 5 & 1 \\ 10 & -1 \end{vmatrix}$ (the same as D but with the x-coefficients replaced by the constants)

$D_y = \begin{vmatrix} 3 & 5 \\ 2 & 10 \end{vmatrix}$ (the same as D but with the y-coefficients replaced by the constants)

Now $D = 3(-1) - 2(1) = -5$, $D_x = 5(-1) - 10(1) = -15$, and $D_y = 3(10) - 2(5) = 20$. The solution values are then

$$x = \frac{D_x}{D} = \frac{-15}{-5} = 3 \quad \text{and} \quad y = \frac{D_y}{D} = \frac{20}{-5} = -4.$$

In other words, the solution set of the system of equations is $\{(3, -4)\}$.

For Group Discussion

1. Apply Cramer's rule to the following system.

$$2x - 4y = 14$$
$$5x + 3y = -30$$

2. Apply Cramer's rule to the following system.

$$3x - 4y = 6$$
$$-12x + 16y = 10$$

3. Why do you think Cramer's rule failed to produce a solution for the system in problem 2 above? Could another method be used to solve the system?

EXAMPLE 2 At the Evergreen Ranch, 6 goats and 5 sheep sell for $305, while 2 goats and 9 sheep cost $285. Find the cost of a goat and the cost of a sheep.

To solve this problem, first write a system of equations. Then use the Gauss-Jordan method to solve the system. Begin by identifying the variables.

$$x = \text{cost of a goat} \quad \text{and} \quad y = \text{cost of a sheep}$$

From the given information, 6 goats and 5 sheep cost a total of $305, so that

$$6x + 5y = 305.$$

Also, 2 goats and 9 sheep cost a total of $285, so that

$$2x + 9y = 285.$$

We must now find the common solution for these two equations, that is, the solution of the linear system

$$6x + 5y = 305$$
$$2x + 9y = 285.$$

Write the augmented matrix and then apply the appropriate row operations.

$$\begin{bmatrix} 6 & 5 & | & 305 \\ 2 & 9 & | & 285 \end{bmatrix}$$

$$\begin{bmatrix} 1 & 5/6 & | & 305/6 \\ 2 & 9 & | & 285 \end{bmatrix} \quad \frac{1}{6}R1$$

$$\begin{bmatrix} 1 & 5/6 & | & 305/6 \\ 0 & 22/3 & | & 550/3 \end{bmatrix} \quad -2R1 + R2$$

$$\begin{bmatrix} 1 & 5/6 & | & 305/6 \\ 0 & 1 & | & 25 \end{bmatrix} \quad \frac{3}{22}R2$$

$$\begin{bmatrix} 1 & 0 & | & 30 \\ 0 & 1 & | & 25 \end{bmatrix} \quad -\frac{5}{6}R2 + R1$$

From the rightmost column, read $x = 30$, $y = 25$. Each goat costs $30, while each sheep costs $25.

EXAMPLE 3 Use the Gauss-Jordan method to solve the system

$$x - y + 5z = -6$$
$$3x + 3y - z = 10$$
$$x + 3y + 2z = 5.$$

Since the system is in proper form, begin by writing the augmented matrix of the linear system.

$$\begin{bmatrix} 1 & -1 & 5 & | & -6 \\ 3 & 3 & -1 & | & 10 \\ 1 & 3 & 2 & | & 5 \end{bmatrix}$$

The final matrix is to be of the form

$$\begin{bmatrix} 1 & 0 & 0 & | & m \\ 0 & 1 & 0 & | & n \\ 0 & 0 & 1 & | & p \end{bmatrix},$$

This is the augmented matrix for the original system in Example 3.

S27

where m, n, and p are real numbers. This final form of the matrix gives the system $x = m$, $y = n$, and $z = p$, so the solution set is $\{(m, n, p)\}$.

The original augmented matrix already has a 1 in the first row, first column. Get a 0 in the second row, first column by multiplying each element in the first row by -3 and adding the result to the corresponding element in the second row, using row operation 3.

$$\begin{bmatrix} 1 & -1 & 5 & | & -6 \\ 0 & 6 & -16 & | & 28 \\ 1 & 3 & 2 & | & 5 \end{bmatrix} \quad -3R1 + R2$$

Now, to change the last element in the first column to a 0, use row operation 3 and multiply each element of the first row by -1, and add the result to the corresponding element of the third row.

$$\begin{bmatrix} 1 & -1 & 5 & | & -6 \\ 0 & 6 & -16 & | & 28 \\ 0 & 4 & -3 & | & 11 \end{bmatrix} \quad -1R1 + R3$$

The same procedure is used to transform the second and third columns. For both of these columns perform the additional step of getting a 1 in the appropriate position of each column. Do this by multiplying the elements of the row by the reciprocal of the number in that position. (As row operations are performed, any fractions appearing in various positions can be reduced to lowest terms.)

$$\begin{bmatrix} 1 & -1 & 5 & | & -6 \\ 0 & 1 & -8/3 & | & 14/3 \\ 0 & 4 & -3 & | & 11 \end{bmatrix} \quad \frac{1}{6}R2$$

$$\begin{bmatrix} 1 & 0 & 7/3 & | & -4/3 \\ 0 & 1 & -8/3 & | & 14/3 \\ 0 & 4 & -3 & | & 11 \end{bmatrix} \quad R2 + R1$$

$$\begin{bmatrix} 1 & 0 & 7/3 & | & -4/3 \\ 0 & 1 & -8/3 & | & 14/3 \\ 0 & 0 & 23/3 & | & -23/3 \end{bmatrix} \quad -4R2 + R3$$

$$\begin{bmatrix} 1 & 0 & 7/3 & | & -4/3 \\ 0 & 1 & -8/3 & | & 14/3 \\ 0 & 0 & 1 & | & -1 \end{bmatrix} \quad \frac{3}{23}R3$$

$$\begin{bmatrix} 1 & 0 & 0 & | & 1 \\ 0 & 1 & -8/3 & | & 14/3 \\ 0 & 0 & 1 & | & -1 \end{bmatrix} \quad -\frac{7}{3}R3 + R1$$

$$\begin{bmatrix} 1 & 0 & 0 & | & 1 \\ 0 & 1 & 0 & | & 2 \\ 0 & 0 & 1 & | & -1 \end{bmatrix} \quad \frac{8}{3}R3 + R2$$

This is the augmented matrix for the final system in Example 3.

The linear system associated with this final matrix is

$$x = 1$$
$$y = 2$$
$$z = -1,$$

and the solution set is $\{(1, 2, -1)\}$. ◢

14.3 EXERCISES

Let $A = \begin{bmatrix} -4 & 0 & 1 \\ 3 & -4 & 2 \\ -1 & 2 & 1 \end{bmatrix}$ and $B = \begin{bmatrix} 2 & -1 & 3 \\ -4 & 0 & 1 \\ 1 & 3 & -3 \end{bmatrix}$.

Apply the row operations indicated in each case, and write out the resulting matrix. (We work here with a square matrix rather than an augmented matrix just to practice row operations.)

1. Interchange rows 1 and 3 of A.
2. Interchange rows 2 and 3 of B.
3. Multiply each element of row 2 of A by -3.
4. Double each element in row 1 of A.
5. Multiply each element of row 2 of B by -4, and add the results to row 1.
6. Multiply each element of row 3 of A by 5, and add the results to row 2.
7. Multiply each element of row 1 of A by 3, and add the results to row 3.
8. Multiply each element of row 3 of B by -1, and add the results to row 2.
9. Form matrix $A + B$. Multiply each element of row 2 of $A + B$ by -3, and add the results to row 1.
10. Form matrix $B - A$. Multiply each element of row 1 of $B - A$ by 5, and add the results to row 3.

State which row operation must be applied to matrix A or B from above to get the following matrices.

11. to A; $\begin{bmatrix} 3 & -4 & 2 \\ -4 & 0 & 1 \\ -1 & 2 & 1 \end{bmatrix}$

12. to B; $\begin{bmatrix} 3 & 2 & 0 \\ -4 & 0 & 1 \\ 1 & 3 & -3 \end{bmatrix}$

13. to A; $\begin{bmatrix} -4 & 0 & 1 \\ 6 & -8 & 4 \\ -1 & 2 & 1 \end{bmatrix}$

14. to A; $\begin{bmatrix} -4 & 0 & 1 \\ 3 & -4 & 2 \\ 1/2 & -1 & -1/2 \end{bmatrix}$

15. to B; $\begin{bmatrix} 2 & -1 & 3 \\ 0 & -2 & 7 \\ 1 & 3 & -3 \end{bmatrix}$

16. to B; $\begin{bmatrix} -1 & -10 & 12 \\ -4 & 0 & 1 \\ 1 & 3 & -3 \end{bmatrix}$

Find the sequence of row operations that will change each of the following matrices into the identity matrix, if possible.

17. $\begin{bmatrix} 1 & 2 \\ 0 & -1 \end{bmatrix}$

18. $\begin{bmatrix} 2 & 1 \\ 1 & -1 \end{bmatrix}$

19. $\begin{bmatrix} -2 & 2 \\ 4 & 1 \end{bmatrix}$

20. $\begin{bmatrix} 0 & -1 \\ -2 & 0 \end{bmatrix}$

21. $\begin{bmatrix} 6 & 3 & 0 \\ 0 & 4 & 0 \\ 0 & 0 & 2 \end{bmatrix}$

22. $\begin{bmatrix} -2 & 2 & 0 \\ 0 & 1 & 0 \\ 1 & 1 & 1 \end{bmatrix}$

Write the augmented matrix for each system. Do not try to solve.

23. $2x + 3y = 11$
$\quad\;\; x + 2y = 8$

24. $3x + 5y = -13$
$\quad\;\; 2x + 3y = -9$

25. $\quad x + 5y = 6$
$\quad 3x - 4y = 1$

26. $\begin{aligned} 2x + 7y &= 1 \\ 5x + y &= -15 \end{aligned}$

27. $\begin{aligned} 2x + y + z &= 3 \\ 3x - 4y + 2z &= -7 \\ x + y + z &= 2 \end{aligned}$

28. $\begin{aligned} 4x - 2y + 3z &= 4 \\ 3x + 5y + z &= 7 \\ 5x - y + 4z &= 7 \end{aligned}$

29. $\begin{aligned} x + y &= 6 \\ 2y + z &= 2 \\ z &= 2 \end{aligned}$

30. $\begin{aligned} x &= 6 \\ y + 2z &= 2 \\ x - 3z &= 2 \end{aligned}$

Use matrix row operations to solve the following systems of equations.

31. $\begin{aligned} x + y &= 5 \\ x - y &= -1 \end{aligned}$

32. $\begin{aligned} x + 2y &= 5 \\ 2x + y &= -2 \end{aligned}$

33. $\begin{aligned} x + y &= -3 \\ 2x - 5y &= -6 \end{aligned}$

34. $\begin{aligned} 3x - 2y &= 4 \\ 3x + y &= -2 \end{aligned}$

35. $\begin{aligned} 2x - 3y &= 10 \\ 2x + 2y &= 5 \end{aligned}$

36. $\begin{aligned} 6x + y &= 5 \\ 5x + y &= 3 \end{aligned}$

37. $\begin{aligned} 2x - 5y &= 10 \\ 3x + y &= 15 \end{aligned}$

38. $\begin{aligned} 4x - y &= 3 \\ -2x + 3y &= 1 \end{aligned}$

39. $\begin{aligned} 2x - 3y &= 2 \\ 4x - 6y &= 1 \end{aligned}$

40. $\begin{aligned} x + 2y &= 1 \\ 2x + 4y &= 3 \end{aligned}$

41. $\begin{aligned} x + y &= -1 \\ y + z &= 4 \\ x + z &= 1 \end{aligned}$

42. $\begin{aligned} x - z &= -3 \\ y + z &= 9 \\ x + z &= 7 \end{aligned}$

43. $\begin{aligned} x + y - z &= 6 \\ 2x - y + z &= -9 \\ x - 2y + 3z &= 1 \end{aligned}$

44. $\begin{aligned} x + 3y - 6z &= 7 \\ 2x - y + z &= 1 \\ x + 2y + 2z &= -1 \end{aligned}$

45. $\begin{aligned} -x + y &= -1 \\ y - z &= 6 \\ x + z &= -1 \end{aligned}$

46. $\begin{aligned} x + y &= 1 \\ 2x - z &= 0 \\ y + 2z &= -2 \end{aligned}$

47. $\begin{aligned} 3x + 2y - w &= 0 \\ 2x + z + 2w &= 5 \\ x + 2y - z &= -2 \\ 2x - y + z + w &= 2 \end{aligned}$

48. $\begin{aligned} x + 3y - 2z - w &= 9 \\ 4x + y + z + 2w &= 2 \\ -3x - y + z - w &= -5 \\ x - y - 3z - 2w &= 2 \end{aligned}$

Use the Gauss-Jordan method to solve each problem.

49. Linda Ramirez is a building contractor. If she hires 7 day laborers and 2 concrete finishers, her payroll for the day is $692, while 1 day laborer and 5 concrete finishers cost $476. Find the daily wage charge for each type of worker.

50. A biologist wants to grow two types of algae, types *A* and *B*. She has available 15 gal of nutrient I and 26 gal of nutrient II. A vat of algae *A* needs 2 gal of nutrient I and 3 gal of nutrient II, while a vat of algae *B* needs 1 gal of I and 2 gal of II. How many vats of each type of algae should the biologist grow in order to use all the nutrients?

51. To make his portrait bust of Millard Fillmore, Harry bought 2 lb of dark clay and 3 lb of light clay, paying $13 for the clay. He later needed one more pound of dark clay and 2 lb of light clay, costing $7 altogether. How much did he pay per pound for each type of clay?

52. The perimeter of a triangle is 21 cm. If two sides are of equal length, and the third side is 3 cm longer than one of the equal sides, find the lengths of the sides.

53. The secretary of the local consumer group bought some decals at 8¢ each and some bumper stickers at 10¢ each to give to the members. He spent a total of $15.52. If he bought a total of 170 items, how many of each kind did he buy?

54. The Matrix and the Patrix, a local musical group, is coming to play at a school festival. The reporter for the school newspaper doesn't know how many guitarists and how many members of the rhythm section there are in the group. Janet, one of the guitarists, says that, not counting herself, there are three times as many members of the rhythm group as guitarists. Steve, a member of the rhythm section, says that, not counting himself, the number of members of the rhythm section is one less than twice the number of guitarists. How many of each are there in the group?

14.4   **Matrix Inverses; Input-Output Models**

Two matrices A and B are said to be **inverses** of each other if $AB = I$ and $BA = I$, where I is the appropriate identity matrix (the same one in both cases). For example, the matrices

$$\begin{bmatrix} 3 & 5 \\ 1 & 2 \end{bmatrix} \quad \text{and} \quad \begin{bmatrix} 2 & -5 \\ -1 & 3 \end{bmatrix}$$

are inverses of each other, since

$$\begin{bmatrix} 3 & 5 \\ 1 & 2 \end{bmatrix} \cdot \begin{bmatrix} 2 & -5 \\ -1 & 3 \end{bmatrix} = \begin{bmatrix} 1 & 0 \\ 0 & 1 \end{bmatrix}$$

and

$$\begin{bmatrix} 2 & -5 \\ -1 & 3 \end{bmatrix} \cdot \begin{bmatrix} 3 & 5 \\ 1 & 2 \end{bmatrix} = \begin{bmatrix} 1 & 0 \\ 0 & 1 \end{bmatrix}.$$

The inverse of matrix A is written A^{-1} (read "A inverse").

Matrix Inverses

Matrices A and A^{-1} are inverses of each other if

$$AA^{-1} = I \quad \text{and} \quad A^{-1}A = I.$$

These screens support the result of Example 1. Notice that the entry in row 1, column 2 of the product is 1×10^{-13}, which is as close as the calculator can get to 0 for this computation. *One must always be aware of the limitations of technology!*

EXAMPLE 1   Determine whether or not

$$\begin{bmatrix} 4 & 5 \\ -1 & 2 \end{bmatrix} \quad \text{and} \quad \begin{bmatrix} 2/13 & -5/13 \\ 1/13 & 4/13 \end{bmatrix}$$

are inverses of each other.

Find the two products.

$$\begin{bmatrix} 4 & 5 \\ -1 & 2 \end{bmatrix} \cdot \begin{bmatrix} 2/13 & -5/13 \\ 1/13 & 4/13 \end{bmatrix} = \begin{bmatrix} 8/13 + 5/13 & -20/13 + 20/13 \\ -2/13 + 2/13 & 5/13 + 8/13 \end{bmatrix}$$

$$= \begin{bmatrix} 1 & 0 \\ 0 & 1 \end{bmatrix}$$

and

$$\begin{bmatrix} 2/13 & -5/13 \\ 1/13 & 4/13 \end{bmatrix} \cdot \begin{bmatrix} 4 & 5 \\ -1 & 2 \end{bmatrix} = \begin{bmatrix} 8/13 + 5/13 & 10/13 - 10/13 \\ 4/13 - 4/13 & 5/13 + 8/13 \end{bmatrix}$$

$$= \begin{bmatrix} 1 & 0 \\ 0 & 1 \end{bmatrix}.$$

Since both products are equal to I (the 2×2 identity matrix in this case), the two given matrices *are* inverses of each other. ◢

Only square matrices can possibly have inverses. (Why is this so?) Furthermore, not all square matrices have inverses. (See Example 4.) As we develop a

S31

way to find inverses, we will at first consider only square matrices of order 2×2.

First, by the definition of matrix inverse, if A is a 2×2 matrix and A^{-1} is its inverse, then $A^{-1}A = I$. Therefore if we can find the matrix multiplier that changes A into I, then we have found A^{-1}.

To begin our search for such a multiplier, we observe that applying any of the three row operations of the previous section to a 2×2 matrix has the same effect as multiplying that matrix by another (appropriate) 2×2 matrix. For example, let $M = \begin{bmatrix} 2 & 4 \\ 3 & 5 \end{bmatrix}$ and multiply M by the 2×2 multiplier $\begin{bmatrix} 0 & 1 \\ 1 & 0 \end{bmatrix}$:

$$\begin{bmatrix} 0 & 1 \\ 1 & 0 \end{bmatrix} \cdot \begin{bmatrix} 2 & 4 \\ 3 & 5 \end{bmatrix} = \begin{bmatrix} 0 \cdot 2 + 1 \cdot 3 & 0 \cdot 4 + 1 \cdot 5 \\ 1 \cdot 2 + 0 \cdot 3 & 1 \cdot 4 + 0 \cdot 5 \end{bmatrix} = \begin{bmatrix} 3 & 5 \\ 2 & 4 \end{bmatrix}.$$

This particular multiplier has the same effect as row operation 1 (interchanging the two rows). In Exercises 27–30, you will see that the other two row operations are also equivalent to multiplying by (appropriate) matrix multipliers.

Since a product of two (or more) 2×2 matrices is another 2×2 matrix, a sequence of row operations, applied in succession, has the net effect of multiplying by some single matrix. Now we know that

$$A^{-1}A = I \qquad \text{and also} \qquad A^{-1}I = A^{-1},$$

so that the multiplier, A^{-1}, that changes A to I will also change I to A^{-1}. This means that any sequence of row operations that changes A to I will also change I to A^{-1}. This fact enables us to use row operations to find A^{-1}. Form a new augmented matrix of the form $[A \,|\, I]$ and apply row operations to change A (on the left) to I. The I (on the right) will automatically become A^{-1}, as illustrated here.

$$[A \,|\, I]$$

Apply row operations to obtain

$$[I \,|\, A^{-1}]$$

 EXAMPLE 2 Find the inverse of the matrix $A = \begin{bmatrix} 2 & -5 \\ -1 & 3 \end{bmatrix}$.

Form the augmented matrix $[A \,|\, I]$ and then change A to I on the left, using row operations as in Section 3.

$$[A \,|\, I]$$
$$\begin{bmatrix} 2 & -5 & | & 1 & 0 \\ -1 & 3 & | & 0 & 1 \end{bmatrix}$$

James Joseph Sylvester (1814–1897) was working as an actuary in the early 1850s in London when Cayley (see facing page) was practicing law there. They met, and while not collaborators as such, they worked side-by-side on the algebra of invariants. Sylvester thought up "matrix" and a number of other terms such as "invariant" and "syzygy" (look that up!). Sylvester's early career was hampered by English law, which required a religious test (Sylvester was Jewish). Thus he did not get his degree from Cambridge until 1872. Sylvester, in contrast to Cayley, taught at several institutions, including a brief stay at the University of Virginia (1841). He was at Johns Hopkins from 1877 to 1883, where his influence helped to establish mathematical research at the university level. He founded the *American Journal of Mathematics*.

Sylvester was also a poet, and he published his *Laws of Verse* in 1870, applying principles of "phonetic syzygy."

First obtain a 1 in row 1, column 1:

$$\begin{bmatrix} 1 & -5/2 & | & 1/2 & 0 \\ -1 & 3 & | & 0 & 1 \end{bmatrix} \quad \tfrac{1}{2}\,R1$$

Next obtain a 0 in row 2, column 1:

$$\begin{bmatrix} 1 & -5/2 & | & 1/2 & 0 \\ 0 & 1/2 & | & 1/2 & 1 \end{bmatrix} \quad R1 + R2$$

Next obtain a 1 in row 2, column 2:

$$\begin{bmatrix} 1 & -5/2 & | & 1/2 & 0 \\ 0 & 1 & | & 1 & 2 \end{bmatrix} \quad 2R2$$

Finally obtain a 0 in row 1, column 2:

$$\begin{bmatrix} 1 & 0 & | & 3 & 5 \\ 0 & 1 & | & 1 & 2 \end{bmatrix} \quad \tfrac{5}{2}\,R2 + R1$$

$$[I \,|\, A^{-1}]$$

This result shows that $A^{-1} = \begin{bmatrix} 3 & 5 \\ 1 & 2 \end{bmatrix}$. You can verify this by computing AA^{-1} and $A^{-1}A$. Both of these products should equal I, the 2×2 identity matrix. ◾

The procedure above generalizes to a square matrix of any order (3×3, 4×4, and so on), as summarized here.

Finding the Inverse of a Matrix

Given any square matrix A, its inverse A^{-1} (if there is an inverse) is found by performing the following steps:

1. Form the augmented matrix $[A \,|\, I]$.
2. Use row operations to obtain a 1 in row 1, column 1.
3. Obtain 0s in all other column 1 positions.
4. Obtain a 1 in row 2, column 2.
5. Obtain 0s in all other column 2 positions.
6. Continue until A is changed into I.
7. The right half of the final result is now A^{-1}.

If any one of these steps is impossible, then matrix A has no inverse.

EXAMPLE 3   Find the inverse of $B = \begin{bmatrix} 1 & 3 & 3 \\ 1 & 4 & 3 \\ 1 & 3 & 4 \end{bmatrix}$.

Perform the steps listed above.

Arthur Cayley (1821–1895) showed such an early affinity for mathematics that he went to Cambridge instead of entering his father's business. Even while Cayley was practicing law (1848–1862), he wrote numerous theoretical papers on mathematics. During this time he and James Sylvester were founding the theory of invariants, out of which grew Cayley's *Memoir on the Theory of Matrices* (1857). Invariants are algebraic expressions that remain virtually unaltered during certain "transformations," such as flips, rotations, and stretches.

In 1863 Cayley became Sadlerian Professor of Pure Mathematics at Cambridge. Except for a lecture series at Johns Hopkins in 1881, his life centered around Cambridge. His work, in contrast, extended to nearly every branch of mathematics. He helped to open the horizons of algebra to include systems that worked even where the commutative law didn't hold. He also helped to free geometry from its three-dimensional Euclidean limitations. Cayley theorized about geometry in *n* dimensions as early as 1843.

Matrix *B* of Example 3 is defined at the top of this screen. Its inverse, B^{-1}, is displayed at the bottom.

Step 1:

$$\left[\begin{array}{ccc|ccc} 1 & 3 & 3 & 1 & 0 & 0 \\ 1 & 4 & 3 & 0 & 1 & 0 \\ 1 & 3 & 4 & 0 & 0 & 1 \end{array}\right]$$

Step 2: There is already a 1 in row 1, column 1.

Step 3:

$$\left[\begin{array}{ccc|ccc} 1 & 3 & 3 & 1 & 0 & 0 \\ 0 & 1 & 0 & -1 & 1 & 0 \\ 0 & 0 & 1 & -1 & 0 & 1 \end{array}\right] \quad \begin{array}{l} -R1 + R2 \\ -R1 + R3 \end{array}$$

Step 4: There is already a 1 in row 2, column 2.

Step 5:

$$\left[\begin{array}{ccc|ccc} 1 & 0 & 3 & 4 & -3 & 0 \\ 0 & 1 & 0 & -1 & 1 & 0 \\ 0 & 0 & 1 & -1 & 0 & 1 \end{array}\right] \quad -3R2 + R1$$

Step 6:

$$\left[\begin{array}{ccc|ccc} 1 & 0 & 0 & 7 & -3 & -3 \\ 0 & 1 & 0 & -1 & 1 & 0 \\ 0 & 0 & 1 & -1 & 0 & 1 \end{array}\right] \quad -3R3 + R1$$

Step 7:

$$B^{-1} = \left[\begin{array}{ccc} 7 & -3 & -3 \\ -1 & 1 & 0 \\ -1 & 0 & 1 \end{array}\right]$$

To check, show that $BB^{-1} = I$ and $B^{-1}B = I$. ◢

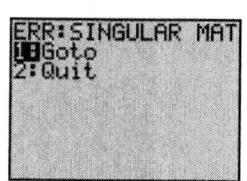

Matrix *C*, as defined in Example 4, has no inverse. Such a matrix is called a *singular matrix*, as seen on the bottom screen.

EXAMPLE 4 Let $C = \begin{bmatrix} 2 & 1 \\ 6 & 3 \end{bmatrix}$. Find C^{-1}.

Proceed as before.

$$\left[\begin{array}{cc|cc} 2 & 1 & 1 & 0 \\ 6 & 3 & 0 & 1 \end{array}\right]$$

$$\left[\begin{array}{cc|cc} 1 & 1/2 & 1/2 & 0 \\ 6 & 3 & 0 & 1 \end{array}\right] \quad \frac{1}{2} R1$$

$$\left[\begin{array}{cc|cc} 1 & 1/2 & 1/2 & 0 \\ 0 & 0 & -3 & 1 \end{array}\right] \quad -6R1 + R2$$

We cannot go further. There is no way to obtain a 1 in row 2, column 2 without losing the 0 just obtained in row 2, column 1. Thus, matrix *C* has no inverse. ◢

The matrix operations introduced in this chapter (addition, subtraction, multiplication by a scalar, and multiplication of two matrices) form the basis of *matrix algebra,* which is similar (but not identical) to real number algebra. Matrix algebra has many applications.

The ability to perform algebraic operations on matrices enables us to formulate the matrix solution of systems of equations in a simpler way. For example, in Example 1 of Section 3, the system

$$3x - 4y = 1$$
$$5x + 2y = 19$$

was solved using row operations. Notice now that if we arrange the x and y coefficients, the variables of the system, and the constants of the system into the three separate matrices

$$A = \begin{bmatrix} 3 & -4 \\ 5 & 2 \end{bmatrix}, \quad X = \begin{bmatrix} x \\ y \end{bmatrix}, \quad \text{and} \quad B = \begin{bmatrix} 1 \\ 19 \end{bmatrix},$$

the system can be written as the single matrix equation

$$AX = B.$$

Verify that the statement

$$\begin{bmatrix} 3 & -4 \\ 5 & 2 \end{bmatrix} \cdot \begin{bmatrix} x \\ y \end{bmatrix} = \begin{bmatrix} 1 \\ 19 \end{bmatrix}$$

is equivalent to the original system of equations.

Now we solve the matrix equation $AX = B$ using matrix algebra as follows.

$AX = B$	
$A^{-1}(AX) = A^{-1}B$	Multiply both sides by A^{-1}.
$(A^{-1}A)X = A^{-1}B$	Use the associative property on the left.
$IX = A^{-1}B$	$A^{-1}A = I$ by the definition of inverse.
$X = A^{-1}B$	$IX = X$ by the definition of identity.

When multiplying both sides of a matrix equation by another matrix (as was done above), be sure to multiply in the same order on both sides of the equation, since matrix multiplication is not commutative.

The matrix X, which now contains the variable values, that is, the solution of the system, is simply the product $A^{-1}B$. We summarize this result as follows.

Solving a Linear System Using Matrix Algebra

A system of linear equations represented by the matrix equation

$$AX = B$$

can be solved by finding A^{-1} and computing the product $A^{-1}B$. If A^{-1} does not exist, the system does not have a unique solution.

A graphing calculator with matrix capability can easily accomplish the system-solving procedure described in Example 5.

EXAMPLE 5 Solve the system

$$3x - 4y = 1$$
$$5x + 2y = 19$$

using matrix algebra.

First find A^{-1} as outlined in this section.

$$\left[\begin{array}{cc|cc} 3 & -4 & 1 & 0 \\ 5 & 2 & 0 & 1 \end{array}\right]$$

$$\left[\begin{array}{cc|cc} 1 & -4/3 & 1/3 & 0 \\ 5 & 2 & 0 & 1 \end{array}\right] \qquad \frac{1}{3} \text{R1}$$

$$\left[\begin{array}{cc|cc} 1 & -4/3 & 1/3 & 0 \\ 0 & 26/3 & -5/3 & 1 \end{array}\right] \qquad -5\text{R1} + \text{R2}$$

$$\left[\begin{array}{cc|cc} 1 & -4/3 & 1/3 & 0 \\ 0 & 1 & -5/26 & 3/26 \end{array}\right] \qquad \frac{3}{26} \text{R2}$$

$$\left[\begin{array}{cc|cc} 1 & 0 & 1/13 & 2/13 \\ 0 & 1 & -5/26 & 3/26 \end{array}\right] \qquad \frac{4}{3} \text{R2} + \text{R1}$$

Now

$$X = A^{-1}B = \left[\begin{array}{cc} 1/13 & 2/13 \\ -5/26 & 3/26 \end{array}\right] \cdot \left[\begin{array}{c} 1 \\ 19 \end{array}\right] = \left[\begin{array}{c} 3 \\ 2 \end{array}\right]$$

so the solution set of the system is $\{(3, 2)\}$. ◢

It may have occurred to you that this matrix algebra method of solving a linear system is really no better than the row operation method of the last section. In fact, finding A^{-1} here required the same sequence of row operations that we used before. In addition, we then had to compute the product $A^{-1}B$.

The real advantage of this last method is that modern calculators (and computers) can easily compute matrix inverses as well as products. So when using a calculator, finding $A^{-1}B$ simply requires entering matrices A and B from the system of equations and then calculating an inverse and a product on the machine. (And these calculations are no more work for large systems than for small ones—except that there are more numbers to enter.)

EXAMPLE 6 Use matrix algebra to solve this system.

$$3x - 5y + 2z = 8$$
$$x + 3y - z = 5$$
$$x - 11y + 4z = -2$$

Start with the coefficient matrix

$$A = \left[\begin{array}{ccc} 3 & -5 & 2 \\ 1 & 3 & -1 \\ 1 & -11 & 4 \end{array}\right].$$

When we try to calculate A^{-1}, we find that A does not have an inverse. (Verify this.) Therefore the given system does not have a unique solution. ◢

S36

Input-Output Models

The economist W. W. Leontief, winner of a Nobel Prize in 1973, developed a method for analyzing an economy which involves matrices. The method is generally known as a **Leontief model,** or an **input-output model.** Suppose that an economy produces n commodities. The production of each uses some (perhaps all) of the other commodities in the economy. Thus, the production of oil requires oil, as well as steel, electricity, and so on. The amounts of all commodities used in the production of one unit of each commodity can be written as an $n \times n$ matrix, called the *input-output matrix,* or the **technological matrix** of the system. Denote the technological matrix A.

Let each of the following be an $n \times 1$ matrix showing the appropriate amounts of all commodities in the economy.

P = Gross Production (total of all commodities produced)
U = Internal Use (amounts of commodities used up in the production process itself)
D = Demand for net production (amounts of commodities needed above and beyond internal use)

The gross production must be sufficient to supply internal use plus the demand for net production:

$$P = U + D.$$

Consider an economy with only two basic products, wheat and oil. Assume that the production of 1 metric ton of wheat requires 1/4 metric ton of wheat and 1/3 metric ton of oil. The production of 1 metric ton of oil requires 1/12 metric ton of wheat and 1/9 metric ton of oil. This leads to the following technological matrix.

$$
A = \text{INPUT} \quad
\begin{array}{c} \\ \text{Wheat} \\ \text{Oil} \end{array}
\overset{\begin{array}{cc}\text{Wheat} & \text{Oil}\end{array}}{\begin{bmatrix} 1/4 & 1/12 \\ 1/3 & 1/9 \end{bmatrix}}, \quad \text{or simply} \quad A = \begin{bmatrix} 1/4 & 1/12 \\ 1/3 & 1/9 \end{bmatrix}
$$

(Notice that input appears on the left of the matrix and output on the top.)
We now claim that the internal use matrix is given by

$$U = AP.$$

To illustrate, suppose the gross production was

$$
P = \begin{array}{c} \\ \text{Wheat} \\ \text{Oil} \end{array}
\overset{\begin{array}{c}\text{Gross} \\ \text{production}\end{array}}{\begin{bmatrix} 864 \\ 4{,}320 \end{bmatrix}}.
$$

Then

$$\begin{pmatrix} \text{Wheat used} \\ \text{internally} \end{pmatrix} = \begin{pmatrix} \text{Wheat} \\ \text{used} \\ \text{per unit} \\ \text{of wheat} \\ \text{produced} \end{pmatrix} \cdot \begin{pmatrix} \text{Units of} \\ \text{wheat} \\ \text{produced} \end{pmatrix} + \begin{pmatrix} \text{Wheat} \\ \text{used} \\ \text{per unit} \\ \text{of oil} \\ \text{produced} \end{pmatrix} \cdot \begin{pmatrix} \text{Units} \\ \text{of oil} \\ \text{produced} \end{pmatrix}$$

$$= \frac{1}{4} \cdot 864 + \frac{1}{12} \cdot 4{,}320$$

$$= 576$$

and

$$\begin{pmatrix} \text{Oil used} \\ \text{internally} \end{pmatrix} = \begin{pmatrix} \text{Oil used} \\ \text{per unit} \\ \text{of wheat} \\ \text{produced} \end{pmatrix} \cdot \begin{pmatrix} \text{Units of} \\ \text{wheat} \\ \text{produced} \end{pmatrix} + \begin{pmatrix} \text{Oil used} \\ \text{per unit} \\ \text{of oil} \\ \text{produced} \end{pmatrix} \cdot \begin{pmatrix} \text{Units} \\ \text{of oil} \\ \text{produced} \end{pmatrix}$$

$$= \frac{1}{3} \cdot 864 + \frac{1}{9} \cdot 4{,}320$$

$$= 768$$

so
$$U = \begin{matrix} \\ \text{Wheat} \\ \text{Oil} \end{matrix} \begin{matrix} \text{Internal} \\ \text{use} \\ \begin{bmatrix} 576 \\ 768 \end{bmatrix} \end{matrix}.$$

But this is just what we obtain from the product AP:

$$AP = \begin{bmatrix} 1/4 & 1/12 \\ 1/3 & 1/9 \end{bmatrix} \cdot \begin{bmatrix} 864 \\ 4{,}320 \end{bmatrix} = \begin{bmatrix} 576 \\ 768 \end{bmatrix}.$$

Since $U = AP$, the equation

$$P = U + D$$

now becomes

$$P = AP + D \qquad \text{or} \qquad P - AP = D.$$

This equation, however, gives D in terms of P. The usual situation is that D is known and we need to find P. So we use matrix algebra to solve for P.

$$P - AP = D$$
$$IP - AP = D \qquad \text{Replace } P \text{ with } IP, \text{ where } I \text{ is the}$$
$$\text{identity matrix with the same order as } A.$$

$$(I - A)P = D \qquad \text{Distributive property}$$
$$(I - A)^{-1}(I - A)P = (I - A)^{-1}D \qquad \text{Multiply both sides by } (I - A)^{-1}.$$
$$IP = (I - A)^{-1}D \qquad \text{Replace } (I - A)^{-1}(I - A) \text{ with } I.$$
$$P = (I - A)^{-1}D \qquad \text{Replace } IP \text{ with } P.$$

We now have a method of finding the gross production, P, required to meet a demand for net production, D.

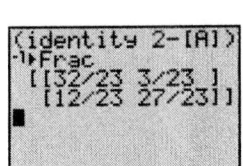

EXAMPLE 7 Find the gross production required in the wheat/oil economy above if the demand for net production is

$$D = \begin{bmatrix} 500 \\ 1,000 \end{bmatrix}.$$

First compute $I - A$:

$$I - A = \begin{bmatrix} 1 & 0 \\ 0 & 1 \end{bmatrix} - \begin{bmatrix} 1/4 & 1/12 \\ 1/3 & 1/9 \end{bmatrix} = \begin{bmatrix} 3/4 & -1/12 \\ -1/3 & 8/9 \end{bmatrix}.$$

Obtain the inverse of $I - A$ (using the procedure described earlier, or a calculator).

$$(I - A)^{-1} = \begin{bmatrix} 32/23 & 3/23 \\ 12/23 & 27/23 \end{bmatrix}$$

Now

$$P = (I - A)^{-1} \cdot D = \begin{bmatrix} 32/23 & 3/23 \\ 12/23 & 27/23 \end{bmatrix} \cdot \begin{bmatrix} 500 \\ 1,000 \end{bmatrix} = \begin{bmatrix} 826 \\ 1,435 \end{bmatrix}.$$

As you read through Example 7, follow these screens from top to bottom to see how a graphing calculator accomplishes the computation.

(Final amounts have been rounded to whole numbers.) A demand for net production of 500 metric tons of wheat and 1,000 metric tons of oil requires a gross production of 826 metric tons of wheat and 1,435 metric tons of oil.

14.4 EXERCISES

Find the inverse of each matrix that has an inverse.

1. $\begin{bmatrix} 1 & 0 \\ 0 & -1 \end{bmatrix}$

2. $\begin{bmatrix} 0 & 1 \\ 1 & 0 \end{bmatrix}$

3. $\begin{bmatrix} 2 & 1 \\ 4 & 3 \end{bmatrix}$

4. $\begin{bmatrix} -3 & 2 \\ 6 & -5 \end{bmatrix}$

5. $\begin{bmatrix} 1 & 1 \\ 1 & 1 \end{bmatrix}$

6. $\begin{bmatrix} -1 & -1 \\ 1 & 1 \end{bmatrix}$

7. $\begin{bmatrix} 1 & 2 & 0 \\ 0 & 1 & 0 \\ 1 & -1 & 1 \end{bmatrix}$

8. $\begin{bmatrix} 0 & 1 & 0 \\ 0 & 0 & -2 \\ 1 & -1 & 0 \end{bmatrix}$

9. $\begin{bmatrix} 4 & 3 & 3 \\ -1 & 0 & -1 \\ -4 & -4 & -3 \end{bmatrix}$

10. $\begin{bmatrix} 1 & 0 & 2 \\ -1 & 0 & -2 \\ 1 & 1 & 1 \end{bmatrix}$

Use matrix algebra to find the unique solution of each system. If the system has no unique solution, state why.

11. $4x + y = 5$
$2x + y = 3$

12. $3x - 7y = 31$
$2x - 4y = 18$

13. $5x - y = 6$
$-10x + 2y = 15$

14. $5x - y = 14$
$x + 8y = 11$

15. $x + y - z = 6$
$2x - y + z = -9$
$x - 2y + 3z = 1$

16. $4x + 2y - 3z = 6$
$x - 4y + z = -4$
$-x + 2z = 2$

17. $2x - y + 3z = 0$
$x + 2y - z = 5$
$2y + z = 1$

18. $x + y = 1$
$2x - z = 0$
$y + 2z = -2$

19. $2x - 3y + z = 4$
$\quad\quad x + y - z = 1$
$\quad\quad -5y + 3z = 2$

20. $\quad\quad x + 3y = 7$
$\quad\quad 2x - y - 5z = 12$
$\quad\quad 7y + 5z = 2$

In each of Exercises 1 and 2, the given matrix was its own inverse. In each of the following cases, find the missing elements to make the given matrix its own inverse.

21. $\begin{bmatrix} 3 & \square \\ 2 & \square \end{bmatrix}$

22. $\begin{bmatrix} \square & 8 \\ \square & 5 \end{bmatrix}$

23. $\begin{bmatrix} 2 & \square \\ \square & -2 \end{bmatrix}$

24. $\begin{bmatrix} \square & 5 \\ -7 & \square \end{bmatrix}$

Assuming that a and b are real numbers, determine whether each of the following statements is sometimes true, *always true,* or never true. *If sometimes true, give the conditions under which it is true.*

25. $\begin{bmatrix} a & 0 \\ 0 & a \end{bmatrix}$ and $\begin{bmatrix} b & 0 \\ 0 & b \end{bmatrix}$ are inverses of each other.

26. $\begin{bmatrix} 0 & a \\ a & 0 \end{bmatrix}$ and $\begin{bmatrix} 0 & b \\ b & 0 \end{bmatrix}$ are inverses of each other.

27. Recall that "row operation 2" is to multiply a given row by some nonzero constant. Show that the following product has the effect (on the second matrix) of multiplying its first row by k.

$$\begin{bmatrix} k & 0 \\ 0 & 1 \end{bmatrix} \cdot \begin{bmatrix} 2 & 4 \\ 3 & 5 \end{bmatrix}$$

28. What 2×2 multiplier, on the left, will change

$$\begin{bmatrix} 2 & 4 \\ 3 & 5 \end{bmatrix} \quad \text{to} \quad \begin{bmatrix} 2 & 4 \\ 3k & 5k \end{bmatrix}$$

(that is, multiply the second row by the constant k)?

29. "Row operation 3" is to add some multiple of one row to another row. Show that the following product has the effect (on the second matrix) of adding twice its first row elements to its corresponding second row elements.

$$\begin{bmatrix} 1 & 0 \\ 2 & 1 \end{bmatrix} \cdot \begin{bmatrix} 2 & 4 \\ 3 & 5 \end{bmatrix}$$

30. What 2×2 multiplier, on the left, will change

$$\begin{bmatrix} 2 & 4 \\ 3 & 5 \end{bmatrix} \quad \text{to} \quad \begin{bmatrix} 11 & 19 \\ 3 & 5 \end{bmatrix}$$

(that is, add three times the second row to the first row)?

The matrix in Example 4 had no inverse. Here are several other 2×2 matrices that do not have inverses:

$$\begin{bmatrix} 5 & 1 \\ 10 & 2 \end{bmatrix}, \quad \begin{bmatrix} 6 & -3 \\ -8 & 4 \end{bmatrix}, \quad \begin{bmatrix} 17 & 22 \\ 34 & 44 \end{bmatrix}.$$

31. Describe the characteristic shared by the above matrices that causes them to not have inverses.

32. Find two additional 2×2 matrices, neither of which has an inverse.

*The **determinant** of a 2×2 matrix is denoted by vertical bars (similar to absolute value signs), so that, for example, the determinant of $\begin{bmatrix} 2 & 6 \\ 5 & 8 \end{bmatrix}$ is denoted $\begin{vmatrix} 2 & 6 \\ 5 & 8 \end{vmatrix}$. The numerical* **value** *of a determinant is defined as follows:*

$$\begin{vmatrix} a & c \\ b & d \end{vmatrix} = ad - bc.$$

Evaluate each determinant.

33. $\begin{vmatrix} 7 & 4 \\ 5 & 3 \end{vmatrix}$

34. $\begin{vmatrix} 2 & 8 \\ -3 & -6 \end{vmatrix}$

35. $\begin{vmatrix} -4 & 8 \\ 5 & -10 \end{vmatrix}$

36. $\begin{vmatrix} 3 & -2 \\ 6 & -4 \end{vmatrix}$

37. Extend the concept of a determinant to 3×3 matrices, and show how to evaluate a 3×3 determinant. (You may want to consult an algebra book.)

38. Give an example of a 3×3 determinant with the value 0.

*A matrix is called **singular** if its determinant has the value 0.*

39. Explain why a system of linear equations has no unique solution if its coefficient matrix is singular.

40. If A is a singular square matrix, what can you say about A^{-1}?

Use a calculator to find the inverse of each matrix. Give all elements to three decimal places.

41. $\begin{bmatrix} 1.2 & 3.7 \\ -4.8 & 5.5 \end{bmatrix}$

42. $\begin{bmatrix} 7/6 & 2/11 \\ 5/13 & 1/9 \end{bmatrix}$

43. $\begin{bmatrix} 14.8 & 18.1 & 11.6 \\ 8.2 & 12.6 & 9.5 \\ 15.1 & 13.8 & 7.4 \end{bmatrix}$

44. $\begin{bmatrix} 125 & 391 & 416 \\ 277 & 143 & 209 \\ 610 & 157 & 504 \end{bmatrix}$

45. In the real number system, how many numbers do not have multiplicative inverses? What are they?

46. In the system of 2×2 matrices, how many matrices do not have multiplicative inverses? What are they?

47. Assume the same basic wheat/oil economy described in the text. Find the gross production required for a net production of 750 metric tons of wheat and 1,000 metric tons of oil. Round final amounts to whole numbers.

48. Find the gross production required in Exercise 47 if production of 1 metric ton of wheat consumes 1/3 metric ton of oil (and no wheat), while the production of 1 metric ton of oil consumes 1/5 metric ton of wheat (and no oil). Round final amounts to whole numbers.

49. Consider an economy depending on three basic commodities: agriculture, manufacturing, and transportation. Suppose 1/4 unit of manufacturing and 1/2 unit of transportation are required to produce 1 unit of agriculture, 1/2 unit of agriculture and 1/4 unit of transportation are required to produce 1 unit of manufacturing, and 1/4 unit of agriculture and 1/4 unit of manufacturing are required to produce 1 unit of transportation. How many units of each commodity should be produced to satisfy a demand for 1,000 units of each commodity? Round final amounts to whole numbers.

50. A simple economy depends on three commodities: oil, corn, and coffee. Production of one unit of oil requires .1 unit of oil, .2 unit of corn, and no units of coffee. To produce one unit of corn requires .2 unit of oil, .1 unit of corn, and .05 unit of coffee. To produce one unit of coffee requires .1 unit of oil, .05 unit of corn, and .1 unit of coffee. Find the gross production required to give a net production of 1,000 units each of oil, corn, and coffee. Round final amounts to whole numbers.

Cryptography

Cryptography, or **code theory,** is one of the areas being continually affected by advancing mathematical theory. "Secret codes," of various forms, have been used throughout history, for purposes that range from international intrigue to childhood pastimes. Today, with more and more information being stored and exchanged within computerized networks, businesses and other interests depend upon advanced cryptographic systems for protection of their data.

A common type of code is constructed by replacing each letter of the alphabet with another letter or symbol, such as

$$A = 3 \quad C = \# \quad E = +$$
$$B = \$ \quad D = 9 \quad F = *$$

and so on. A code like this is very easy for an expert to break. This is because mere substitution of one symbol for another does not change the relative frequency of occurrence of the symbols. Thus, in the substitution of symbols for letters in the English language, $+$ would occur most frequently in any reasonably long message simply because $+$ represents E, and E is the most common letter used in English. (We say "reasonably long message" since in some short messages, such as "summer sessions seldom stimulate", the letter E might not be the most common.) Code breakers have spent a lot of time deciding on the frequency of occurrence of letters. The sample referred to on the opening page of this chapter yields the following percentages for all letters of the alphabet.

Letter	Percent	Letter	Percent	Letter	Percent
E	13.0	D	4.4	G, W	1.6
T	9.3	H, L	3.5	V	1.3
N	7.8	C	3.0	B	.9
R	7.7	F	2.8	X	.5
I, O	7.4	P, U	2.7	K, Q	.3
A	7.3	M	2.5	J	.2
S	6.3	Y	1.9	Z	.1

Governments and computer users need to develop more sophisticated methods of coding and decoding messages. Several of the methods depend on matrix theory. To see how, assign numbers to letters of the alphabet. For simplicity, let A correspond to 1, B to 2, C to 3, and so on. Ignore punctuation and let 27 correspond to a blank space.

A = 1	G = 7	M = 13	S = 19	Y = 25
B = 2	H = 8	N = 14	T = 20	Z = 26
C = 3	I = 9	O = 15	U = 21	space = 27
D = 4	J = 10	P = 16	V = 22	
E = 5	K = 11	Q = 17	W = 23	
F = 6	L = 12	R = 18	X = 24	

Break the message into groups of three letters (and spaces) each. For example, the message SOME CODES ARE EASILY BROKEN becomes

SOM E __ C ODE S __ A RE __ EAS ILY __ BR OKE N __ __ where ___ represents a blank. Each group of letters is then converted to a 3×1 matrix. For example, the letters S, O, and M convert to 19, 15, and 13, respectively, so that

$$\begin{bmatrix} S \\ O \\ M \end{bmatrix} \quad \text{corresponds to} \quad \begin{bmatrix} 19 \\ 15 \\ 13 \end{bmatrix}.$$

Our message corresponds to the following sequence of matrices.

$$\begin{bmatrix} 19 \\ 15 \\ 13 \end{bmatrix} \begin{bmatrix} 5 \\ 27 \\ 3 \end{bmatrix} \begin{bmatrix} 15 \\ 4 \\ 5 \end{bmatrix} \begin{bmatrix} 19 \\ 27 \\ 1 \end{bmatrix} \begin{bmatrix} 18 \\ 5 \\ 27 \end{bmatrix} \begin{bmatrix} 5 \\ 1 \\ 19 \end{bmatrix} \begin{bmatrix} 9 \\ 12 \\ 25 \end{bmatrix} \begin{bmatrix} 27 \\ 2 \\ 18 \end{bmatrix} \begin{bmatrix} 15 \\ 11 \\ 5 \end{bmatrix} \begin{bmatrix} 14 \\ 27 \\ 27 \end{bmatrix}$$

Now choose any 3×3 "multiplier" matrix that has an inverse. Let us choose matrix M as follows.

$$M = \begin{bmatrix} 1 & 3 & 3 \\ 1 & 4 & 3 \\ 1 & 3 & 4 \end{bmatrix}$$

Finding the product of M and each of the preceding matrices gives

$$\begin{bmatrix} 103 \\ 118 \\ 116 \end{bmatrix} \begin{bmatrix} 95 \\ 122 \\ 98 \end{bmatrix} \begin{bmatrix} 42 \\ 46 \\ 47 \end{bmatrix}$$

and so on. (See Exercise 5.) The process of translating the message into this series of matrices is called "encoding." In effect, it disguises the original sequence of matrices. The entries of these product matrices can then be transmitted as the message. The recipient of the message divides the numbers into groups of 3 and converts each group of 3 into a matrix. After multiplying these matrices by the matrix M^{-1}, the message can be read.

A code of this type is simple to use but hard to decode for anyone not knowing the multiplication matrix M. For further information on codes, see *The Codebreakers* by David Kahn. Further information on the substitution of symbols for letters is given in the Sherlock Holmes story "The Dancing Men" and in Edgar Allan Poe's "The Gold Bug" (see the marginal note at the left).

"Shoot from the left eye of the death's head. . . ." In Poe's tale *The Gold-Bug* (1843), the image of a skull on an old piece of parchment starts Legrand, the central character, on a treasure hunt. In the course of it he must decode a message by comparing the frequency of its given symbols with the frequency of letters in the English language. The illustration shows the gold bug (instead of a bullet) dropped from the left eye socket of the skull.

Extension Exercises

1. The message

THE THREE TENORS

is to be encoded by using the matrix method described in the text. The message is broken into groups of two letters (and spaces). Find the sequence of matrices derived from the given message.

2. Use the multiplier matrix $M = \begin{bmatrix} -1 & 2 \\ 2 & -5 \end{bmatrix}$ to encode the sequence of matrices of Exercise 1, and list the resulting sequence of 2×1 matrices.

3. A message that was encoded with the multiplier matrix of Exercise 2 was received as the following sequence of numbers.

$$39, -98, -19, 34, -7, 10, 3, -11, 36,$$
$$-99, 21, -62, 7, -18, 33, -87, 41, -109$$

What multiplier matrix should be used for decoding this message?

4. Find the original message (of Exercise 3).

5. Finish encoding the message SOME CODES ARE EASILY BROKEN given in the text.

6. The person receiving the message of Exercise 5 (SOME CODES ARE EASILY BROKEN) also received the following encoded message (already converted to matrix form).

$$\begin{bmatrix} 99 \\ 119 \\ 107 \end{bmatrix} \begin{bmatrix} 116 \\ 134 \\ 135 \end{bmatrix} \begin{bmatrix} 84 \\ 85 \\ 102 \end{bmatrix} \begin{bmatrix} 98 \\ 125 \\ 102 \end{bmatrix} \begin{bmatrix} 45 \\ 51 \\ 51 \end{bmatrix} \begin{bmatrix} 81 \\ 84 \\ 102 \end{bmatrix} \begin{bmatrix} 153 \\ 173 \\ 180 \end{bmatrix}$$

Decode this second message, assuming it was encoded using the multiplier matrix given in the text.

7. Suppose you are a special agent. The encoding multiplier matrix for today is $M = \begin{bmatrix} 2 & 1 & 2 \\ 3 & 4 & 3 \\ 3 & 1 & 2 \end{bmatrix}$. You need to send the message

DESTROY FILES IMMEDIATELY

to another agent. What sequence of numbers would you transmit?

8. After your transmission of Exercise 7, you receive the response

45, 90, 51, 83, 172, 88, 51, 89, 55, 88, 177, 108, 63, 107, 88.

What is the message?

9. Could the encoding matrix (the multiplier) used in the type of cryptography discussed here be of order 4×4? Explain why or why not.

10. What are the restrictions (if any) on the type of matrix used as the encoding multiplier?

11. Explain why the matrix type code discussed here would be difficult to break.

12. The following message is written in a code in which the frequency of the symbols is the main key to the solution.

)?−−8))6*+8506*3×6;4?*7*&×*−6.48()6)985)?(8+2:;48)81&?(;46*3)6*;
48&(+8(*598+.8()8=8(5*−8−5(81?098;4&+)&15*50:)6)6*;?6;6&*0?−7

Find the frequency of each symbol. By comparing high frequency symbols with the high frequency letters in English (see the text above), try to decipher the message. (*Hint:* look for repeated two-symbol combinations and double letters for added clues. Try to identify vowels first.)

14.5 Matrices and Game Theory*

In this section, we discuss a large and still growing branch of mathematics called **game theory.** While the name may suggest something frivolous, the applications certainly are not. Game theory was developed in the 1940s as a means of analyzing competitive situations in business, warfare, and social settings.

A **two-player game,** the most common case, involves two opponents. These opponents can be two persons, two teams of persons, two countries, and so on. One player may even be a nonpersonal entity. For example, imagine that you are a California citrus farmer in the winter playing a strategic game against nature. You can protect your crop against freezing by burning smudge pots at night at a cost of $1,000. If you burn smudge pots, you will be able to sell your crop for a net profit of $14,000, provided that the freeze does develop. If you do nothing, you will either lose $3,000 in planting costs if the freeze comes, or will gain $8,000 profit if no freeze occurs.

To analyze this situation we set up a **payoff matrix,** which shows the farmer's possible actions, or **strategies,** on the left and nature's strategies (the "States of Nature") on the top. The entries of the matrix are the amounts of profit (or loss) for the various combinations of strategy choices.

$$
\begin{array}{cc}
 & \text{STATES OF NATURE} \\
 & \begin{array}{cc} \text{Freeze} & \text{No freeze} \end{array}
\end{array}
$$

FARMER'S   Use smudge pots $\begin{bmatrix} \$14{,}000 & \$7{,}000 \\ -\$3{,}000 & \$8{,}000 \end{bmatrix}$
STRATEGIES: Don't use them

Several criteria may be used in the decision making. If you are an optimist, you might choose the **maximax** criterion, which selects the action that *maximizes* the *maximum* gain. In our example, if you use smudge pots, your maximum gain would be $14,000, while if you do not use smudge pots, your maximum gain would be $8,000. Using the maximax criterion, you would choose the action that gives the larger of the two maximums and use smudge pots.

On the other hand, you might be a pessimist. In that case, the **maximin** criterion, which *maximizes* the *minimum* payoff, would suit you just fine. The minimum payoffs under the two actions are $7,000, with smudge pots, and −$3,000 if nothing is done. The larger of these occurs if smudge pots are used, so that this is the appropriate action for this criterion, too.

If you are neither an optimist nor a pessimist, and if you can assign some probability p to the "freeze" state of nature, then you can compromise by choosing the action with the greatest expected payoff. Suppose you believe (the weather forecaster has convinced you) that the probability of a freeze is .4. The probability of no freeze would then be .6, with the expected payoffs as follows.

If smudge pots are used: $14{,}000(.4) + 7{,}000(.6) = \$9{,}800$
If no pots are used: $-3{,}000(.4) + 8{,}000(.6) = \$3{,}600$

Economic Behavior In 1944 a new direction in economics was set by the *Theory of Games and Economic Behavior,* containing the famous minimax theorem. It was written by mathematician John von Neumann (see page 853) and economist Oskar Morgenstern. The book's impact relates to the question about which mathematics is proper to economics. Beginning with Antoine Cournot in the 1830s, economists looked to physics for analogies in thermodynamics or mechanics since physics had been so successfully "mathematized." The game-theoretic approach was a break with the past, showing how mathematics other than the calculus could give models of economic behavior.

---

* The material in this section depends somewhat on the ideas of probability and expected value, which were discussed in an earlier chapter.

Con(traption) Game This stamp from Hungary pictures Turk, an automaton built in 1769 that ostensibly played chess—it was actually operated from within by a concealed chess player. Turk was exhibited in the U.S. in the 1830s by Johann Maelzel, inventor of the metronome (and a friend of Beethoven). Edgar Allan Poe's essay on Turk deduces the person inside. Poe observed *Schlumberger*, a European chess player, just before and after Turk's chess game, but never during. Schlumberger is psyched out by Thomas Gavin in his novel *King-kill* (Random House, 1977): Schlumberger hides within Turk to avoid the ordeal of playing chess as his own man. (The title refers to the origin of "checkmate" in the Arabic *shah mat*—"the king is left unable to escape.")

Turk eventually wound up in the Chinese Museum, Philadelphia. It was wrecked by a fire there in 1854. Fire also destroyed Ajeeb, another chess automaton, this time at Coney Island in 1929. The U.S. Chess Master Harry Nelson Pillsbury operated Ajeeb at the turn of the century.

This criterion, choosing the maximum of the expected payoffs, also indicates that smudge pots should be used. Note that, as your subjective beliefs about the probability of a freeze change, so would the expected payoffs. To assign probabilities to such unique events requires a subjective or personal assessment of the event. It works out here that pots should be used as long as you feel the probability of a freeze is greater than $1/18$.

In the example discussed here, all three criteria led to the same action. However, if the cost of using the smudge pots were much larger, or the profit when they were used in the event of a freeze were much smaller, the situation would look very different. Also, for the payoff matrix to be helpful the effect of all important factors must somehow be included. At the least, the use of a payoff matrix does clarify the problem and permit an orderly approach to considering the alternatives.

Notice that in a two-player game player A's strategies (1, 2, and so on) are shown at the left of the payoff matrix, and player B's strategies (I, II, and so on) are shown at the top of the payoff matrix. Each row of the game matrix (the payoff matrix) represents one of A's possible strategies, while each column represents one of B's possible strategies. Each entry in the matrix is the payoff that results for that particular choice of strategies. We assume that if the payoff is a positive number, A receives that amount from B; if it is negative, A pays B. Under this assumption, one player must lose whatever the other wins. This condition defines a **zero-sum game.** Not all games are zero-sum games. The stock market, for example, is *not*. Stocks can go up or down according to outside forces. (In effect, money enters this system from sources other than investors.) Therefore, it is possible that all investors can make money or that they can all lose.

The remainder of this section will be restricted. We discuss two-player, zero-sum games only.

EXAMPLE 1 Assume the payoffs here are dollar amounts. What are the results of each possible combination of strategy choices?

$$
\begin{array}{cc}
& \quad B \\
& \begin{array}{cc} \text{I} & \text{II} \end{array} \\
A \begin{array}{c} 1 \\ 2 \end{array} & \left[\begin{array}{cc} 2 & -1 \\ -3 & 4 \end{array} \right]
\end{array}
$$

From the payoff matrix, we observe the following.

If A applies strategy 1 and B applies strategy I, then A receives \$2 from B.

If A applies strategy 1 and B applies strategy II, then A pays B \$1.

If A applies strategy 2 and B applies strategy I, then A pays B \$3.

If A applies strategy 2 and B applies strategy II, then A receives \$4 from B.

An $m \times n$ (matrix) game is one in which player A has m possible strategies (rows) and player B has n strategies (columns). For example, a 3×3 game is shown here.

$$
\begin{array}{c}
 & & B \\
 & & \text{I} \quad \text{II} \quad \text{III} \\
A \begin{array}{c} 1 \\ 2 \\ 3 \end{array} & & \begin{bmatrix} -3 & -6 & 10 \\ 3 & 0 & 1 \\ 5 & -4 & -8 \end{bmatrix}
\end{array}
$$

From B's viewpoint, strategy II is better than strategy I no matter which strategy A selects, since a gain of \$6 is better than a gain of \$3; breaking even is better than paying \$3 to A; and a gain of \$4 is better than a loss of \$5. Therefore, B should never select strategy I. In a situation like this, strategy II is said to *dominate* strategy I (or strategy I is *dominated* by II). Column II dominates column I since *every* column II payoff is *less than* the corresponding column I payoff.

From A's viewpoint, no strategy (row) in the original matrix above dominates another, since for a row to dominate another, its payoffs must all be greater than the corresponding payoffs in the other row. (Verify that this condition does not occur in the payoff matrix above.)

It is sometimes possible to reduce the order of an $m \times n$ game by eliminating dominated strategies. (No player would ever choose to employ a dominated strategy anyway.)

EXAMPLE 2 Reduce the 3×3 game matrix above by eliminating any dominated strategies.

As observed above, A sees no dominant strategies initially but B would eliminate strategy I, so we arrive at the following reduced matrix.

$$
\begin{array}{c}
 & & B \\
 & & \text{II} \quad \text{III} \\
A \begin{array}{c} 1 \\ 2 \\ 3 \end{array} & & \begin{bmatrix} -6 & 10 \\ 0 & 1 \\ -4 & -8 \end{bmatrix}
\end{array}
$$

But now that strategy I for B has been removed, it turns out that strategy 2 for A dominates strategy 3. Therefore, we can finally reduce the game to a 2×2 matrix as follows.

$$
\begin{array}{c}
 & & B \\
 & & \text{II} \quad \text{III} \\
A \begin{array}{c} 1 \\ 2 \end{array} & & \begin{bmatrix} -6 & 10 \\ 0 & 1 \end{bmatrix}
\end{array}
$$

Which strategies should be chosen by A and B? The goal of game theory is to find *optimum* strategies, those which are most profitable (or least costly) for a player. The resulting payoff, assuming both players select their respective optimum strategies, is called the **value** of the game. We usually find optimum strategies using the **minimax** criterion, in which we *minimize* the *maximum* possible loss. For example, a game for players A and B is shown here.

$$
\begin{array}{c}
& & B \\
& & \text{I} \quad \text{II} \quad \text{III} \\
A & \begin{array}{c} 1 \\ 2 \\ 3 \end{array} & \begin{bmatrix} -7 & 8 & -1 \\ 4 & 7 & 0 \\ -9 & 3 & -6 \end{bmatrix}
\end{array}
$$

In this game, player A's greatest possible losses for his or her strategy choices are $7, $0, and $9, respectively. To minimize the maximum possible loss, player A should select strategy 2. In the same way, B's greatest possible losses are $4, $8, and $0, so that B can minimize possible losses by choosing strategy III. Thus, the payoff will be $0 (strategy 2 for A and III for B), which is the value of the game. A game whose value is $0 is called a **fair game.**

The pair of strategies (2, III) determined by the minimax criterion is called the **saddle point** of the game. The saddle point is the pair of strategies for which the entry in the payoff matrix is both the *minimum* in its row and *maximum* in its column. This fact makes the saddle point easy to determine, if it exists. For example, in the matrix below, by the definition above, the saddle point is (4, I) and the value of the game is $3. (Whenever there are two or more saddle points, they must all yield equal values.)

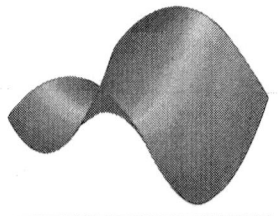

The name **saddle point** comes from a saddle. The seat of the saddle is the maximum from one direction and the minimum from another direction.

$$
\begin{array}{c}
& & B \\
& & \text{I} \quad \text{II} \\
A & \begin{array}{c} 1 \\ 2 \\ 3 \\ 4 \end{array} & \begin{bmatrix} 2 & 2 \\ 0 & 4 \\ 1 & 6 \\ 3 & 7 \end{bmatrix}
\end{array}
$$

Unfortunately, not every $m \times n$ game has a saddle point. When there is no saddle point, another approach must be used. Both players will have to *mix* their strategies. If this mixing were to be done in some systematic fashion, the competitor would soon guess it and play accordingly. For this reason, it is best to mix strategies according to previously determined probabilities. For example, if a player has only two strategies and has decided to select them with equal probability, the random choice can be made by tossing a coin. Heads could represent one strategy; tails the other. Although this would result in the two strategies being used about equally over the long run, on a particular play no player could predetermine which strategy would be used. Some other device, such as a spinner, a die, or random numbers, is necessary for more than two strategies, or when the predetermined probability is different from $1/2$.

To see how to decide on the probability with which a particular strategy is selected, return to the example about the smudge pots. Suppose you must decide several times each season whether or not to use smudge pots, and you don't really know the probability of a freeze. We need to find the fraction of the time (the probability) that you should use smudge pots. There is no saddle point for this game. Thus, let x represent the probability that you will choose strategy 1, with $1 - x$ the probability that you will choose strategy 2.

$$
\begin{array}{cc}
 & \text{NATURE} \\
 & \begin{array}{cc} \text{I} & \text{II} \end{array} \\
\text{YOU} \begin{array}{c} 1 \\ 2 \end{array} & \left[\begin{array}{cc} \$14{,}000 & \$7{,}000 \\ -\$3{,}000 & \$8{,}000 \end{array} \right]
\end{array}
$$

For Nature's strategy I (a freeze) your expected profit is

$$E_\text{I} = 14{,}000x - 3{,}000(1 - x).$$

For Nature's strategy II (no freeze) your expected profit is

$$E_\text{II} = 7{,}000x + 8{,}000(1 - x).$$

You will maximize your profit in the long run if you choose a value of x for which $E_\text{I} = E_\text{II}$. (This fact was proved in 1928 by John von Neumann. We will use it here without proof.) To make $E_\text{I} = E_\text{II}$, solve as follows.

$$E_\text{I} = E_\text{II}$$
$$14{,}000x - 3{,}000(1 - x) = 7{,}000x + 8{,}000(1 - x)$$
$$17{,}000x - 3{,}000 = -1{,}000x + 8{,}000$$
$$18{,}000x = 11{,}000$$
$$x = \frac{11}{18}$$

Thus, the optimum strategy here is to use strategy 1 (use smudge pots) $11/18$ of the time, and strategy 2 (don't use them) a total of

$$1 - x = 1 - \frac{11}{18} = \frac{7}{18}$$

of the time.

EXAMPLE 3 Find the farmer's expected gain from the smudge pot strategy outlined above.

We can substitute $11/18$ for x in either E_I or E_II. Using E_I gives

$$14{,}000\left(\frac{11}{18}\right) - 3{,}000\left(\frac{7}{18}\right) = \frac{133{,}000}{18} = \$7{,}388.89.$$

This result, $\$7{,}388.89$, is the value of the game. The value comes out the same no matter which player's optimum strategy and expected gain are considered.

John von Neumann
(1903–1957) achieved much in a life cut short by cancer. Stories told about him made him a living legend. In 1933 he joined the Institute for Advanced Study, newly founded, and was one of its original six mathematicians. By then he had already written important papers on set theory, quantum mechanics, and the minimax theorem. After 1940 he turned to the applications of mathematics, working with Stanislaw Ulam during World War II and extending game theory with Morgenstern. Von Neumann was intensely interested in the theory and use of computers and automata. His interest in artificial intelligence is expressed in his lecture notes published as *The Computer and the Brain* (Yale paperback).

In the following games, assume that player A chooses rows and player B chooses columns. Eliminate all dominated strategies from each of the following games.

1. $\begin{bmatrix} 1 & 4 \\ 4 & -1 \\ 3 & 5 \\ -4 & 0 \end{bmatrix}$

2. $\begin{bmatrix} 2 & 3 & 1 & -5 \\ -1 & 5 & 4 & 1 \\ 1 & 0 & 2 & -3 \end{bmatrix}$

3. $\begin{bmatrix} 8 & 12 & -7 \\ -2 & 1 & 4 \end{bmatrix}$

4. $\begin{bmatrix} 6 & 2 \\ -1 & 10 \\ 3 & 5 \end{bmatrix}$

Where it exists, find the saddle point and the value of the game for each of the following.

5. $\begin{bmatrix} -6 & 2 \\ -1 & -10 \\ 3 & 5 \end{bmatrix}$

6. $\begin{bmatrix} 7 & 8 \\ -2 & 15 \end{bmatrix}$

7. $\begin{bmatrix} 3 & -4 & 1 \\ 5 & 3 & 2 \end{bmatrix}$

8. $\begin{bmatrix} 2 & 3 & 1 \\ -1 & 4 & -7 \\ 5 & 2 & 0 \\ 8 & -4 & -1 \end{bmatrix}$

9. $\begin{bmatrix} 1 & 4 & -3 & 1 & -1 \\ 2 & 5 & 0 & 4 & 10 \\ 1 & -3 & -2 & 5 & 2 \end{bmatrix}$

10. $\begin{bmatrix} -4 & 2 & -3 & -7 \\ 4 & 3 & 5 & 9 \end{bmatrix}$

Solve each of the following problems.

11. Hillsdale College has sold out all tickets for a jazz concert to be held in the stadium. If it rains, the show will have to be moved into the gym, which has a much smaller seating capacity. The dean must decide in advance whether to set up the seats and the stage in the gym or in the stadium, or both, just in case. The matrix below shows the net profit in each case.

	NATURE Rain	No rain
Set up stadium	−$1,550	$1,500
ACTIONS Set up gym	$1,000	$1,000
Set up both	$750	$1,400

(a) What action should the dean take if he is an optimist?

(b) If he is a pessimist?

(c) If the weather forecaster predicts rain with a probability of .6, what action should the dean take to maximize expected profit?

12. A community is considering an anti-smoking campaign. The city manager has been asked to recommend one of three possible actions: a campaign for everyone in the community over age 10, a campaign for youths only, or no campaign at all. The two states of nature are a true cause-effect relationship between smoking and cancer or no such relationship. The cost to the community (including loss of life and productivity) in each case is shown below.*

	Cause-effect relationship	No such relationship
Campaign for all	$100,000	$800,000
Campaign for youth	$2,820,000	$20,000
No campaign	$3,100,100	$0

*This problem is based on an article by B. G. Greenburg in the September 1969 issue of the *Journal of the American Statistical Association*.

(a) What action should the manager recommend if she is an optimist?

(b) If she is a pessimist?

(c) If the Director of Public Health estimates that the probability of a true cause-effect relationship is .8, which action should be recommended to minimize expected costs?

13. The research department of Allied Manufacturing has developed a new process that they feel will result in an improved product. Management must decide whether or not to market the new product. The new product may be better than the old, or it may not be better. If the new product is better, and the company decides to market it, sales should increase by $50,000. If it is not better and they replace the old product with the new product on the market, they will lose $25,000 to competitors. If they decide not to market the new product, they will lose $40,000 if it is better and research costs of $10,000 if it is not.

(a) Prepare a payoff matrix.

(b) If management believes that the probability is .4 that the new product is better, find the expected profits under each possible course of action, and find the best action.

14. Suppose Allied Manufacturing (of Exercise 13) decides to put their new product on the market with a big advertising campaign. At the same time, they find out that their major competitor, Bates Manufacturing, has also decided on a big advertising campaign for its version of the product. The payoff matrix below shows the increased sales in millions for Allied, which also represent decreases for Bates.

$$
\begin{array}{c}
\quad \text{BATES} \\
\quad \begin{array}{cc} \text{TV} & \text{Radio} \end{array} \\
\text{ALLIED} \quad \begin{array}{c} \text{TV} \\ \text{Radio} \end{array} \begin{bmatrix} 1.0 & -.7 \\ -.5 & .5 \end{bmatrix}
\end{array}
$$

Find the optimum strategy for Allied, and find the value of the game.

In each of the following games, find the optimum strategy for each player, and find the value of the game. Identify any fair games.

15. $\begin{bmatrix} 5 & 1 \\ 3 & 4 \end{bmatrix}$

16. $\begin{bmatrix} -4 & 5 \\ 3 & -4 \end{bmatrix}$

17. $\begin{bmatrix} -2 & 4 \\ 0 & 5 \end{bmatrix}$

18. $\begin{bmatrix} 0 & -4 \\ 4 & 0 \end{bmatrix}$

19. In the game of matching coins, two players each flip a coin. If both coins match (both show heads or both show tails), player A wins $1. If there is no match, player B wins $1, as in the matrix below. Find the optimum strategies for each player, and find the value of the game.

$$
\begin{bmatrix} 1 & -1 \\ -1 & 1 \end{bmatrix}
$$

20. Explain the meaning of a "zero-sum" game. Give an example of a zero-sum game and an example of a non-zero-sum game.

21. Explain these terms: *maximax criterion, maximin criterion,* and *minimax criterion.*

22. Explain why, in a game matrix, a dominant row has entries that are *greater* than those of the dominated row, whereas a dominant column has entries that are *less* than those of the dominated column.

23. Explain what is meant by a "mixed" strategy.

Refer to the original payoff matrix in the text for the citrus farmer. Assume the farmer is neither an optimist nor a pessimist. Each of Exercises 24–26 gives a probability of having a freeze. In each case find (**a**) *the expected payoff for strategy 1 (use smudge pots) and* (**b**) *the expected payoff for strategy 2 (don't use them).*

24. 1/17   **25.** 1/18   **26.** 1/19

27. Discuss how your answers to Exercises 24–26 relate to the claim in the text that "pots should be used as long as you feel the probability of a freeze is greater than 1/18."

28. Refer to Example 3 in the text. Use E_{II} to find the farmer's expected gain for Nature's strategy II. Is the value the same as was obtained in the example using E_1?

In Example 3 it was stated that the value of a game (with no saddle point) comes out the same no matter which player's optimum strategy and expected gain are considered. Work the following exercises to consider the smudge pot question from Nature's viewpoint. Assume the original payoff matrix and suppose that Nature will randomly impose a freeze a certain fraction of the time, given by x.

29. Derive an expression for E_1, the expected payoff in case the farmer chooses to use smudge pots.

30. Derive an expression for E_2, the expected payoff in case the farmer chooses not to use smudge pots.

31. Equate E_1 and E_2 from Exercises 29 and 30 to find Nature's optimum strategy.

32. Find the value (expected payoff) of the game when Nature employs the strategy of Exercise 31. Is the value the same as that arrived at in Example 3?

Another citrus farmer facing the smudge pot decision has calculated the following payoff matrix. Refer to it for Exercises 33–37.

	Freeze	No freeze
Use smudge pots	$8,000	$7,000
Don't use them	−$5,000	$10,000

33. Which strategy would an optimist choose?

34. Which strategy would a pessimist choose?

35. If the farmer is neither an optimist nor a pessimist but is able to reasonably assess the probability of a freeze, how large must that probability be for the farmer's preferred strategy to be to use smudge pots?

36. The payoff matrix above still has no saddle point, so the farmer's best plan is probably to use a mixed strategy. Use the procedure described just before Example 3 to decide what fraction of the time the farmer should use smudge pots.

37. By using smudge pots the fraction of the time computed in Exercise 36, what expected gain does the farmer have? (Compare with Example 3.)

38. For the citrus farmer problem, devise a new 2 × 2 payoff matrix for which an optimist and a pessimist would both choose not to use smudge pots. Describe conditions that might give rise to the payoffs in your matrix.

In this activity, the algebraic structure of the system of 2 × 2 matrices will be compared with that of the system of real numbers.

1. First, as an entire class, review the following description of the real number system to clarify the meanings of the various properties.

   The set of real numbers R, along with the operations of addition ($+$) and multiplication ($\cdot$) and the relation of equality ($=$), is a **mathematical system.** Specifically, R is an **abelian (commutative) group** under the operation $+$ because the following five properties are satisfied. For all a, b, and c in R:

   (1) $a + b$ is in R.   (closure property of $+$)
   (2) $a + b = b + a$.   (commutative property of $+$)
   (3) $(a + b) + c = a + (b + c)$. (associative property of $+$)
   (4) there is an element 0 in R such that $a + 0 = a$.   (identity property of $+$)
   (5) there exists an element $-a$ in R such that $a + (-a) = 0$.   (inverse property of $+$)

   Furthermore, the system R is an **associative ring** because the following three additional properties are satisfied. For all a, b, and c in R:

   (6) $a \cdot b$ is in R.   (closure property of $\cdot$)
   (7) $a \cdot (b \cdot c) = (a \cdot b) \cdot c$.   (associative property of $\cdot$)
   (8) $a \cdot (b + c) = a \cdot b + a \cdot c$ and $(b + c) \cdot a = b \cdot a + c \cdot a$.   (the left and right distributive properties)

   In addition, R is a **commutative ring with unit element** because of the following two properties. For all a and b in R:

   (9) $a \cdot b = b \cdot a$.   (commutative property of $\cdot$)
   (10) there is an element 1 in R such that $a \cdot 1 = 1 \cdot a = a$.   (identity property of $\cdot$)

   Finally, R is a **field** because of one more property. For all a in R (other than 0):

   (11) there exists an element a^{-1} in R such that $a \cdot a^{-1} = 1$.   (inverse property of $\cdot$)

   In summary, the real numbers comprise a field because

   A. all real numbers are an abelian group under $+$, and
   B. all nonzero real numbers are an abelian group under $\cdot$.

2. Next, divide into groups of three or four students each. Each small group is to consider the system of all 2 × 2 matrices with real number entries, together with the operations of $+$ and $\cdot$ and the relation of $=$. Investigate the eleven properties listed above, in turn, for this new system. In each case, try examples, or make use of corresponding properties of the real numbers to prove the results, or use results established in this chapter (including appropriate exercises). Decide, within your group, on answers to the following questions.

   (1) Do the 2 × 2 matrices form a mathematical field? If not, which ones of the eleven properties fail to hold?
   (2) If the system of matrices is not a field, is it at least a commutative ring with unit element?
   (3) If not, is it at least an associative ring?
   (4) If not, is it at least a commutative group under addition?

3. Once the individual groups have decided on their opinions, come back together and share your reasoning. Try to come up with a firm conclusion as a class.

Chapter 14 Test

Let $A = \begin{bmatrix} 2 & -1 & 3 \\ 2 & 0 & 1 \\ 4 & 1 & 3 \end{bmatrix}$ and $B = \begin{bmatrix} -3 & 0 & 1 \\ 0 & 2 & -1 \\ -1 & 0 & 3 \end{bmatrix}$. *Perform the indicated matrix operations.*

1. $A + B$ **2.** $A - B$ **3.** AB **4.** BA **5.** $2A$ **6.** $-3B + A$

Apply the following row operations to matrix A from above.

7. Interchange rows 2 and 3.

8. Multiply each element of row 2 of A by -3, and add the results to row 1.

Find each of the following products, when possible. If not possible, state why not.

9. $\begin{bmatrix} -2 & 1 \\ 3 & 4 \end{bmatrix} \cdot \begin{bmatrix} 2 \\ 1 \end{bmatrix}$ **10.** $\begin{bmatrix} 3 & 4 & 1 \\ 2 & 0 & 8 \end{bmatrix} \cdot \begin{bmatrix} 1 & 0 & 2 \\ 0 & 0 & 1 \\ 3 & 0 & 2 \end{bmatrix}$

11. $\begin{bmatrix} 1 & 6 & 1 \end{bmatrix} \cdot \begin{bmatrix} 3 \\ 2 \\ 1 \end{bmatrix}$ **12.** $\begin{bmatrix} 8 & 9 & 7 \\ 2 & 1 & 3 \end{bmatrix} \begin{bmatrix} 2 & 3 \\ 4 & 2 \end{bmatrix}$

Find the inverse of each of the following matrices, where possible.

13. $\begin{bmatrix} 2 & 1 \\ 5 & 3 \end{bmatrix}$ **14.** $\begin{bmatrix} 1 & 0 & 1 \\ 2 & 3 & 1 \\ 1 & 3 & 2 \end{bmatrix}$

Set up the augmented matrix for each of the following systems of equations. Do not solve the systems.

15. $\begin{aligned} 9x - 4y &= 20 \\ 5x + 10y &= 12 \end{aligned}$ **16.** $\begin{aligned} 2x + y - 6z &= 6 \\ 5x + 12z &= 15 \\ 6y + 3z &= 8 \end{aligned}$

Solve each system of equations by the Gauss-Jordan method (Exercises 17 and 18).

17. $\begin{aligned} 5x + 6y &= 15 \\ 3x + 7y &= 9 \end{aligned}$ **18.** $\begin{aligned} 3x + 4y + z &= 10 \\ x - 3y - 5z &= -3 \\ 2x + 7y &= 1 \end{aligned}$

19. If the system of equations

$$\begin{aligned} x + y &= 1 \\ 2x - y &= -7 \end{aligned}$$

is written as $AX = B$, what exactly is represented by each of the following?
(a) A **(b)** X **(c)** B

20. Given the matrix equation $AX = B$, express X in terms of A and B.

21. Use matrix algebra to solve the system of equations of Exercise 19.

22. Explain the conditions under which the matrix product AB is computable.

The economy of a small country involves bananas and coal. Production of 1 unit of bananas consumes .3 unit of bananas and .1 unit of coal. Production of 1 unit of coal consumes .2 unit of bananas and .4 unit of coal.

23. Set up the technological matrix for this economy.

24. Find the gross production required to meet a demand for net production of 400 units of bananas and 300 units of coal.

25. Remove any dominated strategies from the following game.

$$\begin{bmatrix} 6 & 8 & -3 & 4 \\ 2 & 0 & 2 & -1 \end{bmatrix}$$

26. Identify any saddle points in the following game.

$$\begin{bmatrix} -3 & 1 & 4 & 2 \\ 8 & 9 & 6 & 4 \\ 9 & 10 & 15 & 19 \end{bmatrix}$$

27. Find the optimum strategy for player A and the value of the following game.

$$\begin{array}{cc} & B \\ & \begin{array}{cc} \text{I} & \text{II} \end{array} \\ A \begin{array}{c} 1 \\ 2 \end{array} & \begin{bmatrix} -3 & -4 \\ -4 & 5 \end{bmatrix} \end{array}$$

28. Find two different pairs of values for the missing entries in the matrix

$$A = \begin{bmatrix} \square & -3 \\ 5 & \square \end{bmatrix}$$

that will cause A to be its own inverse.

Arturo Hogan makes silver jewelry inlaid with turquoise. Each ring requires 1.6 units of silver and .7 unit of turquoise, each bracelet requires 5.8 units of silver and 7.5 units of turquoise, and each necklace requires 26.3 units of silver and 18.8 units of turquoise. Arturo pays $5.50 per unit for silver and $2.10 per unit for turquoise.

29. Set up a matrix M relating jewelry items (ring, bracelet, necklace) to materials (silver, turquoise), and another matrix C relating materials to cost (per unit).

30. Perform an appropriate matrix operation to obtain a matrix relating jewelry items to cost (per item) for materials.

14.1 Exercises (Page 812)

1. $\begin{bmatrix} 11 & 1 \\ 9 & 4 \end{bmatrix}$ 3. $\begin{bmatrix} 3 & 3 & -3 \\ 4 & -4 & 0 \end{bmatrix}$ 5. $\begin{bmatrix} -3 & 4 & 2 \\ 8 & 2 & 1 \\ 4 & 3 & 13 \end{bmatrix}$

7. It is not computable because the matrices do not have the same order. 9. $\begin{bmatrix} 0 \\ 12 \\ 7 \end{bmatrix}$ 11. $\begin{bmatrix} -14 & -2 \\ 5 & 10 \end{bmatrix}$

13. $A + B = \begin{bmatrix} -2 & -1 \\ -1 & -4 \end{bmatrix}$ 15. $2A = \begin{bmatrix} -8 & 0 \\ 6 & -8 \end{bmatrix}$ 17. $-4B = \begin{bmatrix} -8 & 4 \\ 16 & 0 \end{bmatrix}$

19. $2A + 3B = \begin{bmatrix} -2 & -3 \\ -6 & -8 \end{bmatrix}$ 21. $(-1)A + A = \begin{bmatrix} 0 & 0 \\ 0 & 0 \end{bmatrix}$

23.
$$\begin{array}{c} \\ \text{I} \\ \text{II} \\ \text{III} \\ \text{IV} \end{array} \begin{array}{ccc} \text{Fat} & \text{Carbohydrates} & \text{Protein} \\ \begin{bmatrix} 5 & 0 & 7 \\ 0 & 10 & 1 \\ 0 & 15 & 2 \\ 10 & 12 & 8 \end{bmatrix} \end{array}$$

25. $C = \begin{array}{c} \\ \text{F1} \\ \text{F2} \end{array} \begin{array}{ccc} \text{W1} & \text{W2} & \text{W3} \\ \begin{bmatrix} 12 & 20 & 25 \\ 16 & 25 & 30 \end{bmatrix} \end{array}$

27. $C + A = \begin{bmatrix} 15 & 18 & 27 \\ 20 & 27 & 28 \end{bmatrix}$ 29. $\begin{bmatrix} 45 & 35 & 20 \\ 65 & 40 & 35 \end{bmatrix} + \begin{bmatrix} 10 & 12 & 5 \\ 15 & 20 & 8 \end{bmatrix} = \begin{bmatrix} 55 & 47 & 25 \\ 80 & 60 & 43 \end{bmatrix}$

31. 25 model-C tables 33. $\begin{bmatrix} 22 & 25 & 38 \\ 31 & 34 & 35 \end{bmatrix} + \begin{bmatrix} 10 & 12 & 5 \\ 15 & 20 & 8 \end{bmatrix} - \begin{bmatrix} 5 & 10 & 8 \\ 11 & 14 & 15 \end{bmatrix} = \begin{bmatrix} 27 & 27 & 35 \\ 35 & 40 & 28 \end{bmatrix}$

35. 9 pounds 37. The given equality is impossible because the two matrices have different orders.
39. $\{(y, z) \mid y = z\}$ 41. $k = 8, m = 1, y = 3$ 43. $x = 1, y = 8, z = 8$

45. The given equality is impossible. In the first row, first column of the matrix $\begin{bmatrix} x & y \\ 3 & 5 \end{bmatrix}$, x must be equal to 10.

But in the second row, first column of the matrix $\begin{bmatrix} -2 & 6 \\ x & 2 \end{bmatrix}$, x must be equal to 4.

47. No. On a calendar, there are seven columns. In order for the days of a given month to form a matrix, the number of days in that month must be divisible by 7. March has 31 days, which is not divisible by 7; therefore the month of March on a calendar will never form a matrix. 49. false 51. true 53. true 55. true

14.2 Exercises (Page 824)

1. $\begin{bmatrix} 8 & 6 \\ -7 & 3 \end{bmatrix}$ 3. $\begin{bmatrix} -2 & -8 \\ -14 & 34 \end{bmatrix}$ 5. $\begin{bmatrix} 17 & 7 & 9 \\ 13 & 6 & 3 \end{bmatrix}$ 7. $\begin{bmatrix} 8 & 3 \\ 11 & -2 \\ 4 & 12 \end{bmatrix}$ 9. It is not computable because the

number of columns in the first matrix is not equal to the number of rows in the second matrix.

11. $\begin{bmatrix} 14 & 4 & 0 \\ -4 & 4 & 0 \\ -6 & 2 & 0 \end{bmatrix}$

13. $AB =$

PURCHASE OPTION

	Large lot	Small lot
Sweet rolls	47.5	57.75
Bread	27	33.75
Cakes	81	95
Pies	12	15

15. $(DA)B =$ Day's orders

	Cost (large lot)	Cost (small lot)
	[11,120	13,555]

17. $RC =$

	Cost per unit
Table	34
Chair	26
Desk	45

19.

	Materials	Labor
Table	34	36
Chair	26	18
Desk	45	45

21.

Team	Level 1 pts	Level 2 pts	Total pts
A	1	2	3
B	2	2	4
C	2	3	5
D	1	1	2

23. (a) $H^2K = \begin{bmatrix} 2 \\ 2 \\ 3 \\ 1 \end{bmatrix}$ (b) H^2K represents the number of Level 2 points earned by each team.

25. $(H + H^2)K = \begin{bmatrix} 3 \\ 4 \\ 5 \\ 2 \end{bmatrix}$; Yes, $(H + H^2)K = HK + H^2K$. **27.** $AB = \begin{bmatrix} 3 & 1 \\ 1 & -5 \end{bmatrix}$ **29.** $(AB)C = \begin{bmatrix} 2 & 3 \\ 6 & 17 \end{bmatrix}$;

$A(BC) = \begin{bmatrix} 2 & 3 \\ 6 & 17 \end{bmatrix}$ **31.** $(A - B)C = \begin{bmatrix} -3 & -11 \\ 1 & 2 \end{bmatrix}$; $AC - BC = \begin{bmatrix} -3 & -11 \\ 1 & 2 \end{bmatrix}$

33. $AB = \begin{bmatrix} 122 & 130 \\ 65 & 57 \end{bmatrix}$; $BA = \begin{bmatrix} 122 & 130 \\ 65 & 57 \end{bmatrix}$; Yes, $AB = BA$.

35. $AB = \begin{bmatrix} 19 & 6 \\ -14 & 20 \end{bmatrix}$; $BA = \begin{bmatrix} 24 & 26 \\ -4 & 15 \end{bmatrix}$; No, AB is not equal to BA.

39. (a) Let $S = \begin{bmatrix} a & b & c \\ d & e & f \\ g & h & j \end{bmatrix}$; $I = \begin{bmatrix} 1 & 0 & 0 \\ 0 & 1 & 0 \\ 0 & 0 & 1 \end{bmatrix}$.

Then $SI = \begin{bmatrix} a \cdot 1 + b \cdot 0 + c \cdot 0 & a \cdot 0 + b \cdot 1 + c \cdot 0 & a \cdot 0 + b \cdot 0 + c \cdot 1 \\ d \cdot 1 + e \cdot 0 + f \cdot 0 & d \cdot 0 + e \cdot 1 + f \cdot 0 & d \cdot 0 + e \cdot 0 + f \cdot 1 \\ g \cdot 1 + h \cdot 0 + j \cdot 0 & g \cdot 0 + h \cdot 1 + j \cdot 0 & g \cdot 0 + h \cdot 0 + j \cdot 1 \end{bmatrix} = \begin{bmatrix} a & b & c \\ d & e & f \\ g & h & j \end{bmatrix} = S$.

43. $M^2 = \begin{bmatrix} 3 & 1 & 1 & 2 & 0 \\ 1 & 2 & 1 & 1 & 1 \\ 1 & 1 & 3 & 0 & 2 \\ 2 & 1 & 0 & 2 & 0 \\ 0 & 1 & 2 & 0 & 2 \end{bmatrix}$ **45.** 2 ways: B to C to A to E and B to C to D to E

49. $\begin{bmatrix} 1 & 0 \\ 0 & -1 \end{bmatrix} \cdot \begin{bmatrix} 1 & 0 \\ 0 & -1 \end{bmatrix} = \begin{bmatrix} 1 & 0 \\ 0 & 1 \end{bmatrix}$; Yes, they are inverses.

51. $\begin{bmatrix} 2 & 1 \\ 4 & 3 \end{bmatrix} \cdot \begin{bmatrix} 3/2 & -1/2 \\ -2 & 1 \end{bmatrix} = \begin{bmatrix} 1 & 0 \\ 0 & 1 \end{bmatrix}$; $\begin{bmatrix} 3/2 & -1/2 \\ -2 & 1 \end{bmatrix} \cdot \begin{bmatrix} 2 & 1 \\ 4 & 3 \end{bmatrix} = \begin{bmatrix} 1 & 0 \\ 0 & 1 \end{bmatrix}$; Yes, they are inverses.

53. No, they are not inverses.   **55.** $\begin{bmatrix} 5 & 6 \\ -10 & -13 \end{bmatrix} \cdot \begin{bmatrix} 13/5 & 6/5 \\ -2 & 1 \end{bmatrix} = \begin{bmatrix} 1 & 12 \\ 0 & -25 \end{bmatrix}$; No, they are not inverses.

57. $\begin{bmatrix} 1 & 3 & 3 \\ 1 & 4 & 3 \\ 1 & 3 & 4 \end{bmatrix} \cdot \begin{bmatrix} 7 & -3 & -3 \\ -1 & 1 & 0 \\ -1 & 0 & 1 \end{bmatrix} = \begin{bmatrix} 1 & 0 & 0 \\ 0 & 1 & 0 \\ 0 & 0 & 1 \end{bmatrix}$; $\begin{bmatrix} 7 & -3 & -3 \\ -1 & 1 & 0 \\ -1 & 0 & 1 \end{bmatrix} \cdot \begin{bmatrix} 1 & 3 & 3 \\ 1 & 4 & 3 \\ 1 & 3 & 4 \end{bmatrix} = \begin{bmatrix} 1 & 0 & 0 \\ 0 & 1 & 0 \\ 0 & 0 & 1 \end{bmatrix}$;
Yes, they are inverses.

61. Product $= \begin{bmatrix} 438.227 & 488.299 & 387.747 & 404.496 & 415.265 & 362.598 \\ 341.127 & 470.054 & 321.549 & 396.768 & 391.883 & 369.323 \\ 296.377 & 380.795 & 260.023 & 314.025 & 285.172 & 266.426 \\ 327.277 & 399.097 & 293.671 & 332.085 & 327.514 & 297.122 \\ 508.767 & 538.464 & 438.303 & 446.607 & 446.589 & 392.418 \end{bmatrix}$

14.3 Exercises   (Page 833)

1. $\begin{bmatrix} -1 & 2 & 1 \\ 3 & -4 & 2 \\ -4 & 0 & 1 \end{bmatrix}$ **3.** $\begin{bmatrix} -4 & 0 & 1 \\ -9 & 12 & -6 \\ -1 & 2 & 1 \end{bmatrix}$ **5.** $\begin{bmatrix} 18 & -1 & -1 \\ -4 & 0 & 1 \\ 1 & 3 & -3 \end{bmatrix}$ **7.** $\begin{bmatrix} -4 & 0 & 1 \\ 3 & -4 & 2 \\ -13 & 2 & 4 \end{bmatrix}$

9. $\begin{bmatrix} 1 & 11 & -5 \\ -1 & -4 & 3 \\ 0 & 5 & -2 \end{bmatrix}$ **11.** Interchange rows 1 and 2.   **13.** Double each element of row 2.   **15.** Multiply
each element of row 1 by 2, and add the results to row 2.   **17.** Multiply row 2 by -1. Multiply row 2 by -2
and add to row 1.   **19.** Multiply row 1 by $-1/2$. Multiply row 1 by -4 and add to row 2. Multiply row 2 by
$1/5$. Multiply row 2 by 1 and add to row 1.   **21.** Multiply row 1 by $1/6$. Multiply row 2 by $1/4$. Multiply row 2
by $-1/2$ and add to row 1. Multiply row 3 by $1/2$.   **23.** $\left[\begin{array}{cc|c} 2 & 3 & 11 \\ 1 & 2 & 8 \end{array}\right]$ **25.** $\left[\begin{array}{cc|c} 1 & 5 & 6 \\ 3 & -4 & 1 \end{array}\right]$

27. $\left[\begin{array}{ccc|c} 2 & 1 & 1 & 3 \\ 3 & -4 & 2 & -7 \\ 1 & 1 & 1 & 2 \end{array}\right]$ **29.** $\left[\begin{array}{ccc|c} 1 & 1 & 0 & 6 \\ 0 & 2 & 1 & 2 \\ 0 & 0 & 1 & 2 \end{array}\right]$ **31.** $\{(2, 3)\}$ **33.** $\{(-3, 0)\}$ **35.** $\{(7/2, -1)\}$

37. $\{(5, 0)\}$ **39.** $\emptyset$ **41.** $\{(-2, 1, 3)\}$ **43.** $\{(-1, 23, 16)\}$ **45.** $\{(3, 2, -4)\}$ **47.** $\{(-1, 2, 5, 1)\}$

49. A laborer charges \$76 per day and a concrete finisher charges \$80 per day.   **51.** Dark clay costs \$5 per lb,
light clay costs \$1 per lb.   **53.** 74 decals and 96 bumper stickers were purchased.

14.4 Exercises   (Page 843)

1. $\begin{bmatrix} 1 & 0 \\ 0 & -1 \end{bmatrix}$ **3.** $\begin{bmatrix} 3/2 & -1/2 \\ -2 & 1 \end{bmatrix}$ **5.** no inverse   **7.** $\begin{bmatrix} 1 & -2 & 0 \\ 0 & 1 & 0 \\ -1 & 3 & 1 \end{bmatrix}$ **9.** $\begin{bmatrix} 4 & 3 & 3 \\ -1 & 0 & -1 \\ -4 & -4 & -3 \end{bmatrix}$

11. $(1, 1)$ **13.** There is no unique solution because the coefficient matrix has no inverse.   **15.** $(-1, 23, 16)$

17. $(2, 1, -1)$ **19.** There is no unique solution because the coefficient matrix has no inverse.   **21.** $\begin{bmatrix} 3 & -4 \\ 2 & -3 \end{bmatrix}$

23. The missing elements can be any two numbers with a product of -3.   **25.** sometimes true (true whenever
the numbers a and b are reciprocals of each other)

27. $\begin{bmatrix} k & 0 \\ 0 & 1 \end{bmatrix} \cdot \begin{bmatrix} 2 & 4 \\ 3 & 5 \end{bmatrix} = \begin{bmatrix} 2k + 0 \cdot 3 & 4k + 0 \cdot 5 \\ 0 \cdot 2 + 1 \cdot 3 & 0 \cdot 4 + 1 \cdot 5 \end{bmatrix} = \begin{bmatrix} 2k & 4k \\ 3 & 5 \end{bmatrix}$ (The first row is multiplied by k.)

29. $\begin{bmatrix} 1 & 0 \\ 2 & 1 \end{bmatrix} \cdot \begin{bmatrix} 2 & 4 \\ 3 & 5 \end{bmatrix} = \begin{bmatrix} 1 \cdot 2 + 0 \cdot 3 & 1 \cdot 4 + 0 \cdot 5 \\ 2 \cdot 2 + 1 \cdot 3 & 2 \cdot 4 + 1 \cdot 5 \end{bmatrix} = \begin{bmatrix} 2 & 4 \\ 2 \cdot 2 + 3 & 2 \cdot 4 + 5 \end{bmatrix}$ **33.** 1 **35.** 0

41. $\begin{bmatrix} .226 & -.152 \\ .197 & .049 \end{bmatrix}$ **43.** $\begin{bmatrix} -.871 & .602 & .594 \\ 1.905 & -1.511 & -1.047 \\ -1.774 & 1.590 & .876 \end{bmatrix}$ **45.** one; 0 **47.** 1,174 metric tons of wheat and 1,565 metric tons of oil **49.** 3,077 units of agriculture; 2,564 units of manufacturing; 3,179 units of transportation

Extension Exercises (Page 847)

1. $\begin{bmatrix} 20 \\ 8 \end{bmatrix}\begin{bmatrix} 5 \\ 27 \end{bmatrix}\begin{bmatrix} 20 \\ 8 \end{bmatrix}\begin{bmatrix} 18 \\ 5 \end{bmatrix}\begin{bmatrix} 5 \\ 27 \end{bmatrix}\begin{bmatrix} 20 \\ 5 \end{bmatrix}\begin{bmatrix} 14 \\ 15 \end{bmatrix}\begin{bmatrix} 18 \\ 19 \end{bmatrix}$ **3.** $\begin{bmatrix} -5 & -2 \\ -2 & -1 \end{bmatrix}$

5. $\begin{bmatrix} 103 \\ 118 \\ 116 \end{bmatrix}\begin{bmatrix} 95 \\ 122 \\ 98 \end{bmatrix}\begin{bmatrix} 42 \\ 46 \\ 47 \end{bmatrix}\begin{bmatrix} 103 \\ 130 \\ 104 \end{bmatrix}\begin{bmatrix} 114 \\ 119 \\ 141 \end{bmatrix}\begin{bmatrix} 65 \\ 66 \\ 84 \end{bmatrix}\begin{bmatrix} 120 \\ 132 \\ 145 \end{bmatrix}\begin{bmatrix} 87 \\ 89 \\ 105 \end{bmatrix}\begin{bmatrix} 63 \\ 74 \\ 68 \end{bmatrix}\begin{bmatrix} 176 \\ 203 \\ 203 \end{bmatrix}$

7. 51, 89, 55, 88, 177, 108, 89, 201, 114, 40, 90, 49, 83, 192, 102, 49, 106, 62, 19, 51, 23, 69, 116, 89, 131, 264, 156

14.5 Exercises (Page 854)

1. $\begin{bmatrix} 4 & -1 \\ 3 & 5 \end{bmatrix}$ **3.** $\begin{bmatrix} 8 & -7 \\ -2 & 4 \end{bmatrix}$ **5.** (3, I); 3 **7.** (2, III); 2 **9.** (2, III); 0 **11. (a)** Set up stadium **(b)** Set up gym **(c)** Set up both **13. (a)**

	Better	Not
Market New	50,000	−25,000
Don't	−40,000	−10,000

(b) $5,000 and −$22,000; Market new **15.** 1: 1/5; 2: 4/5; I: 3/5; II: 2/5; value = 17/5
17. The saddle point gives a value of 0. The game is fair. The first player should select strategy (row) 2, while the second player should select strategy (column) I. **19.** Both A and B should choose either strategy with a probability of 1/2. The value of the game is 0, a fair game. **25. (a)** $7,388.89 **(b)** $7,388.89
29. $7,000x + 7,000$ **31.** Nature should impose a freeze 1/18 of the time. **33.** strategy 2 **35.** greater than 3/16 **37.** $7,187.50

Chapter 14 Test (Page 858)

1. $\begin{bmatrix} -1 & -1 & 4 \\ 2 & 2 & 0 \\ 3 & 1 & 6 \end{bmatrix}$ **2.** $\begin{bmatrix} 5 & -1 & 2 \\ 2 & -2 & 2 \\ 5 & 1 & 0 \end{bmatrix}$ **3.** $\begin{bmatrix} -9 & -2 & 12 \\ -7 & 0 & 5 \\ -15 & 2 & 12 \end{bmatrix}$ **4.** $\begin{bmatrix} -2 & 4 & -6 \\ 0 & -1 & -1 \\ 10 & 4 & 6 \end{bmatrix}$ **5.** $\begin{bmatrix} 4 & -2 & 6 \\ 4 & 0 & 2 \\ 8 & 2 & 6 \end{bmatrix}$

6. $\begin{bmatrix} 11 & -1 & 0 \\ 2 & -6 & 4 \\ 7 & 1 & -6 \end{bmatrix}$ **7.** $\begin{bmatrix} 2 & -1 & 3 \\ 4 & 1 & 3 \\ 2 & 0 & 1 \end{bmatrix}$ **8.** $\begin{bmatrix} -4 & -1 & 0 \\ 2 & 0 & 1 \\ 4 & 1 & 3 \end{bmatrix}$ **9.** $\begin{bmatrix} -3 \\ 10 \end{bmatrix}$ **10.** $\begin{bmatrix} 6 & 0 & 12 \\ 26 & 0 & 20 \end{bmatrix}$

11. [16] **12.** There is no product, since the first matrix has a different number of columns than the second has rows. **13.** $\begin{bmatrix} 3 & -1 \\ -5 & 2 \end{bmatrix}$ **14.** $\begin{bmatrix} 1/2 & 1/2 & -1/2 \\ -1/2 & 1/6 & 1/6 \\ 1/2 & -1/2 & 1/2 \end{bmatrix}$ **15.** $\begin{bmatrix} 9 & -4 & | & 20 \\ 5 & 10 & | & 12 \end{bmatrix}$ **16.** $\begin{bmatrix} 2 & 1 & -6 & | & 6 \\ 5 & 0 & 12 & | & 15 \\ 0 & 6 & 3 & | & 8 \end{bmatrix}$

17. $\{(3, 0)\}$ **18.** $\{(4, -1, 2)\}$ **19. (a)** $\begin{bmatrix} 1 & 1 \\ 2 & -1 \end{bmatrix}$ **(b)** $\begin{bmatrix} x \\ y \end{bmatrix}$ **(c)** $\begin{bmatrix} 1 \\ -7 \end{bmatrix}$ **20.** $X = A^{-1}B$ **21.** $\{(-2, 3)\}$

23. $A = \begin{array}{c} \\ \text{Bananas} \\ \text{Coal} \end{array} \begin{array}{c} \text{Bananas} \quad \text{Coal} \\ \begin{bmatrix} .3 & .2 \\ .1 & .4 \end{bmatrix} \end{array}$ **24.** 750 units of bananas, 625 units of coal   **25.** $\begin{bmatrix} 8 & -3 \\ 0 & 2 \end{bmatrix}$

26. 9   **27.** Select strategy one 9/10 of the time and strategy two 1/10 of the time;   value is $-31/10$.

28. 4 and -4, or -4 and 4

29. $M = \begin{array}{c} \\ \text{Ring} \\ \text{Bracelet} \\ \text{Necklace} \end{array} \begin{array}{c} \text{Silver} \quad \text{Turquoise} \\ \begin{bmatrix} 1.6 & .7 \\ 5.8 & 7.5 \\ 26.3 & 18.8 \end{bmatrix} \end{array}; \quad C = \begin{array}{c} \\ \text{Silver} \\ \text{Turquoise} \end{array} \begin{array}{c} \text{Cost} \\ \text{per unit} \\ \begin{bmatrix} 5.50 \\ 2.10 \end{bmatrix} \end{array}$

30. $MC = \begin{bmatrix} 1.6 & .7 \\ 5.8 & 7.5 \\ 26.3 & 18.8 \end{bmatrix} \cdot \begin{bmatrix} 5.50 \\ 2.10 \end{bmatrix} = \begin{array}{c} \\ \text{Ring} \\ \text{Bracelet} \\ \text{Necklace} \end{array} \begin{array}{c} \text{Cost} \\ \text{per item} \\ \begin{bmatrix} 10.27 \\ 47.65 \\ 184.13 \end{bmatrix} \end{array}$

3.5   Arithmetic in Other Bases

Table 3.16

+	0	1	2	3	4
0	0	1	2	3	4
1	1	2	3	4	10
2	2	3	4	10	11
3	3	4	10	11	12
4	4	10	11	12	13

Addition in any positional system depends on face values, place values, and the ability to add any two single digits. When a sum has two digits we "carry" the left digit to the next position. See Section 3.3. In the decimal system, for example, we need only memorize sums as high as $9 + 9$ (though most of us learn them beyond that).

In a different base, say five, the process is the same. We simply must remember that the place values are now the powers of five rather than ten, and the face values go only as high as 4 rather than 9. Table 3.16 is a base five addition table, though you should be able to quickly find all these sums without the aid of a table. For example, $3 + 4$ is not 7 in this system (since the symbol 7 is not available in base five). "Seven" must be expressed as one 5 and two 1s, so

$$3_{\text{five}} + 4_{\text{five}} = 12_{\text{five}}.$$

Example 1   Add 324_{five} and 223_{five}.

First arrange the numbers just as for ordinary decimal (base ten) addition. Then add in columns, beginning on the right.

Step 1
$$
\begin{array}{r}
{}^{1} \\
3\ 2\ 4 \\
+\ 2\ 2\ 3 \\
\hline
2
\end{array}
\qquad
\begin{array}{l}
4 + 3 = 7_{\text{ten}} = 12_{\text{five}} \\[4pt]
\text{Write 2, carry 1}
\end{array}
$$

Step 2
$$
\begin{array}{r}
{}^{1}\ {}^{1} \\
3\ 2\ 4 \\
+\ 2\ 2\ 3 \\
\hline
0\ 2
\end{array}
\qquad
\begin{array}{l}
1 + 2 + 2 = 5_{\text{ten}} = 10_{\text{five}} \\[4pt]
\text{Write 0, carry 1}
\end{array}
$$

Step 3
$$
\begin{array}{r}
{}^{1}\ {}^{1} \\
3\ 2\ 4 \\
+\ 2\ 2\ 3 \\
\hline
1\ 1\ 0\ 2
\end{array}
\qquad
\begin{array}{l}
1 + 3 + 2 = 6_{\text{ten}} = 11_{\text{five}} \\[4pt]
\text{Write 11}
\end{array}
$$

Finally, $324_{\text{five}} + 223_{\text{five}} = 1102_{\text{five}}$.

Expanded notation shows why this process works. (Notice that the symbol 10 denotes the number five here.)

$$
\begin{array}{rl}
324_{\text{five}} = & (3 \times 10^2) + (2 \times 10^1) + (4 \times 10^0) \\
+223_{\text{five}} = & (2 \times 10^2) + (2 \times 10^1) + (3 \times 10^0) \\
\hline
\text{Sum:} & (10 \times 10^2) + (4 \times 10^1) + (12 \times 10^0)
\end{array}
$$

Now modify the expansion (carry) just as with base ten expansions in Section 3.3.

$$= (10 \times 10^2) + (4 \times 10^1) + (12 \times 10^0)$$

$$= (10 \times 10^2) + (4 \times 10^1) + \overbrace{(10 \times 10^0) + (2 \times 10^0)}$$ Distributive property

$$= (10 \times 10^2) + \underbrace{(4 \times 10^1) + (1 \times 10^1)} + (2 \times 10^0)$$ Distributive property

$$= (10 \times 10^2) + (10 \times 10^1) + (2 \times 10^0)$$

$$= (1 \times 10^3) + (1 \times 10^2) + (2 \times 10^0)$$

$$= 1102_{\text{five}}.$$

Example 2 Add 443_{five}, 1220_{five}, and 4344_{five}.

Work as follows.

Step 1	Step 2	Step 3	Step 4
$\begin{array}{r} {\scriptstyle 1} \\ 4\ 4\ 3 \\ 1\ 2\ 2\ 0 \\ +\ 4\ 3\ 4\ 4 \\ \hline 2 \end{array}$	$\begin{array}{r} {\scriptstyle 2}\ {\scriptstyle 1} \\ 4\ 4\ 3 \\ 1\ 2\ 2\ 0 \\ +\ 4\ 3\ 4\ 4 \\ \hline 1\ 2 \end{array}$	$\begin{array}{r} {\scriptstyle 2}\ {\scriptstyle 2}\ {\scriptstyle 1} \\ 4\ 4\ 3 \\ 1\ 2\ 2\ 0 \\ +\ 4\ 3\ 4\ 4 \\ \hline 1\ 1\ 2 \end{array}$	$\begin{array}{r} {\scriptstyle 2}\ {\scriptstyle 2}\ {\scriptstyle 1} \\ 4\ 4\ 3 \\ 1\ 2\ 2\ 0 \\ +\ 4\ 3\ 4\ 4 \\ \hline 1\ 2\ 1\ 1\ 2 \end{array}$
$3 + 0 + 4$ $= 12_{\text{five}}$	$1 + 4 + 2$ $+ 4 =$ 21_{five}	$2 + 4 + 2$ $+ 3 =$ 21_{five}	$2 + 1 + 4$ $= 12_{\text{five}}$

The answer, 12112_{five}, can be checked by converting the original numbers to decimal (base ten) form, adding in that familiar system, and converting back to base five:

$$443_{\text{five}} = (4 \times 25) + (4 \times 5) + (3 \times 1) = 100 + 20 + 3 = 123$$
$$1220_{\text{five}} = (1 \times 125) + (2 \times 25) + (2 \times 5) = 125 + 50 + 10 = 185$$
$$4344_{\text{five}} = (4 \times 125) + (3 \times 25) + (4 \times 5) + (4 \times 1)$$
$$= 500 + 75 + 20 + 4 = 599.$$

$$\begin{array}{r} 123 \\ 185 \\ +\ 599 \\ \hline 907 \end{array} \longrightarrow \begin{array}{r} 5\ \underline{|\ 907} \\ 5\ \underline{|\ 181}\quad 2 \\ 5\ \underline{|\ 36}\quad 1 \\ 5\ \underline{|\ 7}\quad 1 \\ 5\ \underline{|\ 1}\quad 2 \\ 0\quad 1 \end{array} \longrightarrow \quad \text{Answer: } 12112_{\text{five}}$$

Add in base ten   Convert to base five

Subtraction also is basically the same in any positional system, regardless of the base. Sometimes "borrowing" is required. Again, see Section 3.3.

Work each base five subtraction problem.

(a)
$$343$$
$$-212$$
$$\overline{131}$$

Check by adding 131_{five} and 212_{five}.

(b)
$$432$$
$$-134$$

Begin by borrowing 1 five from the 3 fives in the top number (since 4 cannot be taken from 2).

$$
\begin{array}{r}
2 \\
4\ \overset{1}{\cancel{3}}\ 2 \\
-\ 1\ 3\ 4 \\
\hline
3
\end{array}
\qquad 12_{\text{five}} - 4_{\text{five}} = 3_{\text{five}}
$$

Now borrow from the 4 in the top number.

$$
\begin{array}{r}
3\ \ 12 \\
\cancel{4}\ \cancel{3}\ {}^{1}2 \\
-\ 1\ 3\ 4 \\
\hline
2\ 4\ 3
\end{array}
\qquad 12_{\text{five}} - 3_{\text{five}} = 4_{\text{five}}
$$

and $3_{\text{five}} - 1_{\text{five}} = 2_{\text{five}}$

Check by adding 243_{five} and 134_{five}. ▨

Multiplication (and division) in base five requires a knowledge of products at least up to 4×4. For example, $3 \times 4 = 12_{\text{ten}} = 22_{\text{five}}$. (Twelve consists of two 5s and two 1s.) Table 3.17 gives all base five products of two single digits. Again, the table is a handy reference but we should be able to obtain any of its entries quickly without referring to it. For those of us accustomed to base ten work, a good rule of thumb for working in other bases is: *Reason the steps of a calculation in base ten, but write down the results in the other base.* Whenever a partial result is *written down*, be sure it is written in the other base.

Table 3.17

×	0	1	2	3	4
0	0	0	0	0	0
1	0	1	2	3	4
2	0	2	4	11	13
3	0	3	11	14	22
4	0	4	13	22	31

Example 4 Multiply 24_{five} times 43_{five}.

Step 1
$$
\begin{array}{r}
2 \\
4\ 3 \\
\times\ 2\ 4 \\
\hline
2
\end{array}
\qquad 4 \times 3 = 12_{\text{ten}} = 22_{\text{five}}
$$

Write 2, carry 2

Step 2
$$
\begin{array}{r}
2 \\
4\ 3 \\
\times\ 2\ 4 \\
\hline
3\ 3\ 2
\end{array}
\qquad 4 \times 4 = 16_{\text{ten}}
$$

$16_{\text{ten}} + 2_{\text{ten}} = 18_{\text{ten}} = 33_{\text{five}}$

Write 33

Step 3

$$
\begin{array}{r}
{\scriptstyle 1} \\
4\ 3 \\
\times\ 2\ 4 \\
\hline
3\ 3\ 2 \\
1
\end{array}
$$

$2 \times 3 = 6_{ten} = 11_{five}$

Write 1, carry 1

Step 4

$$
\begin{array}{r}
{\scriptstyle 1} \\
4\ 3 \\
\times\ 2\ 4 \\
\hline
3\ 3\ 2 \\
1\ 4\ 1
\end{array}
$$

$2 \times 4 = 8_{ten}$

$8_{ten} + 1_{ten} = 9_{ten} = 14_{five}$

Write 14

Step 5

$$
\begin{array}{r}
4\ 3 \\
\times\ 2\ 4 \\
\hline
3\ 3\ 2 \\
1\ 4\ 1 \\
\hline
2\ 2\ 4\ 2
\end{array}
$$

Add 332_{five} and 1410_{five}

Answer: 2242_{five} ▨

To divide in base five, reason the steps in base ten, but write results in base five.

Example 5 Divide 4232_{five} by 3_{five}.

The divisor is $3_{five} = 3_{ten}$. Work as follows.

Step 1

$$
\begin{array}{r}
1 \\
3\overline{)4232} \\
3 \\
\hline
1
\end{array}
$$

3 goes into 4 once

Multiply and subtract

Step 2

$$
\begin{array}{r}
12 \\
3\overline{)4232} \\
3 \\
\hline
12 \\
11 \\
\hline
1
\end{array}
$$

Bring down 2

$12_{five} = 7_{ten}$

3 goes into 7 twice

Multiply and subtract

Step 3

$$
\begin{array}{r}
122 \\
3\overline{)4232} \\
3 \\
\hline
12 \\
11 \\
\hline
13 \\
11 \\
\hline
2
\end{array}
$$

Bring down 3

$13_{five} = 8_{ten}$

3 goes into 8 twice

Multiply and subtract

$$\begin{array}{r} \textit{Step 4} \qquad 1224 \\ 3\overline{)4232} \\ \underline{3} \\ 12 \\ \underline{11} \\ 13 \\ \underline{11} \\ 22 \\ \underline{22} \\ 0 \end{array}$$

Bring down 2
$22_{\text{five}} = 12_{\text{ten}}$
3 goes into 12 four times
Multiply and subtract

The remainder is 0, so $4232_{\text{five}} \div 3_{\text{five}} = 1224_{\text{five}}$. ▤

The final example of this section illustrates arithmetic procedures in several other bases.

Example 6   Work each arithmetic problem in the indicated base.

(a) $523_{\text{eight}} + 705_{\text{eight}}$

$$\begin{array}{r} 1 \quad\;\; \\ 5\ 2\ 3 \\ +7\ 0\ 5 \\ \hline 1\ 4\ 3\ 0 \end{array}$$

(b) $T7_{\text{twelve}} \times 8E_{\text{twelve}}$

$$\begin{array}{r} 8\ E \\ \times T\ 7 \\ \hline 5\ 2\ 5 \\ 7\ 5\ 2 \quad \\ \hline 7\ T\ 4\ 5 \end{array}$$

(c) $9CA3_{\text{sixteen}} - ABC_{\text{sixteen}}$

(Recall that ten, eleven, twelve, thirteen, fourteen, and fifteen are denoted A, B, C, D, E, and F.)

$$\begin{array}{r} {}^{B}\; {}^{19}\quad\; \\ 9\ \not C\ \not A\ {}^{1}3 \\ -\quad A\ B\ C \\ \hline 9\ 1\ E\ 7 \end{array}$$

(d) $100110010_{two} \div 110_{two}$

$$
\begin{array}{r}
110011 \\
110\overline{)100110010} \\
\underline{110} \\
111 \\
\underline{110} \\
1001 \\
\underline{110} \\
110 \\
\underline{110} \\
0
\end{array}
$$

3.5 Exercises

Work the following problems in base five.

1. 31 +12

2. 22 +13

3. 142 +303

4. 114 + 34

5. 121 32 +404

6. 101 20 +324

7. 424 − 13

8. 122 − 41

9. 1302 − 433

10. 1222 − 333

11. 241 × 3

12. 403 × 2

13. 24 ×32

14. 12 ×43

15. 413 × 23

16. 2334 × 42

17. 31^2

18. 204^2

19. 12^3

20. 42^3

21. $2\overline{)132}$

22. $3\overline{)212}$

23. $4\overline{)3023}$

24. $3\overline{)1333332}$

25. Complete the base seven addition table.

+	0	1	2	3	4	5	6
0	0	1	2	3	4	5	6
1	1	2	3	4	5	6	10
2	2	3	4	5	6		
3	3	4	5	6		11	
4	4	5	6		11		13
5	5	6		11		13	14
6							

26. Complete the base seven multiplication table.

×	0	1	2	3	4	5	6
0	0	0	0	0	0	0	0
1	0	1	2	3	4	5	6
2	0	2	4	6	11	13	15
3	0	3	6		21		
4	0	4	11		22		33
5	0	5		21		34	42
6	0	6					51

Work the following base seven problems. (You may want to make use of the tables in Exercises 25 and 26.)

27.
$$\begin{array}{r} 36 \\ +41 \\ \hline \end{array}$$

28.
$$\begin{array}{r} 44 \\ +62 \\ \hline \end{array}$$

29.
$$\begin{array}{r} 365 \\ 242 \\ +216 \\ \hline \end{array}$$

30.
$$\begin{array}{r} 245 \\ 345 \\ +466 \\ \hline \end{array}$$

31.
$$\begin{array}{r} 253 \\ -46 \\ \hline \end{array}$$

32.
$$\begin{array}{r} 412 \\ -105 \\ \hline \end{array}$$

33.
$$\begin{array}{r} 4651 \\ -266 \\ \hline \end{array}$$

34.
$$\begin{array}{r} 3654 \\ -666 \\ \hline \end{array}$$

35.
$$\begin{array}{r} 43 \\ \times 6 \\ \hline \end{array}$$

36.
$$\begin{array}{r} 25 \\ \times 6 \\ \hline \end{array}$$

37.
$$\begin{array}{r} 325 \\ \times 42 \\ \hline \end{array}$$

38.
$$\begin{array}{r} 416 \\ \times 55 \\ \hline \end{array}$$

Work the following problems in the indicated bases.

39. $202_{three} + 121_{three}$

40. $82_{nine} + 148_{nine}$

41. $241_{six} - 155_{six}$

42. $222_{four} - 133_{four}$

43. $TE_{twelve} \times 34_{twelve}$

44. $183_{eleven} \times 2T_{eleven}$

45. $1110_{four} \div 32_{four}$

46. $11732_{eight} \div 25_{eight}$

47.
$$\begin{array}{r} 52 \\ 23 \\ +14 \\ \hline \end{array}$$
(base seven)

48.
$$\begin{array}{r} 301 \\ 223 \\ +320 \\ \hline \end{array}$$
(base four)

49.
$$\begin{array}{r} E92 \\ -4E \\ \hline \end{array}$$
(base twelve)

50.
$$\begin{array}{r} CBA \\ -ABC \\ \hline \end{array}$$
(base sixteen)

51.
$$\begin{array}{r} 2021 \\ \times 212 \\ \hline \end{array}$$
(base three)

52.
$$\begin{array}{r} 6012 \\ \times 343 \\ \hline \end{array}$$
(base eight)

53. $26\overline{)13750}$
(base nine)

54. $53\overline{)3211120}$
(base six)

55. 32^2
(base four)

56. $4\overline{)TOT}$
(base eleven)

57. ET^2
(base twelve)

58. D^2
(base sixteen)

59. What is the rule for telling when a base ten numeral represents a number that is divisible by ten?

Use the results of Exercise 59 to help you decide the answers to the following questions.

60. Which of the following base five numerals represent numbers that are divisible by five?

3402, 400, 230, 1002, 4030

61. Which of the following base seven numerals represent numbers that are divisible by seven?

$$50, 63, 105, 240, 5230$$

62. Which of the following base twelve numerals represent numbers that are divisible by twelve?

$$48, 60, 108, 240, 250, 1224, 1970$$

63. Complete the binary addition table below.

+	0	1
0		
1		10

Work these binary addition and subtraction problems.

64.
```
   10
 + 10
```

65.
```
   1010
 + 1101
```

66.
```
  100111
 + 11101
```

67.
```
  1001011
 + 1011010
```

68.
```
   10
    1
 + 11
```

69.
```
   11
   10
 + 11
```

70.
```
  100
  111
 + 101
```

71.
```
  1001
   101
 + 1101
```

72.
```
   1101
    101
 + 1100
```

73.
```
   10110
 -  1011
```

74.
```
  1101110
 - 110101
```

75.
```
  101101010
 -  1011011
```

76. Complete the binary multiplication table below.

×	0	1
0		
1		1

Find each of the following products in binary.

77.
```
   10
 × 10
```

78.
```
   10
 × 11
```

79.
```
  101
 ×  10
```

80.
```
  111
 ×  10
```

81.
```
  10001
 ×   101
```

82.
```
  1110
 ×  110
```

*83.
```
  110110
 ×   1011
```

*84.
```
  110111
 ×    111
```

Find each binary quotient.

85. $11\overline{)11011}$

86. $11\overline{)100111}$

87. $101\overline{)1111000}$

88. $111\overline{)11000100}$

Chapter 3 Summary

Important types of numeration systems

Simple grouping
Multiplicative grouping
Positional

Some numeration systems of history

Egyptian (simple grouping, base 10)

1	10	100	1000	10,000	100,000	1,000,000
I	∩	9	⌐	⌐	⌐	𝕏

Roman (modified simple grouping, base 10)

1	5	10	50	100	500	1000
I	V	X	L	C	D	M

Chinese (modified multiplicative grouping, base 10)

1	2	3	4	5	6	7	8	9	10	100	1000	0
一	二	三	四	五	六	七	八	九	十	百	千	零

Babylonian (combination of base 10 simple grouping within base 60 positional)

1	10
▼	⟨

Hindu-Arabic (positional, base 10)

0	1	2	3	4	5	6	7	8	9

Basics of a positional numeral

Each digit conveys

1. face value: the inherent value of the digit symbol
2. place value: the power of the base associated with the digit's position

Some decimal equivalents in the common computer-oriented bases

Base ten (Decimal)	Base sixteen (Hexadecimal)	Base eight (Octal)	Base two (Binary)
0	0	00	0000
1	1	01	0001
2	2	02	0010
3	3	03	0011
4	4	04	0100
5	5	05	0101
6	6	06	0110
7	7	07	0111
8	8	10	1000
9	9	11	1001
10	A	12	1010
11	B	13	1011
12	C	14	1100
13	D	15	1101
14	E	16	1110
15	F	17	1111

Chapter 3   Test

Identify each of the following base five numerals as simple grouping, multiplicative grouping, or positional. Convert to our system.

1. ΛΛΛΙΙ

2. ⊙N ⊙Λ⊙Ι

3. ⊙⊙⊙⊙⊙

Identify the numeration system for each of the following. Then convert to our system.

4. 𝒮 𝒮 𝒮 999∩∩∩ 99 ∩∩ ΙΙΙΙΙ

5. LXVII

6. ⟨⟨Ι

7. ⟨Ι ⟨ΙΙ ⟨ΙΙΙ

Write each of the following in expanded notation.

8. 28

9. 4690

10. Simplify: $(6 \times 10^3) + (5 \times 10^2) + (7 \times 10^1) + (4 \times 10^0)$.

Convert each of the following to base ten.

11. 475_{eight}

12. 216_{seven}

13. $34T_{twelve}$

14. 110111_{two}

Convert from base ten as indicated.

15. 98 to base four

16. 2914 to base eight

17. 2481 to base twelve

18. 683 to base nine

19. 242 to base two

Perform the following calculations. Use the addition and multiplication tables in the text as needed.

20.
$$\begin{array}{r} 725 \\ + \ 37 \\ \hline \end{array}$$
(base eight)

21.
$$\begin{array}{r} 5365 \\ -2717 \\ \hline \end{array}$$
(base eight)

22.
$$\begin{array}{r} 37 \\ \times 56 \\ \hline \end{array}$$
(base eight)

23.
$$\begin{array}{r} 1101 \\ + \ 101 \\ \hline \end{array}$$
(base two)

24.
$$\begin{array}{r} 5T4 \\ \times \ 6E \\ \hline \end{array}$$
(base twelve)

25. $11\overline{)100111}$

(base two)

1. 43_{five} **3.** 1000_{five} **5.** 1112_{five} **7.** 411_{five} **9.** 314_{five} **11.** 1323_{five} **13.** 1423_{five} **15.** 21104_{five} **17.** 2011_{five}
19. 2333_{five} **21.** 41_{five} **23.** 342_{five} **25.** Row 2: 10, 11; row 3: 10, 12; row 4: 10, 12; row 5: 10, 12; row 6: 6, 10, 11, 12,
13, 14, 15 **27.** 110_{seven} **29.** 1156_{seven} **31.** 204_{seven} **33.** 4352_{seven} **35.** 354_{seven} **37.** 20343_{seven} **39.** 1100_{three} **41.** 42_{six}
43. 3048_{twelve} **45.** 12_{four} **47.** 122_{seven} **49.** $E43_{twelve}$ **51.** 1220222_{three} **53.** 473_{nine} **55.** 3010_{four} **57.** $E804_{twelve}$
59. The numeral must end in 0. **61.** 50; 240; 5230

63.

	0	1
0	0	1
1	1	10

65. 10111_{two} **67.** 10100101_{two} **69.** 1000_{two} **71.** 11011_{two} **73.** 1011_{two} **75.** 100001111_{two} **77.** 100_{two} **79.** 1010_{two}
81. 1010101_{two} **83.** 1001010010_{two} **85.** 1001_{two} **87.** 11000_{two}

Chapter 3 Test *(page 169)*

1. Simple grouping; 17 **2.** Multiplicative grouping; 119 **3.** Positional; 1391 **4.** Egyptian; 3555 **5.** Roman; 67
6. Babylonian; 21 **7.** Babylonian; 40,333 **8.** $(2 \times 10^1) + (8 \times 10^0)$ **9.** $(4 \times 10^3) + (6 \times 10^2) + (9 \times 10^1) + (0 \times 10^0)$
10. 6574 **11.** 317 **12.** 111 **13.** 490 **14.** 55 **15.** 1202_{four} **16.** 5542_{eight} **17.** 1529_{twelve} **18.** 838_{nine}
19. 11110010_{two} **20.** 764_{eight} **21.** 2446_{eight} **22.** 2622_{eight} **23.** 10010_{two} **24.** 34658_{twelve} **25.** 1101_{two}

*4.4 Number Sequences

In Section 2.5 we examined number sequences in conjunction with inductive reasoning. In this section we shall look at two special types of sequences. Recall that a list of numbers having a first number, a second number, a third number, and so on, is called a **sequence**. The numbers in a sequence are called **terms** of the sequence.

Example 1 Examples of sequences:

(a) Even positive integers: 2, 4, 6, 8, 10, . . .

(b) Positive multiples of 5: 5, 10, 15, 20, 25, . . .

(c) Powers of 2: 2, 4, 8, 16, 32, 64, . . .

(d) Divisions on a ruler: $1, \dfrac{1}{2}, \dfrac{1}{4}, \dfrac{1}{8}, \dfrac{1}{16}, \dfrac{1}{32}$

(e) Periodic withdrawals of \$10 from a bank account of \$500 generate the sequence

$$500, 490, 480, 470, 460, \ldots, 20, 10, 0.$$

This sequence would stop when \$0 is reached.

In this section we shall study *arithmetic* and *geometric* sequences. To do so, you should be familiar with the rules for the arithmetic operations with positive and negative numbers. While these rules are covered in detail in Chapter 5, we summarize them (with examples) below.

In adding two numbers with *like* signs, the sum will have the same sign, and the numeral of the sum is obtained by adding the numerals of the addends.

$$5 + 7 = 12 \qquad (-15) + (-4) = -19$$

In adding two numbers with *unlike* signs, the sign of the sum corresponds to the sign of the addend with the larger numeral part. The numeral of the sum is obtained by subtracting the smaller addend numeral from the larger.

$$(-5) + 7 = 2 \qquad (-15) + 4 = -11$$

To subtract $a - b$, rewrite as the sum of a and the opposite of b; that is,

$$a - b = a + (-b)$$
$$4 - 7 = 4 + (-7) = -3 \qquad -3 - (-8) = -3 + 8 = 5$$
$$-6 - 5 = -6 + (-5) = -11$$

When multiplying or dividing signed numbers, the answer is positive if the two numbers have the same sign, while the answer is negative if they have different signs.

$$3 \cdot 8 = 24 \qquad (-3)(8) = -24 \qquad 3(-8) = -24 \qquad (-3)(-8) = 24$$
$$\frac{24}{8} = 3 \qquad \frac{-24}{8} = -3 \qquad \frac{-24}{-8} = 3 \qquad \frac{24}{-3} = -8$$

A negative number raised to an even power gives a positive number, while a negative number raised to an odd power gives a negative number.

$$(-4)^2 = 16 \qquad (-4)^3 = -64 \qquad \left(-\frac{1}{2}\right)^5 = -\frac{1}{32}$$

The sequences in parts **(a)** and **(b)** of Example 1 are examples of *arithmetic sequences*. In an **arithmetic sequence,** each term after the first is found by adding the same number to the preceding term. For example,

$$9, 17, 25, 33, 41, \ldots$$

is an arithmetic sequence. Each term after the first is found by adding 8 to the preceding term. The number 8 is called the *common difference*. To find the **common difference** for an arithmetic sequence, choose any term except the first and subtract the preceding term.

Example 2 Find the common difference in each arithmetic sequence.

(a) 11, 14, 17, 20, 23, 26, 29, . . .

Choose any term except the first and subtract the term coming just before it. Choosing 14 and 17 gives

$$\text{Common difference} = 17 - 14 = 3.$$

(b) 13, 7, 1, -5, -11, -17, . . .

Let us choose 7 and 1.

$$\text{Common difference} = 1 - 7 = -6 \ \blacksquare$$

If the first term and common difference of an arithmetic sequence are known, it is possible to write as many terms in the sequence as desired. For example, suppose the first term of the sequence is 3. The first term of a sequence is often named a_1 (read "a sub one"), so $a_1 = 3$. If the common difference is 5, then the second term of the sequence, a_2, is

$$a_2 = a_1 + 5 = 3 + 5 = 8.$$

Find further terms as follows:

$$a_3 = a_2 + 5 = (a_1 + 5) + 5 = a_1 + 2 \cdot 5 = 3 + 10 = 13$$
$$a_4 = a_3 + 5 = (a_2 + 5) + 5 = (a_1 + 5) + 5 + 5$$
$$= a_1 + 3 \cdot 5 = 3 + 15 = 18$$
$$a_5 = a_4 + 5 = a_1 + 4 \cdot 5 = 3 + 20 = 23, \text{ and so on.}$$

In summary, starting with a_1 gives the pattern shown at the side. Each shaded number is one less than the corresponding "sub" number. Use this pattern to find additional terms of the sequence: for example,

$$a_{12} = a_1 + 11 \cdot 5 \qquad 11 = 12 - 1$$
$$a_{20} = a_1 + 19 \cdot 5 \qquad 19 = 20 - 1.$$

$a_2 = a_1 + 1 \cdot 5$

$a_3 = a_1 + 2 \cdot 5$

$a_4 = a_1 + 3 \cdot 5$

$a_5 = a_1 + 4 \cdot 5$

and so on.

This result can be generalized:

> If a_1 is the first term of an arithmetic sequence, and if d is the common difference for the sequence, then the **general term**, or **nth term**, of the sequence is given by a_n, where
>
> $$a_n = a_1 + (n - 1)d.$$

Example 3 Find the indicated term for each arithmetic sequence.

(a) 7, 12, 17, 22, 27, ... Find the fifteenth term.

The first term of this sequence is $a_1 = 7$, and the common difference is $d = 5$. (Find 5 by subtracting any two adjacent terms.) To find the fifteenth term, a_{15}, replace n with 15 in the formula for a_n.

Doubling "cubes" Doubling in backgammon is a vital aspect of the modern game. A player who is ahead offers to double the stakes; the opponent must agree or concede the game immediately. In return, only the player who accepted the double may redouble later in the game.

The photo shows "super-cubes" from the Chicago Chess and Backgammon Shop. Two of them were shot together to show what either of them looks like on all the sides. (The shape is technically an 8-sided prism.) Numbers on the sides are in geometric sequence, beginning with 2 and doubling. (It is also a sequence of powers of 2 from 2^1 to 2^8.)

$$a_n = a_1 + (n - 1)d \qquad \text{Formula}$$
$$a_{15} = 7 + (15 - 1)5 \qquad \text{Let } n = 15, d = 5, a_1 = 7$$
$$= 7 + (14)5$$
$$= 7 + 70$$
$$a_{15} = 77. \qquad \text{Fifteenth term}$$

(b) $23, 16, 9, 2, -5, -12, \ldots$ Find a_{19}.

For this sequence, $a_1 = 23$ and $d = -7$.

$$a_{19} = a_1 + (19 - 1)d \qquad \text{Let } n = 19$$
$$= 23 + (18)(-7) \qquad \text{Let } a_1 = 23, d = -7$$
$$= 23 + (-126)$$
$$a_{19} = -103 \qquad \text{Nineteenth term}$$

We can also find a formula for the *sum of the first n terms* of an arithmetic sequence. This formula can be developed by a method used by the mathematician K. F. Gauss (1777–1855) when he was a child.

According to an old story,* one of Gauss' teachers was a small-time tyrant. One day he asked the students to find the sum of the first hundred counting numbers, or the sum

$$1 + 2 + 3 + 4 + 5 + 6 + \ldots + 100.$$

The other students in the class began by adding two numbers at a time, but Gauss found a quicker way. He first wrote the sum twice:

$$1 + 2 + 3 + 4 + \ldots + 99 + 100$$
$$100 + 99 + 98 + 97 + \ldots + 2 + 1.$$

He then noticed that by adding vertically, each pair of numbers adds up to 101.

$$\begin{array}{r} 1 + 2 + 3 + 4 + \ldots + 99 + 100 \\ 100 + 99 + 98 + 97 + \ldots + 2 + 1 \\ \hline 101 + 101 + 101 + 101 + \ldots + 101 + 101 \end{array}$$

There are 100 of these sums of 101, for a total of $100 \cdot 101$, or 10,100. However, in finding the total, the numbers 1 through 100 were added twice. So the final result should actually be half of 10,100 or

$$1 + 2 + 3 + 4 + \ldots + 99 + 100 = \frac{10,100}{2} = 5050.$$

Using a method very similar to this would give the following formula for the sum of the first n terms of an arithmetic sequence.

---

*Another version of this story appears in the Exercises of Section 2.5.

Let S_n represent the **sum of the first n terms** of an arithmetic sequence with first term a_1 and common difference d. Then

$$S_n = \frac{n}{2}(a_1 + a_n).$$

Use this result to check the Gauss example: $n = 100$, $a_1 = 1$, and $a_{100} = 100$, so that

$$S_{100} = \frac{100}{2}(1 + 100) = 50 \cdot 101 = 5050.$$

Example 4 Find the sum of the indicated number of terms in each of the following arithmetic sequences.

(a) Find S_9 in 12, 19, 26, 33, 40, . . .

To find S_9, the sum of the first nine terms of this arithmetic sequence, start with the formula for S_n given above. This formula requires a_1, a_9, and n. To find a_9, use the formula $a_n = a_1 + (n - 1)d$, with $n = 9$, $d = 7$, and $a_1 = 12$. Verify that $a_9 = 68$. Now

$$S_n = \frac{n}{2}(a_1 + a_n)$$
$$S_9 = \frac{9}{2}(12 + 68)$$
$$= \frac{9}{2}(80)$$
$$S_9 = 360.$$

(b) Find S_{20} in 5, 13, 21, 29, 37, ...

Finding S_{20} by the formula requires a_{20}. To find a_{20}, use $a_1 = 5$ and $d = 8$. We find that $a_{20} = 5 + (20 - 1)8 = 5 + 152 = 157$. Then

$$S_{20} = \frac{20}{2}(5 + 157) = 10(162) = 1620. \ \blacksquare$$

Geometric sequences occur in nature when a fertilized egg divides into 2 cells, then 4, 8, and so on. The enlargements here show cell division of a frog egg.

In an arithmetic sequence, each term after the first is found by *adding* the same number to the previous term. In a **geometric sequence,** each term after the first is found by *multiplying* the previous term by a fixed number. For example,

$$1, 2, 4, 8, 16, 32, 64, . . .$$

is a geometric sequence, with each term after the first found by multiplying the previous term by 2. The number 2 is called the *common ratio*. The **common ratio** can be found in a geometric sequence by choosing any term

A geometric sequence is formed by the lengths of these nails. Its common ratio is about 1.3.

except the first and then dividing it by the preceding term. In the sequence above, the common ratio could be found by choosing the term 16, for example, and dividing it by the preceding term: 16/8 = 2.

Example 5 Identify any of the following sequences that are geometric. If a sequence is geometric, find the common ratio.

(a) 6, 24, 96, 384, . . .

Each term after the first is found by multiplying the preceding term by 4, so the sequence is geometric, and the common ratio is 4. The common ratio could also have been found by dividing: 96/24 = 4, for example.

(b) 8, −16, 32, −64, 128, . . .

Since each term is found by multiplying the preceding term by −2, the sequence is geometric with common ratio −2.

(c) 100, 90, 81, 73, 66, 60, . . .

This sequence is not geometric. (Is it an arithmetic sequence?) ▤

Working in a manner similar to that for arithmetic sequences would give the following results for geometric sequences. (See a standard college algebra text for details.)

Let a geometric sequence have first term a_1 and common ratio r. Then the **nth term, a_n,** is given by

$$a_n = a_1 \cdot r^{n-1}$$

and the **sum of the first n terms, S_n,** is

$$S_n = \frac{a_1(r^n - 1)}{r - 1}, \quad r \neq 1.$$

Example 6 A geometric sequence has $a_1 = 243$ and $r = -2/3$. Find each of the following.

(a) a_6

The sixth term is found with the formula for a_n given above.

$$a_n = a_1 r^{n-1}$$

Let $n = 6$, $a_1 = 243$, and $r = -2/3$.

$$a_6 = 243 \cdot \left(-\frac{2}{3}\right)^{6-1} = 243\left(-\frac{2}{3}\right)^5 = 243\left(-\frac{32}{243}\right) = -32$$

(b) S_6

The sum of the first six terms of this sequence is

$$S_n = \frac{a_1(r^n - 1)}{r - 1}$$

$$S_6 = \frac{243\left[\left(-\frac{2}{3}\right)^6 - 1\right]}{-\frac{2}{3} - 1}$$

$$= \frac{243\left[\frac{64}{729} - 1\right]}{-\frac{5}{3}}$$

$$= 243\left(\frac{-665}{729}\right)\left(-\frac{3}{5}\right)$$

$$S_6 = 133. \quad\blacksquare$$

Chessboard problem The drawing here is from the early 1400s, but the problem is much older. One medieval Arabic version says that after Sissah ibn Dahir invented chess, his king was happy enough to give him any reward he wanted. Sissah asked for 1 wheat grain on the first square of the board, 2 grains on the second, 4 grains on the third, and so on. Again we get a geometric (and doubling) sequence. The grains total $2^{64} - 1$, or 18,446,744,073,709,551,615.

4.4 Exercises

In each of Exercises 1–16, a formula for the general term of a sequence is given. Use the given formula to find the first five terms of the sequence. Do this by replacing n, in turn, with 1, 2, 3, 4, and 5. Then identify each sequence as arithmetic, geometric, *or* neither.

1. $a_n = 6n + 5$ **2.** $a_n = 12n - 3$ **3.** $a_n = 3n - 7$ **4.** $a_n = 5n - 12$

5. $a_n = -6n + 4$ **6.** $a_n = -11n + 10$ **7.** $a_n = 2^n$ **8.** $a_n = 3^n$

9. $a_n = (-2)^n$ **10.** $a_n = (-3)^n$ **11.** $a_n = 3 \cdot 2^n$ **12.** $a_n = -4 \cdot 2^n$

13. $a_n = \dfrac{n + 1}{n + 2}$ **14.** $a_n = \dfrac{2n}{n + 1}$ **15.** $a_n = \dfrac{1}{n + 1}$ **16.** $a_n = \dfrac{1}{n + 8}$

Identify each sequence as arithmetic, geometric, *or* neither. *For an arithmetic sequence, give the common difference. For a geometric sequence, give the common ratio.*

17. 6, 14, 22, 30, 38, 46, . . .   **18.** 40, 46, 52, 58, 64, . . .

19. 5, 8, 11, 14, 17, 20, 23, . . .   **20.** 23, 34, 45, 56, 67, 78, . . .

21. 4, 12, 36, 108, . . .   **22.** 7, 14, 28, 56, 112, . . .

23. 2, 5, 9, 14, 20, 27, . . .   **24.** 1, 4, 9, 16, 25, 36, . . .

25. 12, 9, 6, 3, 0, −3, −6, . . .   **26.** 37, 31, 25, 19, 13, 7, . . .

27. $-18, -15, -12, -9, -6, \ldots$

28. $-21, -17, -13, -9, -5, \ldots$

29. $3, -6, 12, -24, 48, -96, \ldots$

30. $-5, 10, -20, 40, -80, \ldots$

31. $-5, 6, -7, 8, -9, 10, -11, \ldots$

32. $-12, 9, -6, 3, \ldots$

Find the indicated term for each arithmetic sequence.

33. $a_1 = 10, d = 5$; find a_{13}

34. $a_1 = 6, d = 9$; find a_8

35. $a_1 = 8, d = 3$; find a_{20}

36. $a_1 = 13, d = 7$; find a_{11}

37. $a_1 = 28, d = -3$; find a_8

38. $a_1 = 47, d = -5$; find a_7

39. $a_1 = 12, d = -7$; find a_{12}

40. $a_1 = 18, d = -9$; find a_{13}

41. $6, 9, 12, 15, 18, \ldots$; find a_{25}

42. $14, 17, 20, 23, 26, 29, \ldots$; find a_{13}

***43.** $-9, -13, -17, -21, -25, \ldots$; find a_{15}

***44.** $-4, -11, -18, -25, -32, \ldots$; find a_{18}

Find the sum of the first twelve terms in each arithmetic sequence.

45. $3, 6, 9, 12, 15, 18, \ldots$

46. $11, 13, 15, 17, 19, 21, \ldots$

47. $9, 17, 25, 33, 41, 49, \ldots$

48. $28, 32, 36, 40, 44, 48, \ldots$

49. $88, 98, 108, 118, 128, 138, \ldots$

50. $92, 95, 98, 101, 104, 107, \ldots$

51. $a_1 = 8, d = 9$

52. $a_1 = 12, d = 6$

53. $a_1 = 7, d = -2$

54. $a_1 = 13, d = -5$

55. $a_1 = -8, d = -7$

56. $a_1 = -15, d = -2$

***57.** Find the sum of the first 1000 counting numbers.

***58.** Find the sum of the first 10,000 counting numbers.

Find a_6 and S_6 for each geometric sequence.

59. $6, 18, 54, \ldots$

60. $7, 14, 28, \ldots$

61. $64, 32, 16, \ldots$

62. $729, 243, 81, \ldots$

63. $12, -24, 48, -96, \ldots$

64. $3125, -625, 125, -25, \ldots$

65. $18, -12, 8, -16/3, \ldots$

66. $8, -12, 18, -27, \ldots$

67. $a_1 = 6, r = -3/4$

68. $a_1 = -5, r = -2/5$

69. $a_1 = -3/8, r = -2/3$

70. $a_1 = 15/16, r = -1/2$

71. Fifteen balls are used in the game of pool. The balls are numbered from 1 through 15. In the game of "rotation," when a player "sinks" a ball in a pocket of the table, the player receives as many points as the number on the ball. Answer the following questions about this game. For some of them you can use the formula for the sum of the terms of an arithmetic sequence.

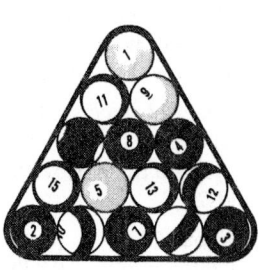

(a) How many points would a player score if he or she sank all fifteen balls?

(b) Suppose player A sank balls 1 through 10 in the pockets, and player B sank balls 11 through 15. Find the total score for player A.

(c) Find the total score for player B.

(d) Who sank more balls into the pockets? Who won the game?

(e) Suppose now that player A sank all the even-numbered balls, and player B sank all the odd-numbered balls. What was each player's score? Who won?

72. Suppose you save the given amounts of money over a five-week period.

Week	1st	2nd	3rd	4th	5th
Money	28¢	45¢	62¢	79¢	96¢

(a) Find the value of a_1.

(b) Find d.

(c) Find the amount that you would save in the 52nd week.

*(d) Find the total amount that you would save in 52 weeks.

73. A man is offered a $10,000 starting salary, with an annual raise of $800.

(a) List his annual salaries for the first five years. Start with $10,000.

(b) Find d.

(c) Find his salary in year 10.

74. A water lily has an area of 8 square inches. These lilies reproduce so fast that the area they cover will double every week.

(a) If two lilies are introduced into a pond, what area will be covered in eight weeks?

(b) in ten weeks?   (c) in twelve weeks?   (d) in fifteen weeks?

75. A vacuum pump removes 1/4 of the air in a cylinder with each stroke of a piston. (Thus, 3/4 of the air remains.)

(a) What fraction of the air will still be in the cylinder after 6 strokes?

(b) after 8 strokes?

76. In a chain letter you receive a list with six names on it. You are to send one dollar to the name at the top of the list, cross off that name, add your name at the bottom, and mail the list to six people, each of whom repeats all these steps. The first person sends six letters, and each of the six recipients sends six letters.

(a) How many letters will be sent in the second mailing?

(b) Each of the 36 recipients then sends 6 letters, producing how many letters in the third mailing?

77. In Exercise 76, how many letters will be sent in each of the following mailings?

(a) Fourth   (b) Sixth   (c) Eighth   (d) Eleventh

The population of the United States is about 230,000,000; by the eleventh mailing more letters will have been sent than there are residents of the country, and the people who started the chain will have made a tidy sum. Chain letters are illegal, however, and postal inspectors go after the originators with a zeal not always shown by mail handlers.

78. A sheet of paper is 1/512 inch thick. If you fold the sheet in half, the total thickness of the two sheets will be 1/256 inch. A second fold produces a stack 1/128 inch thick. How thick would the stack be after the following numbers of folds?

(a) Four folds   (b) Six folds   (c) Eight folds   (d) Ten folds

(e) Fifteen folds (f) Twenty folds (g) Thirty folds

(h) Take a double sheet of newspaper and see how many times you can fold it in half.

79. Suppose that you are offered a job for the month of January. The boss gives you a choice of how you will be paid. You can be paid a flat salary of $10,000 for the month's work, or you can be paid 1 cent on Jan. 1, 2 cents on Jan. 2, 4 cents on Jan. 3, and so on, doubling the previous day's salary each time. What choice would you make, and why? (*Hint:* $2^{31} = 2,147,483,648$)

80. An **equilateral triangle** is a triangle whose sides all measure the same length. The **perimeter** of an equilateral triangle is the sum of all the lengths of its sides, or equivalently, if a side measures x, the perimeter is $3x$. A sequence of equilateral triangles is to be constructed, with each successive triangle being formed by joining the midpoints of the previous triangle.

(a) What is the perimeter of the fifth such triangle?
(b) What is the sum of the perimeters of the first five triangles?

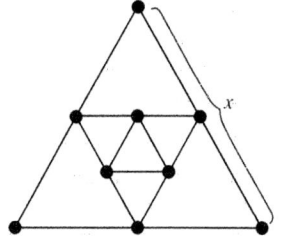

Section 4.4   *(page 195)*

1. 11, 17, 23, 29, 35; arithmetic   **3.** $-4, -1, 2, 5, 8$; arithmetic   **5.** $-2, -8, -14, -20, -26$; arithmetic   **7.** 2, 4, 8, 16, 32; geometric   **9.** $-2, 4, -8, 16, -32$; geometric   **11.** 6, 12, 24, 48, 96; geometric   **13.** 2/3, 3/4, 4/5, 5/6, 6/7; neither   **15.** 1/2, 1/3, 1/4, 1/5, 1/6; neither   **17.** Arithmetic; 8   **19.** Arithmetic; 3   **21.** Geometric; 3   **23.** Neither   **25.** Arithmetic; -3 **27.** Arithmetic; 3   **29.** Geometric; -2 **31.** Neither   **33.** 70   **35.** 65   **37.** 7   **39.** -65 **41.** 78   **43.** -65 **45.** 234   **47.** 636   **49.** 1716   **51.** 690   **53.** -48 **55.** -558 **57.** 500,500   **59.** 1458; 2184   **61.** 2; 126   **63.** -384; -252 **65.** $-64/27$; 266/27   **67.** $-729/512$; 1443/512   **69.** 4/81; $-133/648$ **71.** (a) 120   (b) 55   (c) 65   (d) A; B   (e) 56; 64; B   **73.** (a) $10,000, $10,800, $11,600, $12,400, $13,200   (b) $800   (c) $17,200   **75.** (a) 729/4096 or about 18%   (b) 6561/65,536 or about 10%   **77.** (a) 1296   (b) 46,656   (c) 1,679,616   (d) 362,797,056   **79.** Choose the doubling method. The total wages earned for the month using this method would be $21,474,836.47.